Calculus

A BLAISDELL BOOK IN PURE AND APPLIED MATHEMATICS

CONSULTING EDITOR

George Springer, *Indiana University*

Tom M. Apostol

CALCULUS

VOLUME I

One-Variable Calculus, with an Introduction to Linear Algebra

SECOND EDITION

BLAISDELL PUBLISHING COMPANY

A DIVISION OF GINN AND COMPANY

WALTHAM, MASSACHUSETTS • TORONTO • LONDON

To
Jane and Stephen

PREFACE

Excerpts from the Preface to the First Edition

There seems to be no general agreement as to what should constitute a first course in calculus and analytic geometry. Some people insist that the only way to really understand calculus is to start off with a thorough treatment of the real-number system and develop the subject step by step in a logical and rigorous fashion. Others argue that calculus is primarily a tool for engineers and physicists; they believe the course should stress applications of the calculus by appeal to intuition and by extensive drill on problems which develop manipulative skills. There is much that is sound in both these points of view. Calculus is a deductive science and a branch of pure mathematics. At the same time, it is very important to remember that calculus has strong roots in physical problems and that it derives much of its power and beauty from the variety of its applications. It is possible to combine a strong theoretical development with sound training in technique; this book represents an attempt to strike a sensible balance between the two. While treating the calculus as a deductive science, the book does not neglect applications to physical problems. Proofs of all the important theorems are presented as an essential part of the growth of mathematical ideas; the proofs are often preceded by a geometric or intuitive discussion to give the student some insight into why they take a particular form. Although these intuitive discussions will satisfy readers who are not interested in detailed proofs, the complete proofs are also included for those who prefer a more rigorous presentation.

The approach in this book has been suggested by the historical and philosophical development of calculus and analytic geometry. For example, integration is treated before differentiation. Although to some this may seem unusual, it is historically correct and pedagogically sound. Moreover, it is the best way to make meaningful the true connection between the integral and the derivative.

The concept of the integral is defined first for step functions. Since the integral of a step function is merely a finite sum, integration theory in this case is extremely simple. As the student learns the properties of the integral for step functions, he gains experience in the use of the summation notation and at the same time becomes familiar with the notation for integrals. This sets the stage so that the transition from step functions to more general functions seems easy and natural.

Preface to the Second Edition

The second edition differs from the first in many respects. Linear algebra has been incorporated, the mean-value theorems and routine applications of calculus are introduced at an earlier stage, and many new and easier exercises have been added. A glance at the table of contents reveals that the book has been divided into smaller chapters, each centering on an important concept. Several sections have been rewritten and reorganized to provide better motivation and to improve the flow of ideas.

As in the first edition, a historical introduction precedes each important new concept, tracing its development from an early intuitive physical notion to its precise mathematical formulation. The student is told something of the struggles of the past and of the triumphs of the men who contributed most to the subject. Thus the student becomes an active participant in the evolution of ideas rather than a passive observer of results.

The second edition, like the first, is divided into two volumes. The first two thirds of Volume I deals with the calculus of functions of one variable, including infinite series and an introduction to differential equations. The last third of Volume I introduces linear algebra with applications to geometry and analysis. Much of this material leans heavily on the calculus for examples that illustrate the general theory. It provides a natural blending of algebra and analysis and helps pave the way for the transition from one-variable calculus to multivariable calculus, discussed in Volume II. Further development of linear algebra will occur as needed in the second edition of Volume II.

Once again I acknowledge with pleasure my debt to Professors H. F. Bohnenblust, A. Erdélyi, F. B. Fuller, K. Hoffman, G. Springer, and H. S. Zuckerman. Their influence on the first edition continued into the second. In preparing the second edition, I received additional help from Professor Basil Gordon, who suggested many improvements. Thanks are also due George Springer and William P. Ziemer, who read the final draft. The staff of the Blaisdell Publishing Company has, as always, been helpful; I appreciate their sympathetic consideration of my wishes concerning format and typography.

Finally, it gives me special pleasure to express my gratitude to my wife for the many ways she has contributed during the preparation of both editions. In grateful acknowledgment I happily dedicate this book to her.

T. M. A.

Pasadena, California
September 16, 1966

CONTENTS

I. INTRODUCTION

Part 1. Historical Introduction

Part 2. Some Basic Concepts of the Theory of Sets

Part 3. A Set of Axioms for the Real-Number System

Part 4.   *Mathematical Induction, Summation Notation, and Related Topics*

1. THE CONCEPTS OF INTEGRAL CALCULUS

2. SOME APPLICATIONS OF INTEGRATION

3. CONTINUOUS FUNCTIONS

4. DIFFERENTIAL CALCULUS

5. THE RELATION BETWEEN INTEGRATION AND DIFFERENTIATION

6. THE LOGARITHM, THE EXPONENTIAL, AND THE INVERSE TRIGONOMETRIC FUNCTIONS

7. POLYNOMIAL APPROXIMATIONS TO FUNCTIONS

8. INTRODUCTION TO DIFFERENTIAL EQUATIONS

9. COMPLEX NUMBERS

10. SEQUENCES, INFINITE SERIES, IMPROPER INTEGRALS

11. SEQUENCES AND SERIES OF FUNCTIONS

12. VECTOR ALGEBRA

13. APPLICATIONS OF VECTOR ALGEBRA TO ANALYTIC GEOMETRY

14. CALCULUS OF VECTOR-VALUED FUNCTIONS

15. LINEAR SPACES

16. LINEAR TRANSFORMATIONS AND MATRICES

Calculus

INTRODUCTION

Part 1. Historical Introduction

I 1.1 The two basic concepts of calculus

The remarkable progress that has been made in science and technology during the last century is due in large part to the development of mathematics. That branch of mathematics known as integral and differential calculus serves as a natural and powerful tool for attacking a variety of problems that arise in physics, astronomy, engineering, chemistry, geology, biology, and other fields including, rather recently, some of the social sciences.

To give the reader an idea of the many different types of problems that can be treated by the methods of calculus, we list here a few sample questions selected from the exercises that occur in later chapters of this book.

With what speed should a rocket be fired upward so that it never returns to earth? What is the radius of the smallest circular disk that can cover every isosceles triangle of a given perimeter L? What volume of material is removed from a solid sphere of radius $2r$ if a hole of radius r is drilled through the center? If a strain of bacteria grows at a rate proportional to the amount present and if the population doubles in one hour, by how much will it increase at the end of two hours? If a ten-pound force stretches an elastic spring one inch, how much work is required to stretch the spring one foot?

These examples, chosen from various fields, illustrate some of the technical questions that can be answered by more or less routine applications of calculus.

Calculus is more than a technical tool—it is a collection of fascinating and exciting ideas that have interested thinking men for centuries. These ideas have to do with *speed, area, volume, rate of growth, continuity, tangent line,* and other concepts from a variety of fields. Calculus forces us to stop and think carefully about the meanings of these concepts. Another remarkable feature of the subject is its unifying power. Most of these ideas can be formulated so that they revolve around two rather specialized problems of a geometric nature. We turn now to a brief description of these problems.

Consider a curve C which lies above a horizontal base line such as that shown in Figure I.1. We assume this curve has the property that every vertical line intersects it once at most.

The shaded portion of the figure consists of those points which lie below the curve C, above the horizontal base, and between two parallel vertical segments joining C to the base. The first fundamental problem of calculus is this: *To assign a number which measures the area of this shaded region.*

Consider next a line drawn tangent to the curve, as shown in Figure I.1. The second fundamental problem may be stated as follows: *To assign a number which measures the steepness of this line.*

C

Line tangent to C

FIGURE I.1

Basically, calculus has to do with the precise formulation and solution of these two special problems. It enables us to *define* the concepts of area and tangent line and *to calculate* the area of a given region or the steepness of a given tangent line. *Integral calculus* deals with the problem of area and will be discussed in Chapter 1. *Differential calculus* deals with the problem of tangents and will be introduced in Chapter 4.

The study of calculus requires a certain mathematical background. The present chapter deals with this background material and is divided into four parts: Part 1 provides historical perspective; Part 2 discusses some notation and terminology from the mathematics of sets; Part 3 deals with the real-number system; Part 4 treats mathematical induction and the summation notation. If the reader is acquainted with these topics, he can proceed directly to the development of integral calculus in Chapter 1. If not, he should become familiar with the material in the unstarred sections of this Introduction before proceeding to Chapter 1.

I 1.2   Historical background

The birth of integral calculus occurred more than 2000 years ago when the Greeks attempted to determine areas by a process which they called the *method of exhaustion*. The essential ideas of this method are very simple and can be described briefly as follows: Given a region whose area is to be determined, we inscribe in it a polygonal region which approximates the given region and whose area we can easily compute. Then we choose another polygonal region which gives a better approximation, and we continue the process, taking polygons with more and more sides in an attempt to exhaust the given region. The method is illustrated for a semicircular region in Figure I.2. It was used successfully by Archimedes (287–212 B.C.) to find exact formulas for the area of a circle and a few other special figures.

The development of the method of exhaustion beyond the point to which Archimedes carried it had to wait nearly eighteen centuries until the use of algebraic symbols and techniques became a standard part of mathematics. The elementary algebra that is familiar to most high-school students today was completely unknown in Archimedes' time, and it would have been next to impossible to extend his method to any general class of regions without some convenient way of expressing rather lengthy calculations in a compact and simplified form.

A slow but revolutionary change in the development of mathematical notations began in the 16th century A.D. The cumbersome system of Roman numerals was gradually displaced by the Hindu-Arabic characters used today, the symbols $+$ and $-$ were introduced for the first time, and the advantages of the decimal notation began to be recognized. During this same period, the brilliant successes of the Italian mathematicians Tartaglia,

FIGURE I.2   The method of exhaustion applied to a semicircular region.

Cardano, and Ferrari in finding algebraic solutions of cubic and quartic equations stimulated a great deal of activity in mathematics and encouraged the growth and acceptance of a new and superior algebraic language. With the widespread introduction of well-chosen algebraic symbols, interest was revived in the ancient method of exhaustion and a large number of fragmentary results were discovered in the 16th century by such pioneers as Cavalieri, Toricelli, Roberval, Fermat, Pascal, and Wallis.

Gradually the method of exhaustion was transformed into the subject now called integral calculus, a new and powerful discipline with a large variety of applications, not only to geometrical problems concerned with areas and volumes but also to problems in other sciences. This branch of mathematics, which retained some of the original features of the method of exhaustion, received its biggest impetus in the 17th century, largely due to the efforts of Isaac Newton (1642–1727) and Gottfried Leibniz (1646–1716), and its development continued well into the 19th century before the subject was put on a firm mathematical basis by such men as Augustin-Louis Cauchy (1789–1857) and Bernhard Riemann (1826–1866). Further refinements and extensions of the theory are still being carried out in contemporary mathematics.

I 1.3   The method of exhaustion for the area of a parabolic segment

Before we proceed to a systematic treatment of integral calculus, it will be instructive to apply the method of exhaustion directly to one of the special figures treated by Archimedes himself. The region in question is shown in Figure I.3 and can be described as follows: If we choose an arbitrary point on the base of this figure and denote its distance from 0 by x, then the vertical distance from this point to the curve is x^2. In particular, if the length of the base itself is b, the altitude of the figure is b^2. The vertical distance from x to the curve is called the "ordinate" at x. The curve itself is an example of what is known

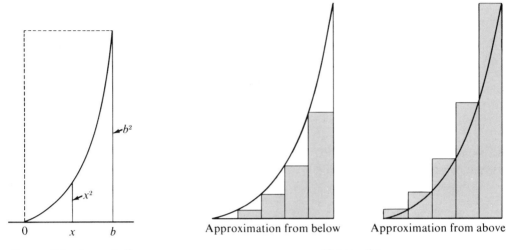

FIGURE I.3   A parabolic
                segment.

FIGURE I.4

as a *parabola*. The region bounded by it and the two line segments is called a *parabolic segment*.

This figure may be enclosed in a rectangle of base b and altitude b^2, as shown in Figure I.3. Examination of the figure suggests that the area of the parabolic segment is less than half the area of the rectangle. Archimedes made the surprising discovery that the area of the parabolic segment is exactly *one-third* that of the rectangle; that is to say, $A = b^3/3$, where A denotes the area of the parabolic segment. We shall show presently how to arrive at this result.

It should be pointed out that the parabolic segment in Figure I.3 is not shown exactly as Archimedes drew it and the details that follow are not exactly the same as those used by him.

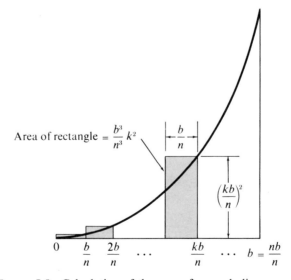

FIGURE I.5   Calculation of the area of a parabolic segment.

Nevertheless, the essential *ideas* are those of Archimedes; what is presented here is the method of exhaustion in modern notation.

The method is simply this: We slice the figure into a number of strips and obtain two approximations to the region, one from below and one from above, by using two sets of rectangles as illustrated in Figure I.4. (We use rectangles rather than arbitrary polygons to simplify the computations.) The area of the parabolic segment is larger than the total area of the inner rectangles but smaller than that of the outer rectangles.

If each strip is further subdivided to obtain a new approximation with a larger number of strips, the total area of the inner rectangles *increases*, whereas the total area of the outer rectangles *decreases*. Archimedes realized that an approximation to the area within any desired degree of accuracy could be obtained by simply taking enough strips.

Let us carry out the actual computations that are required in this case. For the sake of simplicity, we subdivide the base into n *equal* parts, each of length b/n (see Figure I.5). The points of subdivision correspond to the following values of x:

$$0, \frac{b}{n}, \frac{2b}{n}, \frac{3b}{n}, \ldots, \frac{(n-1)b}{n}, \frac{nb}{n} = b .$$

A typical point of subdivision corresponds to $x = kb/n$, where k takes the successive values $k = 0, 1, 2, 3, \ldots, n$. At each point kb/n we construct the outer rectangle of altitude $(kb/n)^2$ as illustrated in Figure I.5. The area of this rectangle is the product of its base and altitude and is equal to

$$\left(\frac{b}{n}\right)\left(\frac{kb}{n}\right)^2 = \frac{b^3}{n^3} k^2.$$

Let us denote by S_n the sum of the areas of all the outer rectangles. Then since the kth rectangle has area $(b^3/n^3)k^2$, we obtain the formula

(I.1) $$S_n = \frac{b^3}{n^3}(1^2 + 2^2 + 3^2 + \cdots + n^2) .$$

In the same way we obtain a formula for the sum s_n of all the inner rectangles:

(I.2) $$s_n = \frac{b^3}{n^3}[1^2 + 2^2 + 3^2 + \cdots + (n-1)^2] .$$

This brings us to a very important stage in the calculation. Notice that the factor multiplying b^3/n^3 in Equation (I.1) is the sum of the squares of the first n integers:

$$1^2 + 2^2 + \cdots + n^2 .$$

[The corresponding factor in Equation (I.2) is similar except that the sum has only $n - 1$ terms.] For a large value of n, the computation of this sum by direct addition of its terms is tedious and inconvenient. Fortunately there is an interesting identity which makes it possible to evaluate this sum in a simpler way, namely,

(I.3) $$1^2 + 2^2 + \cdots + n^2 = \frac{n^3}{3} + \frac{n^2}{2} + \frac{n}{6} .$$ *identity*

This identity is valid for every integer $n \geq 1$ and can be proved as follows: Start with the formula $(k + 1)^3 = k^3 + 3k^2 + 3k + 1$ and rewrite it in the form

$$3k^2 + 3k + 1 = (k + 1)^3 - k^3.$$

Taking $k = 1, 2, \ldots, n - 1$, we get $n - 1$ formulas

$$3 \cdot 1^2 + 3 \cdot 1 + 1 = 2^3 - 1^3$$
$$3 \cdot 2^2 + 3 \cdot 2 + 1 = 3^3 - 2^3$$
$$\cdot$$
$$\cdot$$
$$\cdot$$
$$3(n - 1)^2 + 3(n - 1) + 1 = n^3 - (n - 1)^3.$$

When we add these formulas, all the terms on the right cancel except two and we obtain

$$3[1^2 + 2^2 + \cdots + (n - 1)^2] + 3[1 + 2 + \cdots + (n - 1)] + (n - 1) = n^3 - 1^3.$$

The second sum on the left is the sum of terms in an arithmetic progression and it simplifies to $\frac{1}{2}n(n - 1)$. Therefore this last equation gives us

(I.4) $$1^2 + 2^2 + \cdots + (n - 1)^2 = \frac{n^3}{3} - \frac{n^2}{2} + \frac{n}{6}.$$

Adding n^2 to both members, we obtain (I.3).

For our purposes, we do not need the exact expressions given in the right-hand members of (I.3) and (I.4). All we need are the two *inequalities*

(I.5) $$1^2 + 2^2 + \cdots + (n - 1)^2 < \frac{n^3}{3} < 1^2 + 2^2 + \cdots + n^2$$

which are valid for every integer $n \geq 1$. These inequalities can de deduced easily as consequences of (I.3) and (I.4), or they can be proved directly by induction. (A proof by induction is given in Section I 4.1.)

If we multiply both inequalities in (I.5) by b^3/n^3 and make use of (I.1) and (I.2), we obtain

(I.6) $$s_n < \frac{b^3}{3} < S_n$$

for every n. The inequalities in (I.6) tell us that $b^3/3$ is a number which lies between s_n and S_n for every n. We will now prove that $b^3/3$ is the *only* number which has this property. In other words, we assert that if A is any number which satisfies the inequalities

(I.7) $$s_n < A < S_n$$

for every positive integer n, then $A = b^3/3$. It is because of this fact that Archimedes concluded that the area of the parabolic segment is $b^3/3$.

To prove that $A = b^3/3$, we use the inequalities in (I.5) once more. Adding n^2 to both sides of the leftmost inequality in (I.5), we obtain

$$1^2 + 2^2 + \cdots + n^2 < \frac{n^3}{3} + n^2.$$

Multiplying this by b^3/n^3 and using (I.1), we find

(I.8) $$S_n < \frac{b^3}{3} + \frac{b^3}{n}.$$

Similarly, by subtracting n^2 from both sides of the rightmost inequality in (I.5) and multiplying by b^3/n^3, we are led to the inequality

(I.9) $$\frac{b^3}{3} - \frac{b^3}{n} < s_n.$$

Therefore, any number A satisfying (I.7) must also satisfy

(I.10) $$\frac{b^3}{3} - \frac{b^3}{n} < A < \frac{b^3}{3} + \frac{b^3}{n}$$

for every integer $n \geq 1$. Now there are only three possibilities:

$$A > \frac{b^3}{3}, \qquad A < \frac{b^3}{3}, \qquad A = \frac{b^3}{3}.$$

If we show that each of the first two leads to a contradiction, then we must have $A = b^3/3$, since, in the manner of Sherlock Holmes, this exhausts all the possibilities.

Suppose the inequality $A > b^3/3$ were true. From the second inequality in (I.10) we obtain

(I.11) $$A - \frac{b^3}{3} < \frac{b^3}{n} \quad \text{(by assumption)}$$

for every integer $n \geq 1$. Since $A - b^3/3$ is positive, we may divide both sides of (I.11) by $A - b^3/3$ and then multiply by n to obtain the equivalent statement

$$n < \frac{b^3}{A - b^3/3}$$

for every n. But this inequality is obviously false when $n \geq b^3/(A - b^3/3)$. Hence the inequality $A > b^3/3$ leads to a contradiction. By a similar argument, we can show that the inequality $A < b^3/3$ also leads to a contradiction, and therefore we must have $A = b^3/3$, as asserted.

★I 1.4   Exercises

1. (a) Modify the region in Figure I.3 by assuming that the ordinate at each x is $2x^2$ instead of x^2. Draw the new figure. Check through the principal steps in the foregoing section and find what effect this has on the calculation of the area. Do the same if the ordinate at each x is (b) $3x^2$, (c) $\frac{1}{4}x^2$, (d) $2x^2 + 1$, (e) $ax^2 + c$.

2. Modify the region in Figure I.3 by assuming that the ordinate at each x is x^3 instead of x^2. Draw the new figure.
   (a) Use a construction similar to that illustrated in Figure I.5 and show that the outer and inner sums S_n and s_n are given by

$$S_n = \frac{b^4}{n^4}(1^3 + 2^3 + \cdots + n^3), \qquad s_n = \frac{b^4}{n^4}[1^3 + 2^3 + \cdots + (n-1)^3].$$

   (b) Use the inequalities (which can be proved by mathematical induction; see Section I4.2)

(I.12) $$1^3 + 2^3 + \cdots + (n-1)^3 < \frac{n^4}{4} < 1^3 + 2^3 + \cdots + n^3$$

   to show that $s_n < b^4/4 < S_n$ for every n, and prove that $b^4/4$ is the *only* number which lies between s_n and S_n for every n.
   (c) What number takes the place of $b^4/4$ if the ordinate at each x is $ax^3 + c$?

3. The inequalities (I.5) and (I.12) are special cases of the more general inequalities

(I.13) $$1^k + 2^k + \cdots + (n-1)^k < \frac{n^{k+1}}{k+1} < 1^k + 2^k + \cdots + n^k$$

   that are valid for every integer $n \geq 1$ and every integer $k \geq 1$. Assume the validity of (I.13) and generalize the results of Exercise 2.

I 1.5   A critical analysis of Archimedes' method

From calculations similar to those in Section I 1.3, Archimedes concluded that the area of the parabolic segment in question is $b^3/3$. This fact was generally accepted as a mathematical theorem for nearly 2000 years before it was realized that one must re-examine the result from a more critical point of view. To understand why anyone would question the validity of Archimedes' conclusion, it is necessary to know something about the important changes that have taken place in the recent history of mathematics.

Every branch of knowledge is a collection of ideas described by means of words and symbols, and one cannot understand these ideas unless one knows the exact meanings of the words and symbols that are used. Certain branches of knowledge, known as *deductive systems*, are different from others in that a number of "undefined" concepts are chosen in advance and all other concepts in the system are defined in terms of these. Certain statements about these undefined concepts are taken as *axioms* or *postulates* and other statements that can be deduced from the axioms are called *theorems*. The most familiar example of a deductive system is the Euclidean theory of elementary geometry that has been studied by well-educated men since the time of the ancient Greeks.

The spirit of early Greek mathematics, with its emphasis on the theoretical and postulational approach to geometry as presented in Euclid's *Elements*, dominated the thinking of mathematicians until the time of the Renaissance. A new and vigorous phase in the development of mathematics began with the advent of algebra in the 16th century, and the next 300 years witnessed a flood of important discoveries. Conspicuously absent from this period was the logically precise reasoning of the deductive method with its use of axioms, definitions, and theorems. Instead, the pioneers in the 16th, 17th, and 18th centuries resorted to a curious blend of deductive reasoning combined with intuition, pure guesswork, and mysticism, and it is not surprising to find that some of their work was later shown to be incorrect. However, a surprisingly large number of important discoveries emerged from this era, and a great deal of the work has survived the test of history—a tribute to the unusual skill and ingenuity of these pioneers.

As the flood of new discoveries began to recede, a new and more critical period emerged. Little by little, mathematicians felt forced to return to the classical ideals of the deductive method in an attempt to put the new mathematics on a firm foundation. This phase of the development, which began early in the 19th century and has continued to the present day, has resulted in a degree of logical purity and abstraction that has surpassed all the traditions of Greek science. At the same time, it has brought about a clearer understanding of the foundations of not only calculus but of all of mathematics.

There are many ways to develop calculus as a deductive system. One possible approach is to take the real numbers as the undefined objects. Some of the rules governing the operations on real numbers may then be taken as axioms. One such set of axioms is listed in Part 3 of this Introduction. New concepts, such as *integral, limit, continuity, derivative*, must then be defined in terms of real numbers. Properties of these concepts are then deduced as theorems that follow from the axioms.

Looked at as part of the deductive system of calculus, Archimedes' result about the area of a parabolic segment cannot be accepted as a theorem until a satisfactory definition of area is given first. It is not clear whether Archimedes had ever formulated a precise definition of what he meant by area. He seems to have taken it for granted that every region has an area associated with it. On this assumption he then set out to calculate areas of particular regions. In his calculations he made use of certain facts about area that cannot be proved until we know what is *meant* by area. For instance, he assumed that if one region lies inside another, the area of the smaller region cannot exceed that of the larger region. Also, if a region is decomposed into two or more parts, the sum of the areas of the individual parts is equal to the area of the whole region. All these are properties we would like area to possess, and we shall insist that any definition of area should imply these properties. It is quite possible that Archimedes himself may have taken area to be an undefined concept and then used the properties we just mentioned as *axioms* about area.

Today we consider the work of Archimedes as being important not so much because it helps us to compute areas of particular figures, but rather because it suggests a reasonable way to *define* the concept of area for more or less *arbitrary* figures. As it turns out, the method of Archimedes suggests a way to define a much more general concept known as the *integral*. The integral, in turn, is used to compute not only area but also quantities such as arc length, volume, work and others.

If we look ahead and make use of the terminology of integral calculus, the result of the calculation carried out in Section I 1.3 for the parabolic segment is often stated as follows:

"The integral of x^2 from 0 to b is $b^3/3$."

It is written symbolically as

$$\int_0^b x^2 \, dx = \frac{b^3}{3} \, .$$

The symbol $\int$ (an elongated S) is called an *integral sign*, and it was introduced by Leibniz in 1675. The process which produces the number $b^3/3$ is called *integration*. The numbers 0 and b which are attached to the integral sign are referred to as the *limits of integration*. The symbol $\int_0^b x^2 \, dx$ must be regarded as a whole. Its definition will treat it as such, just as the dictionary describes the word "lapidate" without reference to "lap," "id," or "ate."

Leibniz' symbol for the integral was readily accepted by many early mathematicians because they liked to think of integration as a kind of "summation process" which enabled them to add together infinitely many "infinitesimally small quantities." For example, the area of the parabolic segment was conceived of as a sum of infinitely many infinitesimally thin rectangles of height x^2 and base dx. The integral sign represented the process of adding the areas of all these thin rectangles. This kind of thinking is suggestive and often very helpful, but it is not easy to assign a precise meaning to the idea of an "infinitesimally small quantity." Today the integral is defined in terms of the notion of real number without using ideas like "infinitesimals." This definition is given in Chapter 1.

I 1.6   The approach to calculus to be used in this book

A thorough and complete treatment of either integral or differential calculus depends ultimately on a careful study of the real number system. This study in itself, when carried out in full, is an interesting but somewhat lengthy program that requires a small volume for its complete exposition. The approach in this book is to begin with the real numbers as *undefined objects* and simply to list a number of fundamental properties of real numbers which we shall take as *axioms*. These axioms and some of the simplest theorems that can be deduced from them are discussed in Part 3 of this chapter.

Most of the properties of real numbers discussed here are probably familiar to the reader from his study of elementary algebra. However, there are a few properties of real numbers that do not ordinarily come into consideration in elementary algebra but which play an important role in the calculus. These properties stem from the so-called *least-upper-bound axiom* (also known as the *completeness* or *continuity axiom*) which is dealt with here in some detail. The reader may wish to study Part 3 before proceeding with the main body of the text, or he may postpone reading this material until later when he reaches those parts of the theory that make use of least-upper-bound properties. Material in the text that depends on the least-upper-bound axiom will be clearly indicated.

To develop calculus as a complete, formal mathematical theory, it would be necessary to state, in addition to the axioms for the real number system, a list of the various "methods of proof" which would be permitted for the purpose of deducing theorems from the axioms. Every statement in the theory would then have to be justified either as an "established law" (that is, an axiom, a definition, or a previously proved theorem) or as the result of applying one of the acceptable methods of proof to an established law. A program of this sort would be extremely long and tedious and would add very little to a beginner's understanding of the subject. Fortunately, it is not necessary to proceed in this fashion in order to get a good understanding and a good working knowledge of calculus. In this book the subject is introduced in an informal way, and ample use is made of geometric intuition whenever it is convenient to do so. At the same time, the discussion proceeds in a manner that is consistent with modern standards of precision and clarity of thought. All the important theorems of the subject are explicitly stated and rigorously proved.

To avoid interrupting the principal flow of ideas, some of the proofs appear in separate starred sections. For the same reason, some of the chapters are accompanied by supplementary material in which certain important topics related to calculus are dealt with in detail. Some of these are also starred to indicate that they may be omitted or postponed without disrupting the continuity of the presentation. The extent to which the starred sections are taken up or not will depend partly on the reader's background and skill and partly on the depth of his interests. A person who is interested primarily in the basic techniques may skip the starred sections. Those who wish a more thorough course in calculus, including theory as well as technique, should read some of the starred sections.

Part 2. Some Basic Concepts of the Theory of Sets

I 2.1 Introduction to set theory

In discussing any branch of mathematics, be it analysis, algebra, or geometry, it is helpful to use the notation and terminology of set theory. This subject, which was developed by Boole and Cantor† in the latter part of the 19th century, has had a profound influence on the development of mathematics in the 20th century. It has unified many seemingly disconnected ideas and has helped to reduce many mathematical concepts to their logical foundations in an elegant and systematic way. A thorough treatment of the theory of sets would require a lengthy discussion which we regard as outside the scope of this book. Fortunately, the basic notions are few in number, and it is possible to develop a working knowledge of the methods and ideas of set theory through an informal discussion. Actually, we shall discuss not so much a new theory as an agreement about the precise terminology that we wish to apply to more or less familiar ideas.

In mathematics, the word "set" is used to represent a collection of objects viewed as a single entity. The collections called to mind by such nouns as "flock," "tribe," "crowd," "team," and "electorate" are all examples of sets. The individual objects in the collection are called *elements* or *members* of the set, and they are said to *belong to* or to be *contained in* the set. The set, in turn, is said to *contain* or be *composed of* its elements.

---

† George Boole (1815–1864) was an English mathematician and logician. His book, *An Investigation of the Laws of Thought*, published in 1854, marked the creation of the first workable system of symbolic logic. Georg F. L. P. Cantor (1845–1918) and his school created the modern theory of sets during the period 1874–1895.

We shall be interested primarily in sets of mathematical objects: sets of numbers, sets of curves, sets of geometric figures, and so on. In many applications it is convenient to deal with sets in which nothing special is assumed about the nature of the individual objects in the collection. These are called abstract sets. Abstract set theory has been developed to deal with such collections of arbitrary objects, and from this generality the theory derives its power.

I 2.2 Notations for designating sets

Sets usually are denoted by capital letters: $A, B, C, \ldots, X, Y, Z$; elements are designated by lower-case letters: $a, b, c, \ldots, x, y, z$. We use the special notation

$$x \in S$$

to mean that "x is an element of S" or "x belongs to S." If x does not belong to S, we write $x \notin S$. When convenient, we shall designate sets by displaying the elements in braces; for example, the set of positive even integers less than 10 is denoted by the symbol $\{2, 4, 6, 8\}$ whereas the set of all positive even integers is displayed as $\{2, 4, 6, \ldots\}$, the three dots taking the place of "and so on." The dots are used only when the meaning of "and so on" is clear. The method of listing the members of a set within braces is sometimes referred to as *the roster notation*.

The first basic concept that relates one set to another is *equality* of sets:

DEFINITION OF SET EQUALITY. *Two sets A and B are said to be equal (or identical) if they consist of exactly the same elements, in which case we write $A = B$. If one of the sets contains an element not in the other, we say the sets are unequal and we write $A \neq B$.*

EXAMPLE 1. According to this definition, the two sets $\{2, 4, 6, 8\}$ and $\{2, 8, 6, 4\}$ are equal since they both consist of the four integers 2, 4, 6, and 8. Thus, when we use the roster notation to describe a set, the order in which the elements appear is irrelevant.

EXAMPLE 2. The sets $\{2, 4, 6, 8\}$ and $\{2, 2, 4, 4, 6, 8\}$ are equal even though, in the second set, each of the elements 2 and 4 is listed twice. Both sets contain the four elements 2, 4, 6, 8 and no others; therefore, the definition requires that we call these sets equal. This example shows that we do not insist that the objects listed in the roster notation be distinct. A similar example is the set of letters in the word *Mississippi*, which is equal to the set $\{M, i, s, p\}$, consisting of the four distinct letters M, i, s, and p.

I 2.3 Subsets

From a given set S we may form new sets, called *subsets* of S. For example, the set consisting of those positive integers less than 10 which are divisible by 4 (the set $\{4, 8\}$) is a subset of the set of all even integers less than 10. In general, we have the following definition.

DEFINITION OF A SUBSET. *A set A is said to be a subset of a set B, and we write*

$$A \subseteq B,$$

whenever every element of A also belongs to B. We also say that A is contained in B or that B contains A. The relation $\subseteq$ is referred to as set inclusion.

The statement $A \subseteq B$ does not rule out the possibility that $B \subseteq A$. In fact, we may have both $A \subseteq B$ and $B \subseteq A$, but this happens only if A and B have the same elements. In other words,

$$A = B \qquad \textit{if and only if} \quad A \subseteq B \text{ and } B \subseteq A .$$

This theorem is an immediate consequence of the foregoing definitions of equality and inclusion. If $A \subseteq B$ but $A \neq B$, then we say that A is a *proper subset* of B; we indicate this by writing $A \subset B$.

In all our applications of set theory, we have a fixed set S given in advance, and we are concerned only with subsets of this given set. The underlying set S may vary from one application to another; it will be referred to as the *universal set* of each particular discourse. The notation

$$\{x \mid x \in S \quad \text{and} \quad x \text{ satisfies } P\}$$

will designate the set of all elements x in S which satisfy the property P. When the universal set to which we are referring is understood, we omit the reference to S and write simply $\{x \mid x \text{ satisfies } P\}$. This is read "the set of all x such that x satisfies P." Sets designated in this way are said to be described by a defining property. For example, the set of all positive real numbers could be designated as $\{x \mid x > 0\}$; the universal set S in this case is understood to be the set of all real numbers. Similarly, the set of all even positive integers $\{2, 4, 6, \ldots\}$ can be designated as $\{x \mid x \text{ is a positive even integer}\}$. Of course, the letter x is a dummy and may be replaced by any other convenient symbol. Thus, we may write

$$\{x \mid x > 0\} = \{y \mid y > 0\} = \{t \mid t > 0\}$$

and so on.

It is possible for a set to contain no elements whatever. This set is called the *empty set* or the *void set*, and will be denoted by the symbol $\varnothing$. We will consider $\varnothing$ to be a subset of every set. Some people find it helpful to think of a set as analogous to a container (such as a bag or a box) containing certain objects, its elements. The empty set is then analogous to an empty container.

To avoid logical difficulties, we must distinguish between the element x and the set $\{x\}$ whose only element is x. (A box with a hat in it is conceptually distinct from the hat itself.) In particular, the empty set $\varnothing$ is not the same as the set $\{\varnothing\}$. In fact, the empty set $\varnothing$ contains no elements, whereas the set $\{\varnothing\}$ has one element, $\varnothing$. (A box which contains an empty box is not empty.) Sets consisting of exactly one element are sometimes called *one-element sets*.

Diagrams often help us visualize relations between sets. For example, we may think of a set S as a region in the plane and each of its elements as a point. Subsets of S may then be thought of as collections of points within S. For example, in Figure I.6(b) the shaded portion is a subset of A and also a subset of B. Visual aids of this type, called *Venn diagrams*, are useful for testing the validity of theorems in set theory or for suggesting methods to prove them. Of course, the proofs themselves must rely only on the definitions of the concepts and not on the diagrams.

I 2.4 Unions, intersections, complements

From two given sets A and B, we can form a new set called the *union* of A and B. This new set is denoted by the symbol

$$A \cup B \quad (\text{read: } ``A \text{ union } B")$$

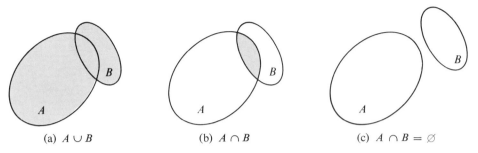

(a) $A \cup B$ (b) $A \cap B$ (c) $A \cap B = \varnothing$

FIGURE I.6   Unions and intersections.

and is defined as the set of those elements which are in A, in B, or in both. That is to say, $A \cup B$ is the set of all elements which belong to at least one of the sets A, B. An example is illustrated in Figure I.6(a), where the shaded portion represents $A \cup B$.

Similarly, the *intersection* of A and B, denoted by

$$A \cap B \quad (\text{read: "}A \text{ intersection } B\text{")},$$

is defined as the set of those elements common to *both* A and B. This is illustrated by the shaded portion of Figure I.6(b). In Figure I.6(c), the two sets A and B have no elements in common; in this case, their intersection is the empty set $\varnothing$. Two sets A and B are said to be *disjoint* if $A \cap B = \varnothing$.

If A and B are sets, the *difference* $A - B$ (also called the *complement of B relative to A*) is defined to be the set of all elements of A which are not in B. Thus, by definition,

$$A - B = \{x \mid x \in A \text{ and } x \notin B\}.$$

In Figure I.6(b) the unshaded portion of A represents $A - B$; the unshaded portion of B represents $B - A$.

The operations of union and intersection have many formal similarities to (as well as differences from) ordinary addition and multiplication of real numbers. For example, since there is no question of order involved in the definitions of union and intersection, it follows that $A \cup B = B \cup A$ and that $A \cap B = B \cap A$. That is to say, union and intersection are *commutative* operations. The definitions are also phrased in such a way that the operations are *associative*:

$$(A \cup B) \cup C = A \cup (B \cup C) \quad \text{and} \quad (A \cap B) \cap C = A \cap (B \cap C).$$

These and other theorems related to the "algebra of sets" are listed as Exercises in Section I 2.5. One of the best ways for the reader to become familiar with the terminology and notations introduced above is to carry out the proofs of each of these laws. A sample of the type of argument that is needed appears immediately after the Exercises.

The operations of union and intersection can be extended to finite or infinite collections of sets as follows: Let $\mathscr{F}$ be a nonempty class† of sets. The union of all the sets in $\mathscr{F}$ is

---

† To help simplify the language, we call a collection of sets a *class*. Capital script letters $\mathscr{A}, \mathscr{B}, \mathscr{C}, \ldots$ are used to denote classes. The usual terminology and notation of set theory applies, of course, to classes. Thus, for example, $A \in \mathscr{F}$ means that A is one of the sets in the class $\mathscr{F}$, and $\mathscr{A} \subseteq \mathscr{B}$ means that every set in $\mathscr{A}$ is also in $\mathscr{B}$, and so forth.

defined as the set of those elements which belong to at least one of the sets in $\mathscr{F}$ and is denoted by the symbol

$$\bigcup_{A\in\mathscr{F}} A.$$

If $\mathscr{F}$ is a finite collection of sets, say $\mathscr{F} = \{A_1, A_2, \ldots, A_n\}$, we write

$$\bigcup_{A\in\mathscr{F}} A = \bigcup_{k=1}^{n} A_k = A_1 \cup A_2 \cup \cdots \cup A_n.$$

Similarly, the intersection of all the sets in $\mathscr{F}$ is defined to be the set of those elements which belong to every one of the sets in $\mathscr{F}$; it is denoted by the symbol

$$\bigcap_{A\in\mathscr{F}} A.$$

For finite collections (as above), we write

$$\bigcap_{A\in\mathscr{F}} A = \bigcap_{k=1}^{n} A_k = A_1 \cap A_2 \cap \cdots \cap A_n.$$

Unions and intersections have been defined in such a way that the associative laws for these operations are automatically satisfied. Hence, there is no ambiguity when we write $A_1 \cup A_2 \cup \cdots \cup A_n$ or $A_1 \cap A_2 \cap \cdots \cap A_n$.

I 2.5   Exercises

1. Use the roster notation to designate the following sets of real numbers.

$$A = \{x \mid x^2 - 1 = 0\}. \qquad D = \{x \mid x^3 - 2x^2 + x = 2\}.$$

$$B = \{x \mid (x - 1)^2 = 0\}. \qquad E = \{x \mid (x + 8)^2 = 9^2\}.$$

$$C = \{x \mid x + 8 = 9\}. \qquad F = \{x \mid (x^2 + 16x)^2 = 17^2\}.$$

2. For the sets in Exercise 1, note that $B \subseteq A$. List all the inclusion relations $\subseteq$ that hold among the sets A, B, C, D, E, F.
3. Let $A = \{1\}$, $B = \{1, 2\}$. Discuss the validity of the following statements (prove the ones that are true and explain why the others are not true).
   (a) $A \subset B$.   (d) $1 \in A$.
   (b) $A \subseteq B$.   (e) $1 \subseteq A$.
   (c) $A \in B$.   (f) $1 \subset B$.
4. Solve Exercise 3 if $A = \{1\}$ and $B = \{\{1\}, 1\}$.
5. Given the set $S = \{1, 2, 3, 4\}$. Display all subsets of S. There are 16 altogether, counting $\varnothing$ and S.
6. Given the following four sets

$$A = \{1, 2\}, \qquad B = \{\{1\}, \{2\}\}, \qquad C = \{\{1\}, \{1, 2\}\}, \qquad D = \{\{1\}, \{2\}, \{1, 2\}\},$$

discuss the validity of the following statements (prove the ones that are true and explain why the others are not true).

(a) $A = B$.   (d) $A \in C$.   (g) $B \subset D$.

(b) $A \subseteq B$.   (e) $A \subset D$.   (h) $B \in D$.

(c) $A \subset C$.   (f) $B \subset C$.   (i) $A \in D$.

7. Prove the following properties of set equality.

    (a) $\{a, a\} = \{a\}$.

    (b) $\{a, b\} = \{b, a\}$.

    (c) $\{a\} = \{b, c\}$ if and only if $a = b = c$.

Prove the set relations in Exercises 8 through 19. (Sample proofs are given at the end of this section).

8. *Commutative laws:* $A \cup B = B \cup A, \quad A \cap B = B \cap A$.

9. *Associative laws:* $A \cup (B \cup C) = (A \cup B) \cup C, \quad A \cap (B \cap C) = (A \cap B) \cap C$.

10. *Distributive laws:* $A \cap (B \cup C) = (A \cap B) \cup (A \cap C), \quad A \cup (B \cap C) = (A \cup B) \cap (A \cup C)$.

11. $A \cup A = A, \quad A \cap A = A$,

12. $A \subseteq A \cup B, \quad A \cap B \subseteq A$.

13. $A \cup \varnothing = A, \quad A \cap \varnothing = \varnothing$.

14. $A \cup (A \cap B) = A, \quad A \cap (A \cup B) = A$.

15. If $A \subseteq C$ and $B \subseteq C$, then $A \cup B \subseteq C$.

16. If $C \subseteq A$ and $C \subseteq B$, then $C \subseteq A \cap B$.

17. (a) If $A \subset B$ and $B \subset C$, prove that $A \subset C$.

    (b) If $A \subseteq B$ and $B \subseteq C$, prove that $A \subseteq C$.

    (c) What can you conclude if $A \subset B$ and $B \subseteq C$?

    (d) If $x \in A$ and $A \subseteq B$, is it necessarily true that $x \in B$?

    (e) If $x \in A$ and $A \in B$, is it necessarily true that $x \in B$?

18. $A - (B \cap C) = (A - B) \cup (A - C)$.

19. Let $\mathscr{F}$ be a class of sets. Then

$$B - \bigcup_{A \in \mathscr{F}} A = \bigcap_{A \in \mathscr{F}} (B - A) \quad \text{and} \quad B - \bigcap_{A \in \mathscr{F}} A = \bigcup_{A \in \mathscr{F}} (B - A).$$

20. (a) Prove that one of the following two formulas is always right and the other one is sometimes wrong:

$$\text{(i)} \quad A - (B - C) = (A - B) \cup C,$$

$$\text{(ii)} \quad A - (B \cup C) = (A - B) - C.$$

(b) State an additional necessary and sufficient condition for the formula which is sometimes incorrect to be always right.

Proof of the commutative law $A \cup B = B \cup A$. Let $X = A \cup B, \quad Y = B \cup A$. To prove that $X = Y$ we prove that $X \subseteq Y$ and $Y \subseteq X$. Suppose that $x \in X$. Then x is in at least one of A or B. Hence, x is in at least one of B or A; so $x \in Y$. Thus, every element of X is also in Y, so $X \subseteq Y$. Similarly, we find that $Y \subseteq X$, so $X = Y$.

Proof of $A \cap B \subseteq A$. If $x \in A \cap B$, then x is in both A and B. In particular, $x \in A$. Thus, every element of $A \cap B$ is also in A; therefore, $A \cap B \subseteq A$.

Part 3.   A Set of Axioms for the Real-Number System

I 3.1   Introduction

There are many ways to introduce the real-number system. One popular method is to begin with the positive integers 1, 2, 3, . . . and use them as building blocks to construct a more comprehensive system having the properties desired. Briefly, the idea of this method is to take the positive integers as undefined concepts, state some axioms concerning them, and then use the positive integers to build a larger system consisting of the positive *rational* numbers (quotients of positive integers). The positive rational numbers, in turn, may then be used as a basis for constructing the positive *irrational* numbers (real numbers like $\sqrt{2}$ and π that are not rational). The final step is the introduction of the negative real numbers and zero. The most difficult part of the whole process is the transition from the rational numbers to the irrational numbers.

Although the need for irrational numbers was apparent to the ancient Greeks from their study of geometry, satisfactory methods for constructing irrational numbers from rational numbers were not introduced until late in the 19th century. At that time, three different theories were outlined by Karl Weierstrass (1815–1897), Georg Cantor (1845–1918), and Richard Dedekind (1831–1916). In 1889, the Italian mathematician Guiseppe Peano (1858–1932) listed five axioms for the positive integers that could be used as the starting point of the whole construction. A detailed account of this construction, beginning with the Peano postulates and using the method of Dedekind to introduce irrational numbers, may be found in a book by E. Landau, *Foundations of Analysis* (New York, Chelsea Publishing Co., 1951).

The point of view we shall adopt here is nonconstructive. We shall start rather far out in the process, taking the real numbers themselves as undefined objects satisfying a number of properties that we use as axioms. That is to say, we shall assume there exists a set **R** of objects, called real numbers, which satisfy the 10 axioms listed in the next few sections. All the properties of real numbers can be deduced from the axioms in the list. When the real numbers are defined by a constructive process, the properties we list as axioms must be proved as theorems.

In the axioms that appear below, lower-case letters $a, b, c, \ldots, x, y, z$ represent arbitrary real numbers unless something is said to the contrary. The axioms fall in a natural way into three groups which we refer to as the *field axioms*, the *order axioms*, and the *least-upper-bound axiom* (also called the *axiom of continuity* or the *completeness axiom*).

I 3.2   The field axioms

Along with the set **R** of real numbers we assume the existence of two operations called *addition* and *multiplication*, such that for every pair of real numbers x and y we can form the *sum* of x and y, which is another real number denoted by $x + y$, and the *product* of x and y, denoted by xy or by $x \cdot y$. It is assumed that the sum $x + y$ and the product xy are *uniquely determined* by x and y. In other words, given x and y, there is exactly one real number $x + y$ and exactly one real number xy. We attach no special meanings to the symbols $+$ and $\cdot$ other than those contained in the axioms.

AXIOM 1.   COMMUTATIVE LAWS. $x + y = y + x, \qquad xy = yx.$

AXIOM 2.   ASSOCIATIVE LAWS. $x + (y + z) = (x + y) + z, \qquad x(yz) = (xy)z.$

AXIOM 3.   DISTRIBUTIVE LAW. $x(y + z) = xy + xz.$

AXIOM 4.   EXISTENCE OF IDENTITY ELEMENTS.   *There exist two distinct real numbers, which we denote by* 0 *and* 1, *such that for every real* x *we have* $x + 0 = x$ *and* $1 \cdot x = x.$

AXIOM 5.   EXISTENCE OF NEGATIVES.   *For every real number* x *there is a real number* y *such that* $x + y = 0.$

AXIOM 6.   EXISTENCE OF RECIPROCALS.   *For every real number* $x \neq 0$ *there is a real number* y *such that* $xy = 1.$

Note: The numbers 0 and 1 in Axioms 5 and 6 are those of Axiom 4.

From the above axioms we can deduce all the usual laws of elementary algebra. The most important of these laws are collected here as a list of theorems. In all these theorems the symbols *a*, *b*, *c*, *d* represent arbitrary real numbers.

THEOREM I.1.   CANCELLATION LAW FOR ADDITION.   *If* $a + b = a + c$, *then* $b = c$. *(In particular, this shows that the number* 0 *of Axiom* 4 *is unique.)*

THEOREM I.2.   POSSIBILITY OF SUBTRACTION.   *Given a and b, there is exactly one x such that* $a + x = b$. *This x is denoted by* $b - a$. *In particular,* $0 - a$ *is written simply* $-a$ *and is called the negative of a.*

THEOREM I.3. $b - a = b + (-a).$

THEOREM I.4. $-(-a) = a.$

THEOREM I.5. $a(b - c) = ab - ac.$

THEOREM I.6. $0 \cdot a = a \cdot 0 = 0.$

THEOREM I.7.   CANCELLATION LAW FOR MULTIPLICATION.   *If* $ab = ac$ *and* $a \neq 0$, *then* $b = c$. *(In particular, this shows that the number* 1 *of Axiom* 4 *is unique.)*

THEOREM I.8.   POSSIBILITY OF DIVISION.   *Given a and b with* $a \neq 0$, *there is exactly one x such that* $ax = b$. *This x is denoted by* b/a *or* $\dfrac{b}{a}$ *and is called the quotient of b and a. In particular,* $1/a$ *is also written* a^{-1} *and is called the reciprocal of a.*

THEOREM I.9.   *If* $a \neq 0$, *then* $b/a = b \cdot a^{-1}.$

THEOREM I.10.   *If* $a \neq 0$, *then* $(a^{-1})^{-1} = a.$

THEOREM I.11.   *If* $ab = 0$, *then* $a = 0$ *or* $b = 0.$

THEOREM I.12. $(-a)b = -(ab)$ *and* $(-a)(-b) = ab.$

THEOREM I.13. $(a/b) + (c/d) = (ad + bc)/(bd)$ *if* $b \neq 0$ *and* $d \neq 0.$

THEOREM I.14. $(a/b)(c/d) = (ac)/(bd)$ *if* $b \neq 0$ *and* $d \neq 0.$

THEOREM I.15. $(a/b)/(c/d) = (ad)/(bc)$ *if* $b \neq 0$, $c \neq 0$, *and* $d \neq 0.$

To illustrate how these statements may be obtained as consequences of the axioms, we shall present proofs of Theorems I.1 through I.4. Those readers who are interested may find it instructive to carry out proofs of the remaining theorems.

Proof of I.1. Given $a + b = a + c$. By Axiom 5, there is a number y such that $y + a = 0$. Since sums are uniquely determined, we have $y + (a + b) = y + (a + c)$. Using the associative law, we obtain $(y + a) + b = (y + a) + c$ or $0 + b = 0 + c$. But by Axiom 4 we have $0 + b = b$ and $0 + c = c$, so that $b = c$. Notice that this theorem shows that there is only one real number having the property of 0 in Axiom 4. In fact, if 0 and $0'$ both have this property, then $0 + 0' = 0$ and $0 + 0 = 0$. Hence $0 + 0' = 0 + 0$ and, by the cancellation law, $0 = 0'$.

Proof of I.2. Given a and b, choose y so that $a + y = 0$ and let $x = y + b$. Then $a + x = a + (y + b) = (a + y) + b = 0 + b = b$. Therefore there is at least one x such that $a + x = b$. But by Theorem I.1 there is at most one such x. Hence there is *exactly* one.

Proof of I.3. Let $x = b - a$ and let $y = b + (-a)$. We wish to prove that $x = y$. Now $x + a = b$ (by the definition of $b - a$) and

$$y + a = [b + (-a)] + a = b + [(-a) + a] = b + 0 = b.$$

Therefore $x + a = y + a$ and hence, by Theorem I.1, $x = y$.

Proof of I.4. We have $a + (-a) = 0$ by the definition of $-a$. But this equation tells us that a is the negative of $-a$. That is, $a = -(-a)$, as asserted.

★I 3.3   Exercises

1. Prove Theorems I.5 through I.15, using Axioms 1 through 6 and Theorems I.1 through I.4.

In Exercises 2 through 10, prove the given statements or establish the given equations. You may use Axioms 1 through 6 and Theorems I.1 through I.15.

2. $-0 = 0$.
3. $1^{-1} = 1$.
4. Zero has no reciprocal.
5. $-(a + b) = -a - b$.
6. $-(a - b) = -a + b$.
7. $(a - b) + (b - c) = a - c$.
8. If $a \neq 0$ and $b \neq 0$, then $(ab)^{-1} = a^{-1}b^{-1}$.
9. $-(a/b) = (-a/b) = a/(-b)$ if $b \neq 0$.
10. $(a/b) - (c/d) = (ad - bc)/(bd)$ if $b \neq 0$ and $d \neq 0$.

I 3.4   The order axioms

This group of axioms has to do with a concept which establishes an *ordering* among the real numbers. This ordering enables us to make statements about one real number being larger or smaller than another. We choose to introduce the order properties as a set of axioms about a new undefined concept called *positiveness* and then to define terms like *less than* and *greater than* in terms of positiveness.

We shall assume that there exists a certain subset $\mathbf{R}^+ \subset \mathbf{R}$, called the set of *positive* numbers, which satisfies the following three order axioms:

AXIOM 7. *If x and y are in $\mathbf{R}^+$, so are $x + y$ and xy.*

AXIOM 8. *For every real $x \neq 0$, either $x \in \mathbf{R}^+$ or $-x \in \mathbf{R}^+$, but not both.*

AXIOM 9. $0 \notin \mathbf{R}^+$.

Now we can define the symbols $<$, $>$, $\leq$, and $\geq$, called, respectively, *less than, greater than, less than or equal to*, and *greater than or equal to*, as follows:

$$x < y \text{ means that } y - x \text{ is positive};$$

$$y > x \text{ means that } x < y;$$

$$x \leq y \text{ means that either } x < y \text{ or } x = y;$$

$$y \geq x \text{ means that } x \leq y.$$

Thus, we have $x > 0$ if and only if x is positive. If $x < 0$, we say that x is *negative*; if $x \geq 0$, we say that x is *nonnegative*. A pair of simultaneous inequalities such as $x < y$, $y < z$ is usually written more briefly as $x < y < z$; similar interpretations are given to the compound inequalities $x \leq y < z$, $x < y \leq z$, and $x \leq y \leq z$.

From the order axioms we can derive all the usual rules for calculating with inequalities. The most important of these are listed here as theorems.

THEOREM I.16. TRICHOTOMY LAW. *For arbitrary real numbers a and b, exactly one of the three relations $a < b$, $b < a$, $a = b$ holds.*

THEOREM I.17. TRANSITIVE LAW. *If $a < b$ and $b < c$, then $a < c$.*

THEOREM I.18. *If $a < b$, then $a + c < b + c$.*

THEOREM I.19. *If $a < b$ and $c > 0$, then $ac < bc$.*

THEOREM I.20. *If $a \neq 0$, then $a^2 > 0$.*

THEOREM I.21. $1 > 0$.

THEOREM I.22. *If $a < b$ and $c < 0$, then $ac > bc$.*

THEOREM I.23. *If $a < b$, then $-a > -b$. In particular, if $a < 0$, then $-a > 0$.*

THEOREM I.24. *If $ab > 0$, then both a and b are positive or both are negative.*

THEOREM I.25. *If $a < c$ and $b < d$, then $a + b < c + d$.*

Again, we shall prove only a few of these theorems as samples to indicate how the proofs may be carried out. Proofs of the others are left as exercises.

Proof of I.16. Let $x = b - a$. If $x = 0$, then $b - a = a - b = 0$, and hence, by Axiom 9, we cannot have $a > b$ or $b > a$. If $x \neq 0$, Axiom 8 tells us that either $x > 0$ or $x < 0$, but not both; that is, either $a < b$ or $b < a$, but not both. Therefore, exactly one of the three relations, $a = b$, $a < b$, $b < a$, holds.

Proof of I.17. If $a < b$ and $b < c$, then $b - a > 0$ and $c - b > 0$. By Axiom 7 we may add to obtain $(b - a) + (c - b) > 0$. That is, $c - a > 0$, and hence $a < c$.

Proof of I.18. Let $x = a + c$, $y = b + c$. Then $y - x = b - a$. But $b - a > 0$ since $a < b$. Hence $y - x > 0$, and this means that $x < y$.

Proof of I.19. If $a < b$, then $b - a > 0$. If $c > 0$, then by Axiom 7 we may multiply c by $(b - a)$ to obtain $(b - a)c > 0$. But $(b - a)c = bc - ac$. Hence $bc - ac > 0$, and this means that $ac < bc$, as asserted.

Proof of I.20. If $a > 0$, then $a \cdot a > 0$ by Axiom 7. If $a < 0$, then $-a > 0$, and hence $(-a) \cdot (-a) > 0$ by Axiom 7. In either case we have $a^2 > 0$.

Proof of I.21. Apply Theorem I.20 with $a = 1$.

⋆I 3.5 Exercises

1. Prove Theorems I.22 through I.25, using the earlier theorems and Axioms 1 through 9.

In Exercises 2 through 10, prove the given statements or establish the given inequalities. You may use Axioms 1 through 9 and Theorems I.1 through I.25.

2. There is no real number x such that $x^2 + 1 = 0$.
3. The sum of two negative numbers is negative.
4. If $a > 0$, then $1/a > 0$; if $a < 0$, then $1/a < 0$.
5. If $0 < a < b$, then $0 < b^{-1} < a^{-1}$.
6. If $a \leq b$ and $b \leq c$, then $a \leq c$.
7. If $a \leq b$ and $b \leq c$, and $a = c$, then $b = c$.
8. For all real a and b we have $a^2 + b^2 \geq 0$. If a and b are not both 0, then $a^2 + b^2 > 0$.
9. There is no real number a such that $x \leq a$ for all real x.
10. If x has the property that $0 \leq x < h$ for *every* positive real number h, then $x = 0$.

I 3.6 Integers and rational numbers

There exist certain subsets of **R** which are distinguished because they have special properties not shared by all real numbers. In this section we shall discuss two such subsets, the *integers* and the *rational numbers*.

To introduce the positive integers we begin with the number 1, whose existence is guaranteed by Axiom 4. The number $1 + 1$ is denoted by 2, the number $2 + 1$ by 3, and so on. The numbers 1, 2, 3, . . . , obtained in this way by repeated addition of 1 are all positive, and they are called the *positive integers*. Strictly speaking, this description of the positive integers is not entirely complete because we have not explained in detail what we mean by the expressions "and so on," or "repeated addition of 1." Although the intuitive meaning of these expressions may seem clear, in a careful treatment of the real-number system it is necessary to give a more precise definition of the positive integers. There are many ways to do this. One convenient method is to introduce first the notion of an *inductive set*.

DEFINITION OF AN INDUCTIVE SET.   *A set of real numbers is called an inductive set if it has the following two properties:*
(a) *The number 1 is in the set.*
(b) *For every x in the set, the number x + 1 is also in the set.*

For example, **R** is an inductive set. So is the set **R**⁺. Now we shall define the positive integers to be those real numbers which belong to every inductive set.

DEFINITION OF POSITIVE INTEGERS.   *A real number is called a positive integer if it belongs to every inductive set.*

Let **P** denote the set of all positive integers. Then **P** is itself an inductive set because (a) it contains 1, and (b) it contains $x + 1$ whenever it contains x. Since the members of **P** belong to every inductive set, we refer to **P** as the *smallest* inductive set. This property of the set **P** forms the logical basis for a type of reasoning that mathematicians call *proof by induction*, a detailed discussion of which is given in Part 4 of this Introduction.

The negatives of the positive integers are called the *negative integers*. The positive integers, together with the negative integers and 0 (zero), form a set **Z** which we call simply the *set of integers.*

In a thorough treatment of the real-number system, it would be necessary at this stage to prove certain theorems about integers. For example, the sum, difference, or product of two integers is an integer, but the quotient of two integers need not be an integer. However, we shall not enter into the details of such proofs.

Quotients of integers a/b (where $b \neq 0$) are called *rational numbers*. The set of rational numbers, denoted by **Q**, contains **Z** as a subset. The reader should realize that all the field axioms and the order axioms are satisfied by **Q**. For this reason, we say that the set of rational numbers is an *ordered field*. Real numbers that are not in **Q** are called *irrational*.

I 3.7   Geometric interpretation of real numbers as points on a line

The reader is undoubtedly familiar with the geometric representation of real numbers by means of points on a straight line. A point is selected to represent 0 and another, to the right of 0, to represent 1, as illustrated in Figure I.7. This choice determines the scale. If one adopts an appropriate set of axioms for Euclidean geometry, then each real number corresponds to exactly one point on this line and, conversely, each point on the line corresponds to one and only one real number. For this reason the line is often called the *real line* or the *real axis*, and it is customary to use the words *real number* and *point* interchangeably. Thus we often speak of the *point x* rather than the point corresponding to the real number x.

The ordering relation among the real numbers has a simple geometric interpretation. If $x < y$, the point x lies to the left of the point y, as shown in Figure I.7. Positive numbers lie to the right of 0 and negative numbers to the left of 0. If $a < b$, a point x satisfies the inequalities $a < x < b$ if and only if x is *between* a and b.

This device for representing real numbers geometrically is a very worthwhile aid that helps us to discover and understand better certain properties of real numbers. However, the reader should realize that all properties of real numbers that are to be accepted as theorems must be deducible from the axioms without any reference to geometry. This does not mean that one should not make use of geometry in studying properties of real numbers. On the contrary, the geometry often suggests the method of proof of a particular theorem, and sometimes a geometric argument is more illuminating than a purely *analytic* proof (one depending entirely on the axioms for the real numbers). In this book, geometric

$$0 \qquad 1 \qquad\qquad x \qquad y$$

FIGURE I.7   Real numbers represented geometrically on a line.

arguments are used to a large extent to help motivate or clarify a particular discussion. Nevertheless, the proofs of all the important theorems are presented in analytic form.

I 3.8   Upper bound of a set, maximum element, least upper bound (supremum)

The nine axioms listed above contain all the properties of real numbers usually discussed in elementary algebra. There is another axiom of fundamental importance in calculus that is ordinarily not discussed in elementary algebra courses. This axiom (or some property equivalent to it) is used to establish the existence of irrational numbers.

Irrational numbers arise in elementary algebra when we try to solve certain quadratic equations. For example, it is desirable to have a real number x such that $x^2 = 2$. From the nine axioms above, we cannot prove that such an x exists in **R**, because these nine axioms are also satisfied by **Q**, and there is no rational number x whose square is 2. (A proof of this statement is outlined in Exercise 11 of Section I 3.12.) Axiom 10 allows us to introduce irrational numbers in the real-number system, and it gives the real-number system a property of continuity that is a keystone in the logical structure of calculus.

Before we describe Axiom 10, it is convenient to introduce some more terminology and notation. Suppose S is a nonempty set of real numbers and suppose there is a number B such that
$$x \le B$$

for every x in S. Then S is said to be *bounded above* by B. The number B is called an *upper bound* for S. We say *an* upper bound because every number greater than B will also be an upper bound. If an upper bound B is also a member of S, then B is called the *largest member* or the *maximum element* of S. There can be at most one such B. If it exists, we write
$$B = \max S \,.$$

Thus, $B = \max S$ if $B \in S$ and $x \le B$ for all x in S. A set with no upper bound is said to be *unbounded above*.

The following examples serve to illustrate the meaning of these terms.

EXAMPLE 1. Let S be the set of all positive real numbers. This set is unbounded above. It has no upper bounds and it has no maximum element.

EXAMPLE 2. Let S be the set of all real x satisfying $0 \leq x \leq 1$. This set is bounded above by 1. In fact, 1 is its maximum element.

EXAMPLE 3. Let T be the set of all real x satisfying $0 \leq x < 1$. This is like the set in Example 2 except that the point 1 is not included. This set is bounded above by 1 but it has no maximum element.

Some sets, like the one in Example 3, are bounded above but have no maximum element. For these sets there is a concept which takes the place of the maximum element. This is called the *least upper bound* of the set and it is defined as follows:

DEFINITION OF LEAST UPPER BOUND. *A number B is called a least upper bound of a nonempty set S if B has the following two properties*:
   (a) *B is an upper bound for S.*
   (b) *No number less than B is an upper bound for S.*

If S has a maximum element, this maximum is also a least upper bound for S. But if S does not have a maximum element, it may still have a least upper bound. In Example 3 above, the number 1 is a least upper bound for T although T has no maximum element. (See Figure I.8.)

(a) S has a largest member: (b) T has no largest member, but it has
    max $S = 1$ a least upper bound: sup $T = 1$

FIGURE I.8   Upper bounds, maximum element, supremum.

THEOREM I.26.   *Two different numbers cannot be least upper bounds for the same set.*

Proof. Suppose that B and C are two least upper bounds for a set S. Property (b) implies that $C \geq B$ since B is a least upper bound; similarly, $B \geq C$ since C is a least upper bound. Hence, we have $B = C$.

This theorem tells us that if there is a least upper bound for a set S, there is *only* one and we may speak of *the* least upper bound.

It is common practice to refer to the least upper bound of a set by the more concise term *supremum*, abbreviated *sup*. We shall adopt this convention and write

$$B = \sup S$$

to express the fact that B is the least upper bound, or supremum, of S.

I 3.9   The least-upper-bound axiom (completeness axiom)

Now we are ready to state the least-upper-bound axiom for the real-number system.

AXIOM 10.   *Every nonempty set S of real numbers which is bounded above has a supremum; that is, there is a real number B such that B = sup S.*

We emphasize once more that the supremum of S need not be a member of S. In fact, sup S belongs to S if and only if S has a maximum element, in which case max S = sup S.

Definitions of the terms *lower bound, bounded below, smallest member* (or *minimum element*) may be similarly formulated. The reader should formulate these for himself. If S has a minimum element, we denote it by min S.

A number L is called a *greatest lower bound* (or *infimum*) of S if (a) L is a lower bound for S, and (b) no number greater than L is a lower bound for S. The infimum of S, when it exists, is uniquely determined and we denote it by inf S. If S has a minimum element, then min S = inf S.

Using Axiom 10, we can prove the following.

THEOREM I.27.   *Every nonempty set S that is bounded below has a greatest lower bound; that is, there is a real number L such that L = inf S.*

Proof. Let $-S$ denote the set of negatives of numbers in S. Then $-S$ is nonempty and bounded above. Axiom 10 tells us that there is a number B which is a supremum for $-S$. It is easy to verify that $-B = $ inf S.

Let us refer once more to the examples in the foregoing section. In Example 1, the set of all positive real numbers, the number 0 is the infimum of S. This set has no minimum element. In Examples 2 and 3, the number 0 is the minimum element.

In all these examples it was easy to decide whether or not the set S was bounded above or below, and it was also easy to determine the numbers sup S and inf S. The next example shows that it may be difficult to determine whether upper or lower bounds exist.

EXAMPLE 4.   Let S be the set of all numbers of the form $(1 + 1/n)^n$, where $n = 1, 2, 3, \ldots$. For example, taking $n = 1$, 2, and 3, we find that the numbers 2, $\frac{9}{4}$, and $\frac{64}{27}$ are in S. Every number in the set is greater than 1, so the set is bounded below and hence has an infimum. With a little effort we can show that 2 is the smallest element of S so inf $S = $ min $S = 2$. The set S is also bounded above, although this fact is not as easy to prove. (Try it!) Once we know that S is bounded above, Axiom 10 tells us that there is a number which is the supremum of S. In this case it is not easy to determine the value of sup S from the description of S. In a later chapter we will learn that sup S is an irrational number approximately equal to 2.718. It is an important number in calculus called the Euler number e.

I 3.10   The Archimedean property of the real-number system

This section contains a number of important properties of the real-number system which are consequences of the least-upper-bound axiom.

THEOREM I.28.   *The set* **P** *of positive integers* 1, 2, 3, . . . *is unbounded above.*

Proof. Assume **P** is bounded above. We shall show that this leads to a contradiction. Since **P** is nonempty, Axiom 10 tells us that **P** has a least upper bound, say b. The number $b - 1$, being less than b, cannot be an upper bound for **P**. Hence, there is at least one positive integer n such that $n > b - 1$. For this n we have $n + 1 > b$. Since $n + 1$ is in **P**, this contradicts the fact that b is an upper bound for **P**.

As corollaries of Theorem I.28, we immediately obtain the following consequences:

THEOREM I.29.   *For every real x there exists a positive integer n such that $n > x$.*

Proof. If this were not so, some x would be an upper bound for **P**, contradicting Theorem I.28.

THEOREM I.30.   *If $x > 0$ and if y is an arbitrary real number, there exists a positive integer n such that $nx > y$.*

Proof. Apply Theorem I.29 with x replaced by y/x.

The property described in Theorem I.30 is called the *Archimedean property* of the real-number system. Geometrically it means that any line segment, no matter how long, may be covered by a finite number of line segments of a given positive length, no matter how small. In other words, a small ruler used often enough can measure arbitrarily large distances. Archimedes realized that this was a fundamental property of the straight line and stated it explicitly as one of the axioms of geometry. In the 19th and 20th centuries, non-Archimedean geometries have been constructed in which this axiom is rejected.

From the Archimedean property, we can prove the following theorem, which will be useful in our discussion of integral calculus.

THEOREM I.31.   *If three real numbers a, x, and y satisfy the inequalities*

(I.14) $$a \le x \le a + \frac{y}{n}$$

for every integer $n \ge 1$, then $x = a$.

Proof. If $x > a$, Theorem I.30 tells us that there is a positive integer n satisfying $n(x - a) > y$, contradicting (I.14). Hence we cannot have $x > a$, so we must have $x = a$.

I 3.11   Fundamental properties of the supremum and infimum

This section discusses three fundamental properties of the supremum and infimum that we shall use in our development of calculus. The first property states that any set of numbers with a supremum contains points arbitrarily close to its supremum; similarly, a set with an infimum contains points arbitrarily close to its infimum.

THEOREM I.32. *Let h be a given positive number and let S be a set of real numbers.*

(a) *If S has a supremum, then for some x in S we have*

$$x > \sup S - h .$$

(b) *If S has an infimum, then for some x in S we have*

$$x < \inf S + h .$$

Proof of (a). If we had $x \leq \sup S - h$ for *all* x in S, then $\sup S - h$ would be an upper bound for S smaller than its least upper bound. Therefore we must have $x > \sup S - h$ for at least one x in S. This proves (a). The proof of (b) is similar.

THEOREM I.33. ADDITIVE PROPERTY. *Given nonempty subsets A and B of* **R**, *let C denote the set*

$$C = \{a + b \mid a \in A, b \in B\} .$$

(a) *If each of A and B has a supremum, then C has a supremum, and*

$$\sup C = \sup A + \sup B .$$

(b) *If each of A and B has an infimum, then C has an infimum, and*

$$\inf C = \inf A + \inf B .$$

Proof. Assume each of A and B has a supremum. If $c \in C$, then $c = a + b$, where $a \in A$ and $b \in B$. Therefore $c \leq \sup A + \sup B$; so $\sup A + \sup B$ is an upper bound for C. This shows that C has a supremum and that

$$\sup C \leq \sup A + \sup B .$$

Now let n be any positive integer. By Theorem I.32 (with $h = 1/n$) there is an a in A and a b in B such that

$$a > \sup A - \frac{1}{n} , \qquad b > \sup B - \frac{1}{n} .$$

Adding these inequalities, we obtain

$$a + b > \sup A + \sup B - \frac{2}{n} , \quad \text{or} \quad \sup A + \sup B < a + b + \frac{2}{n} \leq \sup C + \frac{2}{n} ,$$

since $a + b \leq \sup C$. Therefore we have shown that

$$\sup C \leq \sup A + \sup B < \sup C + \frac{2}{n}$$

for every integer $n \geq 1$. By Theorem I.31, we must have sup $C = $ sup $A + $ sup B. This proves (a), and the proof of (b) is similar.

THEOREM I.34.   *Given two nonempty subsets S and T of* **R** *such that*

$$s \leq t$$

for every s in S and every t in T. Then S has a supremum, and T has an infimum, and they satisfy the inequality

$$\sup S \leq \inf T \, .$$

Proof. Each t in T is an upper bound for S. Therefore S has a supremum which satisfies the inequality sup $S \leq t$ for all t in T. Hence sup S is a lower bound for T, so T has an infimum which cannot be less than sup S. In other words, we have sup $S \leq$ inf T, as asserted.

⋆I 3.12   Exercises

1. If x and y are arbitrary real numbers with $x < y$, prove that there is at least one real z satisfying $x < z < y$.
2. If x is an arbitrary real number, prove that there are integers m and n such that $m < x < n$.
3. If $x > 0$, prove that there is a positive integer n such that $1/n < x$.
4. If x is an arbitrary real number, prove that there is exactly one integer n which satisfies the inequalities $n \leq x < n + 1$. This n is called the greatest integer in x and is denoted by $[x]$. For example, $[5] = 5$, $[\frac{5}{2}] = 2$, $[-\frac{8}{3}] = -3$.
5. If x is an arbitrary real number, prove that there is exactly one integer n which satisfies $x \leq n < x + 1$.
6. If x and y are arbitrary real numbers, $x < y$, prove that there exists at least one rational number r satisfying $x < r < y$, and hence infinitely many. This property is often described by saying that the rational numbers are *dense* in the real-number system.
7. If x is rational, $x \neq 0$, and y irrational, prove that $x + y$, $x - y$, xy, x/y, and y/x are all irrational.
8. Is the sum or product of two irrational numbers always irrational?
9. If x and y are arbitrary real numbers, $x < y$, prove that there exists at least one irrational number z satisfying $x < z < y$, and hence infinitely many.
10. An integer n is called *even* if $n = 2m$ for some integer m, and *odd* if $n + 1$ is even. Prove the following statements:
    (a) An integer cannot be both even and odd.
    (b) Every integer is either even or odd.
    (c) The sum or product of two even integers is even. What can you say about the sum or product of two odd integers?
    (d) If n^2 is even, so is n. If $a^2 = 2b^2$, where a and b are integers, then both a and b are even.
    (e) Every rational number can be expressed in the form a/b, where a and b are integers, at least one of which is odd.
11. Prove that there is no rational number whose square is 2.

    [*Hint:* Argue by contradiction. Assume $(a/b)^2 = 2$, where a and b are integers, at least one of which is odd. Use parts of Exercise 10 to deduce a contradiction.]

12. The Archimedean property of the real-number system was deduced as a consequence of the least-upper-bound axiom. Prove that the set of rational numbers satisfies the Archimedean property but not the least-upper-bound property. This shows that the Archimedean property does not imply the least-upper-bound axiom.

⋆I 3.13   Existence of square roots of nonnegative real numbers

It was pointed our earlier that the equation $x^2 = 2$ has no solutions among the rational numbers. With the help of Axiom 10, we can prove that the equation $x^2 = a$ has a solution among the *real* numbers if $a \geq 0$. Each such x is called a *square root* of a.

First, let us see what we can say about square roots without using Axiom 10. Negative numbers cannot have square roots because if $x^2 = a$, then a, being a square, must be nonnegative (by Theorem I.20). Moreover, if $a = 0$, then $x = 0$ is the only square root (by Theorem I.11). Suppose, then, that $a > 0$. If $x^2 = a$, then $x \neq 0$ and $(-x)^2 = a$, so both x and its negative are square roots. In other words, if a has a square root, then it has two square roots, one positive and one negative. Also, it has *at most two* because if $x^2 = a$ and $y^2 = a$, then $x^2 = y^2$ and $(x - y)(x + y) = 0$, and so, by Theorem I.11, either $x = y$ or $x = -y$. Thus, if a has a square root, it has *exactly* two.

The existence of at least one square root can be deduced from an important theorem in calculus known as the intermediate-value theorem for continuous functions, but it may be instructive to see how the existence of a square root can be proved directly from Axiom 10.

THEOREM I.35.   *Every nonnegative real number a has a unique nonnegative square root.*

Note: If $a \geq 0$, we denote its nonnegative square root by $a^{1/2}$ or by $\sqrt{a}$. If $a > 0$, the negative square root is $-a^{1/2}$ or $-\sqrt{a}$.

Proof. If $a = 0$, then 0 is the only square root. Assume, then, that $a > 0$. Let S be the set of all positive x such that $x^2 \leq a$. Since $(1 + a)^2 > a$, the number $1 + a$ is an upper bound for S. Also, S is nonempty because the number $a/(1 + a)$ is in S; in fact, $a^2 \leq a(1 + a)^2$ and hence $a^2/(1 + a)^2 \leq a$. By Axiom 10, S has a least upper bound which we shall call b. Note that $b \geq a/(1 + a)$ so $b > 0$. There are only three possibilities: $b^2 > a$, $b^2 < a$, or $b^2 = a$.

Suppose $b^2 > a$ and let $c = b - (b^2 - a)/(2b) = \frac{1}{2}(b + a/b)$. Then $0 < c < b$ and $c^2 = b^2 - (b^2 - a) + (b^2 - a)^2/(4b^2) = a + (b^2 - a)^2/(4b^2) > a$. Therefore $c^2 > x^2$ for each x in S, and hence $c > x$ for each x in S. This means that c is an upper bound for S. Since $c < b$, we have a contradiction because b was the *least* upper bound for S. Therefore the inequality $b^2 > a$ is impossible.

Suppose $b^2 < a$. Since $b > 0$, we may choose a positive number c such that $c < b$ and such that $c < (a - b^2)/(3b)$. Then we have

$$(b + c)^2 = b^2 + c(2b + c) < b^2 + 3bc < b^2 + (a - b^2) = a \,.$$

Therefore $b + c$ is in S. Since $b + c > b$, this contradicts the fact that b is an upper bound for S. Therefore the inequality $b^2 < a$ is impossible, and the only remaining alternative is $b^2 = a$.

*I 3.14   Roots of higher order.   Rational powers

The least-upper-bound axiom can also be used to show the existence of roots of higher order.   For example, if n is a positive *odd* integer, then for each real x there is exactly one real y such that $y^n = x$.   This y is called the nth *root* of x and is denoted by

$$(I.15) \qquad\qquad y = x^{1/n} \qquad \text{or} \qquad y = \sqrt[n]{x}.$$

When n is *even*, the situation is slightly different.   In this case, if x is negative, there is no real y such that $y^n = x$ because $y^n \geq 0$ for all real y.   However, if x is positive, it can be shown that there is one and only one positive y such that $y^n = x$.   This y is called the *positive nth root* of x and is denoted by the symbols in (I.15).   Since n is even, $(-y)^n = y^n$ and hence each $x > 0$ has two real nth roots, y and $-y$.   However, the symbols $x^{1/n}$ and $\sqrt[n]{x}$ are reserved for the *positive nth root*.   We do not discuss the proofs of these statements here because they will be deduced later as consequences of the intermediate-value theorem for continuous functions (see Section 3.10).

If r is a positive rational number, say $r = m/n$, where m and n are positive integers, we define x^r to be $(x^m)^{1/n}$, the nth root of x^m, whenever this exists.   If $x \neq 0$, we define $x^{-r} = 1/x^r$ whenever x^r is defined.   From these definitions, it is easy to verify that the usual laws of exponents are valid for rational exponents: $x^r \cdot x^s = x^{r+s}$, $(x^r)^s = x^{rs}$, and $(xy)^r = x^r y^r$.

*I 3.15   Representation of real numbers by decimals

A real number of the form

$$(I.16) \qquad\qquad r = a_0 + \frac{a_1}{10} + \frac{a_2}{10^2} + \cdots + \frac{a_n}{10^n},$$

where a_0 is a nonnegative integer and $a_1, a_2, \ldots, a_n$ are integers satisfying $0 \leq a_i \leq 9$, is usually written more briefly as follows:

$$r = a_0.a_1 a_2 \cdots a_n.$$

This is said to be a *finite decimal representation* of r.   For example,

$$\frac{1}{2} = \frac{5}{10} = 0.5, \qquad \frac{1}{50} = \frac{2}{10^2} = 0.02, \qquad \frac{29}{4} = 7 + \frac{2}{10} + \frac{5}{10^2} = 7.25.$$

Real numbers like these are necessarily rational and, in fact, they all have the form $r = a/10^n$, where a is an integer.   However, not all rational numbers can be expressed with finite decimal representations.   For example, if $\frac{1}{3}$ could be so expressed, then we would have $\frac{1}{3} = a/10^n$ or $3a = 10^n$ for some integer a.   But this is impossible since 3 is not a factor of any power of 10.

Nevertheless, we can approximate an arbitrary real number $x > 0$ to any desired degree of accuracy by a sum of the form (I.16) if we take n large enough.   The reason for this may be seen by the following geometric argument: If x is not an integer, then x lies between two consecutive integers, say $a_0 < x < a_0 + 1$.   The segment joining a_0 and $a_0 + 1$ may be subdivided into ten equal parts. If x is not one of the subdivision points, then x must lie between two consecutive subdivision points. This gives us a pair of inequalities of the form

$$a_0 + \frac{a_1}{10} < x < a_0 + \frac{a_1 + 1}{10},$$

where a_1 is an integer $(0 \leq a_1 \leq 9)$. Next we divide the segment joining $a_0 + a_1/10$ and $a_0 + (a_1 + 1)/10$ into ten equal parts (each of length 10^{-2}) and continue the process. If after a finite number of steps a subdivision point coincides with x, then x is a number of the form (I.16). Otherwise the process continues indefinitely, and it generates an infinite set of integers a_1, a_2, a_3, ... In this case, we say that x has the infinite decimal representation

$$x = a_0.a_1a_2a_3 \cdots.$$

At the nth stage, x satisfies the inequalities

$$a_0 + \frac{a_1}{10} + \cdots + \frac{a_n}{10^n} < x < a_0 + \frac{a_1}{10} + \cdots + \frac{a_n + 1}{10^n}.$$

This gives us two approximations to x, one from above and one from below, by finite decimals that differ by 10^{-n}. Therefore we can achieve any desired degree of accuracy in our approximations by taking n large enough.

When $x = \frac{1}{3}$, it is easy to verify that $a_0 = 0$ and $a_n = 3$ for all $n \geq 1$, and hence the corresponding infinite decimal expansion is

$$\tfrac{1}{3} = 0.333 \cdots.$$

Every irrational number has an infinite decimal representation. For example, when $x = \sqrt{2}$ we may calculate by trial and error as many digits in the expansion as we wish. Thus, $\sqrt{2}$ lies between 1.4 and 1.5, because $(1.4)^2 < 2 < (1.5)^2$. Similarly, by squaring and comparing with 2, we find the following further approximations:

$$1.41 < \sqrt{2} < 1.42, \qquad 1.414 < \sqrt{2} < 1.415, \qquad 1.4142 < \sqrt{2} < 1.4143.$$

Note that the foregoing process generates a succession of intervals of lengths 10^{-1}, 10^{-2}, 10^{-3}, ..., each contained in the preceding and each containing the point x. This is an example of what is known as a sequence of *nested intervals*, a concept that is sometimes used as a basis for constructing the irrational numbers from the rational numbers.

Since we shall do very little with decimals in this book, we shall not develop their properties in any further detail except to mention how decimal expansions may be defined analytically with the help of the least-upper-bound axiom.

If x is a given positive real number, let a_0 denote the largest integer $\leq x$. Having chosen a_0, we let a_1 denote the largest integer such that

$$a_0 + \frac{a_1}{10} \leq x.$$

More generally, having chosen $a_0, a_1, \ldots, a_{n-1}$, we let a_n denote the largest integer such that

(I.17) $$a_0 + \frac{a_1}{10} + \frac{a_2}{10^2} + \cdots + \frac{a_n}{10^n} \leq x .$$

Let S denote the set of all numbers

(I.18) $$a_0 + \frac{a_1}{10} + \frac{a_2}{10^2} + \cdots + \frac{a_n}{10^n}$$

obtained in this way for $n = 0, 1, 2, \ldots$. Then S is nonempty and bounded above, and it is easy to verify that x is actually the least upper bound of S. The integers $a_0, a_1, a_2, \ldots$ so obtained may be used to define a decimal expansion of x if we write

$$x = a_0.a_1a_2a_3 \cdots$$

to mean that the nth digit a_n is the largest integer satisfying (I.17). For example, if $x = \frac{1}{8}$, we find $a_0 = 0$, $a_1 = 1$, $a_2 = 2$, $a_3 = 5$, and $a_n = 0$ for all $n \geq 4$. Therefore we may write

$$\tfrac{1}{8} = 0.125000 \cdots .$$

If in (I.17) we replace the inequality sign $\leq$ by $<$, we obtain a slightly different definition of decimal expansions. The least upper bound of all numbers of the form (I.18) is again x, although the integers $a_0, a_1, a_2, \ldots$ need not be the same as those which satisfy (I.17). For example, if this second definition is applied to $x = \frac{1}{8}$, we find $a_0 = 0$, $a_1 = 1$, $a_2 = 2$, $a_3 = 4$, and $a_n = 9$ for all $n \geq 4$. This leads to the infinite decimal representation

$$\tfrac{1}{8} = 0.124999 \cdots .$$

The fact that a real number might have two different decimal representations is merely a reflection of the fact that two different sets of real numbers can have the same supremum.

Part 4. *Mathematical Induction, Summation Notation, and Related Topics*

I 4.1 An example of a proof by mathematical induction

There is no *largest* integer because when we add 1 to an integer k, we obtain $k + 1$, which is larger than k. Nevertheless, starting with the number 1, we can reach any positive integer whatever in a finite number of steps, passing successively from k to $k + 1$ at each step. This is the basis for a type of reasoning that mathematicians call *proof by induction*. We shall illustrate the use of this method by proving the pair of inequalities used in Section

I 1.3 in the computation of the area of a parabolic segment, namely

(I.19) $$1^2 + 2^2 + \cdots + (n-1)^2 < \frac{n^3}{3} < 1^2 + 2^2 + \cdots + n^2.$$

Consider the leftmost inequality first, and let us refer to this formula as $A(n)$ (an assertion involving n). It is easy to verify this assertion directly for the first few values of n. Thus, for example, when n takes the values 1, 2, and 3, the assertion becomes

$$A(1): 0 < \frac{1^3}{3}, \qquad A(2): 1^2 < \frac{2^3}{3}, \qquad A(3): 1^2 + 2^2 < \frac{3^3}{3},$$

provided we agree to interpret the sum on the left as 0 when $n = 1$.

Our object is to prove that $A(n)$ is true for every positive integer n. The procedure is as follows: Assume the assertion has been proved for a particular value of n, say for $n = k$. That is, assume we have proved

$$A(k): 1^2 + 2^2 + \cdots + (k-1)^2 < \frac{k^3}{3}$$

for a fixed $k \geq 1$. Now *using this*, we shall deduce the corresponding result for $k + 1$:

$$A(k+1): 1^2 + 2^2 + \cdots + k^2 < \frac{(k+1)^3}{3}.$$

Start with $A(k)$ and add k^2 to both sides. This gives the inequality

$$1^2 + 2^2 + \cdots + k^2 < \frac{k^3}{3} + k^2.$$

To obtain $A(k+1)$ as a consequence of this, it suffices to show that

$$\frac{k^3}{3} + k^2 < \frac{(k+1)^3}{3}.$$

But this follows at once from the equation

$$\frac{(k+1)^3}{3} = \frac{k^3 + 3k^2 + 3k + 1}{3} = \frac{k^3}{3} + k^2 + k + \frac{1}{3}.$$

Therefore we have shown that $A(k+1)$ follows from $A(k)$. Now, since $A(1)$ has been verified directly, we conclude that $A(2)$ is also true. Knowing that $A(2)$ is true, we conclude that $A(3)$ is true, and so on. Since every integer can be reached in this way, $A(n)$ is true for all positive integers n. This proves the leftmost inequality in (I.19). The rightmost inequality can be proved in the same way.

I 4.2   The principle of mathematical induction

The reader should make certain that he understands the *pattern* of the foregoing proof. First we proved the assertion $A(n)$ for $n = 1$. Next we showed that *if* the assertion is true for a particular integer, *then* it is also true for the next integer. From this, we concluded that the assertion is true for all positive integers.

The idea of induction may be illustrated in many nonmathematical ways. For example, imagine a row of toy soldiers, numbered consecutively, and suppose they are so arranged that if any one of them falls, say the one labeled k, it will knock over the next one, labeled $k + 1$. Then anyone can visualize what would happen if soldier number 1 were toppled backward. It is also clear that if a later soldier were knocked over first, say the one labeled n_1, then all soldiers behind *him* would fall. This illustrates a slight generalization of the method of induction which can be described in the following way.

Method of proof by induction. Let $A(n)$ be an assertion involving an integer n. We conclude that $A(n)$ is true for every $n \geq n_1$ if we can perform the following two steps:
  (a) Prove that $A(n_1)$ is true.
  (b) Let k be an arbitrary but fixed integer $\geq n_1$. Assume that $A(k)$ is true and prove that $A(k + 1)$ is also true.

In actual practice n_1 is usually 1. The logical justification for this method of proof is the following theorem about real numbers.

THEOREM I.36.   PRINCIPLE OF MATHEMATICAL INDUCTION.   *Let S be a set of positive integers which has the following two properties*:
  (a) *The number 1 is in the set S.*
  (b) *If an integer k is in S, then so is $k + 1$.*
Then every positive integer is in the set S.

Proof. Properties (a) and (b) tell us that S is an inductive set. But the positive integers were defined to be exactly those real numbers which belong to every inductive set. (See Section I 3.6.) Therefore S contains every positive integer.

Whenever we carry out a proof of an assertion $A(n)$ for all $n \geq 1$ by mathematical induction, we are applying Theorem I.36 to the set S of all the integers for which the assertion is true. If we want to prove that $A(n)$ is true only for $n \geq n_1$, we apply Theorem I.36 to the set of n for which $A(n + n_1 - 1)$ is true.

*I 4.3   The well-ordering principle

There is another important property of the positive integers, called the well-ordering principle, that is also used as a basis for proofs by induction. It can be stated as follows.

THEOREM I.37.   WELL-ORDERING PRINCIPLE.   *Every nonempty set of positive integers contains a smallest member.*

Note that the well-ordering principle refers to sets of *positive* integers. The theorem is not true for arbitrary sets of integers. For example, the set of all integers has no smallest member.

The well-ordering principle can be deduced from the principle of induction. This is demonstrated in Section I 4.5. We conclude this section with an example showing how the well-ordering principle can be used to prove theorems about positive integers.

Let $A(n)$ denote the following assertion:

$$A(n): 1^2 + 2^2 + \cdots + n^2 = \frac{n^3}{3} + \frac{n^2}{2} + \frac{n}{6}.$$

Again, we note that $A(1)$ is true, since

$$1^2 = \tfrac{1}{3} + \tfrac{1}{2} + \tfrac{1}{6}.$$

Now there are only two possibilities. We have either
  (i) $A(n)$ is true for every positive integer n, or
  (ii) there is at least one positive integer n for which $A(n)$ is false.
We shall prove that alternative (ii) leads to a contradiction. Assume (ii) holds. Then by the well-ordering principle, there must be a *smallest* positive integer, say k, for which $A(k)$ is false. (We apply the well-ordering principle to the set of all positive integers n for which $A(n)$ is false. Statement (ii) says that this set is nonempty.) This k must be greater than 1, because we have verified that $A(1)$ is true. Also, the assertion must be true for $k - 1$, since k was the smallest integer for which $A(k)$ is false; therefore we may write

$$A(k-1): 1^2 + 2^2 + \cdots + (k-1)^2 = \frac{(k-1)^3}{3} + \frac{(k-1)^2}{2} + \frac{k-1}{6}.$$

Adding k^2 to both sides and simplifying the right-hand side, we find

$$1^2 + 2^2 + \cdots + k^2 = \frac{k^3}{3} + \frac{k^2}{2} + \frac{k}{6}.$$

But this equation states that $A(k)$ is true; therefore we have a contradiction, because k is an integer for which $A(k)$ is false. In other words, statement (ii) leads to a contradiction. Therefore (i) holds, and this proves that the identity in question is valid for all values of $n \geq 1$. An immediate consequence of this identity is the rightmost inequality in (I.19).

A proof like this which makes use of the well-ordering principle is also referred to as a proof by induction. Of course, the proof could also be put in the more usual form in which we verify $A(1)$ and then pass from $A(k)$ to $A(k + 1)$.

I 4.4 Exercises

1. Prove the following formulas by induction:

  (a) $1 + 2 + 3 + \cdots + n = n(n + 1)/2.$

  (b) $1 + 3 + 5 + \cdots + (2n - 1) = n^2.$

  (c) $1^3 + 2^3 + 3^3 + \cdots + n^3 = (1 + 2 + 3 + \cdots + n)^2.$

  (d) $1^3 + 2^3 + \cdots + (n - 1)^3 < n^4/4 < 1^3 + 2^3 + \cdots + n^3.$

2. Note that
$$1 = 1 \,,$$
$$1 - 4 = -(1 + 2) \,,$$
$$1 - 4 + 9 = 1 + 2 + 3 \,,$$
$$1 - 4 + 9 - 16 = -(1 + 2 + 3 + 4) \,.$$

Guess the general law suggested and prove it by induction.

3. Note that
$$1 + \tfrac{1}{2} = 2 - \tfrac{1}{2} \,,$$
$$1 + \tfrac{1}{2} + \tfrac{1}{4} = 2 - \tfrac{1}{4} \,,$$
$$1 + \tfrac{1}{2} + \tfrac{1}{4} + \tfrac{1}{8} = 2 - \tfrac{1}{8} \,.$$

Guess the general law suggested and prove it by induction.

4. Note that
$$1 - \tfrac{1}{2} = \tfrac{1}{2} \,,$$
$$(1 - \tfrac{1}{2})(1 - \tfrac{1}{3}) = \tfrac{1}{3} \,,$$
$$(1 - \tfrac{1}{2})(1 - \tfrac{1}{3})(1 - \tfrac{1}{4}) = \tfrac{1}{4} \,.$$

Guess the general law suggested and prove it by induction.

5. Guess a general law which simplifies the product

$$\left(1 - \frac{1}{4}\right)\left(1 - \frac{1}{9}\right)\left(1 - \frac{1}{16}\right) \cdots \left(1 - \frac{1}{n^2}\right)$$

and prove it by induction.

6. Let $A(n)$ denote the statement: $1 + 2 + \cdots + n = \tfrac{1}{8}(2n + 1)^2$.
   (a) Prove that if $A(k)$ is true for an integer k, then $A(k + 1)$ is also true.
   (b) Criticize the statement: "By induction it follows that $A(n)$ is true for all n."
   (c) Amend $A(n)$ by changing the equality to an inequality that is true for all positive integers n.

7. Let n_1 be the smallest positive integer n for which the inequality $(1 + x)^n > 1 + nx + nx^2$ is true for all $x > 0$. Compute n_1, and prove that the inequality is true for all integers $n \geq n_1$.

8. Given positive real numbers $a_1, a_2, a_3, \ldots$, such that $a_n \leq ca_{n-1}$ for all $n \geq 2$, where c is a fixed positive number, use induction to prove that $a_n \leq a_1 c^{n-1}$ for all $n \geq 1$.

9. Prove the following statement by induction: If a line of unit length is given, then a line of length $\sqrt{n}$ can be constructed with straightedge and compass for each positive integer n.

10. Let b denote a fixed positive integer. Prove the following statement by induction: For every integer $n \geq 0$, there exist nonnegative integers q and r such that

$$n = qb + r, \qquad 0 \leq r < b \,.$$

11. Let n and d denote integers. We say that d is a *divisor* of n if $n = cd$ for some integer c. An integer n is called a *prime* if $n > 1$ and if the only positive divisors of n are 1 and n. Prove, by induction, that every integer $n > 1$ is either a prime or a product of primes.

12. Describe the fallacy in the following "proof" by induction:

   Statement. Given any collection of n blonde girls. If at least one of the girls has blue eyes, then all n of them have blue eyes.

   "*Proof.*" The statement is obviously true when $n = 1$. The step from k to $k + 1$ can be illustrated by going from $n = 3$ to $n = 4$. Assume, therefore, that the statement is true when $n = 3$ and let G_1, G_2, G_3, G_4 be four blonde girls, at least one of which, say G_1, has blue eyes. Taking G_1, G_2, and G_3 together and using the fact that the statement is true when $n = 3$, we find that G_2 and G_3 also have blue eyes. Repeating the process with G_1, G_2, and G_4, we find that G_4 has blue eyes. Thus all four have blue eyes. A similar argument allows us to make the step from k to $k + 1$ in general.

Corollary. All blonde girls have blue eyes.

Proof. Since there exists at least one blonde girl with blue eyes, we can apply the foregoing result to the collection consisting of all blonde girls.

Note: This example is from G. Pólya, who suggests that the reader may want to test the validity of the statement by experiment.

*I 4.5 Proof of the well-ordering principle

In this section we deduce the well-ordering principle from the principle of induction.

Let T be a nonempty collection of positive integers. We want to prove that T has a smallest member, that is, that there is a positive integer t_0 in T such that $t_0 \leq t$ for all t in T.

Suppose T has no smallest member. We shall show that this leads to a contradiction. The integer 1 cannot be in T (otherwise it would be the smallest member of T). Let S denote the collection of all positive integers n such that $n < t$ for all t in T. Now 1 is in S because $1 < t$ for all t in T. Next, let k be a positive integer in S. Then $k < t$ for all t in T. We shall prove that $k + 1$ is also in S. If this were not so, then for some t_1 in T we would have $t_1 \leq k + 1$. Since T has no smallest member, there is an integer t_2 in T such that $t_2 < t_1$, and hence $t_2 < k + 1$. But this means that $t_2 \leq k$, contradicting the fact that $k < t$ for all t in T. Therefore $k + 1$ is in S. By the induction principle, S contains all positive integers. Since T is nonempty, there is a positive integer t in T. But this t must also be in S (since S contains all positive integers). It follows from the definition of S that $t < t$, which is a contradiction. Therefore, the assumption that T has no smallest member leads to a contradiction. It follows that T must have a smallest member, and in turn this proves that the well-ordering principle is a consequence of the principle of induction.

I 4.6 The summation notation

In the calculations for the area of the parabolic segment, we encountered the sum

(I.20) $$1^2 + 2^2 + 3^2 + \cdots + n^2 .$$

Note that a typical term in this sum is of the form k^2, and we get all the terms by letting k run through the values $1, 2, 3, \ldots, n$. There is a very useful and convenient notation which enables us to write sums like this in a more compact form. This is called the *summation notation* and it makes use of the Greek letter sigma, Σ. Using summation notation, we can write the sum in (I.20) as follows:

$$\sum_{k=1}^{n} k^2.$$

This symbol is read: "The sum of k^2 for k running from 1 to n." The numbers appearing under and above the sigma tell us the range of values taken by k. The letter k itself is referred to as the *index of summation*. Of course, it is not important that we use the letter k; any other convenient letter may take its place. For example, instead of $\sum_{k=1}^{n} k^2$ we could write $\sum_{i=1}^{n} i^2$, $\sum_{j=1}^{n} j^2$, $\sum_{m=1}^{n} m^2$, etc., all of which are considered as alternative notations for the same thing. The letters i, j, k, m, etc. that are used in this way are called *dummy indices*. It would not be a good idea to use the letter n for the dummy index in this particular example because n is already being used for the number of terms.

More generally, when we want to form the sum of several real numbers, say $a_1, a_2, \ldots,$ a_n, we denote such a sum by the symbol

$$(I.21) \qquad\qquad\qquad a_1 + a_2 + \cdots + a_n$$

which, using summation notation, can be written as follows:

$$(I.22) \qquad\qquad\qquad \sum_{k=1}^{n} a_k \,.$$

For example, we have

$$\sum_{k=1}^{4} a_k = a_1 + a_2 + a_3 + a_4\,,$$

$$\sum_{i=1}^{5} x_i = x_1 + x_2 + x_3 + x_4 + x_5\,.$$

Sometimes it is convenient to begin summations from 0 or from some value of the index beyond 1. For example, we have

$$\sum_{i=0}^{4} x_i = x_0 + x_1 + x_2 + x_3 + x_4\,,$$

$$\sum_{n=2}^{5} n^3 = 2^3 + 3^3 + 4^3 + 5^3.$$

Other uses of the summation notation are illustrated below:

$$\sum_{m=0}^{4} x^{m+1} = x + x^2 + x^3 + x^4 + x^5,$$

$$\sum_{j=1}^{6} 2^{j-1} = 1 + 2 + 2^2 + 2^3 + 2^4 + 2^5.$$

To emphasize once more that the choice of dummy index is unimportant, we note that the last sum may also be written in each of the following forms:

$$\sum_{q=1}^{6} 2^{q-1} = \sum_{r=0}^{5} 2^r = \sum_{n=0}^{5} 2^{5-n} = \sum_{k=1}^{6} 2^{6-k}.$$

Note: From a strictly logical standpoint, the symbols in (I.21) and (I.22) do not appear among the primitive symbols for the real-number system. In a more careful treatment, we could define these new symbols in terms of the primitive undefined symbols of our system.

This may be done by a process known as *definition by induction* which, like proof by induction, consists of two parts:

(a) We define

$$\sum_{k=1}^{1} a_k = a_1 .$$

(b) Assuming that we have defined $\sum_{k=1}^{n} a_k$ for a fixed $n \geq 1$, we further define

$$\sum_{k=1}^{n+1} a_k = \left(\sum_{k=1}^{n} a_k \right) + a_{n+1} .$$

To illustrate, we may take $n = 1$ in (b) and use (a) to obtain

$$\sum_{k=1}^{2} a_k = \sum_{k=1}^{1} a_k + a_2 = a_1 + a_2 .$$

Now, having defined $\sum_{k=1}^{2} a_k$, we can use (b) again with $n = 2$ to obtain

$$\sum_{k=1}^{3} a_k = \sum_{k=1}^{2} a_k + a_3 = (a_1 + a_2) + a_3 .$$

By the associative law for addition (Axiom 2), the sum $(a_1 + a_2) + a_3$ is the same as $a_1 + (a_2 + a_3)$, and therefore there is no danger of confusion if we drop the parentheses and simply write $a_1 + a_2 + a_3$ for $\sum_{k=1}^{3} a_k$. Similarly, we have

$$\sum_{k=1}^{4} a_k = \sum_{k=1}^{3} a_k + a_4 = (a_1 + a_2 + a_3) + a_4 .$$

In this case we can *prove* that the sum $(a_1 + a_2 + a_3) + a_4$ is the same as $(a_1 + a_2) + (a_3 + a_4)$ or $a_1 + (a_2 + a_3 + a_4)$, and therefore the parentheses can be dropped again without danger of ambiguity, and we agree to write

$$\sum_{k=1}^{4} a_k = a_1 + a_2 + a_3 + a_4 .$$

Continuing in this way, we find that (a) and (b) together give us a complete definition of the symbol in (I.22). The notation in (I.21) is considered to be merely an alternative way of writing (I.22). It is justified by a general associative law for addition which we shall not attempt to state or to prove here.

The reader should notice that *definition by induction* and *proof by induction* involve the same underlying idea. A definition by induction is also called a *recursive definition*.

I 4.7 Exercises

1. Find the numerical values of the following sums:

(a) $\displaystyle\sum_{k=1}^{4} k,$ (c) $\displaystyle\sum_{r=0}^{3} 2^{2r+1},$ (e) $\displaystyle\sum_{i=0}^{5} (2i + 1),$

(b) $\displaystyle\sum_{n=2}^{5} 2^{n-2},$ (d) $\displaystyle\sum_{n=1}^{4} n^n,$ (f) $\displaystyle\sum_{k=1}^{5} \frac{1}{k(k + 1)}.$

2. Establish the following properties of the summation notation:

(a) $\displaystyle\sum_{k=1}^{n} (a_k + b_k) = \sum_{k=1}^{n} a_k + \sum_{k=1}^{n} b_k$ (additive property).

(b) $\displaystyle\sum_{k=1}^{n} (ca_k) = c \sum_{k=1}^{n} a_k$ (homogeneous property).

(c) $\displaystyle\sum_{k=1}^{n} (a_k - a_{k-1}) = a_n - a_0$ (telescoping property).

Use the properties in Exercise 2 whenever possible to derive the formulas in Exercises 3 through 8.

3. $\displaystyle\sum_{k=1}^{n} 1 = n$. (This means $\sum_{k=1}^{n} a_k$, where each $a_k = 1$.)

4. $\displaystyle\sum_{k=1}^{n} (2k - 1) = n^2$.   [*Hint:* $2k - 1 = k^2 - (k - 1)^2$.]

5. $\displaystyle\sum_{k=1}^{n} k = \frac{n^2}{2} + \frac{n}{2}$.   [*Hint:*   Use Exercises 3 and 4.]

6. $\displaystyle\sum_{k=1}^{n} k^2 = \frac{n^3}{3} + \frac{n^2}{2} + \frac{n}{6}$.   [*Hint:* $k^3 - (k - 1)^3 = 3k^2 - 3k + 1$.]

7. $\displaystyle\sum_{k=1}^{n} k^3 = \frac{n^4}{4} + \frac{n^3}{2} + \frac{n^2}{4}$.

8. (a) $\displaystyle\sum_{k=0}^{n} x^k = \frac{1 - x^{n+1}}{1 - x}$ if $x \neq 1$.   *Note:* x^0 is defined to be 1.

[*Hint:*   Apply Exercise 2 to $(1 - x) \sum_{k=0}^{n} x^k$.]

(b) What is the sum equal to when $x = 1$?

9. Prove, by induction, that the sum $\sum_{k=1}^{2n} (-1)^k (2k + 1)$ is proportional to n, and find the constant of proportionality.

10. (a) Give a reasonable definition of the symbol $\sum_{k=m}^{m+n} a_k$.

(b) Prove, by induction, that for $n \geq 1$ we have

$$\sum_{k=n+1}^{2n} \frac{1}{k} = \sum_{m=1}^{2n} \frac{(-1)^{m+1}}{m}.$$

11. Determine whether each of the following statements is true or false. In each case give a reason for your decision.

(a) $\displaystyle\sum_{n=0}^{100} n^4 = \sum_{n=1}^{100} n^4$.

(b) $\displaystyle\sum_{j=0}^{100} 2 = 200$.

(c) $\displaystyle\sum_{k=0}^{100} (2 + k) = 2 + \sum_{k=0}^{100} k$.

(d) $\displaystyle\sum_{i=1}^{100} (i + 1)^2 = \sum_{i=0}^{99} i^2$.

(e) $\displaystyle\sum_{k=1}^{100} k^3 = \left(\sum_{k=1}^{100} k \right) \cdot \left(\sum_{k=1}^{100} k^2 \right)$.

(f) $\displaystyle\sum_{k=0}^{100} k^3 = \left(\sum_{k=0}^{100} k \right)^3$.

12. Guess and prove a general rule which simplifies the sum

$$\sum_{k=1}^{n} \frac{1}{k(k+1)}.$$

13. Prove that $2(\sqrt{n+1} - \sqrt{n}) < \dfrac{1}{\sqrt{n}} < 2(\sqrt{n} - \sqrt{n-1})$ if $n \geq 1$. Then use this to prove that

$$2\sqrt{m} - 2 < \sum_{n=1}^{m} \frac{1}{\sqrt{n}} < 2\sqrt{m} - 1$$

if $m \geq 2$. In particular, when $m = 10^6$, the sum lies between 1998 and 1999.

I 4.8 Absolute values and the triangle inequality

Calculations with inequalities arise quite frequently in calculus. They are of particular importance in dealing with the notion of *absolute value*. If x is a real number, the absolute value of x is a nonnegative real number denoted by $|x|$ and defined as follows:

$$|x| = \begin{cases} x & \text{if } x \geq 0, \\ -x & \text{if } x \leq 0. \end{cases}$$

Note that $-|x| \leq x \leq |x|$. When real numbers are represented geometrically on a real axis, the number $|x|$ is called the *distance* of x from 0. If $a > 0$ and if a point x lies between $-a$ and a, then $|x|$ is nearer to 0 than a is. The analytic statement of this fact is given by the following theorem.

THEOREM I.38. *If $a \geq 0$, then $|x| \leq a$ if and only if $-a \leq x \leq a$.*

Proof. There are two statements to prove: first, that the inequality $|x| \leq a$ implies the two inequalities $-a \leq x \leq a$ and, conversely, that $-a \leq x \leq a$ implies $|x| \leq a$.

Suppose $|x| \leq a$. Then we also have $-a \leq -|x|$. But either $x = |x|$ or $x = -|x|$ and hence $-a \leq -|x| \leq x \leq |x| \leq a$. This proves the first statement.

To prove the converse, assume $-a \leq x \leq a$. Then if $x \geq 0$, we have $|x| = x \leq a$, whereas if $x \leq 0$, we have $|x| = -x \leq a$. In either case we have $|x| \leq a$, and this completes the proof.

Figure I.9 illustrates the geometrical significance of this theorem.

$|x| \leq a$ in this interval

$$-a \qquad 0 \qquad a$$

FIGURE I.9   Geometrical significance of Theorem I.38.

As a consequence of Theorem I.38, it is easy to derive an important inequality which states that the absolute value of a sum of two real numbers cannot exceed the sum of their absolute values.

THEOREM I.39.   *For arbitrary real numbers x and y, we have*

$$|x + y| \leq |x| + |y| \, .$$

Note: This property is called the *triangle inequality*, because when it is generalized to vectors it states that the length of any side of a triangle is less than or equal to the sum of the lengths of the other two sides.

Proof. Adding the inequalities $-|x| \leq x \leq |x|$ and $-|y| \leq y \leq |y|$, we obtain

$$-(|x| + |y|) \leq x + y \leq |x| + |y| \, ,$$

and hence, by Theorem I.38, we conclude that $|x + y| \leq |x| + |y|$.

If we take $x = a - c$ and $y = c - b$, then $x + y = a - b$ and the triangle inequality becomes

$$|a - b| \leq |a - c| + |b - c| \, .$$

This form of the triangle inequality is often used in practice.

Using mathematical induction, we may extend the triangle inequality as follows:

THEOREM I.40.   *For arbitrary real numbers* $a_1, a_2, \ldots, a_n$, *we have*

$$\left| \sum_{k=1}^{n} a_k \right| \leq \sum_{k=1}^{n} |a_k| \, .$$

Proof. When $n = 1$ the inequality is trivial, and when $n = 2$ it is the triangle inequality. Assume, then, that it is true for n real numbers. Then for $n + 1$ real numbers $a_1, a_2, \ldots,$ a_{n+1}, we have

$$\left| \sum_{k=1}^{n+1} a_k \right| = \left| \sum_{k=1}^{n} a_k + a_{n+1} \right| \leq \left| \sum_{k=1}^{n} a_k \right| + |a_{n+1}| \leq \sum_{k=1}^{n} |a_k| + |a_{n+1}| = \sum_{k=1}^{n+1} |a_k| \, .$$

Hence the theorem is true for $n + 1$ numbers if it is true for n. By induction, it is true for every positive integer n.

The next theorem describes an important inequality that we shall use later in connection with our study of vector algebra.

THEOREM I.41.   THE CAUCHY–SCHWARZ INEQUALITY.   *If* $a_1, \ldots, a_n$ *and* $b_1, \ldots, b_n$ *are arbitrary real numbers, we have*

(I.23) $$\left(\sum_{k=1}^{n} a_k b_k \right)^2 \leq \left(\sum_{k=1}^{n} a_k^2 \right) \left(\sum_{k=1}^{n} b_k^2 \right) \, .$$

The equality sign holds if and only if there is a real number x such that $a_k x + b_k = 0$ for each $k = 1, 2, \ldots, n$.

Proof. We have $\sum_{k=1}^{n} (a_k x + b_k)^2 \geq 0$ for every real x because a sum of squares can never be negative. This may be written in the form

(I.24) $Ax^2 + 2Bx + C \geq 0 \,,$

where

$$A = \sum_{k=1}^{n} a_k^2 \,, \qquad B = \sum_{k=1}^{n} a_k b_k \,, \qquad C = \sum_{k=1}^{n} b_k^2 \,.$$

We wish to prove that $B^2 \leq AC$. If $A = 0$, then each $a_k = 0$, so $B = 0$ and the result is trivial. If $A \neq 0$, we may complete the square and write

$$Ax^2 + 2Bx + C = A\left(x + \frac{B}{A}\right)^2 + \frac{AC - B^2}{A} \,.$$

The right side has its smallest value when $x = -B/A$. Putting $x = -B/A$ in (I.24), we obtain $B^2 \leq AC$. This proves (I.23). The reader should verify that the equality sign holds if and only if there is an x such that $a_k x + b_k = 0$ for each k.

I 4.9 Exercises

1. Prove each of the following properties of absolute values.
   (a) $|x| = 0$ if and only if $x = 0$.   (f) $|xy| = |x|\,|y|$.
   (b) $|-x| = |x|$.   (g) $|x/y| = |x|/|y|$ if $y \neq 0$.
   (c) $|x - y| = |y - x|$.   (h) $|x - y| \leq |x| + |y|$.
   (d) $|x|^2 = x^2$.   (i) $|x| - |y| \leq |x - y|$.
   (e) $|x| = \sqrt{x^2}$.   (j) $\bigl| |x| - |y| \bigr| \leq |x - y|$.

2. Each inequality (a_i), listed below, is equivalent to exactly one inequality (b_j). For example, $|x| < 3$ if and only if $-3 < x < 3$, and hence (a_1) is equivalent to (b_2). Determine all equivalent pairs.
   (a_1) $|x| < 3$. (b_1) $4 < x < 6$.
   (a_2) $|x - 1| < 3$. (b_2) $-3 < x < 3$.
   (a_3) $|3 - 2x| < 1$. (b_3) $x > 3$ or $x < -1$.
   (a_4) $|1 + 2x| \leq 1$. (b_4) $x > 2$.
   (a_5) $|x - 1| > 2$. (b_5) $-2 < x < 4$.
   (a_6) $|x + 2| \geq 5$. (b_6) $-\sqrt{3} \leq x \leq -1$ or $1 \leq x \leq \sqrt{3}$.
   (a_7) $|5 - x^{-1}| < 1$. (b_7) $1 < x < 2$.
   (a_8) $|x - 5| < |x + 1|$. (b_8) $x \leq -7$ or $x \geq 3$.
   (a_9) $|x^2 - 2| \leq 1$. (b_9) $\frac{1}{6} < x < \frac{1}{4}$.
   (a_{10}) $x < x^2 - 12 < 4x$. (b_{10}) $-1 \leq x \leq 0$.

3. Determine whether each of the following is true or false. In each case give a reason for your decision.
   (a) $x < 5$ implies $|x| < 5$.
   (b) $|x - 5| < 2$ implies $3 < x < 7$.
   (c) $|1 + 3x| \leq 1$ implies $x \geq -\frac{2}{3}$.
   (d) There is no real x for which $|x - 1| = |x - 2|$.
   (e) For every $x > 0$ there is a $y > 0$ such that $|2x + y| = 5$.

4. Show that the equality sign holds in the Cauchy–Schwarz inequality if and only if there is a real number x such that $a_k x + b_k = 0$ for every $k = 1, 2, \ldots, n$.

*I 4.10   Miscellaneous exercises involving induction

In this section we assemble a number of miscellaneous facts whose proofs are good exercises in the use of mathematical induction. Some of these exercises may serve as a basis for supplementary classroom discussion.

Factorials and binomial coefficients. The symbol $n!$ (read "n *factorial*") may be defined by induction as follows: $0! = 1$, $n! = (n - 1)! \, n$ if $n \geq 1$. Note that $n! = 1 \cdot 2 \cdot 3 \cdots n$.

If $0 \leq k \leq n$, the *binomial coefficient* $\binom{n}{k}$ is defined as follows:

$$\binom{n}{k} = \frac{n!}{k! \, (n - k)!} \, .$$

Note: Sometimes $_nC_k$ is written for $\binom{n}{k}$. These numbers appear as coefficients in the binomial theorem. (See Exercise 4 below.)

1. Compute the values of the following binomial coefficients:
   (a) $\binom{5}{3}$,   (b) $\binom{7}{0}$,   (c) $\binom{7}{1}$,   (d) $\binom{7}{2}$,   (e) $\binom{17}{14}$,   (f) $\binom{0}{0}$.
2. (a) Show that $\binom{n}{k} = \binom{n}{n-k}$.   (c) Find k, given that $\binom{14}{k} = \binom{14}{k-4}$.
   (b) Find n, given that $\binom{n}{10} = \binom{n}{7}$.   (d) Is there a k such that $\binom{12}{k} = \binom{12}{k-3}$?
3. Prove that $\binom{n+1}{k} = \binom{n}{k-1} + \binom{n}{k}$. This is called the *law of Pascal's triangle* and it provides a rapid way of computing binomial coefficients successively. Pascal's triangle is illustrated here for $n \leq 6$.

$$
\begin{array}{ccccccccccccc}
&&&&&& 1 &&&&&& \\
&&&&& 1 && 1 &&&&& \\
&&&& 1 && 2 && 1 &&&& \\
&&& 1 && 3 && 3 && 1 &&& \\
&& 1 && 4 && 6 && 4 && 1 && \\
& 1 && 5 && 10 && 10 && 5 && 1 & \\
1 && 6 && 15 && 20 && 15 && 6 && 1
\end{array}
$$

4. Use induction to prove the binomial theorem

$$(a + b)^n = \sum_{k=0}^{n} \binom{n}{k} a^k b^{n-k} \, .$$

Then use the theorem to derive the formulas

$$\sum_{k=0}^{n} \binom{n}{k} = 2^n \quad \text{and} \quad \sum_{k=0}^{n} (-1)^k \binom{n}{k} = 0, \quad \text{if } n > 0.$$

The product notation. The product of n real numbers $a_1, a_2, \ldots, a_n$ is denoted by the symbol $\prod_{k=1}^{n} a_k$, which may be defined by induction. The symbol $a_1 a_2 \cdots a_n$ is an alternative notation for this product. Note that

$$n! = \prod_{k=1}^{n} k.$$

5. Give a definition by induction for the product $\prod_{k=1}^{n} a_k$.

Prove the following properties of products by induction:

6. $\displaystyle\prod_{k=1}^{n} (a_k b_k) = \left(\prod_{k=1}^{n} a_k\right)\left(\prod_{k=1}^{n} b_k\right)$ (multiplicative property).

An important special case is the relation $\prod_{k=1}^{n} (ca_k) = c^n \prod_{k=1}^{n} a_k$.

7. $\displaystyle\prod_{k=1}^{n} \frac{a_k}{a_{k-1}} = \frac{a_n}{a_0}$ if each $a_k \neq 0$ (telescoping property).

8. If $x \neq 1$, show that

$$\prod_{k=1}^{n} (1 + x^{2^{k-1}}) = \frac{1 - x^{2^n}}{1 - x}.$$

What is the value of the product when $x = 1$?

9. If $a_k < b_k$ for each $k = 1, 2, \ldots, n$, it is easy to prove by induction that $\sum_{k=1}^{n} a_k < \sum_{k=1}^{n} b_k$. Discuss the corresponding inequality for products:

$$\prod_{k=1}^{n} a_k < \prod_{k=1}^{n} b_k.$$

Some special inequalities

10. If $x > 1$, prove by induction that $x^n > x$ for every integer $n \geq 2$. If $0 < x < 1$, prove that $x^n < x$ for every integer $n \geq 2$.

11. Determine all positive integers n for which $2^n < n!$.

12. (a) Use the binomial theorem to prove that for n a positive integer we have

$$\left(1 + \frac{1}{n}\right)^n = 1 + \sum_{k=1}^{n}\left\{\frac{1}{k!} \prod_{r=0}^{k-1}\left(1 - \frac{r}{n}\right)\right\}.$$

   (b) If $n > 1$, use part (a) and Exercise 11 to deduce the inequalities

$$2 < \left(1 + \frac{1}{n}\right)^n < 1 + \sum_{k=1}^{n} \frac{1}{k!} < 3.$$

13. (a) Let p be a positive integer. Prove that

$$b^p - a^p = (b - a)(b^{p-1} + b^{p-2}a + b^{p-3}a^2 + \cdots + ba^{p-2} + a^{p-1}).$$

   [*Hint:* Use the telescoping property for sums.]

   (b) Let p and n denote positive integers. Use part (a) to show that

$$n^p < \frac{(n + 1)^{p+1} - n^{p+1}}{p + 1} < (n + 1)^p.$$

(c) Use induction to prove that

$$\sum_{k=1}^{n-1} k^p < \frac{n^{p+1}}{p+1} < \sum_{k=1}^{n} k^p .$$

Part (b) will assist in making the inductive step from n to $n + 1$.

14. Let $a_1 , \ldots , a_n$ be n real numbers, all having the same sign and all greater than -1. Use induction to prove that

$$(1 + a_1)(1 + a_2) \cdots (1 + a_n) \geq 1 + a_1 + a_2 + \cdots + a_n .$$

In particular, when $a_1 = a_2 = \cdots = a_n = x$, where $x > -1$, this yields

(I.25) $(1 + x)^n \geq 1 + nx$ (*Bernoulli's inequality*).

Show that when $n > 1$ the equality sign holds in (I.25) only for $x = 0$.

15. If $n \geq 2$, prove that $n!/n^n \leq (\frac{1}{2})^k$, where k is the greatest integer $\leq n/2$.

16. The numbers 1, 2, 3, 5, 8, 13, 21, $\ldots$, in which each term after the second is the sum of its two predecessors, are called *Fibonacci numbers*. They may be defined by induction as follows:

$$a_1 = 1, \qquad a_2 = 2, \qquad a_{n+1} = a_n + a_{n-1} \qquad \text{if} \quad n \geq 2 .$$

Prove that

$$a_n < \left(\frac{1 + \sqrt{5}}{2} \right)^n$$

for every $n \geq 1$.

Inequalities relating different types of averages. Let $x_1 , x_2 , \ldots , x_n$ be n positive real numbers. If p is a nonzero integer, the *pth-power mean* M_p of the n numbers is defined as follows:

$$M_p = \left(\frac{x_1^p + \cdots + x_n^p}{n} \right)^{1/p} .$$

The number M_1 is also called the *arithmetic mean*, M_2 the *root mean square*, and M_{-1} the *harmonic mean*.

17. If $p > 0$, prove that $M_p < M_{2p}$ when $x_1 , x_2 , \ldots , x_n$ are not all equal.

[*Hint:* Apply the Cauchy–Schwarz inequality with $a_k = x_k^p$ and $b_k = 1$.]

18. Use the result of Exercise 17 to prove that

$$a^4 + b^4 + c^4 \geq \tfrac{64}{3}$$

if $a^2 + b^2 + c^2 = 8$ and $a > 0, b > 0, c > 0$.

19. Let $a_1 , \ldots , a_n$ be n positive real numbers whose product is equal to 1. Prove that $a_1 + \cdots + a_n \geq n$ and that the equality sign holds only if every $a_k = 1$.

[*Hint:* Consider two cases: (a) All $a_k = 1$; (b) not all $a_k = 1$. Use induction. In case (b) notice that if $a_1 a_2 \cdots a_{n+1} = 1$, then at least one factor, say a_1, exceeds 1 and at least one factor, say a_{n+1}, is less than 1. Let $b_1 = a_1 a_{n+1}$ and apply the induction hypothesis to the product $b_1 a_2 \cdots a_n$, using the fact that $(a_1 - 1)(a_{n+1} - 1) < 0$.]

20. The *geometric mean* G of n positive real numbers $x_1, \ldots, x_n$ is defined by the formula $G = (x_1 x_2 \cdots x_n)^{1/n}$.

    (a) Let M_p denote the pth power mean. Prove that $G \leq M_1$ and that $G = M_1$ only when $x_1 = x_2 = \cdots = x_n$.

    (b) Let p and q be integers, $q < 0 < p$. From part (a) deduce that $M_q < G < M_p$ when $x_1, x_2, \ldots, x_n$ are not all equal.

21. Use the result of Exercise 20 to prove the following statement: If a, b, and c are positive real numbers such that $abc = 8$, then $a + b + c \geq 6$ and $ab + ac + bc \geq 12$.

22. If $x_1, \ldots, x_n$ are positive numbers and if $y_k = 1/x_k$, prove that

$$\left(\sum_{k=1}^{n} x_k \right) \left(\sum_{k=1}^{n} y_k \right) \geq n^2 .$$

23. If a, b, and c are positive and if $a + b + c = 1$, prove that $(1 - a)(1 - b)(1 - c) \geq 8abc$.

1

THE CONCEPTS OF INTEGRAL CALCULUS

In this chapter we present the definition of the integral and some of its basic properties. To understand the definition one must have some acquaintance with the function concept; the next few sections are devoted to an explanation of this and related ideas.

1.1 The basic ideas of Cartesian geometry

As mentioned earlier, one of the applications of the integral is the calculation of area. Ordinarily we do not talk about area by itself. Instead, we talk about the area *of something*. This means that we have certain objects (polygonal regions, circular regions, parabolic segments, etc.) whose areas we wish to measure. If we hope to arrive at a treatment of area that will enable us to deal with many different kinds of objects, we must first find an effective way to describe these objects.

The most primitive way of doing this is by drawing figures, as was done by the ancient Greeks. A much better way was suggested by René Descartes (1596–1650), who introduced the subject of analytic geometry (also known as *Cartesian geometry*). Descartes' idea was to represent geometric points by *numbers*. The procedure for points in a plane is this:

Two perpendicular reference lines (called *coordinate axes*) are chosen, one horizontal (called the "*x*-axis"), the other vertical (the "*y*-axis"). Their point of intersection, denoted by 0, is called the *origin*. On the *x*-axis a convenient point is chosen to the right of 0 and its distance from 0 is called the *unit distance*. Vertical distances along the *y*-axis are usually measured with the same unit distance, although sometimes it is convenient to use a different scale on the *y*-axis. Now each point in the plane (sometimes called the *xy*-plane) is assigned a pair of numbers, called its *coordinates*. These numbers tell us how to locate the point. Figure 1.1 illustrates some examples. The point with coordinates (3, 2) lies three units to the right of the *y*-axis and two units above the *x*-axis. The number 3 is called the *x*-coordinate of the point, 2 its *y*-coordinate. Points to the left of the *y*-axis have a negative *x*-coordinate; those below the *x*-axis have a negative *y*-coordinate. The *x*-coordinate of a point is sometimes called its *abscissa* and the *y*-coordinate is called its *ordinate*.

When we write a pair of numbers such as (a, b) to represent a point, we agree that the abscissa or *x*-coordinate, a, is written first. For this reason, the pair (a, b) is often referred to as an *ordered pair*. It is clear that two ordered pairs (a, b) and (c, d) represent the same point if and only if we have $a = c$ and $b = d$. Points (a, b) with both a and b positive are said to lie in the *first quadrant*; those with $a < 0$ and $b > 0$ are in the *second quadrant*;

those with $a < 0$ and $b < 0$ are in the *third quadrant*; and those with $a > 0$ and $b < 0$ are in the *fourth quadrant*. Figure 1.1 shows one point in each quadrant.

The procedure for points in space is similar. We take three mutually perpendicular lines in space intersecting at a point (the origin). These lines determine three mutually perpendicular planes, and each point in space can be completely described by specifying, with appropriate regard for signs, its distances from these planes. We shall discuss three-dimensional Cartesian geometry in more detail later on; for the present we confine our attention to plane analytic geometry.

A geometric figure, such as a curve in the plane, is a collection of points satisfying one or more special conditions. By translating these conditions into expressions involving the

FIGURE 1.1

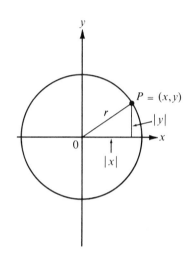

FIGURE 1.2 The circle represented by the Cartesian equation $x^2 + y^2 = r^2$.

coordinates x and y, we obtain one or more equations which characterize the figure in question. For example, consider a circle of radius r with its center at the origin, as shown in Figure 1.2. Let P be an arbitrary point on this circle, and suppose P has coordinates (x, y). Then the line segment OP is the hypotenuse of a right triangle whose legs have lengths $|x|$ and $|y|$ and hence, by the theorem of Pythagoras,

$$x^2 + y^2 = r^2.$$

This equation, called a *Cartesian equation* of the circle, is satisfied by all points (x, y) on the circle and by no others, so the equation completely characterizes the circle. This example illustrates how analytic geometry is used to reduce geometrical statements about points to analytical statements about real numbers.

Throughout their historical development, calculus and analytic geometry have been intimately intertwined. New discoveries in one subject led to improvements in the other. The development of calculus and analytic geometry in this book is similar to the historical development, in that the two subjects are treated together. However, our primary purpose is to discuss calculus. Concepts from analytic geometry that are required for this purpose will be discussed as needed. Actually, only a few very elementary concepts of plane analytic geometry are required to understand the rudiments of calculus. A deeper study of analytic geometry is needed to extend the scope and applications of calculus, and this study will be carried out in later chapters using vector methods as well as the methods of calculus. Until then, all that is required from analytic geometry is a little familiarity with drawing graphs of functions.

1.2 Functions. Informal description and examples

Various fields of human endeavor have to do with relationships that exist between one collection of objects and another. Graphs, charts, curves, tables, formulas, and Gallup polls are familiar to everyone who reads the newspapers. These are merely devices for describing special relations in a quantitative fashion. Mathematicians refer to certain types of these relations as *functions*. In this section, we give an informal description of the function concept. A formal definition is given in Section 1.3.

EXAMPLE 1. The force F necessary to stretch a steel spring a distance x beyond its natural length is proportional to x. That is, $F = cx$, where c is a number independent of x called the spring constant. This formula, discovered by Robert Hooke in the mid-17th century, is called *Hooke's law*, and it is said to express the force as a function of the displacement.

EXAMPLE 2. The volume of a cube is a function of its edge-length. If the edges have length x, the volume V is given by the formula $V = x^3$.

EXAMPLE 3. A *prime* is any integer $n > 1$ that cannot be expressed in the form $n = ab$, where a and b are positive integers, both less than n. The first few primes are 2, 3, 5, 7, 11, 13, 17, 19. For a given real number $x > 0$, it is possible to count the number of primes less than or equal to x. This number is said to be a function of x even though no simple algebraic formula is known for computing it (without counting) when x is known.

The word "function" was introduced into mathematics by Leibniz, who used the term primarily to refer to certain kinds of mathematical formulas. It was later realized that Leibniz's idea of function was much too limited in its scope, and the meaning of the word has since undergone many stages of generalization. Today, the meaning of function is essentially this: Given two sets, say X and Y, a *function* is a correspondence which associates with each element of X one and only one element of Y. The set X is called the *domain* of the function. Those elements of Y associated with the elements in X form a set called the *range* of the function. (This may be all of Y, but it need not be.)

Letters of the English and Greek alphabets are often used to denote functions. The particular letters f, g, h, F, G, H, and φ are frequently used for this purpose. If f is a given function and if x is an object of its domain, the notation $f(x)$ is used to designate that object in the range which is associated to x by the function f, and it is called the *value of f at x* or the *image of x under f*. The symbol $f(x)$ is read as "f of x."

The function idea may be illustrated schematically in many ways. For example, in Figure 1.3(a) the collections X and Y are thought of as sets of points and an arrow is used to suggest a "pairing" of a typical point x in X with the image point $f(x)$ in Y. Another scheme is shown in Figure 1.3(b). Here the function f is imagined to be like a machine into

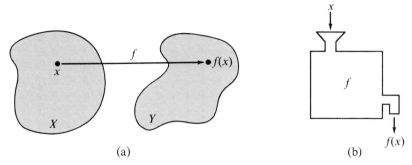

FIGURE 1.3   Schematic representations of the function idea.

which objects of the collection X are fed and objects of Y are produced. When an object x is fed into the machine, the output is the object $f(x)$.

Although the function idea places no restriction on the nature of the objects in the domain X and in the range Y, in elementary calculus we are primarily interested in functions whose domain and range are sets of real numbers. Such functions are called *real-valued functions of a real variable*, or, more briefly, *real functions*, and they may be illustrated geometrically by a graph in the xy-plane. We plot the domain X on the x-axis, and above each point x in X we plot the point (x, y), where $y = f(x)$. The totality of such points (x, y) is called the *graph* of the function.

Now we consider some more examples of real functions.

EXAMPLE 4. *The identity function.* Suppose that $f(x) = x$ for all real x. This function is often called the *identity function.* Its domain is the real line, that is, the set of all real numbers. Here $x = y$ for each point (x, y) on the graph of f. The graph is a straight line making equal angles with the coordinates axes (see Figure 1.4). The range of f is the set of all real numbers.

EXAMPLE 5. *The absolute-value function.* Consider the function which assigns to each real number x the nonnegative number $|x|$. A portion of its graph is shown in Figure 1.5.

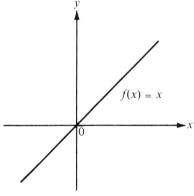

FIGURE 1.4   Graph of the identity function $f(x) = x$.

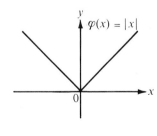

FIGURE 1.5   Absolute-value function $\varphi(x) = |x|$.

Denoting this function by φ, we have $\varphi(x) = |x|$ for all real x. For example, $\varphi(0) = 0$, $\varphi(2) = 2$, $\varphi(-3) = 3$. We list here some properties of absolute values expressed in function notation.

(a) $\varphi(-x) = \varphi(x)$.   (d) $\varphi[\varphi(x)] = \varphi(x)$.

(b) $\varphi(x^2) = x^2$.   (e) $\varphi(x) = \sqrt{x^2}$.

(c) $\varphi(x + y) \le \varphi(x) + \varphi(y)$ (the triangle inequality).

EXAMPLE 6. *The prime-number function.* For any $x > 0$, let $\pi(x)$ be the number of primes less than or equal to x. The domain of π is the set of positive real numbers. Its range is the set of nonnegative integers $\{0, 1, 2, \ldots\}$. A portion of the graph of π is shown in Figure 1.6.

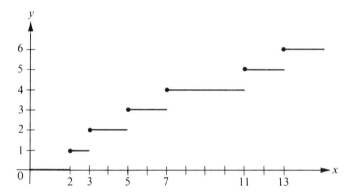

n	$n!$	n	$n!$
1	1	6	720
2	2	7	5,040
3	6	8	40,320
4	24	9	362,880
5	120	10	3,628,800

FIGURE 1.6   The prime-number function.   FIGURE 1.7   The factorial function.

(Different scales are used on the x- and y-axes.) As x increases, the function value $\pi(x)$ remains constant until x reaches a prime, at which point the function value jumps by 1. Therefore the graph of π consists of horizontal line segments. This is an example of a class of functions called *step functions*; they play a fundamental role in the theory of the integral.

EXAMPLE 7. *The factorial function.* For every positive integer n, we define $f(n)$ to be $n! = 1 \cdot 2 \cdots n$. In this example, the domain of f is the set of positive integers. The function values increase so rapidly that it is more convenient to display this function in tabular form rather than as a graph. Figure 1.7 shows a table listing the pairs $(n, n!)$ for $n = 1, 2, \ldots, 10$.

The reader should note two features that all the above examples have in common.

(1) For each x in the domain X there is one and only one image y that is paired with that particular x.

(2) Each function generates a set of pairs (x, y), where x is a typical element of the domain X, and y is the unique element of Y that goes with x.

In most of the above examples, we displayed the pairs (x, y) geometrically as points on a graph. In Example 7 we displayed them as entries in a table. In each case, to know the function is to know, in one way or another, *all* the pairs (x, y) that it generates. This simple observation is the motivation behind the formal definition of the function concept that is given in the next section.

*1.3 Functions. Formal definition as a set of ordered pairs

In the informal discussion of the foregoing section, a function was described as a correspondence which associates with each object in a set X one and only one object in a set Y. The words "correspondence" and "associates with" may not convey exactly the same meaning to all people, so we shall reformulate the whole idea in a different way, basing it on the set concept. First we require the notion of an *ordered pair* of objects.

In the definition of set equality, no mention is made of the *order* in which elements appear. Thus, the sets $\{2, 5\}$ and $\{5, 2\}$ are equal because they consist of exactly the same elements. Sometimes the order *is* important. For example, in plane analytic geometry the coordinates (x, y) of a point represent an ordered pair of numbers. The point with coordinates $(2, 5)$ is not the same as the point with coordinates $(5, 2)$, although the *sets* $\{2, 5\}$ and $\{5, 2\}$ are equal. In the same way, if we have a pair of objects a and b (not necessarily distinct) and if we wish to distinguish one of the objects, say a, as the *first* member and the other, b, as the *second*, we enclose the objects in parentheses, (a, b). We refer to this as an ordered pair. We say that two ordered pairs (a, b) and (c, d) are equal if and only if their first members are equal and their second members are equal. That is to say, we have

$$(a, b) = (c, d) \qquad \text{if and only if} \quad a = c \quad \text{and} \quad b = d \, .$$

Now we may state the formal definition of function.

DEFINITION OF FUNCTION. *A function f is a set of ordered pairs (x, y) no two of which have the same first member.*

If f is a function, the set of all elements x that occur as first members of pairs (x, y) in f is called the *domain* of f. The set of second members y is called the *range* of f, or the set of *values* of f.

Intuitively, a function can be thought of as a table consisting of two columns. Each entry in the table is an ordered pair (x, y); the column of x's is the domain of f, and the column of y's, the range. If two entries (x, y) and (x, z) appear in the table with the same x-value, then for the table to be a function it is necessary that $y = z$. In other words, a function cannot take two different values at a given point x. Therefore, for every x in the domain of f there is exactly one y such that $(x, y) \in f$. Since this y is uniquely determined once x is known, we can introduce a special symbol for it. It is customary to write

$$y = f(x)$$

instead of $(x, y) \in f$ to indicate that the pair (x, y) is in the set f.

As an alternative to describing a function f by specifying explicitly the pairs it contains, it is usually preferable to describe the domain of f, and then, for each x in the domain, to describe how the function value $f(x)$ is obtained. In this connection, we have the following theorem whose proof is left as an exercise for the reader.

THEOREM 1.1.   *Two functions f and g are equal if and only if*
(a) *f and g have the same domain, and*
(b) $f(x) = g(x)$ *for every x in the domain of f.*

It is important to realize that the objects x and $f(x)$ which appear in the ordered pairs $(x, f(x))$ of a function need not be numbers but may be arbitrary objects of any kind. Occasionally we shall use this degree of generality, but for the most part we shall be interested in real functions, that is, functions whose domain and range are subsets of the real line.

Some of the functions that arise in calculus are described in the next few examples.

1.4   More examples of real functions

1. *Constant functions.* A function whose range consists of a single number is called a constant function. An example is shown in Figure 1.8, where $f(x) = 3$ for every real x. The graph is a horizontal line cutting the y-axis at the point $(0, 3)$.

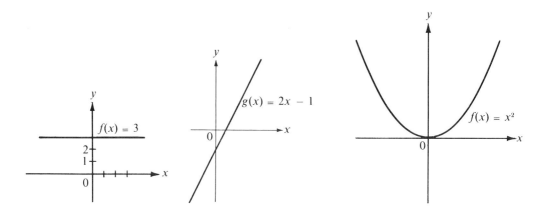

FIGURE 1.8   A constant   FIGURE 1.9   A linear function   FIGURE 1.10   A quadratic
function $f(x) = 3$. $g(x) = 2x - 1$.   polynomial $f(x) = x^2$.

2. *Linear functions.* A function g defined for all real x by a formula of the form

$$g(x) = ax + b$$

is called a linear function because its graph is a straight line. The number b is called the y-intercept of the line; it is the y-coordinate of the point $(0, b)$ where the line cuts the y-axis. The number a is called the slope of the line. One example, $g(x) = x$, is shown in Figure 1.4. Another, $g(x) = 2x - 1$, is shown in Figure 1.9.

3. *The power functions.* For a fixed positive integer n, let f be defined by the equation $f(x) = x^n$ for all real x. When $n = 1$, this is the identity function, shown in Figure 1.4. For $n = 2$, the graph is a parabola, part of which is shown in Figure 1.10. For $n = 3$, the graph is a cubic curve and has the appearance of that in Figure 1.11 (p. 56).

4. *Polynomial functions.* A polynomial function P is one defined for all real x by an equation of the form

$$P(x) = c_0 + c_1 x + \cdots + c_n x^n = \sum_{k=0}^{n} c_k x^k.$$

The numbers c_0, c_1, ..., c_n are called the *coefficients* of the polynomial, and the nonnegative integer n is called its *degree* (if $c_n \neq 0$). They include the constant functions and the power functions as special cases. Polynomials of degree 2, 3, and 4 are called *quadratic*, *cubic*, and *quartic* polynomials, respectively. Figure 1.12 shows a portion of the graph of a quartic polynomial P given by $P(x) = \frac{1}{2}x^4 - 2x^2$.

5. *The circle.* Suppose we return to the Cartesian equation of a circle, $x^2 + y^2 = r^2$ and solve this equation for y in terms of x. There are two solutions given by

$$y = \sqrt{r^2 - x^2} \qquad \text{and} \qquad y = -\sqrt{r^2 - x^2}.$$

(We remind the reader that if $a > 0$, the symbol $\sqrt{a}$ denotes the positive square root of a. The negative square root is $-\sqrt{a}$.) There was a time when mathematicians would say that y is a *double-valued function* of x given by $y = \pm\sqrt{r^2 - x^2}$. However, the more modern point of view does not admit "double-valuedness" as a property of functions. The definition of function requires that for each x in the domain, there corresponds one and only one y in the range. Geometrically, this means that vertical lines which intersect the graph do so at exactly one point. Therefore to make this example fit the theory, we say that the two solutions for y define *two* functions, say f and g, where

$$f(x) = \sqrt{r^2 - x^2} \qquad \text{and} \qquad g(x) = -\sqrt{r^2 - x^2}$$

for each x satisfying $-r \leq x \leq r$. Each of these functions has for its domain the interval extending from $-r$ to r. If $|x| > r$, there is no real y such that $x^2 + y^2 = r^2$, and we say that the functions f and g are *not defined* for such x. Since $f(x)$ is the nonnegative square root of $r^2 - x^2$, the graph of f is the upper semicircle shown in Figure 1.13. The function values of g are ≤ 0, and hence the graph of g is the lower semicircle shown in Figure 1.13.

6. *Sums, products, and quotients of functions.* Let f and g be two real functions having the same domain D. We can construct new functions from f and g by adding, multiplying, or dividing the function values. The function u defined by the equation

$$u(x) = f(x) + g(x) \qquad \text{if} \quad x \in D$$

is called the *sum* of f and g and is denoted by $f + g$. Similarly, the *product* $v = f \cdot g$ and the *quotient* $w = f/g$ are the functions defined by the respective formulas

$$v(x) = f(x)g(x) \quad \text{if} \quad x \in D, \qquad w(x) = f(x)/g(x) \quad \text{if} \quad x \in D \text{ and } g(x) \neq 0.$$

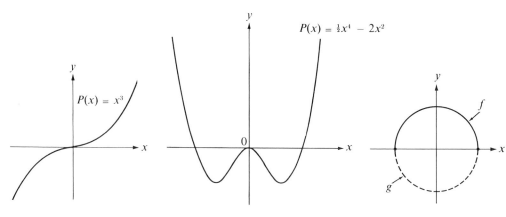

FIGURE 1.11 A cubic polynomial: $P(x) = x^3$.

FIGURE 1.12 A quartic polynomial: $P(x) = \frac{1}{2}x^4 - 2x^2$.

FIGURE 1.13 Graphs of two functions:
$$f(x) = \sqrt{r^2 - x^2},$$
$$g(x) = -\sqrt{r^2 - x^2}.$$

The next set of exercises is intended to give the reader some familiarity with the use of the function notation.

1.5 Exercises

1. Let $f(x) = x + 1$ for all real x. Compute the following: $f(2)$, $f(-2)$, $-f(2)$, $f(\frac{1}{2})$, $1/f(2)$, $f(a + b), f(a) + f(b), f(a)f(b)$.
2. Let $f(x) = 1 + x$ and let $g(x) = 1 - x$ for all real x. Compute the following: $f(2) + g(2)$, $f(2) - g(2), f(2)g(2), f(2)/g(2), f[g(2)], g[f(2)], f(a) + g(-a), f(t)g(-t)$.
3. Let $\varphi(x) = |x - 3| + |x - 1|$ for all real x. Compute the following: $\varphi(0)$, $\varphi(1)$, $\varphi(2)$, $\varphi(3)$, $\varphi(-1), \varphi(-2)$. Find all t for which $\varphi(t + 2) = \varphi(t)$.
4. Let $f(x) = x^2$ for all real x. Verify each of the following formulas. In each case describe the set of real x, y, t, etc., for which the given formula is valid.
   (a) $f(-x) = f(x)$.   (d) $f(2y) = 4f(y)$.
   (b) $f(y) - f(x) = (y - x)(y + x)$.   (e) $f(t^2) = f(t)^2$.
   (c) $f(x + h) - f(x) = 2xh + h^2$.   (f) $\sqrt{f(a)} = |a|$.
5. Let $g(x) = \sqrt{4 - x^2}$ for $|x| \leq 2$. Verify each of the following formulas and tell for which values of x, y, s, and t the given formula is valid.
   (a) $g(-x) = g(x)$.

   (b) $g(2y) = 2\sqrt{1 - y^2}$.

   (c) $g\left(\dfrac{1}{t}\right) = \dfrac{\sqrt{4t^2 - 1}}{|t|}$.

   (d) $g(a - 2) = \sqrt{4a - a^2}$.

   (e) $g\left(\dfrac{s}{2}\right) = \frac{1}{2}\sqrt{16 - s^2}$.

   (f) $\dfrac{1}{2 + g(x)} = \dfrac{2 - g(x)}{x^2}$.
6. Let f be defined as follows: $f(x) = 1$ for $0 \leq x \leq 1$; $f(x) = 2$ for $1 < x \leq 2$. The function is not defined if $x < 0$ or if $x > 2$.
   (a) Draw the graph of f.
   (b) Let $g(x) = f(2x)$. Describe the domain of g and draw its graph.
   (c) Let $h(x) = f(x - 2)$. Describe the domain of h and draw its graph.
   (d) Let $k(x) = f(2x) + f(x - 2)$. Describe the domain of k and draw its graph.

7. The graphs of the two polynomials $g(x) = x$ and $f(x) = x^3$ intersect at three points. Draw enough of their graphs to show how they intersect.

8. The graphs of the two quadratic polynomials $f(x) = x^2 - 2$ and $g(x) = 2x^2 + 4x + 1$ intersect at two points. Draw the portions of the two graphs between the points of intersection.

9. This exercise develops some fundamental properties of polynomials. Let $f(x) = \sum_{k=0}^{n} c_k x^k$ be a polynomial of degree n. Prove each of the following:

   (a) If $n \geq 1$ and $f(0) = 0$, then $f(x) = xg(x)$, where g is a polynomial of degree $n - 1$.

   (b) For each real a, the function p given by $p(x) = f(x + a)$ is a polynomial of degree n.

   (c) If $n \geq 1$ and $f(a) = 0$ for some real a, then $f(x) = (x - a)h(x)$, where h is a polynomial of degree $n - 1$. [*Hint:* Consider $p(x) = f(x + a)$.]

   (d) If $f(x) = 0$ for $n + 1$ distinct real values of x, then every coefficient c_k is zero and $f(x) = 0$ for all real x.

   (e) Let $g(x) = \sum_{k=0}^{m} b_k x^k$ be a polynomial of degree m, where $m \geq n$. If $g(x) = f(x)$ for $m + 1$ distinct real values of x, then $m = n$, $b_k = c_k$ for each k, and $g(x) = f(x)$ for all real x.

10. In each case, find all polynomials p of degree ≤ 2 which satisfy the given conditions.

    (a) $p(0) = p(1) = p(2) = 1$.   (c) $p(0) = p(1) = 1$.

    (b) $p(0) = p(1) = 1, p(2) = 2$.   (d) $p(0) = p(1)$.

11. In each case, find all polynomials p of degree ≤ 2 which satisfy the given conditions for all real x.

    (a) $p(x) = p(1 - x)$.   (c) $p(2x) = 2p(x)$.

    (b) $p(x) = p(1 + x)$.   (d) $p(3x) = p(x + 3)$.

12. Show that the following are polynomials by converting them to the form $\sum_{k=0}^{m} a_k x^k$ for a suitable m. In each case n is a positive integer.

    (a) $(1 + x)^{2n}$.   (b) $\dfrac{1 - x^{n+1}}{1 - x}$, $x \neq 1$.   (c) $\prod_{k=0}^{n} (1 + x^{2^k})$.

1.6 The concept of area as a set function

When a mathematician attempts to develop a general theory encompassing many different concepts, he tries to isolate common properties which seem to be basic to each of the particular applications he has in mind. He then uses these properties as fundamental building blocks of his theory. Euclid used this process when he developed elementary geometry as a deductive system based on a set of axioms. We used the same process in our axiomatic treatment of the real number system, and we shall use it once more in our discussion of area.

When we assign an area to a plane region, we associate a number with a set S in the plane. From a purely mathematical viewpoint, this means that we have a function a (an area function) which assigns a real number $a(S)$ (the area of S) to each set S in some given collection of sets. A function of this kind, whose domain is a collection of sets and whose function values are real numbers, is called a *set function*. The basic problem is this: Given a plane set S, what area $a(S)$ shall we assign to S?

Our approach to this problem is to start with a number of properties we feel area should have and take these as *axioms* for area. Any set function which satisfies these axioms will be called an area function. To make certain we are not discussing an empty theory, it is necessary to show that an area function actually exists. We shall not attempt to do this here. Instead, we assume the existence of an area function and deduce further properties from the axioms. An elementary construction of an area function may be found in Chapters 14 and 22 of Edwin E. Moise, *Elementary Geometry From An Advanced Standpoint*, Addison-Wesley Publishing Co., 1963.

Before we state the axioms for area, we will make a few remarks about the collection of sets in the plane to which an area can be assigned. These sets will be called *measurable sets*; the collection of all measurable sets will be denoted by $\mathcal{M}$. The axioms contain enough information about the sets in $\mathcal{M}$ to enable us to prove that all geometric figures arising in the usual applications of calculus are in $\mathcal{M}$ and that their areas can be calculated by integration.

One of the axioms (Axiom 5) states that every rectangle is measurable and that its area is the product of the lengths of its edges. The term "rectangle" as used here refers to any set congruent† to a set of the form

$$\{(x, y) \mid 0 \leq x \leq h, 0 \leq y \leq k\},$$

where $h \geq 0$ and $k \geq 0$. The numbers h and k are called the lengths of the edges of the rectangle. We consider a line segment or a point to be a special case of a rectangle by allowing h or k (or both) to be zero.

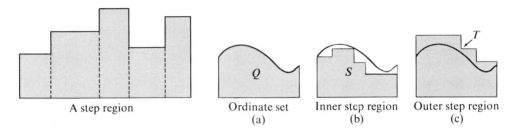

| A step region | Ordinate set | Inner step region | Outer step region |
| | (a) | (b) | (c) |

FIGURE 1.14   FIGURE 1.15   An ordinate set enclosed by two step regions.

From rectangles we can build up more complicated sets. The set shown in Figure 1.14 is the union of a finite collection of adjacent rectangles with their bases resting on the *x*-axis and is called a *step region*. The axioms imply that each step region is measurable and that its area is the sum of the areas of the rectangular pieces.

The region Q shown in Figure 1.15(a) is an example of an *ordinate set*. Its upper boundary is the graph of a nonnegative function. Axiom 6 will enable us to prove that many ordinate sets are measurable and that their areas can be calculated by approximating such sets by inner and outer step regions, as shown in Figure 1.15(b) and (c).

We turn now to the axioms themselves.

AXIOMATIC DEFINITION OF AREA.   *We assume there exists a class $\mathcal{M}$ of measurable sets in the plane and a set function a, whose domain is $\mathcal{M}$, with the following properties:*

1. Nonnegative property. For each set S in $\mathcal{M}$, we have $a(S) \geq 0$.

---

† Congruence is used here in the same sense as in elementary Euclidean geometry. Two sets are said to be congruent if their points can be put in one-to-one correspondence in such a way that distances are preserved. That is, if two points p and q in one set correspond to p' and q' in the other, the distance from p to q must be equal to the distance from p' to q'; this must be true for all choices of p and q.

2. *Additive property*. If S and T are in $\mathcal{M}$, then $S \cup T$ and $S \cap T$ are in $\mathcal{M}$, and we have

$$a(S \cup T) = a(S) + a(T) - a(S \cap T).$$

3. *Difference property*. If S and T are in $\mathcal{M}$ with $S \subseteq T$, then $T - S$ is in $\mathcal{M}$, and we have $a(T - S) = a(T) - a(S)$.

4. *Invariance under congruence*. If a set S is in $\mathcal{M}$ and if T is congruent to S, then T is also in $\mathcal{M}$ and we have $a(S) = a(T)$.

5. *Choice of scale*. Every rectangle R is in $\mathcal{M}$. If the edges of R have lengths h and k, then $a(R) = hk$.

6. *Exhaustion property*. Let Q be a set that can be enclosed between two step regions S and T, so that

(1.1) $$S \subseteq Q \subseteq T.$$

If there is one and only one number c which satisfies the inequalities

$$a(S) \le c \le a(T)$$

for all step regions S and T satisfying (1.1), *then Q is measurable and $a(Q) = c$.*

Axiom 1 simply states that the area of a plane measurable set is either a positive number or zero. Axiom 2 tells us that when a set is formed from two pieces (which may overlap), the area of the union is the sum of the areas of the two parts minus the area of their intersection. In particular, if the intersection has zero area, the area of the whole is the sum of the areas of the two parts.

If we remove a measurable set S from a larger measurable set T, Axiom 3 states that the remaining part, $T - S$, is measurable and its area is obtained by subtraction, $a(T - S) = a(T) - a(S)$. In particular, this axiom implies that the empty set $\varnothing$ is measurable and has zero area. Since $a(T - S) \ge 0$, Axiom 3 also implies the *monotone property*:

$$a(S) \le a(T), \qquad \text{for sets } S \text{ and } T \text{ in } \mathcal{M} \text{ with } S \subseteq T.$$

In other words, a set which is part of another cannot have a larger area.

Axiom 4 assigns equal areas to sets having the same size and shape. The first four axioms would be trivially satisfied if we assigned the number 0 as the area of every set in $\mathcal{M}$. Axiom 5 assigns a nonzero area to some rectangles and thereby excludes this trivial case. Finally, Axiom 6 incorporates the Greek method of exhaustion; it enables us to extend the class of measurable sets from step regions to more general regions.

Axiom 5 assigns zero area to each line segment. Repeated use of the additive property shows that every step region is measurable and that its area is the sum of the areas of the rectangular pieces. Further elementary consequences of the axioms are discussed in the next set of exercises.

1.7   Exercises

The properties of area in this set of exercises are to be deduced from the axioms for area stated in the foregoing section.

1. Prove that each of the following sets is measurable and has zero area: (a) A set consisting of a single point. (b) A set consisting of a finite number of points in a plane. (c) The union of a finite collection of line segments in a plane.

2. Every right triangular region is measurable because it can be obtained as the intersection of two rectangles. Prove that every triangular region is measurable and that its area is one half the product of its base and altitude.

3. Prove that every trapezoid and every parallelogram is measurable and derive the usual formulas for their areas.

4. A point (x, y) in the plane is called a *lattice point* if both coordinates x and y are integers. Let P be a polygon whose vertices are lattice points. The area of P is $I + \frac{1}{2}B - 1$, where I denotes the number of lattice points inside the polygon and B denotes the number on the boundary.
   (a) Prove that the formula is valid for rectangles with sides parallel to the coordinate axes.
   (b) Prove that the formula is valid for right triangles and parallelograms.
   (c) Use induction on the number of edges to construct a proof for general polygons.

5. Prove that a triangle whose vertices are lattice points cannot be equilateral.

   [*Hint:* Assume there is such a triangle and compute its area in two ways, using Exercises 2 and 4.]

6. Let $A = \{1, 2, 3, 4, 5\}$, and let $\mathcal{M}$ denote the class of all subsets of A. (There are 32 altogether, counting A itself and the empty set $\varnothing$.) For each set S in $\mathcal{M}$, let $n(S)$ denote the number of distinct elements in S. If $S = \{1, 2, 3, 4\}$ and $T = \{3, 4, 5\}$, compute $n(S \cup T)$, $n(S \cap T)$, $n(S - T)$, and $n(T - S)$. Prove that the set function n satisfies the first three axioms for area.

1.8   Intervals and ordinate sets

In the theory of integration we are concerned primarily with real functions whose domains are intervals on the x-axis. Sometimes it is important to distinguish between intervals which include their endpoints and those which do not. This distinction is made by introducing the following definitions.

$$a \leq x \leq b \qquad a < x < b \qquad a < x \leq b \qquad a \leq x < b$$

   Closed   Open   Half-open.   Half-open

FIGURE 1.16   Examples of intervals.

If $a < b$, we denote by $[a, b]$ the set of all x satisfying the inequalities $a \leq x \leq b$ and refer to this set as the *closed interval* from a to b. The corresponding *open interval*, written (a, b), is the set of all x satisfying $a < x < b$. The closed interval $[a, b]$ includes the endpoints a and b, whereas the open interval does not. (See Figure 1.16.) The open interval (a, b) is also called the *interior* of $[a, b]$. Half-open intervals $(a, b]$ and $[a, b)$, which include just one endpoint are defined by the inequalities $a < x \leq b$ and $a \leq x < b$, respectively.

Let f be a nonnegative function whose domain is a closed interval $[a, b]$. The portion of the plane between the graph of f and the x-axis is called the *ordinate set* of f. More precisely, the ordinate set of f is the collection of all points (x, y) satisfying the inequalities

$$a \leq x \leq b, \qquad 0 \leq y \leq f(x).$$

In each of the examples shown in Figure 1.17 the shaded portion represents the ordinate set of the corresponding function.

Ordinate sets are the geometric objects whose areas we want to compute by means of the integral calculus. We shall define the concept of integral first for step functions and then use the integral of a step function to formulate the definition of integral for more general

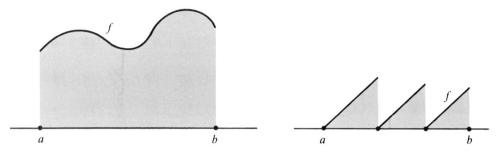

FIGURE 1.17 Examples of ordinate sets.

functions. Integration theory for step functions is extremely simple and leads in a natural way to the corresponding theory for more general functions. To start this program, it is necessary to have an analytic definition of a step function. This may be given most simply in terms of the concept of a *partition*, to which we turn now.

1.9 Partitions and step functions

Suppose we decompose a given closed interval $[a, b]$ into n subintervals by inserting $n - 1$ points of subdivision, say $x_1, x_2, \ldots, x_{n-1}$, subject only to the restriction

(1.2) $$a < x_1 < x_2 < \cdots < x_{n-1} < b.$$

It is convenient to denote the point a itself by x_0 and the point b by x_n. A collection of points satisfying (1.2) is called a *partition* P of $[a, b]$, and we use the symbol

$$P = \{x_0, x_1, \ldots, x_n\}$$

to designate this partition. The partition P determines n closed subintervals

$$[x_0, x_1], [x_1, x_2], \ldots, [x_{n-1}, x_n].$$

A typical closed subinterval is $[x_{k-1}, x_k]$, and it is referred to as the kth closed subinterval of P; an example is shown in Figure 1.18. The corresponding open interval (x_{k-1}, x_k) is called the kth open subinterval of P.

Now we are ready to formulate an analytic definition of a step function.

FIGURE 1.18   An example of a partition of $[a, b]$.

DEFINITION OF A STEP FUNCTION.   *A function s, whose domain is a closed interval* $[a, b]$, *is called a step function if there is a partition* $P = \{x_0, x_1, \ldots, x_n\}$ *of* $[a, b]$ *such that s is constant on each open subinterval of P.   That is to say, for each* $k = 1, 2, \ldots, n$, *there is a real number* s_k *such that*

$$s(x) = s_k \qquad if \qquad x_{k-1} < x < x_k .$$

Step functions are sometimes called piecewise constant functions.

   Note: At each of the endpoints x_{k-1} and x_k the function must have some well-defined value, but this need not be the same as s_k.

   EXAMPLE.   A familiar example of a step function is the "postage function," whose graph is shown in Figure 1.19. Assume that the charge for first-class mail for parcels weighing up to 20 pounds is 5 cents for every ounce or fraction thereof.   The graph shows the number of 5-cent stamps required for mail weighing up to 4 ounces.   In this case the line segments on the graph are half-open intervals containing their right endpoints.   The domain of the function is the interval $[0, 320]$.

   From a given partition P of $[a, b]$, we can always form a new partition P' by adjoining more subdivision points to those already in P.   Such a partition P' is called a *refinement* of P and is said to be *finer than P*.   For example, $P = \{0, 1, 2, 3, 4\}$ is a partition of the interval $[0, 4]$.   If we adjoint the points $3/4$, $\sqrt{2}$, and $7/2$, we obtain a new partition P' of

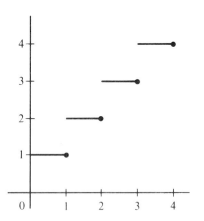

FIGURE 1.19   The postage function.

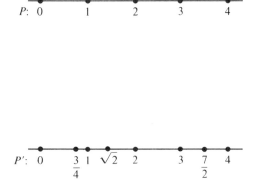

FIGURE 1.20   A partition P of $[0, 4]$ and a refinement P'.

[0, 4], namely, $P' = \{0, 3/4, 1, \sqrt{2}, 2, 3, 7/2, 4\}$, which is a refinement of P. (See Figure 1.20.) If a step function is constant on the open subintervals of P, then it is also constant on the open subintervals of every refinement P'.

1.10 Sum and product of step functions

New step functions may be formed from given step functions by adding corresponding function values. For example, suppose s and t are step functions, both defined on the same interval $[a, b]$. Let P_1 and P_2 be partitions of $[a, b]$ such that s is constant on the open subintervals of P_1 and t is constant on the open subintervals of P_2. Let $u = s + t$ be the function defined by the equation

$$u(x) = s(x) + t(x) \qquad \text{if} \qquad a \le x \le b .$$

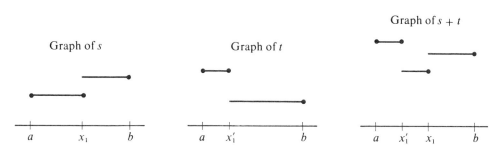

FIGURE 1.21 The sum of two step functions.

To show that u is actually a step function, we must exhibit a partition P such that u is constant on the open subintervals of P. For the new partition P, we take all the points of P_1 along with all the points of P_2. This partition, the union of P_1 and P_2, is called the *common refinement* of P_1 and P_2. Since both s and t are constant on the open subintervals of the common refinement, the same is true of u. An example is illustrated in Figure 1.21. The partition P_1 is $\{a, x_1, b\}$, the partition P_2 is $\{a, x'_1, b\}$, and the common refinement is $\{a, x'_1, x_1, b\}$.

Similarly, the product $v = s \cdot t$ of two step functions is another step function. An important special case occurs when one of the factors, say t, is constant throughout $[a, b]$. If $t(x) = c$ for each x in $[a, b]$, then each function value $v(x)$ is obtained by multiplying the step function $s(x)$ by the constant c.

1.11 Exercises

In this set of exercises, $[x]$ denotes the greatest integer $\le x$.
1. Let $f(x) = [x]$ and let $g(x) = [2x]$ for all real x. In each case, draw the graph of the function h defined over the interval $[-1, 2]$ by the formula given.
   (a) $h(x) = f(x) + g(x)$. (c) $h(x) = f(x)g(x)$.
   (b) $h(x) = f(x) + g(x/2)$. (d) $h(x) = \frac{1}{4}f(2x)g(x/2)$.
2. In each case, f is a function defined over the interval $[-2, 2]$ by the formula given. Draw the graph of f. If f is a step function, find a partition P of $[-2, 2]$ such that f is constant on the open subintervals of P.

(a) $f(x) = x + [x]$.   (d) $f(x) = 2[x]$.
(b) $f(x) = x - [x]$.   (e) $f(x) = [x + \frac{1}{2}]$.
(c) $f(x) = [-x]$.   (f) $f(x) = [x] + [x + \frac{1}{2}]$.

3. In each case, sketch the graph of the function f defined by the formula given.

    (a) $f(x) = [\sqrt{x}]$ for $0 \le x \le 10$.   (c) $f(x) = \sqrt{[x]}$ for $0 \le x \le 10$.
    (b) $f(x) = [x^2]$ for $0 \le x \le 3$.   (d) $f(x) = [x]^2$ for $0 \le x \le 3$.

4. Prove that the greatest-integer function has the properties indicated.

    (a) $[x + n] = [x] + n$ for every integer n.

    (b) $[-x] = \begin{cases} -[x] & \text{if } x \text{ is an integer,} \\ -[x] - 1 & \text{otherwise.} \end{cases}$

    (c) $[x + y] = [x] + [y]$ or $[x] + [y] + 1$.
    (d) $[2x] = [x] + [x + \frac{1}{2}]$.
    (e) $[3x] = [x] + [x + \frac{1}{3}] + [x + \frac{2}{3}]$.

Optional exercises.

5. The formulas in Exercises 4(d) and 4(e) suggest a generalization for $[nx]$. State and prove such a generalization.

6. Recall that a lattice point (x, y) in the plane is one whose coordinates are integers. Let f be a nonnegative function whose domain is the interval $[a, b]$, where a and b are integers, $a < b$. Let S denote the set of points (x, y) satisfying $a \le x \le b, 0 < y \le f(x)$. Prove that the number of lattice points in S is equal to the sum

$$\sum_{n=a}^{b} [f(n)].$$

7. If a and b are positive integers with no common factor, we have the formula

$$\sum_{n=1}^{b-1} \left[\frac{na}{b} \right] = \frac{(a - 1)(b - 1)}{2}.$$

When $b = 1$, the sum on the left is understood to be 0.

(a) Derive this result by a geometric argument, counting lattice points in a right triangle.

(b) Derive the result analytically as follows: By changing the index of summation, note that $\sum_{n=1}^{b-1} [na/b] = \sum_{n=1}^{b-1} [a(b - n)/b]$. Now apply Exercises 4(a) and (b) to the bracket on the right.

8. Let S be a set of points on the real line. The *characteristic function* of S is, by definition, the function χ_S such that $\chi_S(x) = 1$ for every x in S, and $\chi_S(x) = 0$ for those x not in S. Let f be a step function which takes the constant value c_k on the kth open subinterval I_k of some partition of an interval $[a, b]$. Prove that for each x in the union $I_1 \cup I_2 \cup \cdots \cup I_n$ we have

$$f(x) = \sum_{k=1}^{n} c_k \chi_{I_k}(x).$$

This property is described by saying that every step function is a linear combination of characteristic functions of intervals.

1.12   The definition of the integral for step functions

In this section we introduce the integral for step functions. The definition is constructed so that the integral of a nonnegative step function is equal to the area of its ordinate set.

Let s be a step function defined on $[a, b]$, and let $P = \{x_0, x_1, \ldots, x_n\}$ be a partition of $[a, b]$ such that s is constant on the open subintervals of P. Denote by s_k the constant value that s takes in the kth open subinterval, so that

$$s(x) = s_k \quad \text{if} \quad x_{k-1} < x < x_k, \quad k = 1, 2, \ldots, n.$$

DEFINITION OF THE INTEGRAL OF STEP FUNCTIONS. *The integral of s from a to b, denoted by the symbol $\int_a^b s(x)\, dx$, is defined by the following formula:*

$$(1.3) \qquad \int_a^b s(x)\, dx = \sum_{k=1}^{n} s_k \cdot (x_k - x_{k-1}).$$

That is to say, to compute the integral, we multiply each constant value s_k by the length of the kth subinterval, and then we add together all these products.

Note that the values of s at the subdivision points are immaterial since they do not appear on the right-hand side of (1.3). In particular, if s is constant on the open interval (a, b), say $s(x) = c$ if $a < x < b$, then we have

$$\int_a^b s(x)\, dx = c \sum_{k=1}^{n} (x_k - x_{k-1}) = c(b - a),$$

regardless of the values $s(a)$ and $s(b)$. If $c > 0$ and if $s(x) = c$ for all x in the closed interval $[a, b]$, the ordinate set of s is a rectangle of base $b - a$ and altitude c; the integral of s is $c(b - a)$, the area of this rectangle. Changing the value of s at one or both endpoints a or b changes the ordinate set but does not alter the integral of s or the area of its ordinate set. For example, the two ordinate sets shown in Figure 1.22 have equal areas.

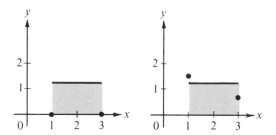

FIGURE 1.22 Changes in function values at two points do not alter area of ordinate set.

FIGURE 1.23 The ordinate set of a step function.

The ordinate set of any nonnegative step function s consists of a finite number of rectangles, one for each interval of constancy; the ordinate set may also contain or lack certain vertical line segments, depending on how s is defined at the subdivision points. The integral of s is equal to the sum of the areas of the individual rectangles, regardless of the values s takes at the subdivision points. This is consistent with the fact that the vertical segments have zero area and make no contribution to the area of the ordinate set. In Figure 1.23, the step function s takes the constant values 2, 1, and $\frac{9}{4}$ in the open intervals $(1, 2)$, $(2, 5)$, and $(5, 6)$, respectively. Its integral is equal to

$$\int_1^6 s(x)\, dx = 2 \cdot (2 - 1) + 1 \cdot (5 - 2) + \tfrac{9}{4} \cdot (6 - 5) = \tfrac{29}{4}.$$

It should be noted that the formula for the integral in (1.3) is independent of the choice of the partition P as long as s is constant on the open subintervals of P. For example, suppose we change from P to a finer partition P' by inserting exactly one new subdivision point t, where $x_0 < t < x_1$. Then the first term on the right of (1.3) is replaced by the two terms $s_1 \cdot (t - x_0)$ and $s_1 \cdot (x_1 - t)$, and the rest of the terms are unchanged. Since

$$s_1 \cdot (t - x_0) + s_1 \cdot (x_1 - t) = s_1 \cdot (x_1 - x_0),$$

the value of the entire sum is unchanged. We can proceed from P to any finer partition P' by inserting the new subdivision points one at a time. At each stage, the sum in (1.3) remains unchanged, so the integral is the same for all refinements of P.

1.13   Properties of the integral of a step function

In this section we describe a number of fundamental properties satisfied by the integral of a step function. Most of these properties seem obvious when they are interpreted geometrically, and some of them may even seem trivial. All these properties carry over to integrals of more general functions, and it will be a simple matter to prove them in the general case once we have established them for step functions. The properties are listed below as theorems, and in each case a geometric interpretation for nonnegative step functions is given in terms of areas. Analytic proofs of the theorems are outlined in Section 1.15.

FIGURE 1.24   Illustrating the additive property of the integral.

The first property states that the integral of a sum of two step functions is equal to the sum of the integrals. This is known as the *additive* property and it is illustrated in Figure 1.24.

THEOREM 1.2.   ADDITIVE PROPERTY.

$$\int_a^b [s(x) + t(x)]\, dx = \int_a^b s(x)\, dx + \int_a^b t(x)\, dx .$$

The next property, illustrated in Figure 1.25, is called the *homogeneous* property. It states that if all the function values are multiplied by a constant c, then the integral is also multiplied by c.

THEOREM 1.3.   HOMOGENEOUS PROPERTY.   *For every real number c, we have*

$$\int_a^b c \cdot s(x)\, dx = c \int_a^b s(x)\, dx .$$

These two theorems can be combined into one formula known as the linearity property.

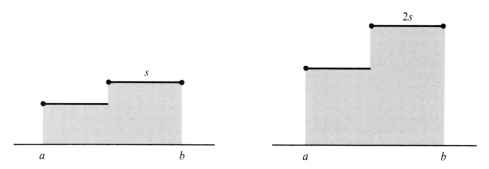

FIGURE 1.25   Illustrating the homogeneous property of the integral (with $c = 2$).

THEOREM 1.4.   LINEARITY PROPERTY.   *For every real c_1 and c_2, we have*

$$\int_a^b [c_1 s(x) + c_2 t(x)]\, dx = c_1 \int_a^b s(x)\, dx + c_2 \int_a^b t(x)\, dx.$$

Next, we have a *comparison* theorem which tells us that if one step function has larger values than another throughout $[a, b]$, its integral over this interval is also larger.

THEOREM 1.5.   COMPARISON THEOREM.   *If $s(x) < t(x)$ for every x in $[a, b]$, then*

$$\int_a^b s(x)\, dx < \int_a^b t(x)\, dx.$$

Interpreted geometrically, this theorem reflects the monotone property of area. If the ordinate set of a nonnegative step function lies inside another, the area of the smaller region is less than that of the larger.

The foregoing properties all refer to step functions defined on a common interval. The integral has further important properties that relate integrals over different intervals. Among these we have the following.

THEOREM 1.6.   ADDITIVITY WITH RESPECT TO THE INTERVAL OF INTEGRATION.

$$\int_a^c s(x)\, dx + \int_c^b s(x)\, dx = \int_a^b s(x)\, dx \qquad if \qquad a < c < b.$$

This theorem reflects the additive property of area, illustrated in Figure 1.26. If an ordinate set is decomposed into two ordinate sets, the sum of the areas of the two parts is equal to the area of the whole.

The next theorem may be described as *invariance under translation*. If the ordinate set of a step function s is "shifted" by an amount c, the resulting ordinate set is that of another step function t related to s by the equation $t(x) = s(x - c)$. If s is defined on $[a, b]$, then t is defined on $[a + c, b + c]$, and their ordinate sets, being congruent, have equal areas.

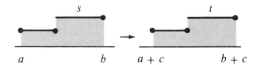

FIGURE 1.26   Additivity with respect
to the interval of integration.

FIGURE 1.27   Illustrating invariance of the
integral under translation: $t(x) = s(x - c)$.

This property is expressed analytically as follows:

THEOREM 1.7.   INVARIANCE UNDER TRANSLATION.

$$\int_a^b s(x)\,dx = \int_{a+c}^{b+c} s(x - c)\,dx \qquad \text{for every real } c.$$

Its geometric meaning is illustrated in Figure 1.27 for $c > 0$. When $c < 0$, the ordinate
set is shifted to the left.

The homogeneous property (Theorem 1.3) explains what happens to an integral under a
change of scale on the y-axis. The following theorem deals with a change of scale on the
x-axis. If s is a step function defined on an interval $[a, b]$ and if we distort the scale in the
horizontal direction by multiplying all x-coordinates by a factor $k > 0$, then the new graph
is that of another step function t defined on the interval $[ka, kb]$ and related to s by the
equation

$$t(x) = s\left(\frac{x}{k}\right) \qquad \text{if} \qquad ka \le x \le kb.$$

An example with $k = 2$ is shown in Figure 1.28 and it suggests that the distorted figure has
an area twice that of the original figure. More generally, distortion by a positive factor k

FIGURE 1.28   Change of scale on the x-axis: $t(x) = s(x/2)$.

has the effect of multiplying the integral by k. Expressed analytically, this property assumes
the following form:

THEOREM 1.8.   EXPANSION OR CONTRACTION OF THE INTERVAL OF INTEGRATION.

$$\int_{ka}^{kb} s\left(\frac{x}{k}\right) dx = k \int_a^b s(x)\,dx \qquad \text{for every } k > 0.$$

Until now, when we have used the symbol $\int_a^b$, it has been understood that the lower limit
a was less than the upper limit b. It is convenient to extend our ideas somewhat and consider
integrals with a lower limit larger than the upper limit. This is done by defining

(1.4) $$\int_b^a s(x)\,dx = -\int_a^b s(x)\,dx \qquad \text{if} \qquad a < b.$$

We also define

$$\int_a^a s(x)\, dx = 0 ,$$

a definition that is suggested by putting $a = b$ in (1.4). These conventions allow us to conclude that Theorem 1.6 is valid not only when c is between a and b but for any arrangement of the points a, b, c. Theorem 1.6 is sometimes written in the form

$$\int_a^c s(x)\, dx + \int_c^b s(x)\, dx + \int_b^a s(x)\, dx = 0 .$$

Similarly, we can extend the range of validity of Theorem 1.8 and allow the constant k to be negative. In particular, when $k = -1$, Theorem 1.8 and Equation (1.4) give us

$$\int_a^b s(x)\, dx = \int_{-b}^{-a} s(-x)\, dx .$$

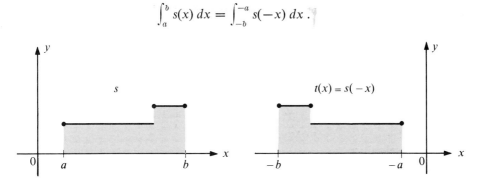

FIGURE 1.29   Illustrating the reflection property of the integral.

We shall refer to this as the *reflection property* of the integral, since the graph of the function t given by $t(x) = s(-x)$ is obtained from that of s by reflection through the y-axis. An example is shown in Figure 1.29.

1.14 Other notations for integrals

The letter x that appears in the symbol $\int_a^b s(x)\, dx$ plays no essential role in the definition of the integral. Any other letter would serve equally well. The letters t, u, v, z are frequently used for this purpose, and it is agreed that instead of $\int_a^b s(x)\, dx$ we may write $\int_a^b s(t)\, dt$, $\int_a^b s(u)\, du$, etc., all these being considered as alternative notations for the same thing. The symbols x, t, u, etc. that are used in this way are called "dummy variables." They are analogous to dummy indices used in the summation notation.

There is a tendency among some authors of calculus textbooks to omit the dummy variable and the d-symbol altogether and to write simply $\int_a^b s$ for the integral. One good reason for using this abbreviated symbol is that it suggests more strongly that the integral depends only on the *function s* and on the *interval* $[a, b]$. Also, certain formulas appear simpler in this notation. For example, the additive property becomes $\int_a^b (s + t) = \int_a^b s + \int_a^b t$. On the other hand, it becomes awkward to write formulas like Theorems 1.7 and 1.8 in the abbreviated notation. More important than this, we shall find later that the original Leibniz notation has certain practical advantages. The symbol dx, which appears to be rather superfluous at this stage, turns out to be an extremely useful computational device in connection with many routine calculations with integrals.

1.15 Exercises

1. Compute the value of each of the following integrals. You may use the theorems of Section 1.13 whenever it is convenient to do so. The notation $[x]$ denotes the greatest integer $\leq x$.

   (a) $\int_{-1}^{3} [x]\, dx.$ (d) $\int_{-1}^{3} 2[x]\, dx.$

   (b) $\int_{-1}^{3} [x + \frac{1}{2}]\, dx.$ (e) $\int_{-1}^{3} [2x]\, dx.$

   (c) $\int_{-1}^{3} ([x] + [x + \frac{1}{2}])\, dx.$ (f) $\int_{-1}^{3} [-x]\, dx.$

2. Give an example of a step function s, defined on the closed interval $[0, 5]$, which has the following properties: $\int_{0}^{2} s(x)\, dx = 5$, $\int_{0}^{5} s(x)\, dx = 2$.

3. Show that $\int_{a}^{b} [x]\, dx + \int_{a}^{b} [-x]\, dx = a - b$.

4. (a) If n is a positive integer, prove that $\int_{0}^{n} [t]\, dt = n(n - 1)/2$.
   (b) If $f(x) = \int_{0}^{x} [t]\, dt$ for $x \geq 0$, draw the graph of f over the interval $[0, 4]$.

5. (a) Prove that $\int_{0}^{2} [t^2]\, dt = 5 - \sqrt{2} - \sqrt{3}$.
   (b) Compute $\int_{-3}^{3} [t^2]\, dt$.

6. (a) If n is a positive integer, prove that $\int_{0}^{n} [t]^2\, dt = n(n - 1)(2n - 1)/6$.
   (b) If $f(x) = \int_{0}^{x} [t]^2\, dt$ for $x \geq 0$, draw the graph of f over the interval $[0, 3]$.
   (c) Find all $x > 0$ for which $\int_{0}^{x} [t]^2\, dt = 2(x - 1)$.

7. (a) Compute $\int_{0}^{9} [\sqrt{t}]\, dt$.
   (b) If n is a positive integer, prove that $\int_{0}^{n^2} [\sqrt{t}]\, dt = n(n - 1)(4n + 1)/6$.

8. Show that the translation property (Theorem 1.7) may be expressed in the equivalent form

$$\int_{a+c}^{b+c} f(x)\, dx = \int_{a}^{b} f(x + c)\, dx .$$

9. Show that the following property is equivalent to Theorem 1.8:

$$\int_{ka}^{kb} f(x)\, dx = k \int_{a}^{b} f(kx)\, dx .$$

10. Given a positive integer p. A step function s is defined on the interval $[0, p]$ as follows: $s(x) = (-1)^n n$ if x lies in the interval $n \leq x < n + 1$, where $n = 0, 1, 2, \ldots, p - 1$; $s(p) = 0$. Let $f(p) = \int_{0}^{p} s(x)\, dx$.
    (a) Calculate $f(3)$, $f(4)$, and $f(f(3))$.
    (b) For what value (or values) of p is $|f(p)| = 7$?

11. If, instead of defining integrals of step functions by using formula (1.3), we used the definition

$$\int_{a}^{b} s(x)\, dx = \sum_{k=1}^{n} s_k^3 \cdot (x_k - x_{k-1}) ,$$

a new and different theory of integration would result. Which of the following properties would remain valid in this new theory?

(a) $\int_a^b s + \int_b^c s = \int_a^c s.$

(c) $\int_a^b c \cdot s = c \int_a^b s.$

(b) $\int_a^b (s + t) = \int_a^b s + \int_a^b t.$

(d) $\int_{a+c}^{b+c} s(x) \, dx = \int_a^b s(x + c) \, dx.$

(e) If $s(x) < t(x)$ for each x in $[a, b]$, then $\int_a^b s < \int_a^b t.$

12. Solve Exercise 11 if we use the definition

$$\int_a^b s(x) \, dx = \sum_{k=1}^n s_k \cdot (x_k^2 - x_{k-1}^2) .$$

Analytic proofs of the properties of the integral given in Section 1.13 are requested in the following exercises. The proofs of Theorems 1.3 and 1.8 are worked out here as samples. Hints are given for the others.

Proof of Theorem 1.3: $\int_a^b c \cdot s(x) \, dx = c \int_a^b s(x) \, dx$ for every real c.

Let $P = \{x_0, x_1, \ldots, x_n\}$ be a partition of $[a, b]$ such that s is constant on the open subintervals of P. Assume $s(x) = s_k$ if $x_{k-1} < x < x_k$ ($k = 1, 2, \ldots, n$). Then $c \cdot s(x) = c \cdot s_k$ if $x_{k-1} < x < x_k$, and hence by the definition of an integral we have

$$\int_a^b c \cdot s(x) \, dx = \sum_{k=1}^n c \cdot s_k \cdot (x_k - x_{k-1}) = c \sum_{k=1}^n s_k \cdot (x_k - x_{k-1}) = c \int_a^b s(x) \, dx .$$

Proof of Theorem 1.8:

$$\int_{ka}^{kb} s\left(\frac{x}{k}\right) dx = k \int_a^b s(x) \, dx \qquad \text{if} \quad k > 0 .$$

Let $P = \{x_0, x_1, \ldots, x_n\}$ be a partition of the interval $[a, b]$ such that s is constant on the open subintervals of P. Assume that $s(x) = s_i$ if $x_{i-1} < x < x_i$. Let $t(x) = s(x/k)$ if $ka \le x \le kb$. Then $t(x) = s_i$ if x lies in the open interval (kx_{i-1}, kx_i); hence $P' = \{kx_0, kx_1, \ldots, kx_n\}$ is a partition of $[ka, kb]$ and t is constant on the open subintervals of P'. Therefore t is a step function whose integral is

$$\int_{ka}^{kb} t(x) \, dx = \sum_{i=1}^n s_i \cdot (kx_i - kx_{i-1}) = k \sum_{i=1}^n s_i \cdot (x_i - x_{i-1}) = k \int_a^b s(x) \, dx .$$

13. Prove Theorem 1.2 (the additive property).

[*Hint:* Use the additive property for sums: $\sum_{k=1}^n (a_k + b_k) = \sum_{k=1}^n a_k + \sum_{k=1}^n b_k .$]

14. Prove Theorem 1.4 (the linearity property).

[*Hint:* Use the additive property and the homogeneous property.]

15. Prove Theorem 1.5 (the comparison theorem).

[*Hint:* Use the corresponding property for sums: $\sum_{k=1}^n a_k < \sum_{k=1}^n b_k$ if $a_k < b_k$ for $k = 1, 2, \ldots, n.$]

16. Prove Theorem 1.6 (additivity with respect to the interval).

   [*Hint:* If P_1 is a partition of $[a, c]$ and P_2 a partiton of $[c, b]$, then the points of P_1 along with those of P_2 form a partition of $[a, b]$.]

17. Prove Theorem 1.7 (invariance under translation).

   [*Hint:* If $P = \{x_0, x_1, \ldots, x_n\}$ is a partition of $[a, b]$, then $P' = \{x_0 + c, x_1 + c, \ldots, x_n + c\}$ is a partition of $[a + c, b + c]$.]

1.16   The integral of more general functions

The integral $\int_a^b s(x)\, dx$ has been defined when s is a step function. In this section we shall formulate a definition of $\int_a^b f(x)\, dx$ that will apply to more general functions f. The definition will be constructed so that the resulting integral has all the properties listed in Section 1.13.

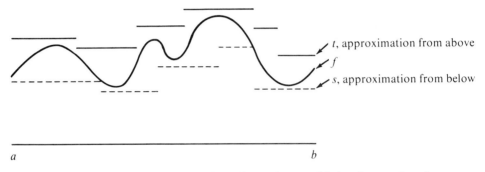

FIGURE 1.30   Approximating a function f from above and below by step functions.

The approach will be patterned somewhat after the method of Archimedes, which was explained above in Section I 1.3. The idea is simply this: We begin by approximating the function f from below and from above by step functions, as suggested in Figure 1.30. That is, we choose an arbitrary step function, say s, whose graph lies below that of f, and a arbitrary step function, say t, whose graph lies above that of f. Next, we consider the collection of all the numbers $\int_a^b s(x)\, dx$ and $\int_a^b t(x)\, dx$ obtained by choosing s and t in all possible ways. In general, we have

$$\int_a^b s(x)\, dx < \int_a^b t(x)\, dx$$

because of the comparison theorem. If the integral of f is to obey the comparison theorem, then it must be a number which falls between $\int_a^b s(x)\, dx$ and $\int_a^b t(x)\, dx$ for every pair of approximating functions s and t. If there is *only one* number which has this property we define the integral of f to be this number.

   There is only one thing that can cause trouble in this procedure, and it occurs in the very first step. Unfortunately, it is not possible to approximate *every* function from above and from below by step functions. For example, the function f given by the equations

$$f(x) = \frac{1}{x} \quad \text{if} \quad x \neq 0, \quad f(0) = 0,$$

is defined for all real x, but on any interval $[a, b]$ containing the origin we cannot surround f by step functions. This is due to the fact that f has arbitrarily large values near the origin or, as we say, f is *unbounded* in every neighborhood of the origin (see Figure 1.31). Therefore, we shall first restrict ourselves to those functions that are *bounded* on $[a, b]$, that is, to those functions f for which there exists a number $M > 0$ such that

(1.5) $$-M \leq f(x) \leq M$$

for every x in $[a, b]$. Geometrically, the graph of such a function lies between the graphs of two constant step functions s and t having the values $-M$ and $+M$, respectively. (See

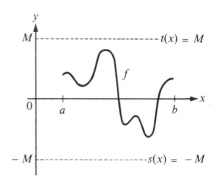

FIGURE 1.31   An unbounded function.   FIGURE 1.32   A bounded function.

Figure 1.32.) In a case like this, we say that f is bounded by M. The two inequalities in (1.5) can also be written as

$$|f(x)| \leq M.$$

With this point taken care of, we can proceed to carry out the plan described above and to formulate the definition of the integral.

DEFINITION OF THE INTEGRAL OF A BOUNDED FUNCTION. *Let f be a function defined and bounded on $[a, b]$. Let s and t denote arbitrary step functions defined on $[a, b]$ such that*

(1.6) $$s(x) \leq f(x) \leq t(x)$$

for every x in $[a, b]$. If there is one and only one number I such that

(1.7) $$\int_a^b s(x)\, dx \leq I \leq \int_a^b t(x)\, dx$$

for every pair of step functions s and t satisfying (1.6), then this number I is called the integral of f from a to b, and is denoted by the symbol $\int_a^b f(x)\, dx$ or by $\int_a^b f$. When such an I exists, the function f is said to be integrable on $[a, b]$.

If $a < b$, we define $\int_b^a f(x)\,dx = -\int_a^b f(x)\,dx$, provided f is integrable on $[a, b]$. We also define $\int_a^a f(x)\,dx = 0$. If f is integrable on $[a, b]$, we say that the integral $\int_a^b f(x)\,dx$ exists. The function f is called the *integrand*, the numbers a and b are called the *limits of integration*, and the interval $[a, b]$ the *interval of integration*.

1.17 Upper and lower integrals

Assume f is bounded on $[a, b]$. If s and t are step functions satisfying (1.6), we say s is *below* f, and t is *above* f, and we write $s \leq f \leq t$.

Let S denote the set of all numbers $\int_a^b s(x)\,dx$ obtained as s runs through all step functions below f, and let T be the set of all numbers $\int_a^b t(x)\,dx$ obtained as t runs through all step functions above f. That is, let

$$S = \left\{ \int_a^b s(x)\,dx \,\middle|\, s \leq f \right\}, \qquad T = \left\{ \int_a^b t(x)\,dx \,\middle|\, f \leq t \right\}.$$

Both sets S and T are nonempty since f is bounded. Also, $\int_a^b s(x)\,dx \leq \int_a^b t(x)\,dx$ if $s \leq f \leq t$, so every number in S is less than every number in T. Therefore, by Theorem I.34, S has a supremum, and T has an infimum, and they satisfy the inequalities

$$\int_a^b s(x)\,dx \leq \sup S \leq \inf T \leq \int_a^b t(x)\,dx$$

for all s and t satisfying $s \leq f \leq t$. This shows that both numbers $\sup S$ and $\inf T$ satisfy (1.7). Therefore, f is integrable on $[a, b]$ if and only if $\sup S = \inf T$, in which case we have

$$\int_a^b f(x)\,dx = \sup S = \inf T.$$

The number $\sup S$ is called the *lower integral* of f and is denoted by $\underline{I}(f)$. The number $\inf T$ is called the *upper* integral of f and is denoted by $\bar{I}(f)$. Thus, we have

$$\underline{I}(f) = \sup \left\{ \int_a^b s(x)\,dx \,\middle|\, s \leq f \right\}, \qquad \bar{I}(f) = \inf \left\{ \int_a^b t(x)\,dx \,\middle|\, f \leq t \right\}.$$

The foregoing argument proves the following theorem.

THEOREM 1.9.   *Every function f which is bounded on $[a, b]$ has a lower integral $\underline{I}(f)$ and an upper integral $\bar{I}(f)$ satisfying the inequalities*

$$\int_a^b s(x)\,dx \leq \underline{I}(f) \leq \bar{I}(f) \leq \int_a^b t(x)\,dx$$

for all step functions s and t with $s \leq f \leq t$. The function f is integrable on $[a, b]$ if and only if its upper and lower integrals are equal, in which case we have

$$\int_a^b f(x)\,dx = \underline{I}(f) = \bar{I}(f).$$

1.18   The area of an ordinate set expressed as an integral

The concept of area was introduced axiomatically in Section 1.6 as a set function having certain properties. From these properties we proved that the area of the ordinate set of a nonnegative step function is equal to the integral of the function. Now we show that the same is true for any integrable nonnegative function. We recall that the ordinate set of a nonnegative function f over an interval $[a, b]$ is the set of all points (x, y) satisfying the inequalities $0 \leq y \leq f(x)$, $a \leq x \leq b$.

THEOREM 1.10.   *Let f be a nonnegative function, integrable on an interval $[a, b]$, and let Q denote the ordinate set of f over $[a, b]$. Then Q is measurable and its area is equal to the integral $\int_a^b f(x)\, dx$.*

Proof. Let S and T be two step regions satisfying $S \subseteq Q \subseteq T$. Then there are two step functions s and t satisfying $s \leq f \leq t$ on $[a, b]$, such that

$$a(S) = \int_a^b s(x)\, dx \qquad \text{and} \qquad a(T) = \int_a^b t(x)\, dx \, .$$

Since f is integrable on $[a, b]$, the number $I = \int_a^b f(x)\, dx$ is the only number satisfying the inequalities

$$\int_a^b s(x)\, dx \leq I \leq \int_a^b t(x)\, dx$$

for all step functions s and t with $s \leq f \leq t$. Therefore this is also the only number satisfying $a(S) \leq I \leq a(T)$ for all step regions S and T with $S \subseteq Q \subseteq T$. By the exhaustion property, this proves that Q is measurable and that $a(Q) = I$.

Let Q denote the ordinate set of Theorem 1.10, and let Q' denote the set that remains if we remove from Q those points on the graph of f. That is, let

$$Q' = \{(x, y) \mid a \leq x \leq b, 0 \leq y < f(x)\} \, .$$

The argument used to prove Theorem 1.10 also shows that Q' is measurable and that $a(Q') = a(Q)$. Therefore, by the difference property of area, the set $Q - Q'$ is measurable and

$$a(Q - Q') = a(Q) - a(Q') = 0 \, .$$

In other words, we have proved the following theorem.

THEOREM 1.11.   *Let f be a nonnegative function, integrable on an interval $[a, b]$. Then the graph of f, that is, the set*

$$\{(x, y) \mid a \leq x \leq b, y = f(x)\} \, ,$$

is measurable and has area equal to 0.

1.19   Informal remarks on the theory and technique of integration

Two fundamental questions arise at this stage: (1) *Which bounded functions are integrable?* (2) *Given that a function f is integrable, how do we compute the integral of f?*

The first question comes under the heading "Theory of Integration" and the second under the heading "Technique of Integration." A complete answer to question (1) lies beyond the scope of an introductory course and will not be given in this book. Instead, we shall give partial answers which require only elementary ideas.

First we introduce an important class of functions known as *monotonic functions*. In the following section we define these functions and give a number of examples. Then we prove that all bounded monotonic functions are integrable. Fortunately, most of the functions that occur in practice are monotonic or sums of monotonic functions, so the results of this miniature theory of integration are quite comprehensive.

The discussion of "Technique of Integration" begins in Section 1.23, where we calculate the integral $\int_0^b x^p \, dx$, when p is a positive integer. Then we develop general properties of the integral, such as linearity and additivity, and show how these properties help us to extend our knowledge of integrals of specific functions.

1.20 Monotonic and piecewise monotonic functions. Definitions and examples

A function f is said to be *increasing* on a set S if $f(x) \leq f(y)$ for every pair of points x and y in S with $x < y$. If the strict inequality $f(x) < f(y)$ holds for all $x < y$ in S, the function is said to be *strictly increasing* on S. Similarly, f is called *decreasing* on S if

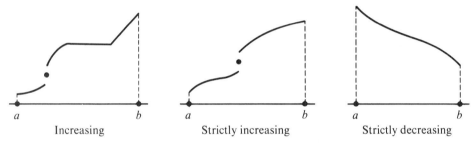

Increasing	Strictly increasing	Strictly decreasing

FIGURE 1.33   Monotonic functions.

$f(x) \geq f(y)$ for all $x < y$ in S. If $f(x) > f(y)$ for all $x < y$ in S, then f is called *strictly decreasing* on S. A function is called *monotonic* on S if it is increasing on S or if it is decreasing on S. The term *strictly monotonic* means that f is strictly increasing on S or strictly decreasing on S. Ordinarily, the set S under consideration is either an open interval or a closed interval. Examples are shown in Figure 1.33.

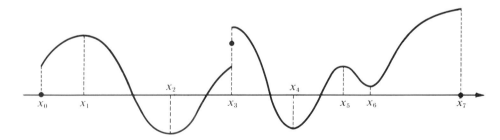

FIGURE 1.34   A piecewise monotonic function.

A function f is said to be *piecewise monotonic* on an interval if its graph consists of a finite number of monotonic pieces. That is to say, f is piecewise monotonic on $[a, b]$ if there is a partition P of $[a, b]$ such that f is monotonic on each of the open subintervals of P. In particular, step functions are piecewise monotonic, as are all the examples shown in Figures 1.33 and 1.34.

EXAMPLE 1. *The power functions.* If p is a positive integer, we have the inequality

$$x^p < y^p \qquad \text{if} \quad 0 \le x < y,$$

which is easily proved by mathematical induction. This shows that the power function f, defined for all real x by the equation $f(x) = x^p$, is strictly increasing on the nonnegative real axis. It is also strictly monotonic on the negative real axis (it is decreasing if p is even and increasing if p is odd). Therefore, f is piecewise monotonic on every finite interval.

EXAMPLE 2. *The square-root function.* Let $f(x) = \sqrt{x}$ for $x \ge 0$. This function is strictly increasing on the nonnegative real axis. In fact, if $0 \le x < y$, we have

$$\sqrt{y} - \sqrt{x} = \frac{y - x}{\sqrt{y} + \sqrt{x}} ;$$

hence, $\sqrt{y} - \sqrt{x} > 0$.

EXAMPLE 3. The graph of the function g defined by the equation

$$g(x) = \sqrt{r^2 - x^2} \qquad \text{if} \quad -r \le x \le r$$

is a semicircle of radius r. This function is strictly increasing on the interval $-r \le x \le 0$ and strictly decreasing on the interval $0 \le x \le r$. Hence, g is piecewise monotonic on $[-r, r]$.

1.21 Integrability of bounded monotonic functions

The importance of monotonic functions in integration theory is due to the following theorem.

THEOREM 1.12. *If f is monotonic on a closed interval $[a, b]$, then f is integrable on $[a, b]$.*

Proof. We shall prove the theorem for increasing functions. The proof for decreasing functions is analogous. Assume f is increasing and let $\underline{I}(f)$ and $\bar{I}(f)$ denote its lower and upper integrals, respectively. We shall prove that $\underline{I}(f) = \bar{I}(f)$.

Let n be a positive integer and construct two special approximating step functions s_n and t_n as follows: Let $P = \{x_0, x_1, \ldots, x_n\}$ be a partition of $[a, b]$ into n *equal* subintervals, that is, subintervals $[x_{k-1}, x_k]$ with $x_k - x_{k-1} = (b - a)/n$ for each k. Now define s_n and t_n by the formulas

$$s_n(x) = f(x_{k-1}), \qquad t_n(x) = f(x_k) \qquad \text{if} \quad x_{k-1} < x < x_k.$$

At the subdivision points, define s_n and t_n so as to preserve the relations $s_n(x) \le f(x) \le t_n(x)$ throughout $[a, b]$. An example is shown in Figure 1.35(a). For this choice of step functions, we have

$$\int_a^b t_n - \int_a^b s_n = \sum_{k=1}^n f(x_k)(x_k - x_{k-1}) - \sum_{k=1}^n f(x_{k-1})(x_k - x_{k-1})$$

$$= \frac{b-a}{n} \sum_{k=1}^n [f(x_k) - f(x_{k-1})] = \frac{(b-a)[f(b) - f(a)]}{n},$$

where the last equation is a consequence of the telescoping property of finite sums. This last relation has a simple geometric interpretation. The difference $\int_a^b t_n - \int_a^b s_n$ is equal to the sum of the areas of the shaded rectangles in Figure 1.35(a). By sliding these rectangles to the right so that they rest on a common base as in Figure 1.35(b), we see that they fill out a

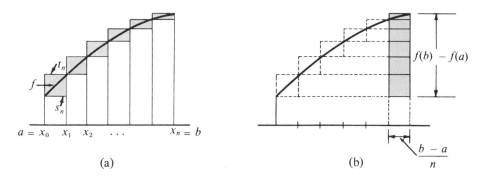

(a)   (b)

FIGURE 1.35   Proof of integrability of an increasing function.

rectangle of base $(b - a)/n$ and altitude $f(b) - f(a)$; the sum of the areas is therefore C/n, where $C = (b - a)[f(b) - f(a)]$.

Now we rewrite the foregoing relation in the form

(1.8) $$\int_a^b t_n - \int_a^b s_n = \frac{C}{n}.$$

The lower and upper integrals of f satisfy the inequalities

$$\int_a^b s_n \le \underline{I}(f) \le \int_a^b t_n \qquad \text{and} \qquad \int_a^b s_n \le \bar{I}(f) \le \int_a^b t_n.$$

Multiplying the first set of inequalities by (-1) and adding the result to the second set, we obtain

$$\bar{I}(f) - \underline{I}(f) \le \int_a^b t_n - \int_a^b s_n.$$

Using (1.8) and the relation $\underline{I}(f) \le \bar{I}(f)$, we obtain

$$0 \le \bar{I}(f) - \underline{I}(f) \le \frac{C}{n}.$$

for every integer $n \geq 1$. Therefore, by Theorem I.31, we must have $\underline{I}(f) = \overline{I}(f)$. This proves that f is integrable on $[a, b]$.

1.22 Calculation of the integral of a bounded monotonic function

The proof of Theorem 1.12 not only shows that the integral of a bounded increasing function *exists*, but it also suggests a method for computing the value of the integral. This is described by the following theorem.

THEOREM 1.13.   *Assume f is increasing on a closed interval $[a, b]$. Let $x_k = a + k(b - a)/n$ for $k = 0, 1, \ldots, n$. If I is any number which satisfies the inequalities*

(1.9)
$$\frac{b - a}{n} \sum_{k=0}^{n-1} f(x_k) \leq I \leq \frac{b - a}{n} \sum_{k=1}^{n} f(x_k)$$

for every integer $n \geq 1$, then $I = \int_a^b f(x) \, dx$.

Proof. Let s_n and t_n be the special approximating step functions obtained by subdivision of the interval $[a, b]$ into n equal parts, as described in the proof of Theorem 1.12. Then, inequalities (1.9) state that

$$\int_a^b s_n \leq I \leq \int_a^b t_n$$

for every $n \geq 1$. But the integral $\int_a^b f(x) \, dx$ satisfies the same inequalities as I. Using Equation (1.8) we see that

$$0 \leq \left| I - \int_a^b f(x) \, dx \right| \leq \frac{C}{n}$$

for every integer $n \geq 1$. Therefore, by Theorem I.31, we have $I = \int_a^b f(x) \, dx$, as asserted.

An analogous argument gives a proof of the corresponding theorem for decreasing functions.

THEOREM 1.14.   *Assume f is decreasing on $[a, b]$. Let $x_k = a + k(b - a)/n$ for $k = 0, 1, \ldots, n$. If I is any number which satisfies the inequalities*

$$\frac{b - a}{n} \sum_{k=1}^{n} f(x_k) \leq I \leq \frac{b - a}{n} \sum_{k=0}^{n-1} f(x_k)$$

for every integer $n \geq 1$, then $I = \int_a^b f(x) \, dx$.

1.23 Calculation of the integral $\int_0^b x^p \, dx$ when p is a positive integer

To illustrate the use of Theorem 1.13 we shall calculate the integral $\int_0^b x^p \, dx$ where $b > 0$ and p is any positive integer. The integral exists because the integrand is bounded and increasing on $[0, b]$.

THEOREM 1.15.   *If p is a positive integer and $b > 0$, we have*

$$\int_0^b x^p \, dx = \frac{b^{p+1}}{p+1} \, .$$

Proof. We begin with the inequalities

$$\sum_{k=1}^{n-1} k^p < \frac{n^{p+1}}{p+1} < \sum_{k=1}^{n} k^p$$

valid for every integer $n \geq 1$ and every integer $p \geq 1$. These inequalities may be easily proved by mathematical induction. (A proof is outlined in Exercise 13 of Section I 4.10.) Multiplication of these inequalities by b^{p+1}/n^{p+1} gives us

$$\frac{b}{n} \sum_{k=1}^{n-1} \left(\frac{kb}{n}\right)^p < \frac{b^{p+1}}{p+1} < \frac{b}{n} \sum_{k=1}^{n} \left(\frac{kb}{n}\right)^p \, .$$

If we let $f(x) = x^p$ and $x_k = kb/n$, for $k = 0, 1, 2, \ldots, n$, these inequalities become

$$\frac{b}{n} \sum_{k=0}^{n-1} f(x_k) < \frac{b^{p+1}}{p+1} < \frac{b}{n} \sum_{k=1}^{n} f(x_k) \, .$$

Therefore, the inequalities (1.9) of Theorem 1.13 are satisfied with $f(x) = x^p$, $a = 0$, and $I = b^{p+1}/(p+1)$. It follows that $\int_0^b x^p \, dx = b^{p+1}/(p+1)$.

1.24   The basic properties of the integral

From the definition of the integral, it is possible to deduce the following properties. Proofs are given in Section 1.27.

THEOREM 1.16.   LINEARITY WITH RESPECT TO THE INTEGRAND.   *If both f and g are integrable on $[a, b]$, so is $c_1 f + c_2 g$ for every pair of constants c_1 and c_2. Furthermore, we have*

$$\int_a^b [c_1 f(x) + c_2 g(x)] \, dx = c_1 \int_a^b f(x) \, dx + c_2 \int_a^b g(x) \, dx \, .$$

Note: By use of mathematical induction, the linearity property can be generalized as follows: If $f_1, \ldots, f_n$ are integrable on $[a, b]$, then so is $c_1 f_1 + \cdots + c_n f_n$ for all real $c_1, \ldots, c_n$, and

$$\int_a^b \sum_{k=1}^{n} c_k f_k(x) \, dx = \sum_{k=1}^{n} c_k \int_a^b f_k(x) \, dx \, .$$

THEOREM 1.17.   ADDITIVITY WITH RESPECT TO THE INTERVAL OF INTEGRATION.   *If two of the following three integrals exist, the third also exists, and we have*

$$\int_a^b f(x) \, dx + \int_b^c f(x) \, dx = \int_a^c f(x) \, dx \, .$$

Note: In particular, if f is monotonic on $[a, b]$ and also on $[b, c]$, then both integrals $\int_a^b f$ and $\int_b^c f$ exist, so $\int_a^c f$ also exists and is equal to the sum of the other two integrals.

THEOREM 1.18. INVARIANCE UNDER TRANSLATION. *If f is integrable on $[a, b]$, then for every real c we have*

$$\int_a^b f(x)\, dx = \int_{a+c}^{b+c} f(x - c)\, dx \, .$$

THEOREM 1.19. EXPANSION OR CONTRACTION OF THE INTERVAL OF INTEGRATION. *If f is integrable on $[a, b]$, then for every real $k \neq 0$ we have*

$$\int_a^b f(x)\, dx = \frac{1}{k} \int_{ka}^{kb} f\left(\frac{x}{k}\right) dx \, .$$

Note: In both Theorems 1.18 and 1.19, the existence of one of the integrals implies the existence of the other. When $k = -1$, Theorem 1.19 is called the *reflection property*.

THEOREM 1.20. COMPARISON THEOREM. *If both f and g are integrable on $[a, b]$ and if $g(x) \leq f(x)$ for every x in $[a, b]$, then we have*

$$\int_a^b g(x)\, dx \leq \int_a^b f(x)\, dx \, .$$

An important special case of Theorem 1.20 occurs when $g(x) = 0$ for every x. In this case, the theorem states that if $f(x) \geq 0$ everywhere on $[a, b]$, then $\int_a^b f(x)\, dx \geq 0$. In other words, a nonnegative function has a nonnegative integral. It can also be shown that if we have the *strict* inequality $g(x) < f(x)$ for all x in $[a, b]$, then the same strict inequality holds for the integrals, but the proof is not easy to give at this stage.

In Chapter 5 we shall discuss various methods for calculating the value of an integral without the necessity of using the definition in each case. These methods, however, are applicable to only a relatively small number of functions, and for most integrable functions the actual numerical value of the integral can only be estimated. This is usually done by approximating the integrand above and below by step functions or by other simple functions whose integrals can be evaluated exactly. Then the comparison theorem is used to obtain corresponding approximations for the integral of the function in question. This idea will be explored more fully in Chapter 7.

1.25 Integration of polynomials

In Section 1.23 we established the integration formula

(1.10)
$$\int_0^b x^p\, dx = \frac{b^{p+1}}{p + 1}$$

for $b > 0$ and p any positive integer. The formula is also valid if $b = 0$, since both members are zero. We can use Theorem 1.19 to show that (1.10) also holds for negative b. We simply take $k = -1$ in Theorem 1.19 to obtain

$$\int_0^{-b} x^p \, dx = -\int_0^b (-x)^p \, dx = (-1)^{p+1} \int_0^b x^p \, dx = \frac{(-b)^{p+1}}{p+1},$$

which shows that (1.10) holds for negative b. The additive property $\int_a^b x^p \, dx = \int_0^b x^p \, dx - \int_0^a x^p \, dx$ now leads to the more general formula

$$\int_a^b x^p \, dx = \frac{b^{p+1} - a^{p+1}}{p+1},$$

valid for all real a and b, and any integer $p \geq 0$.

Sometimes the special symbol

$$P(x) \Big|_a^b$$

is used to designate the difference $P(b) - P(a)$. Thus the foregoing formula may also be written as follows:

$$\int_a^b x^p \, dx = \frac{x^{p+1}}{p+1} \Big|_a^b = \frac{b^{p+1} - a^{p+1}}{p+1}.$$

This formula, along with the linearity property, enables us to integrate every polynomial. For example, to compute the integral $\int_1^3 (x^2 - 3x + 5) \, dx$, we find the integral of each term and then add the results. Thus, we have

$$\int_1^3 (x^2 - 3x + 5) \, dx = \int_1^3 x^2 \, dx - 3 \int_1^3 x \, dx + 5 \int_1^3 dx = \frac{x^3}{3} \Big|_1^3 - 3 \frac{x^2}{2} \Big|_1^3 + 5x \Big|_1^3$$

$$= \frac{3^3 - 1^3}{3} - 3 \frac{3^2 - 1^2}{2} + 5 \frac{3^1 - 1^1}{1} = \frac{26}{3} - 12 + 10 = \frac{20}{3}.$$

More generally, to compute the integral of any polynomial we integrate term by term:

$$\int_a^b \sum_{k=0}^n c_k x^k \, dx = \sum_{k=0}^n c_k \int_a^b x^k \, dx = \sum_{k=0}^n c_k \frac{b^{k+1} - a^{k+1}}{k+1}.$$

We can also integrate more complicated functions formed by piecing together various polynomials. For example, consider the integral $\int_0^1 |x(2x - 1)| \, dx$. Because of the absolute-value signs, the integrand is not a polynomial. However, by considering the sign of

$x(2x - 1)$, we can split the interval $[0, 1]$ into two subintervals, in each of which the integrand is a polynomial. As x varies from 0 to 1, the product $x(2x - 1)$ changes sign at the point $x = \frac{1}{2}$; it is negative if $0 < x < \frac{1}{2}$ and positive if $\frac{1}{2} < x < 1$. Therefore, we use the additive property to write

$$\int_0^1 |x(2x - 1)|\, dx = -\int_0^{1/2} x(2x - 1)\, dx + \int_{1/2}^1 x(2x - 1)\, dx$$

$$= \int_0^{1/2} (x - 2x^2)\, dx + \int_{1/2}^1 (2x^2 - x)\, dx$$

$$= (\tfrac{1}{8} - \tfrac{1}{12}) + (\tfrac{7}{12} - \tfrac{3}{8}) = \tfrac{1}{4}.$$

1.26 Exercises

Compute each of the following integrals.

1. $\int_0^3 x^2\, dx.$

2. $\int_{-3}^3 x^2\, dx.$

3. $\int_0^2 4x^3\, dx.$

4. $\int_{-2}^2 4x^3\, dx.$

5. $\int_0^1 5t^4\, dt.$

6. $\int_{-1}^1 5t^4\, dt.$

7. $\int_0^1 (5x^4 - 4x^3)\, dx.$

8. $\int_{-1}^1 (5x^4 - 4x^3)\, dx.$

9. $\int_{-1}^2 (t^2 + 1)\, dt.$

10. $\int_2^3 (3x^2 - 4x + 2)\, dx.$

11. $\int_0^{1/2} (8t^3 + 6t^2 - 2t + 5)\, dt.$

12. $\int_{-2}^4 (u - 1)(u - 2)\, du.$

13. $\int_{-1}^0 (x + 1)^2\, dx.$

14. $\int_0^{-1} (x + 1)^2\, dx.$

15. $\int_0^2 (x - 1)(3x - 1)\, dx.$

16. $\int_0^2 |(x - 1)(3x - 1)|\, dx.$

17. $\int_0^3 (2x - 5)^3\, dx.$

18. $\int_{-3}^3 (x^2 - 3)^3\, dx.$

19. $\int_0^5 x^2(x - 5)^4\, dx.$

20. $\int_{-2}^{-4} (x + 4)^{10}\, dx.$ [*Hint:* Theorem 1.18.]

21. Find all values of c for which

    (a) $\int_0^c x(1 - x)\, dx = 0,$ (b) $\int_0^c |x(1 - x)|\, dx = 0.$

22. Compute each of the following integrals. Draw the graph of f in each case.

    (a) $\int_0^2 f(x)\, dx$ where $f(x) = \begin{cases} x^2 & \text{if } 0 \le x \le 1, \\ 2 - x & \text{if } 1 \le x \le 2. \end{cases}$

    (b) $\int_0^1 f(x)\, dx$ where $f(x) = \begin{cases} x & \text{if } 0 \le x \le c, \\ c\,\dfrac{1 - x}{1 - c} & \text{if } c \le x \le 1; \end{cases}$

    c is a fixed real number, $0 < c < 1.$

23. Find a quadratic polynomial P for which $P(0) = P(1) = 0$ and $\int_0^1 P(x)\, dx = 1.$

24. Find a cubic polynomial P for which $P(0) = P(-2) = 0$, $P(1) = 15$, and $3\int_{-2}^0 P(x)\, dx = 4.$

Optional exercises

25. Let f be a function whose domain contains $-x$ whenever it contains x. We say that f is an
    even function if $f(-x) = f(x)$ and an *odd* function if $f(-x) = -f(x)$ for all x in the domain
    of f. If f is integrable on $[0, b]$, prove that

    (a) $\int_{-b}^{b} f(x)\,dx = 2\int_{0}^{b} f(x)\,dx$ if f is even;

    (b) $\int_{-b}^{b} f(x)\,dx = 0$ if f is odd.

26. Use Theorems 1.18 and 1.19 to derive the formula

$$\int_{a}^{b} f(x)\,dx = (b-a)\int_{0}^{1} f[a + (b-a)x]\,dx\,.$$

27. Theorems 1.18 and 1.19 suggest a common generalization for the integral $\int_{a}^{b} f(Ax + B)\,dx$.
    Guess the formula suggested and prove it with the help of Theorems 1.18 and 1.19. Discuss
    also the case $A = 0$.

28. Use Theorems 1.18 and 1.19 to derive the formula

$$\int_{a}^{b} f(c-x)\,dx = \int_{c-b}^{c-a} f(x)\,dx\,.$$

1.27   Proofs of the basic properties of the integral

This section contains proofs of the basic properties of the integral listed in Theorems
1.16 through 1.20 in Section 1.24. We make repeated use of the fact that every function f
which is bounded on an interval $[a, b]$ has a lower integral $\underline{I}(f)$ and an upper integral $\bar{I}(f)$
given by

$$\underline{I}(f) = \sup\left\{\int_{a}^{b} s \,\Big|\, s \le f\right\}\,, \qquad \bar{I}(g) = \inf\left\{\int_{a}^{b} t \,\Big|\, f \le t\right\}\,,$$

where s and t denote arbitrary step functions below and above f, respectively. We know,
by Theorem 1.9, that f is integrable if and only if $\underline{I}(f) = \bar{I}(f)$, in which case the value of the
integral of f is the common value of the upper and lower integrals.

Proof of the Linearity Property (*Theorem 1.16*). We decompose the linearity property into
two parts:

(A) $$\int_{a}^{b} (f + g) = \int_{a}^{b} f + \int_{a}^{b} g\,,$$

(B) $$\int_{a}^{b} cf = c\int_{a}^{b} f\,.$$

To prove (A), let $\underline{I}(f) = \int_{a}^{b} f$ and let $\underline{I}(g) = \int_{a}^{b} g$. We shall prove that $\underline{I}(f + g) = \bar{I}(f + g) = \underline{I}(f) + \underline{I}(g)$.

Let s_1 and s_2 denote arbitrary step functions below f and g, respectively. Since f and g
are integrable, we have

$$\underline{I}(f) = \sup\left\{\int_{a}^{b} s_1 \,\Big|\, s_1 \le f\right\}\,, \qquad \underline{I}(g) = \sup\left\{\int_{a}^{b} s_2 \,\Big|\, s_2 \le g\right\}\,.$$

By the additive property of the supremum (Theorem I.33), we also have

(1.11) $$I(f) + I(g) = \sup \left\{ \int_a^b s_1 + \int_a^b s_2 \,\bigg|\, s_1 \leq f, s_2 \leq g \right\}.$$

But if $s_1 \leq f$ and $s_2 \leq g$, then the sum $s = s_1 + s_2$ is a step function below $f + g$, and we have

$$\int_a^b s_1 + \int_a^b s_2 = \int_a^b s \leq \underline{I}(f + g).$$

Therefore, the number $\underline{I}(f + g)$ is an upper bound for the set appearing on the right of (1.11). This upper bound cannot be less than the least upper bound of the set, so we have

(1.12) $$\underline{I}(f) + \underline{I}(g) \leq \underline{I}(f + g).$$

Similarly, if we use the relations

$$\bar{I}(f) = \inf \left\{ \int_a^b t_1 \,\bigg|\, f \leq t_1 \right\}, \qquad \bar{I}(g) = \inf \left\{ \int_a^b t_2 \,\bigg|\, g \leq t_2 \right\},$$

where t_1 and t_2 denote arbitrary step functions above f and g, respectively, we obtain the inequality

(1.13) $$\bar{I}(f + g) \leq \bar{I}(f) + \bar{I}(g).$$

Inequalities (1.12) and (1.13) together show that $\underline{I}(f + g) = \bar{I}(f + g) = I(f) + I(g)$. Therefore $f + g$ is integrable and relation (A) holds.

Relation (B) is trivial if $c = 0$. If $c > 0$, we note that every step function s_1 below cf is of the form $s_1 = cs$, where s is a step function below f. Similarly, every step function t_1 above cf is of the form $t_1 = ct$, where t is a step function above f. Therefore we have

$$\underline{I}(cf) = \sup \left\{ \int_a^b s_1 \,\bigg|\, s_1 \leq cf \right\} = \sup \left\{ c \int_a^b s \,\bigg|\, s \leq f \right\} = c\underline{I}(f)$$

and

$$\bar{I}(cf) = \inf \left\{ \int_a^b t_1 \,\bigg|\, cf \leq t_1 \right\} = \inf \left\{ c \int_a^b t \,\bigg|\, f \leq t \right\} = c\bar{I}(f).$$

Therefore $\underline{I}(cf) = \bar{I}(cf) = cI(f)$. Here we have used the following properties of the supremum and infimum:

(1.14) $\sup \{cx \mid x \in A\} = c \sup \{x \mid x \in A\}$, $\quad \inf \{cx \mid x \in A\} = c \inf \{x \mid x \in A\}$,

which hold if $c > 0$. This proves (B) if $c > 0$.

If $c < 0$, the proof of (B) is basically the same, except that every step function s_1 below cf is of the form $s_1 = ct$, where t is a step function *above* f, and every step function t_1 above cf is of the form $t_1 = cs$, where s is a step function *below* f. Also, instead of (1.14) we use the relations

$$\sup \{cx \mid x \in A\} = c \inf \{x \mid x \in A\}, \qquad \inf \{cx \mid x \in A\} = c \sup \{x \mid x \in A\},$$

which hold if $c < 0$. We now have

$$I(cf) = \sup \left\{ \int_a^b s_1 \mid s_1 \leq cf \right\} = \sup \left\{ c \int_a^b t \mid f \leq t \right\} = c \inf \left\{ \int_a^b t \mid f \leq t \right\} = cI(f).$$

Similarly, we find $\bar{I}(cf) = cI(f)$. Therefore (B) holds for all real c.

Proof of Additivity with Respect to the Interval of Integration (*Theorem* 1.17). Suppose that $a < b < c$, and assume that the two integrals $\int_a^b f$ and $\int_b^c f$ exist. Let $I(f)$ and $\bar{I}(f)$ denote the upper and lower integrals of f over the interval $[a, c]$. We shall prove that

(1.15) $$I(f) = \bar{I}(f) = \int_a^b f + \int_b^c f.$$

If s is any step function below f on $[a, c]$, we have

$$\int_a^c s = \int_a^b s + \int_b^c s.$$

Conversely, if s_1 and s_2 are step functions below f on $[a, b]$ and on $[b, c]$, respectively, then the function s which is equal to s_1 on $[a, b)$ and equal to s_2 on $[b, c]$ is a step function below f on $[a, c]$ for which we have

$$\int_a^c s = \int_a^b s_1 + \int_b^c s_2.$$

Therefore, by the additive property of the supremum (Theorem 1.33), we have

$$I(f) = \sup \left\{ \int_a^c s \mid s \leq f \right\} = \sup \left\{ \int_a^b s_1 \mid s_1 \leq f \right\} + \sup \left\{ \int_b^c s_2 \mid s_2 \leq f \right\} = \int_a^b f + \int_b^c f.$$

Similarly, we find

$$\bar{I}(f) = \int_a^b f + \int_b^c f,$$

which proves (1.15) when $a < b < c$. The proof is similar for any other arrangement of the points a, b, c.

Proof of the Translation Property (*Theorem* 1.18). Let g be the function defined on the interval $[a + c, b + c]$ by the equation $g(x) = f(x - c)$. Let $I(g)$ and $\bar{I}(g)$ denote the lower and upper integrals of g on the interval $[a + c, b + c]$. We shall prove that

(1.16) $$I(g) = \bar{I}(g) = \int_a^b f(x)\,dx.$$

Let s be any step function below g on the interval $[a + c, b + c]$. Then the function s_1 defined on $[a, b]$ by the equation $s_1(x) = s(x + c)$ is a step function below f on $[a, b]$. Moreover, every step function s_1 below f on $[a, b]$ has this form for some s below g. Also, by the translation property for integrals of step functions, we have

$$\int_{a+c}^{b+c} s(x)\,dx = \int_a^b s(x + c)\,dx = \int_a^b s_1(x)\,dx.$$

Therefore we have

$$I(g) = \sup \left\{ \int_{a+c}^{b+c} s \mid s \leq g \right\} = \sup \left\{ \int_a^b s_1 \mid s_1 \leq f \right\} = \int_a^b f(x)\, dx\,.$$

Similarly, we find $\bar{I}(g) = \int_a^b f(x)\, dx$, which proves (1.16).

Proof of the Expansion Property (*Theorem* 1.19).   Assume $k > 0$ and define g on the interval $[ka, kb]$ by the equation $g(x) = f(x/k)$. Let $I(g)$ and $\bar{I}(g)$ denote the lower and upper integrals of g on $[ka, kb]$.   We shall prove that

$$(1.17) \qquad\qquad I(g) = \bar{I}(g) = k \int_a^b f(x)\, dx\,.$$

Let s be any step function below g on $[ka, kb]$.   Then the function s_1 defined on $[a, b]$ by the equation $s_1(x) = s(kx)$ is a step function below f on $[a, b]$.   Moreover, every step function s_1 below f on $[a, b]$ has this form.   Also, by the expansion property for integrals of step functions, we have

$$\int_{ka}^{kb} s(x)\, dx = k \int_a^b s(kx)\, dx = k \int_a^b s_1(x)\, dx\,.$$

Therefore we have

$$I(g) = \sup \left\{ \int_{ka}^{kb} s \mid s \leq g \right\} = \sup \left\{ k \int_a^b s_1 \mid s_1 \leq f \right\} = k \int_a^b f(x)\, dx\,.$$

Similarly, we find $\bar{I}(g) = k\int_a^b f(x)\, dx$, which proves (1.17) if $k > 0$.   The same type of proof can be used if $k < 0$.

Proof of the Comparison Theorem (*Theorem* 1.20).   Assume $g \leq f$ on the interval $[a, b]$. Let s be any step function below g, and let t be any step function above f.   Then we have $\int_a^b s \leq \int_a^b t$, and hence Theorem I.34 gives us

$$\int_a^b g = \sup \left\{ \int_a^b s \mid s \leq g \right\} \leq \inf \left\{ \int_a^b t \mid f \leq t \right\} = \int_a^b f\,.$$

This proves that $\int_a^b g \leq \int_a^b f$, as required.

2

SOME APPLICATIONS OF INTEGRATION

2.1 Introduction

In Section 1.18 we expressed the area of the ordinate set of a nonnegative function as an integral. In this chapter we will show that areas of more general regions can also be expressed as integrals. We will also discuss further applications of the integral to concepts such as volume, work, and averages. Then, at the end of the chapter, we will study properties of functions defined by integrals.

2.2 The area of a region between two graphs expressed as an integral

If two functions f and g are related by the inequality $f(x) \leq g(x)$ for all x in an interval $[a, b]$, we write $f \leq g$ on $[a, b]$. Figure 2.1 shows two examples. If $f \leq g$ on $[a, b]$, the set S consisting of all points (x, y) satisfying the inequalities

$$f(x) \leq y \leq g(x), \qquad a \leq x \leq b,$$

is called the region between the graphs of f and g. The following theorem tells us how to express the area of S as an integral.

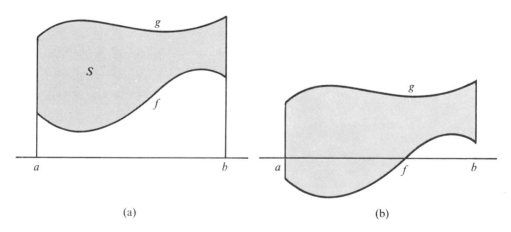

(a)   (b)

FIGURE 2.1   The area of a region between two graphs expressed as an integral:

$$a(S) = \int_a^b [g(x) - f(x)]\, dx.$$

THEOREM 2.1. *Assume f and g are integrable and satisfy f ≤ g on [a, b]. Then the region S between their graphs is measurable and its area a(S) is given by the integral*

(2.1) $$a(S) = \int_a^b [g(x) - f(x)]\, dx \,.$$

Proof. Assume first that f and g are nonnegative, as shown in Figure 2.1(a). Let F and G denote the following sets:

$$F = \{(x, y) \mid a \le x \le b, 0 \le y < f(x)\}\,, \qquad G = \{(x, y) \mid a \le x \le b, 0 \le y \le g(x)\}\,.$$

That is, G is the ordinate set of g, and F is the ordinate set of f, minus the graph of f. The region S between the graphs of f and g is the difference $S = G - F$. By Theorems 1.10 and 1.11, both F and G are measurable. Since $F \subseteq G$, the difference $S = G - F$ is also measurable, and we have

$$a(S) = a(G) - a(F) = \int_a^b g(x)\, dx - \int_a^b f(x)\, dx = \int_a^b [g(x) - f(x)]\, dx\,.$$

This proves (2.1) when f and g are nonnegative.

Now consider the general case where $f \le g$ on $[a, b]$, but f and g are not necessarily nonnegative. An example is shown in Figure 2.1(b). We can reduce this to the previous case by sliding the region upward until it lies above the x-axis. That is, we choose a positive number c large enough to ensure that $0 \le f(x) + c \le g(x) + c$ for all x in $[a, b]$. By what we have already proved, the new region T between the graphs of $f + c$ and $g + c$ is measurable, and its area is given by the integral

$$a(T) = \int_a^b [(g(x) + c) - (f(x) + c)]\, dx = \int_a^b [g(x) - f(x)]\, dx\,.$$

But T is congruent to S; so S is also measurable and we have

$$a(S) = a(T) = \int_a^b [g(x) - f(x)]\, dx\,.$$

This completes the proof.

2.3 Worked examples

EXAMPLE 1. Compute the area of the region S between the graphs of f and g over the interval $[0, 2]$ if $f(x) = x(x - 2)$ and $g(x) = x/2$.

Solution. The two graphs are shown in Figure 2.2. The shaded portion represents S. Since $f \le g$ over the interval $[0, 2]$, we use Theorem 2.1 to write

$$a(S) = \int_0^2 [g(x) - f(x)]\, dx = \int_0^2 \left(\frac{5}{2}x - x^2\right) dx = \frac{5}{2}\frac{2^2}{2} - \frac{2^3}{3} = \frac{7}{3}\,.$$

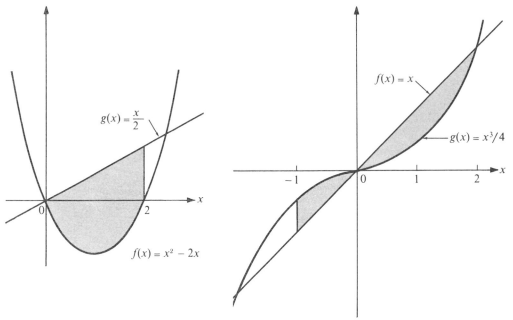

FIGURE 2.2 Example 1.   FIGURE 2.3 Example 2.

EXAMPLE 2. Compute the area of the region S between the graphs of f and g over the interval $[-1, 2]$ if $f(x) = x$ and $g(x) = x^3/4$.

Solution.   The region S is shown in Figure 2.3. Here we do not have $f \le g$ throughout the interval $[-1, 2]$. However, we do have $f \le g$ over the subinterval $[-1, 0]$ and $g \le f$ over the subinterval $[0, 2]$. Applying Theorem 2.1 to each subinterval, we have

$$a(S) = \int_{-1}^{0} [g(x) - f(x)] \, dx + \int_{0}^{2} [f(x) - g(x)] \, dx$$

$$= \int_{-1}^{0} \left(\frac{x^3}{4} - x \right) dx + \int_{0}^{2} \left(x - \frac{x^3}{4} \right) dx$$

$$= -\frac{1}{4} \frac{(-1)^4}{4} + \frac{(-1)^2}{2} + \frac{2^2}{2} - \frac{1}{4} \frac{2^4}{4} = \frac{23}{16} .$$

In examples like this one, where the interval $[a, b]$ can be broken up into a finite number of subintervals such that either $f \le g$ or $g \le f$ in each subinterval, formula (2.1) of Theorem 2.1 becomes

$$a(S) = \int_{a}^{b} |g(x) - f(x)| \, dx .$$

EXAMPLE 3. *Area of a circular disk.* A circular disk of radius r is the set of all points inside or on the boundary of a circle of radius r. Such a disk is congruent to the region between the graphs of the two functions f and g defined on the interval $[-r, r]$ by the formulas

$$g(x) = \sqrt{r^2 - x^2} \quad \text{and} \quad f(x) = -\sqrt{r^2 - x^2}.$$

Each function is bounded and monotonic on $[-r, r]$ so each is integrable on $[-r, r]$. Theorem 2.1 tells us that the region between their graphs is measurable and that its area is $\int_{-r}^{r} [g(x) - f(x)]\, dx$. Let $A(r)$ denote the area of the disk. We will prove that

$$A(r) = r^2 A(1).$$

That is, *the area of a disk of radius r is r^2 times the area of a unit disk* (a disk of radius 1). Since $g(x) - f(x) = 2g(x)$, Theorem 2.1 gives us

$$A(r) = \int_{-r}^{r} 2g(x)\, dx = 2 \int_{-r}^{r} \sqrt{r^2 - x^2}\, dx .$$

In particular, when $r = 1$, we have the formula

$$A(1) = 2 \int_{-1}^{1} \sqrt{1 - x^2}\, dx .$$

Now we change the scale on the x-axis, using Theorem 1.19 with $k = 1/r$, to obtain

$$A(r) = 2 \int_{-r}^{r} g(x)\, dx = 2r \int_{-1}^{1} g(rx)\, dx = 2r \int_{-1}^{1} \sqrt{r^2 - (rx)^2}\, dx$$

$$= 2r^2 \int_{-1}^{1} \sqrt{1 - x^2}\, dx = r^2 A(1) .$$

This proves that $A(r) = r^2 A(1)$, as asserted.

DEFINITION.   *We define the number π to be the area of a unit disk.*

The formula just proved states that $A(r) = \pi r^2$.

The foregoing example illustrates the behavior of area under expansion or contraction of plane regions. Suppose S is a given set of points in the plane and consider a new set of points obtained by multiplying the coordinates of each point of S by a constant factor $k > 0$. We denote this set by kS and say that it is *similar to S*. The process which produces kS from S is called a *similarity transformation*. Each point is moved along a straight line which passes through the origin to k times its original distance from the origin. If $k > 1$, the transformation is also called a *stretching* or an *expansion* (from the origin) and, if $0 < k < 1$, it is called a *shrinking* or a *contraction* (toward the origin).

For example, if S is the region bounded by a unit circle with center at the origin, then kS is a concentric circular region of radius k. In Example 3 we showed that for circular regions, the area of kS is k^2 times the area of S. Now we prove that this property of area holds for any ordinate set.

EXAMPLE 4. *Behavior of the area of an ordinate set under a similarity transformation.*
Let f be nonnegative and integrable on $[a, b]$ and let S be its ordinate set. An example is
shown in Figure 2.4(a). If we apply a similarity transformation with a positive factor k,
then kS is the ordinate set of a new function, say g, over the interval $[ka, kb]$. [See Figure
2.4(b).] A point (x, y) is on the graph of g if and only if the point $(x/k, y/k)$ is on the graph
of f. Hence $y/k = f(x/k)$, so $y = kf(x/k)$. In other words, the new function g is related to
f by the formula

$$g(x) = kf(x/k)$$

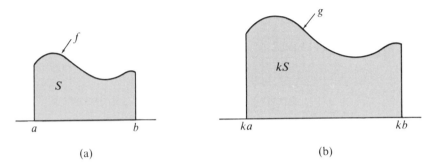

(a)   (b)

FIGURE 2.4   The area of kS is k^2 times that of S.

for each x in $[ka, kb]$. Therefore, the area of kS is given by

$$a(kS) = \int_{ka}^{kb} g(x) \, dx = k \int_{ka}^{kb} f(x/k) \, dx = k^2 \int_{a}^{b} f(x) \, dx \, ,$$

where in the last step we used the expansion property for integrals (Theorem 1.19). Since
$\int_{a}^{b} f(x) \, dx = a(S)$, this proves that $a(kS) = k^2 a(S)$. In other words, the area of kS is k^2 times
that of S.

EXAMPLE 5. *Calculation of the integral $\int_{0}^{a} x^{1/2} \, dx$.* The integral for area is a two-edged
sword. Although we ordinarily use the integral to calculate areas, sometimes we can use
our knowledge of area to calculate integrals. We illustrate by computing the value of the
integral $\int_{0}^{a} x^{1/2} \, dx$, where $a > 0$. (The integral exists since the integrand is increasing and
bounded on $[0, a]$.)

Figure 2.5 shows the graph of the function f given by $f(x) = x^{1/2}$ over the interval $[0, a]$.
Its ordinate set S has an area given by

$$a(S) = \int_{0}^{a} x^{1/2} \, dx \, .$$

Now we compute this area another way. We simply observe that in Figure 2.5 the region
S and the shaded region T together fill out a rectangle of base a and altitude $a^{1/2}$. Therefore,
$a(S) + a(T) = a^{3/2}$, so we have

$$a(S) = a^{3/2} - a(T) \, .$$

But T is the ordinate set of a function g defined over the interval $[0, a^{1/2}]$ on the y-axis by the equation $g(y) = y^2$. Thus, we have

$$a(T) = \int_0^{a^{1/2}} g(y)\, dy = \int_0^{a^{1/2}} y^2\, dy = \tfrac{1}{3} a^{3/2},$$

so $a(S) = a^{3/2} - \tfrac{1}{3} a^{3/2} = \tfrac{2}{3} a^{3/2}$. This proves that

$$\int_0^a x^{1/2}\, dx = \tfrac{2}{3}\, a^{3/2}.$$

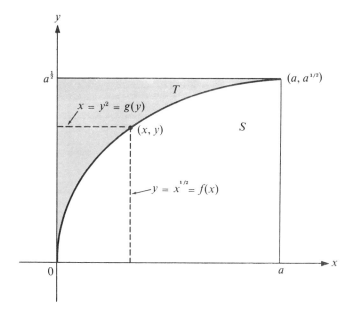

FIGURE 2.5   Calculation of the integral $\int_0^a x^{1/2}\, dx$.

More generally, if $a > 0$ and $b > 0$, we may use the additive property of the integral to obtain the formula

$$\int_a^b x^{1/2}\, dx = \tfrac{2}{3}(b^{3/2} - a^{3/2}).$$

The foregoing argument can also be used to compute the integral $\int_a^b x^{1/n}\, dx$, if n is a positive integer. We state the result as a theorem.

THEOREM 2.2.   *For $a > 0$, $b > 0$ and n a positive integer, we have*

(2.2)
$$\int_a^b x^{1/n}\, dx = \frac{b^{1+1/n} - a^{1+1/n}}{1 + 1/n}.$$

The proof is so similar to that in Example 5 that we leave the details to the reader.

2.4   Exercises

In Exercises 1 through 14, compute the area of the region S between the graphs of f and g over the interval $[a, b]$ specified in each case.   Make a sketch of the two graphs and indicate S by shading.

1. $f(x) = 4 - x^2$, $g(x) = 0$, $a = -2$, $b = 2$.
2. $f(x) = 4 - x^2$, $g(x) = 8 - 2x^2$, $a = -2$, $b = 2$.
3. $f(x) = x^3 + x^2$, $g(x) = x^3 + 1$, $a = -1$, $b = 1$.
4. $f(x) = x - x^2$, $g(x) = -x$, $a = 0$, $b = 2$.
5. $f(x) = x^{1/3}$, $g(x) = x^{1/2}$, $a = 0$, $b = 1$.
6. $f(x) = x^{1/3}$, $g(x) = x^{1/2}$, $a = 1$, $b = 2$.
7. $f(x) = x^{1/3}$, $g(x) = x^{1/2}$, $a = 0$, $b = 2$.
8. $f(x) = x^{1/2}$, $g(x) = x^2$, $a = 0$, $b = 2$.
9. $f(x) = x^2$, $g(x) = x + 1$, $a = -1$, $b = (1 + \sqrt{5})/2$.
10. $f(x) = x(x^2 - 1)$, $g(x) = x$, $a = -1$, $b = \sqrt{2}$.
11. $f(x) = |x|$, $g(x) = x^2 - 1$, $a = -1$, $b = 1$.
12. $f(x) = |x - 1|$, $g(x) = x^2 - 2x$, $a = 0$, $b = 2$.
13. $f(x) = 2|x|$, $g(x) = 1 - 3x^3$, $a = -\sqrt{3}/3$, $b = \frac{1}{3}$.
14. $f(x) = |x| + |x - 1|$, $g(x) = 0$, $a = -1$, $b = 2$.
15. The graphs of $f(x) = x^2$ and $g(x) = cx^3$, where $c > 0$, intersect at the points $(0, 0)$ and $(1/c, 1/c^2)$. Find c so that the region which lies between these graphs and over the interval $[0, 1/c]$ has area $\frac{2}{3}$.
16. Let $f(x) = x - x^2$, $g(x) = ax$. Determine a so that the region above the graph of g and below the graph of f has area $\frac{9}{2}$.
17. We have defined π to be the area of a unit circular disk. In Example 3 of Section 2.3, we proved that $\pi = 2 \int_{-1}^{1} \sqrt{1 - x^2}\, dx$. Use properties of the integral to compute the following in terms of π:

   (a) $\displaystyle\int_{-3}^{3} \sqrt{9 - x^2}\, dx$;   (b) $\displaystyle\int_{0}^{2} \sqrt{1 - \tfrac{1}{4}x^2}\, dx$;   (c) $\displaystyle\int_{-2}^{2} (x - 3)\sqrt{4 - x^2}\, dx$.

18. Calculate the areas of regular dodecagons (twelve-sided polygons) inscribed and circumscribed about a unit circular disk and thereby deduce the inequalities $3 < \pi < 12(2 - \sqrt{3})$.
19. Let C denote the unit circle, whose Cartesian equation is $x^2 + y^2 = 1$. Let E be the set of points obtained by multiplying the x-coordinate of each point (x, y) on C by a constant factor $a > 0$ and the y-coordinate by a constant factor $b > 0$. The set E is called an ellipse. (When $a = b$, the ellipse is another circle.)
   (a) Show that each point (x, y) on E satisfies the Cartesian equation $(x/a)^2 + (y/b)^2 = 1$.
   (b) Use properties of the integral to prove that the region enclosed by this ellipse is measurable and that its area is πab.
20. Exercise 19 is a generalization of Example 3 of Section 2.3. State and prove a corresponding generalization of Example 4 of Section 2.3.
21. Use an argument similar to that in Example 5 of Section 2.3 to prove Theorem 2.2.

2.5   The trigonometric functions

Before we introduce further applications of integration, we will digress briefly to discuss the trigonometric functions. We assume that the reader has some knowledge of the properties of the six trigonometric functions, sine, cosine, tangent, cotangent, secant, and cosecant; and their inverses, arc sine, arc cosine, arc tangent, etc. These functions are discussed in elementary trigonometry courses in connection with various problems involving the sides and angles of triangles.

The trigonometric functions are important in calculus, not so much because of their relation to the sides and angles of a triangle, but rather because of the properties they possess as *functions*. The six trigonometric functions have in common an important property known as periodicity.

A function *f* is said to be *periodic* with period $p \neq 0$ if its domain contains $x + p$ whenever it contains x and if $f(x + p) = f(x)$ for every x in the domain of *f*. The sine and cosine functions are periodic with period 2π, where π is the area of a unit circular disk. Many problems in physics and engineering deal with periodic phenomena (such as vibrations, planetary and wave motion) and the sine and cosine functions form the basis for the mathematical analysis of such problems.

The sine and cosine functions can be introduced in many different ways. For example, there are geometric definitions which relate the sine and cosine functions to angles, and there are analytic definitions which introduce these functions without any reference whatever to geometry. All these methods are equivalent, in the sense that they all lead to the same functions.

Ordinarily, when we work with the sine and cosine we are not concerned so much with their definitions as we are with the properties that can be deduced from the definitions. Some of these properties, which are of importance in calculus, are listed below. As usual, we denote the values of the sine and cosine functions at x by sin x, cos x, respectively.

FUNDAMENTAL PROPERTIES OF THE SINE AND COSINE.

1. *Domain of definition. The sine and cosine functions are defined everywhere on the real line.*

2. *Special values. We have* $\cos 0 = \sin \frac{1}{2}\pi = 1$, $\cos \pi = -1$.

3. *Cosine of a difference. For all x and y, we have*

$$(2.3) \qquad \cos(y - x) = \cos y \cos x + \sin y \sin x.$$

4. *Fundamental inequalities. For* $0 < x < \frac{1}{2}\pi$, *we have*

$$(2.4) \qquad 0 < \cos x < \frac{\sin x}{x} < \frac{1}{\cos x}.$$

From these four properties we can deduce all the properties of the sine and cosine that are of importance in calculus. This suggests that we might introduce the trigonometric functions axiomatically. That is, we could take properties 1 through 4 as axioms about the sine and cosine and deduce all further properties as theorems. To make certain we are not discussing an empty theory, it is necessary to show that there are functions satisfying the above properties. We shall by-pass this problem for the moment. First we assume that functions exist which satisfy these fundamental properties and show how further properties can then be deduced. Then, in Section 2.7, we indicate a geometric method of defining the sine and cosine so as to obtain functions with the desired properties. In Chapter 11 we also outline an analytic method for defining the sine and cosine.

THEOREM 2.3. *If two functions* sin *and* cos *satisfy properties 1 through 4, then they also satisfy the following properties:*

(a) *Pythagorean identity.* $\sin^2 x + \cos^2 x = 1$ *for all* x.
(b) *Special values.* $\sin 0 = \cos \frac{1}{2}\pi = \sin \pi = 0$.
(c) *Even and odd properties. The cosine is an even function and the sine is an odd function. That is, for all x we have*

$$\cos(-x) = \cos x, \qquad \sin(-x) = -\sin x.$$

(d) *Co-relations. For all x, we have*

$$\sin(\tfrac{1}{2}\pi + x) = \cos x, \qquad \cos(\tfrac{1}{2}\pi + x) = -\sin x.$$

(e) *Periodicity. For all x, we have* $\sin(x + 2\pi) = \sin x$, $\cos(x + 2\pi) = \cos x$.
(f) *Addition formulas. For all x and y, we have*

$$\cos(x + y) = \cos x \cos y - \sin x \sin y,$$

$$\sin(x + y) = \sin x \cos y + \cos x \sin y.$$

(g) *Difference formulas. For all a and b, we have*

$$\sin a - \sin b = 2 \sin \frac{a - b}{2} \cos \frac{a + b}{2},$$

$$\cos a - \cos b = -2 \sin \frac{a - b}{2} \sin \frac{a + b}{2}.$$

(h) *Monotonicity. In the interval $[0, \frac{1}{2}\pi]$, the sine is strictly increasing and the cosine is strictly decreasing.*

Proof. Part (a) follows at once if we take $x = y$ in (2.3) and use the relation $\cos 0 = 1$. Property (b) follows from (a) by taking $x = 0$, $x = \frac{1}{2}\pi$, $x = \pi$ and using the relation $\sin \frac{1}{2}\pi = 1$. The even property of the cosine also follows from (2.3) by taking $y = 0$. Next we deduce the formula

$$(2.5) \qquad\qquad \cos(\tfrac{1}{2}\pi - x) = \sin x,$$

by taking $y = \frac{1}{2}\pi$ in (2.3). From this and (2.3), we find that the sine is odd, since

$$\sin(-x) = \cos\left(\frac{\pi}{2} + x\right) = \cos\left[\pi - \left(\frac{\pi}{2} - x\right)\right]$$

$$= \cos \pi \cos\left(\frac{\pi}{2} - x\right) + \sin \pi \sin\left(\frac{\pi}{2} - x\right) = -\sin x.$$

This proves (c). To prove (d), we again use (2.5), first with x replaced by $\frac{1}{2}\pi + x$ and then with x replaced by $-x$. Repeated use of (d) then gives us the periodicity relations (e).

To prove the addition formula for the cosine, we simply replace x by $-x$ in (2.3) and use the even and odd properties. Then we use part (d) and the addition formula for the cosine to obtain

$$\sin (x + y) = -\cos \left(x + y + \frac{\pi}{2}\right) = -\cos x \cos \left(y + \frac{\pi}{2}\right) + \sin x \sin \left(y + \frac{\pi}{2}\right)$$

$$= \cos x \sin y + \sin x \cos y \,.$$

This proves (f). To deduce the difference formulas (g), we first replace y by $-y$ in the addition formula for $\sin (x + y)$ to obtain

$$\sin (x - y) = \sin x \cos y - \cos x \sin y \,.$$

Subtracting this from the formula for $\sin (x + y)$ and doing the same for the cosine function, we get

$$\sin (x + y) - \sin (x - y) = 2 \sin y \cos x \,,$$

$$\cos (x + y) - \cos (x - y) = -2 \sin y \sin x \,.$$

Taking $x = (a + b)/2$, $y = (a - b)/2$, we find that these become the difference formulas in (g).

Properties (a) through (g) were deduced from properties 1 through 3 alone. Property 4 is used to prove (h). The inequalities (2.4) show that $\cos x$ and $\sin x$ are positive if $0 < x < \frac{1}{2}\pi$. Now, if $0 < b < a < \frac{1}{2}\pi$, the numbers $(a + b)/2$ and $(a - b)/2$ are in the interval $(0, \frac{1}{2}\pi)$, and the difference formulas (g) show that $\sin a > \sin b$ and $\cos a < \cos b$. This completes the proof of Theorem 2.3.

Further properties of the sine and cosine functions are discussed in the next set of exercises (page 104). We mention, in particular, two formulas that are used frequently in calculus. These are called the *double-angle* or *duplication formulas*. We have

$$\sin 2x = 2 \sin x \cos x \,, \qquad \cos 2x = \cos^2 x - \sin^2 x = 1 - 2 \sin^2 x \,.$$

These are, of course, merely special cases of the addition formulas obtained by taking $y = x$. The second formula for $\cos 2x$ follows from the first by use of the Pythagorean identity. The Pythagorean identity also shows that $|\cos x| \leq 1$ and $|\sin x| \leq 1$ for all x.

2.6　Integration formulas for the sine and cosine

The monotonicity properties in part (h) of Theorem 2.3, along with the co-relations and the periodicity properties, show that the sine and cosine functions are piecewise monotonic on every interval. Therefore, by repeated use of Theorem 1.12, we see that the sine and cosine are integrable on every finite interval. Now we shall calculate their integrals by applying Theorem 1.14. This calculation makes use of a pair of inequalities which we state as a separate theorem.

THEOREM 2.4.　*If* $0 < a \leq \frac{1}{2}\pi$ *and* $n \geq 1$, *we have*

(2.6)
$$\frac{a}{n} \sum_{k=1}^{n} \cos \frac{ka}{n} < \sin a < \frac{a}{n} \sum_{k=0}^{n-1} \cos \frac{ka}{n} \,.$$

Proof. The inequalities in (2.6) will be deduced from the trigonometric identity

(2.7) $$2 \sin \tfrac{1}{2}x \sum_{k=1}^{n} \cos kx = \sin (n + \tfrac{1}{2})x - \sin \tfrac{1}{2}x ,$$

which is valid for $n \geq 1$ and all real x. To prove (2.7), we use one of the difference formulas (g) of Theorem 2.3 to write

$$2 \sin \tfrac{1}{2}x \cos kx = \sin (k + \tfrac{1}{2})x - \sin (k - \tfrac{1}{2})x .$$

Taking $k = 1, 2, \ldots, n$ and adding these equations, we find that the sum on the right telescopes and we obtain (2.7).

If $\tfrac{1}{2}x$ is not an integer multiple of π we can divide both members of (2.7) by $2 \sin \tfrac{1}{2}x$ to obtain

$$\sum_{k=1}^{n} \cos kx = \frac{\sin (n + \tfrac{1}{2})x - \sin \tfrac{1}{2}x}{2 \sin \tfrac{1}{2}x} .$$

Replacing n by $n - 1$ and adding 1 to both members we also obtain

$$\sum_{k=0}^{n-1} \cos kx = \frac{\sin (n - \tfrac{1}{2})x + \sin \tfrac{1}{2}x}{2 \sin \tfrac{1}{2}x} .$$

Both these formulas are valid if $x \neq 2m\pi$, where m is an integer. Taking $x = a/n$, where $0 < a \leq \tfrac{1}{2}\pi$ we find that the pair of inequalities in (2.6) is equivalent to the pair

$$\frac{\sin (n + \tfrac{1}{2}) \dfrac{a}{n} - \sin \left(\dfrac{a}{2n}\right)}{\dfrac{a}{n} \cdot 2 \sin \left(\dfrac{a}{2n}\right)} < \sin a < \frac{\sin (n - \tfrac{1}{2}) \dfrac{a}{n} + \sin \left(\dfrac{a}{2n}\right)}{\dfrac{a}{n} \cdot 2 \sin \left(\dfrac{a}{2n}\right)} .$$

This pair, in turn, is equivalent to the pair

(2.8) $$\sin (n + \tfrac{1}{2}) \frac{a}{n} - \sin \left(\frac{a}{2n}\right) < \frac{\sin \left(\dfrac{a}{2n}\right)}{\left(\dfrac{a}{2n}\right)} \sin a < \sin (n - \tfrac{1}{2}) \frac{a}{n} + \sin \left(\frac{a}{2n}\right) .$$

Therefore, proving (2.6) is equivalent to proving (2.8). We shall prove that we have

(2.9) $$\sin (2n + 1)\theta - \sin \theta < \frac{\sin \theta}{\theta} \sin 2n\theta < \sin (2n - 1)\theta + \sin \theta$$

for $0 < 2n\theta \leq \tfrac{1}{2}\pi$. When $\theta = a/(2n)$ this reduces to (2.8).

To prove the leftmost inequality in (2.9), we use the addition formula for the sine to write

$$(2.10) \quad \sin(2n+1)\theta = \sin 2n\theta \cos \theta + \cos 2n\theta \sin \theta < \sin 2n\theta \, \frac{\sin \theta}{\theta} + \sin \theta \, ,$$

where we have also used the inequalities

$$\cos \theta < \frac{\sin \theta}{\theta} \, , \qquad 0 < \cos 2n\theta \leq 1 \, , \qquad \sin \theta > 0 \, ,$$

all of which are valid since $0 < 2n\theta \leq \frac{1}{2}\pi$. Inequality (2.10) is equivalent to the leftmost inequality in (2.9).

To prove the rightmost inequality in (2.9), we again use the addition formula for the sine and write

$$\sin(2n-1)\theta = \sin 2n\theta \cos \theta - \cos 2n\theta \sin \theta \, .$$

Adding $\sin \theta$ to both members, we obtain

$$(2.11) \qquad \sin(2n-1)\theta + \sin \theta = \sin 2n\theta \left(\cos \theta + \sin \theta \, \frac{1 - \cos 2n\theta}{\sin 2n\theta} \right) .$$

But since we have

$$\frac{1 - \cos 2n\theta}{\sin 2n\theta} = \frac{2 \sin^2 n\theta}{2 \sin n\theta \cos n\theta} = \frac{\sin n\theta}{\cos n\theta} \, ,$$

the right member of (2.11) is equal to

$$\sin 2n\theta \left(\cos \theta + \sin \theta \, \frac{\sin n\theta}{\cos n\theta} \right) = \sin 2n\theta \, \frac{\cos \theta \cos n\theta + \sin \theta \sin n\theta}{\cos n\theta}$$

$$= \sin 2n\theta \, \frac{\cos(n-1)\theta}{\cos n\theta} \, .$$

Therefore, to complete the proof of (2.9), we need only show that

$$(2.12) \qquad\qquad \frac{\cos(n-1)\theta}{\cos n\theta} > \frac{\sin \theta}{\theta} \, .$$

But we have

$$\cos n\theta = \cos(n-1)\theta \cos \theta - \sin(n-1)\theta \sin \theta$$

$$< \cos(n-1)\theta \cos \theta < \cos(n-1)\theta \, \frac{\theta}{\sin \theta} \, ,$$

where we have again used the fundamental inequality $\cos \theta < \theta/(\sin \theta)$. This last relation implies (2.12), so the proof of Theorem 2.4 is complete.

THEOREM 2.5.   *If two functions* sin *and* cos *satisfy the fundamental properties 1 through 4, then for every real a we have*

$$(2.13) \qquad\qquad \int_0^a \cos x \, dx = \sin a \,,$$

$$(2.14) \qquad\qquad \int_0^a \sin x \, dx = 1 - \cos a \,.$$

Proof.   First we prove (2.13), and then we use (2.13) to deduce (2.14). Assume that $0 < a \le \frac{1}{2}\pi$. Since the cosine is decreasing on $[0, a]$, we can apply Theorem 1.14 in conjunction with the inequalities of Theorem 2.4 to obtain (2.13). The formula also holds trivially for $a = 0$, since both members are zero. The general properties of the integral can now be used to extend its validity to all real a.

For example, if $-\frac{1}{2}\pi \le a \le 0$, then $0 \le -a \le \frac{1}{2}\pi$, and the reflection property gives us

$$\int_0^a \cos x \, dx = -\int_0^{-a} \cos(-x) \, dx = -\int_0^{-a} \cos x \, dx = -\sin(-a) = \sin a \,.$$

Thus (2.13) is valid in the interval $[-\frac{1}{2}\pi, \frac{1}{2}\pi]$. Now suppose that $\frac{1}{2}\pi \le a \le \frac{3}{2}\pi$. Then $-\frac{1}{2}\pi \le a - \pi \le \frac{1}{2}\pi$, so we have

$$\int_0^a \cos x \, dx = \int_0^{\pi/2} \cos x \, dx + \int_{\pi/2}^a \cos x \, dx = \sin \frac{1}{2}\pi + \int_{-\pi/2}^{a-\pi} \cos(x + \pi) \, dx$$

$$= 1 - \int_{-\pi/2}^{a-\pi} \cos x \, dx = 1 - \sin(a - \pi) + \sin(-\tfrac{1}{2}\pi) = \sin a \,.$$

Thus (2.13) holds for all a in the interval $[-\frac{1}{2}\pi, \frac{3}{2}\pi]$. But this interval has length 2π, so formula (2.13) holds for all a since both members are periodic in a with period 2π.

Now we use (2.13) to deduce (2.14). First we prove that (2.14) holds when $a = \pi/2$. Applying, in succession, the translation property, the co-relation $\sin(x + \frac{1}{2}\pi) = \cos x$, and the reflection property, we find

$$\int_0^{\pi/2} \sin x \, dx = \int_{-\pi/2}^0 \sin\left(x + \frac{\pi}{2}\right) dx = \int_{-\pi/2}^0 \cos x \, dx = \int_0^{\pi/2} \cos(-x) \, dx \,.$$

Using the relation $\cos(-x) = \cos x$ and Equation (2.13), we obtain

$$\int_0^{\pi/2} \sin x \, dx = 1 \,.$$

Now, for any real a, we may write

$$\int_0^a \sin x \, dx = \int_0^{\pi/2} \sin x \, dx + \int_{\pi/2}^a \sin x \, dx = 1 + \int_0^{a-\pi/2} \sin\left(x + \frac{\pi}{2}\right) dx$$

$$= 1 + \int_0^{a-\pi/2} \cos x \, dx = 1 + \sin\left(a - \frac{\pi}{2}\right) = 1 - \cos a \,.$$

This shows that Equation (2.13) implies (2.14).

EXAMPLE 1. Using (2.13) and (2.14) in conjunction with the additive property

$$\int_a^b f(x)\, dx = \int_0^b f(x)\, dx - \int_0^a f(x)\, dx,$$

we get the more general integration formulas

$$\int_a^b \cos x\, dx = \sin b - \sin a$$

and

$$\int_a^b \sin x\, dx = (1 - \cos b) - (1 - \cos a) = -(\cos b - \cos a)\,.$$

If again we use the special symbol $f(x)\,\big|_a^b$ to denote the difference $f(b) - f(a)$, we can write these integration formulas in the form

$$\int_a^b \cos x\, dx = \sin x\,\Big|_a^b \quad \text{and} \quad \int_a^b \sin x\, dx = -\cos x\,\Big|_a^b\,.$$

EXAMPLE 2. Using the results of Example 1 and the expansion property

$$\int_a^b f(x)\, dx = \frac{1}{c}\int_{ca}^{cb} f(x/c)\, dx\,,$$

we obtain the following formulas, valid for $c \neq 0$:

$$\int_a^b \cos cx\, dx = \frac{1}{c}\int_{ca}^{cb} \cos x\, dx = \frac{1}{c}(\sin cb - \sin ca)\,,$$

and

$$\int_a^b \sin cx\, dx = \frac{1}{c}\int_{ca}^{cb} \sin x\, dx = -\frac{1}{c}(\cos cb - \cos ca)\,.$$

EXAMPLE 3. The identity $\cos 2x = 1 - 2\sin^2 x$ implies $\sin^2 x = \frac{1}{2}(1 - \cos 2x)$ so, from Example 2, we obtain

$$\int_0^a \sin^2 x\, dx = \frac{1}{2}\int_0^a (1 - \cos 2x)\, dx = \frac{a}{2} - \frac{1}{4}\sin 2a\,.$$

Since $\sin^2 x + \cos^2 x = 1$, we also find

$$\int_0^a \cos^2 x\, dx = \int_0^a (1 - \sin^2 x)\, dx = a - \int_0^a \sin^2 x\, dx = \frac{a}{2} + \frac{1}{4}\sin 2a\,.$$

2.7 A geometric description of the sine and cosine functions

In this section we indicate a geometric method for defining the sine and cosine functions, and we give a geometric interpretation of the fundamental properties listed in the Section 2.5.

Consider a circle of radius r with its center at the origin. Denote the point $(r, 0)$ by A, and let P be any other point on the circle. The two line segments OA and OP determine a geometric configuration called an angle which we denote by the symbol $\angle AOP$. An example is shown in Figure 2.6. We wish to assign to this angle a nonnegative real number x which can be used as a measurement of its size. The most common way of doing this is to take a circle of radius 1 and let x be the length of the circular arc AP, traced counterclockwise

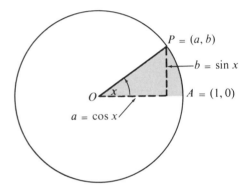

FIGURE 2.6   An angle $\angle AOP$ consisting of x radians.

FIGURE 2.7   Geometric description of $\sin x$ and $\cos x$.

from A to P, and to say that the measure of $\angle AOP$ is x radians. From a logical point of view, this is unsatisfactory at the present stage because we have not yet discussed the concept of arc length. Arc length will be discussed later in Chapter 14. Since the concept of area has already been discussed, we prefer to use the area of the circular sector AOP rather than the length of the arc AP as a measure of the size of $\angle AOP$. It is understood that the sector AOP is the smaller portion of the circular disk when P is above the real axis, and the larger portion when P is below the real axis.

Later, when arc length is discussed, we shall find that the length of arc AP is exactly twice the area of sector AOP. Therefore, to get the same scale of measurement for angles by both methods, we shall use *twice* the area of the sector AOP as a measure of the angle $\angle AOP$. However, to obtain a "dimensionless" measure of angles, that is, a measure independent of the unit of distance in our coordinate system, we shall define the measure of $\angle AOP$ to be *twice the area of sector AOP divided by the square of the radius*. This ratio does not change if we expand or contract the circle, and therefore there is no loss in generality in restricting our considerations to a unit circle. The unit of measure so obtained is called the *radian*. Thus, we say the measure of an angle $\angle AOP$ is x radians if $x/2$ is the area of the sector AOP cut from a unit circular disk.

We have already introduced the symbol π to denote the area of a unit circular disk. When $P = (-1, 0)$, the sector AOP is a semicircular disk of area $\frac{1}{2}\pi$, so it subtends an angle of π radians. The entire disk is a sector consisting of 2π radians. If P is initially at $(1, 0)$ and if

P moves once around the circle in a counterclockwise direction, the area of sector AOP increases from 0 to π, taking every value in the interval $[0, \pi]$ exactly once. This property, which is geometrically plausible, can be proved by expressing the area as an integral, but we shall not discuss the proof.

The next step is to define the sine and cosine of an angle. Actually, we prefer to speak of the sine and cosine of a *number* rather than of an *angle*, so that the sine and cosine will be *functions* defined on the real line. We proceed as follows: Choose a number x satisfying $0 < x < 2\pi$ and let P be the point on the unit circle such that the area of sector AOP is equal to $x/2$. Let (a, b) denote the coordinates of P. An example is shown in Figure 2.7. The numbers a and b are completely determined by x. We define the sine and cosine of x as follows:

$$\cos x = a , \qquad \sin x = b .$$

In other words, $\cos x$ is the abscissa of P and $\sin x$ is its ordinate.

For example, when $x = \pi$, we have $P = (-1, 0)$ so that $\cos \pi = -1$ and $\sin \pi = 0$. Similarly, when $x = \frac{1}{2}\pi$ we have $P = (0, 1)$ and hence $\cos \frac{1}{2}\pi = 0$ and $\sin \frac{1}{2}\pi = 1$. This procedure describes the sine and cosine as functions defined in the open interval $(0, 2\pi)$. We extend the definitions to the whole real axis by means of the following equations:

$$\sin 0 = 0 , \qquad \cos 0 = 1 , \qquad \sin (x + 2\pi) = \sin x , \qquad \cos (x + 2\pi) = \cos x .$$

The other four trigonometric functions are now defined in terms of the sine and cosine by the usual formulas,

$$\tan x = \frac{\sin x}{\cos x} , \qquad \cot x = \frac{\cos x}{\sin x} , \qquad \sec x = \frac{1}{\cos x} , \qquad \csc x = \frac{1}{\sin x} .$$

These functions are defined for all real x except for certain isolated points where the denominators may be zero. They all satisfy the periodicity property $f(x + 2\pi) = f(x)$. The tangent and cotangent have the smaller period π.

Now we give geometric arguments to indicate how these definitions lead to the fundamental properties listed in Section 2.5. Properties 1 and 2 have already been taken care of by the way we have defined the sine and cosine. The Pythagorean identity becomes evident when we refer to Figure 2.7. The line segment OP is the hypotenuse of a right triangle whose legs have lengths $|\cos x|$ and $|\sin x|$. Hence the Pythagorean theorem for right triangles implies the identity $\cos^2 x + \sin^2 x = 1$.

Now we use the Pythagorean theorem for right triangles again to give a geometric proof of formula (2.3) for $\cos (y - x)$. Refer to the two right triangles PAQ and PBQ shown in Figure 2.8. In triangle PAQ, the length of side AQ is $|\sin y - \sin x|$, the absolute value of the difference of the ordinates of Q and P. Similarly, AP has length $|\cos x - \cos y|$. If d denotes the length of the hypotenuse PQ, we have, by the Pythagorean theorem,

$$d^2 = (\sin y - \sin x)^2 + (\cos x - \cos y)^2 .$$

On the other hand, in right triangle PBQ the leg BP has length $|1 - \cos (y - x)|$ and the leg BQ has length $|\sin (y - x)|$. Therefore, the Pythagorean theorem gives us

$$d^2 = [1 - \cos (y - x)]^2 + \sin^2 (y - x) .$$

Equating the two expressions for d^2 and solving for $\cos(y - x)$, we obtain the desired formula (2.3) for $\cos(y - x)$.

Finally, geometric proofs of the fundamental inequalities in property 4 may be given by referring to Figure 2.9. We simply compare the area of sector OAP with that of triangles OQP and OAB. Because of the way we have defined angular measure, the area of sector OAP is $\frac{1}{2}x$. Triangle OAB has base 1 and altitude h, say. By similar triangles, we find $h/1 = (\sin x)/(\cos x)$, so the area of triangle OAB is $\frac{1}{2}h = \frac{1}{2}(\sin x)/(\cos x)$. Therefore, comparison of areas gives us the inequalities

$$\frac{1}{2}\sin x \cos x < \frac{1}{2}x < \frac{1}{2}\frac{\sin x}{\cos x}.$$

FIGURE 2.8   Geometric proof of the formula for $\cos(y - x)$.

FIGURE 2.9   Geometric proof of the inequalities
$$0 < \cos x < \frac{\sin x}{x} < \frac{1}{\cos x}.$$

Dividing by $\frac{1}{2}\sin x$ and taking reciprocals, we obtain the fundamental inequalities (2.4).

We remind the reader once more that the discussion of this section is intended to provide a geometric interpretation of the sine and cosine and their fundamental properties. An analytic treatment of these functions, making no use of geometry, will be described in Section 11.11.

Extensive tables of values of the sine, cosine, tangent, and cotangent appear in most mathematical handbooks. The graphs of the six trigonometric functions are shown in Figure 2.10 (page 107) as they appear over one complete period-interval. The rest of the graph in each case is obtained by appealing to periodicity.

2.8   Exercises

In this set of exercises, you may use the properties of the sine and cosine listed in Sections 2.5 through 2.7.

1. (a) Prove that $\sin n\pi = 0$ for every integer n and that these are the only values of x for which $\sin x = 0$.
   (b) Find all real x such that $\cos x = 0$.
2. Find all real x such that (a) $\sin x = 1$; (b) $\cos x = 1$; (c) $\sin x = -1$; (d) $\cos x = -1$.
3. Prove that $\sin(x + \pi) = -\sin x$ and $\cos(x + \pi) = -\cos x$ for all x.
4. Prove that $\sin 3x = 3\sin x - 4\sin^3 x$ and $\cos 3x = \cos x - 4\sin^2 x \cos x$ for all real x. Prove also that $\cos 3x = 4\cos^3 x - 3\cos x$.

5. (a) Prove that $\sin \frac{1}{6}\pi = \frac{1}{2}$, $\cos \frac{1}{6}\pi = \frac{1}{2}\sqrt{3}$. [*Hint:* Use Exercise 4.]

   (b) Prove that $\sin \frac{1}{3}\pi = \frac{1}{2}\sqrt{3}$, $\cos \frac{1}{3}\pi = \frac{1}{2}$.

   (c) Prove that $\sin \frac{1}{4}\pi = \cos \frac{1}{4}\pi = \frac{1}{2}\sqrt{2}$.

6. Prove that $\tan (x - y) = (\tan x - \tan y)/(1 + \tan x \tan y)$ for all x and y with $\tan x \tan y \ne -1$. Obtain corresponding formulas for $\tan (x + y)$ and $\cot (x + y)$.

7. Find numbers A and B such that $3 \sin (x + \frac{1}{3}\pi) = A \sin x + B \cos x$ for all x.

8. Prove that if C and α are given real numbers, there exist real numbers A and B such that $C \sin (x + \alpha) = A \sin x + B \cos x$ for all x.

9. Prove that if A and B are given real numbers, there exist numbers C and α, with $C \ge 0$, such that the formula of Exercise 8 holds.

10. Determine C and α, with $C > 0$, such that $C \sin (x + \alpha) = -2 \sin x - 2 \cos x$ for all x.

11. Prove that if A and B are given real numbers, there exist numbers C and α, with $C \ge 0$, such that $C \cos (x + \alpha) = A \sin x + B \cos x$. Determine C and α if $A = B = 1$.

12. Find all real x such that $\sin x = \cos x$.

13. Find all real x such that $\sin x - \cos x = 1$.

14. Prove that the following identities hold for all x and y.

   (a) $2 \cos x \cos y = \cos (x - y) + \cos (x + y)$.

   (b) $2 \sin x \sin y = \cos (x - y) - \cos (x + y)$.

   (c) $2 \sin x \cos y = \sin (x - y) + \sin (x + y)$.

15. If $h \ne 0$, prove that the following identities hold for all x:

$$\frac{\sin (x + h) - \sin x}{h} = \frac{\sin (h/2)}{h/2} \cos \left(x + \frac{h}{2}\right),$$

$$\frac{\cos (x + h) - \cos x}{h} = -\frac{\sin (h/2)}{h/2} \sin \left(x + \frac{h}{2}\right).$$

   These formulas are used in differential calculus.

16. Prove or disprove each of the following statements.

   (a) For all $x \ne 0$, we have $\sin 2x \ne 2 \sin x$.

   (b) For every x, there is a y such that $\cos (x + y) = \cos x + \cos y$.

   (c) There is an x such that $\sin (x + y) = \sin x + \sin y$ for all y.

   (d) There is a $y \ne 0$ such that $\int_0^y \sin x \, dx = \sin y$.

17. Calculate the integral $\int_a^b \sin x \, dx$ for each of the following values of a and b. In each case interpret your result geometrically in terms of areas.

   (a) $a = 0, b = \pi/6$.   (e) $a = 0, b = \pi$.

   (b) $a = 0, b = \pi/4$.   (f) $a = 0, b = 2\pi$.

   (c) $a = 0, b = \pi/3$.   (g) $a = -1, b = 1$.

   (d) $a = 0, b = \pi/2$.   (h) $a = -\pi/6, b = \pi/4$.

   Evaluate the integrals in Exercises 18 through 27.

18. $\int_0^\pi (x + \sin x) \, dx$.

19. $\int_0^{\pi/2} (x^2 + \cos x) \, dx$.

20. $\int_0^{\pi/2} (\sin x - \cos x) \, dx$.

21. $\int_0^{\pi/2} |\sin x - \cos x| \, dx$.

22. $\int_0^\pi (\frac{1}{2} + \cos t) \, dt$.

23. $\int_0^\pi |\frac{1}{2} + \cos t| \, dt$.

24. $\int_{-\pi}^x |\frac{1}{2} + \cos t| \, dt$,   if $0 \le x \le \pi$.

25. $\int_x^{x^2} (t^2 + \sin t) \, dt$.

26. $\int_0^{\pi/2} \sin 2x \, dx$.

27. $\int_0^{\pi/3} \cos \frac{x}{2} \, dx$.

28. Prove the following integration formulas, valid for $b \neq 0$:

$$\int_0^x \cos(a + bt)\, dt = \frac{1}{b}[\sin(a + bx) - \sin a],$$

$$\int_0^x \sin(a + bt)\, dt = -\frac{1}{b}[\cos(a + bx) - \cos a].$$

29. (a) Use the identity $\sin 3t = 3 \sin t - 4 \sin^3 t$ to deduce the integration formula

$$\int_0^x \sin^3 t\, dt = \tfrac{2}{3} - \tfrac{1}{3}(2 + \sin^2 x) \cos x.$$

 (b) Derive the identity $\cos 3t = 4 \cos^3 t - 3 \cos t$ and use it to prove that

$$\int_0^x \cos^3 t\, dt = \tfrac{1}{3}(2 + \cos^2 x) \sin x.$$

30. If a function f is periodic with period $p > 0$ and integrable on $[0, p]$, prove that $\int_0^p f(x)\, dx = \int_a^{a+p} f(x)\, dx$ for all a.

31. (a) Prove that $\int_0^{2\pi} \sin nx\, dx = \int_0^{2\pi} \cos nx\, dx = 0$ for all integers $n \neq 0$.
 (b) Use part (a) and the addition formulas for the sine and cosine to establish the following formulas, valid for integers m and n, $m^2 \neq n^2$;

$$\int_0^{2\pi} \sin nx \cos mx\, dx = \int_0^{2\pi} \sin nx \sin mx\, dx = \int_0^{2\pi} \cos nx \cos mx\, dx = 0,$$

$$\int_0^{2\pi} \sin^2 nx\, dx = \int_0^{2\pi} \cos^2 nx\, dx = \pi, \quad \text{if} \quad n \neq 0.$$

These formulas are known as the orthogonality relations for the sine and cosine.

32. Use the identity

$$2 \sin \frac{x}{2} \cos kx = \sin(2k + 1)\frac{x}{2} - \sin(2k - 1)\frac{x}{2}$$

and the telescoping property of finite sums to prove that if $x \neq 2m\pi$ (m an integer), we have

$$\sum_{k=1}^{n} \cos kx = \frac{\sin \frac{1}{2}nx \cos \frac{1}{2}(n + 1)x}{\sin \frac{1}{2}x}.$$

33. If $x \neq 2m\pi$ (m an integer), prove that

$$\sum_{k=1}^{n} \sin kx = \frac{\sin \frac{1}{2}nx \sin \frac{1}{2}(n + 1)x}{\sin \frac{1}{2}x}.$$

34. Refer to Figure 2.7. By comparing the area of triangle OAP with that of the circular sector OAP, prove that $\sin x < x$ if $0 < x < \frac{1}{2}\pi$. Then use the fact that $\sin(-x) = -\sin x$ to prove that $|\sin x| < |x|$ if $0 < |x| < \frac{1}{2}\pi$.

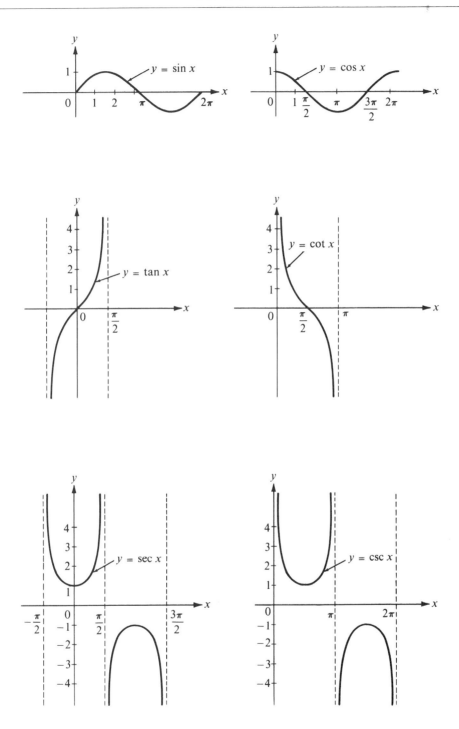

FIGURE 2.10 Graphs of the trigonometric functions as they appear over one
period-interval.

2.9 Polar coordinates

Up to now we have located points in the plane with rectangular coordinates. We can also locate them with polar coordinates. This is done as follows. Let P be a point distinct from the origin. Suppose the line segment joining P to the origin has length $r > 0$ and makes an angle of θ radians with the positive x-axis. An example is shown in Figure 2.11. The two numbers r and θ are called *polar coordinates* of P. They are related to the rectangular coordinates (x, y) by the equations

(2.15) $x = r \cos \theta, \qquad y = r \sin \theta.$

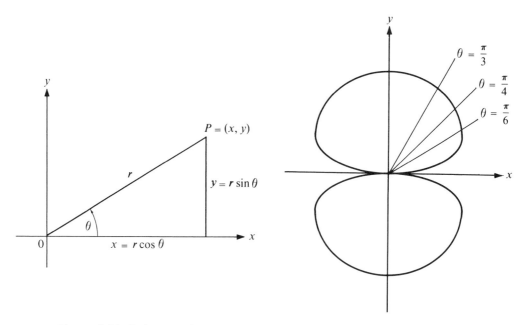

FIGURE 2.11   Polar coordinates.   FIGURE 2.12   A figure-eight curve with polar
                                          equation $r = \sqrt{|\sin \theta|}$.

The positive number r is called the *radial distance* of P, and θ is called a *polar angle*. We say *a* polar angle rather than *the* polar angle because if θ satisfies (2.15), so does $\theta + 2n\pi$ for any integer n. We agree to call all pairs of real numbers (r, θ) polar coordinates of P if they satisfy (2.15) with $r > 0$. Thus, a given point has more than one pair of polar coordinates. The radial distance r is uniquely determined, $r = \sqrt{x^2 + y^2}$, but the polar angle θ is determined only up to integer multiples of 2π.

When P is the origin, the equations in (2.15) are satisfied with $r = 0$ and any θ. For this reason we assign to the origin the radial distance $r = 0$, and we agree that *any* real θ may be used as a polar angle.

Let f be a nonnegative function defined on an interval $[a, b]$. The set of all points with polar coordinates (r, θ) satisfying $r = f(\theta)$ is called the graph of f in polar coordinates. The equation $r = f(\theta)$ is called a polar equation of this graph. For some curves, polar equations may be simpler and more convenient to use than Cartesian equations. For example, the circle with Cartesian equation $x^2 + y^2 = 4$ has the simpler polar equation $r = 2$. The equations in (2.15) show how to convert from rectangular to polar coordinates.

EXAMPLE. Figure 2.12 shows a curve in the shape of a figure eight whose Cartesian equation is $(x^2 + y^2)^3 = y^2$. Using (2.15), we find $x^2 + y^2 = r^2$, so the polar coordinates of the points on this curve satisfy the equation $r^6 = r^2 \sin^2 \theta$, or $r^2 = |\sin \theta|$, $r = \sqrt{|\sin \theta|}$. It is not difficult to sketch this curve from the polar equation. For example, in the interval $0 \le \theta \le \pi/2$, $\sin \theta$ increases from 0 to 1, so r also increases from 0 to 1. Plotting a few values which are easy to calculate, for example, those corresponding to $\theta = \pi/6$, $\pi/4$, and $\pi/3$, we quickly sketch the portion of the curve in the first quadrant. The rest of the curve is obtained by appealing to symmetry in the Cartesian equation, or to the symmetry and periodicity of $|\sin \theta|$. It would be a more difficult task to sketch this curve from its Cartesian equation alone.

2.10 The integral for area in polar coordinates

Let f be a nonnegative function defined on an interval $[a, b]$, where $0 \le b - a \le 2\pi$. The set of all points with polar coordinates (r, θ) satisfying the inequalities

$$0 \le r \le f(\theta), \qquad a \le \theta \le b,$$

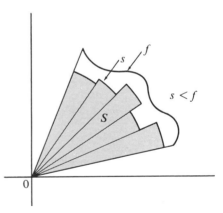

FIGURE 2.13 The radial set of f over an interval $[a, b]$.

FIGURE 2.14 The radial set of a step function s is a union of circular sectors. Its area is $\frac{1}{2} \int_a^b s^2(\theta)\, d\theta$.

is called the *radial set* of f over $[a, b]$. The shaded region shown in Figure 2.13 is an example. If f is constant on $[a, b]$, its radial set is a circular sector subtending an angle of $b - a$ radians. Figure 2.14 shows the radial set S of a step function s. Over each of the n open subintervals (θ_{k-1}, θ_k) of $[a, b]$ in which s is constant, say $s(\theta) = s_k$, the graph of s in polar coordinates is a circular arc of radius s_k, and its radial set is a circular sector subtending an angle of $\theta_k - \theta_{k-1}$ radians. Because of the way we have defined angular measure, the area of this sector is $\frac{1}{2}(\theta_k - \theta_{k-1})s_k^2$. Since $b - a \le 2\pi$, none of these sectors overlap so, by additivity, the area of the radial set of s over the full interval $[a, b]$ is given by

$$a(S) = \tfrac{1}{2} \sum_{k=1}^{n} s_k^2 \cdot (\theta_k - \theta_{k-1}) = \tfrac{1}{2} \int_a^b s^2(\theta)\, d\theta \, ,$$

where $s^2(\theta)$ means the square of $s(\theta)$. Thus, for step functions, the area of the radial set has been expressed as an integral. Now we prove that this integral formula holds more generally.

THEOREM 2.6. *Let R denote the radial set of a nonnegative function f over an interval $[a, b]$, where $0 \le b - a \le 2\pi$, and assume that R is measurable. If f^2 is integrable on $[a, b]$ the area of R is given by the integral*

$$a(R) = \tfrac{1}{2} \int_a^b f^2(\theta)\, d\theta \, .$$

Proof. Choose two step functions s and t satisfying

$$0 \le s(\theta) \le f(\theta) \le t(\theta)$$

for all θ in $[a, b]$, and let S and T denote their radial sets, respectively. Since $s \le f \le t$ on $[a, b]$, the radial sets are related by the inclusion relations $S \subseteq R \subseteq T$. Hence, by the monotone property of area, we have $a(S) \le a(R) \le a(T)$. But S and T are radial sets of step functions, so $a(S) = \tfrac{1}{2}\int_a^b s^2(\theta)\, d\theta$ and $a(T) = \tfrac{1}{2}\int_a^b t^2(\theta)\, d\theta$. Therefore we have the inequalities

$$\int_a^b s^2(\theta)\, d\theta \le 2a(R) \le \int_a^b t^2(\theta)\, d\theta \, ,$$

for all step functions s and t satisfying $s \le f \le t$ on $[a, b]$. But s^2 and t^2 are arbitrary step functions satisfying $s^2 \le f^2 \le t^2$ on $[a, b]$ hence, since f^2 is integrable, we must have $2a(R) = \int_a^b f^2(\theta)\, d\theta$. This proves the theorem.

Note: It can be proved that the measurability of R is a consequence of the hypothesis that f^2 is integrable, but we shall not discuss the proof.

EXAMPLE. To calculate the area of the radial set R enclosed by the figure-eight curve shown in Figure 2.12, we calculate the area of the portion in the first quadrant and multiply by four. For this curve, we have $f^2(\theta) = |\sin \theta|$ and, since $\sin \theta \ge 0$ for $0 \le \theta \le \pi/2$, we find

$$a(R) = 4\int_0^{\pi/2} \tfrac{1}{2} f^2(\theta)\, d\theta = 2\int_0^{\pi/2} \sin \theta\, d\theta = 2\left(\cos 0 - \cos \frac{\pi}{2}\right) = 2 \, .$$

2.11 Exercises

In each of Exercises 1 through 4, show that the set of points whose rectangular coordinates (x, y) satisfy the given Cartesian equation is equal to the set of all points whose polar coordinates (r, θ) satisfy the corresponding polar equation.

1. $(x - 1)^2 + y^2 = 1;$ $r = 2 \cos \theta,$ $\cos \theta > 0.$
2. $x^2 + y^2 - x = \sqrt{x^2 + y^2};$ $r = 1 + \cos \theta.$
3. $(x^2 + y^2)^2 = x^2 - y^2, y^2 \leq x^2;$ $r = \sqrt{\cos 2\theta},$ $\cos 2\theta \geq 0.$
4. $(x^2 + y^2)^2 = |x^2 - y^2|;$ $r = \sqrt{|\cos 2\theta|}.$

In each of Exercises 5 through 15, sketch the graph of f in polar coordinates and compute the area of the radial set of f over the interval specified. You may assume each set is measurable.

5. *Spiral of Archimedes:* $f(\theta) = \theta,$ $0 \leq \theta \leq 2\pi.$
6. *Circle tangent to y-axis:* $f(\theta) = 2 \cos \theta,$ $-\pi/2 \leq \theta \leq \pi/2.$
7. *Two circles tangent to y-axis:* $f(\theta) = 2 |\cos \theta|,$ $0 \leq \theta \leq 2\pi.$
8. *Circle tangent to x-axis:* $f(\theta) = 4 \sin \theta,$ $0 \leq \theta \leq \pi.$
9. *Two circles tangent to x-axis:* $f(\theta) = 4 |\sin \theta|,$ $0 \leq \theta \leq 2\pi.$
10. *Rose petal:* $f(\theta) = \sin 2\theta,$ $0 \leq \theta \leq \pi/2.$
11. *Four-leaved rose:* $f(\theta) = |\sin 2\theta|,$ $0 \leq \theta \leq 2\pi.$
12. *Lazy eight:* $f(\theta) = \sqrt{|\cos \theta|},$ $0 \leq \theta \leq 2\pi.$
13. *Four-leaf clover:* $f(\theta) = \sqrt{|\cos 2\theta|},$ $0 \leq \theta \leq 2\pi.$
14. *Cardioid:* $f(\theta) = 1 + \cos \theta,$ $0 \leq \theta \leq 2\pi.$
15. *Limaçon:* $f(\theta) = 2 + \cos \theta,$ $0 \leq \theta \leq 2\pi.$

2.12 Application of integration to the calculation of volume

In Section 1.6 we introduced the concept of area as a set function satisfying certain properties which we took as axioms for area. Then, in Sections 1.18 and 2.2, we showed that the areas of many regions could be calculated by integration. The same approach can be used to discuss the concept of volume.

We assume there exist certain sets S of points in three-dimensional space, which we call *measurable sets*, and a set function v, called a *volume function*, which assigns to each measurable set S a number $v(S)$, called the volume of S. We use the symbol $\mathscr{A}$ to denote the class of all measurable sets in three-dimensional space, and we call each set S in $\mathscr{A}$ a *solid*.

As in the case of area, we list a number of properties we would like volume to have and take these as axioms for volume. The choice of axioms enables us to prove that the volumes of many solids can be computed by integration.

The first three axioms, like those for area, describe the nonnegative, additive, and difference properties. Instead of an axiom of invariance under congruence, we use a different type of axiom, called *Cavalieri's principle*. This assigns equal volumes to congruent solids and also to certain solids which, though not congruent, have equal cross-sectional areas cut by planes perpendicular to a given line. More precisely, suppose S is a given solid and L a given line. If a plane F is perpendicular to L, the intersection $F \cap S$ is called a cross-section perpendicular to L. If every cross-section perpendicular to L is a measurable set in its own plane, we call S a *Cavalieri solid*. Cavalieri's principle assigns equal volumes to two Cavalieri solids, S and T, if $a(S \cap F) = a(T \cap F)$ for every plane F perpendicular to the given line L.

Cavalieri's principle can be illustrated intuitively as follows. Imagine a Cavalieri solid as being a stack of thin sheets of material, like a deck of cards, each sheet being perpendicular to a given line L. If we slide each sheet in its own plane we can change the shape of the solid but not its volume.

The next axiom states that the volume of a rectangular parallelepiped is the product of the lengths of its edges. A rectangular parallelepiped is any set congruent to a set of the form

(2.16) $\{(x, y, z) \mid 0 \leq x \leq a, \quad 0 \leq y \leq b, \quad 0 \leq z \leq c\}.$

We shall use the shorter term "box" rather than "rectangular parallelepiped." The non-negative numbers a, b, c in (2.16) are called the lengths of the edges of the box.

Finally, we include an axiom which states that every convex set is measurable. A set is called *convex* if, for every pair of points P and Q in the set, the line segment joining P and Q is also in the set. This axiom, along with the additive and difference properties, ensures that all the elementary solids that occur in the usual applications of calculus are measurable.

The axioms for volume can now be stated as follows.

AXIOMATIC DEFINITION OF VOLUME. *We assume there exists a class $\mathcal{A}$ of solids and a set function v, whose domain is $\mathcal{A}$, with the following properties:*

1. *Nonnegative property.* *For each set S in $\mathcal{A}$ we have $v(S) \geq 0$.*
2. *Additive property.* *If S and T are in $\mathcal{A}$, then $S \cup T$ and $S \cap T$ are in $\mathcal{A}$, and we have*

$$v(S \cup T) = v(S) + v(T) - v(S \cap T).$$

3. *Difference property.* *If S and T are in $\mathcal{A}$ with $S \subseteq T$, then $T - S$ is in $\mathcal{A}$, and we have $v(T - S) = v(T) - v(S)$.*
4. *Cavalieri's principle.* *If S and T are two Cavalieri solids in $\mathcal{A}$ with $a(S \cap F) \leq a(T \cap F)$ for every plane F perpendicular to a given line, then $v(S) \leq v(T)$.*
5. *Choice of scale.* *Every box B is in $\mathcal{A}$. If the edges of B have lengths a, b, and c, then $v(B) = abc$.*
6. *Every convex set is in $\mathcal{A}$.*

Axiom 3 shows that the empty set $\varnothing$ is in $\mathcal{A}$ and has zero volume. Since $v(T - S) \geq 0$, Axiom 3 also implies the following monotone property:

$$v(S) \leq v(T), \qquad \text{for sets } S \text{ and } T \text{ in } \mathcal{A} \text{ with } S \subseteq T.$$

The monotone property, in turn, shows that every bounded plane set S in $\mathcal{A}$ has zero volume. A plane set is called *bounded* if it is a subset of some square in the plane. If we consider a box B of altitude c having this square as its base, then $S \subseteq B$ so that we have $v(S) \leq v(B) = a^2c$, where a is the length of each edge of the square base. If we had $v(S) > 0$, we could choose c so that $c < v(S)/a^2$, contradicting the inequality $v(S) \leq a^2c$. This shows that $v(S)$ cannot be positive, so $v(S) = 0$, as asserted.

Note that Cavalieri's principle has been stated in the form of inequalities. If $a(S \cap F) = a(T \cap F)$ for every plane F perpendicular to a given line, we may apply Axiom 5 twice to deduce $v(S) \leq v(T)$ and $v(T) \leq v(S)$, and hence we have $v(T) = v(S)$.

Next we show that the volume of a right cylindrical solid is equal to the area of its base multiplied by its altitude. By a right cylindrical solid we mean a set congruent to a set S of the form

$$S = \{(x, y, z) \mid (x, y) \in B, \quad a \leq z \leq b\},$$

where B is a bounded plane measurable set. The areas of the cross sections of S perpendicular to the z-axis determine a cross-sectional area function a_S which takes the constant value $a(B)$ on the interval $a \le z \le b$, and the value 0 outside $[a, b]$.

Now let T be a box with cross-sectional area function a_T equal to a_S. Axiom 5 tells us that $v(T) = a(B)(b - a)$, where $a(B)$ is the area of the base of T, and $b - a$ is its altitude. Cavalieri's principle states that $v(S) = v(T)$, so the volume of S is the area of its base, $a(B)$, multiplied by its altitude, $b - a$. Note that the product $a(B)(b - a)$ is the integral of the function a_S over the interval $[a, b]$. In other words, the volume of a right cylindrical solid is equal to the integral of its cross-sectional area function,

$$v(S) = \int_a^b a_S(z) \, dz \, .$$

We can extend this formula to more general Cavalieri solids. Let R be a Cavalieri solid with measurable cross-sections perpendicular to a given line L. Introduce a coordinate axis along L (call it the u-axis), and let $a_R(u)$ be the area of the cross section cut by a plane perpendicular to L at the point u. The volume of R can be computed by the following theorem.

THEOREM 2.7.   *Let R be a Cavalieri solid in $\mathscr{A}$ with a cross-sectional area function a_R which is integrable on an interval $[a, b]$ and zero outside $[a, b]$. Then the volume of R is equal to the integral of the cross-sectional area:*

$$v(R) = \int_a^b a_R(u) \, du \, .$$

Proof. Choose step functions s and t such that $s \le a_R \le t$ on $[a, b]$ and define s and t to be zero outside $[a, b]$. For each subinterval of $[a, b]$ on which s is constant, we can imagine a cylindrical solid (for example, a right circular cylinder) constructed so that its cross-sectional area on this subinterval has the same constant value as s. The union of these cylinders over all intervals of constancy of s is a solid S whose volume $v(S)$ is, by additivity, equal to the integral $\int_a^b s(u) \, du$. Similarly, there is a solid T, a union of cylinders, whose volume $v(T) = \int_a^b t(u) \, du$. But $a_S(u) = s(u) \le a_R(u) \le t(u) = a_T(u)$ for all u in $[a, b]$, so Cavalieri's principle implies that $v(S) \le v(R) \le v(T)$. In other words, $v(R)$ satisfies the inequalities

$$\int_a^b s(u) \, du \le v(R) \le \int_a^b t(u) \, du$$

for all step functions s and t satisfying $s \le a_S \le t$ on $[a, b]$. Since a_S is integrable on $[a, b]$, it follows that $v(R) = \int_a^b a_S(u) \, du$.

EXAMPLE.   *Volume of a solid of revolution.* Let f be a function which is nonnegative and integrable on an interval $[a, b]$. If the ordinate set of this function is revolved about the x-axis, it sweeps out a solid of revolution. Each cross section cut by a plane perpendicular to the x-axis is a circular disk. The area of the circular disk cut at the point x is $\pi f^2(x)$, where $f^2(x)$ means the square of $f(x)$. Therefore, by Theorem 2.7, the volume of the solid (if the solid is in $\mathscr{A}$) is equal to the integral $\int_a^b \pi f^2(x) \, dx$, if the integral exists. In particular, if $f(x) = \sqrt{r^2 - x^2}$ for $-r \leq x \leq r$, the ordinate set of f is a semicircular disk of radius r and the solid swept out is a sphere of radius r. The sphere is convex. Its volume is equal to

$$\int_{-r}^{r} \pi f^2(x)\, dx = \pi \int_{-r}^{r} (r^2 - x^2)\, dx = 2\pi \int_{0}^{r} (r^2 - x^2)\, dx = \tfrac{4}{3}\pi r^3 .$$

More generally, suppose we have two nonnegative functions f and g which are integrable on an interval $[a, b]$ and satisfy $f \leq g$ on $[a, b]$. When the region between their graphs is rotated about the x-axis, it sweeps out a solid of revolution such that each cross section cut by a plane perpendicular to the x-axis at the point x is an annulus (a region bounded by two concentric circles) with area $\pi g^2(x) - \pi f^2(x)$. Therefore, if $g^2 - f^2$ is integrable, the volume of such a solid (if the solid is in $\mathscr{A}$) is given by the integral

$$\int_{a}^{b} \pi[g^2(x) - f^2(x)]\, dx .$$

2.13 Exercises

1. Use integration to compute the volume of a right circular cone generated by revolving the ordinate set of a linear function $f(x) = cx$ over the interval $0 \leq x \leq b$. Show that the result is one-third the area of the base times the altitude of the cone.

In each of Exercises 2 through 7, compute the volume of the solid generated by revolving the ordinate set of the function f over the interval indicated. Sketch each of the ordinate sets.

2. $f(x) = \sqrt{x}$, $0 \leq x \leq 1$.
3. $f(x) = x^{1/4}$, $0 \leq x \leq 1$.
4. $f(x) = x^2$, $-1 \leq x \leq 2$.
5. $f(x) = \sin x$, $0 \leq x \leq \pi$.
6. $f(x) = \cos x$, $0 \leq x \leq \pi/2$.
7. $f(x) = \sin x + \cos x$, $0 \leq x \leq \pi$.

In each of Exercises 8 through 11, sketch the region between the graphs of f and g and compute the volume of the solid obtained by rotating this region about the x-axis.

8. $f(x) = \sqrt{x}$, $g(x) = 1$, $0 \leq x \leq 1$.
9. $f(x) = \sqrt{x}$, $g(x) = x^2$, $0 \leq x \leq 1$.
10. $f(x) = \sin x$, $g(x) = \cos x$, $0 \leq x \leq \pi/4$.
11. $f(x) = \sqrt{4 - x^2}$, $g(x) = 1$, $0 \leq x \leq \sqrt{3}$.
12. Sketch the graphs of $f(x) = \sqrt{x}$ and $g(x) = x/2$ over the interval $[0, 2]$. Find a number t, $1 < t < 2$, so that when the region between the graphs of f and g over the interval $[0, t]$ is rotated about the x-axis, it sweeps out a solid of revolution whose volume is equal to $\pi t^3/3$.
13. What volume of material is removed from a solid sphere of radius $2r$ by drilling a hole of radius r through the center?
14. A napkin-ring is formed by drilling a cylindrical hole symmetrically through the center of a solid sphere. If the length of the hole is $2h$, prove that the volume of the napkin-ring is πah^3, where a is a rational number.
15. A solid has a circular base of radius 2. Each cross section cut by a plane perpendicular to a fixed diameter is an equilateral triangle. Compute the volume of the solid.
16. The cross sections of a solid are squares perpendicular to the x-axis with their centers on the axis. If the square cut off at x has edge $2x^2$, find the volume of the solid between $x = 0$ and $x = a$. Make a sketch.
17. Find the volume of a solid whose cross section, made by a plane perpendicular to the x-axis, has the area $ax^2 + bx + c$ for each x in the interval $0 \leq x \leq h$. Express the volume in terms of the areas B_1, M, and B_2 of the cross sections corresponding to $x = 0$, $x = h/2$, and $x = h$, respectively. The resulting formula is known as the *prismoid formula*.

18. Make a sketch of the region in the xy-plane consisting of all points (x, y) satisfying the simultaneous inequalities $0 \leq x \leq 2$, $\frac{1}{4}x^2 \leq y \leq 1$. Compute the volume of the solid obtained by rotating this region about (a) the x-axis; (b) the y-axis; (c) the vertical line passing through $(2, 0)$; (d) the horizontal line passing through $(0, 1)$.

2.14 Application of integration to the concept of work

Thus far our applications of integration have been to area and volume, concepts from geometry. Now we discuss an application to *work*, a concept from physics.

Work is a measure of the energy expended by a force in moving a particle from one point to another. In this section we consider only the simplest case, linear motion. That is, we assume that the motion takes place along a line (which we take as the x-axis) from one point, say $x = a$, to another point, $x = b$, and we also assume that the force acts along this line. We permit either $a < b$ or $b < a$. We assume further that the force acting on the particle is a function of the position. If the particle is at x, we denote by $f(x)$ the force acting on it, where $f(x) > 0$ if the force acts in the direction of the positive x-axis, and $f(x) < 0$ if the force acts in the opposite direction. When the force is constant, say $f(x) = c$ for all x between a and b, we define the work done by f to be the number $c \cdot (b - a)$, force times displacement. The work may be positive or negative.

If force is measured in pounds and distance in feet, we measure work in *foot-pounds*; if force is in *dynes* and distance in *centimeters* (the *cgs* system), work is measured in *dyne-centimeters*. One dyne-centimeter of work is called an *erg*. If force is in *newtons* and distance in *meters* (the *mks* system), work is in *newton-meters*. One newton-meter of work is called a *joule*. One newton is 10^5 dynes, and one joule is 10^7 ergs.

EXAMPLE. A stone weighing 3 pounds (lb) is thrown upward along a straight line, rising to a height of 15 feet (ft) and returning to the ground. We take the x-axis pointing up along the line of motion. The constant force of gravity acts downward, so $f(x) = -3$ lb for each x, $0 \leq x \leq 15$. The work done by gravity in moving the stone from, say, $x = 6$ ft to $x = 15$ ft is $-3 \cdot (15 - 6) = -27$ foot-pounds (ft-lb). When the same stone falls from $x = 15$ ft to $x = 6$ ft, the work done by gravity is $-3(6 - 15) = 27$ ft-lb.

Now suppose the force is not necessarily constant but is a given function of position defined on the interval joining a and b. How do we define the work done by f in moving a particle from a to b? We proceed much as we did for area and volume. We state some properties of work which are dictated by physical requirements. Then we prove that for any definition of work which has these properties, the work done by an integrable force function f is equal to the integral $\int_a^b f(x)\,dx$.

FUNDAMENTAL PROPERTIES OF WORK. *Let $W_a(f)$ denote the work done by a force function f in moving a particle from a to b. Then work has the following properties:*

1. *Additive property. If $a < c < b$, then $W_a^b(f) = W_a^c(f) + W_c^b(f)$.*
2. *Monotone property. If $f \leq g$ on $[a, b]$, then $W_a^b(f) \leq W_a^b(g)$. That is, a greater force does greater work.*
3. *Elementary formula. If f is constant, say $f(x) = c$ for all x in the open interval (a, b), then $W_a^b(f) = c \cdot (b - a)$.*

The additive property can be extended by induction to any finite number of intervals.

That is, if $a = x_0 < x_1 < \cdots < x_n = b$, we have

$$W_a^b(f) = \sum_{k=1}^{n} W_k \,,$$

where W_k is the work done by f from x_{k-1} to x_k. In particular, if the force is a step function s which takes a constant value s_k on the open interval (x_{k-1}, x_k), property 3 states that $W_k = s_k \cdot (x_k - x_{k-1})$, so we have

$$W_a^b(s) = \sum_{k=1}^{n} s_k \cdot (x_k - x_{k-1}) = \int_a^b s(x)\, dx \,.$$

Thus, for step functions, work has been expressed as an integral. Now it is an easy matter to prove that this holds true more generally.

THEOREM 2.8.   *Suppose work has been defined for a class of force functions f in such a way that it satisfies properties 1, 2, and 3. Then the work done by an integrable force function f in moving a particle from a to b is equal to the integral of f,*

$$W_a^b(f) = \int_a^b f(x)\, dx \,.$$

Proof. Let s and t be two step functions satisfying $s \leq f \leq t$ on $[a, b]$. The monotone property of work states that $W_a^b(s) \leq W_a^b(f) \leq W_a^b(t)$. But $W_a^b(s) = \int_a^b s(x)\, dx$ and $W_a^b(t) = \int_a^b t(x)\, dx$, so the number $W_a^b(f)$ satisfies the inequalities

$$\int_a^b s(x)\, dx \leq W_a^b(f) \leq \int_a^b t(x)\, dx$$

for all step functions s and t satisfying $s \leq f \leq t$ on $[a, b]$. Since f is integrable on $[a, b]$, it follows that $W_a^b(f) = \int_a^b f(x)\, dx$.

   Note: Many authors simply define work to be the integral of the force function. The foregoing discussion serves as motivation for this definition.

   EXAMPLE. *Work required to stretch a spring.* Assume that the force $f(x)$ needed to stretch a steel spring a distance x beyond its natural length is proportional to x (*Hooke's law*). We place the x-axis along the axis of the spring. If the stretching force acts in the positive direction of the axis, we have $f(x) = cx$, where the spring constant c is positive. (The value of c can be determined if we know the force $f(x)$ for a particular value of $x \neq 0$.) The work required to stretch the spring a distance a is $\int_0^a f(x)\, dx = \int_0^a cx\, dx = ca^2/2$, a number proportional to the square of the displacement.

   A discussion of work for motion along curves other than straight lines is carried out in Volume II with the aid of line integrals.

2.15 Exercises

   In Exercises 1 and 2 assume the force on the spring obeys Hooke's law.
1. If a ten-pound force stretches an elastic spring one inch, how much work is done in stretching the spring one foot?

2. A spring has a natural length of 1 meter (m). A force of 100 newtons compresses it to 0.9 m. How many joules of work are required to compress it to half its natural length? What is the length of the spring when 20 joules of work have been expended?

3. A particle is moved along the x-axis by a propelling force $f(x) = 3x^2 + 4x$ newtons. Calculate how many joules of work are done by the force to move the particle (a) from $x = 0$ to $x = 7$ m; (b) from $x = 2$ m to $x = 7$ m.

4. A particle is to be moved along the x-axis by a quadratic propelling force $f(x) = ax^2 + bx$ dynes. Calculate a and b so that 900 ergs of work are required to move the particle 10 centimeters (cm) from the origin, if the force is 65 dynes when $x = 5$ cm.

5. A cable 50 feet in length and weighing 4 pounds per foot (lb/ft) hangs from a windlass. Calculate the work done in winding up 25 ft of the cable. Neglect all forces except gravity.

6. Solve Exercise 5 if a 50 pound weight is attached to the end of the cable.

7. A weight of 150 pounds is attached at one end of a long flexible chain weighing 2 lb/ft. The weight is initially suspended with 10 feet of chain over the edge of a building 100 feet in height. Neglect all forces except gravity and calculate the amount of work done by the force of gravity when the load is lowered to a position 10 feet above the ground.

8. In Exercise 7, suppose that the chain is only 60 feet long and that the load and chain are allowed to drop to the ground, starting from the same initial position as before. Calculate the amount of work done by the force of gravity when the weight reaches the ground.

9. Let $V(q)$ denote the voltage required to place a charge q on the plates of a condensor. The work required to charge a condensor from $q = a$ to $q = b$ is defined to be the integral $\int_a^b V(q)\, dq$. If the voltage is proportional to the charge, prove that the work done to place a charge Q on an uncharged condensor is $\frac{1}{2}QV(Q)$.

2.16 Average value of a function

In scientific work it is often necessary to make several measurements under similar conditions and then compute an *average* or *mean* for the purpose of summarizing the data. There are many useful types of averages, the most common being the *arithmetic mean*. If $a_1, a_2, \ldots, a_n$ are n real numbers, their arithmetic mean $\bar{a}$ is defined by the equation

(2.17)
$$\bar{a} = \frac{1}{n} \sum_{k=1}^{n} a_k \,.$$

If the numbers a_k are the values of a function f at n distinct points, say $a_k = f(x_k)$, then the number

$$\frac{1}{n} \sum_{k=1}^{n} f(x_k)$$

is the arithmetic mean of the function values $f(x_1), \ldots, f(x_n)$. We can extend this concept to compute an average value not only for a finite number of values of $f(x)$ but for all values of $f(x)$ where x runs through an interval. The following definition serves this purpose.

DEFINITION OF AVERAGE VALUE OF A FUNCTION ON AN INTERVAL. *If f is integrable on an interval $[a, b]$, we define $A(f)$, the average value of f on $[a, b]$, by the formula*

(2.18)
$$A(f) = \frac{1}{b-a} \int_a^b f(x)\, dx \,.$$

When f is nonnegative, this formula has a simple geometric interpretation. Written in the form $(b - a)A(f) = \int_a^b f(x)\, dx$, it states that the rectangle of altitude $A(f)$ and base $[a, b]$ has an area equal to that of the ordinate set of f over $[a, b]$.

Now we can show that formula (2.18) is actually an extension of the concept of the arithmetic mean. Let f be a step function which is constant on n equal subintervals of $[a, b]$. Specifically, let $x_k = a + k(b - a)/n$ for $k = 0, 1, 2, \ldots, n$, and suppose that $f(x) = f(x_k)$, if $x_{k-1} < x < x_k$. Then $x_k - x_{k-1} = (b - a)/n$, so we have

$$A(f) = \frac{1}{b - a} \int_a^b f(x)\, dx = \frac{1}{b - a} \sum_{k=1}^{n} f(x_k) \frac{b - a}{n} = \frac{1}{n} \sum_{k=1}^{n} f(x_k).$$

Thus, for step functions, the average $A(f)$ is the same as the arithmetic mean of the values $f(x_1), \ldots, f(x_n)$ taken on the intervals of constancy.

Weighted arithmetic means are often used in place of the ordinary arithmetic mean in (2.17). If $w_1, w_2, \ldots, w_n$ are n nonnegative numbers (called *weights*), not all zero, the weighted arithmetic mean $\bar{a}$ of $a_1, a_2, \ldots, a_n$ is defined by the formula

$$\bar{a} = \frac{\displaystyle\sum_{k=1}^{n} w_k a_k}{\displaystyle\sum_{k=1}^{n} w_k}.$$

When the weights are all equal, this reduces to the ordinary arithmetic mean. The extension of this concept to integrable functions is given by the formula

$$(2.19) \qquad\qquad A(f) = \frac{\displaystyle\int_a^b w(x) f(x)\, dx}{\displaystyle\int_a^b w(x)\, dx},$$

where w is a nonnegative weight function with $\int_a^b w(x)\, dx \neq 0$.

Weighted averages are widely used in physics and engineering, as well as in mathematics. For example, consider a straight rod of length a made of a material of varying density. Place the rod along the positive x-axis with one end at the origin 0, and let $m(x)$ denote the mass of a portion of the rod of length x, measured from 0. If $m(x) = \int_0^x \rho(t)\, dt$ for some integrable function ρ (ρ is the Greek letter *rho*), then ρ is called the *mass density* of the rod. A *uniform* rod is one whose mass density is constant. The integral $\int_0^a x\rho(x)\, dx$ is called the *first moment* of the rod about 0, and the *center of mass* is the point whose x-coordinate is

$$\bar{x} = \frac{\displaystyle\int_0^a x\rho(x)\, dx}{\displaystyle\int_0^a \rho(x)\, dx}.$$

This is an example of a weighted average. We are averaging the distance function $f(x) = x$ with the mass density ρ as weight function.

The integral $\int_0^a x^2\rho(x)\,dx$ is called the *second moment*, or *moment of inertia*, of the rod about 0, and the positive number r given by the formula

$$r^2 = \frac{\displaystyle\int_0^a x^2\rho(x)\,dx}{\displaystyle\int_0^a \rho(x)\,dx}$$

is called the *radius of gyration* of the rod. In this case, the function being averaged is the square of the distance function, $f(x) = x^2$, with the mass density ρ as the weight function.

Weighted averages like these also occur in the mathematical theory of probability where the concepts of *expectation* and *variance* play the same role as center of mass and moment of inertia.

2.17 Exercises

In Exercises 1 through 10, compute the average $A(f)$ for the given function f over the specified interval.

1. $f(x) = x^2$, $a \le x \le b$.
2. $f(x) = x^2 + x^3$, $0 \le x \le 1$.
3. $f(x) = x^{1/2}$, $0 \le x \le 4$.
4. $f(x) = x^{1/3}$, $1 \le x \le 8$.
5. $f(x) = \sin x$, $0 \le x \le \pi/2$.
6. $f(x) = \cos x$, $-\pi/2 \le x \le \pi/2$.
7. $f(x) = \sin 2x$, $0 \le x \le \pi/2$.
8. $f(x) = \sin x \cos x$, $0 \le x \le \pi/4$.
9. $f(x) = \sin^2 x$, $0 \le x \le \pi/2$.
10. $f(x) = \cos^2 x$, $0 \le x \le \pi$.

11. (a) If $f(x) = x^2$ for $0 \le x \le a$, find a number c satisfying $0 < c < a$ such that $f(c)$ is equal to the average of f in $[0, a]$.
    (b) Solve part (a) if $f(x) = x^n$, where n is any positive integer.
12. Let $f(x) = x^2$ for $0 \le x \le 1$. The average value of f on $[0, 1]$ is $\frac{1}{3}$. Find a nonnegative weight function w such that the weighted average of f on $[0, 1]$, as defined by Equation (2.19) is (a) $\frac{1}{2}$; (b) $\frac{3}{5}$; (c) $\frac{2}{3}$.
13. Let $A(f)$ denote the average of f over an interval $[a, b]$. Prove that the average has the following properties:
    (a) *Additive property:* $A(f + g) = A(f) + A(g)$.
    (b) *Homogenous property:* $A(cf) = cA(f)$ if c is any real number.
    (c) *Monotone property:* $A(f) \le A(g)$ if $f \le g$ on $[a, b]$.
14. Which of the properties in Exercise 13 are valid for weighted averages as defined by Equation (2.19)?
15. Let $A_a^b(f)$ denote the average of f on an interval $[a, b]$.
    (a) If $a < c < b$, prove that there is a number t satisfying $0 < t < 1$ such that $A_a^b(f) = tA_a^c(f) + (1 - t)A_c^b(f)$. Thus, $A_a^b(f)$ is a weighted arithmetic mean of $A_a^c(f)$ and $A_c^b(f)$.
    (b) Prove that the result of part (a) also holds for weighted averages as defined by Equation (2.19).

Each of Exercises 16 through 21 refers to a rod of length L placed on the x-axis with one end at the origin. For the mass density ρ as described in each case, calculate (a) the center of mass of the rod, (b) the moment of inertia about the origin, and (c) the radius of gyration.

16. $\rho(x) = 1$ for $0 \le x \le L$.

17. $\rho(x) = 1$ for $0 \le x \le \dfrac{L}{2}$, $\rho(x) = 2$ for $\dfrac{L}{2} < x \le L$.

18. $\rho(x) = x$ for $0 \le x \le L$.

19. $\rho(x) = x$ for $0 \le x \le \dfrac{L}{2}$, $\rho(x) = \dfrac{L}{2}$ for $\dfrac{L}{2} \le x \le L$.

20. $\rho(x) = x^2$ for $0 \le x \le L$.

21. $\rho(x) = x^2$ for $0 \le x \le \dfrac{L}{2}$, $\rho(x) = \dfrac{L^2}{4}$ for $\dfrac{L}{2} \le x \le L$.

22. Determine a mass density ρ so that the center of mass of a rod of length L will be at a distance $L/4$ from one end of the rod.

23. In an electrical circuit, the voltage $e(t)$ at time t is given by the formula $e(t) = 3 \sin 2t$. Calculate the following: (a) the average voltage over the time interval $[0, \pi/2]$; (b) the root-mean-square of the voltage; that is, the square root of the average of the function e^2 in the interval $[0, \pi/2]$.

24. In an electrical circuit, the voltage $e(t)$ and the current $i(t)$ at time t are given by the formulas $e(t) = 160 \sin t$, $i(t) = 2 \sin (t - \pi/6)$. The average power is defined to be

$$\frac{1}{T} \int_0^T e(t)i(t)\, dt\,,$$

where T is the period of both the voltage and the current. Determine T and calculate the average power.

2.18 The integral as a function of the upper limit. Indefinite integrals

In this section we assume that f is a function such that the integral $\int_a^x f(t)\, dt$ exists for each x in an interval $[a, b]$. We shall keep a and f fixed and study this integral as a function of x. We denote the value of the integral by $A(x)$, so that we have

(2.20) $A(x) = \displaystyle\int_a^x f(t)\, dt$ if $a \le x \le b$.

An equation like this enables us to construct a new function A from a given function f, the value of A at each point in $[a, b]$ being determined by Equation (2.20). The function A is sometimes referred to as an *indefinite integral* of f, and it is said to be obtained from f by integration. We say *an* indefinite integral rather than *the* indefinite integral because A also depends on the lower limit a. Different values of a will lead to different functions A. If we use a different lower limit, say c, and define another indefinite integral F by the equation

$$F(x) = \int_c^x f(t)\, dt\,,$$

then the additive property tells us that

$$A(x) - F(x) = \int_a^x f(t)\, dt - \int_c^x f(t)\, dt = \int_a^c f(t)\, dt\,,$$

and hence the difference $A(x) - F(x)$ is *independent* of x. Therefore any two indefinite integrals of the same function differ only by a constant (the constant depends on the choice of a and c).

When an indefinite integral of f is known, the value of an integral such as $\int_a^b f(t)\, dt$ may be evaluated by a simple subtraction. For example, if n is a nonnegative integer, we have the formula of Theorem 1.15,

$$\int_0^x t^n\, dt = \frac{x^{n+1}}{n + 1}\,,$$

and the additive property implies that

$$\int_a^b t^n \, dt = \int_0^b t^n \, dt - \int_0^a t^n \, dt = \frac{b^{n+1} - a^{n+1}}{n+1} \, .$$

In general, if $F(x) = \int_c^x f(t) \, dt$, then we have

(2.21) $$\int_a^b f(t) \, dt = \int_c^b f(t) \, dt - \int_c^a f(t) \, dt = F(b) - F(a) \, .$$

A different choice of c merely changes $F(x)$ by a constant; this does not alter the difference $F(b) - F(a)$, because the constant cancels out in the subtraction.

If we use the special symbol

$$F(x) \Big|_a^b$$

to denote the difference $F(b) - F(a)$, Equation (2.21) may be written as

$$\int_a^b f(x) \, dx = F(x) \Big|_a^b = F(b) - F(a) \, .$$

There is, of course, a very simple geometric relationship between a function f and its indefinite integrals. An example is illustrated in Figure 2.15(a), where f is a nonnegative function and the number $A(x)$ is equal to the area of the shaded region under the graph of f from a to x. If f assumes both positive and negative values, as in Figure 2.15(b), the integral $A(x)$ gives the sum of the areas of the regions above the x-axis minus the sum of the areas below the x-axis.

Many of the functions that occur in various branches of science arise exactly in this way, as indefinite integrals of other functions. This is one of the reasons that a large part of calculus is devoted to the study of indefinite integrals.

Sometimes a knowledge of a special property of f implies a corresponding special property of the indefinite integral. For example, if f is nonnegative on $[a, b]$, then the indefinite integral A is increasing, since we have

$$A(y) - A(x) = \int_a^y f(t) \, dt - \int_a^x f(t) \, dt = \int_x^y f(t) \, dt \geq 0 \, ,$$

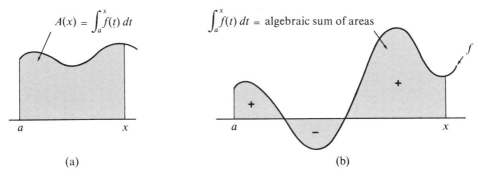

FIGURE 2.15   Indefinite integral interpreted geometrically in terms of area.

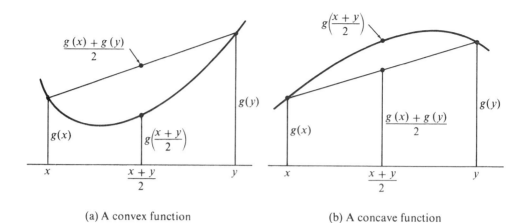

(a) A convex function   (b) A concave function

FIGURE 2.16   Geometric interpretation of convexity and concavity.

whenever $a \leq x \leq y \leq b$. Interpreted geometrically, this means that the area under the graph of a nonnegative function from a to x cannot decrease as x increases.

Now we discuss another property which is not immediately evident geometrically. Suppose f is increasing on $[a, b]$. We can prove that the indefinite integral A has a property known as *convexity*. Its graph bends upward, as illustrated in Figure 2.16(a); that is, the chord joining any two points on the graph always lies above the graph. An analytic definition of convexity may be given as follows.

DEFINITION OF A CONVEX FUNCTION.   *A function g is said to be convex on an interval $[a, b]$ if, for all x and y in $[a, b]$ and for every α satisfying $0 < α < 1$, we have*

(2.22) $g(z) \leq \alpha g(y) + (1 - \alpha)g(x), \quad where \quad z = \alpha y + (1 - \alpha)x$.

We say g is concave on $[a, b]$ if the reverse inequality holds,

$$g(z) \geq \alpha g(y) + (1 - \alpha)g(x), \quad where \quad z = \alpha y + (1 - \alpha)x .$$

These inequalities have a simple geometric interpretation. The point $z = \alpha y + (1 - \alpha)x$ satisfies $z - x = \alpha(y - x)$. If $x < y$, this point divides the interval $[x, y]$ into two sub-intervals, $[x, z]$ and $[z, y]$, the length of $[x, z]$ being α times that of $[x, y]$. As α runs from 0 to 1, the point $\alpha g(y) + (1 - \alpha)g(x)$ traces out the line segment joining the points $(x, g(x))$ and $(y, g(y))$ on the graph of g. Inequality (2.22) states that the graph of g never goes above this line segment. Figure 2.16(a) shows an example with $\alpha = \frac{1}{2}$. For a concave function, the graph never goes below the line segment, as illustrated by the example in Figure 2.16(b).

THEOREM 2.9.   *Let $A(x) = \int_a^x f(t)\, dt$. Then A is convex on every interval where f is increasing, and concave on every interval where f is decreasing.*

Proof.   Assume f is increasing on $[a, b]$, choose $x < y$, and let $z = \alpha y + (1 - \alpha)x$. We are to prove that $A(z) \leq \alpha A(y) + (1 - \alpha)A(x)$. Since $A(z) = \alpha A(z) + (1 - \alpha)A(z)$, this is the same as proving that $\alpha A(z) + (1 - \alpha)A(z) \leq \alpha A(y) + (1 - \alpha)A(x)$, or that

$$(1 - \alpha)[A(z) - A(x)] \leq \alpha[A(y) - A(z)] .$$

Since we have $A(z) - A(x) = \int_x^z f(t)\, dt$ and $A(y) - A(z) = \int_z^y f(t)\, dt$, we are to prove that

$$(2.23) \qquad\qquad (1 - \alpha) \int_x^z f(t)\, dt \leq \alpha \int_z^y f(t)\, dt .$$

But f is increasing, so we have the inequalities

$$f(t) \leq f(z) \quad\text{if}\quad x \leq t \leq z, \quad\text{and}\quad f(z) \leq f(t) \quad\text{if}\quad z \leq t \leq y .$$

Integrating these inequalities we find

$$\int_x^z f(t)\, dt \leq f(z)(z - x), \quad\text{and}\quad f(z)(y - z) \leq \int_z^y f(t)\, dt .$$

But $(1 - \alpha)(z - x) = \alpha(y - z)$, so these inequalities give us

$$(1 - \alpha) \int_x^z f(t)\, dt \leq (1 - \alpha)f(z)(z - x) = \alpha f(z)(y - z) \leq \alpha \int_z^y f(t)\, dt ,$$

which proves (2.23). This proves that A is convex when f is increasing. When f is decreasing, we may apply the result just proved to $-f$.

EXAMPLE. The cosine function decreases in the interval $[0, \pi]$. Since $\sin x = \int_0^x \cos t\, dt$, the graph of the sine function is concave in the interval $[0, \pi]$. In the interval $[\pi, 2\pi]$, the cosine increases and the sine function is convex.

Figure 2.17 illustrates further properties of indefinite integrals. The graph on the left is that of the greatest-integer function, $f(x) = [x]$; the graph on the right is that of the indefinite integral $A(x) = \int_0^x [t]\, dt$. On those intervals where f is constant, the function A is linear. We describe this by saying that *the integral of a step function is piecewise linear.*

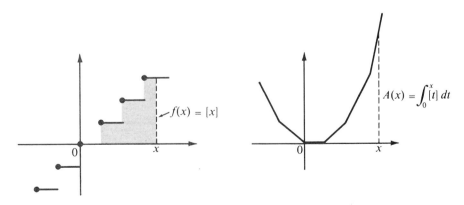

FIGURE 2.17   The indefinite integral of a step function is piecewise linear.

Observe also that the graph of f is made up of disconnected line segments. There are points on the graph of f where a small change in x produces a sudden jump in the value of the function. Note, however, that the corresponding indefinite integral does not exhibit this behavior. A small change in x produces only a small change in $A(x)$. That is why the graph of A is not disconnected. This illustrates a general property of indefinite integrals known as *continuity*. In the next chapter we shall discuss the concept of continuity in detail and prove that the indefinite integral is always a continuous function.

2.19 Exercises

Evaluate the integrals in Exercises 1 through 16.

1. $\int_0^x (1 + t + t^2)\, dt.$

2. $\int_0^{2y} (1 + t + t^2)\, dt.$

3. $\int_{-1}^{2x} (1 + t + t^2)\, dt.$

4. $\int_1^{1-x} (1 - 2t + 3t^2)\, dt.$

5. $\int_{-2}^x t^2(t^2 + 1)\, dt.$

6. $\int_x^{x^2} (t^2 + 1)^2\, dt.$

7. $\int_1^x (t^{1/2} + 1)\, dt, \qquad x > 0.$

8. $\int_x^{x^2} (t^{1/2} + t^{1/4})\, dt, \qquad x > 0.$

9. $\int_{-\pi}^x \cos t\, dt.$

10. $\int_0^{x^2} (\tfrac{1}{2} + \cos t)\, dt.$

11. $\int_x^{x^2} (\tfrac{1}{2} - \sin t)\, dt.$

12. $\int_0^x (u^2 + \sin 3u)\, du.$

13. $\int_x^{x^2} (v^2 + \sin 3v)\, dv.$

14. $\int_0^y (\sin^2 x + x)\, dx.$

15. $\int_0^x \left(\sin 2w + \cos \dfrac{w}{2}\right) dw.$

16. $\int_{-\pi}^x (\tfrac{1}{2} + \cos t)^2\, dt.$

17. Find all real values of x such that

$$\int_0^x (t^3 - t)\, dt = \tfrac{1}{3}\int_{\sqrt{2}}^x (t - t^3)\, dt.$$

Draw a suitable figure and interpret the equation geometrically.

18. Let $f(x) = x - [x] - \tfrac{1}{2}$ if x is not an integer, and let $f(x) = 0$ if x is an integer. (As usual, $[x]$ denotes the greatest integer $\leq x$.) Define a new function P as follows:

$$P(x) = \int_0^x f(t)\, dt \qquad \text{for every real } x.$$

(a) Draw the graph of f over the interval $[-3, 3]$ and prove that f is periodic with period 1: $f(x + 1) = f(x)$ for all x.
(b) Prove that $P(x) = \tfrac{1}{2}(x^2 - x)$, if $0 \leq x \leq 1$ and that P is periodic with period 1.
(c) Express $P(x)$ in terms of $[x]$.
(d) Determine a constant c such that $\int_0^1 (P(t) + c)\, dt = 0.$
(e) For the constant c of part (d), let $Q(x) = \int_0^x (P(t) + c)\, dt.$ Prove that Q is periodic with period 1 and that

$$Q(x) = \frac{x^3}{6} - \frac{x^2}{4} + \frac{x}{12} \qquad \text{if } 0 \leq x \leq 1.$$

19. Given an odd function f, defined everywhere, periodic with period 2, and integrable on every interval. Let $g(x) = \int_0^x f(t)\,dt$.
    (a) Prove that $g(2n) = 0$ for every integer n.
    (b) Prove that g is even and periodic with period 2.
20. Given an even function f, defined everywhere, periodic with period 2, and integrable on every interval. Let $g(x) = \int_0^x f(t)\,dt$, and let $A = g(1)$.
    (a) Prove that g is odd and that $g(x + 2) - g(x) = g(2)$.
    (b) Compute $g(2)$ and $g(5)$ in terms of A.
    (c) For what value of A will g be periodic with period 2?
21. Given two functions f and g, integrable on every interval and having the following properties: f is odd, g is even, $f(5) = 7$, $f(0) = 0$, $g(x) = f(x + 5)$, $f(x) = \int_0^x g(t)\,dt$ for all x. Prove that (a) $f(x - 5) = -g(x)$ for all x; (b) $\int_0^5 f(t)\,dt = 7$; (c) $\int_0^x f(t)\,dt = g(0) - g(x)$.

3

CONTINUOUS FUNCTIONS

3.1 Informal description of continuity

This chapter deals with the concept of continuity, one of the most important and also one of the most fascinating ideas in all of mathematics. Before we give a precise technical definition of continuity, we shall briefly discuss the concept in an informal and intuitive way to give the reader a feeling for its meaning.

Roughly speaking, the situation is this: Suppose a function f has the value $f(p)$ at a certain point p. Then f is said to be continuous at p if at every nearby point x the function

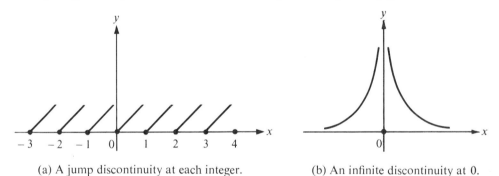

(a) A jump discontinuity at each integer.   (b) An infinite discontinuity at 0.

FIGURE 3.1   Illustrating two kinds of discontinuities.

value $f(x)$ is close to $f(p)$. Another way of putting it is as follows: If we let x move toward p, we want the corresponding function values $f(x)$ to become arbitrarily close to $f(p)$, regardless of the manner in which x approaches p. We do *not* want sudden jumps in the values of a continuous function, as in the examples in Figure 3.1.

Figure 3.1(a) shows the graph of the function f defined by the equation $f(x) = x - [x]$, where $[x]$ denotes the greatest integer $\leq x$. At each integer we have what is known as a *jump discontinuity*. For example, $f(2) = 0$, but as x approaches 2 from the left, $f(x)$ approaches the value 1, which is not equal to $f(2)$. Therefore we have a discontinuity at 2. Note that $f(x)$ *does* approach $f(2)$ if we let x approach 2 *from the right*, but this by itself is not enough to establish continuity at 2. In a case like this, the function is called *continuous from the right* at 2 and *discontinuous from the left* at 2. Continuity at a point requires both continuity from the left and from the right.

126

In the early development of calculus almost all functions that were dealt with were continuous and there was no real need at that time for a penetrating look into the exact meaning of continuity. It was not until late in the 18th century that discontinuous functions began appearing in connection with various kinds of physical problems. In particular, the work of J. B. J. Fourier (1758–1830) on the theory of heat forced mathematicians of the early 19th century to examine more carefully the exact meaning of such concepts as *function* and *continuity*. Although the meaning of the word "continuous" seems intuitively clear to most people, it is not obvious how a good definition of this idea should be formulated. One popular dictionary explains continuity as follows:

Continuity: Quality or state of being continuous.

Continuous: Having continuity of parts.

Trying to learn the meaning of continuity from these two statements alone is like trying to learn Chinese with only a Chinese dictionary. A satisfactory mathematical definition of continuity, expressed entirely in terms of properties of the real-number system, was first formulated in 1821 by the French mathematician, Augustin-Louis Cauchy (1789–1857). His definition, which is still used today, is most easily explained in terms of the limit concept to which we turn now.

3.2 The definition of the limit of a function

Let f be a function defined in some open interval containing a point p, although we do not insist that f be defined at the point p itself. Let A be a real number. The equation

$$\lim_{x \to p} f(x) = A$$

is read: "The limit of $f(x)$, as x approaches p, is equal to A," or "$f(x)$ approaches A as x approaches p." It is also written without the limit symbol, as follows:

$$f(x) \to A \qquad \text{as} \quad x \to p.$$

This symbolism is intended to convey the idea that we can make $f(x)$ as close to A as we please, provided we choose x sufficiently close to p.

Our first task is to explain the meaning of these symbols entirely in terms of real numbers. We shall do this in two stages. First we introduce the concept of a *neighborhood* of a point, then we define limits in terms of neighborhoods.

DEFINITION OF NEIGHBORHOOD OF A POINT. *Any open interval containing a point p as its midpoint is called a neighborhood of p.*

Notation. We denote neighborhoods by $N(p)$, $N_1(p)$, $N_2(p)$, etc. Since a neighborhood $N(p)$ is an open interval symmetric about p, it consists of all real x satisfying $p - r < x < p + r$ for some $r > 0$. The positive number r is called the *radius* of the neighborhood. We designate $N(p)$ by $N(p; r)$ if we wish to specify its radius. The inequalities $p - r < x < p + r$ are equivalent to $-r < x - p < r$, and to $|x - p| < r$. Thus, $N(p; r)$ consists of all points x whose distance from p is less than r.

In the next definition, we assume that A is a real number and that f is a function defined on some neighborhood of a point p (except possibly at p). The function f may also be defined at p but this is irrelevant in the definition.

DEFINITION OF LIMIT OF A FUNCTION.   *The symbolism*

$$\lim_{x \to p} f(x) = A \qquad [or \quad f(x) \to A \quad as \quad x \to p]$$

means that for every neighborhood $N_1(A)$ there is some neighborhood $N_2(p)$ such that

(3.1) $f(x) \in N_1(A)$ *whenever* $x \in N_2(p)$ *and* $x \neq p$.

The first thing to note about this definition is that it involves *two* neighborhoods, $N_1(A)$ and $N_2(p)$. The neighborhood $N_1(A)$ is specified *first;* it tells us how close we wish $f(x)$ to

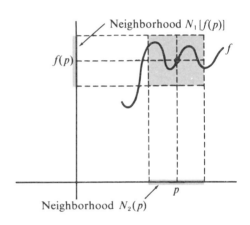

FIGURE 3.2   Here $\lim\limits_{x \to p} f(x) = A$, but there is no assertion about f at p.

FIGURE 3.3   Here f is defined at p and $\lim\limits_{x \to p} f(x) = f(p)$, hence f is continuous at p.

be to the limit A. The second neighborhood, $N_2(p)$, tells us how close x should be to p so that $f(x)$ will be within the first neighborhood $N_1(A)$. The essential part of the definition is that, for *every* $N_1(A)$, *no matter how small*, there is *some* neighborhood $N_2(p)$ to satisfy (3.1). In general, the neighborhood $N_2(p)$ will depend on the choice of $N_1(A)$. A neighborhood $N_2(p)$ that works for one particular $N_1(A)$ will also work, of course, for every larger $N_1(A)$, but it may not be suitable for any smaller $N_1(A)$.

The definition of limit may be illustrated geometrically as in Figure 3.2. A neighborhood $N_1(A)$ is shown on the y-axis. A neighborhood $N_2(p)$ corresponding to $N_1(A)$ is shown on the x-axis. The shaded rectangle consists of all points (x, y) for which $x \in N_2(p)$ and $y \in N_1(A)$. The definition of limit asserts that the entire graph of f above the interval $N_2(p)$ lies within this rectangle, except possibly for the point on the graph above p itself.

The definition of limit can also be formulated in terms of the *radii* of the neighborhoods $N_1(A)$ and $N_2(p)$. It is customary to denote the radius of $N_1(A)$ by ϵ (the Greek letter *epsilon*) and the radius of $N_2(p)$ by δ (the Greek letter *delta*). The statement $f(x) \in N_1(A)$ is equivalent to the inequality $|f(x) - A| < \epsilon$, and the statement $x \in N_2(p)$, $x \neq p$, is equivalent to the inequalities $0 < |x - p| < \delta$. Therefore, the definition of limit can also be expressed as follows:

The symbol $\lim_{x \to p} f(x) = A$ means that for every $\epsilon > 0$, there is a $\delta > 0$ such that

$$(3.2) \qquad |f(x) - A| < \epsilon \qquad whenever \quad 0 < |x - p| < \delta .$$

We note that the three statements,

$$\lim_{x \to p} f(x) = A , \qquad \lim_{x \to p} (f(x) - A) = 0 , \qquad \lim_{x \to p} |f(x) - A| = 0 ,$$

are all equivalent. This equivalence becomes apparent as soon as we write each of these statements in the ϵ, δ-terminology (3.2).

In dealing with limits as $x \to p$, we sometimes find it convenient to denote the difference $x - p$ by a new symbol, say h, and to let $h \to 0$. This simply amounts to a change in notation, because, as can be easily verified, the following two statements are equivalent:

$$\lim_{x \to p} f(x) = A , \qquad \lim_{h \to 0} f(p + h) = A .$$

EXAMPLE 1. *Limit of a constant function.* Let $f(x) = c$ for all x. It is easy to prove that for every p, we have $\lim_{x \to p} f(x) = c$. In fact, given any neighborhood $N_1(c)$, relation (3.1) is trivially satisfied for any choice of $N_2(p)$ because $f(x) = c$ for all x and $c \in N_1(c)$ for all neighborhoods $N_1(c)$. In limit notation, we write

$$\lim_{x \to p} c = c .$$

EXAMPLE 2. *Limit of the identity function.* Here $f(x) = x$ for all x. We can easily prove that $\lim_{x \to p} f(x) = p$. Choose any neighborhood $N_1(p)$ and take $N_2(p) = N_1(p)$. Then relation (3.1) is trivially satisfied. In limit notation, we write

$$\lim_{x \to p} x = p .$$

"One-sided" limits may be defined in a similar way. For example, if $f(x) \to A$ as $x \to p$ through values greater than p, we say that A is the *right-hand limit* of f at p, and we indicate this by writing

$$\lim_{x \to p+} f(x) = A .$$

In neighborhood terminology this means that for every neighborhood $N_1(A)$, there is some neighborhood $N_2(p)$ such that

$$(3.3) \qquad f(x) \in N_1(A) \qquad whenever \quad x \in N_2(p) \qquad and \quad x > p.$$

Left-hand limits, denoted by writing $x \to p-$, are similarly defined by restricting x to values less than p.

If f has a limit A at p, then it also has a right-hand limit and a left-hand limit at p, both of these being equal to A. But a function can have a right-hand limit at p different from the left-hand limit, as indicated in the next example.

EXAMPLE 3. Let $f(x) = [x]$ for all x, and let p be any integer. For x near p, $x < p$, we have $f(x) = p - 1$, and for x near p, $x > p$, we have $f(x) = p$. Therefore we see that

$$\lim_{x \to p-} f(x) = p - 1 \qquad \text{and} \qquad \lim_{x \to p+} f(x) = p .$$

In an example like this one, where the right- and left-hand limits are unequal, the limit of f at p *does not exist*.

EXAMPLE 4. Let $f(x) = 1/x^2$ if $x \neq 0$, and let $f(0) = 0$. The graph of f near zero is shown in Figure 3.1(b). In this example, f takes arbitrarily large values near 0 so it has no right-hand limit and no left-hand limit at 0. To prove rigorously that there is no real number A such that $\lim_{x \to 0+} f(x) = A$, we may argue as follows: Suppose there were such an A, say $A \geq 0$. Choose a neighborhood $N_1(A)$ of length 1. In the interval $0 < x < 1/(A + 2)$, we have $f(x) = 1/x^2 > (A + 2)^2 > A + 2$, so $f(x)$ cannot lie in the neighborhood $N_1(A)$. Thus, every neighborhood $N(0)$ contains points $x > 0$ for which $f(x)$ is outside $N_1(A)$, so (3.3) is violated for this choice of $N_1(A)$. Hence f has no right-hand limit at 0.

EXAMPLE 5. Let $f(x) = 1$ if $x \neq 0$, and let $f(0) = 0$. This function takes the constant value 1 everywhere except at 0, where it has the value 0. Both the right- and left-hand limits are 1 at every point p, so the limit of $f(x)$, as x approaches p, exists and equals 1. Note that the limit of f is 1 at the point 0, even though $f(0) = 0$.

3.3   The definition of continuity of a function

In the definition of limit we made no assertion about the behavior of f at the point p itself. Statement (3.1) refers to those $x \neq p$ which lie in $N_2(p)$, so it is not necessary that f be defined at p. Moreover, even if f is defined at p, its value there need not be equal to the limit A. However, if it happens that f is defined at p and if it also happens that $f(p) = A$, then we say the function f is continuous at p. In other words, we have the following definition.

DEFINITION OF CONTINUITY OF A FUNCTION AT A POINT. *A function f is said to be continuous at a point p if*

(a) f *is defined at p, and*

(b) $\lim_{x \to p} f(x) = f(p) .$

This definition can also be formulated in terms of neighborhoods. A function f is continuous at p if for every neighborhood $N_1[f(p)]$ there is a neighborhood $N_2(p)$ such that

(3.4) $f(x) \in N_1[f(p)] \qquad \text{whenever} \quad x \in N_2(p) .$

Since $f(p)$ always belongs to $N_1[f(p)]$, we do not need the condition $x \neq p$ in (3.4). In the ϵ, δ-terminology, where we specify the radii of the neighborhoods, the definition of continuity can be restated as follows:

A function f is continuous at p if for every $\epsilon > 0$ there is a $\delta > 0$ such that

$$|f(x) - f(p)| < \epsilon \qquad \text{whenever} \quad |x - p| < \delta.$$

The definition of continuity is illustrated geometrically in Figure 3.3. This is like Figure 3.2 except that the limiting value, A, is equal to the function value $f(p)$ so the entire graph of f above $N_2(p)$ lies in the shaded rectangle.

EXAMPLE 1. *Constant functions are continuous everywhere.* If $f(x) = c$ for all x, then

$$\lim_{x \to p} f(x) = \lim_{x \to p} c = c = f(p)$$

for every p, so f is continuous everywhere.

EXAMPLE 2. *The identity function is continuous everywhere.* If $f(x) = x$ for all x, we have

$$\lim_{x \to p} f(x) = \lim_{x \to p} x = p = f(p)$$

for every p, so the identity function is continuous everywhere.

EXAMPLE 3. Let $f(x) = [x]$ for all x. This function is continuous at every point p which is not an integer. At the integers it is discontinuous, since the limit of f does not exist, the right- and left-hand limits being unequal. A discontinuity of this type, where the right- and left-hand limits exist but are unequal, is called a *jump discontinuity*. However, since the right-hand limit equals $f(p)$ at each integer p, we say that f is *continuous from the right* at p.

EXAMPLE 4. The function f for which $f(x) = 1/x^2$ for $x \neq 0$, $f(0) = 0$, is discontinuous at 0. [See Figure 3.1(b).] We say there is an *infinite discontinuity* at 0 because the function takes arbitrarily large values near 0.

EXAMPLE 5. Let $f(x) = 1$ for $x \neq 0$, $f(0) = 0$. This function is continuous everywhere except at 0. It is discontinuous at 0 because $f(0)$ is not equal to the limit of $f(x)$ as $x \to 0$. In this example, the discontinuity could be removed by redefining the function at 0 to have the value 1 instead of 0. For this reason, a discontinuity of this type is called a *removable discontinuity*. Note that jump discontinuities, such as those possessed by the greatest-integer function, cannot be removed by simply changing the value of f at one point.

3.4 The basic limit theorems. More examples of continuous functions

Calculations with limits may often be simplified by the use of the following theorem which provides basic rules for operating with limits.

THEOREM 3.1.   *Let f and g be functions such that*

$$\lim_{x \to p} f(x) = A , \qquad \lim_{x \to p} g(x) = B .$$

Then we have

(i) $\lim_{x \to p} [f(x) + g(x)] = A + B ,$

(ii) $\lim_{x \to p} [f(x) - g(x)] = A - B ,$

(iii) $\lim_{x \to p} f(x) \cdot g(x) = A \cdot B ,$

(iv) $\lim_{x \to p} f(x)/g(x) = A/B \qquad \text{if} \quad B \neq 0 .$

Note: An important special case of (iii) occurs when f is constant, say $f(x) = A$ for all x. In this case, (iii) is written as $\lim_{x \to p} A \cdot g(x) = A \cdot B$.

The proof of Theorem 3.1 is not difficult but it is somewhat lengthy so we have placed it in a separate section (Section 3.5). We discuss here some simple consequences of the theorem.

First we note that the statements in the theorem may be written in a slightly different form. For example, (i) can be written as follows:

$$\lim_{x \to p} [f(x) + g(x)] = \lim_{x \to p} f(x) + \lim_{x \to p} g(x) .$$

It tells us that the limit of a sum is the sum of the limits.

It is customary to denote by $f + g, f - g, f \cdot g$, and f/g the functions whose values at each x under consideration are

$$f(x) + g(x), \qquad f(x) - g(x), \qquad f(x) \cdot g(x), \qquad \text{and} \qquad f(x)/g(x) ,$$

respectively. These functions are called the *sum, difference, product,* and *quotient* of f and g. Of course, the quotient f/g is defined only at those points for which $g(x) \neq 0$. The following corollary to Theorem 3.1 is stated in this terminology and notation and is concerned with continuous functions.

THEOREM 3.2.   *Let f and g be continuous at a point p. Then the sum $f + g$, the difference $f - g$, and the product $f \cdot g$ are also continuous at p. The same is true of the quotient f/g if $g(p) \neq 0$.*

Proof.   Since f and g are continuous at p, we have $\lim_{x \to p} f(x) = f(p)$ and $\lim_{x \to p} g(x) = g(p)$. Therefore we may apply the limit formulas in Theorem 3.1 with $A = f(p)$ and $B = g(p)$ to deduce Theorem 3.2.

We have already seen that the identity function and constant functions are continuous everywhere. Using these examples and Theorem 3.2, we may construct many more examples of continuous functions.

EXAMPLE 1. *Continuity of polynomials.* If we take $f(x) = g(x) = x$, the result on continuity of products proves the continuity at each point for the function whose value at each x is x^2. By mathematical induction, it follows that for every real c and every positive integer n, the function f for which $f(x) = cx^n$ is continuous for all x. Since the sum of two continuous functions is itself continuous, by induction it follows that the same is true for the sum of any finite number of continuous functions. Therefore every polynomial $p(x) = \sum_{k=0}^{n} c_k x^k$ is continuous at all points.

EXAMPLE 2. *Continuity of rational functions.* The quotient of two polynomials is called a *rational function*. If r is a rational function, then we have

$$r(x) = \frac{p(x)}{q(x)},$$

where p and q are polynomials. The function r is defined for all real x for which $q(x) \neq 0$. Since quotients of continuous functions are continuous, we see that every rational function is continuous wherever it is defined. A simple example is $r(x) = 1/x$ if $x \neq 0$. This function is continuous everywhere except at $x = 0$, where it fails to be defined.

The next theorem shows that if a function g is squeezed between two other functions which have equal limits as $x \to p$, then g also has this limit as $x \to p$.

THEOREM 3.3. SQUEEZING PRINCIPLE. *Suppose that $f(x) \leq g(x) \leq h(x)$ for all $x \neq p$ in some neighborhood $N(p)$. Suppose also that*

$$\lim_{x \to p} f(x) = \lim_{x \to p} h(x) = a .$$

Then we also have $\lim_{x \to p} g(x) = a$.

Proof. Let $G(x) = g(x) - f(x)$, and $H(x) = h(x) - f(x)$. The inequalities $f \leq g \leq h$ imply $0 \leq g - f \leq h - f$, or

$$0 \leq G(x) \leq H(x)$$

for all $x \neq p$ in $N(p)$. To prove the theorem, it suffices to show that $G(x) \to 0$ as $x \to p$, given that $H(x) \to 0$ as $x \to p$.

Let $N_1(0)$ be any neighborhood of 0. Since $H(x) \to 0$ as $x \to p$, there is a neighborhood $N_2(p)$ such that

$$H(x) \in N_1(0) \quad \text{whenever} \quad x \in N_2(p) \quad \text{and} \quad x \neq p .$$

We can assume that $N_2(p) \subseteq N(p)$. Then the inequality $0 \leq G \leq H$ states that $G(x)$ is no further from 0 than $H(x)$ if x is in $N_2(p)$, $x \neq p$. Therefore $G(x) \in N_1(0)$ for such x, and hence $G(x) \to 0$ as $x \to p$. This proves the theorem. The same proof is valid if all the limits are one-sided limits.

The squeezing principle is useful in practice because it is often possible to find squeezing functions f and h which are easier to deal with than g. We shall use the result now to prove that every indefinite integral is a continuous function.

THEOREM 3.4. CONTINUITY OF INDEFINITE INTEGRALS. *Assume f is integrable on $[a, x]$ for every x in $[a, b]$, and let*

$$A(x) = \int_a^x f(t)\, dt \; .$$

Then the indefinite integral A is continuous at each point of $[a, b]$. (At each endpoint we have one-sided continuity.)

Proof. Choose p in $[a, b]$. We are to prove that $A(x) \to A(p)$ as $x \to p$. We have

(3.5) $$A(x) - A(p) = \int_p^x f(t)\, dt \; .$$

Now we estimate the size of this integral. Since f is bounded on $[a, b]$, there is a constant $M > 0$ such that $-M \leq f(t) \leq M$ for all t in $[a, b]$. If $x > p$, we integrate these inequalities over the interval $[p, x]$ to obtain

$$-M(x - p) \leq A(x) - A(p) \leq M(x - p) \; .$$

If $x < p$, we obtain the same inequalities with $x - p$ replaced by $p - x$. Therefore, in either case we can let $x \to p$ and apply the squeezing principle to find that $A(x) \to A(p)$. This proves the theorem. If p is an endpoint of $[a, b]$, we must let $x \to p$ from inside the interval, so the limits are one-sided.

EXAMPLE 3. *Continuity of the sine and cosine.* Since the sine function is an indefinite integral, $\sin x = \int_0^x \cos t\, dt$, the foregoing theorem tells us that the sine is continuous everywhere. Similarly, the cosine is everywhere continuous since $\cos x = 1 - \int_0^x \sin t\, dt$. The continuity of these functions can also be deduced without making use of the fact that they are indefinite integrals. An alternate proof is outlined in Exercise 26 of Section 3.6.

EXAMPLE 4. In this example we prove an important limit formula,

(3.6) $$\lim_{x \to 0} \frac{\sin x}{x} = 1 \; ,$$

that is needed later in our discussion of differential calculus. Since the denominator of the quotient $(\sin x)/x$ approaches 0 as $x \to 0$, we cannot apply the quotient theorem on limits to deduce (3.6). Instead, we use the squeezing principle. From Section 2.5 we have the fundamental inequalities

$$0 < \frac{\sin x}{x} < \frac{1}{\cos x},$$

valid for $0 < x < \frac{1}{2}\pi$. They are also valid for $-\frac{1}{2}\pi < x < 0$ since $\cos(-x) = \cos x$ and $\sin(-x) = -x$, and hence they hold for all $x \neq 0$ in the neighborhood $N(0; \frac{1}{2}\pi)$. When $x \to 0$, we find $\cos x \to 1$ since the cosine is continuous at 0, and hence $1/(\cos x) \to 1$. Therefore, by the squeezing principle, we deduce (3.6). If we define $f(x) = (\sin x)/x$ for $x \neq 0$, $f(0) = 1$, then f is continuous everywhere. Its graph is shown in Figure 3.4.

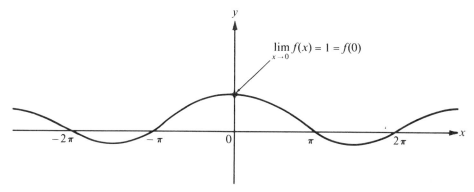

FIGURE 3.4 $f(x) = (\sin x)/x$ if $x \neq 0$, $f(0) = 1$. This function is continuous everywhere.

EXAMPLE 5. *Continuity of f when $f(x) = x^r$ for $x > 0$, where r is a positive rational number.* From Theorem 2.2 we have the integration formula

$$\int_0^x t^{1/n}\, dt = \frac{x^{1+1/n}}{1 + 1/n},$$

valid for all $x > 0$ and every integer $n \geq 1$. Using Theorems 3.4 and 3.1, we find that the function A given by $A(x) = x^{1+1/n}$ is continuous at all points $p > 0$. Now let $g(x) = x^{1/n} = A(x)/x$ for $x > 0$. Since g is a quotient of two continuous functions it, too, is continuous at all points $p > 0$. More generally, if $f(x) = x^{m/n}$, where m is a positive integer, then f is a product of continuous functions and hence is continuous at all points $p > 0$. This establishes the continuity of the rth-power function, $f(x) = x^r$, when r is any positive rational number, at all points $p > 0$. At $p = 0$ we have right-hand continuity.

The continuity of the rth-power function for rational r can also be deduced without using integrals. An alternate proof is given in Section 3.13.

3.5 Proofs of the basic limit theorems

In this section we prove Theorem 3.1 which describes the basic rules for dealing with limits of sums, products, and quotients. The principal algebraic tools used in the proof are two properties of absolute values that were mentioned earlier in Sections I4.8 and I4.9. They are (1) the triangle inequality, which states that $|a + b| \leq |a| + |b|$ for all real a and b, and (2) the equation $|ab| = |a|\,|b|$, which states that the absolute value of a product is the product of absolute values.

Proofs of (i) *and* (ii). Since the two statements

$$\lim_{x \to p} f(x) = A \qquad \text{and} \qquad \lim_{x \to p} [f(x) - A] = 0$$

are equivalent, and since we have

$$f(x) + g(x) - (A + B) = [f(x) - A] + [g(x) - B],$$

it suffices to prove part (i) of the theorem when the limits A and B are both zero.

Suppose, then, that $f(x) \to 0$ and $g(x) \to 0$ as $x \to p$. We shall prove that $f(x) + g(x) \to 0$ as $x \to p$. This means we must show that for every $\epsilon > 0$ there is a $\delta > 0$ such that

(3.7) $|f(x) + g(x)| < \epsilon$ whenever $0 < |x - p| < \delta$.

Let ϵ be given. Since $f(x) \to 0$ as $x \to p$, there is a $\delta_1 > 0$ such that

(3.8) $|f(x)| < \dfrac{\epsilon}{2}$ whenever $0 < |x - p| < \delta_1$.

Similarly, since $g(x) \to 0$ as $x \to p$, there is a $\delta_2 > 0$ such that

(3.9) $|g(x)| < \dfrac{\epsilon}{2}$ whenever $0 < |x - p| < \delta_2$.

If we let δ denote the smaller of the two numbers δ_1 and δ_2, then both inequalities (3.8) and (3.9) are valid if $0 < |x - p| < \delta$ and hence, by the triangle inequality, we find that

$$|f(x) + g(x)| \leq |f(x)| + |g(x)| < \frac{\epsilon}{2} + \frac{\epsilon}{2} = \epsilon.$$

This proves (3.7) which, in turn, proves (i). The proof of (ii) is entirely similar, except that in the last step we use the inequality $|f(x) - g(x)| \leq |f(x)| + |g(x)|$.

Proof of (iii). Suppose that we have proved part (iii) for the special case in which one of the limits is 0. Then the general case follows easily from this special case. In fact, all we need to do is write

$$f(x)g(x) - AB = f(x)[g(x) - B] + B[f(x) - A].$$

The special case implies that each term on the right approaches 0 as $x \to p$ and, by property (i), the sum of the two terms also approaches 0. Therefore, it remains to prove (iii) in the special case where one of the limits, say B, is 0.

Suppose, then, that $f(x) \to A$ and $g(x) \to 0$ as $x \to p$. We wish to prove that $f(x)g(x) \to 0$ as $x \to p$. To do this we must show that if a positive ϵ is given, there is a $\delta > 0$ such that

$$(3.10) \qquad |f(x)g(x)| < \epsilon \qquad \text{whenever} \quad 0 < |x - p| < \delta .$$

Since $f(x) \to A$ as $x \to p$, there is a δ_1 such that

$$(3.11) \qquad |f(x) - A| < 1 \qquad \text{whenever} \quad 0 < |x - p| < \delta_1 .$$

For such x, we have $|f(x)| = |f(x) - A + A| \leq |f(x) - A| + |A| < 1 + |A|$, and hence

$$(3.12) \qquad |f(x)g(x)| = |f(x)|\,|g(x)| < (1 + |A|)\,|g(x)|.$$

Since $g(x) \to 0$ as $x \to p$, for every $\epsilon > 0$ there is a δ_2 such that

$$(3.13) \qquad |g(x)| < \frac{\epsilon}{1 + |A|} \qquad \text{whenever} \quad 0 < |x - p| < \delta_2 .$$

Therefore, if we let δ be the smaller of the two numbers δ_1 and δ_2, then both inequalities (3.12) and (3.13) are valid whenever $0 < |x - p| < \delta$, and for such x we deduce (3.10). This completes the proof of (iii).

Proof of (iv). Since the quotient $f(x)/g(x)$ is the product of $f(x)/B$ with $B/g(x)$, it suffices to prove that $B/g(x) \to 1$ as $x \to p$ and then appeal to (iii). Let $h(x) = g(x)/B$. Then $h(x) \to 1$ as $x \to p$, and we wish to prove that $1/h(x) \to 1$ as $x \to p$.

Let $\epsilon > 0$ be given. We must show that there is a $\delta > 0$ such that

$$(3.14) \qquad \left| \frac{1}{h(x)} - 1 \right| < \epsilon \qquad \text{whenever} \quad 0 < |x - p| < \delta .$$

The difference to be estimated may be written as follows.

$$(3.15) \qquad \left| \frac{1}{h(x)} - 1 \right| = \frac{|h(x) - 1|}{|h(x)|} .$$

Since $h(x) \to 1$ as $x \to p$, we can choose a $\delta > 0$ such that both inequalities

$$(3.16) \qquad |h(x) - 1| < \frac{\epsilon}{2} \qquad \text{and} \qquad |h(x) - 1| < \frac{1}{2}$$

are satisfied whenever $0 < |x - p| < \delta$. The second of these inequalities implies $h(x) > \frac{1}{2}$ so $1/|h(x)| = 1/h(x) < 2$ for such x. Using this in (3.15) along with the first inequality in (3.16), we obtain (3.14). This completes the proof of (iv).

3.6 Exercises

In Exercises 1 through 10, compute the limits and explain which limit theorems you are using in each case.

1. $\lim\limits_{x \to 2} \dfrac{1}{x^2}$.

2. $\lim\limits_{x \to 0} \dfrac{25x^3 + 2}{75x^7 - 2}$.

3. $\lim\limits_{x \to 2} \dfrac{x^2 - 4}{x - 2}$.

4. $\lim\limits_{x \to 1} \dfrac{2x^2 - 3x + 1}{x - 1}$.

5. $\lim\limits_{h \to 0} \dfrac{(t + h)^2 - t^2}{h}$.

6. $\lim\limits_{x \to 0} \dfrac{x^2 - a^2}{x^2 + 2ax + a^2}$, $a \neq 0$.

7. $\lim\limits_{a \to 0} \dfrac{x^2 - a^2}{x^2 + 2ax + a^2}$, $x \neq 0$.

8. $\lim\limits_{x \to a} \dfrac{x^2 - a^2}{x^2 + 2ax + a^2}$, $a \neq 0$.

9. $\lim\limits_{t \to 0} \tan t$.

10. $\lim\limits_{t \to 0} (\sin 2t + t^2 \cos 5t)$.

11. $\lim\limits_{x \to 0+} \dfrac{|x|}{x}$.

12. $\lim\limits_{x \to 0-} \dfrac{|x|}{x}$.

13. $\lim\limits_{x \to 0+} \dfrac{\sqrt{x^2}}{x}$.

14. $\lim\limits_{x \to 0-} \dfrac{\sqrt{x^2}}{x}$.

Use the relation $\lim_{x \to 0} (\sin x)/x = 1$ to establish the limit formulas in Exercises 15 through 20.

15. $\lim\limits_{x \to 0} \dfrac{\sin 2x}{x} = 2$.

16. $\lim\limits_{x \to 0} \dfrac{\tan 2x}{\sin x} = 2$.

17. $\lim\limits_{x \to 0} \dfrac{\sin 5x}{\sin x} = 5$.

18. $\lim\limits_{x \to 0} \dfrac{\sin 5x - \sin 3x}{x} = 2$.

19. $\lim\limits_{x \to 0} \dfrac{\sin x - \sin a}{x - a} = \cos a$.

20. $\lim\limits_{x \to 0} \dfrac{1 - \cos x}{x^2} = \tfrac{1}{2}$.

21. Show that $\lim\limits_{x \to 0} \dfrac{1 - \sqrt{1 - x^2}}{x^2} = \tfrac{1}{2}$. [*Hint:* $(1 - \sqrt{u})(1 + \sqrt{u}) = 1 - u$.]

22. A function f is defined as follows:

$$f(x) = \begin{cases} \sin x & \text{if } x \leq c, \\ ax + b & \text{if } x > c, \end{cases}$$

where a, b, c are constants. If b and c are given, find all values of a (if any exist) for which f is continuous at the point $x = c$.

23. Solve Exercise 22 if f is defined as follows:

$$f(x) = \begin{cases} 2 \cos x & \text{if } x \leq c, \\ ax^2 + b & \text{if } x > c. \end{cases}$$

24. At what points are the tangent and cotangent functions continuous?

25. Let $f(x) = (\tan x)/x$ if $x \neq 0$. Sketch the graph of f over the half-open intervals $[-\tfrac{1}{4}\pi, 0)$ and $(0, \tfrac{1}{4}\pi]$. What happens to $f(x)$ as $x \to 0$? Can you define $f(0)$ so that f becomes continuous at 0?

26. This exercise outlines an alternate proof of the continuity of the sine and cosine functions.
    (a) The inequality $|\sin x| < |x|$, valid for $0 < |x| < \frac{1}{2}\pi$, was proved in Exercise 34 of Section 2.8. Use this inequality to prove that the sine function is continuous at 0.
    (b) Use part (a) and the identity $\cos 2x = 1 - 2 \sin^2 x$ to prove that the cosine is continuous at 0.
    (c) Use the addition formulas for $\sin (x + h)$ and $\cos (x + h)$ to prove that the sine and cosine are continuous at any real x.

27. Figure 3.5 shows a portion of the graph of the function f defined as follows:

$$f(x) = \sin \frac{1}{x} \qquad \text{if} \quad x \neq 0 \,.$$

For $x = 1/(n\pi)$, where n is an integer, we have $\sin (1/x) = \sin (n\pi) = 0$. Between two such points, the function values rise to $+1$ and drop back to 0 or else drop to -1 and rise back to 0.

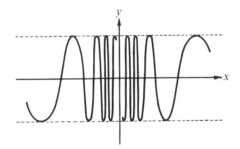

FIGURE 3.5 $f(x) = \sin (1/x)$ if $x \neq 0$. This function is discontinuous at 0 no matter how $f(0)$ is defined.

Therefore, between any such point and the origin, the curve has an infinite number of oscillations. This suggests that the function values do not approach any fixed value as $x \to 0$. Prove that there is no real number A such that $f(x) \to A$ as $x \to 0$. This shows that it is not possible to define $f(0)$ in such a way that f becomes continuous at 0.

[*Hint:* Assume such an A exists and obtain a contradiction.]

28. For $x \neq 0$, let $f(x) = [1/x]$, where $[t]$ denotes the greatest integer $\leq t$. Sketch the graph of f over the intervals $[-2, -\frac{1}{5}]$ and $[\frac{1}{5}, 2]$. What happens to $f(x)$ as $x \to 0$ through positive values? through negative values? Can you define $f(0)$ so that f becomes continuous at 0?

29. Same as Exercise 28, when $f(x) = (-1)^{[1/x]}$ for $x \neq 0$.

30. Same as Exercise 28, when $f(x) = x(-1)^{[1/x]}$ for $x \neq 0$.

31. Give an example of a function that is continuous at one point of an interval and discontinuous at all other points of the interval, or prove that there is no such function.

32. Let $f(x) = x \sin (1/x)$ if $x \neq 0$. Define $f(0)$ so that f will be continuous at 0.

33. Let f be a function such that $|f(u) - f(v)| \leq |u - v|$ for all u and v in an interval $[a, b]$.
    (a) Prove that f is continuous at each point of $[a, b]$.
    (b) Assume that f is integrable on $[a, b]$. Prove that

$$\left| \int_a^b f(x)\, dx - (b - a)f(a) \right| \leq \frac{(b - a)^2}{2} \,.$$

(c) More generally, prove that for any c in $[a, b]$, we have

$$\left| \int_a^b f(x)\, dx - (b - a)f(c) \right| \leq \frac{(b - a)^2}{2}.$$

3.7 Composite functions and continuity

We can create new functions from given ones by addition, subtraction, multiplication, and division. In this section we learn a new way to construct functions by an operation known as composition. We illustrate with an example.

Let $f(x) = \sin(x^2)$. To compute $f(x)$, we first square x and then take the sine of x^2. Thus, $f(x)$ is obtained by combining two other functions, the squaring function and the sine function. If we let $v(x) = x^2$ and $u(x) = \sin x$, we can express $f(x)$ in terms of u and v by writing

$$f(x) = u[v(x)].$$

We say that f is the *composition* of u and v (in that order). If we compose v and u in the opposite order, we obtain a different result, $v[u(x)] = (\sin x)^2$. That is, to compute $v[u(x)]$, we take the sine of x first and then square $\sin x$.

Now we can carry out this process more generally. Let u and v be any two given functions. The composite or composition of u and v (in that order) is defined to be the function f for which

$$f(x) = u[v(x)] \qquad \text{(read as ``} u \text{ of } v \text{ of } x \text{'').}$$

That is, to evaluate f at x we first compute $v(x)$ and then evaluate u at the point $v(x)$. Of course, this presupposes that it makes sense to evaluate u at $v(x)$, and therefore f will be defined only at those points x for which $v(x)$ is in the domain of u.

For example, if $u(x) = \sqrt{x}$ and $v(x) = 1 - x^2$, then the composite f is given by $f(x) = \sqrt{1 - x^2}$. Note that v is defined for all real x, whereas u is defined only for $x \geq 0$. Therefore the composite f is defined only for those x satisfying $1 - x^2 \geq 0$.

Formally, $f(x)$ is obtained by substituting $v(x)$ for x in the expression $u(x)$. For this reason, the function f is sometimes denoted by the symbol $f = u(v)$ (read as ``$u$ of $v$''). Another notation that we shall use to denote composition is $f = u \circ v$ (read as ``u circle v''). This resembles the notation for the product $u \cdot v$. In fact, we shall see in a moment that the operation of composition has some of the properties possessed by multiplication.

The composite of three or more functions may be found by composing them two at a time. Thus, the function f given by

$$f(x) = \cos[\sin(x^2)]$$

is a composition, $f = u \circ (v \circ w)$, where

$$u(x) = \cos x, \qquad v(x) = \sin x, \qquad \text{and} \qquad w(x) = x^2.$$

Notice that the same f can be obtained by composing u and v first and then composing $u \circ v$

with w, thus: $f = (u \circ v) \circ w$. This illustrates the *associative law* for composition which states that

(3.17) $$u \circ (v \circ w) = (u \circ v) \circ w$$

for all functions u, v, w, provided it makes sense to form all the composites in question. The reader will find that the proof of (3.17) is a straightforward exercise.

It should be noted that the *commutative law*, $u \circ v = v \circ u$, does not always hold for composition. For example, if $u(x) = \sin x$ and $v(x) = x^2$, the composite $f = u \circ v$ is given by $f(x) = \sin x^2$ (which means $\sin (x^2)$), whereas the composition $g = v \circ u$ is given by $g(x) = \sin^2 x$ [which means $(\sin x)^2$].

Now we shall prove a theorem which tells us that the property of continuity is preserved under the operation of composition. More precisely, we have the following.

THEOREM 3.5.   *Assume v is continuous at p and that u is continuous at q, where $q = v(p)$. Then the composite function $f = u \circ v$ is continuous at p.*

Proof. Since u is continuous at q, for every neighborhood $N_1[u(q)]$ there is a neighborhood $N_2(q)$ such that

(3.18) $$u(y) \in N_1[u(q)] \quad \text{whenever} \quad y \in N_2(q).$$

But $q = v(p)$ and v is continuous at p, so for the neighborhood $N_2(q)$ there is another neighborhood $N_3(p)$ such that

(3.19) $$v(x) \in N_2(q) \quad \text{whenever} \quad x \in N_3(p).$$

If we let $y = v(x)$ and combine (3.18) with (3.19), we find that for every neighborhood $N_1(u[v(p)])$ there is a neighborhood $N_3(p)$ such that

$$u[v(x)] \in N_1(u[v(p)]) \quad \text{whenever} \quad x \in N_3(p),$$

or, in other words, since $f(x) = u[v(x)]$,

$$f(x) \in N_1[f(p)] \quad \text{whenever} \quad x \in N_3(p).$$

This means that f is continuous at p, as asserted.

EXAMPLE 1. Let $f(x) = \sin x^2$. This is the composition of two functions continuous everywhere so f is continuous everywhere.

EXAMPLE 2. Let $f(x) = \sqrt{1 - x^2} = u[v(x)]$, where $u(x) = \sqrt{x}$, $v(x) = 1 - x^2$. The function v is continuous everywhere but u is continuous only for points $x \geq 0$. Hence f is continuous at those points x for which $v(x) \geq 0$, that is at all points satisfying $x^2 \leq 1$.

3.8 Exercises

In Exercises 1 through 10, the functions f and g are defined by the formulas given. Unless otherwise noted, the domains of f and g consist of all real numbers. Let $h(x) = f[g(x)]$ whenever $g(x)$ lies in the domain of f. In each case, describe the domain of h and give one or more formulas for determining $h(x)$.

1. $f(x) = x^2 - 2x$, $g(x) = x + 1$.
2. $f(x) = x + 1$, $g(x) = x^2 - 2x$.
3. $f(x) = \sqrt{x}$ if $x \geq 0$, $g(x) = x^2$.
4. $f(x) = \sqrt{x}$ if $x \geq 0$, $g(x) = -x^2$.
5. $f(x) = x^2$, $g(x) = \sqrt{x}$ if $x \geq 0$.
6. $f(x) = -x^2$, $g(x) = \sqrt{x}$ if $x \geq 0$.
7. $f(x) = \sin x$, $g(x) = \sqrt{x}$ if $x \geq 0$.
8. $f(x) = \sqrt{x}$ if $x \geq 0$, $g(x) = \sin x$.
9. $f(x) = \sqrt{x}$ if $x > 0$, $g(x) = x + \sqrt{x}$ if $x > 0$.
10. $f(x) = \sqrt{x + \sqrt{x}}$ if $x > 0$, $g(x) = x + \sqrt{x}$ if $x > 0$.

Calculate the limits in Exercises 11 through 20 and explain which limit theorems you are using in each case.

11. $\lim\limits_{x \to -2} \dfrac{x^3 + 8}{x^2 - 4}$.

12. $\lim\limits_{x \to 4} \sqrt{1 + \sqrt{x}}$.

13. $\lim\limits_{t \to 0} \dfrac{\sin (\tan t)}{\sin t}$.

14. $\lim\limits_{x \to \pi/2} \dfrac{\sin (\cos x)}{\cos x}$.

15. $\lim\limits_{t \to \pi} \dfrac{\sin (t - \pi)}{t - \pi}$.

16. $\lim\limits_{x \to 1} \dfrac{\sin (x^2 - 1)}{x - 1}$.

17. $\lim\limits_{x \to 0} x \sin \dfrac{1}{x}$.

18. $\lim\limits_{x \to 0} \dfrac{1 - \cos 2x}{x^2}$.

19. $\lim\limits_{x \to 0} \dfrac{\sqrt{1 + x} - \sqrt{1 - x}}{x}$.

20. $\lim\limits_{x \to 0} \dfrac{1 - \sqrt{1 - 4x^2}}{x^2}$.

21. Let f and g be two functions defined as follows:

$$f(x) = \frac{x + |x|}{2} \quad \text{for all } x, \qquad g(x) = \begin{cases} x & \text{for } x < 0, \\ x^2 & \text{for } x \geq 0. \end{cases}$$

Find a formula (or formulas) for computing the composite function $h(x) = f[g(x)]$. For what values of x is h continuous?

22. Solve Exercise 21 when f and g are defined as follows:

$$f(x) = \begin{cases} 1 & \text{if } |x| \leq 1, \\ 0 & \text{if } |x| > 1, \end{cases} \qquad g(x) = \begin{cases} 2 - x^2 & \text{if } |x| \leq 2, \\ 2 & \text{if } |x| > 2. \end{cases}$$

23. Solve Exercise 21 when $h(x) = g[f(x)]$.

3.9 Bolzano's theorem for continuous functions

In the rest of this chapter we shall discuss certain special properties of continuous functions that are used quite frequently. Most of these properties appear obvious when interpreted geometrically; consequently many people are inclined to accept them as self-evident.

However, it is important to realize that these statements are no more self-evident than the definition of continuity itself, and therefore they require proof if they are to be used with any degree of generality. The proofs of most of these properties make use of the least-upper-bound axiom for the real number system.

Bernard Bolzano (1781–1848), a Catholic priest who made many important contributions to mathematics in the first half of the 19th century, was one of the first to recognize that many "obvious" statements about continuous functions require proof. His observations concerning continuity were published posthumously in 1850 in an important book, *Paradoxien des Unendlichen*. One of his results, now known as the theorem of Bolzano, is illustrated in Figure 3.6, where the graph of a continuous function *f* is shown. The graph lies below the *x*-axis at $x = a$ and above the axis at $x = b$. Bolzano's theorem asserts that the curve must cross the axis somewhere between *a* and *b*. This property, first published by Bolzano in 1817, may be stated formally as follows.

THEOREM 3.6.   BOLZANO'S THEOREM.   *Let f be continuous at each point of a closed interval* [a, b] *and assume that f(a) and f(b) have opposite signs. Then there is at least one c in the open interval* (a, b) *such that f(c) = 0.*

We shall base our proof of Bolzano's theorem on the following property of continuous functions which we state here as a separate theorem.

THEOREM 3.7.   SIGN-PRESERVING PROPERTY OF CONTINUOUS FUNCTIONS.   *Let f be continuous at c and suppose that f(c) ≠ 0. Then there is an interval* (c − δ, c + δ) *about c in which f has the same sign as f(c).*

Proof of Theorem 3.7. Suppose $f(c) > 0$. By continuity, for every $\epsilon > 0$ there is a $\delta > 0$ such that

$$(3.20) \qquad f(c) - \epsilon < f(x) < f(c) + \epsilon \qquad \text{whenever} \quad c - \delta < x < c + \delta \, .$$

If we take the δ corresponding to $\epsilon = f(c)/2$ (this ϵ is *positive*), then (3.20) becomes

$$\tfrac{1}{2}f(c) < f(x) < \tfrac{3}{2}f(c) \qquad \text{whenever} \quad c - \delta < x < c + \delta \, .$$

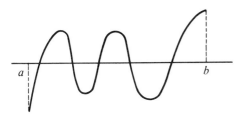

FIGURE 3.6   Illustrating Bolzano's theorem.

FIGURE 3.7   Here $f(x) > 0$ for x near c because $f(c) > 0$.

(See Figure 3.7). Therefore $f(x) > 0$ in this interval, and hence $f(x)$ and $f(c)$ have the same sign. If $f(c) < 0$, we take the δ corresponding to $\epsilon = -\frac{1}{2}f(c)$ and arrive at the same conclusion.

> *Note:* If there is one-sided continuity at c, then there is a corresponding one-sided interval $[c, c + \delta)$ or $(c - \delta, c]$ in which f has the same sign as $f(c)$.

Proof of Bolzano's theorem. To be specific, assume $f(a) < 0$ and $f(b) > 0$, as shown in Figure 3.6. There may be many values of x between a and b for which $f(x) = 0$. Our problem is to find *one*. We shall do this by finding the largest x for which $f(x) = 0$. For this purpose we let S denote the set of all those points x in the interval $[a, b]$ for which $f(x) \leq 0$. There is at least one point in S because $f(a) < 0$. Therefore S is a nonempty set. Also, S is bounded above since all of S lies within $[a, b]$, so S has a supremum. Let $c = \sup S$. We shall prove that $f(c) = 0$.

There are only three possibilities: $f(c) > 0$, $f(c) < 0$, and $f(c) = 0$. If $f(c) > 0$, there is an interval $(c - \delta, c + \delta)$, or $(c - \delta, c]$ if $c = b$, in which f is positive. Therefore no points of S can lie to the right of $c - \delta$, and hence $c - \delta$ is an upper bound for the set S. But $c - \delta < c$, and c is the *least* upper bound of S. Therefore the inequality $f(c) > 0$ is impossible. If $f(c) < 0$, there is an interval $(c - \delta, c + \delta)$, or $[c, c + \delta)$ if $c = a$, in which f is negative. Hence $f(x) < 0$ for some $x > c$, contradicting the fact that c is an upper bound for S. Therefore $f(c) < 0$ is also impossible, and the only remaining possibility is $f(c) = 0$. Also, $a < c < b$ because $f(a) < 0$ and $f(b) > 0$. This proves Bolzano's theorem.

3.10 The intermediate-value theorem for continuous functions

An immediate consequence of Bolzano's theorem is the *intermediate-value theorem* for continuous functions, illustrated in Figure 3.8.

THEOREM 3.8. *Let f be continuous at each point of a closed interval $[a, b]$. Choose two arbitrary points $x_1 < x_2$ in $[a, b]$ such that $f(x_1) \neq f(x_2)$. Then f takes on every value between $f(x_1)$ and $f(x_2)$ somewhere in the interval (x_1, x_2).*

Proof. Suppose $f(x_1) < f(x_2)$ and let k be any value between $f(x_1)$ and $f(x_2)$. Let g be the function defined on $[x_1, x_2]$ as follows:

$$g(x) = f(x) - k .$$

FIGURE 3.8 Illustrating the intermediate-value theorem.

FIGURE 3.9 An example for which Bolzano's theorem is not applicable.

Then g is continuous at each point of $[x_1, x_2]$, and we have

$$g(x_1) = f(x_1) - k < 0, \qquad g(x_2) = f(x_2) - k > 0.$$

Applying Bolzano's theorem to g, we have $g(c) = 0$ for some c between x_1 and x_2. But this means $f(c) = k$, and the proof is complete.

> *Note:* In both Bolzano's theorem and the intermediate-value theorem, it is assumed that f is continuous at each point of $[a, b]$, including the endpoints a and b. To understand why continuity at both endpoints is necessary, we refer to the curve in Figure 3.9. Here f is continuous everywhere in $[a, b]$ except at a. Although $f(a)$ is negative and $f(b)$ is positive, there is no x in $[a, b]$ for which $f(x) = 0$.

We conclude this section with an application of the intermediate-value theorem in which we prove that every positive real number has a positive nth root, a fact mentioned earlier in Section I 3.14. We state this as a formal theorem.

THEOREM 3.9. *If n is a positive integer and if $a > 0$, then there is exactly one positive b such that $b^n = a$.*

Proof. Choose $c > 1$ such that $0 < a < c$, and consider the function f defined on the interval $[0, c]$ by the equation $f(x) = x^n$. This function is continuous on $[0, c]$, and at the endpoints we have $f(0) = 0$, $f(c) = c^n$. Since $0 < a < c < c^n$, the given number a lies between the function values $f(0)$ and $f(c)$. Therefore, by the intermediate-value theorem, we have $f(x) = a$ for some x in $(0, c)$, say for $x = b$. This proves the existence of at least one positive b such that $b^n = a$. There cannot be more than one such b because f is strictly increasing on $[0, c]$. This completes the proof.

3.11 Exercises

1. Let f be a polynomial of degree n, say $f(x) = \sum_{k=0}^{n} c_k x^k$, such that the first and last coefficients c_0 and c_n have opposite signs. Prove that $f(x) = 0$ for at least one positive x.

2. A real number x_1, such that $f(x_1) = 0$, is said to be a real root of the equation $f(x) = 0$. We say that a real root of an equation has been *isolated* if we exhibit an interval $[a, b]$ containing this root and no others. With the aid of Bolzano's theorem, isolate the real roots of each of the following equations (each has four real roots).
   (a) $3x^4 - 2x^3 - 36x^2 + 36x - 8 = 0$.
   (b) $2x^4 - 14x^2 + 14x - 1 = 0$.
   (c) $x^4 + 4x^3 + x^2 - 6x + 2 = 0$.

3. If n is an odd positive integer and $a < 0$, prove that there is exactly one negative b such that $b^n = a$.

4. Let $f(x) = \tan x$. Although $f(\pi/4) = 1$ and $f(3\pi/4) = -1$, there is no x in the interval $[\pi/4, 3\pi/4]$ such that $f(x) = 0$. Explain why this does not contradict Bolzano's theorem.

5. Given a real-valued function f which is continuous on the closed interval $[0, 1]$. Assume that $0 \le f(x) \le 1$ for each x in $[0, 1]$. Prove that there is at least one point c in $[0, 1]$ for which $f(c) = c$. Such a point is called a *fixed point* of f. The result of this exercise is a special case of *Brouwer's fixed-point theorem*. [*Hint:* Apply Bolzano's theorem to $g(x) = f(x) - x$.]

6. Given a real-valued function f which is continuous on the closed interval $[a, b]$. Assume that $f(a) \le a$ and that $f(b) \ge b$. Prove that f has a fixed point in $[a, b]$. (See Exercise 5.)

3.12   The process of inversion

This section describes another important method that is often used to construct new functions from given ones. Before we describe the method in detail, we will illustrate it with a simple example.

Consider the function f defined on the interval $[0, 2]$ by the equation $f(x) = 2x + 1$. The range of f is the interval $[1, 5]$. Each point x in $[0, 2]$ is carried by f onto exactly one point y in $[1, 5]$, namely

$$(3.21) \qquad\qquad\qquad y = 2x + 1.$$

Conversely, for every y in $[1, 5]$, there is exactly one x in $[0, 2]$ for which $y = f(x)$. To find this x, we solve Equation (3.21) to obtain

$$x = \tfrac{1}{2}(y - 1).$$

This equation defines x as a function of y. If we denote this function by g, we have

$$g(y) = \tfrac{1}{2}(y - 1)$$

for each y in $[1, 5]$. The function g is called the *inverse* of f. Note that $g[f(x)] = x$ for each x in $[0, 2]$, and that $f[g(y)] = y$ for each y in $[1, 5]$.

Consider now a more general function f with domain A and range B. For each x in A, there is exactly one y in B such that $y = f(x)$. For each y in B, there is at least one x in A such that $f(x) = y$. Suppose that there is *exactly one* such x. Then we can define a new function g on B as follows:

$$g(y) = x \qquad \text{means} \quad y = f(x).$$

In other words, the value of g at each point y in B is that unique x in A such that $f(x) = y$. This new function g is called the *inverse* of f. The process by which g is obtained from f is called *inversion*. Note that $g[f(x)] = x$ for all x in A, and that $f[g(y)] = y$ for all y in B.

The process of inversion can be applied to any function f having the property that for each y in the range of f, there is exactly one x in the domain of f such that $f(x) = y$. In particular, a function that is continuous and strictly monotonic on an interval $[a, b]$ has this property. An example is shown in Figure 3.10. Let $c = f(a)$, $d = f(b)$. The intermediate-value theorem for continuous functions tells us that in the interval $[a, b]$, f takes on every value between c and d. Moreover, f cannot take on the same value twice because $f(x_1) \neq f(x_2)$ whenever $x_1 \neq x_2$. Therefore, every continuous strictly monotonic function has an inverse.

The relation between a function f and its inverse g can also be simply explained in the ordered-pair formulation of the function concept. In Section 1.3 we described a function f as a set of ordered pairs (x, y) no two of which have the same first element. The inverse function g is formed by taking the pairs (x, y) in f and interchanging the elements x and y. That is, $(y, x) \in g$ if and only if $(x, y) \in f$. If f is strictly monotonic, then no two pairs in f have the same second element, and hence no two pairs of g have the same first element. Thus g is, indeed, a function.

EXAMPLE. *The nth-root function.* If n is a positive integer, let $f(x) = x^n$ for $x \geq 0$. Then f is strictly increasing on every interval $[a, b]$ with $0 \leq a \leq b$. The inverse function g is the nth-root function, defined for $y \geq 0$ by the equation

$$g(y) = y^{1/n}.$$

3.13 Properties of functions preserved by inversion

Many properties possessed by the function f are transmitted to the inverse g. Figure 3.11 illustrates the relationship between their graphs. One can be obtained from the other merely by reflection through the line $y = x$, because a point (u, v) lies on the graph of f if and only if the point (v, u) lies on the graph of g.

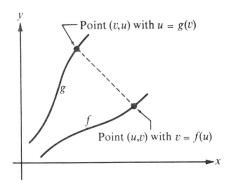

FIGURE 3.10 A continuous, strictly increasing function.

FIGURE 3.11 Illustrating the process of inversion.

The properties of monotonicity and continuity possessed by f are transmitted to the inverse function g, as described by the following theorem.

THEOREM 3.10. *Assume f is strictly increasing and continuous on an interval $[a, b]$. Let $c = f(a)$ and $d = f(b)$ and let g be the inverse of f. That is, for each y in $[c, d]$, let $g(y)$ be that x in $[a, b]$ such that $y = f(x)$. Then*
   (a) *g is strictly increasing on $[c, d]$;*
   (b) *g is continuous on $[c, d]$.*

Proof. Choose $y_1 < y_2$ in $[c, d]$ and let $x_1 = g(y_1)$, $x_2 = g(y_2)$. Then $y_1 = f(x_1)$ and $y_2 = f(x_2)$. Since f is strictly increasing, the relation $y_1 < y_2$ implies $x_1 < x_2$, which, in turn, implies g is strictly increasing on $[c, d]$. This proves part (a).

Now we prove (b). The proof is illustrated in Figure 3.12. Choose a point y_0 in the open interval (c, d). To prove g is continuous at y_0, we must show that for every $\epsilon > 0$ there is a $\delta > 0$ such that

(3.22) $\qquad g(y_0) - \epsilon < g(y) < g(y_0) + \epsilon \qquad$ whenever $\quad y_0 - \delta < y < y_0 + \delta$.

Let $x_0 = g(y_0)$, so that $f(x_0) = y_0$. Suppose ϵ is given. (There is no loss in generality if we consider only those ϵ small enough so that both $x_0 - \epsilon$ and $x_0 + \epsilon$ are in $[a, b]$.) Let δ

be the smaller of the two numbers

$$f(x_0) - f(x_0 - \epsilon) \qquad \text{and} \qquad f(x_0 + \epsilon) - f(x_0).$$

It is easy to check that this δ works in (3.22). A slight modification of the argument proves that g is continuous from the right at c, and continuous from the left at d.

There is a corresponding theorem for decreasing functions. That is, the inverse of a strictly decreasing continuous function f is strictly decreasing and continuous. This follows by applying Theorem 3.10 to $-f$.

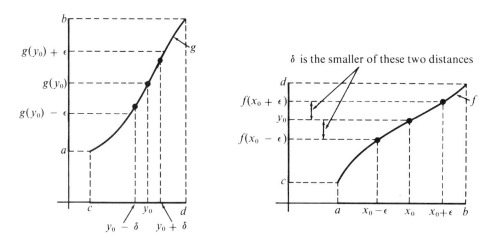

FIGURE 3.12   Proof of the continuity of the inverse function.

EXAMPLE. *Continuity of the nth-root function.* The nth-root function g, defined for $y \geq 0$ by the equation $g(y) = y^{1/n}$, is strictly increasing and continuous on every interval $[c, d]$ with $0 \leq c < d$, since it is the inverse of a strictly increasing continuous function. This gives an alternate proof of the continuity of the nth-root function, independent of the theory of integration. Since the product of continuous functions is continuous, we again deduce the continuity of the rth-power function, $h(y) = y^r$, where $r = m/n$ is a positive rational number and $y \geq 0$.

3.14   Inverses of piecewise monotonic functions

Suppose we try to apply the process of inversion to a function that is not monotonic on $[a, b]$. For example, suppose that $f(x) = x^2$ on an interval of the form $[-c, c]$ on the x-axis. Each point x in this interval is carried by f into exactly one point y in the interval $[0, c^2]$, namely,

(3.23) $y = x^2 .$

We can solve Equation (3.23) for x in terms of y, but there are *two* values of x corresponding to each y in $(0, c^2]$, namely,

$$x = \sqrt{y} \qquad \text{and} \qquad x = -\sqrt{y}.$$

As we have mentioned once before, there was a time when mathematicians would have said that the inverse g in this case is a *double-valued function* defined by

$$g(y) = \pm\sqrt{y}\,.$$

But since the more modern point of view does not admit double-valuedness as a property of functions, in a case like this we say that the process of inversion gives rise to *two* new functions, say g_1 and g_2, where

(3.24) $\qquad g_1(y) = \sqrt{y} \quad$ and $\quad g_2(y) = -\sqrt{y} \quad$ for each y in $[0, c^2]$.

To fit this in with the notion of inverse as explained above, we can look upon the equation $y = x^2$ as defining not *one* function f but *two* functions f_1 and f_2, say, where

$$f_1(x) = x^2 \quad \text{if} \ \ 0 \le x \le c \quad \text{and} \quad f_2(x) = x^2 \quad \text{if} \ \ -c \le x \le 0\,.$$

These may be considered as *distinct* functions because they have different domains. Each function is monotonic on its domain and each has an inverse, the inverse of f_1 being g_1 and the inverse of f_2 being g_2, where g_1 and g_2 are given by (3.24).

This illustrates how the process of inversion can be applied to piecewise monotonic functions. We simply consider such a function as a union of monotonic functions and invert each monotonic piece.

We shall make extensive use of the process of inversion in Chapter 6.

3.15 Exercises

In each of Exercises 1 through 5, show that f is strictly monotonic on the whole real axis. Let g denote the inverse of f. Describe the domain of g in each case. Write $y = f(x)$ and solve for x in terms of y; thus find a formula (or formulas) for computing $g(y)$ for each y in the domain of g.

1. $f(x) = x + 1$.
2. $f(x) = 2x + 5$.
3. $f(x) = 1 - x$.

4. $f(x) = x^3$.

5. $f(x) = \begin{cases} x & \text{if} \ \ x < 1, \\ x^2 & \text{if} \ \ 1 \le x \le 4, \\ 8x^{1/2} & \text{if} \ \ x > 4. \end{cases}$

Mean values. Let f be continuous and strictly monotonic on the positive real axis and let g denote the inverse of f. If $a_1 < a_2 < \cdots < a_n$ are n given positive real numbers, we define their *mean value* (or *average*) *with respect to* f to be the number M_f defined as follows:

$$M_f = g\left(\frac{1}{n}\sum_{i=1}^{n} f(a_i)\right).$$

In particular, when $f(x) = x^p$ for $p \neq 0$, M_f is called the pth *power mean* (See also Section I 4.10.) The exercises which follow deal with properties of mean values.

6. Show that $f(M_f) = (1/n)\sum_{i=1}^{n} f(a_i)$. In other words, the value of f at the average M_f is the arithmetic mean of the function values $f(a_1), \ldots, f(a_n)$.
7. Show that $a_1 < M_f < a_n$. In other words, the average of $a_1, \ldots, a_n$ lies between the largest and smallest of the a_i.
8. If $h(x) = af(x) + b$, where $a \neq 0$, show that $M_h = M_f$. This shows that different functions may lead to the same average. Interpret this theorem geometrically by comparing the graphs of h and f.

3.16   The extreme-value theorem for continuous functions

Let f be a real-valued function defined on a set S of real numbers. The function f is said to have an *absolute maximum* on the set S if there is at least one point c in S such that

$$f(x) \leq f(c) \qquad \text{for all } x \text{ in } S.$$

The number $f(c)$ is called the absolute maximum value of f on S. We say that f has an *absolute minimum* on S if there is a point d in S such that

$$f(x) \geq f(d) \qquad \text{for all } x \text{ in } S.$$

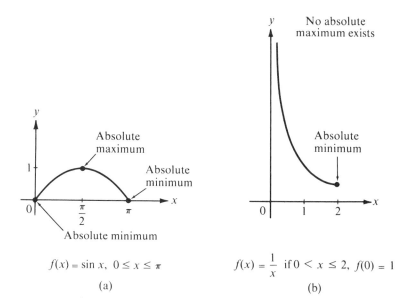

FIGURE 3.13   Maximum and minimum values of functions.

These concepts are illustrated in Figure 3.13. In Figure 3.13(a), S is the closed interval $[0, \pi]$ and $f(x) = \sin x$. The absolute minimum, which occurs at both endpoints of the interval, is 0. The absolute maximum is $f(\tfrac{1}{2}\pi) = 1$.

In Figure 3.13(b), S is the closed interval $[0, 2]$ and $f(x) = 1/x$ if $x > 0$, $f(0) = 1$. In this example, f has an absolute minimum at $x = 2$, but it has no absolute maximum. It fails to have a maximum because of a discontinuity at a point of S.

We wish to prove that if S is a closed interval and if f is continuous everywhere on S, then f has both an absolute maximum and an absolute minimum on S. This result, known as the extreme-value theorem for continuous functions, will be deduced as a simple consequence of the following theorem.

THEOREM 3.11.   BOUNDEDNESS THEOREM FOR CONTINUOUS FUNCTIONS.   *Let f be continuous on a closed interval $[a, b]$. Then f is bounded on $[a, b]$. That is, there is a number $C \geq 0$ such that $|f(x)| \leq C$ for all x in $[a, b]$.*

Proof. We argue by contradiction, using a technique called the method of successive bisection. Assume that f is *unbounded* (not bounded) on $[a, b]$. Let c be the midpoint of $[a, b]$. Since f is unbounded on $[a, b]$ it is unbounded on at least one of the subintervals $[a, c]$ or $[c, b]$. Let $[a_1, b_1]$ be that half of $[a, b]$ in which f is unbounded. If f is unbounded in both halves, let $[a_1, b_1]$ be the left half, $[a, c]$. Now continue the bisection process repeatedly, denoting by $[a_{n+1}, b_{n+1}]$ that half of $[a_n, b_n]$ in which f is unbounded, with the understanding that we choose the left half if f is unbounded in both halves. Since the length of each interval is half that of its predecessor, we note that the length of $[a_n, b_n]$ is $(b - a)/2^n$.

Let A denote the set of leftmost endpoints $a, a_1, a_2, \ldots$, so constructed, and let α be the supremum of A. Then α lies in $[a, b]$. By continuity of f at α, there is an interval of the form $(\alpha - \delta, \alpha + \delta)$ in which

$$(3.25) \qquad |f(x) - f(\alpha)| < 1 .$$

If $\alpha = a$ this interval has the form $[a, a + \delta)$, and if $\alpha = b$ it has the form $(b - \delta, b]$. Inequality (3.25) implies

$$|f(x)| < 1 + |f(\alpha)| ,$$

so f is bounded by $1 + |f(\alpha)|$ in this interval. However, the interval $[a_n, b_n]$ lies inside $(\alpha - \delta, \alpha + \delta)$ when n is so large that $(b - a)/2^n < \delta$. Therefore f is also bounded in $[a_n, b_n]$, contradicting the fact that f is unbounded on $[a_n, b_n]$. This contradiction completes the proof.

If f is bounded on $[a, b]$, then the set of all function values $f(x)$ is bounded above and below. Therefore, this set has a supremum and an infimum which we denote by sup f and inf f, respectively. That is, we write

$$\sup f = \sup \{f(x) \mid a \leq x \leq b\}, \qquad \inf f = \inf \{f(x) \mid a \leq x \leq b\} .$$

For any bounded function we have $\inf f \leq f(x) \leq \sup f$ for all x in $[a, b]$. Now we prove that a continuous function takes on both values inf f and sup f somewhere in $[a, b]$.

THEOREM 3.12. EXTREME-VALUE THEOREM FOR CONTINUOUS FUNCTIONS. *Assume f is continuous on a closed interval $[a, b]$. Then there exist points c and d in $[a, b]$ such that*

$$f(c) = \sup f \qquad and \qquad f(d) = \inf f.$$

Proof. It suffices to prove that f attains its supremum in $[a, b]$. The result for the infimum then follows as a consequence because the infimum of f is the supremum of $-f$.

Let $M = \sup f$. We shall assume that there is no x in $[a, b]$ for which $f(x) = M$ and obtain a contradiction. Let $g(x) = M - f(x)$. Then $g(x) > 0$ for all x in $[a, b]$ so the reciprocal $1/g$ is continuous on $[a, b]$. By Theorem 3.11, $1/g$ is bounded on $[a, b]$, say $1/g(x) < C$ for all x in $[a, b]$, where $C > 0$. This implies $M - f(x) > 1/C$, so that $f(x) < M - 1/C$ for all x in $[a, b]$. This contradicts the fact that M is the least upper bound of f on $[a, b]$. Hence, $f(x) = M$ for at least one x in $[a, b]$.

Note: This theorem shows that if f is continuous on $[a, b]$, then sup f is its absolute maximum, and inf f its absolute minimum. Hence, by the intermediate-value theorem, the range of f is the closed interval $[\inf f, \sup f]$.

3.17   The small-span theorem for continuous functions (uniform continuity)

Let f be real-valued and continuous on a closed interval $[a, b]$ and let $M(f)$ and $m(f)$ denote, respectively, the maximum and minimum values of f on $[a, b]$. We shall call the difference

$$M(f) - m(f)$$

the *span* of f in the interval $[a, b]$. Some authors use the term *oscillation* instead of span. However, oscillation has the disadvantage of suggesting undulating or wavelike functions. Older texts use the word *saltus*, which is Latin for *leap*. The word "span" seems more suggestive of what is being measured here. We note that the span of f in any subinterval of $[a, b]$ cannot exceed the span of f in $[a, b]$.

We shall prove next that the interval $[a, b]$ can be partitioned so that the span of f in each subinterval is arbitrarily small. More precisely, we have the following theorem which we call the *small-span theorem* for continuous functions. It is usually referred to in the literature as the theorem on uniform continuity.

THEOREM 3.13.   *Let f be continuous on a closed interval $[a, b]$. Then, for every $\epsilon > 0$ there is a partition of $[a, b]$ into a finite number of subintervals such that the span of f in every subinterval is less than ϵ.*

Proof. We argue by contradiction, using the method of successive bisections. Assume the theorem is *false*. That is, assume that for some ϵ, say for $\epsilon = \epsilon_0$, the interval $[a, b]$ cannot be partitioned into a finite number of subintervals in each of which the span of f is less than ϵ_0. Let c be the midpoint of $[a, b]$. Then for the same ϵ_0, the theorem is false in at least one of the two subintervals $[a, c]$ or $[c, b]$. (If the theorem were true in both intervals $[a, c]$ and $[c, b]$, it would also be true in the full interval $[a, b]$.) Let $[a_1, b_1]$ be that half of $[a, b]$ in which the theorem is false for ϵ_0. If it is false in both halves, let $[a_1, b_1]$ be the left half, $[a, c]$. Now continue the bisection process repeatedly, denoting by $[a_{n+1}, b_{n+1}]$ that half of $[a_n, b_n]$ in which the theorem is false for ϵ_0, with the understanding that we choose the left half if the theorem is false in both halves of $[a_n, b_n]$. Note that the span of f in each subinterval $[a_n, b_n]$ so constructed is at least ϵ_0.

Let A denote the collection of leftmost endpoints $a, a_1, a_2, \ldots$, so constructed, and let α be the least upper bound of A. Then α lies in $[a, b]$. By continuity of f at α, there is an interval $(\alpha - \delta, \alpha + \delta)$ in which the span of f is less than ϵ_0. (If $\alpha = a$, this interval is $[a, a + \delta)$, and if $\alpha = b$, it is $(b - \delta, b]$.) However, the interval $[a_n, b_n]$ lies inside $(\alpha - \delta, \alpha + \delta)$ when n is so large that $(b - a)/2^n < \delta$, so the span of f in $[a_n, b_n]$ is also less than ϵ_0, contradicting the fact that the span of f is at least ϵ_0 in $[a_n, b_n]$. This contradiction completes the proof of Theorem 3.13.

3.18   The integrability theorem for continuous functions

The small-span theorem can be used to prove that a function which is continuous on $[a, b]$ is also integrable on $[a, b]$.

THEOREM 3.14. INTEGRABILITY OF CONTINUOUS FUNCTIONS. *If a function f is continuous at each point of a closed interval [a, b], then f is integrable on [a, b].*

Proof. Theorem 3.11 shows that f is bounded on $[a, b]$, so f has an upper integral, $\bar{I}(f)$, and a lower integral, $\underline{I}(f)$. We shall prove that $\underline{I}(f) = \bar{I}(f)$.

Choose an integer $N \geq 1$ and let $\epsilon = 1/N$. By the small-span theorem, for this choice of ϵ there is a partition $P = \{x_0, x_1, \ldots, x_n\}$ of $[a, b]$ into n subintervals such that the span of f in every subinterval is less than ϵ. Denote by $M_k(f)$ and $m_k(f)$, respectively, the absolute maximum and minimum values of f in the kth subinterval $[x_{k-1}, x_k]$. Then we have

$$M_k(f) - m_k(f) < \epsilon$$

for each $k = 1, 2, \ldots, n$. Now let s_n and t_n be two step functions defined on $[a, b]$ as follows:

$$s_n(x) = m_k(f) \quad \text{if} \quad x_{k-1} < x \leq x_k, \qquad s_n(a) = m_1(f),$$

$$t_n(x) = M_k(f) \quad \text{if} \quad x_{k-1} \leq x < x_k, \qquad t_n(b) = M_n(f).$$

Then we have $s_n(x) \leq f(x) \leq t_n(x)$ for all x in $[a, b]$. Also, we have

$$\int_a^b s_n = \sum_{k=1}^n m_k(f)(x_k - x_{k-1}) \qquad \text{and} \qquad \int_a^b t_n = \sum_{k=1}^n M_k(f)(x_k - x_{k-1}).$$

The difference of these two integrals is

$$\int_a^b t_n - \int_a^b s_n = \sum_{k=1}^n [M_k(f) - m_k(f)](x_k - x_{k-1}) < \epsilon \sum_{k=1}^n (x_k - x_{k-1}) = \epsilon(b - a).$$

Since $\epsilon = 1/N$, this inequality can be written in the form

(3.26) $$\int_a^b t_n - \int_a^b s_n < \frac{b - a}{N}.$$

On the other hand, the upper and lower integrals of f satisfy the inequalities

$$\int_a^b s_n \leq \underline{I}(f) \leq \int_a^b t_n \qquad \text{and} \qquad \int_a^b s_n \leq \bar{I}(f) \leq \int_a^b t_n.$$

Multiplying the first set of inequalities by (-1) and adding the result to the second set, we obtain

$$\bar{I}(f) - \underline{I}(f) \leq \int_a^b t_n - \int_a^b s_n.$$

Using (3.26) and the relation $\underline{I}(f)) \leq \bar{I}(f)$, we have

$$0 \leq \bar{I}(f) - \underline{I}(f) < \frac{b - a}{N}$$

for every integer $N \geq 1$. Therefore, by Theorem I.31, we must have $\underline{I}(f) = \bar{I}(f)$. This proves that f is integrable on $[a, b]$.

3.19   Mean-value theorems for integrals of continuous functions

In Section 2.16 we defined the average value $A(f)$ of a function f over an interval $[a, b]$ to be the quotient $\int_a^b f(x)\, dx/(b - a)$. When f is continuous, we can prove that this average value is equal to the value of f at some point in $[a, b]$.

THEOREM 3.15.   MEAN-VALUE THEOREM FOR INTEGRALS.   *If f is continuous on $[a, b]$, then for some c in $[a, b]$ we have*

$$\int_a^b f(x)\, dx = f(c)(b - a).$$

Proof. Let m and M denote, respectively, the minimum and maximum values of f on $[a, b]$. Then $m \leq f(x) \leq M$ for all x in $[a, b]$. Integrating these inequalities and dividing by $b - a$, we find $m \leq A(f) \leq M$, where $A(f) = \int_a^b f(x)\, dx/(b - a)$. But now the intermediate-value theorem tells us that $A(f) = f(c)$ for some c in $[a, b]$. This completes the proof.

There is a corresponding result for weighted mean values.

THEOREM 3.16.   WEIGHTED MEAN-VALUE THEOREM FOR INTEGRALS.   *Assume f and g are continuous on $[a, b]$. If g never changes sign in $[a, b]$ then, for some c in $[a, b]$, we have*

$$(3.27) \qquad \int_a^b f(x)g(x)\, dx = f(c) \int_a^b g(x)\, dx .$$

Proof. Since g never changes sign in $[a, b]$, g is always nonnegative or always nonpositive on $[a, b]$. Let us assume that g is nonnegative on $[a, b]$. Then we may argue as in the proof of Theorem 3.15, except that we integrate the inequalities $mg(x) \leq f(x)g(x) \leq Mg(x)$ to obtain

$$(3.28) \qquad m\int_a^b g(x)\, dx \leq \int_a^b f(x)g(x)\, dx \leq M\int_a^b g(x)\, dx.$$

If $\int_a^b g(x)\, dx = 0$, this inequality shows that $\int_a^b f(x)g(x)\, dx = 0$. In this case, Equation (3.27) holds trivially for any choice of c since both members are zero. Otherwise, the integral of g is positive, and we may divide by this integral in (3.28) and apply the intermediate-value theorem as before to complete the proof. If g is nonpositive, we apply the same argument to $-g$.

The weighted mean-value theorem sometimes leads to a useful estimate for the integral of a product of two functions, especially if the integral of one of the factors is easy to compute. Examples are given in the next set of exercises.

3.20 Exercises

1. Use Theorem 3.16 to establish the following inequalities:

$$\frac{1}{10\sqrt{2}} \le \int_0^1 \frac{x^9}{\sqrt{1+x}}\, dx \le \frac{1}{10} .$$

2. Note that $\sqrt{1-x^2} = (1-x^2)/\sqrt{1-x^2}$ and use Theorem 3.16 to obtain the inequalities

$$\frac{11}{24} \le \int_0^{1/2} \sqrt{1-x^2}\, dx \le \frac{11}{24}\sqrt{\frac{4}{3}} .$$

3. Use the identity $1 + x^6 = (1+x^2)(1-x^2+x^4)$ and Theorem 3.16 to prove that for $a > 0$, we have

$$\frac{1}{1+a^6}\left(a - \frac{a^3}{3} + \frac{a^5}{5}\right) \le \int_0^a \frac{dx}{1+x^2} \le a - \frac{a^3}{3} + \frac{a^5}{5} .$$

   Take $a = 1/10$ and calculate the value of the integral rounded off to six decimal places.
4. One of the following two statements is incorrect. Explain why it is wrong.
   (a) The integral $\int_{2\pi}^{4\pi} (\sin t)/t\, dt > 0$ because $\int_{2\pi}^{3\pi} (\sin t)/t\, dt > \int_{3\pi}^{4\pi} |\sin t|/t\, dt$.
   (b) The integral $\int_{2\pi}^{4\pi} (\sin t)/t\, dt = 0$ because, by Theorem 3.16, for some c between 2π and 4π we have

$$\int_{2\pi}^{4\pi} \frac{\sin t}{t}\, dt = \frac{1}{c}\int_{2\pi}^{4\pi} \sin t\, dt = \frac{\cos(2\pi) - \cos(4\pi)}{c} = 0 .$$

5. If n is a positive integer, use Theorem 3.16 to show that

$$\int_{\sqrt{n\pi}}^{\sqrt{(n+1)\pi}} \sin(t^2)\, dt = \frac{(-1)^n}{c} , \qquad \text{where } \sqrt{n\pi} \le c \le \sqrt{(n+1)\pi} .$$

6. Assume f is continuous on $[a, b]$. If $\int_a^b f(x)\, dx = 0$, prove that $f(c) = 0$ for at least one c in $[a, b]$.
7. Assume that f is integrable and nonnegative on $[a, b]$. If $\int_a^b f(x)\, dx = 0$, prove that $f(x) = 0$ at each point of continuity of f. [*Hint:* If $f(c) > 0$ at a point of continuity c, there is an interval about c in which $f(x) > \frac{1}{2}f(c)$.]
8. Assume f is continuous on $[a, b]$. Assume also that $\int_a^b f(x)g(x)\, dx = 0$ for every function g that is continuous on $[a, b]$. Prove that $f(x) = 0$ for all x in $[a, b]$.

4

DIFFERENTIAL CALCULUS

4.1 Historical introduction

Newton and Leibniz, quite independently of one another, were largely responsible for developing the ideas of integral calculus to the point where hitherto insurmountable problems could be solved by more or less routine methods. The successful accomplishments of these men were primarily due to the fact that they were able to fuse together the integral calculus with the second main branch of calculus, differential calculus.

The central idea of differential calculus is the notion of *derivative*. Like the integral, the derivative originated from a problem in geometry—the problem of finding the tangent line at a point of a curve. Unlike the integral, however, the derivative evolved very late in the history of mathematics. The concept was not formulated until early in the 17th century when the French mathematician Pierre de Fermat, attempted to determine the maxima and minima of certain special functions.

Fermat's idea, basically very simple, can be understood if we refer to the curve in Figure 4.1. It is assumed that at each of its points this curve has a definite direction that can be described by a tangent line. Some of these tangents are indicated by broken lines in the figure. Fermat noticed that at certain points where the curve has a maximum or

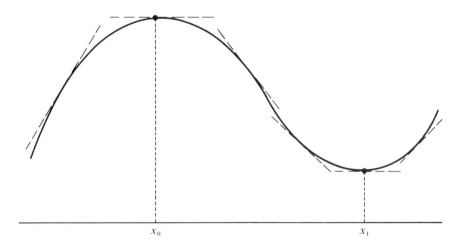

FIGURE 4.1 The curve has horizontal tangents above the points x_0 and x_1.

minimum, such as those shown in the figure with abscissae x_0 and x_1, the tangent line must be horizontal. Thus the problem of locating such extreme values is seen to depend on the solution of another problem, that of locating the horizontal tangents.

This raises the more general question of determining the direction of the tangent line at an *arbitrary point* of the curve. It was the attempt to solve this general problem that led Fermat to discover some of the rudimentary ideas underlying the notion of derivative.

At first sight there seems to be no connection whatever between the problem of finding the area of a region lying under a curve and the problem of finding the tangent line at a point of a curve. The first person to realize that these two seemingly remote ideas are, in fact, rather intimately related appears to have been Newton's teacher, Isaac Barrow (1630–1677). However, Newton and Leibniz were the first to understand the real importance of this relation and they exploited it to the fullest, thus inaugurating an unprecedented era in the development of mathematics.

Although the derivative was originally formulated to study the problem of tangents, it was soon found that it also provides a way to calculate *velocity* and, more generally, the *rate of change* of a function. In the next section we shall consider a special problem involving the calculation of a velocity. The solution of this problem contains all the essential features of the derivative concept and may help to motivate the general definition of derivative which is given in Section 4.3.

4.2 A problem involving velocity

Suppose a projectile is fired straight up from the ground with initial velocity of 144 feet per second. Neglect friction, and assume the projectile is influenced only by gravity so that it moves up and back along a straight line. Let $f(t)$ denote the height in feet that the projectile attains t seconds after firing. If the force of gravity were not acting on it, the projectile would continue to move upward with a constant velocity, traveling a distance of 144 feet every second, and at time t we would have $f(t) = 144t$. In actual practice, gravity causes the projectile to slow down until its velocity decreases to zero and then it drops back to earth. Physical experiments suggest that as long as the projectile is aloft, its height $f(t)$ is given by the formula

$$(4.1) \qquad f(t) = 144t - 16t^2 .$$

The term $-16t^2$ is due to the influence of gravity. Note that $f(t) = 0$ when $t = 0$ and when $t = 9$. This means that the projectile returns to earth after 9 seconds and it is to be understood that formula (4.1) is valid only for $0 \leq t \leq 9$.

The problem we wish to consider is this: *To determine the velocity of the projectile at each instant of its motion.* Before we can understand this problem, we must decide on what is *meant* by the velocity at each instant. To do this, we introduce first the notion of *average velocity during a time interval*, say from time t to time $t + h$. This is defined to be the quotient

$$\frac{\text{change in distance during time interval}}{\text{length of time interval}} = \frac{f(t + h) - f(t)}{h} .$$

This quotient, called a *difference quotient*, is a number which may be calculated whenever both t and $t + h$ are in the interval $[0, 9]$. The number h may be positive or negative, but not zero. We shall keep t fixed and see what happens to the difference quotient as we take values of h with smaller and smaller absolute value.

For example, consider the instant $t = 2$. The distance traveled after 2 seconds is

$$f(2) = 288 - 64 = 224.$$

At time $t = 2 + h$, the distance covered is

$$f(2 + h) = 144(2 + h) - 16(2 + h)^2 = 224 + 80h - 16h^2.$$

Therefore the average velocity in the interval from $t = 2$ to $t = 2 + h$ is

$$\frac{f(2 + h) - f(2)}{h} = \frac{80h - 16h^2}{h} = 80 - 16h.$$

As we take values of h with smaller and smaller absolute value, this average velocity gets closer and closer to 80. For example, if $h = 0.1$, we get an average velocity of 78.4; when $h = 0.001$, we get 79.984; when $h = 0.00001$, we obtain the value 79.99984; and when $h = -0.00001$, we obtain 80.00016. The important thing is that we can make the average velocity as close to 80 as we please by taking $|h|$ sufficiently small. In other words, the average velocity approaches 80 as a limit when h approaches zero. It seems natural to call this limiting value the *instantaneous velocity* at time $t = 2$.

The same kind of calculation can be carried out for any other instant. The average velocity for an arbitrary time interval from t to $t + h$ is given by the quotient

$$\frac{f(t + h) - f(t)}{h} = \frac{[144(t + h) - 16(t + h)^2] - [144t - 16t^2]}{h} = 144 - 32t - 16h.$$

When h approaches zero, the expression on the right approaches $144 - 32t$ as a limit, and this limit is defined to be the *instantaneous velocity* at time t. If we denote the instantaneous velocity by $v(t)$, we may write

(4.2) $v(t) = 144 - 32t.$

The formula in (4.1) for the distance $f(t)$ defines a function f which tells us how high the projectile is at each instant of its motion. We may refer to f as the *position function*. Its domain is the closed interval $[0, 9]$ and its graph is shown in Figure 4.2(a). [The scale on the vertical axis is distorted in both Figures 4.2(a) and (b).] The formula in (4.2) for the velocity $v(t)$ defines a new function v which tells us how fast the projectile is moving at each instant of its motion. This is called the *velocity function*, and its graph is shown in Figure 4.2(b). As t increases from 0 to 9, $v(t)$ decreases steadily from $v(0) = 144$ to $v(9) = -144$. To find the time t for which $v(t) = 0$, we solve the equation $144 = 32t$ to obtain $t = 9/2$. Therefore, at the midpoint of the motion the influence of gravity reduces the velocity to zero, and the projectile is momentarily at rest. The height at this instant is $f(9/2) = 324$. When $t > 9/2$, the velocity is negative, indicating that the height is decreasing.

The limit process by which $v(t)$ is obtained from the difference quotient is written symbolically as follows:

(4.3)
$$v(t) = \lim_{h \to 0} \frac{f(t + h) - f(t)}{h}.$$

This equation is used to define velocity not only for this particular example but, more generally, for any particle moving along a straight line, provided the position function f is such that the difference quotient tends to a definite limit as h approaches zero.

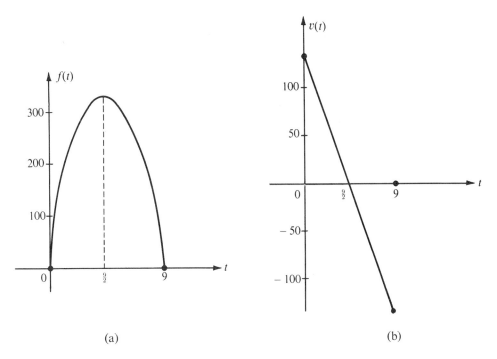

(a)

(b)

FIGURE 4.2 (a) Graph of the position function $f(t) = 144t - 16t^2$. (b) Graph of the velocity function: $v(t) = 144 - 32t$.

4.3 The derivative of a function

The example described in the foregoing section points the way to the introduction of the concept of derivative. We begin with a function f defined at least on some open interval (a, b) on the x-axis. Then we choose a fixed point x in this interval and introduce the difference quotient

$$\frac{f(x + h) - f(x)}{h},$$

where the number h, which may be positive or negative (but not zero), is such that $x + h$ also lies in (a, b). The numerator of this quotient measures the change in the function when x changes from x to $x + h$. The quotient itself is referred to as the *average rate of change* of f in the interval joining x to $x + h$.

Now we let h approach zero and see what happens to this quotient. If the quotient approaches some definite value as a limit (which implies that the limit is the same whether h approaches zero through positive values or through negative values), then this limit is called the *derivative* of f at x and is denoted by the symbol $f'(x)$ (read as "f prime of x"). Thus, the formal definition of $f'(x)$ may be stated as follows:

DEFINITION OF DERIVATIVE.   *The derivative $f'(x)$ is defined by the equation*

(4.4)
$$f'(x) = \lim_{h \to 0} \frac{f(x + h) - f(x)}{h},$$

provided the limit exists. The number $f'(x)$ is also called the rate of change of f at x.

By comparing (4.4) with (4.3), we see that the concept of instantaneous velocity is merely an example of the concept of derivative. The velocity $v(t)$ is equal to the derivative $f'(t)$, where f is the function which measures position. This is often described by saying that velocity is the rate of change of position with respect to time. In the example worked out in Section 4.2, the position function f is described by the equation

$$f(t) = 144t - 16t^2,$$

and its derivative f' is a new function (velocity) given by

$$f'(t) = 144 - 32t.$$

In general, the limit process which produces $f'(x)$ from $f(x)$ gives us a way of obtaining a new function f' from a given function f. The process is called *differentiation*, and f' is called the *first derivative* of f. If f', in turn, is defined on an open interval, we can try to compute *its* first derivative, denoted by f'' and called the *second derivative* of f. Similarly, the nth derivative of f, denoted by $f^{(n)}$, is defined to be the first derivative of $f^{(n-1)}$. We make the convention that $f^{(0)} = f$, that is, the zeroth derivative is the function itself.

For rectilinear motion, the first derivative of velocity (second derivative of position) is called *acceleration*. For example, to compute the acceleration in the example of Section 4.2, we can use Equation (4.2) to form the difference quotient

$$\frac{v(t + h) - v(t)}{h} = \frac{[144 - 32(t + h)] - [144 - 32t]}{h} = \frac{-32h}{h} = -32.$$

Since this quotient has the constant value -32 for each $h \neq 0$, its limit as $h \to 0$ is also -32. Thus, the acceleration in this problem is constant and equal to -32. This result tells us that the velocity is decreasing at the rate of 32 feet per second every second. In 9 seconds the total decrease in velocity is $9 \cdot 32 = 288$ feet per second. This agrees with the fact that during the 9 seconds of motion the velocity changes from $v(0) = 144$ to $v(9) = -144$.

4.4 Examples of derivatives

EXAMPLE 1. *Derivative of a constant function.* Suppose f is a constant function, say $f(x) = c$ for all x. The difference quotient is

$$\frac{f(x + h) - f(x)}{h} = \frac{c - c}{h} = 0 .$$

Since the quotient is 0 for all $h \neq 0$, its limit, $f'(x)$, is also 0 for every x. In other words, a constant function has a zero derivative everywhere.

EXAMPLE 2. *Derivative of a linear function.* Suppose f is a linear function, say $f(x) = mx + b$ for all real x. If $h \neq 0$, we have

$$\frac{f(x + h) - f(x)}{h} = \frac{m(x + h) + b - (mx + b)}{h} = \frac{mh}{h} = m .$$

Since the difference quotient does not change when h approaches 0, we conclude that

$$f'(x) = m \qquad \text{for every } x.$$

Thus, the derivative of a linear function is a constant function.

EXAMPLE 3. *Derivative of a positive integer power function.* Consider next the case $f(x) = x^n$, where n is a positive integer. The difference quotient becomes

$$\frac{f(x + h) - f(x)}{h} = \frac{(x + h)^n - x^n}{h} .$$

To study this quotient as h approaches 0, we can proceed in two ways, either by factoring the numerator as a difference of two nth powers or by using the binomial theorem to expand $(x + h)^n$. We shall carry out the details by the first method and leave the other method as an exercise for the reader. (See Exercise 39 in Section 4.6.)

From elementary algebra we have the identity†

$$a^n - b^n = (a - b) \sum_{k=0}^{n-1} a^k b^{n-1-k} .$$

If we take $a = x + h$ and $b = x$ and divide both sides by h, this identity becomes

$$\frac{(x + h)^n - x^n}{h} = \sum_{k=0}^{n-1} (x + h)^k x^{n-1-k} .$$

---

† This identity is an immediate consequence of the telescoping property of finite sums. In fact, if we multiply each term of the sum by $(a - b)$, we find

$$(a - b) \sum_{k=0}^{n-1} a^k b^{n-1-k} = \sum_{k=0}^{n-1} (a^{k+1} b^{n-(k+1)} - a^k b^{n-k}) = a^n - b^n.$$

There are n terms in the sum. As h approaches 0, $(x + h)^k$ approaches x^k, the kth term approaches $x^k x^{n-1-k} = x^{n-1}$, and therefore the sum of all n terms approaches nx^{n-1}. From this it follows that

$$f'(x) = nx^{n-1} \qquad \text{for every } x.$$

EXAMPLE 4. *Derivative of the sine function.* Let $s(x) = \sin x$. The difference quotient in question is

$$\frac{s(x + h) - s(x)}{h} = \frac{\sin (x + h) - \sin x}{h}.$$

To transform this into a form that makes it possible to calculate the limit as $h \to 0$, we use the trigonometric identity

$$\sin y - \sin x = 2 \sin \frac{y - x}{2} \cos \frac{y + x}{2}$$

with $y = x + h$. This leads to the formula

$$\frac{\sin (x + h) - \sin x}{h} = \frac{\sin (h/2)}{h/2} \cos \left(x + \frac{h}{2} \right).$$

As $h \to 0$, the factor $\cos (x + \frac{1}{2}h) \to \cos x$ because of the continuity of the cosine. Also, the limit formula

$$\lim_{x \to 0} \frac{\sin x}{x} = 1,$$

established earlier in Section 3.4, shows that

(4.5) $$\frac{\sin (h/2)}{h/2} \to 1 \qquad \text{as} \quad h \to 0.$$

Therefore the difference quotient has the limit $\cos x$ as $h \to 0$. In other words, $s'(x) = \cos x$ for every x; the derivative of the sine function is the cosine function.

EXAMPLE 5. *The derivative of the cosine function.* Let $c(x) = \cos x$. We shall prove that $c'(x) = -\sin x$; that is, the derivative of the cosine function is minus the sine function. We start with the identity

$$\cos y - \cos x = -2 \sin \frac{y - x}{2} \sin \frac{y + x}{2}$$

and take $y = x + h$. This leads to the formula

$$\frac{\cos (x + h) - \cos x}{h} = - \frac{\sin (h/2)}{h/2} \sin \left(x + \frac{h}{2} \right).$$

Continuity of the sine shows that $\sin (x + \tfrac{1}{2}h) \to \sin x$ as $h \to 0$; from (4.5), we obtain $c'(x) = -\sin x$.

EXAMPLE 6. *Derivative of the nth-root function.* If n is a positive integer, let $f(x) = x^{1/n}$ for $x > 0$. The difference quotient for f is

$$\frac{f(x + h) - f(x)}{h} = \frac{(x + h)^{1/n} - x^{1/n}}{h}.$$

Let $u = (x + h)^{1/n}$ and let $v = x^{1/n}$. Then we have $u^n = x + h$ and $v^n = x$, so $h = u^n - v^n$, and the difference quotient becomes

$$\frac{f(x + h) - f(x)}{h} = \frac{u - v}{u^n - v^n} = \frac{1}{u^{n-1} + u^{n-2}v + \cdots + uv^{n-2} + v^{n-1}}.$$

The continuity of the nth-root function shows that $u \to v$ as $h \to 0$. Therefore each term in the denominator on the right has the limit v^{n-1} as $h \to 0$. There are n terms altogether, so the difference quotient has the limit v^{1-n}/n. Since $v = x^{1/n}$, this proves that

$$f'(x) = \frac{1}{n}x^{1/n-1}.$$

EXAMPLE 7. *Continuity of functions having derivatives.* If a function f has a derivative at a point x, then it is also continuous at x. To prove this, we use the identity

$$f(x + h) = f(x) + h\left(\frac{f(x + h) - f(x)}{h}\right)$$

which is valid for $h \neq 0$. If we let $h \to 0$, the difference quotient on the right approaches $f'(x)$ and, since this quotient is multiplied by a factor which tends to 0, the second term on the right approaches $0 \cdot f'(x) = 0$. This shows that $f(x + h) \to f(x)$ as $h \to 0$, and hence that f is continuous at x.

This example provides a new way of showing that functions are continuous. Every time we establish the existence of a derivative $f'(x)$, we also establish, at the same time, the continuity of f at x. It should be noted, however, that the converse is not true. Continuity at x does not necessarily mean that the derivative $f'(x)$ exists. For example, when $f(x) = |x|$, the point $x = 0$ is a point of continuity of f [since $f(x) \to 0$ as $x \to 0$] but there is no derivative at 0. (See Figure 4.3.) The difference quotient $[f(0 + h) - f(0)]/h$ is

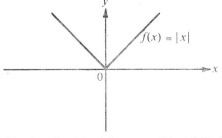

FIGURE 4.3 The function is continuous at 0 but $f'(0)$ does not exist.

equal to $|h|/h$. This has the value $+1$ if $h > 0$ and -1 if $h < 0$, and hence does not tend to a limit as $h \to 0$.

4.5   The algebra of derivatives

Just as the limit theorems of Section 3.4 tell us how to compute limits of the sum, difference, product, and quotient of two functions, so the next theorem provides us with a corresponding set of rules for computing derivatives.

THEOREM 4.1.   *Let f and g be two functions defined on a common interval. At each point where f and g have a derivative, the same is true of the sum $f + g$, the difference $f - g$, the product $f \cdot g$, and the quotient f/g. (For f/g we need the extra proviso that g is not zero at the point in question.)   The derivatives of these functions are given by the following formulas:*

(i) $(f + g)' = f' + g'$,

(ii) $(f - g)' = f' - g'$,

(iii) $(f \cdot g)' = f \cdot g' + g \cdot f'$,

(iv) $\left(\dfrac{f}{g}\right)' = \dfrac{g \cdot f' - f \cdot g'}{g^2}$ *at points x where $g(x) \neq 0$* .

We shall prove this theorem in a moment, but first we want to mention some of its consequences. A special case of (iii) occurs when one of the two functions is constant, say $g(x) = c$ for all x under consideration. In this case, (iii) becomes $(c \cdot f)' = c \cdot f'$. In other words, the derivative of a constant times f is the constant times the derivative of f. Combining this with the fact that the derivative of a sum is the sum of derivatives [property (i)], we find that for every pair of constants c_1 and c_2 we have

$$(c_1 f + c_2 g)' = c_1 f' + c_2 g'.$$

This is called the *linearity property* of the derivative, and it is analogous to the linearity property of the integral. Using mathematical induction, we can extend the linearity property to arbitrary finite sums as follows:

$$\left(\sum_{i=1}^{n} c_i \cdot f_i\right)' = \sum_{i=1}^{n} c_i \cdot f_i',$$

where $c_1, \ldots, c_n$ are constants and $f_1, \ldots, f_n$ are functions with derivatives $f_1', \ldots, f_n'$.

Every derivative formula can be written in two ways, either as an equality between two *functions* or as an equality involving *numbers*. The properties of Theorem 4.1, as written above, are equations involving functions. For example, property (i) states that the derivative of the function $f + g$ is the sum of the two functions f' and g'. When these functions are evaluated at a point x, we obtain formulas involving numbers. Thus formula (i) implies

$$(f + g)'(x) = f'(x) + g'(x).$$

We proceed now to the proof of Theorem 4.1.

Proof of (i). Let x be a point where both derivatives $f'(x)$ and $g'(x)$ exist. The difference quotient for $f + g$ is

$$\frac{[f(x + h) + g(x + h)] - [f(x) + g(x)]}{h} = \frac{f(x + h) - f(x)}{h} + \frac{g(x + h) - g(x)}{h}.$$

When $h \to 0$ the first quotient on the right approaches $f'(x)$, the second approaches $g'(x)$, and hence the sum approaches $f'(x) + g'(x)$. This proves (i), and the proof of (ii) is similar.

Proof of (iii). The difference quotient for the product $f \cdot g$ is

(4.6)
$$\frac{f(x + h)g(x + h) - f(x)g(x)}{h}.$$

To study this quotient as $h \to 0$, we add and subtract in the numerator a term which enables us to write (4.6) as a sum of two terms involving difference quotients of f and g. Adding and subtracting $g(x)f(x + h)$, we see that (4.6) becomes

$$\frac{f(x + h)g(x + h) - f(x)g(x)}{h} = g(x)\frac{f(x + h) - f(x)}{h} + f(x + h)\frac{g(x + h) - g(x)}{h}.$$

When $h \to 0$ the first term on the right approaches $g(x)f'(x)$. Since f is continuous at x, we have $f(x + h) \to f(x)$, so the second term approaches $f(x)g'(x)$. This proves (iii).

Proof of (iv). A special case of (iv) occurs when $f(x) = 1$ for all x. In this case $f'(x) = 0$ for all x and (iv) reduces to the formula

(4.7)
$$\left(\frac{1}{g}\right)' = -\frac{g'}{g^2}$$

provided $g(x) \neq 0$. We can deduce the general formula (iv) from this special case by writing f/g as a product and using (iii), since

$$\left(f \cdot \frac{1}{g}\right)' = \frac{1}{g} \cdot f' + f \cdot \left(\frac{1}{g}\right)' = \frac{f'}{g} - \frac{f \cdot g'}{g^2} = \frac{g \cdot f' - f \cdot g'}{g^2}.$$

Therefore it remains to prove (4.7). The difference quotient for $1/g$ is

(4.8)
$$\frac{[1/g(x + h)] - [1/g(x)]}{h} = -\frac{g(x + h) - g(x)}{h} \cdot \frac{1}{g(x)} \cdot \frac{1}{g(x + h)}.$$

When $h \to 0$, the first quotient on the right approaches $g'(x)$ and the third factor approaches $1/g(x)$. The continuity of g at x is required since we are using the fact that $g(x + h) \to g(x)$ as $h \to 0$. Hence the quotient in (4.8) approaches $-g'(x)/g(x)^2$, and this proves (4.7).

Note: In order to write (4.8) we need to know that $g(x + h) \neq 0$ for all sufficiently small h. This follows from Theorem 3.7.

Theorem 4.1, when used in conjunction with the examples worked out in Section 4.4, enables us to derive new examples of differentiation formulas.

EXAMPLE 1. *Polynomials.* In Example 3 of Section 4.4 we showed that if $f(x) = x^n$, where n is a positive integer, then $f'(x) = nx^{n-1}$. The reader may find it instructive to rederive this result as a consequence of the special case $n = 1$, using mathematical induction in conjunction with the formula for differentiating a product.

Using this result along with the linearity property, we can differentiate any polynomial by computing the derivative of each term and adding the derivatives. Thus, if

$$f(x) = \sum_{k=0}^{n} c_k x^k ,$$

then, by differentiating term by term, we obtain

$$f'(x) = \sum_{k=0}^{n} k c_k x^{k-1} .$$

Note that the derivative of a polynomial of degree n is a new polynomial of degree $n - 1$. For example, if $f(x) = 2x^3 + 5x^2 - 7x + 8$, then $f'(x) = 6x^2 + 10x - 7$.

EXAMPLE 2. *Rational functions.* If r is the quotient of two polynomials, say $r(x) = p(x)/q(x)$, then the derivative $r'(x)$ may be computed by the quotient formula (iv) in Theorem 4.1. The derivative $r'(x)$ exists at every x for which the denominator $q(x) \neq 0$. Note that the function r' so defined is itself a rational function. In particular, when $r(x) = 1/x^m$, where m is a positive integer and $x \neq 0$, we find

$$r'(x) = \frac{x^m \cdot 0 - mx^{m-1}}{x^{2m}} = \frac{-m}{x^{m+1}} .$$

If this is written in the form $r'(x) = -mx^{-m-1}$, it provides an extension from positive exponents to negative exponents of the formula for differentiating nth powers.

EXAMPLE 3. *Rational powers.* Let $f(x) = x^r$ for $x > 0$, where r is a rational number. We have already proved the differentiation formula

(4.9) $$f'(x) = rx^{r-1}$$

for $r = 1/n$, where n is a positive integer. Now we extend it to all rational powers. The formula for differentiating a product shows that Equation (4.9) is also valid for $r = 2/n$

and, by induction, for $r = m/n$, where m is any positive integer. (The induction argument refers to m.) Therefore Equation (4.9) is valid for all positive rational r. The formula for differentiating a quotient now shows that (4.9) is also valid for negative rational r. Thus, if $f(x) = x^{2/3}$, we have $f'(x) = \frac{2}{3}x^{-1/3}$. If $f(x) = x^{-1/2}$, then $f'(x) = -\frac{1}{2}x^{-3/2}$. In each case, we require $x > 0$.

4.6 Exercises

1. If $f(x) = 2 + x - x^2$, compute $f'(0), f'(\frac{1}{2}), f'(1), f'(-10)$.
2. If $f(x) = \frac{1}{3}x^3 + \frac{1}{2}x^2 - 2x$, find all x for which (a) $f'(x) = 0$; (b) $f'(x) = -2$; (c) $f'(x) = 10$.

In Exercises 3 through 12, obtain a formula for $f'(x)$ if $f(x)$ is described as indicated.

3. $f(x) = x^2 + 3x + 2$.

4. $f(x) = x^4 + \sin x$.

5. $f(x) = x^4 \sin x$.

6. $f(x) = \dfrac{1}{x+1}$, $\quad x \neq -1$.

7. $f(x) = \dfrac{1}{x^2+1} + x^5 \cos x$.

8. $f(x) = \dfrac{x}{x-1}$, $\quad x \neq 1$.

9. $f(x) = \dfrac{1}{2+\cos x}$.

10. $f(x) = \dfrac{x^2+3x+2}{x^4+x^2+1}$.

11. $f(x) = \dfrac{2-\sin x}{2-\cos x}$.

12. $f(x) = \dfrac{x \sin x}{1+x^2}$.

13. Assume that the height $f(t)$ of a projectile, t seconds after being fired directly upward from the ground with an initial velocity of v_0 ft/sec, is given by the formula

$$f(t) = v_0 t - 16t^2.$$

(a) Use the method described in Section 4.2 to show that the average velocity of the projectile during a time interval from t to $t + h$ is $v_0 - 32t - 16h$ ft/sec, and that the instantaneous velocity at time t is $v_0 - 32t$ ft/sec.
(b) Compute (in terms of v_0) the time required for the velocity to drop to zero.
(c) What is the velocity on return to earth?
(d) What must the initial velocity be for the projectile to return to earth after 1 sec? after 10 sec? after T sec?
(e) Show that the projectile moves with constant acceleration.
(f) Give an example of another formula for the height which will lead to a constant acceleration of -20 ft/sec/sec.
14. What is the rate of change of the volume of a cube with respect to the length of each edge?
15. (a) The area of a circle of radius r is πr^2 and its circumference is $2\pi r$. Show that the rate of change of the area with respect to the radius is equal to the circumference.
(b) The volume of a sphere of radius r is $4\pi r^3/3$ and its surface area is $4\pi r^2$. Show that the rate of change of the volume with respect to the radius is equal to the surface area.

In Exercises 16 through 23, obtain a formula for $f'(x)$ if $f(x)$ is defined as indicated.

16. $f(x) = \sqrt{x}$, $\quad x > 0$.

17. $f(x) = \dfrac{1}{1+\sqrt{x}}$, $\quad x > 0$.

18. $f(x) = x^{3/2}$, $\quad x > 0$.

19. $f(x) = x^{-3/2}$, $\quad x > 0$.

20. $f(x) = x^{1/2} + x^{1/3} + x^{1/4}, \qquad x > 0.$ 22. $f(x) = \dfrac{\sqrt{x}}{1+x}, \qquad x > 0.$

21. $f(x) = x^{-1/2} + x^{-1/3} + x^{-1/4}, \qquad x > 0.$ 23. $f(x) = \dfrac{x}{1+\sqrt{x}}, \qquad x > 0.$

24. Let $f_1, \ldots, f_n$ be n functions having derivatives $f_1', \ldots, f_n'$. Develop a rule for differentiating the product $g = f_1 \cdots f_n$ and prove it by mathematical induction. Show that for those points x, where none of the function values $f_1(x), \ldots, f_n(x)$ are zero, we have

$$\frac{g'(x)}{g(x)} = \frac{f_1'(x)}{f_1(x)} + \cdots + \frac{f_n'(x)}{f_n(x)}.$$

25. Verify the entries in the following short table of derivatives. It is understood that the formulas hold for those x for which $f(x)$ is defined.

$f(x)$	$f'(x)$	$f(x)$	$f'(x)$
$\tan x$	$\sec^2 x$	$\sec x$	$\tan x \sec x$
$\cot x$	$-\csc^2 x$	$\csc x$	$-\cot x \csc x$

In Exercises 26 through 35, compute the derivative $f'(x)$. It is understood that each formula holds for those x for which $f(x)$ is defined.

26. $f(x) = \tan x \sec x.$

27. $f(x) = x \tan x.$

28. $f(x) = \dfrac{1}{x} + \dfrac{2}{x^2} + \dfrac{3}{x^3}.$

29. $f(x) = \dfrac{2x}{1-x^2}.$

30. $f(x) = \dfrac{1+x-x^2}{1-x+x^2}.$

31. $f(x) = \dfrac{\sin x}{x}.$

32. $f(x) = \dfrac{1}{x+\sin x}.$

33. $f(x) = \dfrac{ax+b}{cx+d}.$

34. $f(x) = \dfrac{\cos x}{2x^2+3}.$

35. $f(x) = \dfrac{ax^2+bx+c}{\sin x + \cos x}.$

36. If $f(x) = (ax+b)\sin x + (cx+d)\cos x$, determine values of the constants a, b, c, d such that $f'(x) = x \cos x$.

37. If $g(x) = (ax^2 + bx + c)\sin x + (dx^2 + ex + f)\cos x$, determine values of the constants a, b, c, d, e, f such that $g'(x) = x^2 \sin x$.

38. Given the formula

$$1 + x + x^2 + \cdots + x^n = \frac{x^{n+1} - 1}{x - 1}$$

(valid if $x \neq 1$), determine, by differentiation, formulas for the following sums:
(a) $1 + 2x + 3x^2 + \cdots + nx^{n-1}$,
(b) $1^2 x + 2^2 x^2 + 3^2 x^3 + \cdots + n^2 x^n$.

39. Let $f(x) = x^n$, where n is a positive integer. Use the binomial theorem to expand $(x + h)^n$ and derive the formula

$$\frac{f(x + h) - f(x)}{h} = nx^{n-1} + \frac{n(n - 1)}{2} x^{n-2}h + \cdots + nxh^{n-2} + h^{n-1}.$$

Express the sum on the right in summation notation. Let $h \to 0$ and deduce that $f'(x) = nx^{n-1}$. State which limit theorems you are using. (This result was derived in another way in Example 3 of Section 4.4.)

4.7 Geometric interpretation of the derivative as a slope

The procedure used to define the derivative has a geometric interpretation which leads in a natural way to the idea of a tangent line to a curve. A portion of the graph of a function f is shown in Figure 4.4. Two of its points P and Q are shown with respective coordinates

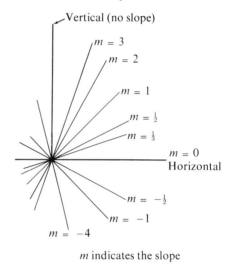

FIGURE 4.4 Geometric interpretation of the difference quotient as the tangent of an angle.

FIGURE 4.5 Lines of various slopes.

$(x, f(x))$ and $(x + h, f(x + h))$. Consider the right triangle with hypotenuse PQ; its altitude, $f(x + h) - f(x)$, represents the difference of the ordinates of the two points Q and P. Therefore, the difference quotient

(4.10)
$$\frac{f(x + h) - f(x)}{h}$$

represents the trigonometric tangent of the angle α that PQ makes with the horizontal. The real number $\tan \alpha$ is called the *slope* of the line through P and Q and it provides a way of measuring the "steepness" of this line. For example, if f is a linear function, say $f(x) = mx + b$, the difference quotient (4.10) has the value m, so m is the slope of the line.

Some examples of lines of various slopes are shown in Figure 4.5. For a horizontal line,

$\alpha = 0$ and the slope, $\tan \alpha$, is also 0. If α lies between 0 and $\frac{1}{2}\pi$, the line is rising as we move from left to right and the slope is positive. If α lies between $\frac{1}{2}\pi$ and π, the line is falling as we move from left to right and the slope is negative. A line for which $\alpha = \frac{1}{4}\pi$ has slope 1. As α increases from 0 to $\frac{1}{2}\pi$, $\tan \alpha$ increases without bound, and the corresponding lines of slope $\tan \alpha$ approach a vertical position. Since $\tan \frac{1}{2}\pi$ is not defined, we say that *vertical lines have no slope*.

Suppose now that f has a derivative at x. This means that the difference quotient approaches a certain limit $f'(x)$ as h approaches 0. When this is interpreted geometrically it tells us that, as h gets nearer to 0, the point P remains fixed, Q moves along the curve toward P, and the line through PQ changes its direction in such a way that its slope approaches the number $f'(x)$ as a limit. For this reason it seems natural to define the *slope of the curve* at P to be the number $f'(x)$. The line through P having this slope is called the *tangent line* at P.

> *Note:* The concept of a line tangent to a circle (and to a few other special curves) was considered by the ancient Greeks. They defined a tangent line to a circle as a line having one of its points on the circle and all its other points outside the circle. From this definition, many properties of tangent lines to circles can be derived. For example, we can prove that the tangent at any point is perpendicular to the radius at that point. However, the Greek definition of tangent line is not easily extended to more general curves. The method described above, where the tangent line is defined in terms of a derivative, has proved to be far more satisfactory. Using this definition, we can prove that for a circle the tangent line has all the properties ascribed to it by the Greek geometers. Concepts such as perpendicularity and parallelism can be explained rather simply in analytic terms making use of slopes of lines. For example, from the trigonometric identity
>
> $$\tan (\alpha - \beta) = \frac{\tan \alpha - \tan \beta}{1 + \tan \alpha \tan \beta},$$
>
> it follows that two nonvertical lines with the same slope are parallel. Also, from the identity
>
> $$\cot (\alpha - \beta) = \frac{1 + \tan \alpha \tan \beta}{\tan \alpha - \tan \beta},$$
>
> we find that two nonvertical lines with slopes having product -1 are perpendicular.

The algebraic sign of the derivative of a function gives us useful information about the behavior of its graph. For example, if x is a point in an open interval where the derivative is *positive*, then the graph is rising in the immediate vicinity of x as we move from left to right. This occurs at x_3 in Figure 4.6. A *negative* derivative in an interval means the graph is falling, as shown at x_1, while a zero derivative at a point means a horizontal tangent line. At a maximum or minimum, such as those shown at x_2, x_5, and x_6, the slope must be zero. Fermat was the first to notice that points like x_2, x_5, and x_6, where f has a maximum or minimum, must occur among the roots of the equation $f'(x) = 0$. It is important to realize that $f'(x)$ may also be zero at points where there is no maximum or minimum, such as above the point x_4. Note that this particular tangent line crosses the graph. This is an example of a situation not covered by the Greek definition of tangency.

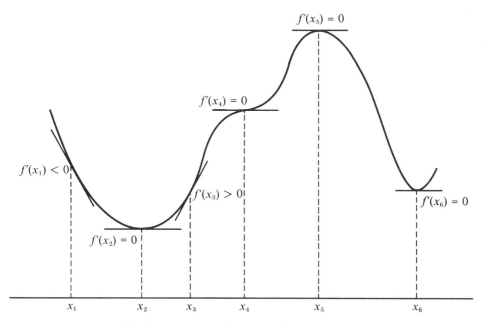

FIGURE 4.6   Geometric significance of the sign of the derivative.

The foregoing remarks concerning the significance of the algebraic sign of the derivative may seem quite obvious when we interpret them geometrically. Analytic proofs of these statements, based on general properties of derivatives, will be given in Section 4.16.

4.8   Other notations for derivatives

Notation has played an extremely important role in the development of mathematics. Some mathematical symbols, such as x^n or $n!$, are merely abbreviations that compress long statements or formulas into a short space. Others, like the integration symbol $\int_a^b f(x)\, dx$, not only remind us of the process being represented but also help us in carrying out computations.

Sometimes several different notations are used for the same idea, preference for one or another being dependent on the circumstances that surround the use of the symbols. This is especially true in differential calculus where many different notations are used for derivatives. The derivative of a function f has been denoted in our previous discussions by f', a notation introduced by J. L. Lagrange (1736–1813) late in the 18th century. This emphasizes the fact that f' is a new function obtained from f by differentiation, its value at x being denoted by $f'(x)$. Each point (x, y) on the graph of f has its coordinates x and y related by the equation $y = f(x)$, and the symbol y' is also used to represent the derivative $f'(x)$. Similarly, $y'', \ldots, y^{(n)}$ represent the higher derivatives $f''(x), \ldots, f^{(n)}(x)$. For example, if $y = \sin x$, then $y' = \cos x$, $y'' = -\sin x$, etc. Lagrange's notation is not too far removed from that used by Newton who wrote $\dot{y}$ and $\ddot{y}$, instead of y' and y''. Newton's dots are still used by some authors, especially to denote velocity and acceleration.

Another symbol was introduced in 1800 by L. Arbogast (1759–1803) who denoted the derivative of f by Df, a symbol that has widespread use today. The symbol D is called a *differentiation operator*, and it helps to suggest that Df is a new function obtained from f by the operation of differentiation. Higher derivatives f'', f''', ..., $f^{(n)}$ are written $D^2 f$, $D^3 f$, ..., $D^n f$, respectively, the values of these derivatives at x being written $D^2 f(x)$, $D^3 f(x)$, ..., $D^n f(x)$. Thus, we have $D \sin x = \cos x$ and $D^2 \sin x = D \cos x = -\sin x$. The rule for differentiating a sum of two functions becomes, in the D-notation, $D(f + g) = Df + Dg$. Evaluation of the derivatives at x leads to the formula $[D(f + g)](x) = Df(x) + Dg(x)$ which is also written in the form $D[f(x) + g(x)] = Df(x) + Dg(x)$. The reader may easily formulate the product and quotient rules in the D-notation.

Among the early pioneers of mathematical analysis, Leibniz, more than anyone else, understood the importance of well-chosen symbols. He experimented at great length and carried on extensive correspondence with other mathematicians, debating the merits or drawbacks of various notations. The tremendous impact that calculus has had on the development of modern mathematics is due in part to its well-developed and highly suggestive symbols, many of them originated by Leibniz.

Leibniz developed a notation for derivatives quite different from those mentioned above. Using y for $f(x)$, he wrote the difference quotient

$$\frac{f(x + h) - f(x)}{h}$$

in the form

$$\frac{\Delta y}{\Delta x},$$

where Δx (read as "delta x") was written for h, and Δy for $f(x + h) - f(x)$. The symbol Δ is called a *difference operator*. For the limit of the difference quotient, that is, for the derivative $f'(x)$, Leibniz wrote dy/dx. In this notation, the definition of derivative becomes

$$\frac{dy}{dx} = \lim_{\Delta x \to 0} \frac{\Delta y}{\Delta x}.$$

Not only was Leibniz's notation different, but his way of thinking about derivatives was different. He thought of the limit dy/dx as a quotient of "infinitesimal" quantities dy and dx called "differentials," and he referred to the derivative dy/dx as a "differential quotient." Leibniz imagined infinitesimals as entirely new types of numbers which, although not zero, were smaller than every positive real number.

Even though Leibniz was not able to give a satisfactory definition of infinitesimals, he and his followers used them freely in their development of calculus. Consequently, many people found calculus somewhat mysterious and began to question the validity of the methods. The work of Cauchy and others in the 19th century gradually led to the replacement of infinitesimals by the classical theory of limits. Nevertheless, many people have found it helpful to try to think as Leibniz did in terms of infinitesimals. This kind of thinking has intuitive appeal and often leads quickly to results that can be proved correct by more conventional means.

Recently Abraham Robinson has shown that the real number system can be extended to incorporate infinitesimals as envisaged by Leibniz. A discussion of this extension and its impact on many branches of mathematics is given in Robinson's book, *Non-standard Analysis*, North-Holland Publishing Company, Amsterdam, 1966.

Although some of Leibniz's ideas fell into temporary disrepute, the same cannot be said of his notations. The symbol dy/dx for the derivative has the obvious advantage that it summarizes the whole process of forming the difference quotient and passing to the limit. Later we shall find the further advantage that certain formulas become easier to remember and to work with when derivatives are written in the Leibniz notation.

4.9 Exercises

1. Let $f(x) = \frac{1}{3}x^3 - 2x^2 + 3x + 1$ for all x. Find the points on the graph of f at which the tangent line is horizontal.

2. Let $f(x) = \frac{2}{3}x^3 + \frac{1}{2}x^2 - x - 1$ for all x. Find the points on the graph of f at which the slope is: (a) 0; (b) -1; (c) 5.

3. Let $f(x) = x + \sin x$ for all x. Find all points x for which the graph of f at $(x, f(x))$ has slope zero.

4. Let $f(x) = x^2 + ax + b$ for all x. Find values of a and b such that the line $y = 2x$ is tangent to the graph of f at the point $(2, 4)$.

5. Find values of the constants a, b, and c for which the graphs of the two polynomials $f(x) = x^2 + ax + b$ and $g(x) = x^3 - c$ will intersect at the point $(1, 2)$ and have the same tangent line at that point.

6. Consider the graph of the function f defined by the equation $f(x) = x^2 + ax + b$, where a and b are constants.
   (a) Find the slope of the chord joining the points on the graph for which $x = x_1$ and $x = x_2$.
   (b) Find, in terms of x_1 and x_2, all values of x for which the tangent line at $(x, f(x))$ has the same slope as the chord in part (a).

7. Show that the line $y = -x$ is tangent to the curve given by the equation $y = x^3 - 6x^2 + 8x$. Find the point of tangency. Does this tangent line intersect the curve anywhere else?

8. Make a sketch of the graph of the cubic polynomial $f(x) = x - x^3$ over the closed interval $-2 \le x \le 2$. Find constants m and b such that the line $y = mx + b$ will be tangent to the graph of f at the point $(-1, 0)$. A second line through $(-1, 0)$ is also tangent to the graph of f at a point (a, c). Determine the coordinates a and c.

9. A function f is defined as follows:

$$f(x) = \begin{cases} x^2 & \text{if } x \le c, \\ ax + b & \text{if } x > c, \end{cases} \qquad (a, b, c \text{ constants}).$$

   Find values of a and b (in terms of c) such that $f'(c)$ exists.

10. Solve Exercise 9 when f is defined as follows:

$$f(x) = \begin{cases} \dfrac{1}{|x|} & \text{if } |x| > c, \\ a + bx^2 & \text{if } |x| \le c. \end{cases}$$

11. Solve Exercise 9 when f is defined as follows:

$$f(x) = \begin{cases} \sin x & \text{if } x \le c, \\ ax + b & \text{if } x > c. \end{cases}$$

12. If $f(x) = (1 - \sqrt{x})/(1 + \sqrt{x})$ for $x > 0$, find formulas for $Df(x)$, $D^2f(x)$, and $D^3f(x)$.

13. There is a polynomial $P(x) = ax^3 + bx^2 + cx + d$ such that $P(0) = P(1) = -2$, $P'(0) = -1$, and $P''(0) = 10$. Compute a, b, c, d.

14. Two functions f and g have first and second derivatives at 0 and satisfy the relations

$$f(0) = 2/g(0), \qquad f'(0) = 2g'(0) = 4g(0), \qquad g''(0) = 5f''(0) = 6f(0) = 3 .$$

(a) Let $h(x) = f(x)/g(x)$, and compute $h'(0)$.
(b) Let $k(x) = f(x)g(x) \sin x$, and compute $k'(0)$.
(c) Compute the limit of $g'(x)/f'(x)$ as $x \to 0$.

15. Given that the derivative $f'(a)$ exists. State which of the following statements are true and which are false. Give a reason for your decision in each case.

(a) $f'(a) = \lim\limits_{h \to a} \dfrac{f(h) - f(a)}{h - a}$.

(c) $f'(a) = \lim\limits_{t \to 0} \dfrac{f(a + 2t) - f(a)}{t}$.

(b) $f'(a) = \lim\limits_{h \to 0} \dfrac{f(a) - f(a - h)}{h}$.

(d) $f'(a) = \lim\limits_{t \to 0} \dfrac{f(a + 2t) - f(a + t)}{2t}$.

16. Suppose that instead of the usual definition of the derivative $Df(x)$, we define a new kind of derivative, $D^*f(x)$, by the formula

$$D^*f(x) = \lim\limits_{h \to 0} \frac{f^2(x + h) - f^2(x)}{h} ,$$

where $f^2(x)$ means $[f(x)]^2$.

(a) Derive formulas for computing the derivative D^* of a sum, difference, product, and quotient.
(b) Express $D^*f(x)$ in terms of $Df(x)$.
(c) For what functions does $D^*f = Df$?

4.10   The chain rule for differentiating composite functions

With the differentiation formulas developed thus far, we can find derivatives of functions f for which $f(x)$ is a finite sum of products or quotients of constant multiples of $\sin x$, $\cos x$, and x^r (r rational). As yet, however, we have not learned to deal with something like $f(x) = \sin(x^2)$ without going back to the definition of derivative. In this section we shall present a theorem, called the *chain rule*, that enables us to differentiate composite functions such as $f(x) = \sin(x^2)$. This increases substantially the number of functions that we can differentiate.

We recall that if u and v are functions such that the domain of u includes the range of v, we can define the composite function $f = u \circ v$ by the equation

$$f(x) = u[v(x)] .$$

The chain rule tells us how to express the derivative of f in terms of the derivatives u' and v'.

THEOREM 4.2.   CHAIN RULE.   *Let f be the composition of two functions u and v, say $f = u \circ v$. Suppose that both derivatives $v'(x)$ and $u'(y)$ exist, where $y = v(x)$. Then the* *derivative $f'(x)$ also exists and is given by the formula*

(4.11)
$$f'(x) = u'(y) \cdot v'(x) .$$

In other words, to compute the derivative of $u \circ v$ at x, we first compute the derivative of u at the point y, where $y = v(x)$, and multiply this by $v'(x)$.

Before we discuss the proof of (4.11), we shall mention some alternative ways of expressing the chain rule formula. If we write (4.11) entirely in terms of x, we obtain the formula

$$f'(x) = u'[v(x)] \cdot v'(x) .$$

Expressed as an equation involving *functions* rather than numbers, the chain rule assumes the following form

$$(u \circ v)' = (u' \circ v) \cdot v'.$$

In the $u(v)$-notation, let us write $u(v)'$ for the derivative of the composite function $u(v)$ and $u'(v)$ for the composition $u' \circ v$. Then the last formula becomes

$$u(v)' = u'(v) \cdot v'.$$

Proof of Theorem 4.2. We turn now to the proof of (4.11). We assume that v has a derivative at x and that u has a derivative at $v(x)$, and we wish to prove that f has a derivative at x given by the product $u'[v(x)] \cdot v'(x)$. The difference quotient for f is

(4.12)
$$\frac{f(x + h) - f(x)}{h} = \frac{u[v(x + h)] - u[v(x)]}{h} .$$

It is helpful at this stage to introduce some new notation. Let $y = v(x)$ and let $k = v(x + h) - v(x)$. (It is important to realize that k depends on h.) Then we have $v(x + h) = y + k$ and (4.12) becomes

(4.13)
$$\frac{f(x + h) - f(x)}{h} = \frac{u(y + k) - u(y)}{h} .$$

The right-hand side of (4.13) resembles the difference quotient whose limit defines $u'(y)$ except that h appears in the denominator instead of k. If $k \neq 0$, it is easy to complete the proof. We simply multiply numerator and denominator by k, and the right-hand side of (4.13) becomes

(4.14)
$$\frac{u(y + k) - u(y)}{k} \cdot \frac{k}{h} = \frac{u(y + k) - u(y)}{k} \cdot \frac{v(x + h) - v(x)}{h} .$$

When $h \to 0$, the last quotient on the right tends to $v'(x)$. Also, $k \to 0$ as $h \to 0$ because

$k = v(x + h) - v(x)$ and v is continuous at x. Therefore the first quotient on the right of (4.14) approaches $u'(y)$ as $h \to 0$, and this leads at once to (4.11).

Although the foregoing argument seems to be the most natural way to proceed, it is not completely general. Since $k = v(x + h) - v(x)$, it may happen that $k = 0$ for infinitely many values of h as $h \to 0$, in which case the passage from (4.13) to (4.14) is not valid. To overcome this difficulty, a slight modification of the proof is needed.

Let us return to Equation (4.13) and express the quotient on the right in a form that does not involve k in the denominator. For this purpose we introduce the difference between the derivative $u'(y)$ and the difference quotient whose limit is $u'(y)$. That is, we define a new function g as follows:

$$(4.15) \qquad g(t) = \frac{u(y + t) - u(y)}{t} - u'(y) \qquad \text{if} \quad t \neq 0 \, .$$

This equation defines $g(t)$ only if $t \neq 0$. Multiplying by t and rearranging terms, we may write (4.15) in the following form:

$$(4.16) \qquad u(y + t) - u(y) = t[g(t) + u'(y)] \, .$$

Although (4.16) has been derived under the hypothesis that $t \neq 0$, it also holds for $t = 0$, provided we assign some definite value to $g(0)$. Since $g(t) \to 0$ as $t \to 0$, we shall define $g(0)$ to be 0. This will ensure the continuity of g at 0. If, now, we replace t in (4.16) by k, where $k = v(x + h) - v(x)$, and substitute the right-hand side of (4.16) in (4.13), we obtain

$$(4.17) \qquad \frac{f(x + h) - f(x)}{h} = \frac{k}{h}[g(k) + u'(y)] \, ,$$

a formula that is valid even if $k = 0$. When $h \to 0$ the quotient $k/h \to v'(x)$ and $g(k) \to 0$ so the right-hand side of (4.17) approaches the limit $u'(y) \cdot v'(x)$. This completes the proof of the chain rule.

4.11 Applications of the chain rule. Related rates and implicit differentiation

The chain rule is an excellent example to illustrate the usefulness of the Leibniz notation for derivatives. In fact, if we write (4.11) in the Leibniz notation, it assumes the appearance of a trivial algebraic identity. First we introduce new symbols, say

$$y = v(x) \qquad \text{and} \qquad z = u(y) \, .$$

Then we write dy/dx for the derivative $v'(x)$, and dz/dy for $u'(y)$. The formation of the composite function is indicated by writing

$$z = u(y) = u[v(x)] = f(x) \, ,$$

and dz/dx is written for the derivative $f'(x)$. The chain rule, as expressed in Equation

(4.11), now becomes

(4.18)
$$\frac{dz}{dx} = \frac{dz}{dy}\frac{dy}{dx}.$$

The strong suggestive power of this formula is obvious. It is especially attractive to people who use calculus in physical problems. For example, suppose the foregoing symbol z represents a physical quantity measured in terms of other physical quantities x and y. The equation $z = f(x)$ tells us how to find z if x is given, and the equation $z = u(y)$ tells us how to find z if y is given. The relation between x and y is expressed by the equation $y = v(x)$. The chain rule, as expressed in (4.18), tells us that the rate of change of z with respect to x is equal to the product of the rate of change of z with respect to y and the rate of change of y with respect to x. The following example illustrates how the chain rule may be used in a special physical problem.

EXAMPLE 1. Suppose a gas is pumped into a spherical balloon at a constant rate of 50 cubic centimeters per second. Assume that the gas pressure remains constant and that the balloon always has a spherical shape. How fast is the radius of the balloon increasing when the radius is 5 centimeters?

Solution. Let r denote the radius and V the volume of the balloon at time t. We are given dV/dt, the rate of change of volume with respect to time, and we want to determine dr/dt, the rate of change of the radius with respect to time, at the instant when $r = 5$. The chain rule provides the connection between the given data and the unknown. It states that

(4.19)
$$\frac{dV}{dt} = \frac{dV}{dr}\frac{dr}{dt}.$$

To compute dV/dr, we use the formula $V = 4\pi r^3/3$ which expresses the volume of the sphere in terms of its radius. Differentiation gives us $dV/dr = 4\pi r^2$, and hence (4.19) becomes

$$\frac{dV}{dt} = 4\pi r^2 \frac{dr}{dt}.$$

Substituting $dV/dt = 50$ and $r = 5$, we obtain $dr/dt = 1/(2\pi)$. That is to say, the radius is increasing at a rate of $1/(2\pi)$ centimeters per second at the instant when $r = 5$.

The foregoing example is called a problem in *related rates*. Note that it was not necessary to express r as a function of t in order to determine the derivative dr/dt. It is this fact that makes the chain rule especially useful in related-rate problems.

The next two examples show how the chain rule may be used to obtain new differentiation formulas.

EXAMPLE 2. Given $f(x) = \sin(x^2)$, compute $f'(x)$.

Solution. The function f is a composition, $f(x) = u[v(x)]$, where $v(x) = x^2$ and $u(x) = \sin x$. To use the chain rule, we need to determine $u'[v(x)] = u'(x^2)$. Since $u'(x) = \cos x$, we have $u'(x^2) = \cos(x^2)$, and hence (4.11) gives us

$$f'(x) = \cos(x^2) \cdot v'(x) = \cos(x^2) \cdot 2x.$$

We may also solve the problem using the Leibniz notation. If we write $y = x^2$ and $z = f(x)$, then $z = \sin y$ and $dz/dx = f'(x)$. The chain rule yields

$$\frac{dz}{dx} = \frac{dz}{dy}\frac{dy}{dx} = (\cos y)(2x) = \cos(x^2) \cdot 2x ,$$

which agrees with the foregoing result for $f'(x)$.

EXAMPLE 3. If $f(x) = [v(x)]^n$, where n is a positive integer, compute $f'(x)$ in terms of $v(x)$ and $v'(x)$.

Solution. The function f is a composition, $f(x) = u[v(x)]$, where $u(x) = x^n$. Since $u'(x) = nx^{n-1}$, we have $u'[v(x)] = n[v(x)]^{n-1}$, and the chain rule yields

$$f'(x) = n[v(x)]^{n-1}v'(x) .$$

If we omit the reference to x and write this as an equality involving functions, we obtain the important formula

$$(v^n)' = nv^{n-1}v'$$

which tells us how to differentiate the nth power of v when v' exists. The formula is also valid for *rational* powers if v^n and v^{n-1} are defined. To solve the problem in the Leibniz notation, we write $y = v(x)$ and $z = f(x)$. Then $z = y^n$, $dz/dx = f'(x)$, and the chain rule gives us

$$\frac{dz}{dx} = \frac{dz}{dy}\frac{dy}{dx} = ny^{n-1}v'(x) = n[v(x)]^{n-1}v'(x) ,$$

which agrees with the first solution.

EXAMPLE 4. The equation $x^2 + y^2 = r^2$ represents a circle of radius r and center at the origin. If we solve this equation for y in terms of x, we obtain two solutions which serve to define two functions f and g given on the interval $[-r, r]$ by the formulas

$$f(x) = \sqrt{r^2 - x^2} \qquad \text{and} \qquad g(x) = -\sqrt{r^2 - x^2} .$$

(The graph of f is the upper semicircle and the graph of g the lower semicircle.) We may compute the derivatives of f and g by the chain rule. For f we use the result of Example 3 with $v(x) = r^2 - x^2$ and $n = \frac{1}{2}$ to obtain

(4.20) $$f'(x) = \tfrac{1}{2}(r^2 - x^2)^{-1/2}(-2x) = \frac{-x}{\sqrt{r^2 - x^2}} = \frac{-x}{f(x)}$$

whenever $f(x) \neq 0$. The same method, applied to g, gives us

(4.21) $$g'(x) = -\frac{-x}{\sqrt{r^2 - x^2}} = \frac{-x}{g(x)}$$

whenever $g(x) \neq 0$. Notice that if we let y stand for either $f(x)$ or $g(x)$, then both formulas (4.20) and (4.21) can be combined into one, namely,

$$(4.22) \qquad\qquad y' = \frac{-x}{y} \quad \text{if} \quad y \neq 0.$$

Another useful application of the chain rule has to do with a technique known as *implicit differentiation*. We shall explain the method and illustrate its advantages by rederiving the result of Example 4 in a simpler way.

EXAMPLE 5. *Implicit differentiation.* Formula (4.22) may be derived directly from the equation $x^2 + y^2 = r^2$ without the necessity of solving for y. We remember that y is a function of x [either $y = f(x)$ or $y = g(x)$]. Assuming that y' exists, we differentiate both sides of the equation $x^2 + y^2 = r^2$ to obtain

$$(4.23) \qquad\qquad 2x + 2yy' = 0.$$

(The term $2yy'$ comes from differentiating y^2 as explained in Example 3.) When Equation (4.23) is solved for y' it yields (4.22).

The equation $x^2 + y^2 = r^2$ is said to define y *implicitly* as a function of x (it actually defines *two* functions), and the process by which (4.23) is obtained from this equation is called *implicit differentiation*. The end result is valid for either of the two functions f and g so defined. Notice that at a point (x, y) on the circle with $x \neq 0$ and $y \neq 0$, the tangent line has a slope $-x/y$, whereas the radius from the center to (x, y) has the slope y/x. The product of the two slopes is -1 so the tangent is perpendicular to the radius.

4.12 Exercises

In Exercises 1 through 14, determine the derivative $f'(x)$. In each case it is understood that x is restricted to those values for which the formula for $f(x)$ is meaningful.

1. $f(x) = \cos 2x - 2 \sin x$.

2. $f(x) = \sqrt{1 + x^2}$.

3. $f(x) = (2 - x^2) \cos x^2 + 2x \sin x^3$.

4. $f(x) = \sin (\cos^2 x) \cdot \cos (\sin^2 x)$.

5. $f(x) = \sin^n x \cdot \cos nx$.

6. $f(x) = \sin [\sin (\sin x)]$.

7. $f(x) = \dfrac{\sin^2 x}{\sin x^2}$.

8. $f(x) = \tan \dfrac{x}{2} - \cot \dfrac{x}{2}$.

9. $f(x) = \sec^2 x + \csc^2 x$.

10. $f(x) = x\sqrt{1 + x^2}$.

11. $f(x) = \dfrac{x}{\sqrt{4 - x^2}}$.

12. $f(x) = \left(\dfrac{1 + x^3}{1 - x^3} \right)^{1/3}$.

13. $f(x) = \dfrac{1}{\sqrt{1 + x^2}\,(x + \sqrt{1 + x^2})}$.

14. $f(x) = \sqrt{x + \sqrt{x + \sqrt{x}}}$.

15. Compute $f'(x)$ if $f(x) = (1 + x)(2 + x^2)^{1/2}(3 + x^3)^{1/3}$, $x^3 \neq -3$.

16. Let $f(x) = \dfrac{1}{1 + 1/x}$ if $x \neq 0$, and let $g(x) = \dfrac{1}{1 + 1/f(x)}$. Compute $f'(x)$ and $g'(x)$.

17. The following table of values was computed for a pair of functions f and g and their derivatives f' and g'. Construct a corresponding table for the two composite functions h and k given by $h(x) = f[g(x)]$, $k(x) = g[f(x)]$.

x	$f(x)$	$f'(x)$	$g(x)$	$g'(x)$
0	1	5	2	−5
1	3	−2	0	1
2	0	2	3	1
3	2	4	1	−6

18. A function f and its first two derivatives are tabulated as shown. Let $g(x) = xf(x^2)$ and make a table of g and its first two derivatives for $x = 0, 1, 2$.

x	$f(x)$	$f'(x)$	$f''(x)$
0	0	1	2
1	1	1	1
2	3	2	1
4	6	3	0

19. Determine the derivative $g'(x)$ in terms of $f'(x)$ if:
    (a) $g(x) = f(x^2)$;
    (b) $g(x) = f(\sin^2 x) + f(\cos^2 x)$;
    (c) $g(x) = f[f(x)]$;
    (d) $g(x) = f\{f[f(x)]\}$.

Related rates and implicit differentiation.

20. Each edge of a cube is expanding at the rate of 1 centimeter (cm) per second. How fast is the volume changing when the length of each edge is (a) 5 cm? (b) 10 cm? (c) x cm?

21. An airplane flies in level flight at constant velocity, eight miles above the ground. (In this exercise assume the earth is flat.) The flight path passes directly over a point P on the ground. The distance from the plane to P is decreasing at the rate of 4 miles per minute at the instant when this distance is 10 miles. Compute the velocity of the plane in miles per hour.

22. A baseball diamond is a 90-foot square. A ball is batted along the third-base line at a constant speed of 100 feet per second. How fast is its distance from first base changing when (a) it is halfway to third base? (b) it reaches third base?

23. A boat sails parallel to a straight beach at a constant speed of 12 miles per hour, staying 4 miles offshore. How fast is it approaching a lighthouse on the shoreline at the instant it is exactly 5 miles from the lighthouse?

24. A reservoir has the shape of a right-circular cone. The altitude is 10 feet, and the radius of the base is 4 ft. Water is poured into the reservoir at a constant rate of 5 cubic feet per minute. How fast is the water level rising when the depth of the water is 5 feet if (a) the vertex of the cone is up? (b) the vertex of the cone is down?

25. A water tank has the shape of a right-circular cone with its vertex down. Its altitude is 10 feet and the radius of the base is 15 feet. Water leaks out of the bottom at a constant rate of 1 cubic foot per second. Water is poured into the tank at a constant rate of c cubic feet per second. Compute c so that the water level will be rising at the rate of 4 feet per second at the instant when the water is 2 feet deep.

26. Water flows into a hemispherical tank of radius 10 feet (flat side up). At any instant, let h denote the depth of the water, measured from the bottom, r the radius of the surface of the water, and V the volume of the water in the tank. Compute dV/dh at the instant when $h = 5$ feet. If the water flows in at a constant rate of $5\sqrt{3}$ cubic feet per second, compute dr/dt, the rate at which r is changing, at the instant t when $h = 5$ feet.

27. A variable right triangle ABC in the xy-plane has its right angle at vertex B, a fixed vertex A at the origin, and the third vertex C restricted to lie on the parabola $y = 1 + \frac{7}{36} x^2$. The point B starts at the point $(0, 1)$ at time $t = 0$ and moves upward along the y-axis at a constant velocity of 2 cm/sec. How fast is the area of the triangle increasing when $t = 7/2$ sec?

28. The radius of a right-circular cylinder increases at a constant rate. Its altitude is a linear function of the radius and increases three times as fast as the radius. When the radius is 1 foot the altitude is 6 feet. When the radius is 6 feet, the volume is increasing at a rate of 1 cubic foot per second. When the radius is 36 feet, the volume is increasing at a rate of n cubic feet per second, where n is an integer. Compute n.

29. A particle is constrained to move along a parabola whose equation is $y = x^2$. (a) At what point on the curve are the abscissa and the ordinate changing at the same rate? (b) Find this rate if the motion is such that at time t we have $x = \sin t$ and $y = \sin^2 t$.

30. The equation $x^3 + y^3 = 1$ defines y as one or more functions of x. (a) Assuming the derivative y' exists, and without attempting to solve for y, show that y' satisfies the equation $x^2 + y^2 y' = 0$. (b) Assuming the second derivative y'' exists, show that $y'' = -2xy^{-5}$ whenever $y \neq 0$.

31. If $0 < x < 5$, the equation $x^{1/2} + y^{1/2} = 5$ defines y as a function of x. Without solving for y, show that the derivative y' has a fixed sign. (You may assume the existence of y'.)

32. The equation $3x^2 + 4y^2 = 12$ defines y implicitly as two functions of x if $|x| \leq 2$. Assuming the second derivative y'' exists, show that it satisfies the equation $4y^3 y'' = -9$.

33. The equation $x \sin xy + 2x^2 = 0$ defines y implicitly as a function of x. Assuming the derivative y' exists, show that it satisfies the equation $y'x^2 \cos xy + xy \cos xy + \sin xy + 4x = 0$.

34. If $y = x^r$, where r is a rational number, say $r = m/n$, then $y^n = x^m$. Assuming the existence of the derivative y', derive the formula $y' = rx^{r-1}$ using implicit differentiation and the corresponding formula for integer exponents.

4.13 Applications of differentiation to extreme values of functions

Differentiation can be used to help locate maxima and minima of functions. Actually, there are two different uses of the word "maximum" in calculus, and they are distinguished by the two prefixes *absolute* and *relative*. The concept of absolute maximum was introduced in Chapter 3. We recall that a real-valued function f is said to have an absolute maximum on a set S if there is at least one point c in S such that

$$f(x) \leq f(c) \qquad \text{for all } x \text{ in } S .$$

The concept of relative maximum is defined as follows.

DEFINITION OF RELATIVE MAXIMUM. *A function f, defined on a set S, is said to have a relative maximum at a point c in S if there is some open interval I containing c such that*

$$f(x) \le f(c) \quad \text{for all } x \text{ which lie in } I \cap S.$$

The concept of relative minimum is similarly defined by reversing the inequality.

In other words, a relative maximum at c is an absolute maximum in some neighborhood of c, although this need not be an absolute maximum on the whole of S. Examples are shown in Figure 4.7. Of course, every absolute maximum is, in particular, a relative maximum.

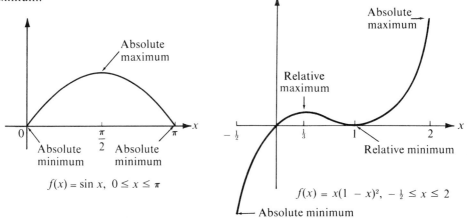

FIGURE 4.7   Extrema of functions.

DEFINITION OF EXTREMUM. *A number which is either a relative maximum or a relative minimum of a function f is called an extreme value or an extremum of f.*

The next theorem, which is illustrated in Figure 4.7, relates extrema of a function to horizontal tangents of its graph.

THEOREM 4.3.   VANISHING OF THE DERIVATIVE AT AN INTERIOR EXTREMUM. *Let f be defined on an open interval I, and assume that f has a relative maximum or a relative minimum at an interior point c of I. If the derivative f'(c) exists, then f'(c) = 0.*

Proof. Define a function Q on I as follows:

$$Q(x) = \frac{f(x) - f(c)}{x - c} \quad \text{if} \quad x \ne c, \qquad Q(c) = f'(c).$$

Since $f'(c)$ exists, $Q(x) \to Q(c)$ as $x \to c$, so Q is continuous at c. We wish to prove that $Q(c) = 0$. We shall do this by showing that each of the inequalities $Q(c) > 0$ and $Q(c) < 0$ leads to a contradiction.

Assume $Q(c) > 0$. By the sign-preserving property of continuous functions, there is an interval about c in which $Q(x)$ is positive. Therefore the numerator of the quotient $Q(x)$ has the same sign as the denominator for all $x \neq c$ in this interval. In other words, $f(x) > f(c)$ when $x > c$, and $f(x) < f(c)$ when $x < c$. This contradicts the assumption that f has an extremum at c. Hence, the inequality $Q(c) > 0$ is impossible. A similar argument shows that we cannot have $Q(c) < 0$. Therefore $Q(c) = 0$, as asserted. Since $Q(c) = f'(c)$, this proves the theorem.

It is important to realize that a zero derivative at c does not imply an extremum at c. For example, let $f(x) = x^3$. The graph of f is shown in Figure 4.8. Here $f'(x) = 3x^2$, so

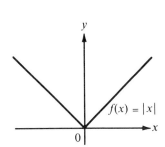

FIGURE 4.8   Here $f'(0)$ equals 0 but there is no extremum at 0.

FIGURE 4.9   There is an extremum at 0, but $f'(0)$ does not exist.

$f'(0) = 0$. However, this function is increasing in every interval containing 0 so there is no extremum at 0. This example shows that a zero derivative at c is *not sufficient* for an extremum at c.

Another example, $f(x) = |x|$, shows that a zero derivative does not always occur at an extremum. Here there is a relative minimum at 0, as shown in Figure 4.9, but at the point 0 itself the graph has a sharp corner and there is no derivative. Theorem 4.3 assumes that the derivative $f'(c)$ *exists* at the extremum. In other words, Theorem 4.3 tells us that, *in the absence of sharp corners*, the derivative must necessarily vanish at an extremum if this extremum occurs in the interior of an interval.

In a later section we shall describe a test for extrema which is comprehensive enough to include both the examples in Figure 4.7 and also the example in Figure 4.9. This test, which is described in Theorem 4.8, tells us that an extremum always occurs at a point where the derivative changes its sign. Although this fact may seem geometrically evident, a proof is not easy to give with the materials developed thus far. We shall deduce this result as a consequence of the mean-value theorem for derivatives which we discuss next.

4.14   The mean-value theorem for derivatives

The mean-value theorem for derivatives holds a position of importance in calculus because many properties of functions can easily be deduced from it. Before we state the mean-value theorem, we will examine one of its special cases from which the more general theorem will be deduced. This special case was discovered in 1690 by Michel Rolle (1652–1719), a French mathematician.

THEOREM 4.4. ROLLE'S THEOREM. *Let f be a function which is continuous everywhere on a closed interval* [a, b] *and has a derivative at each point of the open interval* (a, b). *Also, assume that*

$$f(a) = f(b) .$$

Then there is at least one point c in the open interval (a, b) *such that* $f'(c) = 0$.

The geometric significance of Rolle's theorem is illustrated in Figure 4.10. The theorem simply asserts that the curve shown must have a horizontal tangent somewhere between a and b.

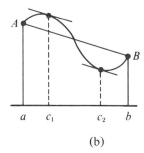

(a)   (b)

FIGURE 4.10   Geometric interpre-   FIGURE 4.11   Geometric significance of the mean-value
tation of Rolle's theorem.   theorem.

Proof. We assume that $f'(x) \neq 0$ for every x in the open interval (a, b), and we arrive at a contradiction as follows: By the extreme-value theorem for continuous functions, f must take on its absolute maximum M and its absolute minimum m somewhere in the closed interval [a, b]. Theorem 4.3 tells us that neither extreme value can be taken at any interior point (otherwise the derivative would vanish there). Hence, both extreme values are taken on at the endpoints a and b. But since $f(a) = f(b)$, this means that $m = M$, and hence f is constant on [a, b]. This contradicts the fact that $f'(x) \neq 0$ for all x in (a, b). It follows that $f'(c) = 0$ for at least one c satisfying $a < c < b$, which proves the theorem.

We can use Rolle's theorem to prove the mean-value theorem. Before we state the mean-value theorem, it may be helpful to examine its geometric significance. Each of the curves shown in Figure 4.11 is the graph of a continuous function f with a tangent line above each point of the open interval (a, b). At the point $(c, f(c))$ shown in Figure 4.11(a), the tangent line is parallel to the chord AB. In Figure 4.11(b), there are two points where the tangent line is parallel to the chord AB. The mean-value theorem guarantees that there will be *at least one point* with this property.

To translate this geometric property into an analytic statement, we need only observe that parallelism of two lines means equality of their slopes. Since the slope of the chord

AB is the quotient $[f(b) - f(a)]/(b - a)$ and since the slope of the tangent line at c is the derivative $f'(c)$, the above assertion states that

(4.24)
$$\frac{f(b) - f(a)}{b - a} = f'(c)$$

for *some* c in the open interval (a, b).

To exhibit strong intuitive evidence for the truth of (4.24), we may think of $f(t)$ as the distance traveled by a moving particle at time t. Then the quotient on the left of (4.24) represents the *mean* or *average* speed in the time interval $[a, b]$, and the derivative $f'(t)$ represents the instantaneous speed at time t. The equation asserts that there must be some moment when the instantaneous speed is equal to the average speed. For example, if the average speed during an automobile trip is 45 mph, then the speedometer must register 45 mph *at least once* during the trip.

The mean-value theorem may be stated formally as follows.

THEOREM 4.5. MEAN-VALUE THEOREM FOR DERIVATIVES. *Assume that f is continuous everywhere on a closed interval $[a, b]$ and has a derivative at each point of the open interval (a, b). Then there is at least one interior point c of (a, b) for which*

(4.25)
$$f(b) - f(a) = f'(c)(b - a).$$

Proof. To apply Rolle's theorem we need a function which has equal values at the endpoints a and b. To construct such a function, we modify f as follows. Let

$$h(x) = f(x)(b - a) - x[f(b) - f(a)].$$

Then $h(a) = h(b) = bf(a) - af(b)$. Also, h is continuous on $[a, b]$ and has a derivative in the open interval (a, b). Applying Rolle's theorem to h, we find that $h'(c) = 0$ for some c in (a, b). But

$$h'(x) = f'(x)(b - a) - [f(b) - f(a)].$$

When $x = c$, this gives us Equation (4.25).

Notice that the theorem makes no assertion about the exact location of the one or more "mean values" c, except to say that they all lie *somewhere* between a and b. For some functions the position of the mean values may be specified exactly, but in most cases it is very difficult to make an accurate determination of these points. Nevertheless, the real usefulness of the theorem lies in the fact that many conclusions can be drawn from the knowledge of the mere *existence* of at least one mean value.

Note: It is important to realize that the conclusion of the mean-value theorem may fail to hold if there is any point between a and b where the derivative does not exist. For example, the function f defined by the equation $f(x) = |x|$ is continuous everywhere on the real axis and has a derivative everywhere except at 0. Let $A = (-1, f(-1))$ and let $B = (2, f(2))$. The slope of the chord joining A and B is

$$\frac{f(2) - f(-1)}{2 - (-1)} = \frac{2 - 1}{3} = \frac{1}{3}$$

but the derivative is nowhere equal to $\frac{1}{3}$.

The following extension of the mean-value theorem is often useful.

THEOREM 4.6. CAUCHY'S MEAN-VALUE FORMULA. *Let f and g be two functions continuous on a closed interval $[a, b]$ and having derivatives in the open interval (a, b). Then, for some c in (a, b), we have*

$$f'(c)[g(b) - g(a)] = g'(c)[f(b) - f(a)].$$

Proof. The proof is similar to that of Theorem 4.5. We let

$$h(x) = f(x)[g(b) - g(a)] - g(x)[f(b) - f(a)].$$

Then $h(a) = h(b) = f(a)g(b) - g(a)f(b)$. Applying Rolle's theorem to h, we find that $h'(c) = 0$ for some c in (a, b). Computing $h'(c)$ from the formula defining h, we obtain Cauchy's mean-value formula. Theorem 4.5 is the special case obtained by taking $g(x) = x$.

4.15 Exercises

1. Show that on the graph of any quadratic polynomial the chord joining the points for which $x = a$ and $x = b$ is parallel to the tangent line at the midpoint $x = (a + b)/2$.
2. Use Rolle's theorem to prove that, regardless of the value of b, there is at most one point x in the interval $-1 \leq x \leq 1$ for which $x^3 - 3x + b = 0$.
3. Define a function f as follows:

$$f(x) = \frac{3 - x^2}{2} \quad \text{if} \quad x \leq 1, \qquad f(x) = \frac{1}{x} \quad \text{if} \quad x \geq 1.$$

(a) Sketch the graph of f for x in the interval $0 \leq x \leq 2$.
(b) Show that f satisfies the conditions of the mean-value theorem over the interval $[0, 2]$ and determine all the mean values provided by the theorem.
4. Let $f(x) = 1 - x^{2/3}$. Show that $f(1) = f(-1) = 0$, but that $f'(x)$ is never zero in the interval $[-1, 1]$. Explain how this is possible, in view of Rolle's theorem.
5. Show that $x^2 = x \sin x + \cos x$ for exactly two real values of x.
6. Show that the mean-value formula can be expressed in the form

$$f(x + h) = f(x) + hf'(x + \theta h) \qquad \text{where} \quad 0 < \theta < 1.$$

Determine θ in terms of x and h when (a) $f(x) = x^2$; (b) $f(x) = x^3$. Keep x fixed, $x \neq 0$, and find the limit of θ in each case as $h \to 0$.
7. Let f be a polynomial. A real number α is said to be a *zero* of f of multiplicity m if $f(x) = (x - \alpha)^m g(x)$, where $g(\alpha) \neq 0$.

(a) If f has r zeros in an interval $[a, b]$, prove that f' has at least $r - 1$ zeros, and in general, the kth derivative $f^{(k)}$ has at least $r - k$ zeros in $[a, b]$. (The zeros are to be counted as often as their multiplicity indicates.)

(b) If the kth derivative $f^{(k)}$ has *exactly* r zeros in $[a, b]$, what can you conclude about the number of zeros of f in $[a, b]$?

8. Use the mean-value theorem to deduce the following inequalities:

(a) $|\sin x - \sin y| \le |x - y|$.

(b) $ny^{n-1}(x - y) \le x^n - y^n \le nx^{n-1}(x - y)$ if $0 < y \le x$, $n = 1, 2, 3, \ldots$.

9. A function f, continuous on $[a, b]$, has a second derivative f'' everywhere on the open interval (a, b). The line segment joining $(a, f(a))$ and $(b, f(b))$ intersects the graph of f at a third point $(c, f(c))$, where $a < c < b$. Prove that $f''(t) = 0$ for at least one point t in (a, b).

10. This exercise outlines a proof of the intermediate-value theorem for derivatives. *Assume f has a derivative everywhere on an open interval I. Choose $a < b$ in I. Then f' takes on every value between $f'(a)$ and $f'(b)$ somewhere in (a, b).*

(a) Define a new function g on $[a, b]$ as follows:

$$g(x) = \frac{f(x) - f(a)}{x - a} \quad \text{if} \quad x \ne a, \quad g(a) = f'(a).$$

Prove that g takes on every value between $f'(a)$ and $g(b)$ in the open interval (a, b). Use the mean-value theorem for derivatives to show that f' takes on every value between $f'(a)$ and $g(b)$ in the open interval (a, b).

(b) Define a new function h on $[a, b]$ as follows:

$$h(x) = \frac{f(x) - f(b)}{x - b} \quad \text{if} \quad x \ne b, \quad h(b) = f'(b).$$

By an argument similar to that in part (a), show that f' takes on every value between $f'(b)$ and $h(a)$ in (a, b). Since $h(a) = g(b)$, this proves the intermediate-value theorem for derivatives.

4.16 Applications of the mean-value theorem to geometric properties of functions

The mean-value theorem may be used to deduce properties of a function from a knowledge of the algebraic sign of its derivative. This is illustrated by the following theorem.

THEOREM 4.7. *Let f be a function which is continuous on a closed interval $[a, b]$ and assume f has a derivative at each point of the open interval (a, b). Then we have:*

(a) *If $f'(x) > 0$ for every x in (a, b), f is strictly increasing on $[a, b]$;*

(b) *If $f'(x) < 0$ for every x in (a, b), f is strictly decreasing on $[a, b]$;*

(c) *If $f'(x) = 0$ for every x in (a, b), f is constant throughout $[a, b]$.*

Proof. To prove (a) we must show that $f(x) < f(y)$ whenever $a \le x < y \le b$. Therefore, suppose $x < y$ and apply the mean-value theorem to the closed subinterval $[x, y]$. We obtain

(4.26) $f(y) - f(x) = f'(c)(y - x), \quad \text{where} \quad x < c < y.$

Since both $f'(c)$ and $y - x$ are positive, so is $f(y) - f(x)$, and this means $f(x) < f(y)$, as asserted. This proves (a), and the proof of (b) is similar. To prove (c), we use Equation (4.26) with $x = a$. Since $f'(c) = 0$, we have $f(y) = f(a)$ for every y in $[a, b]$, so f is constant on $[a, b]$.

We can use Theorem 4.7 to prove that an extremum occurs whenever the derivative changes sign.

THEOREM 4.8.   *Assume f is continuous on a closed interval $[a, b]$ and assume that the derivative f' exists everywhere in the open interval (a, b), except possibly at a point c.*
  (a) *If $f'(x)$ is positive for all $x < c$ and negative for all $x > c$, then f has a relative maximum at c.*
  (b) *If, on the other hand, $f'(x)$ is negative for all $x < c$ and positive for all $x > c$, then f has a relative minimum at c.*

Proof.   In case (a), Theorem 4.7(a) tells us that f is strictly increasing on $[a, c]$ and strictly decreasing on $[c, b]$. Hence $f(x) < f(c)$ for all $x \neq c$ in (a, b), so f has a relative

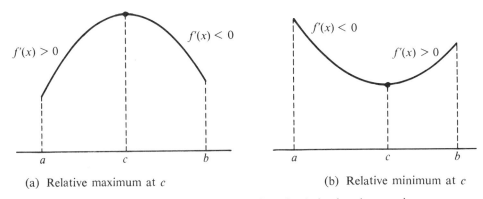

(a) Relative maximum at c (b) Relative minimum at c

FIGURE 4.12   An extremum occurs when the derivative changes sign.

maximum at c. This proves (a) and the proof of (b) is entirely analogous. The two cases are illustrated in Figure 4.12.

4.17 Second-derivative test for extrema

If a function f is continuous on a closed interval $[a, b]$, the extreme-value theorem tells us that it has an absolute maximum and an absolute minimum somewhere in $[a, b]$. If f has a derivative at each interior point, then the only places where extrema can occur are:
  (1) at the endpoints a and b;
  (2) at those interior points x where $f'(x) = 0$.
Points of type (2) are often called *critical points* of f. To decide whether there is a maximum or a minimum (or neither) at a critical point c, we need more information about f. Usually the behavior of f at a critical point can be determined from the algebraic sign of the derivative near c. The next theorem shows that a study of the sign of the second derivative near c can also be helpful.

THEOREM 4.9. SECOND-DERIVATIVE TEST FOR AN EXTREMUM AT A CRITICAL POINT. *Let c be a critical point of f in an open interval (a, b); that is, assume $a < c < b$ and $f'(c) = 0$. Assume also that the second derivative f'' exists in (a, b). Then we have the following:*
  (a) *If f'' is negative in (a, b), f has a relative maximum at c.*
  (b) *If f'' is positive in (a, b), f has a relative minimum at c.*

The two cases are illustrated in Figure 4.12.

Proof. Consider case (a), $f'' < 0$ in (a, b). By Theorem 4.7 (applied to f'), the function f' is strictly decreasing in (a, b). But $f'(c) = 0$, so f' changes its sign from positive to negative at c, as shown in Figure 4.12(a). Hence, by Theorem 4.8, f has a relative maximum at c. The proof in case (b) is entirely analogous.

If f'' is continuous at c, and if $f''(c) \neq 0$, there will be a neighborhood of c in which f'' has the same sign as $f''(c)$. Therefore, if $f'(c) = 0$, the function f has a relative maximum at c if $f''(c)$ is negative, and a relative minimum if $f''(c)$ is positive. This test suffices for many examples that occur in practice.

The sign of the second derivative also governs the convexity or the concavity of f. The next theorem shows that the function is convex in intervals where f'' is positive, as illustrated by Figure 4.12(b). In Figure 4.12(a), f is concave because f'' is negative. It suffices to discuss only the convex case, because if f is convex, then $-f$ is concave.

THEOREM 4.10. DERIVATIVE TEST FOR CONVEXITY. *Assume f is continuous on $[a, b]$ and has a derivative in the open interval (a, b). If f' is increasing on (a, b), then f is convex on $[a, b]$. In particular, f is convex if f'' exists and is nonnegative in (a, b).*

Proof. Take $x < y$ in $[a, b]$ and let $z = \alpha y + (1 - \alpha)x$, where $0 < \alpha < 1$. We wish to prove that $f(z) \leq \alpha f(y) + (1 - \alpha)f(x)$. Since $f(z) = \alpha f(z) + (1 - \alpha)f(z)$, this is the same as proving that

$$(1 - \alpha)[f(z) - f(x)] \leq \alpha[f(y) - f(z)].$$

By the mean-value theorem (applied twice), there exist points c and d satisfying $x < c < z$ and $z < d < y$ such that

$$f(z) - f(x) = f'(c)(z - x), \quad \text{and} \quad f(y) - f(z) = f'(d)(y - z).$$

Since f' is increasing, we have $f'(c) \leq f'(d)$. Also, we have $(1 - \alpha)(z - x) = \alpha(y - z)$, so we may write

$$(1 - \alpha)[f(z) - f(x)] = (1 - \alpha)f'(c)(z - x) \leq \alpha f'(d)(y - z) = \alpha[f(y) - f(z)],$$

which proves the required inequality for convexity.

4.18 Curve sketching

The information gathered in the theorems of the last few sections is often useful in curve sketching. In drawing the graph of a function f, we should first determine the domain of f

[the set of x for which $f(x)$ is defined] and, if it is easy to do so, we should find the range of f (the set of values taken on by f). A knowledge of the domain and range gives us an idea of the extent of the curve $y = f(x)$, since it specifies a portion of the xy-plane in which the entire curve must lie. Then it is a good idea to try to locate those points (if any) where the curve crosses the coordinate axes. These are called *intercepts* of the graph. The y-intercept is simply the point $(0, f(0))$, assuming 0 is in the domain of f, and the x-intercepts are those points $(x, 0)$ for which $f(x) = 0$. Computing the x-intercepts may be extremely difficult in practice, and we may have to be content with approximate values only.

We should also try to determine intervals in which f is monotonic by examining the sign of f', and to determine intervals of convexity and concavity by studying the sign of f''. Special attention should be paid to those points where the graph has horizontal tangents.

EXAMPLE 1. *The graph of $y = f(x)$, where $f(x) = x + 1/x$ for $x \neq 0$.*

In this case, there are no intercepts on either axis. The first two derivatives are given by the formulas

$$f'(x) = 1 - 1/x^2, \qquad f''(x) = 2/x^3.$$

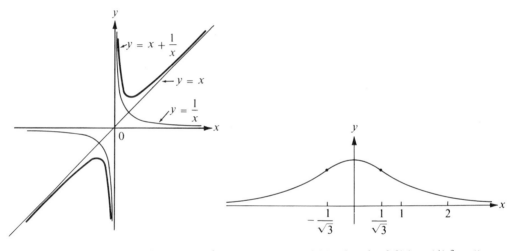

FIGURE 4.13   Graph of $f(x) = x + 1/x$.   FIGURE 4.14   Graph of $f(x) = 1/(x^2 + 1)$.

The first derivative is positive if $x^2 > 1$, negative if $x^2 < 1$, and zero if $x^2 = 1$. Hence there is a relative minimum at $x = 1$ and a relative maximum at $x = -1$. For $x > 0$, the second derivative is positive so the first derivative is strictly increasing. For $x < 0$, the second derivative is negative, and therefore the first derivative is strictly decreasing. For x near 0, the term x is small compared to $1/x$, and the curve behaves like the curve $y = 1/x$. (See Figure 4.13.) On the other hand, for very large x (positive or negative), the term $1/x$ is small compared to x, and the curve behaves very much like the line $y = x$. In this example, the function is odd, $f(-x) = -f(x)$, so the graph is symmetric with respect to the origin.

In the foregoing example, the line $y = x$ is an asymptote of the curve. In general, a nonvertical line with equation $y = mx + b$ is called an *asymptote* of the graph of $y = f(x)$ if the difference $f(x) - (mx + b)$ tends to 0 as x takes arbitrarily large positive values or arbitrarily large negative values. A vertical line, $x = a$, is called a *vertical asymptote* if $|f(x)|$ takes arbitrarily large values as $x \to a$ from the right or from the left. In the foregoing example, the y-axis is a vertical asymptote.

EXAMPLE 2. *The graph of* $y = f(x)$, *where* $f(x) = 1/(x^2 + 1)$.

This is an even function, positive for all x, and has the x-axis as a horizontal asymptote. The first derivative is given by

$$f'(x) = \frac{-2x}{(x^2 + 1)^2},$$

so $f'(x) < 0$ if $x > 0$, $f'(x) > 0$ if $x < 0$, and $f'(x) = 0$ when $x = 0$. Therefore the function increases over the negative axis, decreases over the positive axis, and has a relative maximum at $x = 0$. Differentiating once more, we find that

$$f''(x) = \frac{(x^2 + 1)^2(-2) - (-2x)2(x^2 + 1)(2x)}{(x^2 + 1)^4} = \frac{2(3x^2 - 1)}{(x^2 + 1)^3}.$$

Thus $f''(x) > 0$ if $3x^2 > 1$, and $f''(x) < 0$ if $3x^2 < 1$. Hence, the first derivative increases when $x^2 > \frac{1}{3}$ and decreases when $x^2 < \frac{1}{3}$. This information suffices to draw the curve in Figure 4.14. The two points on the graph corresponding to $x^2 = \frac{1}{3}$, where the second derivative changes its sign, are called *points of inflection*.

4.19 Exercises

In the following exercises, (a) find all points x such that $f'(x) = 0$; (b) examine the sign of f' and determine those intervals in which f is monotonic; (c) examine the sign of f'' and determine those intervals in which f' is monotonic; (d) make a sketch of the graph of f. In each case, the function is defined for all x for which the given formula for $f(x)$ is meaningful.

1. $f(x) = x^2 - 3x + 2$.

2. $f(x) = x^3 - 4x$.
3. $f(x) = (x - 1)^2(x + 2)$.
4. $f(x) = x^3 - 6x^2 + 9x + 5$.
5. $f(x) = 2 + (x - 1)^4$.
6. $f(x) = 1/x^2$.
7. $f(x) = x + 1/x^2$.

8. $f(x) = \dfrac{1}{(x - 1)(x - 3)}$.

9. $f(x) = x/(1 + x^2)$.
10. $f(x) = (x^2 - 4)/(x^2 - 9)$.
11. $f(x) = \sin^2 x$.
12. $f(x) = x - \sin x$.
13. $f(x) = x + \cos x$.
14. $f(x) = \frac{1}{6}x^2 + \frac{1}{12} \cos 2x$.

4.20 Worked examples of extremum problems

Many extremum problems in both pure and applied mathematics can be attacked systematically with the use of differential calculus. As a matter of fact, the rudiments of differential calculus were first developed when Fermat tried to find general methods for determining maxima and minima. We shall solve a few examples in this section and give the reader an opportunity to solve others in the next set of exercises.

First we formulate two simple principles which can be used to solve many extremum problems.

EXAMPLE 1. *Constant-sum, maximum-product principle.* Given a positive number S. Prove that among all choices of positive numbers x and y with $x + y = S$, the product xy is largest when $x = y = \frac{1}{2}S$.

Proof. If $x + y = S$, then $y = S - x$ and the product xy is equal to $x(S - x) = xS - x^2$. Let $f(x) = xS - x^2$. This quadratic polynomial has first derivative $f'(x) = S - 2x$ which is positive for $x < \frac{1}{2}S$ and negative for $x > \frac{1}{2}S$. Hence the maximum of xy occurs when $x = \frac{1}{2}S$, $y = S - x = \frac{1}{2}S$. This can also be proved without the use of calculus. We simply write $f(x) = \frac{1}{4}S^2 - (x - \frac{1}{2}S)^2$ and note that $f(x)$ is largest when $x = \frac{1}{2}S$.

EXAMPLE 2. *Constant-product, minimum-sum principle.* Given a positive number P. Prove that among all choices of positive numbers x and y with $xy = P$, the sum $x + y$ is smallest when $x = y = \sqrt{P}$.

Proof. We must determine the minimum of the function $f(x) = x + P/x$ for $x > 0$. The first derivative is $f'(x) = 1 - P/x^2$. This is negative for $x^2 < P$ and positive for $x^2 > P$, so $f(x)$ has its minimum at $x = \sqrt{P}$. Hence, the sum $x + y$ is smallest when $x = y = \sqrt{P}$.

EXAMPLE 3. Among all rectangles of given perimeter, the square has the largest area.

Proof. We use the result of Example 1. Let x and y denote the sides of a general rectangle. If the perimeter is fixed, then $x + y$ is constant, so the area xy has its largest value when $x = y$. Hence, the maximizing rectangle is a square.

EXAMPLE 4. The geometric mean of two positive numbers does not exceed their arithmetic mean. That is, $\sqrt{ab} \leq \frac{1}{2}(a + b)$.

Proof. Given $a > 0$, $b > 0$, let $P = ab$. Among all positive x and y with $xy = P$, the sum $x + y$ is smallest when $x = y = \sqrt{P}$. In other words, if $xy = P$, then $x + y \geq \sqrt{P} + \sqrt{P} = 2\sqrt{P}$. In particular, $a + b \geq 2\sqrt{P} = 2\sqrt{ab}$, so $\sqrt{ab} \leq \frac{1}{2}(a + b)$. Equality occurs if and only if $a = b$.

EXAMPLE 5. A block of weight W is to be moved along a flat table by a force inclined at an angle θ with the line of motion, where $0 \leq \theta \leq \frac{1}{2}\pi$, as shown in Figure 4.15. Assume the motion is resisted by a frictional force which is proportional to the normal force with which the block presses perpendicularly against the surface of the table. Find the angle θ for which the propelling force needed to overcome friction will be as small as possible.

Solution. Let $F(\theta)$ denote the propelling force. It has an upward vertical component $F(\theta) \sin \theta$, so the net normal force pressing against the table is $N = W - F(\theta) \sin \theta$. The frictional force is μN, where μ (the Greek letter *mu*) is a constant called the coefficient of friction. The horizontal component of the propelling force is $F(\theta) \cos \theta$. When this is equated to the frictional force, we get $F(\theta) \cos \theta = \mu[W - F(\theta) \sin \theta]$ from which we find

$$F(\theta) = \frac{\mu W}{\cos \theta + \mu \sin \theta} \, .$$

To minimize $F(\theta)$, we maximize the denominator $g(\theta) = \cos \theta + \mu \sin \theta$ in the interval $0 \le \theta \le \frac{1}{2}\pi$. At the endpoints, we have $g(0) = 1$ and $g(\frac{1}{2}\pi) = \mu$. In the interior of the interval, we have

$$g'(\theta) = -\sin \theta + \mu \cos \theta \, ,$$

so g has a critical point at $\theta = \alpha$, where $\sin \alpha = \mu \cos \alpha$. This gives $g(\alpha) = \cos \alpha + \mu^2 \cos \alpha = (1 + \mu^2) \cos \alpha$. We can express $\cos \alpha$ in terms of μ. Since $\mu^2 \cos^2 \alpha = \sin^2 \alpha = 1 - \cos^2 \alpha$, we find $(1 + \mu^2) \cos^2 \alpha = 1$, so $\cos \alpha = 1/\sqrt{1 + \mu^2}$. Thus $g(\alpha) = \sqrt{1 + \mu^2}$.

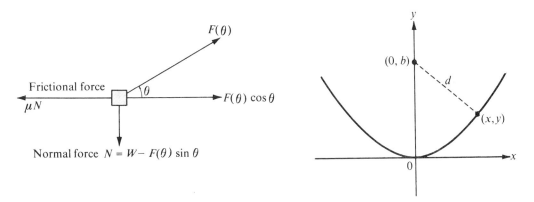

FIGURE 4.15 Example 5.   FIGURE 4.16 Example 6.

Since $g(\alpha)$ exceeds $g(0)$ and $g(\frac{1}{2}\pi)$, the maximum of g occurs at the critical point. Hence the minimum force required is

$$F(\alpha) = \frac{\mu W}{g(\alpha)} = \frac{\mu W}{\sqrt{1 + \mu^2}} \, .$$

EXAMPLE 6. Find the shortest distance from a given point $(0, b)$ on the y-axis to the parabola $x^2 = 4y$. (The number b may have any real value.)

Solution. The parabola is shown in Figure 4.16. The quantity to be minimized is the distance d, where

$$d = \sqrt{x^2 + (y - b)^2} \, ,$$

subject to the restriction $x^2 = 4y$. It is clear from the figure that when b is *negative* the minimum distance is $|b|$. As the point $(0, b)$ moves upward along the positive y-axis, the minimum is b until the point reaches a certain special position, above which the minimum is $<b$. The exact location of this special position will now be determined.

First of all, we observe that the point (x, y) that minimizes d also minimizes d^2. (This observation enables us to avoid differentiation of square roots.) At this stage, we may express d^2 in terms of x alone or else in terms of y alone. We shall express d^2 in terms of y and leave it as an exercise for the reader to carry out the calculations when d^2 is expressed in terms of x.

Therefore the function f to be minimized is given by the formula

$$f(y) = d^2 = 4y + (y - b)^2 .$$

Although $f(y)$ is defined for all real y, the nature of the problem requires that we seek the minimum only among those $y \geq 0$. The derivative, given by $f'(y) = 4 + 2(y - b)$, is zero only when $y = b - 2$. When $b < 2$, this leads to a negative critical point y which is excluded by the restriction $y \geq 0$. In other words, if $b < 2$, the minimum does not occur at a critical point. In fact, when $b < 2$, we see that $f'(y) > 0$ when $y \geq 0$, and hence f is strictly increasing for $y \geq 0$. Therefore the absolute minimum occurs at the endpoint $y = 0$. The corresponding minimum d is $\sqrt{b^2} = |b|$.

If $b \geq 2$, there is a legitimate critical point at $y = b - 2$. Since $f''(y) = 2$ for all y, the derivative f' is increasing, and hence the *absolute minimum* of f occurs at this critical point. The minimum d is $\sqrt{4(b - 2) + 4} = 2\sqrt{b - 1}$. Thus we have shown that the minimum distance is $|b|$ if $b < 2$ and is $2\sqrt{b - 1}$ if $b \geq 2$. (The value $b = 2$ is the special value referred to above.)

4.21 Exercises

1. Prove that among all rectangles of a given area, the square has the smallest perimeter.
2. A farmer has L feet of fencing to enclose a rectangular pasture adjacent to a long stone wall. What dimensions give the maximum area of the pasture?
3. A farmer wishes to enclose a rectangular pasture of area A adjacent to a long stone wall. What dimensions require the least amount of fencing?
4. Given $S > 0$. Prove that among all positive numbers x and y with $x + y = S$, the sum $x^2 + y^2$ is smallest when $x = y$.
5. Given $R > 0$. Prove that among all positive numbers x and y with $x^2 + y^2 = R$, the sum $x + y$ is largest when $x = y$.
6. Each edge of a square has length L. Prove that among all squares inscribed in the given square, the one of minimum area has edges of length $\frac{1}{2}L\sqrt{2}$.
7. Each edge of a square has length L, Find the size of the square of largest area that can be circumscribed about the given square.
8. Prove that among all rectangles that can be inscribed in a given circle, the square has the largest area.
9. Prove that among all rectangles of a given area, the square has the smallest circumscribed circle.
10. Given a sphere of radius R. Find the radius r and altitude h of the right circular cylinder with largest lateral surface area $2\pi rh$ that can be inscribed in the sphere.
11. Among all right circular cylinders of given lateral surface area, prove that the smallest circumscribed sphere has radius $\sqrt{2}$ times that of the cylinder.

12. Given a right circular cone with radius R and altitude H. Find the radius and altitude of the right circular cylinder of largest lateral surface area that can be inscribed in the cone.

13. Find the dimensions of the right circular cylinder of maximum volume that can be inscribed in a right circular cone of radius R and altitude H.

14. Given a sphere of radius R. Compute, in terms of R, the radius r and the altitude h of the right circular cone of maximum volume that can be inscribed in this sphere.

15. Find the rectangle of largest area that can be inscribed in a semicircle, the lower base being on the diameter.

16. Find the trapezoid of largest area that can be inscribed in a semicircle, the lower base being on the diameter.

17. An open box is made from a rectangular piece of material by removing equal squares at each corner and turning up the sides. Find the dimensions of the box of largest volume that can be made in this manner if the material has sides (a) 10 and 10; (b) 12 and 18.

18. If a and b are the legs of a right triangle whose hypotenuse is 1, find the largest value of $2a + b$.

19. A truck is to be driven 300 miles on a freeway at a constant speed of x miles per hour. Speed laws require $30 \leq x \leq 60$. Assume that fuel costs 30 cents per gallon and is consumed at the rate of $2 + x^2/600$ gallons per hour. If the driver's wages are D dollars per hour and if he obeys all speed laws, find the most economical speed and the cost of the trip if (a) $D = 0$, (b) $D = 1$, (c) $D = 2$, (d) $D = 3$, (e) $D = 4$.

20. A cylinder is obtained by revolving a rectangle about the x-axis, the base of the rectangle lying on the x-axis and the entire rectangle lying in the region between the curve $y = x/(x^2 + 1)$ and the x-axis. Find the maximum possible volume of the cylinder.

21. The lower right-hand corner of a page is folded over so as to reach the leftmost edge. (See Figure 4.17.) If the width of the page is six inches, find the minimum length of the crease. What angle will this minimal crease make with the rightmost edge of the page? Assume the page is long enough to prevent the crease reaching the top of the page.

FIGURE 4.17   Exercise 21.

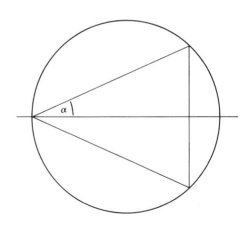

FIGURE 4.18   Exercise 22.

22. (a) An isosceles triangle is inscribed in a circle of radius r as shown in Figure 4.18. If the angle 2α at the apex is restricted to lie between 0 and $\frac{1}{2}\pi$, find the largest value and the smallest value of the perimeter of the triangle. Give full details of your reasoning.

(b) What is the radius of the smallest circular disk large enough to cover *every* isosceles triangle of a given perimeter L? Give full details of your reasoning.

23. A window is to be made in the form of a rectangle surmounted by a semicircle with diameter equal to the base of the rectangle. The rectangular portion is to be of clear glass, and the semicircular portion is to be of a colored glass admitting only half as much light per square foot as the clear glass. The total perimeter of the window frame is to be a fixed length P. Find, in terms of P, the dimensions of the window which will admit the most light.

24. A log 12 feet long has the shape of a frustum of a right circular cone with diameters 4 feet and $(4 + h)$ feet at its ends, where $h \geq 0$. Determine, as a function of h, the volume of the largest right circular cylinder that can be cut from the log, if its axis coincides with that of the log.

25. Given n real numbers $a_1, \ldots, a_n$. Prove that the sum $\sum_{k=1}^{n} (x - a_k)^2$ is smallest when x is the arithmetic mean of $a_1, \ldots, a_n$.

26. If $x > 0$, let $f(x) = 5x^2 + Ax^{-5}$, where A is a positive constant. Find the smallest A such that $f(x) \geq 24$ for all $x > 0$.

27. For each real t, let $f(x) = -\frac{1}{3}x^3 + t^2 x$, and let $m(t)$ denote the minimum of $f(x)$ over the interval $0 \leq x \leq 1$. Determine the value of $m(t)$ for each t in the interval $-1 \leq t \leq 1$. Remember that for some values of t the minimum of $f(x)$ may occur at the endpoints of the interval $0 \leq x \leq 1$.

28. A number x is known to lie in an interval $a \leq x \leq b$, where $a > 0$. We wish to approximate x by another number t in $[a, b]$ so that the relative error, $|t - x|/x$, will be as small as possible. Let $M(t)$ denote the maximum value of $|t - x|/x$ as x varies from a to b. (a) Prove that this maximum occurs at one of the endpoints $x = a$ or $x = b$. (b) Prove that $M(t)$ is smallest when t is the harmonic mean of a and b, that is, when $1/t = \frac{1}{2}(1/a + 1/b)$.

★4.22 Partial derivatives

This section explains the concept of partial derivative and introduces the reader to some notation and terminology. We shall not make use of the results of this section anywhere else in Volume I, so this material may be omitted or postponed without loss in continuity.

In Chapter 1, a function was defined to be a correspondence which associates with each object in a set X one and only one object in another set Y; the set X is referred to as the *domain* of the function. Up to now, we have dealt with functions having a domain consisting of points on the x-axis. Such functions are usually called *functions of one real variable*. It is not difficult to extend many of the ideas of calculus to functions of two or more real variables.

By a *real-valued function of two real variables* we mean one whose domain X is a set of points in the xy-plane. If f denotes such a function, its value at a point (x, y) is a real number, written $f(x, y)$. It is easy to imagine how such a function might arise in a physical problem. For example, suppose a flat metal plate in the shape of a circular disk of radius 4 centimeters is placed on the xy-plane, with the center of the disk at the origin and with the disk heated in such a way that its temperature at each point (x, y) is $16 - x^2 - y^2$ degrees centigrade. If we denote the temperature at (x, y) by $f(x, y)$, then f is a function of two variables defined by the equation

$$(4.27) \qquad\qquad f(x, y) = 16 - x^2 - y^2.$$

The domain of this function is the set of all points (x, y) whose distance from the origin does not exceed 4. The theorem of Pythagoras tells us that all points (x, y) at a distance

r from the origin satisfy the equation

(4.28) $$x^2 + y^2 = r^2.$$

Therefore the domain in this case consists of all points (x, y) which satisfy the inequality $x^2 + y^2 \leq 16$. Note that on the circle described by (4.28), the temperature is $f(x, y) = 16 - r^2$. That is, the function f is constant on each circle with center at the origin. (See Figure 4.19.)

We shall describe two useful methods for obtaining a geometric picture of a function of two variables. One is by means of a *surface* in space. To construct this surface, we introduce a third coordinate axis (called the z-axis); it passes through the origin and is perpendicular

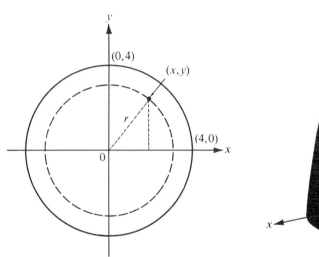

FIGURE 4.19   The temperature is constant on each circle with center at the origin.

FIGURE 4.20   The surface represented by the equation $z = 16 - x^2 - y^2$.

to the xy-plane. Above each point (x, y) we plot the point (x, y, z) whose z-coordinate is obtained from the equation $z = f(x, y)$.

The surface for the example described above is shown in Figure 4.20. If we placed a thermometer at a point (x, y) on the plate, the top of the mercury column would just touch the surface at the point (x, y, z) where $z = f(x, y)$ provided, of course, that unit distances on the z-axis are properly chosen.

A different kind of picture of a function of two variables can be drawn entirely in the xy-plane. This is the method of *contour lines* that is used by map makers to represent a three-dimensional landscape by a two-dimensional drawing. We imagine that the surface described above has been cut by various horizontal planes (parallel to the xy-plane). They intersect the surface at those points (x, y, z) whose elevation z is constant. By projecting these points on the xy-plane, we get a family of contour lines or *level curves*. Each level curve consists of those and only those points (x, y) whose coordinates satisfy the equation

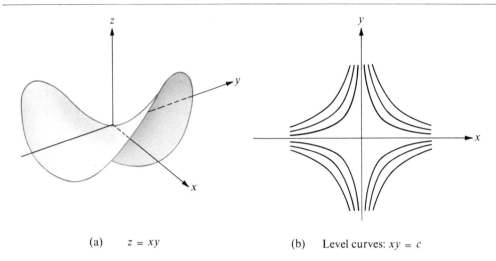

(a) $z = xy$ (b)   Level curves: $xy = c$

FIGURE 4.21   (a) A surface whose equation is $z = xy$.   (b) The corresponding level
curves $xy = $ constant.

$f(x, y) = c$, where c is the constant elevation for that particular curve. In the example
mentioned above, the level curves are concentric circles, and they represent curves of
constant temperature, or *isothermals*, as might be drawn on a weather map. Another
example of a surface and its level curves is shown in Figure 4.21. The equation in this case
is $z = xy$. The "saddle-shaped" surface is known as a *hyperbolic paraboloid*.

Contour lines on topographic maps are often shown for every 100 ft of elevation. When
they are close together, the elevation is changing rapidly as we move from one contour to
the next; this happens in the vicinity of a steep mountain. When the contour lines are far
apart the elevation is changing slowly. We can get a general idea of the steepness of a

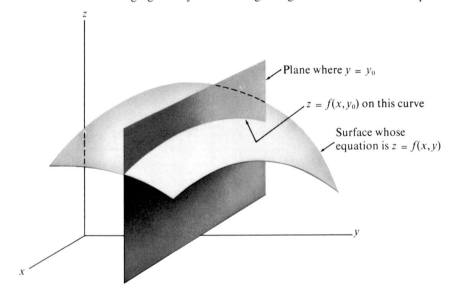

FIGURE 4.22   The curve of intersection of a surface $z = f(x, y)$ and a plane $y = y_0$.

landscape by considering the spacing of its level curves. However, to get precise information concerning the rate of change of the elevation, we must describe the surface in terms of a function to which we can apply the ideas of differential calculus.

The rate at which the elevation is changing at a point (x_0, y_0) depends on the direction in which we move away from this point. For the sake of simplicity, we shall consider at this time just the two special directions parallel to the x- and y-axes. Suppose we examine a surface described by an equation of the form $z = f(x, y)$; let us cut this surface with a plane perpendicular to the y-axis, as shown in Figure 4.22. Such a plane consists of all points (x, y, z) in space for which the y-coordinate is constant, say $y = y_0$. (The equation $y = y_0$ is called an equation of this plane.) The intersection of this plane with the surface is a plane curve, all points of which satisfy the equation $z = f(x, y_0)$. On this curve the elevation $f(x, y_0)$ is a function of x alone.

Suppose now we move from a point (x_0, y_0) to a point $(x_0 + h, y_0)$. The corresponding change in elevation is $f(x_0 + h, y_0) - f(x_0, y_0)$. This suggests that we form the difference quotient

(4.29)
$$\frac{f(x_0 + h, y_0) - f(x_0, y_0)}{h}$$

and let $h \to 0$. If this quotient approaches a definite limit as $h \to 0$, we call this limit the *partial derivative of f with respect to x* at (x_0, y_0). There are various symbols that are used to denote partial derivatives, some of the most common ones being

$$\frac{\partial f(x_0, y_0)}{\partial x}, \qquad f'_x(x_0, y_0), \qquad f_x(x_0, y_0), \qquad f_1(x_0, y_0), \qquad D_1 f(x_0, y_0).$$

The subscript 1 in the last two notations refers to the fact that only the first coordinate is allowed to change when we form the difference quotient in (4.29). Thus we have

$$f_1(x_0, y_0) = \lim_{h \to 0} \frac{f(x_0 + h, y_0) - f(x_0, y_0)}{h}.$$

Similarly, we define the *partial derivative with respect to y* at (x_0, y_0) by the equation

$$f_2(x_0, y_0) = \lim_{k \to 0} \frac{f(x_0, y_0 + k) - f(x_0, y_0)}{k},$$

alternative notations being

$$\frac{\partial f(x_0, y_0)}{\partial y}, \qquad f'_y(x_0, y_0), \qquad f_y(x_0, y_0), \qquad D_2 f(x_0, y_0).$$

If we write $z = f(x, y)$, then $\partial z/\partial x$ and $\partial z/\partial y$ are also used to denote partial derivatives.

Partial differentiation is not a new concept. If we introduce another function g of one variable, defined by the equation

$$g(x) = f(x, y_0),$$

then the ordinary derivative $g'(x_0)$ is exactly the same as the partial derivative $f_1(x_0, y_0)$. Geometrically, the partial derivative $f_1(x, y_0)$ represents the slope of the tangent line at a typical point of the curve shown in Figure 4.22. In the same way, when x is constant, say $x = x_0$, the equation $z = f(x_0, y)$ describes the curve of intersection of the surface with the plane whose equation is $x = x_0$. The partial derivative $f_2(x_0, y)$ gives the slope of the line tangent to this curve. From these remarks we see that to compute the partial derivative of $f(x, y)$ with respect to x, we can treat y as though it were constant and use the ordinary rules of differential calculus. Thus, for example, if $f(x, y) = 16 - x^2 - y^2$, we get $f_1(x, y) = -2x$. Similarly, if we hold x fixed, we find $f_2(x, y) = -2y$.

Another example is the function given by

$$(4.30) \qquad f(x, y) = x \sin y + y^2 \cos xy .$$

Its partial derivatives are

$$f_1(x, y) = \sin y - y^3 \sin xy , \qquad f_2(x, y) = x \cos y - xy^2 \sin xy + 2y \cos xy .$$

Partial differentiation is a process which produces new functions $f_1 = \partial f / \partial x$ and $f_2 = \partial f / \partial y$ from a given function f. Since f_1 and f_2 are also functions of two variables, we can consider *their* partial derivatives. These are called *second-order* partial derivatives of f, denoted as follows:

$$f_{1,1} = f_{xx} = \frac{\partial^2 f}{\partial x^2} , \qquad f_{1,2} = f_{xy} = \frac{\partial^2 f}{\partial y \, \partial x} , \qquad f_{2,1} = f_{yx} = \frac{\partial^2 f}{\partial x \, \partial y} , \qquad f_{2,2} = f_{yy} = \frac{\partial^2 f}{\partial y^2} .$$

Notice that $f_{1,2}$ means $(f_1)_2$, the partial derivative of f_1 with respect to y. In the ∂-notation, we indicate the order of derivatives by writing

$$\frac{\partial^2 f}{\partial y \, \partial x} = \frac{\partial}{\partial y} \left(\frac{\partial f}{\partial x} \right) .$$

This does not always yield the same result as the other mixed partial derivative,

$$\frac{\partial^2 f}{\partial x \, \partial y} = \frac{\partial}{\partial x} \left(\frac{\partial f}{\partial y} \right) .$$

However, equality of the two mixed partial derivatives does hold under certain conditions that are usually satisfied by most functions that occur in practice. We shall discuss these conditions further in Volume II.

Referring to the example in (4.27), we find that its second-order partial derivatives are given by the following formulas:

$$f_{1,1}(x, y) = -2, \qquad f_{1,2}(x, y) = f_{2,1}(x, y) = 0, \qquad f_{2,2}(x, y) = -2 .$$

For the example in (4.30), we obtain

$$f_{1,1}(x, y) = -y^4 \cos xy \,,$$
$$f_{1,2}(x, y) = \cos y - xy^3 \cos xy - 3y^2 \sin xy \,,$$
$$f_{2,1}(x, y) = \cos y - xy^3 \cos xy - y^2 \sin xy - 2y^2 \sin xy = f_{1,2}(x, y) \,,$$
$$f_{2,2}(x, y) = -x \sin y - x^2 y^2 \cos xy - 2xy \sin xy - 2xy \sin xy + 2 \cos xy$$
$$= -x \sin y - x^2 y^2 \cos xy - 4xy \sin xy + 2 \cos xy \,.$$

A more detailed study of partial derivatives will be undertaken in Volume II.

⋆4.23 Exercises

In Exercises 1 through 8, compute all first- and second-order partial derivatives. In each case verify that the mixed partial derivatives $f_{1,2}(x, y)$ and $f_{2,1}(x, y)$ are equal.

1. $f(x, y) = x^4 + y^4 - 4x^2 y^2$.

2. $f(x, y) = x \sin (x + y)$.

3. $f(x, y) = xy + \dfrac{x}{y} \qquad (y \neq 0)$.

4. $f(x, y) = \sqrt{x^2 + y^2}$.

5. $f(x, y) = \sin (x^2 y^3)$.

6. $f(x, y) = \sin [\cos (2x - 3y)]$.

7. $f(x, y) = \dfrac{x + y}{x - y} \qquad (x \neq y)$.

8. $f(x, y) = \dfrac{x}{\sqrt{x^2 + y^2}} \qquad (x, y) \neq (0, 0)$.

9. Show that $x(\partial z/\partial x) + y(\partial z/\partial y) = 2z$ if (a) $z = (x - 2y)^2$, (b) $z = (x^4 + y^4)^{1/2}$.

10. If $f(x, y) = xy/(x^2 + y^2)^2$ for $(x, y) \neq (0, 0)$, show that

$$\frac{\partial^2 f}{\partial x^2} + \frac{\partial^2 f}{\partial y^2} = 0.$$

5

THE RELATION BETWEEN INTEGRATION AND DIFFERENTIATION

5.1 The derivative of an indefinite integral. The first fundamental theorem of calculus

We come now to the remarkable connection that exists between integration and differentiation. The relationship between these two processes is somewhat analogous to that which holds between "squaring" and "taking the square root." If we square a positive number and then take the positive square root of the result, we get the original number back again. Similarly, if we operate on a continuous function f by integration, we get a new function (an indefinite integral of f) which, when differentiated, leads back to the original function f. For example, if $f(x) = x^2$, then an indefinite integral A of f may be defined by the equation

$$A(x) = \int_c^x f(t) \, dt = \int_c^x t^2 \, dt = \frac{x^3}{3} - \frac{c^3}{3},$$

where c is a constant. Differentiating, we find $A'(x) = x^2 = f(x)$. This example illustrates a general result, called the first fundamental theorem of calculus, which may be stated as follows:

THEOREM 5.1. FIRST FUNDAMENTAL THEOREM OF CALCULUS. *Let f be a function that is integrable on $[a, x]$ for each x in $[a, b]$. Let c be such that $a \leq c \leq b$ and define a new function A as follows:*

$$A(x) = \int_c^x f(t) \, dt \qquad if \qquad a \leq x \leq b \,.$$

Then the derivative $A'(x)$ exists at each point x in the open interval (a, b) where f is continuous, and for such x we have

(5.1) $A'(x) = f(x) \,.$

First we give a geometric argument which suggests why the theorem ought to be true; then we give an analytic proof.

202

Geometric motivation. Figure 5.1 shows the graph of a function f over an interval $[a, b]$. In the figure, h is positive and

$$\int_x^{x+h} f(t)\, dt = \int_c^{x+h} f(t)\, dt - \int_c^x f(t)\, dt = A(x+h) - A(x).$$

The example shown is continuous throughout the interval $[x, x + h]$. Therefore, by the mean-value theorem for integrals, we have

$$A(x+h) - A(x) = hf(z), \qquad \text{where} \quad x \le z \le x + h.$$

Hence we have

(5.2) $$\frac{A(x+h) - A(x)}{h} = f(z),$$

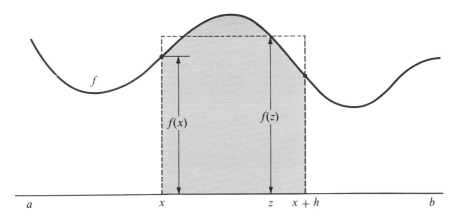

f

$f(x)$

$f(z)$

$a \qquad\qquad x \qquad\qquad z \quad x+h \qquad\qquad b$

FIGURE 5.1   Geometric motivation for the first fundamental theorem of calculus.

and, since $x \le z \le x + h$, we find that $f(z) \to f(x)$ as $h \to 0$ through positive values. A similar argument is valid if $h \to 0$ through negative values. Therefore, $A'(x)$ exists and is equal to $f(x)$.

This argument assumes that the function f is continuous in some *neighborhood* of the point x. However, the hypothesis of the theorem refers only to continuity of f at a *single point* x. Therefore, we use a different method to prove the theorem under this weaker hypothesis.

Analytic Proof.   Let x be a point of continuity of f, keep x fixed, and form the quotient

$$\frac{A(x+h) - A(x)}{h}.$$

To prove the theorem we must show that this quotient approaches the limit $f(x)$ as $h \to 0$. The numerator is

$$A(x+h) - A(x) = \int_c^{x+h} f(t)\, dt - \int_c^x f(t)\, dt = \int_x^{x+h} f(t)\, dt.$$

If we write $f(t) = f(x) + [f(t) - f(x)]$ in the last integral, we obtain

$$A(x + h) - A(x) = \int_x^{x+h} f(x)\, dt + \int_x^{x+h} [f(t) - f(x)]\, dt$$

$$= hf(x) + \int_x^{x+h} [f(t) - f(x)]\, dt\,,$$

from which we find

(5.3) $$\frac{A(x + h) - A(x)}{h} = f(x) + \frac{1}{h} \int_x^{x+h} [f(t) - f(x)]\, dt\,.$$

Therefore, to complete the proof of (5.1), all we need to do is show that

$$\lim_{h \to 0} \frac{1}{h} \int_x^{x+h} [f(t) - f(x)]\, dt = 0\,.$$

It is this part of the proof that makes use of the continuity of f at x.

Let us denote the second term on the right of (5.3) by $G(h)$. We are to prove that $G(h) \to 0$ as $h \to 0$. Using the definition of limit, we must show that for every $\epsilon > 0$ there is a $\delta > 0$ such that

(5.4) $$|G(h)| < \epsilon \qquad \text{whenever} \quad 0 < |h| < \delta\,.$$

Continuity of f at x tells us that, if ϵ is given, there is a positive δ such that

(5.5) $$|f(t) - f(x)| < \tfrac{1}{2}\epsilon$$

whenever

(5.6) $$x - \delta < t < x + \delta\,.$$

If we choose h so that $0 < h < \delta$, then every t in the interval $[x, x + h]$ satisfies (5.6) and hence (5.5) holds for every such t. Using the property $|\int_x^{x+h} g(t)\, dt| \leq \int_x^{x+h} |g(t)|\, dt$ with $g(t) = f(t) - f(x)$, we see that the inequality in (5.5) leads to the relation

$$\left| \int_x^{x+h} [f(t) - f(x)]\, dt \right| \leq \int_x^{x+h} |f(t) - f(x)|\, dt \leq \int_x^{x+h} \tfrac{1}{2}\epsilon\, dt = \tfrac{1}{2}h\epsilon < h\epsilon\,.$$

If we divide by h, we see that (5.4) holds for $0 < h < \delta$. If $h < 0$, a similar argument proves that (5.4) holds whenever $0 < |h| < \delta$, and this completes the proof.

5.2 The zero-derivative theorem

If a function f is constant on an open interval (a, b), its derivative is zero everywhere on (a, b). We proved this fact earlier as an immediate consequence of the definition of derivative. We also proved, as part (c) of Theorem 4.7, the converse of this statement which we restate here as a separate theorem.

THEOREM 5.2. ZERO-DERIVATIVE THEOREM. *If $f'(x) = 0$ for each x in an open interval I, then f is constant on I.*

This theorem, when used in combination with the first fundamental theorem of calculus, leads to the second fundamental theorem which is described in the next section.

5.3 Primitive functions and the second fundamental theorem of calculus

DEFINITION OF PRIMITIVE FUNCTION. *A function P is called a primitive (or an antiderivative) of a function f on an open interval I if the derivative of P is f, that is, if $P'(x) = f(x)$ for all x in I.*

For example, the sine function is a primitive of the cosine on every interval because the derivative of the sine is the cosine. We speak of *a* primitive, rather than *the* primitive, because if P is a primitive of f then so is $P + k$ for every constant k. Conversely, any two primitives P and Q of the same function f can differ only by a constant because their difference $P - Q$ has the derivative

$$P'(x) - Q'(x) = f(x) - f(x) = 0$$

for every x in I and hence, by Theorem 5.2, $P - Q$ is constant on I.

The first fundamental theorem of calculus tells us that we can always construct a primitive of a continuous function by integration. When we combine this with the fact that two primitives of the same function can differ only by a constant, we obtain the second fundamental theorem of calculus.

THEOREM 5.3. SECOND FUNDAMENTAL THEOREM OF CALCULUS. *Assume f is continuous on an open interval I, and let P be any primitive of f on I. Then, for each c and each x in I, we have*

(5.7) $$P(x) = P(c) + \int_c^x f(t)\, dt\,.$$

Proof. Let $A(x) = \int_c^x f(t)\, dt$. Since f is continuous at each x in I, the first fundamental theorem tells us that $A'(x) = f(x)$ for all x in I. In other words, A is a primitive of f on I. Since two primitives of f can differ only by a constant, we must have $A(x) - P(x) = k$ for some constant k. When $x = c$, this formula implies $-P(c) = k$, since $A(c) = 0$. Therefore, $A(x) - P(x) = -P(c)$, from which we obtain (5.7).

Theorem 5.3 tells us how to find every primitive P of a continuous function f. We simply integrate f from a fixed point c to an arbitrary point x and add the constant $P(c)$ to get $P(x)$. But the real power of the theorem becomes apparent when we write Equation (5.7) in the following form:

(5.8) $$\int_c^x f(t)\, dt = P(x) - P(c)\,.$$

In this form it tells us that we can compute the value of an integral by a mere subtraction if we know a primitive P. The problem of evaluating an integral is transferred to another problem—that of finding a primitive P of f. In actual practice, the second problem is a great deal easier to deal with than the first. Every differentiation formula, when read in reverse, gives us an example of a primitive of some function f and this, in turn, leads to an integration formula for this function.

From the differentiation formulas worked out thus far we can derive the following integration formulas as consequences of the second fundamental theorem.

EXAMPLE 1. *Integration of rational powers.* The integration formula

$$(5.9) \qquad \int_a^b x^n \, dx = \frac{b^{n+1} - a^{n+1}}{n + 1} \qquad (n = 0, 1, 2, \ldots)$$

was proved in Section 1.23 directly from the definition of the integral. The result may be rederived and generalized to rational exponents by using the second fundamental theorem. First of all, we observe that the function P defined by the equation

$$(5.10) \qquad P(x) = \frac{x^{n+1}}{n + 1}$$

has the derivative $P'(x) = x^n$ if n is any nonnegative integer. Since this is valid for all real x, we may use (5.8) to write

$$\int_a^b x^n \, dx = P(b) - P(a) = \frac{b^{n+1} - a^{n+1}}{n + 1}$$

for all intervals $[a, b]$. This formula, proved for all integers $n \geq 0$, also holds for all negative integers except $n = -1$, which is excluded because $n + 1$ appears in the denominator. To prove (5.9) for negative n, it suffices to show that (5.10) implies $P'(x) = x^n$ when n is negative and $\neq -1$, a fact which is easily verified by differentiating P as a rational function. Of course, when n is negative, neither $P(x)$ nor $P'(x)$ is defined for $x = 0$, and when we use (5.9) for negative n, it is important to exclude those intervals $[a, b]$ that contain the point $x = 0$.

The results of Example 3 in Section 4.5 enable us to extend (5.9) to all *rational* exponents (except -1), provided the integrand is defined everywhere on the interval $[a, b]$ under consideration. For example, if $0 < a < b$ and $n = -\frac{1}{2}$, we find

$$\int_a^b \frac{1}{\sqrt{x}} \, dx = \int_a^b x^{-1/2} dx = \frac{x^{1/2}}{\frac{1}{2}} \Big|_a^b = 2(\sqrt{b} - \sqrt{a}) \,.$$

This result was proved earlier, using the area axioms. The present proof makes no use of these axioms.

In the next chapter we shall define a general power function f such that $f(x) = x^c$ for *every real exponent* c. We shall find that this function has the derivative $f'(x) = cx^{c-1}$ and the primitive $P(x) = x^{c+1}/(c + 1)$ if $c \neq -1$. This will enable us to extend (5.9) to all real exponents except -1.

Note that we cannot get $P'(x) = 1/x$ by differentiation of any function of the form $P(x) = x^n$. Nevertheless, there exists a function P whose derivative is $P'(x) = 1/x$. To exhibit such a function all we need to do is write a suitable indefinite integral; for example,

$$P(x) = \int_1^x \frac{1}{t}\, dt \qquad \text{if} \qquad x > 0 \,.$$

This integral exists because the integrand is monotonic. The function so defined is called the *logarithm* (more specifically, the *natural logarithm*). Its properties are developed systematically in Chapter 6.

EXAMPLE 2. *Integration of the sine and cosine.* Since the derivative of the sine is the cosine and the derivative of the cosine is minus the sine, the second fundamental theorem also gives us the following formulas:

$$\int_a^b \cos x \, dx = \sin x \,\Big|_a^b = \sin b - \sin a \,,$$

$$\int_a^b \sin x \, dx = (-\cos x) \,\Big|_a^b = \cos a - \cos b \,.$$

These formulas were also proved in Chapter 2 directly from the definition of the integral.

Further examples of integration formulas can be obtained from Examples 1 and 2 by taking finite sums of terms of the form Ax^n, $B \sin x$, $C \cos x$, where A, B, C are constants.

5.4 Properties of a function deduced from properties of its derivative

If a function f has a continuous derivative f' on an open interval I, the second fundamental theorem states that

$$(5.11) \qquad\qquad f(x) = f(c) + \int_c^x f'(t) \, dt$$

for every choice of points x and c in I. This formula, which expresses f in terms of its derivative f', enables us to deduce properties of a function from properties of its derivative. Although the following properties have already been discussed in Chapter 4, it may be of interest to see how they can also be deduced as simple consequences of Equation (5.11).

Suppose f' is continuous and nonnegative on I. If $x > c$, then $\int_c^x f'(t) \, dt \geq 0$, and hence $f(x) \geq f(c)$. In other words, if the derivative is continuous and nonnegative on I, the function is increasing on I.

In Theorem 2.9 we proved that the indefinite integral of an increasing function is convex. Therefore, if f' is continuous and increasing on I, Equation (5.11) shows that f is convex on I. Similarly, f is concave on those intervals where f' is continuous and decreasing.

5.5   Exercises

In each of Exercises 1 through 10, find a primitive of f; that is, find a function P such that $P'(x) = f(x)$ and use the second fundamental theorem to evaluate $\int_a^b f(x)\,dx$.

1. $f(x) = 5x^3$.

2. $f(x) = 4x^4 - 12x$.

3. $f(x) = (x + 1)(x^3 - 2)$.

4. $f(x) = \dfrac{x^4 + x - 3}{x^3}$, $x \neq 0$.

5. $f(x) = (1 + \sqrt{x})^2$, $x > 0$.

6. $f(x) = \sqrt{2x} + \sqrt{\tfrac{1}{2}x}$, $x > 0$.

7. $f(x) = \dfrac{2x^2 - 6x + 7}{2\sqrt{x}}$, $x > 0$.

8. $f(x) = 2x^{1/3} - x^{-1/3}$, $x > 0$.

9. $f(x) = 3 \sin x + 2x^5$.

10. $f(x) = x^{4/3} - 5 \cos x$.

11. Prove that there is no polynomial f whose derivative is given by the formula $f'(x) = 1/x$.

12. Show that $\int_0^x |t|\,dt = \tfrac{1}{2}x|x|$ for all real x.

13. Show that
$$\int_0^x (t + |t|)^2\,dt = \frac{2x^2}{3}(x + |x|) \qquad \text{for all real } x\,.$$

14. A function f is continuous everywhere and satisfies the equation
$$\int_0^x f(t)\,dt = -\tfrac{1}{2} + x^2 + x \sin 2x + \tfrac{1}{2}\cos 2x$$
for all x. Compute $f(\tfrac{1}{4}\pi)$ and $f'(\tfrac{1}{4}\pi)$.

15. Find a function f and a value of the constant c such that
$$\int_c^x f(t)\,dt = \cos x - \tfrac{1}{2} \qquad \text{for all real } x\,.$$

16. Find a function f and a value of the constant c such that
$$\int_c^x tf(t)\,dt = \sin x - x \cos x - \tfrac{1}{2}x^2 \qquad \text{for all real } x\,.$$

17. There is a function f, defined and continuous for all real x, which satisfies an equation of the form
$$\int_0^x f(t)\,dt = \int_x^1 t^2 f(t)\,dt + \frac{x^{16}}{8} + \frac{x^{18}}{9} + c\,,$$
where c is a constant. Find an explicit formula for $f(x)$ and find the value of the constant c.

18. A function f is defined for all real x by the formula
$$f(x) = 3 + \int_0^x \frac{1 + \sin t}{2 + t^2}\,dt\,.$$

Without attempting to evaluate this integral, find a quadratic polynomial $p(x) = a + bx + cx^2$ such that $p(0) = f(0)$, $p'(0) = f'(0)$, and $p''(0) = f''(0)$.

19. Given a function g, continuous everywhere, such that $g(1) = 5$ and $\int_0^1 g(t)\,dt = 2$. Let $f(x) = \frac{1}{2}\int_0^x (x - t)^2 g(t)\,dt$. Prove that

$$f'(x) = x \int_0^x g(t)\,dt - \int_0^x tg(t)\,dt\,,$$

then compute $f''(1)$ and $f'''(1)$.

20. Without attempting to evaluate the following indefinite integrals, find the derivative $f'(x)$ in each case if $f(x)$ is equal to

(a) $\int_0^x (1 + t^2)^{-3}\,dt\,,$ (b) $\int_0^{x^2} (1 + t^2)^{-3}\,dt\,,$ (c) $\int_{x^3}^{x^2} (1 + t^2)^{-3}\,dt\,.$

21. Without attempting to evaluate the integral, compute $f'(x)$ if f is defined by the formula

$$f(x) = \int_{x^3}^{x^2} \frac{t^6}{1 + t^4}\,dt\,.$$

22. In each case, compute $f(2)$ if f is continuous and satisfies the given formula for all $x \geq 0$.

(a) $\int_0^x f(t)\,dt = x^2(1 + x)\,.$ (c) $\int_0^{f(x)} t^2\,dt = x^2(1 + x)\,.$

(b) $\int_0^{x^2} f(t)\,dt = x^2(1 + x)\,.$ (d) $\int_0^{x^2(1+x)} f(t)\,dt = x\,.$

23. The base of a solid is the ordinate set of a nonnegative function f over the interval $[0, a]$. All cross sections perpendicular to this interval are squares. The volume of the solid is

$$a^3 - 2a\cos a + (2 - a^2)\sin a$$

for every $a \geq 0$. Assume f is continuous on $[0, a]$ and calculate $f(a)$.

24. A mechanism propels a particle along a straight line. It is designed so that the displacement of the particle at time t from an initial point 0 on the line is given by the formula $f(t) = \frac{1}{2}t^2 + 2t\sin t$. The mechanism works perfectly until time $t = \pi$ when an unexpected malfunction occurs. From then on the particle moves with constant velocity (the velocity it acquires at time $t = \pi$). Compute the following: (a) its velocity at time $t = \pi$; (b) its acceleration at time $t = \frac{1}{2}\pi$; (c) its acceleration at time $t = \frac{3}{2}\pi$; (d) its displacement from 0 at time $t = \frac{5}{2}\pi$. (e) Find a time $t > \pi$ when the particle returns to the initial point 0, or else prove that it never returns to 0.

25. A particle moves along a straight line. Its position at time t is $f(t)$. When $0 \leq t \leq 1$, the position is given by the integral

$$f(t) = \int_0^t \frac{1 + 2\sin \pi x \cos \pi x}{1 + x^2}\,dx\,.$$

(Do not attempt to evaluate this integral.) For $t \geq 1$, the particle moves with constant acceleration (the acceleration it acquires at time $t = 1$). Compute the following: (a) its acceleration at time $t = 2$; (b) its velocity when $t = 1$; (c) its velocity when $t > 1$; (d) the difference $f(t) - f(1)$ when $t > 1$.

26. In each case, find a function f with a continuous second derivative f'' which satisfies all the given conditions or else explain why such an example cannot exist.

(a) $f''(x) > 0$ for every x, $f'(0) = 1$, $f'(1) = 0$.
(b) $f''(x) > 0$ for every x, $f'(0) = 1$, $f'(1) = 3$.
(c) $f''(x) > 0$ for every x, $f'(0) = 1$, $f(x) \leq 100$ for all $x > 0$.
(d) $f''(x) > 0$ for every x, $f'(0) = 1$, $f(x) \leq 100$ for all $x < 0$.

27. A particle moves along a straight line, its position at time t being $f(t)$. It starts with an initial velocity $f'(0) = 0$ and has a continuous acceleration $f''(t) \geq 6$ for all t in the interval $0 \leq t \leq 1$. Prove that the velocity $f'(t) \geq 3$ for all t in some interval $[a, b]$, where $0 \leq a < b \leq 1$, with $b - a = \frac{1}{2}$.

28. Given a function f such that the integral $A(x) = \int_a^x f(t)\,dt$ exists for each x in an interval $[a, b]$. Let c be a point in the open interval (a, b). Consider the following ten statements about this f and this A:

(a) f is continuous at c.   (α) A is continuous at c.
(b) f is discontinuous at c.   (β) A is discontinuous at c.
(c) f is increasing on (a, b).   (γ) A is convex on (a, b).
(d) $f'(c)$ exists.   (δ) $A'(c)$ exists.
(e) f' is continuous at c.   (ϵ) A' is continuous at c.

In a table like the one shown here, mark T in the appropriate square if the statement labeled with a Latin letter always implies the statement labeled with a Greek letter. Leave the other squares blank. For example, if (a) implies (α), mark T in the upper left-hand corner square, etc.

	α	β	γ	δ	ϵ
a					
b					
c					
d					
e					

5.6 The Leibniz notation for primitives

We return now to a further study of the relationship between integration and differentiation. First we discuss some notation introduced by Leibniz.

We have defined a primitive P of a function f to be any function for which $P'(x) = f(x)$. If f is continuous on an interval, one primitive is given by a formula of the form

$$P(x) = \int_c^x f(t)\,dt \,,$$

and all other primitives can differ from this one only by a constant. Leibniz used the symbol $\int f(x)\,dx$ to denote a general primitive of f. In this notation, an equation like

(5.12) $$\int f(x)\,dx = P(x) + C$$

is considered to be merely an alternative way of writing $P'(x) = f(x)$. For example, since the derivative of the sine is the cosine, we may write

(5.13) $$\int \cos x\,dx = \sin x + C \,.$$

Similarly, since the derivative of $x^{n+1}/(n + 1)$ is x^n, we may write

(5.14) $$\int x^n\,dx = \frac{x^{n+1}}{n + 1} + C \,,$$

for any rational power $n \neq -1$. The symbol C represents an arbitrary constant so each of Equations (5.13) and (5.14) is really a statement about a whole set of functions.

Despite similarity in appearance, the symbol $\int f(x)\, dx$ is conceptually distinct from the integration symbol $\int_a^b f(x)\, dx$. The symbols originate from two entirely different processes—differentiation and integration. Since, however, the two processes are related by the fundamental theorems of calculus, there are corresponding relationships between the two symbols.

The first fundamental theorem states that any indefinite integral of f is also a primitive of f. Therefore we may replace $P(x)$ in Equation (5.12) by $\int_c^x f(t)\, dt$ for some lower limit c and write (5.12) as follows:

$$(5.15) \qquad \int f(x)\, dx = \int_c^x f(t)\, dt + C \,.$$

This means that we can think of the symbol $\int f(x)\, dx$ as representing some indefinite integral of f, plus a constant.

The second fundamental theorem tells us that for any primitive P of f and for any constant C, we have

$$\int_a^b f(x)\, dx = [P(x) + C]\Big|_a^b \,.$$

If we replace $P(x) + C$ by $\int f(x)\, dx$, this formula may be written in the form

$$(5.16) \qquad \int_a^b f(x)\, dx = \int f(x)\, dx \Big|_a^b \,.$$

The two formulas in (5.15) and (5.16) may be thought of as symbolic expressions of the first and second fundamental theorems of calculus.

Because of long historical usage, many calculus textbooks refer to the symbol $\int f(x)\, dx$ as an "indefinite integral" rather than as a primitive or an antiderivative. This is justified, in part, by Equation (5.15), which tells us that the symbol $\int f(x)\, dx$ is, apart from an additive constant C, an indefinite integral of f. For the same reason, many handbooks of mathematical tables contain extensive lists of formulas labeled "tables of indefinite integrals" which, in reality, are tables of primitives. To distinguish the symbol $\int f(x)\, dx$ from $\int_a^b f(x)\, dx$, the latter is called a *definite* integral. Since the second fundamental theorem reduces the problem of integration to that of finding a primitive, the term "technique of integration" is used to refer to any systematic method for finding primitives. This terminology is widely used in the mathematical literature, and it will be adopted also in this book. Thus, for example, when one is asked to "integrate" $\int f(x)\, dx$, it is to be understood that what is wanted is the most general primitive of f.

There are three principal techniques that are used to construct tables of indefinite integrals, and they should be learned by anyone who desires a good working knowledge of calculus. They are (1) *integration by substitution* (to be described in the next section), a method based on the chain rule; (2) *integration by parts*, a method based on the formula for differentiating a product (to be described in Section 5.9); and (3) *integration by partial fractions*, an algebraic technique which is discussed at the end of Chapter 6. These techniques not only explain how tables of indefinite integrals are constructed, but also they tell us how certain formulas are converted to the basic forms listed in the tables.

5.7   Integration by substitution

Let Q be a composition of two functions P and g, say $Q(x) = P[g(x)]$ for all x in some interval I. If we know the derivative of P, say $P'(x) = f(x)$, the chain rule tells us that the derivative of Q is given by the formula $Q'(x) = P'[g(x)]g'(x)$. Since $P' = f$, this states that $Q'(x) = f[g(x)]g'(x)$. In other words,

$$(5.17) \qquad P'(x) = f(x) \qquad \text{implies} \qquad Q'(x) = f[g(x)]g'(x) .$$

In Leibniz notation, this statement can be written as follows: If we have the integration formula

$$(5.18) \qquad \int f(x)\,dx = P(x) + C ,$$

then we also have the more general formula

$$(5.19) \qquad \int f[g(x)]g'(x)\,dx = P[g(x)] + C .$$

For example, if $f(x) = \cos x$, then (5.18) holds with $P(x) = \sin x$, so (5.19) becomes

$$(5.20) \qquad \int \cos g(x) \cdot g'(x)\,dx = \sin g(x) + C .$$

In particular, if $g(x) = x^3$, this gives us

$$\int \cos x^3 \cdot 3x^2\,dx = \sin x^3 + C ,$$

a result that is easily verified directly since the derivative of $\sin x^3$ is $3x^2 \cos x^3$.

Now we notice that the general formula in (5.19) is related to (5.18) by a simple mechanical process. Suppose we replace $g(x)$ everywhere in (5.19) by a new symbol u and replace $g'(x)$ by du/dx, the Leibniz notation for derivatives. Then (5.19) becomes

$$\int f(u)\,\frac{du}{dx}\,dx = P(u) + C .$$

At this stage the temptation is strong to replace the combination $\dfrac{du}{dx}\,dx$ by du. If we do this, the last formula becomes

$$(5.21) \qquad \int f(u)\,du = P(u) + C .$$

Notice that this has exactly the same form as (5.18), except that the symbol u appears everywhere instead of x. In other words, every integration formula such as (5.18) can be made to yield a more general integration formula if we simply substitute symbols. We replace x in (5.18) by a new symbol u to obtain (5.21), and then we think of u as representing a new function of x, say $u = g(x)$. Then we replace the symbol du by the combination $g'(x)\,dx$, and Equation (5.21) reduces to the general formula in (5.19).

For example, if we replace x by u in the formula $\int \cos x\,dx = \sin x + C$, we obtain

$$\int \cos u\,du = \sin u + C\,.$$

In this latter formula, u may be replaced by $g(x)$ and du by $g'(x)\,dx$, and a correct integration formula, (5.20), results.

When this mechanical process is used *in reverse*, it becomes the method of *integration by substitution*. The object of the method is to transform an integral with a complicated integrand, such as $\int 3x^2 \cos x^3\,dx$, into a more familiar integral, such as $\int \cos u\,du$. The method is applicable whenever the original integral can be written in the form

$$\int f[g(x)]g'(x)\,dx\,,$$

since the substitution

$$u = g(x), \qquad du = g'(x)\,dx\,,$$

transforms this to $\int f(u)\,du$. If we succeed in carrying out the integration indicated by $\int f(u)\,du$, we obtain a primitive, say $P(u)$, and then the original integral may be evaluated by replacing u by $g(x)$ in the formula for $P(u)$.

The reader should realize that we have attached no meanings to the symbols dx and du by themselves. They are used as purely formal devices to help us perform the mathematical operations in a mechanical way. Each time we use the process, we are really applying the statement (5.17).

Success in this method depends on one's ability to determine at the outset which part of the integrand should be replaced by the symbol u, and this ability comes from a lot of experience in working out specific examples. The following examples illustrate how the method is carried out in actual practice.

EXAMPLE 1. Integrate $\int x^3 \cos x^4\,dx$.

Solution. Let us keep in mind that we are trying to write $x^3 \cos x^4$ in the form $f[g(x)]g'(x)$ with a suitable choice of f and g. Since $\cos x^4$ is a composition, this suggests that we take $f(x) = \cos x$ and $g(x) = x^4$ so that $\cos x^4$ becomes $f[g(x)]$. This choice of g gives $g'(x) = 4x^3$, and hence $f[g(x)]g'(x) = (\cos x^4)(4x^3)$. The extra factor 4 is easily taken care of by multiplying and dividing the integrand by 4. Thus we have

$$x^3 \cos x^4 = \tfrac{1}{4}(\cos x^4)(4x^3) = \tfrac{1}{4}f[g(x)]g'(x)\,.$$

Now, we make the substitution $u = g(x) = x^4$, $du = g'(x)\,dx = 4x^3\,dx$, and obtain

$$\int x^3 \cos x^4\,dx = \tfrac{1}{4}\int f(u)\,du = \tfrac{1}{4}\int \cos u\,du = \tfrac{1}{4}\sin u + C\,.$$

Replacing u by x^4 in the end result, we obtain the formula

$$\int x^3 \cos x^4 \, dx = \tfrac{1}{4} \sin x^4 + C \, ,$$

which can be verified directly by differentiation.

After a little practice one can perform some of the above steps mentally, and the entire calculation can be given more briefly as follows: Let $u = x^4$. Then $du = 4x^3 \, dx$, and we obtain

$$\int x^3 \cos x^4 \, dx = \tfrac{1}{4} \int (\cos x^4)(4x^3 \, dx) = \tfrac{1}{4} \int \cos u \, du = \tfrac{1}{4} \sin u + C = \tfrac{1}{4} \sin x^4 + C \, .$$

Notice that the method works in this example because the factor x^3 has an exponent one less than the power of x which appears in $\cos x^4$.

EXAMPLE 2. Integrate $\int \cos^2 x \sin x \, dx$.

Solution. Let $u = \cos x$. Then $du = -\sin x \, dx$, and we get

$$\int \cos^2 x \sin x \, dx = -\int (\cos x)^2 (-\sin x \, dx) = -\int u^2 \, du = -\frac{u^3}{3} + C = -\frac{\cos^3 x}{3} + C \, .$$

Again, the final result is easily verified by differentiation.

EXAMPLE 3. Integrate $\displaystyle\int \frac{\sin \sqrt{x}}{\sqrt{x}} \, dx$.

Solution. Let $u = \sqrt{x} = x^{1/2}$. Then $du = \tfrac{1}{2} x^{-1/2} \, dx$, or $dx/\sqrt{x} = 2 \, du$. Hence

$$\int \frac{\sin \sqrt{x}}{\sqrt{x}} \, dx = 2 \int \sin u \, du = -2 \cos u + C = -2 \cos \sqrt{x} + C \, .$$

EXAMPLE 4. Integrate $\displaystyle\int \frac{x \, dx}{\sqrt{1 + x^2}}$.

Solution. Let $u = 1 + x^2$. Then $du = 2x \, dx$ so $x \, dx = \tfrac{1}{2} \, du$, and we obtain

$$\int \frac{x \, dx}{\sqrt{1 + x^2}} = \frac{1}{2} \int \frac{du}{\sqrt{u}} = \frac{1}{2} \int u^{-1/2} \, du = u^{1/2} + C = \sqrt{1 + x^2} + C \, .$$

The method of substitution is, of course, also applicable to definite integrals. For example, to evaluate the definite integral $\int_0^{\pi/2} \cos^2 x \sin x \, dx$, we first determine the indefinite integral, as explained in Example 2, and then we use the second fundamental theorem to write

$$\int_0^{\pi/2} \cos^2 x \sin x \, dx = -\frac{1}{3} \cos^3 x \, \Big|_0^{\pi/2} = -\frac{1}{3}\left(\cos^3 \frac{\pi}{2} - \cos^3 0\right) = \frac{1}{3}.$$

Sometimes it is desirable to apply the second fundamental theorem directly to the integral expressed in terms of u. This may be done by using new limits of integration. We shall illustrate how this is carried out in a particular example, and then we shall justify the process with a general theorem.

EXAMPLE 5. Evaluate $\displaystyle\int_2^3 \frac{(x+1)\,dx}{\sqrt{x^2 + 2x + 3}}$.

Solution. Let $u = x^2 + 2x + 3$. Then $du = (2x + 2)\,dx$, so that

$$\frac{(x+1)\,dx}{\sqrt{x^2 + 2x + 3}} = \frac{1}{2}\frac{du}{\sqrt{u}} \, .$$

Now we obtain new limits of integration by noting that $u = 11$ when $x = 2$, and that $u = 18$ when $x = 3$. Then we write

$$\int_2^3 \frac{(x+1)\,dx}{\sqrt{x^2 + 2x + 3}} = \frac{1}{2}\int_{11}^{18} u^{-1/2}\,du = \sqrt{u}\,\Big|_{11}^{18} = \sqrt{18} - \sqrt{11} \, .$$

The same result is arrived at by expressing everything in terms of x. Thus we have

$$\int_2^3 \frac{(x+1)\,dx}{\sqrt{x^2 + 2x + 3}} = \sqrt{x^2 + 2x + 3}\,\Big|_2^3 = \sqrt{18} - \sqrt{11} \, .$$

Now we prove a general theorem which justifies the process used in Example 5.

THEOREM 5.4. SUBSTITUTION THEOREM FOR INTEGRALS. *Assume g has a continuous derivative g' on an open interval I. Let J be the set of values taken by g on I and assume that f is continuous on J. Then for each x and c in I, we have*

(5.22) $$\int_c^x f[g(t)]g'(t)\,dt = \int_{g(c)}^{g(x)} f(u)\,du \, .$$

Proof. Let $a = g(c)$ and define two new functions P and Q as follows:

$$P(x) = \int_a^x f(u)\,du \quad \text{if} \quad x \in J, \qquad Q(x) = \int_c^x f[g(t)]g'(t)\,dt \quad \text{if} \quad x \in I.$$

Since P and Q are indefinite integrals of continuous functions, they have derivatives given by the formulas

$$P'(x) = f(x), \qquad Q'(x) = f[g(x)]g'(x).$$

Now let R denote the composite function, $R(x) = P[g(x)]$. Using the chain rule, we find

$$R'(x) = P'[g(x)]g'(x) = f[g(x)]g'(x) = Q'(x).$$

Applying the second fundamental theorem twice, we obtain

$$\int_{g(c)}^{g(x)} f(u)\, du = \int_{g(c)}^{g(x)} P'(u)\, du = P[g(x)] - P[g(c)] = R(x) - R(c),$$

and

$$\int_{c}^{x} f[g(t)]g'(t)\, dt = \int_{c}^{x} Q'(t)\, dt = \int_{c}^{x} R'(t)\, dt = R(x) - R(c).$$

This shows that the two integrals in (5.22) are equal.

5.8   Exercises

In Exercises 1 through 20, evaluate the integrals by the method of substitution.

1. $\int \sqrt{2x + 1}\, dx.$

2. $\int x\sqrt{1 + 3x}\, dx.$

3. $\int x^2 \sqrt{x + 1}\, dx.$

4. $\int_{-2/3}^{1/3} \dfrac{x\, dx}{\sqrt{2 - 3x}}.$

5. $\int \dfrac{(x + 1)\, dx}{(x^2 + 2x + 2)^3}.$

6. $\int \sin^3 x\, dx.$

7. $\int z(z - 1)^{1/3}\, dz.$

8. $\int \dfrac{\cos x\, dx}{\sin^3 x}.$

9. $\int_{0}^{\pi/4} \cos 2x\sqrt{4 - \sin 2x}\, dx.$

10. $\int \dfrac{\sin x\, dx}{(3 + \cos x)^2}.$

11. $\int \dfrac{\sin x\, dx}{\sqrt{\cos^3 x}}.$

12. $\int_{3}^{8} \dfrac{\sin \sqrt{x + 1}\, dx}{\sqrt{x + 1}}.$

13. $\int x^{n-1} \sin x^n\, dx, \qquad n \neq 0.$

14. $\int \dfrac{x^5\, dx}{\sqrt{1 - x^6}}.$

15. $\int t(1 + t)^{1/4}\, dt.$

16. $\int (x^2 + 1)^{-3/2}\, dx.$

17. $\int x^2(8x^3 + 27)^{2/3}\, dx.$

18. $\int \dfrac{(\sin x + \cos x)\, dx}{(\sin x - \cos x)^{1/3}}.$

19. $\int \dfrac{x\, dx}{\sqrt{1 + x^2 + \sqrt{(1 + x^2)^3}}}.$

20. $\int \dfrac{(x^2 + 1 - 2x)^{1/5}\, dx}{1 - x}.$

21. Deduce the formulas in Theorems 1.18 and 1.19 by the method of substitution.
22. Let

$$F(x, a) = \int_0^x \frac{t^p}{(t^2 + a^2)^q}\, dt\,,$$

where $a > 0$, and p and q are positive integers. Show that $F(x, a) = a^{p+1-2q}F(x/a, 1)$.

23. Show that

$$\int_x^1 \frac{dt}{1 + t^2} = \int_1^{1/x} \frac{dt}{1 + t^2} \qquad \text{if} \quad x > 0\,.$$

24. If m and n are positive integers, show that

$$\int_0^1 x^m(1 - x)^n\, dx = \int_0^1 x^n(1 - x)^m\, dx\,.$$

25. If m is a positive integer, show that

$$\int_0^{\pi/2} \cos^m x \sin^m x\, dx = 2^{-m} \int_0^{\pi/2} \cos^m x\, dx\,.$$

26. (a) Show that

$$\int_0^{\pi} xf(\sin x)\, dx = \frac{\pi}{2}\int_0^{\pi} f(\sin x)\, dx\,. \qquad [\textit{Hint:} \quad u = \pi - x.]$$

   (b) Use part (a) to deduce the formula

$$\int_0^{\pi} \frac{x \sin x}{1 + \cos^2 x}\, dx = \pi \int_0^1 \frac{dx}{1 + x^2}\,.$$

27. Show that $\int_0^1 (1 - x^2)^{n-1/2}\, dx = \int_0^{\pi/2} \cos^{2n} u\, du$ if n is a positive integer. [*Hint:* $x = \sin u$.] The integral on the right can be evaluated by the method of integration by parts, to be discussed in the next section.

5.9 Integration by parts

We proved in Chapter 4 that the derivative of a product of two functions f and g is given by the formula

$$h'(x) = f(x)g'(x) + f'(x)g(x)\,,$$

where $h(x) = f(x)g(x)$. When this is translated into the Leibniz notation for primitives, it becomes $\int f(x)g'(x)\, dx + \int f'(x)g(x)\, dx = f(x)g(x) + C$, usually written as follows:

(5.23) $$\int f(x)g'(x)\, dx = f(x)g(x) - \int f'(x)g(x)\, dx + C\,.$$

This equation, known as the formula for *integration by parts*, provides us with a new integration technique.

To evaluate an integral, say $\int k(x)\,dx$, using (5.23), we try to find two functions f and g such that $k(x)$ can be written in the form $f(x)g'(x)$. If we can do this, then (5.23) tells us that we have

$$\int k(x)\,dx = f(x)g(x) - \int g(x)f'(x)\,dx + C \, ,$$

and the difficulty has been transferred to the evaluation of $\int g(x)f'(x)\,dx$. If f and g are properly chosen, this last integral may be easier to evaluate than the original one. Sometimes two or more applications of (5.23) will lead to an integral that is easily evaluated or that may be found in a table. The examples worked out below have been chosen to illustrate the advantages of this method. For definite integrals, (5.23) leads to the formula

$$\int_a^b f(x)g'(x)\,dx = f(b)g(b) - f(a)g(a) - \int_a^b f'(x)g(x)\,dx \, .$$

If we introduce the substitutions $u = f(x)$, $v = g(x)$, $du = f'(x)\,dx$, and $dv = g'(x)\,dx$, the formula for integration by parts assumes an abbreviated form that many people find easier to remember, namely

$$(5.24) \qquad\qquad \int u\,dv = uv - \int v\,du + C \, .$$

EXAMPLE 1. Integrate $\int x \cos x\,dx$.

Solution. We choose $f(x) = x$ and $g'(x) = \cos x$. This means that we have $f'(x) = 1$ and $g(x) = \sin x$, so (5.23) becomes

$$(5.25) \qquad \int x \cos x\,dx = x \sin x - \int \sin x\,dx + C = x \sin x + \cos x + C \, .$$

Note that in this case the second integral is one we have already calculated.

To carry out the same calculation in the abbreviated notation of (5.24), we write

$$u = x, \qquad dv = \cos x\,dx \, ,$$

$$du = dx, \qquad v = \int \cos x\,dx = \sin x \, ,$$

$$\int x \cos x\,dx = uv - \int v\,du = x \sin x - \int \sin x\,dx + C = x \sin x + \cos x + C \, .$$

Had we chosen $u = \cos x$ and $dv = x\,dx$, we would have obtained $du = -\sin x\,dx$, $v = \tfrac{1}{2}x^2$, and (5.24) would have given us

$$\int x \cos x\,dx = \tfrac{1}{2}x^2 \cos x - \tfrac{1}{2}\int x^2(-\sin x)\,dx + C = \tfrac{1}{2}x^2 \cos x + \tfrac{1}{2}\int x^2 \sin x\,dx + C \, .$$

Since the last integral is one which we have not yet calculated, this choice of u and v is not as useful as the first choice. Notice, however, that we can solve this last equation for $\int x^2 \sin x \, dx$ and use (5.25) to obtain

$$\int x^2 \sin x \, dx = 2x \sin x + 2 \cos x - x^2 \cos x + C \, .$$

EXAMPLE 2. Integrate $\int x^2 \cos x \, dx$.

Solution. Let $u = x^2$ and $dv = \cos x \, dx$. Then $du = 2x \, dx$ and $v = \int \cos x \, dx = \sin x$, so we have

$$(5.26) \quad \int x^2 \cos x \, dx = \int u \, dv = uv - \int v \, du + C = x^2 \sin x - 2 \int x \sin x \, dx + C \, .$$

The last integral can be evaluated by applying integration by parts once more. Since it is similar to Example 1, we simply state the result:

$$\int x \sin x \, dx = -x \cos x + \sin x + C \, .$$

Substituting in (5.26) and consolidating the two arbitrary constants into one, we obtain

$$\int x^2 \cos x \, dx = x^2 \sin x + 2x \cos x - 2 \sin x + C \, .$$

EXAMPLE 3. The method sometimes fails because it leads back to the original integral. For example, let us try to integrate $\int x^{-1} \, dx$ by parts. If we let $u = x$ and $dv = x^{-2} \, dx$, then $\int x^{-1} \, dx = \int u \, dv$. For this choice of u and v, we have $du = dx$ and $v = -x^{-1}$, so (5.24) gives us

$$(5.27) \quad \int x^{-1} \, dx = \int u \, dv = uv - \int v \, du + C = -1 + \int x^{-1} \, dx + C \, ,$$

and we are back where we started. Moreover, the situation does not improve if we try $u = x^n$ and $dv = x^{-n-1} \, dx$.

This example is often used to illustrate the importance of paying attention to the arbitrary constant C. If formula (5.27) is written without C, it leads to the equation $\int x^{-1} \, dx = -1 + \int x^{-1} \, dx$, which is sometimes used to give a fallacious proof that $0 = -1$.

As an application of the method of integration by parts, we obtain another version of the weighted mean-value theorem for integrals (Theorem 3.16).

THEOREM 5.5. SECOND MEAN-VALUE THEOREM FOR INTEGRALS. *Assume g is continuous on $[a, b]$, and assume f has a derivative which is continuous and never changes sign in $[a, b]$. Then, for some c in $[a, b]$, we have*

$$(5.28) \quad \int_a^b f(x)g(x) \, dx = f(a) \int_a^c g(x) \, dx + f(b) \int_c^b g(x) \, dx \, .$$

Proof. Let $G(x) = \int_a^x g(t)\, dt$. Since g is continuous, we have $G'(x) = g(x)$. Therefore, integration by parts gives us

(5.29) $$\int_a^b f(x)g(x)\, dx = \int_a^b f(x)G'(x)\, dx = f(b)G(b) - \int_a^b f'(x)G(x)\, dx\,,$$

since $G(a) = 0$. By the weighted mean-value theorem, we have

$$\int_a^b f'(x)G(x)\, dx = G(c) \int_a^b f'(x)\, dx = G(c)[f(b) - f(a)]$$

for some c in $[a, b]$. Therefore, (5.29) becomes

$$\int_a^b f(x)g(x)\, dx = f(b)G(b) - G(c)[f(b) - f(a)] = f(a)G(c) + f(b)[G(b) - G(c)]\,.$$

This proves (5.28) since $G(c) = \int_a^c g(x)\, dx$ and $G(b) - G(c) = \int_c^b g(x)\, dx$.

5.10   Exercises

Use integration by parts to evaluate the integrals in Exercises 1 through 6.

1. $\int x \sin x\, dx$.

2. $\int x^2 \sin x\, dx$.

3. $\int x^3 \cos x\, dx$.

4. $\int x^3 \sin x\, dx$.

5. $\int \sin x \cos x\, dx$.

6. $\int x \sin x \cos x\, dx$.

7. Use integration by parts to deduce the formula

$$\int \sin^2 x\, dx = -\sin x \cos x + \int \cos^2 x\, dx\,.$$

In the second integral, write $\cos^2 x = 1 - \sin^2 x$ and thereby deduce the formula

$$\int \sin^2 x\, dx = \tfrac{1}{2}x - \tfrac{1}{4}\sin 2x\,.$$

8. Use integration by parts to deduce the formula

$$\int \sin^n x\, dx = -\sin^{n-1} x \cos x + (n - 1) \int \sin^{n-2} x \cos^2 x\, dx\,.$$

In the second integral, write $\cos^2 x = 1 - \sin^2 x$ and thereby deduce the recursion formula

$$\int \sin^n x\, dx = -\frac{\sin^{n-1} x \cos x}{n} + \frac{n - 1}{n} \int \sin^{n-2} x\, dx\,.$$

9. Use the results of Exercises 7 and 8 to show that

(a) $\displaystyle\int_0^{\pi/2} \sin^2 x\, dx = \frac{\pi}{4}$.

(b) $\displaystyle\int_0^{\pi/2} \sin^4 x \, dx = \frac{3}{4} \int_0^{\pi/2} \sin^2 x \, dx = \frac{3\pi}{16}$.

(c) $\displaystyle\int_0^{\pi/2} \sin^6 x \, dx = \frac{5}{6} \int_0^{\pi/2} \sin^4 x \, dx = \frac{5\pi}{32}$.

10. Use the results of Exercises 7 and 8 to derive the following formulas.

   (a) $\displaystyle\int \sin^3 x \, dx = -\frac{3}{4} \cos x + \frac{1}{12} \cos 3x$.

   (b) $\displaystyle\int \sin^4 x \, dx = \frac{3}{8} x - \frac{1}{4} \sin 2x + \frac{1}{32} \sin 4x$.

   (c) $\displaystyle\int \sin^5 x \, dx = -\frac{5}{8}x + \frac{5}{48} \cos 3x - \frac{1}{80} \cos 5x$.

11. Use integration by parts and the results of Exercises 7 and 10 to deduce the following formulas.

   (a) $\displaystyle\int x \sin^2 x \, dx = \frac{1}{4} x^2 - \frac{1}{4} x \sin 2x - \frac{1}{8} \cos 2x$.

   (b) $\displaystyle\int x \sin^3 x \, dx = \frac{3}{4} \sin x - \frac{1}{36} \sin 3x - \frac{3}{4}x \cos x + \frac{1}{12} x \cos 3x$.

   (c) $\displaystyle\int x^2 \sin^2 x \, dx = \frac{1}{6}x^3 + (\frac{1}{8} - \frac{1}{4}x^2) \sin 2x - \frac{1}{4}x \cos 2x$.

12. Use integration by parts to derive the recursion formula

$$\int \cos^n x \, dx = \frac{\cos^{n-1} x \sin x}{n} + \frac{n-1}{n} \int \cos^{n-2} x \, dx \ .$$

13. Use the result of Exercise 12 to obtain the following formulas.

   (a) $\displaystyle\int \cos^2 x \, dx = \frac{1}{2}x + \frac{1}{4} \sin 2x$.

   (b) $\displaystyle\int \cos^3 x \, dx = \frac{3}{4} \sin x + \frac{1}{12} \sin 3x$.

   (c) $\displaystyle\int \cos^4 x \, dx = \frac{3}{8}x + \frac{1}{4} \sin 2x + \frac{1}{32} \sin 4x$.

14. Use integration by parts to show that

$$\int \sqrt{1 - x^2} \, dx = x\sqrt{1 - x^2} + \int \frac{x^2}{\sqrt{1 - x^2}} \, dx.$$

   Write $x^2 = x^2 - 1 + 1$ in the second integral and deduce the formula

$$\int \sqrt{1 - x^2} \, dx = \frac{1}{2}x\sqrt{1 - x^2} + \frac{1}{2} \int \frac{1}{\sqrt{1 - x^2}} \, dx.$$

15. (a) Use integration by parts to derive the formula

$$\int (a^2 - x^2)^n \, dx = \frac{x(a^2 - x^2)^n}{2n + 1} + \frac{2a^2 n}{2n + 1} \int (a^2 - x^2)^{n-1} \, dx + C \ .$$

   (b) Use part (a) to evaluate $\int_0^a (a^2 - x^2)^{5/2} \, dx$.

16. (a) If $I_n(x) = \int_0^x t^n(t^2 + a^2)^{-1/2} dt$, use integration by parts to show that

$$nI_n(x) = x^{n-1}\sqrt{x^2 + a^2} - (n - 1)a^2 I_{n-2}(x) \qquad \text{if} \quad n \geq 2.$$

   (b) Use part (a) to show that $\int_0^2 x^5(x^2 + 5)^{-1/2} dx = 168/5 - 40\sqrt{5}/3$.

17. Evaluate the integral $\int_{-1}^3 t^3(4 + t^3)^{-1/2} dt$, given that $\int_{-1}^3 (4 + t^3)^{1/2} dt = 11.35$. Leave the answer in terms of $\sqrt{3}$ and $\sqrt{31}$.

18. Use integration by parts to derive the formula

$$\int \frac{\sin^{n+1} x}{\cos^{m+1} x} dx = \frac{1}{m} \frac{\sin^n x}{\cos^m x} - \frac{n}{m} \int \frac{\sin^{n-1} x}{\cos^{m-1} x} dx.$$

   Apply the formula to integrate $\int \tan^2 x \, dx$ and $\int \tan^4 x \, dx$.

19. Use integration by parts to derive the formula

$$\int \frac{\cos^{m+1} x}{\sin^{n+1} x} dx = -\frac{1}{n} \frac{\cos^m x}{\sin^n x} - \frac{m}{n} \int \frac{\cos^{m-1} x}{\sin^{n-1} x} dx.$$

   Apply the formula to integrate $\int \cot^2 x \, dx$ and $\int \cot^4 x \, dx$.

20. (a) Find an integer n such that $n \int_0^1 xf''(2x) \, dx = \int_0^2 tf''(t) \, dt$.
   (b) Compute $\int_0^1 xf''(2x) \, dx$, given that $f(0) = 1$, $f(2) = 3$, and $f'(2) = 5$.

21. (a) If ϕ'' is continuous and nonzero on $[a, b]$, and if there is a constant $m > 0$ such that $\phi'(t) \geq m$ for all t in $[a, b]$, use Theorem 5.5 to prove that

$$\left| \int_a^b \sin \phi(t) \, dt \right| \leq \frac{4}{m}.$$

   [*Hint:*   Multiply and divide the integrand by $\phi'(t)$.]

   (b) If $a > 0$, show that $|\int_a^x \sin (t^2) \, dt| \leq 2/a$ for all $x > a$.

*5.11   Miscellaneous review exercises

1. Let f be a polynomial with $f(0) = 1$ and let $g(x) = x^n f(x)$. Compute $g(0), g'(0), \ldots, g^{(n)}(0)$.
2. Find a polynomial P of degree ≤ 5 with $P(0) = 1, P(1) = 2, P'(0) = P''(0) = P'(1) = P''(1) = 0$.
3. If $f(x) = \cos x$ and $g(x) = \sin x$, prove that

$$f^{(n)}(x) = \cos (x + \tfrac{1}{2}n\pi) \qquad \text{and} \qquad g^{(n)}(x) = \sin (x + \tfrac{1}{2}n\pi).$$

4. If $h(x) = f(x)g(x)$, prove that the nth derivative of h is given by the formula

$$h^{(n)}(x) = \sum_{k=0}^n \binom{n}{k} f^{(k)}(x) g^{(n-k)}(x),$$

   where $\binom{n}{k}$ denotes the binomial coefficient. This is called *Leibniz's formula*.
5. Given two functions f and g whose derivatives f' and g' satisfy the equations

$$(5.30) \qquad\qquad f'(x) = g(x), \qquad g'(x) = -f(x), \qquad f(0) = 0, \qquad g(0) = 1,$$

   for every x in some open interval J containing 0. For example, these equations are satisfied when $f(x) = \sin x$ and $g(x) = \cos x$.

(a) Prove that $f^2(x) + g^2(x) = 1$ for every x in J.

(b) Let F and G be another pair of functions satisfying (5.30). Prove that $F(x) = f(x)$ and $G(x) = g(x)$ for every x in J. [*Hint:* Consider $h(x) = [F(x) - f(x)]^2 + [G(x) - g(x)]^2$.]

(c) What more can you say about functions f and g satisfying (5.30)?

6. A function f, defined for all positive real numbers, satisfies the equation $f(x^2) = x^3$ for every $x > 0$. Determine $f'(4)$.

7. A function g, defined for all positive real numbers, satisfies the following two conditions: $g(1) = 1$ and $g'(x^2) = x^3$ for all $x > 0$. Compute $g(4)$.

8. Show that

$$\int_0^x \frac{\sin t}{t + 1}\, dt \geq 0 \qquad \text{for all} \quad x \geq 0.$$

9. Let C_1 and C_2 be two curves passing through the origin as indicated in Figure 5.2. A curve C is said to "bisect in area" the region between C_1 and C_2 if, for each point P of C, the two shaded regions A and B shown in the figure have equal areas. Determine the upper curve C_2, given that the bisecting curve C has the equation $y = x^2$ and that the lower curve C_1 has the equation $y = \frac{1}{2}x^2$.

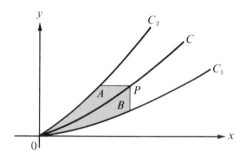

FIGURE 5.2   Exercise 9.

10. A function f is defined for all x as follows:

$$f(x) = \begin{cases} x^2 & \text{if} \quad x \text{ is rational}, \\ 0 & \text{if} \quad x \text{ is irrational}. \end{cases}$$

Let $Q(h) = f(h)/h$ if $h \neq 0$. (a) Prove that $Q(h) \to 0$ as $h \to 0$. (b) Prove that f has a derivative at 0, and compute $f'(0)$.

In Exercises 11 through 20, evaluate the given integrals. Try to simplify the calculations by using the method of substitution and/or integration by parts whenever possible.

11. $\int (2 + 3x) \sin 5x\, dx$.

12. $\int x\sqrt{1 + x^2}\, dx$.

13. $\int_{-2}^1 x(x^2 - 1)^9\, dx$.

14. $\int_0^1 \frac{2x + 3}{(6x + 7)^3}\, dx$.

15. $\int x^4(1 + x^5)^5\, dx$.

16. $\int_0^1 x^4(1 - x)^{20}\, dx$.

17. $\int_1^2 x^{-2} \sin \frac{1}{x}\, dx$.

18. $\int \sin \sqrt[4]{x - 1}\, dx$.

19. $\int x \sin x^2 \cos x^2\, dx$.

20. $\int \sqrt{1 + 3 \cos^2 x}\, \sin 2x\, dx$.

21. Show that the value of the integral $\int_0^2 375 x^5 (x^2 + 1)^{-4}\, dx$ is 2^n for some integer n.

22. Determine a pair of numbers a and b for which $\int_0^1 (ax + b)(x^2 + 3x + 2)^{-2}\, dx = 3/2$.

23. Let $I_n = \int_0^1 (1 - x^2)^n\, dx$. Show that $(2n + 1)I_n = 2n\, I_{n-1}$, then use this relation to compute I_2, I_3, I_4, and I_5.

24. Let $F(m, n) = \int_0^x t^m (1 + t)^n\, dt$, $m > 0$, $n > 0$. Show that

$$(m + 1)F(m, n) + nF(m + 1, n - 1) = x^{m+1}(1 + x)^n.$$

Use this to evaluate $F(10, 2)$.

25. Let $f(n) = \int_0^{\pi/4} \tan^n x\, dx$ where $n \geq 1$. Show that

(a) $f(n + 1) < f(n)$.

(b) $f(n) + f(n - 2) = \dfrac{1}{n - 1}$ if $n > 2$.

(c) $\dfrac{1}{n + 1} < 2f(n) < \dfrac{1}{n - 1}$ if $n > 2$.

26. Compute $f(0)$, given that $f(\pi) = 2$ and that $\int_0^\pi [f(x) + f''(x)] \sin x\, dx = 5$.

27. Let A denote the value of the integral

$$\int_0^\pi \frac{\cos x}{(x + 2)^2}\, dx\,.$$

Compute the following integral in terms of A:

$$\int_0^{\pi/2} \frac{\sin x \cos x}{x + 1}\, dx\,.$$

The formulas in Exercises 28 through 33 appear in integral tables. Verify each of these formulas by any method.

28. $\displaystyle \int \frac{\sqrt{a + bx}}{x}\, dx = 2\sqrt{a + bx} + a \int \frac{dx}{x\sqrt{a + bx}} + C.$

29. $\displaystyle \int x^n \sqrt{ax + b}\, dx = \frac{2}{a(2n + 3)}\left(x^n(ax + b)^{3/2} - nb \int x^{n-1}\sqrt{ax + b}\, dx \right) + C \quad (n \neq -\tfrac{3}{2}).$

30. $\displaystyle \int \frac{x^m}{\sqrt{a + bx}}\, dx = \frac{2}{(2m + 1)b}\left(x^m \sqrt{a + bx} - ma \int \frac{x^{m-1}}{\sqrt{a + bx}}\, dx \right) + C \quad (m \neq -\tfrac{1}{2}).$

31. $\displaystyle \int \frac{dx}{x^n \sqrt{ax + b}} = -\frac{\sqrt{ax + b}}{(n - 1)bx^{n-1}} - \frac{(2n - 3)a}{(2n - 2)b} \int \frac{dx}{x^{n-1}\sqrt{ax + b}} + C \quad (n \neq 1).$

32. $\displaystyle \int \frac{\cos^m x}{\sin^n x}\, dx = \frac{\cos^{m-1} x}{(m - n)\sin^{n-1}x} + \frac{m - 1}{m - n} \int \frac{\cos^{m-2} x}{\sin^n x}\, dx + C \quad (m \neq n).$

33. $\displaystyle \int \frac{\cos^m x}{\sin^n x}\, dx = -\frac{\cos^{m+1} x}{(n - 1)\sin^{n-1} x} - \frac{m - n + 2}{n - 1} \int \frac{\cos^m x}{\sin^{n-2} x}\, dx + C \quad (n \neq 1).$

34. (a) Find a polynomial $P(x)$ such that $P'(x) - 3P(x) = 4 - 5x + 3x^2$. Prove that there is only one solution.

(b) If $Q(x)$ is a given polynomial, prove that there is one and only one polynomial $P(x)$ such that $P'(x) - 3P(x) = Q(x)$.

35. A sequence of polynomials (called the *Bernoulli polynomials*) is defined inductively as follows:

$$P_0(x) = 1; \qquad P'_n(x) = nP_{n-1}(x) \qquad \text{and} \qquad \int_0^1 P_n(x)\, dx = 0 \qquad \text{if} \quad n \geq 1.$$

(a) Determine explicit formulas for $P_1(x), P_2(x), \ldots, P_5(x)$.

(b) Prove, by induction, that $P_n(x)$ is a polynomial in x of degree n, the term of highest degree being x^n.

(c) Prove that $P_n(0) = P_n(1)$ if $n \geq 2$.

(d) Prove that $P_n(x + 1) - P_n(x) = nx^{n-1}$ if $n \geq 1$.

(e) Prove that for $n \geq 2$ we have

$$\sum_{r=1}^{k-1} r^n = \int_0^k P_n(x)\, dx = \frac{P_{n+1}(k) - P_{n+1}(0)}{n + 1}.$$

(f) Prove that $P_n(1 - x) = (-1)^n P_n(x)$ if $n \geq 1$.

(g) Prove that $P_{2n+1}(0) = 0$ and $P_{2n-1}(\frac{1}{2}) = 0$ if $n \geq 1$.

36. Assume that $|f''(x)| \leq m$ for each x in the interval $[0, a]$, and assume that f takes on its largest value at an interior point of this interval. Show that $|f'(0)| + |f'(a)| \leq am$. You may assume that f'' is continuous in $[0, a]$.

6

THE LOGARITHM, THE EXPONENTIAL,
AND THE INVERSE TRIGONOMETRIC FUNCTIONS

6.1 Introduction

Whenever man focuses his attention on quantitative relationships, he is either studying the properties of a known function or trying to discover the properties of an unknown function. The function concept is so broad and so general that it is not surprising to find an endless variety of functions occurring in nature. What *is* surprising is that a few rather special functions govern so many totally different kinds of natural phenomena. We shall study some of these functions in this chapter—first of all, the logarithm and its inverse (the exponential function) and secondly, the inverses of the trigonometric functions. Anyone who studies mathematics, either as an abstract discipline or as a tool for some other scientific field, will find that a good working knowledge of these functions and their properties is indispensable.

The reader probably has had occasion to work with logarithms to the base 10 in an elementary algebra or trigonometry course. The definition usually given in elementary algebra is this: If $x > 0$, the logarithm of x to the base 10, denoted by $\log_{10} x$, is that real number u such that $10^u = x$. If $x = 10^u$ and $y = 10^v$, the law of exponents yields $xy = 10^{u+v}$. In terms of logarithms, this becomes

$$(6.1) \qquad \log_{10}(xy) = \log_{10} x + \log_{10} y.$$

It is this fundamental property that makes logarithms particularly adaptable to computations involving multiplication. The number 10 is useful as a base because real numbers are commonly written in the decimal system, and certain important numbers like 0.01, 0.1, 1, 10, 100, 1000, ... have for their logarithms the integers $-2, -1, 0, 1, 2, 3, \ldots$, respectively.

It is not necessary to restrict ourselves to base 10. Any other positive base $b \neq 1$ would serve equally well. Thus

$$(6.2) \qquad u = \log_b x \qquad \text{means} \qquad x = b^u,$$

and the fundamental property in (6.1) becomes

$$(6.3) \qquad \log_b(xy) = \log_b x + \log_b y.$$

226

If we examine the definition in (6.2) from a critical point of view, we find that it suffers from several logical gaps. First of all, to understand (6.2) we must know what is meant by b^u. This is easy to define when u is an *integer* or a *rational number* (the quotient of two integers), but it is not a trivial matter to define b^u when u is *irrational*. For example, how should we define $10^{\sqrt{2}}$? Even if we manage to obtain a satisfactory definition for b^u, there are further difficulties to overcome before we can use (6.2) as a good definition of logarithms. It must be shown that for every $x > 0$, there actually *exists* a number u such that $x = b^u$. Also, the law of exponents, $b^u b^v = b^{u+v}$, must be established for all real exponents u and v in order to derive (6.3) from (6.2).

It is possible to overcome these difficulties and arrive at a satisfactory definition of logarithms by this method, but the process is long and tedious. Fortunately, however, the study of logarithms can proceed in an entirely different way which is much simpler and which illustrates the power and elegance of the methods of calculus. The idea is to introduce logarithms *first*, and then use logarithms to define b^u.

6.2 Motivation for the definition of the natural logarithm as an integral

The logarithm is an example of a mathematical concept that can be defined in many different ways. When a mathematician tries to formulate a definition of a concept, such as the logarithm, he usually has in mind a number of properties he wants this concept to have. By examining these properties, he is often led to a simple formula or process that might serve as a definition from which all the desired properties spring forth as logical deductions. We shall illustrate how this procedure may be used to arrive at the definition of the logarithm which is given in the next section.

One of the properties we want logarithms to have is that the logarithm of a product should be the sum of the logarithms of the individual factors. Let us consider this property by itself and see where it leads us. If we think of the logarithm as a function f, then we want this function to have the property expressed by the formula

$$(6.4) \qquad\qquad f(xy) = f(x) + f(y)$$

whenever x, y, and xy are in the domain of f.

An equation like (6.4), which expresses a relationship between the values of a function at two or more points, is called a *functional equation*. Many mathematical problems can be reduced to solving a functional equation, a solution being any function which satisfies the equation. Ordinarily an equation of this sort has many different solutions, and it is usually very difficult to find them all. It is easier to seek only those solutions which have some additional property such as continuity or differentiability. For the most part, these are the only solutions we are interested in anyway. We shall adopt this point of view and determine all differentiable solutions of (6.4). But first let us try to deduce what information we can from (6.4) alone, without any further restrictions on f.

One solution of (6.4) is the function that is zero everywhere on the real axis. In fact, this is the only solution of (6.4) that is defined for all real numbers. To prove this, let f be any function that satisfies (6.4). If 0 is in the domain of f, then we may put $y = 0$ in (6.4) to obtain $f(0) = f(x) + f(0)$, and this implies that $f(x) = 0$ for every x in the domain of f. In other words, if 0 is in the domain of f, then f must be identically zero. Therefore, a solution of (6.4) that is not identically zero cannot be defined at 0.

If f is a solution of (6.4) and if the domain of f includes 1, we may put $x = y = 1$ in (6.4) to obtain $f(1) = 2f(1)$, and this implies

$$f(1) = 0.$$

If both 1 and -1 are in the domain of f, we may take $x = -1$ and $y = -1$ to deduce that $f(1) = 2f(-1)$; hence $f(-1) = 0$. If now x, $-x$, 1, and -1 are in the domain of f, we may put $y = -1$ in (6.4) to deduce $f(-x) = f(-1) + f(x)$ and, since $f(\quad) = 0$, we find

$$f(-x) = f(x).$$

In other words, any solution of (6.4) is necessarily an *even* function.

Suppose, now, we assume that f has a derivative $f'(x)$ at each $x \neq 0$. If we hold y fixed in (6.4) and differentiate with respect to x (using the chain rule on the left), we find

$$yf'(xy) = f'(x).$$

When $x = 1$, this gives us $yf'(y) = f'(1)$, and hence we have

$$f'(y) = \frac{f'(1)}{y} \qquad \text{for each} \qquad y \neq 0.$$

From this equation we see that the derivative f' is monotonic and hence integrable on every closed interval not containing the origin. Also, f' is continuous on every such interval, and we may apply the second fundamental theorem of calculus to write

$$f(x) - f(c) = \int_c^x f'(t)\, dt = f'(1) \int_c^x \frac{1}{t}\, dt.$$

If $x > 0$, this equation holds for any positive c, and if $x < 0$, it holds for any negative c. Since $f(1) = 0$, the choice $c = 1$ gives us

$$f(x) = f'(1) \int_1^x \frac{1}{t}\, dt \qquad \text{if} \qquad x > 0.$$

If x is negative then $-x$ is positive and, since $f(x) = f(-x)$, we find

$$f(x) = f'(1) \int_1^{-x} \frac{1}{t}\, dt \qquad \text{if} \qquad x < 0.$$

These two formulas for $f(x)$ may be combined into one formula that is valid for both positive and negative x, namely,

(6.5)
$$f(x) = f'(1) \int_1^{|x|} \frac{1}{t}\, dt \qquad \text{if} \quad x \neq 0.$$

Therefore we have shown that if there is a solution of (6.4) which has a derivative at each point $x \neq 0$, then this solution must necessarily be given by the integral formula in (6.5). If $f'(1) = 0$, then (6.5) implies that $f(x) = 0$ for all $x \neq 0$, and this solution agrees with the solution that is identically zero. Therefore, if f is not identically zero, we must have $f'(1) \neq 0$, in which case we can divide both sides of (6.5) by $f'(1)$ to obtain

$$(6.6) \qquad g(x) = \int_1^{|x|} \frac{1}{t}\, dt \qquad \text{if} \quad x \neq 0 \,,$$

where $g(x) = f(x)/f'(1)$. The function g is also a solution of (6.4), since cf is a solution whenever f is. This proves that if (6.4) has a solution that is not identically zero and if this solution has a derivative everywhere except at the origin, then the function g given by (6.6) is also a solution, and *all* solutions may be obtained from this one by multiplying g by a suitable constant.

It should be emphasized that this argument does not prove that the function g in (6.6) actually *is* a solution, because we derived (6.6) on the assumption that there is at least one solution that is not identically zero. Formula (6.6) suggests a way to construct such a solution. We simply operate in reverse. That is, we use the integral in (6.6) to define a function g, and then we verify directly that this function actually satisfies (6.4). This suggests that we should define the logarithm to be the function g given by (6.6). If we did so, this function would have the property that $g(-x) = g(x)$ or, in other words, distinct numbers would have the same logarithm. For some of the things we want to do later, it is preferable to define the logarithm in such a way that no two distinct numbers have the same logarithm. This latter property may be achieved by defining the logarithm only for positive numbers. Therefore we use the following definition.

6.3 The definition of the logarithm. Basic properties

DEFINITION. *If x is a positive real number, we define the natural logarithm of x, denoted temporarily by $L(x)$, to be the integral*

$$(6.7) \qquad L(x) = \int_1^x \frac{1}{t}\, dt \,.$$

When $x > 1$, $L(x)$ may be interpreted geometrically as the area of the shaded region shown in Figure 6.1.

THEOREM 6.1. *The logarithm function has the following properties:*
(a) $L(1) = 0$.

(b) $L'(x) = \dfrac{1}{x}$ *for every $x > 0$.*

(c) $L(ab) = L(a) + L(b)$ *for every $a > 0, b > 0$.*

Proof. Part (a) follows at once from the definition. To prove (b), we simply note that L is an indefinite integral of a continuous function and apply the first fundamental theorem of calculus. Property (c) follows from the additive property of the integral. We write

$$L(ab) = \int_1^{ab} \frac{dt}{t} = \int_1^a \frac{dt}{t} + \int_a^{ab} \frac{dt}{t} = L(a) + \int_a^{ab} \frac{dt}{t}.$$

In the last integral we make the substitution $u = t/a$, $du = dt/a$, and we find that the integral reduces to $L(b)$, thus proving (c).

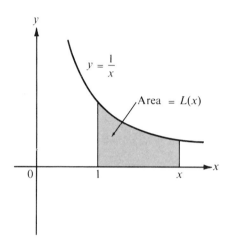

FIGURE 6.1 Interpretation of the logarithm as an area.

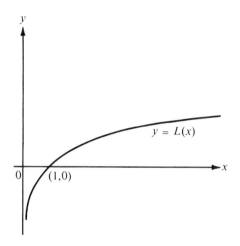

FIGURE 6.2 The graph of the natural logarithm.

6.4 The graph of the natural logarithm

The graph of the logarithm function has the general shape shown in Figure 6.2. Many properties of this curve can be discovered without undue calculation simply by referring to the properties in Theorem 6.1. For example, from (b) we see that L has a positive derivative everywhere so it is strictly increasing on every interval. Since $L(1) = 0$, the graph lies above the x-axis if $x > 1$ and below the axis if $0 < x < 1$. The curve has slope 1 when $x = 1$. For $x > 1$, the slope gradually decreases toward zero as x increases indefinitely. For small values of x, the slope is large and, moreover, it increases without bound as x decreases toward zero. The second derivative is $L''(x) = -1/x^2$ which is negative for all x, so L is a concave function.

6.5 Consequences of the functional equation $L(ab) = L(a) + L(b)$

Since the graph of the logarithm tends to level off as x increases indefinitely, it might be suspected that the values of L have an upper bound. Actually, the function is unbounded above; that is, for every positive number M (no matter how large) there exist values of x such that

(6.8) $L(x) > M$.

We can deduce this from the functional equation. When $a = b$, we get $L(a^2) = 2L(a)$. Using the functional equation once more with $b = a^2$, we obtain $L(a^3) = 3L(a)$. By induction we find the general formula

$$L(a^n) = nL(a)$$

for every integer $n \geq 1$. When $a = 2$, this becomes $L(2^n) = nL(2)$, and hence we have

(6.9) $$L(2^n) > M \qquad \text{when} \quad n > \frac{M}{L(2)} .$$

This proves the assertion in (6.8). Taking $b = 1/a$ in the functional equation, we find $L(1/a) = -L(a)$. In particular, when $a = 2^n$, where n is chosen as in (6.9), we have

$$L\left(\frac{1}{2^n}\right) = -L(2^n) < -M ,$$

which shows that there is also no lower bound to the function values.

Finally we observe that the graph crosses every horizontal line exactly once. That is, given an *arbitrary* real number b (positive, negative, or zero), there is *one and only one* $a > 0$ such that

(6.10) $$L(a) = b .$$

To prove this we can argue as follows: If $b > 0$, choose any integer $n > b/L(2)$. Then $L(2^n) > b$ because of (6.9). Now examine the function L on the closed interval $[1, 2^n]$. Its value at the left endpoint is $L(1) = 0$, and its value at the right endpoint is $L(2^n)$. Since $0 < b < L(2^n)$, the intermediate-value theorem for continuous functions (Theorem 3.8 in Section 3.10) guarantees the existence of at least one a such that $L(a) = b$. There cannot be another value a' such that $L(a') = b$ because this would mean $L(a) = L(a')$ for $a \neq a'$, thus contradicting the increasing property of the logarithm. Therefore the assertion in (6.10) has been proved for $b > 0$. The proof for negative b follows from this if we use the equation $L(1/a) = -L(a)$. In other words, we have proved the following.

THEOREM 6.2.   *For every real number b there is exactly one positive real number a whose logarithm, $L(a)$, is equal to b.*

In particular, there is exactly one number whose natural logarithm is equal to 1. This number, like π, occurs repeatedly in so many mathematical formulas that it was inevitable that a special symbol would be adopted for it. Leonard Euler (1707–1783) seems to have been the first to recognize the importance of this number, and he modestly denoted it by e, a notation which soon became standard.

DEFINITION.   *We denote by e that number for which*

(6.11) $$L(e) = 1 .$$

In Chapter 7 we shall obtain explicit formulas that enable us to calculate the decimal expansion of e to any desired degree of accuracy. Its value, correct to ten decimal places, is 2.7182818285. In Chapter 7 we also prove that e is irrational.

Natural logarithms are also called *Napierian logarithms*, in honor of their inventor, John Napier (1550–1617). It is common practice to use the symbols ln x or log x instead of $L(x)$ to denote the logarithm of x.

6.6   Logarithms referred to any positive base $b \neq 1$

The work of Section 6.2 tells us that the most general f which is differentiable on the positive real axis and which satisfies the functional equation $f(xy) = f(x) + f(y)$ is given by the formula

(6.12)
$$f(x) = c \log x,$$

where c is a constant. For each c, we could call this $f(x)$ the logarithm of x associated with c although, of course, its value would not be necessarily the same as the natural logarithm of x. When $c = 0$, f is identically zero, so this case is uninteresting. If $c \neq 0$, we may indicate in another way the dependence of f on c by introducing the concept of a *base* for logarithms.

From (6.12) we see that when $c \neq 0$, there exists a unique real number $b > 0$ such that $f(b) = 1$. This b is related to c by the equation $c \log b = 1$; hence $b \neq 1$, $c = 1/\log b$, and (6.12) becomes

$$f(x) = \frac{\log x}{\log b}.$$

For this choice of c we say that $f(x)$ is *the logarithm of x to the base b* and we write $\log_b x$ for $f(x)$.

DEFINITION.   *If $b > 0$, $b \neq 1$, and if $x > 0$, the logarithm of x to the base b is the number*

$$\log_b x = \frac{\log x}{\log b},$$

where the logarithms on the right are natural logarithms.

Note that $\log_b b = 1$. Also, when $b = e$, we have $\log_e x = \log x$, so natural logarithms are those with base e. Since logarithms to base e are used so frequently in mathematics, the word logarithm almost invariably means *natural* logarithm. Later, in Section 6.15, we shall define b^u in such a way that the equation $b^u = x$ will mean exactly the same as the equation $u = \log_b x$.

Since logarithms to the base b are obtained from natural logarithms by multiplying by the constant $1/\log b$, the graph of the equation $y = \log_b x$ may be obtained from that of the equation $y = \log x$ by simply multiplying all ordinates by the same factor. When $b > 1$, this factor is positive, and, when $b < 1$, it is negative. Examples with $b > 1$ are

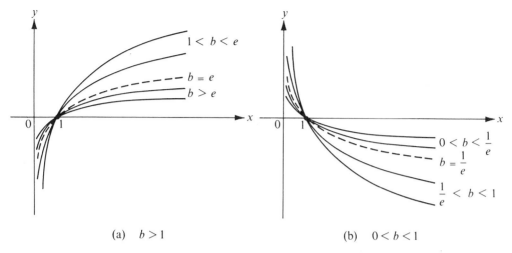

FIGURE 6.3   The graph of $y = \log_b x$ for various values of b.

shown in Figure 6.3(a). When $b < 1$, we note that $1/b > 1$ and $\log b = -\log (1/b)$, so the graph of $y = \log_b x$ may be obtained from that of $y = \log_{1/b} x$ by reflection through the x-axis. Examples are shown in Figure 6.3(b).

6.7   Differentiation and integration formulas involving logarithms

Since the derivative of the logarithm is given by the formula $D \log x = 1/x$ for $x > 0$, we have the integration formula

$$\int \frac{1}{x} dx = \log x + C .$$

More generally, if $u = f(x)$, where f has a continuous derivative, we have

(6.13) $\displaystyle\int \frac{du}{u} = \log u + C$ or $\displaystyle\int \frac{f'(x)}{f(x)} dx = \log f(x) + C .$

Some care must be exercised when using (6.13) because the logarithm is not defined for negative numbers. Therefore, the integration formulas in (6.13) are valid only if u, or $f(x)$, is positive.

Fortunately it is easy to extend the range of validity of these formulas to accommodate functions that are negative or positive (but *nonzero*). We simply introduce a new function L_0 defined for all real $x \neq 0$ by the equation

(6.14) $$L_0(x) = \log |x| = \int_1^{|x|} \frac{1}{t} dt ,$$

a definition suggested by Equation (6.6) of Section 6.2. The graph of L_0 is symmetric about the y-axis, as shown in Figure 6.4. The portion to the right of the y-axis is exactly the same as the logarithmic curve of Figure 6.2.

Since $\log |xy| = \log (|x| |y|) = \log |x| + \log |y|$, the function L_0 also satisfies the basic functional equation in (6.4). That is, we have

$$L_0(xy) = L_0(x) + L_0(y)$$

for all real x and y except 0. For $x > 0$, we have $L_0'(x) = 1/x$ since $L_0(x)$ is the same as $\log x$ for positive x. This derivative formula also holds for $x < 0$ because, in this case, $L_0(x) = L(-x)$, and hence $L_0'(x) = -L'(-x) = -1/(-x) = 1/x$. Therefore we have

(6.15) $$L_0'(x) = \frac{1}{x} \qquad \text{for all real } x \neq 0 .$$

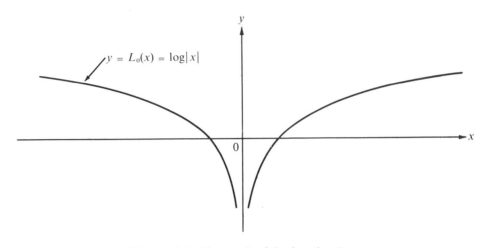

FIGURE 6.4   The graph of the function L_0.

Hence, if we use L_0 instead of L in the foregoing integration formulas, we can extend their scope to include functions which assume negative values as well as positive values. For example, (6.13) can be generalized as follows:

(6.16) $$\int \frac{du}{u} = \log |u| + C , \qquad \int \frac{f'(x)}{f(x)} \, dx = \log |f(x)| + C .$$

Of course, when we use (6.16) along with the second fundamental theorem of calculus to evaluate a definite integral, we must avoid intervals that include points where u or $f(x)$ might be zero.

EXAMPLE 1. Integrate $\int \tan x \, dx$.

Solution. The integral has the form $-\int du/u$, where $u = \cos x$, $du = -\sin x \, dx$. Therefore we have

$$\int \tan x \, dx = -\int \frac{du}{u} = -\log |u| + C = -\log |\cos x| + C ,$$

a formula which is valid on any interval in which $\cos x \neq 0$.

The next two examples illustrate the use of integration by parts.

EXAMPLE 2. Integrate $\int \log x \, dx$.

Solution. Let $u = \log x$, $dv = dx$. Then $du = dx/x$, $v = x$, and we obtain

$$\int \log x \, dx = \int u \, dv = uv - \int v \, du = x \log x - \int x \frac{1}{x} \, dx = x \log x - x + C \,.$$

EXAMPLE 3. Integrate $\int \sin (\log x) \, dx$.

Solution. Let $u = \sin (\log x)$, $v = x$. Then $du = \cos (\log x)(1/x) \, dx$, and we find

$$\int \sin (\log x) \, dx = \int u \, dv = uv - \int v \, du = x \sin (\log x) - \int \cos (\log x) \, dx \,.$$

In the last integral we use integration by parts once more to get

$$\int \cos (\log x) \, dx = x \cos (\log x) + \int \sin (\log x) \, dx \,.$$

Combining this with the foregoing equation, we find that

$$\int \sin (\log x) \, dx = \tfrac{1}{2} x \sin (\log x) - \tfrac{1}{2} x \cos (\log x) + C \,,$$

and

$$\int \cos (\log x) \, dx = \tfrac{1}{2} x \sin (\log x) + \tfrac{1}{2} x \cos (\log x) + C \,.$$

6.8 Logarithmic differentiation

We shall describe now a technique known as *logarithmic differentiation* which is often a great help in computing derivatives. The method was developed in 1697 by Johann Bernoulli (1667–1748), and all it amounts to is a simple application of the chain rule.

Suppose we form the composition of L_0 with any differentiable function f; say we let

$$g(x) = L_0[f(x)] = \log |f(x)|$$

for those x such that $f(x) \neq 0$. The chain rule, used in conjunction with (6.15), yields the formula

(6.17) $$g'(x) = L_0'[f(x)] \cdot f'(x) = \frac{f'(x)}{f(x)} \,.$$

If the derivative $g'(x)$ can be found in some other way, then we may use (6.17) to obtain $f'(x)$ by simply multiplying $g'(x)$ by $f(x)$. The process is useful in practice because in many cases $g'(x)$ is easier to compute than $f'(x)$ itself. In particular, this is true when f is a product or quotient of several simpler functions. The following example is typical.

EXAMPLE. Compute $f'(x)$ if $f(x) = x^2 \cos x (1 + x^4)^{-7}$.

Solution. We take the logarithm of the absolute value of $f(x)$ and then we differentiate. Let

$$g(x) = \log |f(x)| = \log x^2 + \log |\cos x| + \log (1 + x^4)^{-7}$$

$$= 2 \log |x| + \log |\cos x| - 7 \log (1 + x^4).$$

Differentiation yields

$$g'(x) = \frac{f'(x)}{f(x)} = \frac{2}{x} - \frac{\sin x}{\cos x} - \frac{28x^3}{1 + x^4} \, .$$

Multiplying by $f(x)$, we obtain

$$f'(x) = \frac{2x \cos x}{(1 + x^4)^7} - \frac{x^2 \sin x}{(1 + x^4)^7} - \frac{28x^5 \cos x}{(1 + x^4)^8} \, .$$

6.9   Exercises

1. (a) Find all c such that $\log x = c + \int_e^x t^{-1} \, dt$ for all $x > 0$.
   (b) Let $f(x) = \log [(1 + x)/(1 - x)]$ if $x > 0$. If a and b are given numbers, with $ab \neq -1$, find all x such that $f(x) = f(a) + f(b)$.
2. In each case, find a real x satisfying the given equation.
   (a) $\log (1 + x) = \log (1 - x)$.   (c) $2 \log x = x \log 2, \quad x \neq 2$.
   (b) $\log (1 + x) = 1 + \log (1 - x)$.   (d) $\log (\sqrt{x} + \sqrt{x + 1}) = 1$.
3. Let $f(x) = (\log x)/x$ if $x > 0$. Describe the intervals in which f is increasing, decreasing, convex, and concave. Sketch the graph of f.

In Exercises 4 through 15, find the derivative $f'(x)$. In each case, the function f is assumed to be defined for all real x for which the given formula for $f(x)$ is meaningful.

4. $f(x) = \log (1 + x^2)$.
5. $f(x) = \log \sqrt{1 + x^2}$.
6. $f(x) = \log \sqrt{4 - x^2}$.
7. $f(x) = \log (\log x)$.
8. $f(x) = \log(x^2 \log x)$.
9. $f(x) = \frac{1}{4} \log \dfrac{x^2 - 1}{x^2 + 1}$.

10. $f(x) = (x + \sqrt{1 + x^2})^n$
11. $f(x) = \sqrt{x + 1} - \log (1 + \sqrt{x + 1})$.
12. $f(x) = x \log (x + \sqrt{1 + x^2}) - \sqrt{1 + x^2}$.
13. $f(x) = \dfrac{1}{2\sqrt{ab}} \log \dfrac{\sqrt{a} + x\sqrt{b}}{\sqrt{a} - x\sqrt{b}} \, .$
14. $f(x) = x[\sin (\log x) - \cos (\log x)]$.
15. $f(x) = \log_x e$.

In Exercises 16 through 26, evaluate the integrals.

16. $\displaystyle\int \frac{dx}{2 + 3x} \, .$
17. $\int \log^2 x \, dx$.
18. $\int x \log x \, dx$.
19. $\int x \log^2 x \, dx$.

20. $\displaystyle\int_0^{e^3 - 1} \frac{dt}{1 + t} \, .$
21. $\int \cot x \, dx$.
22. $\int x^n \log (ax) \, dx$.
23. $\int x^2 \log^2 x \, dx$.

24. $\int \dfrac{dx}{x \log x}$.

26. $\int \dfrac{\log |x|}{x\sqrt{1 + \log |x|}}\, dx$.

25. $\int_0^{1-e^{-2}} \dfrac{\log (1 - t)}{1 - t}\, dt$.

27. Derive the recursion formula

$$\int x^m \log^n x\, dx = \frac{x^{m+1} \log^n x}{m + 1} - \frac{n}{m + 1}\int x^m \log^{n-1} x\, dx$$

and use it to integrate $\int x^3 \log^3 x\, dx$.

28. (a) If $x > 0$, let $f(x) = x - 1 - \log x$, $g(x) = \log x - 1 + 1/x$. Examine the signs of f' and g' to prove that the inequalities

$$1 - \frac{1}{x} < \log x < x - 1$$

are valid for $x > 0$, $x \neq 1$. When $x = 1$, they become equalities.
(b) Sketch graphs of the functions A and B defined by the equations $A(x) = x - 1$ and $B(x) = 1 - 1/x$ for $x > 0$, and interpret geometrically the inequalities in part (a).

29. Prove the limit relation

$$\lim_{x \to 0} \frac{\log (1 + x)}{x} = 1$$

by the following two methods: (a) using the definition of the derivative $L'(1)$; (b) using the result of Exercise 28.

30. If $a > 0$, use the functional equation for the logarithm to prove that $\log (a^r) = r \log a$ for every rational number r.

31. Let $P = \{a_0, a_1, a_2, \ldots, a_n\}$ be any partition of the interval $[1, x]$, where $x > 1$.
(a) Integrate suitable step functions that are constant on the open subintervals of P to derive the following inequalities:

$$\sum_{k=1}^{n}\left(\frac{a_k - a_{k-1}}{a_k}\right) < \log x < \sum_{k=1}^{n}\left(\frac{a_k - a_{k-1}}{a_{k-1}}\right).$$

(b) Interpret the inequalities of part (a) geometrically in terms of areas.
(c) Specialize the partition to show that for every integer $n > 1$,

$$\sum_{k=2}^{n} \frac{1}{k} < \log n < \sum_{k=1}^{n-1} \frac{1}{k}.$$

32. Prove the following formulas for changing from one logarithmic base to another:

(a) $\log_b x = \log_b a \log_a x$;

(b) $\log_b x = \dfrac{\log_a x}{\log_a b}$.

33. Given that $\log_e 10 = 2.302585$, correct to six decimal places, compute $\log_{10} e$ using one of the formulas in Exercise 32. How many correct decimal places can you be certain of in the result of your calculation? *Note:* A table, correct to six decimal places, gives $\log_{10} e = 0.434294$.

34. A function f, continuous on the positive real axis, has the property that for all choices of $x > 0$ and $y > 0$, the integral

$$\int_x^{xy} f(t)\, dt$$

is independent of x (and therefore depends only on y). If $f(2) = 2$, compute the value of the integral $A(x) = \int_1^x f(t)\, dt$ for all $x > 0$.

35. A function f, continuous on the positive real axis, has the property that

$$\int_1^{xy} f(t)\, dt = y \int_1^x f(t)\, dt + x \int_1^y f(t)\, dt$$

for all $x > 0$ and all $y > 0$. If $f(1) = 3$, compute $f(x)$ for each $x > 0$.

36. The base of a solid is the ordinate set of a function f which is continuous over the interval $[1, a]$. All cross sections perpendicular to the interval $[1, a]$ are squares. The volume of the solid is $\frac{1}{3}a^3 \log^2 a - \frac{2}{9}a^3 \log a + \frac{2}{27}a^3 - \frac{2}{27}$ for every $a \geq 1$. Compute $f(a)$.

6.10 Polynomial approximations to the logarithm

In this section we will show that the logarithm function can be approximated by certain polynomials which can be used to compute logarithms to any desired degree of accuracy.

To simplify the resulting formulas, we first replace x by $1 - x$ in the integral defining the logarithm to obtain

$$\log (1 - x) = \int_1^{1-x} \frac{dt}{t},$$

which is valid if $x < 1$. The change of variable $t = 1 - u$ converts this to the form

$$-\log (1 - x) = \int_0^x \frac{du}{1 - u}, \qquad \text{valid for} \quad x < 1.$$

Now we approximate the integrand $1/(1 - u)$ by polynomials which we then integrate to obtain corresponding approximations for the logarithm. To illustrate the method, we begin with a simple linear approximation to the integrand.

From the algebraic identity $1 - u^2 = (1 - u)(1 + u)$, we obtain the formula

(6.18)
$$\frac{1}{1 - u} = 1 + u + \frac{u^2}{1 - u},$$

valid for any real $u \neq 1$. Integrating this from 0 to x, where $x < 1$, we have

(6.19)
$$-\log (1 - x) = x + \frac{x^2}{2} + \int_0^x \frac{u^2}{1 - u}\, du .$$

The graph of the quadratic polynomial $P(x) = x + \frac{1}{2}x^2$ which appears on the right of (6.19) is shown in Figure 6.5 along with the curve $y = -\log (1 - x)$. Note that for x near zero the polynomial $P(x)$ is a good approximation to $-\log (1 - x)$. In the next theorem we use a polynomial of degree $n - 1$ to approximate $1/(1 - u)$, and thereby obtain a polynomial of degree n which approximates $\log (1 - x)$.

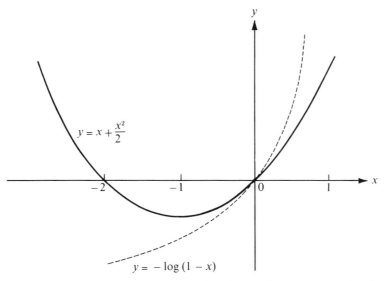

FIGURE 6.5   A quadratic polynomial approximation to the curve $y = -\log(1 - x)$.

THEOREM 6.3.   *Let P_n denote the polynomial of degree n given by*

$$P_n(x) = x + \frac{x^2}{2} + \frac{x^3}{3} + \cdots + \frac{x^n}{n} = \sum_{k=1}^{n} \frac{x^k}{k}.$$

Then, for every $x < 1$ and every $n \geq 1$, we have

(6.20) $$-\log(1 - x) = P_n(x) + \int_0^x \frac{u^n}{1 - u} \, du \ .$$

Proof. From the algebraic identity

$$1 - u^n = (1 - u)(1 + u + u^2 + \cdots + u^{n-1}),$$

we obtain the formula

$$\frac{1}{1 - u} = 1 + u + u^2 + \cdots + u^{n-1} + \frac{u^n}{1 - u},$$

which is valid for $u \neq 1$. Integrating this from 0 to x, where $x < 1$, we obtain (6.20).
We can rewrite (6.20) in the form

(6.21) $$-\log(1 - x) = P_n(x) + E_n(x),$$

where $E_n(x)$ is the integral,

$$E_n(x) = \int_0^x \frac{u^n}{1 - u} \, du \ .$$

The quantity $E_n(x)$ represents the error made when we approximate $-\log(1-x)$ by the polynomial $P_n(x)$. To use (6.21) in computations, we need to know whether the error is positive or negative and how large it can be. The next theorem tells us that for small positive x the error $E_n(x)$ is positive, but for negative x the error has the same sign as $(-1)^{n+1}$, where n is the degree of the approximating polynomial. The theorem also gives useful upper and lower bounds for the error.

THEOREM 6.4.   *If $0 < x < 1$, we have the inequalities*

$$(6.22) \qquad \frac{x^{n+1}}{n+1} \leq E_n(x) \leq \frac{1}{1-x}\frac{x^{n+1}}{n+1} .$$

If $x < 0$, the error $E_n(x)$ has the same sign as $(-1)^{n+1}$, and we have

$$(6.23) \qquad 0 < (-1)^{n+1}E_n(x) \leq \frac{|x|^{n+1}}{n+1} .$$

Proof. Assume that $0 < x < 1$. In the integral defining $E_n(x)$ we have $0 \leq u \leq x$, so $1 - x \leq 1 - u \leq 1$, and hence the integrand satisfies the inequalities

$$u^n \leq \frac{u^n}{1-u} \leq \frac{u^n}{1-x} .$$

Integrating these inequalities, we obtain (6.22).

To prove (6.23), assume $x < 0$ and let $t = -x = |x|$. Then $t > 0$ and we have

$$E_n(x) = E_n(-t) = \int_0^{-t} \frac{u^n}{1-u}\, du = -\int_0^t \frac{(-v)^n}{1+v}\, dv = (-1)^{n+1}\int_0^t \frac{v^n}{1+v}\, dv .$$

This shows that $E_n(x)$ has the same sign as $(-1)^{n+1}$. Also, we have

$$(-1)^{n+1}E_n(x) = \int_0^t \frac{v^n}{1+v}\, dv \leq \int_0^t v^n\, dv = \frac{t^{n+1}}{n+1} = \frac{|x|^{n+1}}{n+1} ,$$

which completes the proof of (6.23).

The next theorem gives a formula which is admirably suited for computations of logarithms.

THEOREM 6.5.   *If $0 < x < 1$ and if $m \geq 1$, we have*

$$\log \frac{1+x}{1-x} = 2\left(x + \frac{x^3}{3} + \cdots + \frac{x^{2m-1}}{2m-1}\right) + R_m(x) ,$$

where the error term, $R_m(x)$, satisfies the inequalities

(6.24)
$$\frac{x^{2m+1}}{2m+1} < R_m(x) \le \frac{2-x}{1-x} \frac{x^{2m+1}}{2m+1}.$$

Proof. Equation (6.21) is valid for any real $x < 1$. If we replace x by $-x$ in (6.21), keeping $x > -1$, we obtain the formula

(6.25)
$$-\log(1+x) = P_n(-x) + E_n(-x).$$

If $-1 < x < 1$, both (6.21) and (6.25) are valid. Subtracting (6.25) from (6.21), we find

(6.26)
$$\log\frac{1+x}{1-x} = P_n(x) - P_n(-x) + E_n(x) - E_n(-x).$$

In the difference $P_n(x) - P_n(-x)$, the even powers of x cancel and the odd powers double up. Therefore, if n is even, say $n = 2m$, we have

$$P_{2m}(x) - P_{2m}(-x) = 2\left(x + \frac{x^3}{3} + \cdots + \frac{x^{2m-1}}{2m-1}\right),$$

and Equation (6.26) becomes

$$\log\frac{1+x}{1-x} = 2\left(x + \frac{x^3}{3} + \cdots + \frac{x^{2m-1}}{2m-1}\right) + R_m(x),$$

where $R_m(x) = E_{2m}(x) - E_{2m}(-x)$. This formula is valid if x lies in the open interval $-1 < x < 1$. Now we restrict x to the interval $0 < x < 1$. Then the estimates of Theorem 6.4 give us

$$\frac{x^{2m+1}}{2m+1} \le E_{2m}(x) \le \frac{1}{1-x}\frac{x^{2m+1}}{2m+1} \quad \text{and} \quad 0 < -E_{2m}(-x) \le \frac{x^{2m+1}}{2m+1}.$$

Adding these, we obtain the inequalities in (6.24), since $1 + 1/(1-x) = (2-x)/(1-x)$.

EXAMPLE. Taking $m = 2$ and $x = \frac{1}{3}$, we have $(1+x)/(1-x) = 2$, and we obtain the formula

$$\log 2 = 2(\tfrac{1}{3} + \tfrac{1}{81}) + R_2(\tfrac{1}{3}), \quad \text{where} \quad \tfrac{1}{5}(\tfrac{1}{3})^5 < R_2(\tfrac{1}{3}) \le \tfrac{1}{2}(\tfrac{1}{3})^5 = \tfrac{1}{486}.$$

This gives us the inequalities $0.6921 < \log 2 < 0.6935$ with very little calculation.

6.11   Exercises

1. Use Theorem 6.5 with $x = \frac{1}{3}$ and $m = 5$ to calculate approximations to log 2. Retain nine decimals in your calculations and obtain the inequalities $0.6931460 < \log 2 < 0.6931476$.
2. If $x = \frac{1}{5}$, then $(1 + x)/(1 - x) = \frac{3}{2}$. Thus, Theorem 6.5 enables us to compute log 3 in terms of log 2. Take $x = \frac{1}{5}$ and $m = 5$ in Theorem 6.5 and use the results of Exercise 1 to obtain the inequalities $1.098611 < \log 3 < 1.098617$.
   Note: Since $\log 2 < \log e < \log 3$, it follows that $2 < e < 3$.
3. Use Theorem 6.5 with $x = \frac{1}{9}$ to calculate log 5 in terms of log 2. Choose the degree of the approximating polynomial high enough to obtain the inequalities $1.609435 < \log 5 < 1.609438$.
4. Use Theorem 6.5 with $x = \frac{1}{6}$ to calculate log 7 in terms of log 5. Choose the degree of the approximating polynomial high enough to obtain the inequalities $1.945907 < \log 7 < 1.945911$.
5. Use the results of Exercises 1 through 4 to calculate a short table listing log n for $n = 2, 3, \ldots,$ 10. Tabulate each entry with as many *correct* decimal places as you can be certain of from the inequalities in Exercises 1 through 4.

6.12   The exponential function

Theorem 6.2 shows that for every real x there is one and only one y such that $L(y) = x$. Therefore we can use the process of inversion to define y as a function of x. The resulting inverse function is called the *exponential function*, or the *antilogarithm*, and is denoted by E.

DEFINITION.   *For any real x, we define $E(x)$ to be that number y whose logarithm is x. That is, $y = E(x)$ means that $L(y) = x$.*

The domain of E is the entire real axis; its range is the set of positive real numbers. The graph of E, which is shown in Figure 6.6, is obtained from the graph of the logarithm by

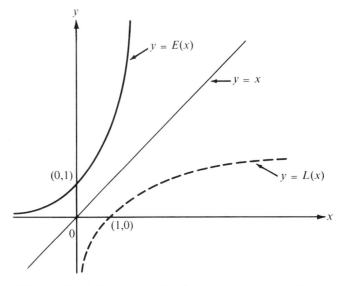

FIGURE 6.6   The graph of the exponential function is obtained from that of the logarithm by reflection through the line $y = x$.

reflection through the line $y = x$. Since L and E are inverses of each other, we have

$$L[E(x)] = x \quad \text{for all } x \quad \text{and} \quad E[L(y)] = y \quad \text{for all } y > 0 \,.$$

Each property of the logarithm can be translated into a property of the exponential. For example, since the logarithm is strictly increasing and continuous on the positive real axis, it follows from Theorem 3.10 that the exponential is strictly increasing and continuous on the entire real axis. The counterpart of Theorem 6.1 is given by the following theorem.

THEOREM 6.6. *The exponential function has the following properties:*
(a) $E(0) = 1, \quad E(1) = e.$
(b) $E'(x) = E(x) \quad$ *for every* x.
(c) $E(a + b) = E(a)E(b) \quad$ *for all* a *and* b.

Proof. Part (a) follows from the equations $L(1) = 0$ and $L(e) = 1$. Next we prove (c), the functional equation for the exponential. Assume that a and b are given and let

$$x = E(a), \quad y = E(b), \quad c = L(xy) \,.$$

Then we have

$$L(x) = a, \quad L(y) = b, \quad E(c) = xy \,.$$

But $c = L(xy) = L(x) + L(y) = a + b$. That is, $c = a + b$. Hence, $E(c) = E(a + b)$. On the other hand, $E(c) = xy = E(a)E(b)$, so $E(a + b) = E(a)E(b)$, which proves (c).

Now we use the functional equation to help us prove (b). The difference quotient for the derivative $E'(x)$ is

$$\frac{E(x + h) - E(x)}{h} = \frac{E(x)E(h) - E(x)}{h} = E(x)\frac{E(h) - 1}{h} \,.$$

Therefore, to prove (b) we must show that

$$(6.27) \qquad\qquad \lim_{h \to 0} \frac{E(h) - 1}{h} = 1 \,.$$

We shall express the quotient in (6.27) in terms of the logarithm. Let $k = E(h) - 1$. Then $k + 1 = E(h)$ so $L(k + 1) = h$ and the quotient is equal to

$$(6.28) \qquad\qquad \frac{E(h) - 1}{h} = \frac{k}{L(k + 1)} \,.$$

Now as $h \to 0$, $E(h) \to 1$ because the exponential function is continuous at 1. Since $k = E(h) - 1$, we have $k \to 0$ as $h \to 0$. But

$$\frac{L(k + 1)}{k} = \frac{L(k + 1) - L(1)}{k} \to L'(1) = 1 \quad \text{as} \quad k \to 0 \,.$$

In view of (6.28), this proves (6.27) which, in turn, proves (b).

6.13   Exponentials expressed as powers of e

The functional equation $E(a + b) = E(a)E(b)$ has many interesting consequences. For example, we can use it to prove that

$$(6.29) \qquad\qquad E(r) = e^r$$

for every rational number r.

First we take $b = -a$ in the functional equation to get

$$E(a)E(-a) = E(0) = 1 \, ,$$

and hence $E(-a) = 1/E(a)$ for every real a. Taking $b = a$, $b = 2a, \ldots, b = na$ in the functional equation we obtain, successively, $E(2a) = E(a)^2$, $E(3a) = E(a)^3$, and, in general, we have

$$(6.30) \qquad\qquad E(na) = E(a)^n$$

for every positive integer n. In particular, when $a = 1$, we obtain

$$E(n) = e^n \, ,$$

whereas for $a = 1/n$, we obtain $E(1) = E(1/n)^n$. Since $E(1/n) > 0$, this implies

$$(6.31) \qquad\qquad E\left(\frac{1}{n}\right) = e^{1/n} \, .$$

Therefore, if we put $a = 1/m$ in (6.30) and use (6.31), we find

$$E\left(\frac{n}{m}\right) = E\left(\frac{1}{m}\right)^n = e^{n/m}$$

for all positive integers m and n. In other words, we have proved (6.29) for every positive rational number r. Since $E(-r) = 1/E(r) = e^{-r}$, it also holds for all negative rational r.

6.14   The definition of e^x for arbitrary real x

In the foregoing section we *proved* that $e^x = E(x)$ when x is any *rational* number. Now we shall *define* e^x for irrational x by writing

$$(6.32) \qquad\qquad e^x = E(x) \qquad \text{for every real } x \, .$$

One justification for this definition is that we can use it to prove that the law of exponents

$$(6.33) \qquad\qquad e^a e^b = e^{a+b}$$

is valid for all real exponents a and b. When we use the definition in (6.32), the proof of (6.33) is a triviality because (6.33) is nothing but a restatement of the functional equation.

The notation e^x for $E(x)$ is the one that is commonly used for the exponential. Occasionally $\exp(x)$ is written instead of e^x, especially when complicated formulas appear in the exponent. We shall continue to use $E(x)$ from time to time in this chapter, but later we shall switch to e^x.

We have defined the exponential function so that the two equations

$$y = e^x \quad \text{and} \quad x = \log y$$

mean exactly the same thing. In the next section we shall define more general powers so that the two equations $y = a^x$ and $x = \log_a y$ will be equivalent.

6.15 The definition of a^x for $a > 0$ and x real

Now that we have defined e^x for arbitrary real x, there is absolutely no difficulty in formulating a definition of a^x for every $a > 0$. One way to proceed is to let a^x denote that number y such that $\log_a y = x$. But this does not work for $a = 1$, since logarithms to the base 1 have not been defined. Another way is to define a^x by the formula

$$(6.34) \qquad a^x = e^{x \log a} .$$

The second method is preferable because, first of all, it is meaningful for all positive a (including $a = 1$) and, secondly, it makes it easy to prove the following properties of exponentials:

$$\log a^x = x \log a . \qquad (ab)^x = a^x b^x .$$

$$a^x a^y = a^{x+y} . \qquad (a^x)^y = (a^y)^x = a^{xy} .$$

$$\textit{If } a \neq 1, \textit{ then } y = a^x \textit{ if and only if } x = \log_a y .$$

The proofs of these properties are left as exercises for the reader.

Just as the graph of the exponential function was obtained from that of the logarithm by reflection through the line $y = x$, so the graph of $y = a^x$ can be obtained from that of $y = \log_a x$ by reflection through the same line; examples are shown in Figure 6.7. The curves in Figures 6.7 were obtained by reflection of those in Figures 6.3. The graph corresponding to $a = 1$ is, of course, the horizontal line $y = 1$.

6.16 Differentiation and integration formulas involving exponentials

One of the most remarkable properties of the exponential function is the formula

$$(6.35) \qquad E'(x) = E(x) ,$$

which tells us that this function is its own derivative. If we use this along with the chain rule, we can obtain differentiation formulas for exponential functions with any positive base a.

Suppose $f(x) = a^x$ for $x > 0$. By the definition of a^x, we may write

$$f(x) = e^{x \log a} = E(x \log a) ;$$

hence, by the chain rule, we find

(6.36) $f'(x) = E'(x \log a) \cdot \log a = E(x \log a) \cdot \log a = a^x \log a$.

In other words, differentiation of a^x simply multiplies a^x by the constant factor $\log a$, this factor being 1 when $a = e$.

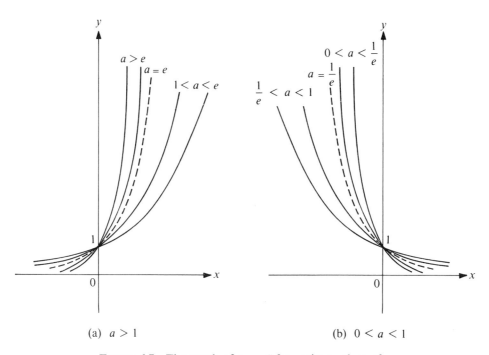

(a) $a > 1$ (b) $0 < a < 1$

FIGURE 6.7   The graph of $y = a^x$ for various values of a.

Of course, these differentiation formulas automatically lead to corresponding integration formulas. For example, (6.35) yields the result

(6.37) $\int e^x \, dx = e^x + C$,

whereas (6.36) gives us the more general formula

(6.38) $\int a^x \, dx = \dfrac{a^x}{\log a} + C \qquad (a > 0, a \neq 1)$.

These may be generalized further by the method of substitution. We simply replace x everywhere in (6.37) and (6.38) by u to obtain

(6.39) $\int e^u \, du = e^u + C , \qquad \int a^u \, du = \dfrac{a^u}{\log a} + C \qquad (a > 0, a \neq 1),$

where u now represents any function with a continuous derivative. If we write $u = f(x)$, and $du = f'(x)\, dx$, the formulas in (6.39) become

$$\int e^{f(x)} f'(x)\, dx = e^{f(x)} + C\,, \qquad \int a^{f(x)} f'(x)\, dx = \frac{a^{f(x)}}{\log a} + C\,,$$

the second of these being valid for $a > 0$, $a \neq 1$.

EXAMPLE 1. Integrate $\int x^2 e^{x^3}\, dx$.

Solution. Let $u = x^3$. Then $du = 3x^2\, dx$, and we obtain

$$\int x^2 e^{x^3}\, dx = \tfrac{1}{3} \int e^{x^3} (3x^2\, dx) = \tfrac{1}{3} \int e^u\, du = \tfrac{1}{3} e^u + C = \tfrac{1}{3} e^{x^3} + C\,.$$

EXAMPLE 2. Integrate $\displaystyle\int \frac{2^{\sqrt{x}}}{\sqrt{x}}\, dx$.

Solution. Let $u = \sqrt{x} = x^{1/2}$. Then $du = \tfrac{1}{2} x^{-1/2}\, dx = \tfrac{1}{2}\, dx/\sqrt{x}$. Hence we have

$$\int \frac{2^{\sqrt{x}}}{\sqrt{x}}\, dx = 2 \int 2^{\sqrt{x}} \left(\frac{1}{2} \frac{dx}{\sqrt{x}} \right) = 2 \int 2^u\, du = 2\, \frac{2^u}{\log 2} + C = \frac{2^{1+\sqrt{x}}}{\log 2} + C\,.$$

EXAMPLE 3. Integrate $\int \cos x\, e^{2 \sin x}\, dx$.

Solution. Let $u = 2 \sin x$. Then $du = 2 \cos x\, dx$, and hence we obtain

$$\int \cos x\, e^{2 \sin x}\, dx = \tfrac{1}{2} \int e^{2 \sin x} (2 \cos x\, dx) = \tfrac{1}{2} \int e^u\, du = \tfrac{1}{2} e^u + C = \tfrac{1}{2} e^{2 \sin x} + C\,.$$

EXAMPLE 4. Integrate $\int e^x \sin x\, dx$.

Solution. Let $u = e^x$, $dv = \sin x\, dx$. Then $du = e^x\, dx$, $v = -\cos x$, and we find

$$(6.40) \qquad \int e^x \sin x\, dx = \int u\, dv = uv - \int v\, du = -e^x \cos x + \int e^x \cos x\, dx + C\,.$$

The integral $\int e^x \cos x\, dx$ is treated in the same way. We let $u = e^x$, $dv = \cos x\, dx$, $du = e^x\, dx$, $v = \sin x$, and we obtain

$$(6.41) \qquad \int e^x \cos x\, dx = e^x \sin x - \int e^x \sin x\, dx + C\,.$$

Substituting this in (6.40), we may solve for $\int e^x \sin x\, dx$ and consolidate the arbitrary constants to obtain

$$\int e^x \sin x\, dx = \frac{e^x}{2} (\sin x - \cos x) + C\,.$$

Notice that we can use this in (6.41) to obtain also

$$\int e^x \cos x\, dx = \frac{e^x}{2} (\cos x + \sin x) + C\,.$$

EXAMPLE 5. Integrate $\displaystyle\int \frac{dx}{1 + e^x}$.

Solution. One way to treat this example is to rewrite the integrand as follows:

$$\frac{1}{1 + e^x} = \frac{e^{-x}}{e^{-x} + 1} .$$

Now put $u = e^{-x} + 1$. Then $du = -e^{-x}\, dx$, and we get

$$\int \frac{e^{-x}}{e^{-x} + 1}\, dx = -\int \frac{-e^{-x}\, dx}{e^{-x} + 1} = -\int \frac{du}{u} = -\log |u| + C = -\log (1 + e^{-x}) + C .$$

The result can be written in other ways if we manipulate the logarithm. For instance,

$$-\log (1 + e^{-x}) = \log \frac{1}{1 + e^{-x}} = \log \frac{e^x}{e^x + 1}$$

$$= \log (e^x) - \log (e^x + 1) = x - \log (1 + e^x) .$$

Another way to treat this same example is to write

$$\frac{1}{1 + e^x} = 1 - \frac{e^x}{1 + e^x} .$$

Then we have

$$\int \frac{dx}{1 + e^x} = x - \int \frac{e^x}{1 + e^x}\, dx = x - \int \frac{du}{u} ,$$

where $u = 1 + e^x$. Thus we find

$$\int \frac{dx}{1 + e^x} = x - \log (1 + e^x) + C ,$$

which is one of the forms obtained above.

6.17   Exercises

In Exercises 1 through 12, find the derivative $f'(x)$. In each case the function f is assumed to be defined for all real x for which the given formula for $f(x)$ is meaningful.

1. $f(x) = e^{3x-1}$.
2. $f(x) = e^{4x^2}$.
3. $f(x) = e^{-x^2}$.
4. $f(x) = e^{\sqrt{x}}$.
5. $f(x) = e^{1/x}$.
6. $f(x) = 2^x$.

7. $f(x) = 2^{x^2}$ [which means $2^{(x^2)}$].
8. $f(x) = e^{\sin x}$.
9. $f(x) = e^{\cos^2 x}$.
10. $f(x) = e^{\log x}$.
11. $f(x) = e^{e^x}$ [which means $e^{(e^x)}$].
12. $f(x) = e^{e^{e^x}}$ [which means $\exp (e^{(e^x)})$].

Evaluate the indefinite integrals in Exercises 13 through 18.

13. $\int x\,e^x\,dx.$

16. $\int x^2\,e^{-2x}\,dx.$

14. $\int x\,e^{-x}\,dx.$

17. $\int e^{\sqrt{x}}\,dx.$

15. $\int x^2\,e^x\,dx.$

18. $\int x^3 e^{-x^2}\,dx.$

19. Determine all constants a and b such that $e^x = b + \int_a^x e^t\,dt$.

20. Let $A = \int e^{ax}\cos bx\,dx$ and $B = \int e^{ax}\sin bx\,dx$, where a and b are constants, not both zero. Use integration by parts to show that

$$aA - bB = e^{ax}\cos bx + C_1, \qquad aB + bA = e^{ax}\sin bx + C_2,$$

where C_1 and C_2 are arbitrary constants. Solve for A and B to deduce the following integration formulas:

$$\int e^{ax}\cos bx\,dx = \frac{e^{ax}(a\cos bx + b\sin bx)}{a^2 + b^2} + C,$$

$$\int e^{ax}\sin bx\,dx = \frac{e^{ax}(a\sin bx - b\cos bx)}{a^2 + b^2} + C.$$

In Exercises 21 through 34, find the derivative $f'(x)$. In each case, the function f is assumed to be defined for all real x for which the given formula for $f(x)$ is meaningful. Logarithmic differentiation may simplify the work in some cases.

21. $f(x) = x^x.$

22. $f(x) = (1 + x)(1 + e^{x^2}).$

23. $f(x) = \dfrac{e^x - e^{-x}}{e^x + e^{-x}}.$

24. $f(x) = x^{a^a} + a^{x^a} + a^{a^x}.$

25. $f(x) = \log\,[\log\,(\log x)].$

26. $f(x) = \log\,(e^x + \sqrt{1 + e^{2x}}).$

27. $f(x) = x^{x^x}.$

28. $f(x) = (\log x)^x.$

29. $f(x) = x^{\log x}.$

30. $f(x) = \dfrac{(\log x)^x}{x^{\log x}}.$

31. $f(x) = (\sin x)^{\cos x} + (\cos x)^{\sin x}.$

32. $f(x) = x^{1/x}.$

33. $f(x) = \dfrac{x^2(3 - x)^{1/3}}{(1 - x)(3 + x)^{2/3}}.$

34. $f(x) = \displaystyle\prod_{i=1}^{n} (x - a_i)^{b_i}.$

35. Let $f(x) = x^r$, where $x > 0$ and r is any real number. The formula $f'(x) = rx^{r-1}$ was proved earlier for *rational r*.
    (a) Show that this formula also holds for arbitrary real r. [*Hint:* Write $x^r = e^{r\log x}$.]
    (b) Discuss under what conditions the result of part (a) applies for $x \le 0$.

36. Use the definition $a^x = e^{x\log a}$ to derive the following properties of general exponentials:
    (a) $\log a^x = x\log a$.
    (b) $(ab)^x = a^x b^x$.
    (c) $a^x a^y = a^{x+y}$.
    (d) $(a^x)^y = (a^y)^x = a^{xy}$.
    (e) If $a \ne 1$, *then* $y = a^x$ if and only if $x = \log_a y$.

37. Let $f(x) = \frac{1}{2}(a^x + a^{-x})$ if $a > 0$. Show that

$$f(x + y) + f(x - y) = 2f(x)f(y).$$

38. Let $f(x) = e^{cx}$, where c is a constant. Show that $f'(0) = c$, and use this to deduce the following limit relation:

$$\lim_{x \to 0} \frac{e^{cx} - 1}{x} = c .$$

39. Let f be a function defined everywhere on the real axis, with a derivative f' which satisfies the equation

$$f'(x) = cf(x) \qquad \text{for every } x ,$$

where c is a constant. Prove that there is a constant K such that $f(x) = Ke^{cx}$ for every x. [*Hint:* Let $g(x) = f(x)e^{-cx}$ and consider $g'(x)$.]

40. Let f be a function defined everywhere on the real axis. Suppose also that f satisfies the functional equation

(i) $$f(x + y) = f(x)f(y) \qquad \text{for all } x \text{ and } y .$$

(a) Using only the functional equation, prove that $f(0)$ is either 0 or 1. Also, prove that if $f(0) \neq 0$ then $f(x) \neq 0$ for *all* x.
Assume, in addition to (i), that $f'(x)$ exists for all x, and prove the following statements:
(b) $f'(x)f(y) = f'(y)f(x)$ for all x and y.
(c) There is a constant c such that $f'(x) = cf(x)$ for all x.
(d) $f(x) = e^{cx}$ if $f(0) \neq 0$.   [*Hint:* See Exercise 39.]

41. (a) Let $f(x) = e^x - 1 - x$ for all x. Prove that $f'(x) \geq 0$ if $x \geq 0$ and $f'(x) \leq 0$ if $x \leq 0$. Use this fact to deduce the inequalities

$$e^x > 1 + x , \qquad e^{-x} > 1 - x ,$$

valid for all $x > 0$. (When $x = 0$, these become equalities.)
Integrate these inequalities to derive the following further inequalities, all valid for $x > 0$:

(b) $e^x > 1 + x + \dfrac{x^2}{2!} ,$ $e^{-x} < 1 - x + \dfrac{x^2}{2!} .$

(c) $e^x > 1 + x + \dfrac{x^2}{2!} + \dfrac{x^3}{3!} ,$ $e^{-x} > 1 - x + \dfrac{x^2}{2!} - \dfrac{x^3}{3!} .$

(d) Guess the generalization suggested and prove your result.

42. If n is a positive integer and if $x > 0$, show that

$$\left(1 + \frac{x}{n}\right)^n < e^x , \qquad \text{and that} \qquad e^x < \left(1 - \frac{x}{n}\right)^{-n} \qquad \text{if } x < n .$$

By choosing a suitable value of n, deduce that $2.5 < e < 2.99$.

43. Let $f(x, y) = x^y$ where $x > 0$. Show that

$$\frac{\partial f}{\partial x} = yx^{y-1} \qquad \text{and} \qquad \frac{\partial f}{\partial y} = x^y \log x .$$

6.18   The hyperbolic functions

Certain combinations of exponential functions occur quite frequently in analysis, and it is worth while to give these combinations special names and to study them as examples of new functions. These combinations, called the *hyperbolic sine* (sinh), the *hyperbolic cosine* (cosh), the *hyperbolic tangent* (tanh), etc., are defined as follows:

$$\sinh x = \frac{e^x - e^{-x}}{2}, \qquad \cosh x = \frac{e^x + e^{-x}}{2}, \qquad \tanh x = \frac{\sinh x}{\cosh x} = \frac{e^x - e^{-x}}{e^x + e^{-x}},$$

$$\operatorname{csch} x = \frac{1}{\sinh x}, \qquad \operatorname{sech} x = \frac{1}{\cosh x}, \qquad \coth x = \frac{1}{\tanh x}.$$

$y = \sinh x$ $y = \cosh x$ $y = \tanh x$

FIGURE 6.8   Graphs of hyperbolic functions.

The prefix "hyperbolic" is due to the fact that these functions are related geometrically to a hyperbola in much the same way as the trigonometric functions are related to a circle. This relation will be discussed in more detail in Chapter 14 when we study the hyperbola. The graphs of the sinh, cosh, and tanh are shown in Figure 6.8.

The hyperbolic functions possess many properties that resemble those of the trigonometric functions. Some of these are listed as exercises in the following section.

6.19   Exercises

Derive the properties of the hyperbolic functions listed in Exercises 1 through 15 and compare them, whenever possible, with the corresponding properties of the trigonometric functions.

1. $\cosh^2 x - \sinh^2 x = 1$.
2. $\sinh(-x) = -\sinh x$.
3. $\cosh(-x) = \cosh x$.
4. $\tanh(-x) = -\tanh x$.
5. $\sinh(x + y) = \sinh x \cosh y + \cosh x \sinh y$.
6. $\cosh(x + y) = \cosh x \cosh y + \sinh x \sinh y$.
7. $\sinh 2x = 2 \sinh x \cosh x$.
8. $\cosh 2x = \cosh^2 x + \sinh^2 x$.
9. $\cosh x + \sinh x = e^x$.
10. $\cosh x - \sinh x = e^{-x}$.
11. $(\cosh x + \sinh x)^n = \cosh nx + \sinh nx$ (n an integer).
12. $2 \sinh^2 \frac{1}{2}x = \cosh x - 1$.

13. $2 \cosh^2 \frac{1}{2}x = \cosh x + 1$.
14. $\tanh^2 x + \operatorname{sech}^2 x = 1$.
15. $\coth^2 x - \operatorname{csch}^2 x = 1$.
16. Find $\cosh x$ if $\sinh x = \frac{4}{3}$.
17. Find $\sinh x$ if $\cosh x = \frac{5}{4}$ and $x > 0$.
18. Find $\sinh x$ and $\cosh x$ if $\tanh x = \frac{5}{13}$.
19. Find $\cosh (x + y)$ if $\sinh x = \frac{4}{3}$ and $\sinh y = \frac{3}{4}$.
20. Find $\tanh 2x$ if $\tanh x = \frac{3}{4}$.

In Exercises 21 through 26, prove the differentiation formulas.

21. $D \sinh x = \cosh x$.
22. $D \cosh x = \sinh x$.
23. $D \tanh x = \operatorname{sech}^2 x$.

24. $D \coth x = -\operatorname{csch}^2 x$.
25. $D \operatorname{sech} x = -\operatorname{sech} x \tanh x$.
26. $D \operatorname{csch} x = -\operatorname{csch} x \coth x$.

6.20 Derivatives of inverse functions

We have applied the process of inversion to construct the exponential function from the logarithm. In the next section, we shall invert the trigonometric functions. It is convenient at this point to discuss a general theorem which shows that the process of inversion transmits differentiability from a function to its inverse.

THEOREM 6.7. *Assume f is strictly increasing and continuous on an interval $[a, b]$, and let g be the inverse of f. If the derivative $f'(x)$ exists and is nonzero at a point x in (a, b), then the derivative $g'(y)$ also exists and is nonzero at the corresponding point y, where $y = f(x)$. Moreover, the two derivatives are reciprocals of each other; that is, we have*

(6.42)
$$g'(y) = \frac{1}{f'(x)}.$$

Note: If we use the Leibniz notation and write y for $f(x)$, dy/dx for $f'(x)$, x for $g(y)$, and dx/dy for $g'(y)$, then Equation (6.42) becomes

$$\frac{dx}{dy} = \frac{1}{\left(\dfrac{dy}{dx}\right)},$$

which has the appearance of a trivial algebraic identity.

Proof. Assume x is a point in (a, b) where $f'(x)$ exists and is nonzero, and let $y = f(x)$. We shall show that the difference quotient

$$\frac{g(y + k) - g(y)}{k}$$

approaches the limit $1/f'(x)$ as $k \to 0$.

Let $h = g(y + k) - g(y)$. Since $x = g(y)$, this implies $h = g(y + k) - x$ or $x + h = g(y + k)$. Therefore $y + k = f(x + h)$, and hence $k = f(x + h) - f(x)$. Note that

$h \neq 0$ if $k \neq 0$ because g is strictly increasing. Therefore, if $k \neq 0$, the difference quotient in question is

(6.43)
$$\frac{g(y + k) - g(y)}{k} = \frac{h}{f(x + h) - f(x)} = \frac{1}{[f(x + h) - f(x)]/h}.$$

As $k \to 0$, the difference $g(y + k) - g(y) \to 0$ because of the continuity of g at y [property (b) of Theorem 3.10]. This means that $h \to 0$ as $k \to 0$. But we know that the difference quotient in the denominator on the extreme right of (6.43) approaches $f'(x)$ as $h \to 0$ [since $f'(x)$ exists]. Therefore, when $k \to 0$, the quotient on the extreme left of (6.43) approaches the limit $1/f'(x)$. This proves Theorem 6.7.

6.21 Inverses of the trigonometric functions

The process of inversion may be applied to the trigonometric functions. Suppose we begin with the sine function. To determine a unique inverse, we must consider the sine over some interval where it is monotonic. There are, of course, many such intervals, for

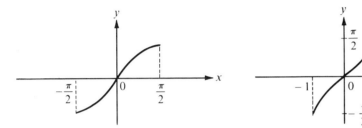

FIGURE 6.9 $y = \sin x$.   FIGURE 6.10 $y = \arcsin x$.

example $[-\frac{1}{2}\pi, \frac{1}{2}\pi]$, $[\frac{1}{2}\pi, \frac{3}{2}\pi]$, $[-\frac{3}{2}\pi, -\frac{1}{2}\pi]$, etc., and it really does not matter which one of these we choose. It is customary to select $[-\frac{1}{2}\pi, \frac{1}{2}\pi]$ and define a new function f as follows:

$$f(x) = \sin x \quad \text{if} \quad -\frac{\pi}{2} \leq x \leq \frac{\pi}{2}.$$

The function f so defined is strictly increasing and it assumes every value between -1 and $+1$ exactly once on the interval $[-\frac{1}{2}\pi, \frac{1}{2}\pi]$. (See Figure 6.9.) Hence there is a uniquely determined function g defined on $[-1, 1]$ which assigns to each number y in $[-1, 1]$ that number x in $[-\frac{1}{2}\pi, \frac{1}{2}\pi]$ for which $y = \sin x$. This function g is called the *inverse sine* or *arc sine*, and its value at y is denoted by $\arcsin y$, or by $\sin^{-1} y$. Thus,

$$u = \arcsin v \quad \text{means} \quad v = \sin u \quad \text{and} \quad -\frac{\pi}{2} \leq u \leq \frac{\pi}{2}.$$

The graph of the arc sine is shown in Figure 6.10. Note that the arc sine is not defined outside the interval $[-1, 1]$.

The derivative of the arc sine can be obtained from formula (6.42) of Section 6.20. In this case we have $f'(x) = \cos x$ and this is nonzero in the open interval $(-\frac{1}{2}\pi, \frac{1}{2}\pi)$. Therefore formula (6.42) yields

$$g'(y) = \frac{1}{f'(x)} = \frac{1}{\cos x} = \frac{1}{\sqrt{1 - \sin^2 x}} = \frac{1}{\sqrt{1 - y^2}} \qquad \text{if} \quad -1 < y < 1 .$$

With a change in notation we can write this result as follows:

(6.44) $$\qquad\qquad D \arcsin x = \frac{1}{\sqrt{1 - x^2}} \qquad \text{if} \quad -1 < x < 1 .$$

Of course, this now gives us a new integration formula,

(6.45) $$\qquad\qquad \int_0^x \frac{1}{\sqrt{1 - t^2}} \, dt = \arcsin x ,$$

which is valid for $-1 < x < 1$.

> *Note:* This formula may be used as the starting point for a completely analytic theory of the trigonometric functions, without any reference to geometry. Briefly, the idea is to begin with the arc sine function, defining it by the integral in (6.45), just as we defined the logarithm as an integral. Next, the sine function is defined as the inverse of the arc sine, and the cosine as the derivative of the sine. Many details are required to carry out this program completely and we shall not attempt to describe them here. An alternative method for introducing the trigonometric functions analytically will be mentioned in Chapter 11.

In the Leibniz notation for indefinite integrals we may write formula (6.45) in the form

(6.46) $$\qquad\qquad \int \frac{dx}{\sqrt{1 - x^2}} = \arcsin x + C .$$

Integration by parts yields the following further integration formula:

$$\int \arcsin x \, dx = x \arcsin x - \int \frac{x \, dx}{\sqrt{1 - x^2}} = x \arcsin x + \sqrt{1 - x^2} + C .$$

The cosine and tangent are inverted in a similar fashion. For the cosine it is customary to choose the interval $[0, \pi]$ in which to perform the inversion. (See Figure 6.11.) The resulting inverse function, called the arc cosine, is defined as follows:

$$u = \arccos v \qquad \text{means} \qquad v = \cos u \qquad \text{and} \qquad 0 \leq u \leq \pi .$$

The graph of the arc cosine function is shown in Figure 6.12.

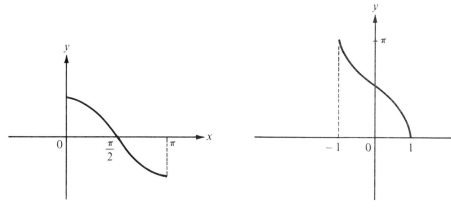

FIGURE 6.11 $y = \cos x$.   FIGURE 6.12 $y = \arccos x$.

To invert the tangent we choose the open interval $(-\frac{1}{2}\pi, \frac{1}{2}\pi)$ (see Figure 6.13) and we define the arc tangent as follows:

$$u = \arctan v \quad \text{means} \quad v = \tan u \quad \text{and} \quad -\frac{\pi}{2} < u < \frac{\pi}{2}.$$

Figure 6.14 shows a portion of the graph of the arc tangent function.

The argument used to derive (6.44) can also be applied to the arc cosine and arc tangent functions, and it yields the following differentiation formulas:

(6.47) $$D \arccos x = \frac{-1}{\sqrt{1 - x^2}},$$

valid for $-1 < x < 1$, and

(6.48) $$D \arctan x = \frac{1}{1 + x^2},$$

valid for all real x.

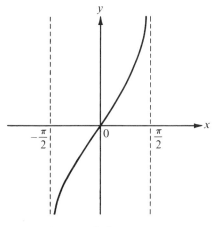

FIGURE 6.13 $y = \tan x$.

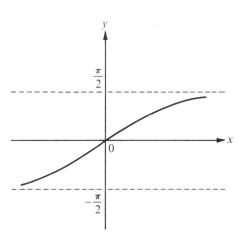

FIGURE 6.14 $y = \arctan x$.

When (6.47) is translated into an integration formula it becomes

(6.49)
$$\int_0^x \frac{1}{\sqrt{1-t^2}}\, dt = -(\arccos x - \arccos 0) = \frac{\pi}{2} - \arccos x$$

if $-1 < x < 1$. By comparing (6.49) with (6.45), we deduce the relation $\frac{1}{2}\pi - \arccos x = \arcsin x$. (This may also be deduced from the familiar identity $\sin(\frac{1}{2}\pi - y) = \cos y$ if we write $y = \arccos x$.) In the Leibniz notation for indefinite integrals, we may write (6.49) as follows:

(6.50)
$$\int \frac{dx}{\sqrt{1-x^2}} = -\arccos x + C .$$

Similarly, from (6.48) we obtain

(6.51)
$$\int_0^x \frac{dt}{1+t^2} = \arctan x \qquad \text{or} \qquad \int \frac{dx}{1+x^2} = \arctan x + C .$$

Using integration by parts in conjunction with (6.50) and (6.51), we can derive the following further integration formulas:

$$\int \arccos x\, dx = x \arccos x + \int \frac{x\, dx}{\sqrt{1-x^2}} = x \arccos x - \sqrt{1-x^2} + C ,$$

$$\int \arctan x\, dx = x \arctan x - \int \frac{x\, dx}{1+x^2} = x \arctan x - \tfrac{1}{2}\log(1+x^2) + C .$$

The inverses of the cotangent, secant, and cosecant can be defined by means of the following formulas:

(6.52)
$$\operatorname{arccot} x = \frac{\pi}{2} - \arctan x \qquad \text{for all real } x ,$$

(6.53)
$$\operatorname{arcsec} x = \arccos \frac{1}{x} \qquad \text{when } |x| \geq 1 ,$$

(6.54)
$$\operatorname{arccsc} x = \arcsin \frac{1}{x} \qquad \text{when } |x| \geq 1 .$$

Differentiation and integration formulas for these functions are listed in the following exercises.

6.22 Exercises

Derive the differentiation formulas in Exercises 1 through 5.

1. $D \arccos x = \dfrac{-1}{\sqrt{1-x^2}} \qquad$ if $-1 < x < 1.$

2. $D \arctan x = \dfrac{1}{1+x^2} \qquad$ for all real $x.$

3. $D \operatorname{arccot} x = \dfrac{-1}{1 + x^2}$ for   all real x.

4. $D \operatorname{arcsec} x = \dfrac{1}{|x|\sqrt{x^2 - 1}}$ if $|x| > 1$.

5. $D \operatorname{arccsc} x = \dfrac{-1}{|x|\sqrt{x^2 - 1}}$ if $|x| > 1$.

Derive the integration formulas in Exercises 6 through 10.

6. $\int \operatorname{arccot} x \, dx = x \operatorname{arccot} x + \frac{1}{2}\log(1 + x^2) + C$.

7. $\int \operatorname{arcsec} x \, dx = x \operatorname{arcsec} x - \dfrac{x}{|x|} \log|x + \sqrt{x^2 - 1}| + C$.

8. $\int \operatorname{arccsc} x \, dx = x \operatorname{arccsc} x + \dfrac{x}{|x|} \log|x + \sqrt{x^2 - 1}| + C$.

9. $\int (\arcsin x)^2 \, dx = x(\arcsin x)^2 - 2x + 2\sqrt{1 - x^2}\,\arcsin x + C$.

10. $\int \dfrac{\arcsin x}{x^2} \, dx = \log\left|\dfrac{1 - \sqrt{1 - x^2}}{x}\right| - \dfrac{\arcsin x}{x} + C$.

11. (a) Show that $D\left(\operatorname{arccot} x - \arctan \dfrac{1}{x}\right) = 0$ for all $x \neq 0$.

    (b) Prove that there is no constant C such that $\operatorname{arccot} x - \arctan(1/x) = C$ for all $x \neq 0$. Explain why this does not contradict the zero-derivative theorem (Theorem 5.2).

In Exercises 12 through 25, find the derivative $f'(x)$. In each case the function f is assumed to be defined for all real x for which the given formula for $f(x)$ is meaningful.

12. $f(x) = \arcsin \dfrac{x}{2}$.

13. $f(x) = \arccos \dfrac{1 - x}{\sqrt{2}}$.

14. $f(x) = \arccos \dfrac{1}{x}$.

15. $f(x) = \arcsin(\sin x)$.

16. $f(x) = \sqrt{x} - \arctan \sqrt{x}$.

17. $f(x) = \arctan x + \frac{1}{3}\arctan(x^3)$.

18. $f(x) = \arcsin \dfrac{1 - x^2}{1 + x^2}$.

19. $f(x) = \arctan(\tan^2 x)$.

20. $f(x) = \arctan(x + \sqrt{1 + x^2})$.

21. $f(x) = \arcsin(\sin x - \cos x)$.

22. $f(x) = \arccos \sqrt{1 - x^2}$.

23. $f(x) = \arctan \dfrac{1 + x}{1 - x}$.

24. $f(x) = [\arccos(x^2)]^{-2}$.

25. $f(x) = \log\left(\arccos \dfrac{1}{\sqrt{x}}\right)$.

26. Show that $dy/dx = (x + y)/(x - y)$ if $\arctan(y/x) = \log\sqrt{x^2 + y^2}$.

27. Compute d^2y/dx^2 if $y = (\arcsin x)/\sqrt{1 - x^2}$ for $|x| < 1$.

28. Let $f(x) = \arctan x - x + \frac{1}{3}x^3$. Examine the sign of f' to prove that

$$x - \dfrac{x^3}{3} < \arctan x \quad \text{if} \quad x > 0.$$

In Exercises 29 through 47, evaluate the indefinite integrals.

29. $\int \dfrac{dx}{\sqrt{a^2 - x^2}}$, $\quad a \neq 0$.

30. $\int \dfrac{dx}{\sqrt{1 - 2x - x^2}}$.

31. $\int \dfrac{dx}{a^2 + x^2}$, $\quad a \neq 0$.

32. $\int \dfrac{dx}{a + bx^2}$ $\quad (ab \neq 0)$.

33. $\int \dfrac{dx}{x^2 - x + 2}$.

34. $\int x \arctan x \, dx$.

35. $\int x^2 \arccos x \, dx$.

36. $\int x(\arctan x)^2 \, dx$.

37. $\int \arctan \sqrt{x} \, dx$.

47. $\int \dfrac{dx}{\sqrt{(x - a)(b - x)}}$, $\quad b \neq a$. $\quad$ [*Hint:* $x - a = (b - a) \sin^2 u$.]

38. $\int \dfrac{\arctan \sqrt{x}}{\sqrt{x}(1 + x)} \, dx$.

39. $\int \sqrt{1 - x^2} \, dx$. $\quad$ [*Hint:* $x = \sin u$.]

40. $\int \dfrac{x \, e^{\arctan x}}{(1 + x^2)^{3/2}} \, dx$.

41. $\int \dfrac{e^{\arctan x}}{(1 + x^2)^{3/2}} \, dx$.

42. $\int \dfrac{x^2}{(1 + x^2)^2} \, dx$.

43. $\int \dfrac{e^x}{1 + e^{2x}} \, dx$.

44. $\int \dfrac{\text{arccot } e^x}{e^x} \, dx$.

45. $\int \left(\dfrac{a + x}{a - x}\right)^{1/2} dx$, $\quad a > 0$.

46. $\int \sqrt{(x - a)(b - x)} \, dx$, $\quad b \neq a$.

6.23 Integration by partial fractions

We recall that a quotient of two polynomials is called a rational function. Differentiation of a rational function leads to a new rational function which may be obtained by the quotient rule for derivatives. On the other hand, integration of a rational function may lead to functions that are not rational. For example, we have

$$\int \frac{dx}{x} = \log |x| + C \quad \text{and} \quad \int \frac{dx}{1 + x^2} = \arctan x + C .$$

We shall describe a method for computing the integral of any rational function, and we shall find that the result can always be expressed in terms of polynomials, rational functions, inverse tangents, and logarithms.

The basic idea of the method is to decompose a given rational function into a sum of simpler fractions (called partial fractions) that can be integrated by the techniques discussed earlier. We shall describe the general procedure by means of a number of simple examples that illustrate all the essential features of the method.

EXAMPLE 1. In this example we begin with two simple fractions, $1/(x - 1)$ and $1/(x + 3)$, which we know how to integrate, and see what happens when we form a linear combination of these fractions. For example, if we take twice the first fraction plus three times the second, we obtain

$$\frac{2}{x - 1} + \frac{3}{x + 3} = \frac{2(x + 3) + 3(x - 1)}{(x - 1)(x + 3)} = \frac{5x + 3}{x^2 + 2x - 3} .$$

If, now, we read this formula from right to left, it tells us that the rational function r given by $r(x) = (5x + 3)/(x^2 + 2x - 3)$ has been expressed as a linear combination of $1/(x - 1)$ and $1/(x + 3)$. Therefore, we may evaluate the integral of r by writing

$$\int \frac{5x + 3}{x^2 + 2x - 3} \, dx = 2 \int \frac{dx}{x - 1} + 3 \int \frac{dx}{x + 3} = 2 \log |x - 1| + 3 \log |x + 3| + C.$$

EXAMPLE 2. The foregoing example suggests a procedure for dealing with integrals of the form $\int (ax + b)/(x^2 + 2x - 3) \, dx$. For example, to evaluate $\int (2x + 5)/(x^2 + 2x - 3) \, dx$, we try to express the integral as a linear combination of $1/(x - 1)$ and $1/(x + 3)$ by writing

(6.55)
$$\frac{2x + 5}{x^2 + 2x - 3} = \frac{A}{x - 1} + \frac{B}{x + 3}$$

with constants A and B to be determined. If we can choose A and B so that Equation (6.55) is an identity, then the integral of the fraction on the left is equal to the sum of the integrals of the simpler fractions on the right. To find A and B, we multiply both sides of (6.55) by $(x - 1)(x + 3)$ to remove the fractions. This gives us

(6.56)
$$A(x + 3) + B(x - 1) = 2x + 5.$$

At this stage there are two methods commonly used to find A and B. One method is to equate coefficients of like powers of x in (6.56). This leads to the equations $A + B = 2$ and $3A - B = 5$. Solving this pair of simultaneous equations, we obtain $A = \frac{7}{4}$ and $B = \frac{1}{4}$. The other method involves the substitution of two values of x in (6.56) and leads to another pair of equations for A and B. In this particular case, the presence of the factors $x - 1$ and $x + 3$ suggests that we use the values $x = 1$ and $x = -3$. When we put $x = 1$ in (6.56), the coefficient of B vanishes, and we find $4A = 7$, or $A = \frac{7}{4}$. Similarly, we can make the coefficient of A vanish by putting $x = -3$. This gives us $-4B = -1$, or $B = \frac{1}{4}$. In any event, we have found values of A and B to satisfy (6.55), so we have

$$\int \frac{2x + 5}{x^2 + 2x - 3} \, dx = \frac{7}{4} \int \frac{dx}{x - 1} + \frac{1}{4} \int \frac{dx}{x + 3} = \frac{7}{4} \log |x - 1| + \frac{1}{4} \log |x + 3| + C.$$

It is clear that the method described in Example 2 also applies to integrals of the form $\int f(x)/g(x) \, dx$ in which f is a linear polynomial and g is a quadratic polynomial that can be factored into distinct linear factors with real coefficients, say $g(x) = (x - x_1)(x - x_2)$. In this case the quotient $f(x)/g(x)$ can be expressed as a linear combination of $1/(x - x_1)$ and $1/(x - x_2)$, and integration of $f(x)/g(x)$ leads to a corresponding combination of the logarithmic terms $\log |x - x_1|$ and $\log |x - x_2|$.

The foregoing examples involve rational functions f/g in which the degree of the numerator is less than that of the denominator. A rational function with this property is said to be a *proper* rational function. If f/g is *improper*, that is, if the degree of f is not less than that of g, then we can express f/g as the sum of a polynomial and a proper rational function. In fact, we simply divide f by g to obtain

$$\frac{f(x)}{g(x)} = Q(x) + \frac{R(x)}{g(x)},$$

where Q and R are polynomials (called the *quotient* and *remainder*, respectively) such that the remainder has degree less than that of g. For example,

$$\frac{x^3 + 3x}{x^2 - 2x - 3} = x + 2 + \frac{10x + 6}{x^2 - 2x - 3}.$$

Therefore, in the study of integration technique, there is no loss in generality if we restrict ourselves to *proper* rational functions, and from now on we consider $\int f(x)/g(x)\, dx$, where f has degree less than that of g.

A general theorem in algebra states that every proper rational function can be expressed as a finite sum of fractions of the forms

$$\frac{A}{(x + a)^k} \quad \text{and} \quad \frac{Bx + C}{(x^2 + bx + c)^m},$$

where k and m are positive integers and A, B, C, a, b, c are constants with $b^2 - 4c < 0$. The condition $b^2 - 4c < 0$ means that the quadratic polynomial $x^2 + bx + c$ cannot be factored into linear factors with real coefficients or, what amounts to the same thing, the quadratic equation $x^2 + bx + c = 0$ has no real roots. Such a quadratic factor is said to be *irreducible*. When a rational function has been so expressed, we say that it has been decomposed into *partial fractions*. Therefore the problem of integrating this rational function reduces to that of integrating its partial fractions. These may be easily dealt with by the techniques described in the examples which follow.

We shall not bother to prove that partial-fraction decompositions always exist. Instead, we shall show (by means of examples) how to obtain the partial fractions in specific problems. In each case that arises the partial-fraction decomposition can be verified directly.

It is convenient to separate the discussion into cases depending on the way in which the denominator of the quotient $f(x)/g(x)$ can be factored.

CASE 1. The denominator is a product of distinct linear factors. Suppose that $g(x)$ splits into n distinct linear factors, say

$$g(x) = (x - x_1)(x - x_2) \cdots (x - x_n).$$

Now notice that a linear combination of the form

$$\frac{A_1}{x - x_1} + \cdots + \frac{A_n}{x - x_n}$$

may be expressed as a single fraction with the common denominator $g(x)$, and the numerator of this fraction will be a polynomial of degree $< n$ involving the A's. Therefore, if we can find A's to make this numerator equal to $f(x)$, we shall have the decomposition

$$\frac{f(x)}{g(x)} = \frac{A_1}{x - x_1} + \cdots + \frac{A_n}{x - x_n},$$

and the integral of $f(x)/g(x)$ will be equal to $\sum_{i=1}^{n} A_i \log |x - x_i|$. In the next example, we work out a case with $n = 3$.

EXAMPLE 3. Integrate $\displaystyle\int \frac{2x^2 + 5x - 1}{x^3 + x^2 - 2x} \, dx$.

Solution. Since $x^3 + x^2 - 2x = x(x - 1)(x + 2)$, the denominator is a product of distinct linear factors, and we try to find A_1, A_2, and A_3 such that

$$\frac{2x^2 + 5x - 1}{x^3 + x^2 - 2x} = \frac{A_1}{x} + \frac{A_2}{x - 1} + \frac{A_3}{x + 2}.$$

Clearing the fractions, we obtain

$$2x^2 + 5x - 1 = A_1(x - 1)(x + 2) + A_2 x(x + 2) + A_3 x(x - 1).$$

When $x = 0$, we find $-2A_1 = -1$, so $A_1 = \frac{1}{2}$. When $x = 1$, we obtain $3A_2 = 6$, $A_2 = 2$, and when $x = -2$, we find $6A_3 = -3$, or $A_3 = -\frac{1}{2}$. Therefore we have

$$\int \frac{2x^2 + 5x - 1}{x^3 + x^2 - 2x} \, dx = \frac{1}{2} \int \frac{dx}{x} + 2 \int \frac{dx}{x - 1} - \frac{1}{2} \int \frac{dx}{x + 2}$$

$$= \tfrac{1}{2} \log |x| + 2 \log |x - 1| - \tfrac{1}{2} \log |x + 2| + C.$$

CASE 2. The denominator is a product of linear factors, some of which are repeated. We illustrate this case with an example.

EXAMPLE 4. Integrate $\displaystyle\int \frac{x^2 + 2x + 3}{(x - 1)(x + 1)^2} \, dx$.

Solution. Here we try to find A_1, A_2, A_3 so that

(6.57)
$$\frac{x^2 + 2x + 3}{(x - 1)(x + 1)^2} = \frac{A_1}{x - 1} + \frac{A_2}{x + 1} + \frac{A_3}{(x + 1)^2}.$$

We need both $A_2/(x + 1)$ and $A_3/(x + 1)^2$ as well as $A_1/(x - 1)$ in order to get a polynomial of degree two in the numerator and to have as many constants as equations when we try to determine the A's. Clearing the fractions, we obtain

(6.58)
$$x^2 + 2x + 3 = A_1(x + 1)^2 + A_2(x - 1)(x + 1) + A_3(x - 1).$$

Substituting $x = 1$, we find $4A_1 = 6$, so $A_1 = \frac{3}{2}$. When $x = -1$, we obtain $-2A_3 = 2$ and $A_3 = -1$. We need one more equation to determine A_2. Since there are no other choices of x that will make any factor vanish, we choose a convenient x that will help to simplify the calculations. For example, the choice $x = 0$ leads to the equation $3 = A_1 - A_2 - A_3$ from which we find $A_2 = -\frac{1}{2}$. An alternative method is to differentiate both sides of (6.58) and then substitute a convenient x. Differentiation of (6.58) leads to the equation

$$2x + 2 = 2A_1(x + 1) + A_2(x - 1) + A_2(x + 1) + A_3,$$

and, if we put $x = -1$, we find $0 = -2A_2 + A_3$, so $A_2 = \frac{1}{2}A_3 = -\frac{1}{2}$, as before. Therefore we have found A's to satisfy (6.57), so we have

$$\int \frac{x^2 + 2x + 3}{(x - 1)(x + 1)^2}\, dx = \frac{3}{2}\int \frac{dx}{x - 1} - \frac{1}{2}\int \frac{dx}{x + 1} - \int \frac{dx}{(x + 1)^2}$$

$$= \frac{3}{2}\log|x - 1| - \frac{1}{2}\log|x + 1| + \frac{1}{x + 1} + C.$$

If, on the left of (6.57), the factor $(x + 1)^3$ had appeared instead of $(x + 1)^2$, we would have added an extra term $A_4/(x + 1)^3$ on the right. More generally, if a linear factor $x + a$ appears p times in the denominator, then for this factor we must allow for a sum of p terms, namely

(6.59)
$$\sum_{k=1}^{p} \frac{A_k}{(x + a)^k},$$

where the A's are constants. A sum of this type is to be used for each repeated linear factor.

CASE 3. The denominator contains irreducible quadratic factors, none of which are repeated.

EXAMPLE 5. Integrate $\displaystyle\int \frac{3x^2 + 2x - 2}{x^3 - 1}\, dx$.

Solution. The denominator can be split as the product $x^3 - 1 = (x - 1)(x^2 + x + 1)$, where $x^2 + x + 1$ is irreducible, and we try a decomposition of the form

$$\frac{3x^2 + 2x - 2}{x^3 - 1} = \frac{A}{x - 1} + \frac{Bx + C}{x^2 + x + 1}.$$

In the fraction with denominator $x^2 + x + 1$, we have used a linear polynomial $Bx + C$ in the numerator in order to have as many constants as equations when we solve for A, B, C. Clearing the fractions and solving for A, B, and C, we find $A = 1$, $B = 2$, and $C = 3$. Therefore we have

$$\int \frac{3x^2 + 2x - 2}{x^3 - 1}\, dx = \int \frac{dx}{x - 1} + \int \frac{2x + 3}{x^2 + x + 1}\, dx.$$

The first integral on the right is $\log|x - 1|$. To evaluate the second integral, we write

$$\int \frac{2x + 3}{x^2 + x + 1}\, dx = \int \frac{2x + 1}{x^2 + x + 1}\, dx + \int \frac{2}{x^2 + x + 1}\, dx$$

$$= \log(x^2 + x + 1) + 2\int \frac{dx}{(x + \frac{1}{2})^2 + \frac{3}{4}}.$$

If we let $u = x + \frac{1}{2}$ and $\alpha = \sqrt{\frac{3}{4}}$, the last integral is

$$2 \int \frac{du}{u^2 + \alpha^2} = \frac{2}{\alpha} \arctan \frac{u}{\alpha} = \frac{4}{3} \sqrt{3} \arctan \frac{2x + 1}{\sqrt{3}}.$$

Therefore, we have

$$\int \frac{3x^2 + 2x - 2}{x^3 - 1} \, dx = \log|x - 1| + \log(x^2 + x + 1) + \frac{4}{3} \sqrt{3} \arctan \frac{2x + 1}{\sqrt{3}} + C.$$

CASE 4. The denominator contains irreducible quadratic factors, some of which are repeated. Here the situation is analogous to Case 2. In the partial-fraction decomposition of $f(x)/g(x)$ we allow, first of all, a sum of the form (6.59) for each linear factor, as already described. In addition, if an irreducible quadratic factor $x^2 + bx + c$ is repeated m times, we allow a sum of m terms, namely

$$\sum_{k=1}^{m} \frac{B_k x + C_k}{(x^2 + bx + c)^k},$$

where each numerator is linear.

EXAMPLE 6. Integrate $\displaystyle \int \frac{x^4 - x^3 + 2x^2 - x + 2}{(x - 1)(x^2 + 2)^2} \, dx$.

Solution. We write

$$\frac{x^4 - x^3 + 2x^2 - x + 2}{(x - 1)(x^2 + 2)^2} = \frac{A}{x - 1} + \frac{Bx + C}{x^2 + 2} + \frac{Dx + E}{(x^2 + 2)^2}.$$

Clearing the fractions and solving for A, B, C, D, and E, we find that

$$A = \tfrac{1}{3}, \qquad B = \tfrac{2}{3}, \qquad C = -\tfrac{1}{3}, \qquad D = -1, \qquad E = 0.$$

Therefore, we have

$$\int \frac{x^4 - x^3 + 2x^2 - x + 2}{(x - 1)(x^2 + 2)^2} \, dx = \frac{1}{3} \int \frac{dx}{x - 1} + \int \frac{\frac{2}{3}x - \frac{1}{3}}{x^2 + 2} \, dx - \int \frac{x \, dx}{(x^2 + 2)^2}$$

$$= \frac{1}{3} \int \frac{dx}{x - 1} + \frac{1}{3} \int \frac{2x \, dx}{x^2 + 2} - \frac{1}{3} \int \frac{dx}{x^2 + 2} - \frac{1}{2} \int \frac{2x \, dx}{(x^2 + 2)^2}$$

$$= \frac{1}{3} \log|x - 1| + \frac{1}{3} \log(x^2 + 2) - \frac{\sqrt{2}}{6} \arctan \frac{x}{\sqrt{2}}$$

$$+ \frac{1}{2} \frac{1}{x^2 + 2} + C.$$

The foregoing examples are typical of what happens in general. The problem of integrating a proper rational function reduces to that of calculating integrals of the forms

$$\int \frac{dx}{(x+a)^n} , \qquad \int \frac{x \, dx}{(x^2+bx+c)^m} , \qquad \text{and} \qquad \int \frac{dx}{(x^2+bx+c)^m} .$$

The first integral is $\log |x+a|$ if $n=1$ and $(x+a)^{1-n}/(1-n)$ if $n>1$. To treat the other two, we express the quadratic as a sum of two squares by writing

$$x^2 + bx + c = \left(x + \frac{b}{2}\right)^2 + \left(c - \frac{b^2}{4}\right) = u^2 + \alpha^2 ,$$

where $u = x + b/2$ and $\alpha = \frac{1}{2}\sqrt{4c - b^2}$. (This is possible because $4c - b^2 > 0$.) The substitution $u = x + b/2$ reduces the problem to that of computing

(6.60) $$\int \frac{u \, du}{(u^2 + \alpha^2)^m} \qquad \text{and} \qquad \int \frac{du}{(u^2 + \alpha^2)^m} .$$

The first of these is $\frac{1}{2} \log (u^2 + \alpha^2)$ if $m = 1$, and $\frac{1}{2}(u^2 + \alpha^2)^{1-m}/(1-m)$ if $m > 1$. When $m = 1$, the second integral in (6.60) is evaluated by the formula

$$\int \frac{du}{u^2 + \alpha^2} = \frac{1}{\alpha} \arctan \frac{u}{\alpha} + C .$$

The case $m > 1$ may be reduced to the case $m = 1$ by repeated application of the recursion formula

$$\int \frac{du}{(u^2 + \alpha^2)^m} = \frac{1}{2\alpha^2(m-1)} \frac{u}{(u^2 + \alpha^2)^{m-1}} + \frac{2m-3}{2\alpha^2(m-1)} \int \frac{du}{(u^2 + \alpha^2)^{m-1}} ,$$

which is obtained by integration by parts. This discussion shows that every rational function may be integrated in terms of polynomials, rational functions, inverse tangents, and logarithms.

6.24 Integrals which can be transformed into integrals of rational functions

A function of two variables defined by an equation of the form

$$P(x, y) = \sum_{m=0}^{p} \sum_{n=0}^{q} a_{m,n} x^m y^n$$

is called a *polynomial in two variables.* The quotient of two such polynomials is called a *rational function of two variables.* Integrals of the form $\int R(\sin x, \cos x) \, dx$, where R is a rational function of two variables, may be reduced by the substitution $u = \tan \frac{1}{2}x$ to integrals of the form $\int r(u) \, du$ where r is a rational function of one variable. The latter integral may be evaluated by the techniques just described. We illustrate the method with a particular example.

EXAMPLE 1. Integrate $\int \dfrac{1}{\sin x + \cos x} \, dx$.

Solution. The substitution $u = \tan \frac{1}{2}x$ gives us

$$x = 2 \arctan u\,, \qquad dx = \frac{2}{1 + u^2}\, du\,,$$

$$\sin x = 2 \sin \frac{x}{2} \cos \frac{x}{2} = \frac{2 \tan \frac{1}{2}x}{\sec^2 \frac{1}{2}x} = \frac{2u}{1 + u^2}\,,$$

$$\cos x = 2 \cos^2 \frac{x}{2} - 1 = \frac{2}{\sec^2 \frac{1}{2}x} - 1 = \frac{2}{1 + u^2} - 1 = \frac{1 - u^2}{1 + u^2}\,,$$

and

$$\sin x + \cos x = \frac{2u + 1 - u^2}{1 + u^2}\,.$$

Therefore, we have

$$\int \frac{dx}{\sin x + \cos x} = -2 \int \frac{du}{u^2 - 2u - 1} = -2 \int \frac{du}{(u - a)(u - b)}\,,$$

where $a = 1 + \sqrt{2}$ and $b = 1 - \sqrt{2}$. The method of partial fractions leads to

$$\int \frac{du}{(u - a)(u - b)} = \frac{1}{a - b} \int \left(\frac{1}{u - a} - \frac{1}{u - b} \right) du$$

and, since $a - b = 2\sqrt{2}$, we obtain

$$(6.61) \qquad \int \frac{dx}{\sin x + \cos x} = \frac{\sqrt{2}}{2} \log \left| \frac{u - b}{u - a} \right| + C = \frac{\sqrt{2}}{2} \log \left| \frac{\tan \frac{1}{2}x - 1 + \sqrt{2}}{\tan \frac{1}{2}x - 1 - \sqrt{2}} \right| + C\,.$$

The final answer may be simplified somewhat by using suitable trigonometric identities. First we note that $\sqrt{2} - 1 = \tan \frac{1}{8}\pi$ so the numerator of the last fraction in (6.61) is $\tan \frac{1}{2}x + \tan \frac{1}{8}\pi$. In the denominator we write

$$\left| \tan \frac{x}{2} - 1 - \sqrt{2} \right| = (\sqrt{2} + 1) \left| (\sqrt{2} - 1) \tan \frac{x}{2} - 1 \right| = (\sqrt{2} + 1) \left| 1 - \tan \frac{x}{2} \tan \frac{\pi}{8} \right|\,.$$

Taking logarithms as indicated in (6.61), we may combine the term $-\frac{1}{2}\sqrt{2} \log (\sqrt{2} + 1)$ with the arbitrary constant and rewrite (6.61) as follows:

$$\int \frac{dx}{\sin x + \cos x} = \frac{\sqrt{2}}{2} \log \left| \tan \left(\frac{x}{2} + \frac{\pi}{8} \right) \right| + C\,.$$

In an earlier section we derived the integration formula

$$\int \frac{dx}{\sqrt{1 - x^2}} = \arcsin x$$

as a consequence of the formula for differentiating arcsin x. The presence of arcsin x suggests that we could also evaluate this integral by the trigonometric substitution $t = \arcsin x$. We then have

$$x = \sin t, \qquad dx = \cos t \, dt, \qquad \sqrt{1 - x^2} = \sqrt{1 - \sin^2 t} = \cos t,$$

and we find that

$$\int \frac{dx}{\sqrt{1 - x^2}} = \int \frac{\cos t \, dt}{\cos t} = \int dt = t = \arcsin x.$$

This is always a good substitution to try if the integrand involves $\sqrt{1 - x^2}$. More generally, any integral of the form $\int R(x, \sqrt{a^2 - x^2}) \, dx$, where R is a rational function of two variables, can be transformed by the substitution

$$x = a \sin t, \qquad dx = a \cos t \, dt,$$

into an integral of the form $\int R(a \sin t, a \cos t) a \cos t \, dt$. This, in turn, can always be integrated by one of the methods described above.

EXAMPLE 2. Integrate $\displaystyle\int \frac{x \, dx}{4 - x^2 + \sqrt{4 - x^2}}$.

Solution. We let $x = 2 \sin t$, $dx = 2 \cos t \, dt$, $\sqrt{4 - x^2} = 2 \cos t$, and we find that

$$\int \frac{x \, dx}{4 - x^2 + \sqrt{4 - x^2}} = \int \frac{4 \sin t \cos t \, dt}{4 \cos^2 t + 2 \cos t} = \int \frac{\sin t \, dt}{\cos t + \frac{1}{2}}$$

$$= -\log |\tfrac{1}{2} + \cos t| + C = -\log (1 + \sqrt{4 - x^2}) + C.$$

The same method works for integrals of the form

$$\int R(x, \sqrt{a^2 - (cx + d)^2}) \, dx \; ;$$

we use the trigonometric substitution $cx + d = a \sin t$.

We can deal similarly with integrals of the form

$$\int R(x, \sqrt{a^2 + (cx + d)^2}) \, dx$$

by the substitution $cx + d = a \tan t$, $c \, dx = a \sec^2 t \, dt$. For integrals of the form

$$\int R(x, \sqrt{(cx + d)^2 - a^2}) \, dx,$$

we use the substitution $cx + d = a \sec t$, $c \, dx = a \sec t \tan t \, dt$. In either case, the new integrand becomes a rational function of $\sin t$ and $\cos t$.

6.25 Exercises

Evaluate the following integrals:

1. $\int \dfrac{2x + 3}{(x - 2)(x + 5)}\, dx.$

2. $\int \dfrac{x\, dx}{(x + 1)(x + 2)(x + 3)}.$

3. $\int \dfrac{x\, dx}{x^3 - 3x + 2}.$

4. $\int \dfrac{x^4 + 2x - 6}{x^3 + x^2 - 2x}\, dx.$

5. $\int \dfrac{8x^3 + 7}{(x + 1)(2x + 1)^3}\, dx.$

6. $\int \dfrac{4x^2 + x + 1}{x^3 - 1}\, dx.$

7. $\int \dfrac{x^4\, dx}{x^4 + 5x^2 + 4}.$

8. $\int \dfrac{x + 2}{x^2 + x}\, dx.$

9. $\int \dfrac{dx}{x(x^2 + 1)^2}.$

10. $\int \dfrac{dx}{(x + 1)(x + 2)^2(x + 3)^3}.$

11. $\int \dfrac{x\, dx}{(x + 1)^2}.$

12. $\int \dfrac{dx}{x^3 - x}.$

13. $\int \dfrac{x^2\, dx}{x^2 + x - 6}.$

14. $\int \dfrac{(x + 2)\, dx}{x^2 - 4x + 4}.$

15. $\int \dfrac{dx}{(x^2 - 4x + 4)(x^2 - 4x + 5)}.$

16. $\int \dfrac{(x - 3)\, dx}{x^3 + 3x^2 + 2x}.$

17. $\int \dfrac{dx}{(x^2 - 1)^2}.$

18. $\int \dfrac{x + 1}{x^3 - 1}\, dx.$

19. $\int \dfrac{x^4 + 1}{x(x^2 + 1)^2}\, dx.$

20. $\int \dfrac{dx}{x^4 - 2x^3}.$

21. $\int \dfrac{1 - x^3}{x(x^2 + 1)}\, dx.$

22. $\int \dfrac{dx}{x^4 - 1}.$

23. $\int \dfrac{dx}{x^4 + 1}.$

24. $\int \dfrac{x^2\, dx}{(x^2 + 2x + 2)^2}.$

25. $\int \dfrac{4x^5 - 1}{(x^5 + x + 1)^2}\, dx.$

26. $\int \dfrac{dx}{2 \sin x - \cos x + 5}.$

27. $\int \dfrac{dx}{1 + a \cos x} \qquad (0 < a < 1).$

28. $\int \dfrac{dx}{1 + a \cos x} \qquad (a > 1).$

29. $\int \dfrac{\sin^2 x}{1 + \sin^2 x}\, dx.$

30. $\int \dfrac{dx}{a^2 \sin^2 x + b^2 \cos^2 x} \qquad (ab \neq 0).$

31. $\int \dfrac{dx}{(a \sin x + b \cos x)^2} \qquad (a \neq 0).$

32. $\int_0^{\pi/2} \dfrac{\sin x\, dx}{1 + \cos x + \sin x}.$

33. $\int \sqrt{3 - x^2}\, dx.$

34. $\int \dfrac{x}{\sqrt{3 - x^2}}\, dx.$

35. $\int \dfrac{\sqrt{3 - x^2}}{x}\, dx.$

36. $\int \dfrac{\sqrt{x^2 + x}}{x}\, dx.$

37. $\int \sqrt{x^2 + 5}\, dx.$

38. $\int \dfrac{x}{\sqrt{x^2 + x + 1}}\, dx.$

39. $\displaystyle\int \frac{dx}{\sqrt{x^2 + x}}$.

40. $\displaystyle\int \frac{\sqrt{2 - x - x^2}}{x^2}\, dx$.

[*Hint:* In Exercise 40, multiply numerator and denominator by $\sqrt{2 - x - x^2}$.]

6.26   Miscellaneous review exercises

1. Let $f(x) = \int_1^x (\log t)/(t + 1)\, dt$ if $x > 0$. Compute $f(x) + f(1/x)$. As a check, you should obtain $f(2) + f(\tfrac{1}{2}) = \tfrac{1}{2}\log^2 2$.

2. Find a function f, continuous for all x (and not everywhere zero), such that

$$f^2(x) = \int_0^x f(t)\,\frac{\sin t}{2 + \cos t}\, dt \; .$$

3. Try to evaluate $\int e^x/x\, dx$ by using integration by parts.

4. Integrate $\int_0^{\pi/2} \log\,(e^{\cos x})\, dx$.

5. A function f is defined by the equation

$$f(x) = \sqrt{\frac{4x + 2}{x(x + 1)(x + 2)}} \qquad \text{if} \quad x > 0\;.$$

(a) Find the slope of the graph of f at the point for which $x = 1$.

(b) The region under the graph and above the interval $[1, 4]$ is rotated about the x-axis, thus generating a solid of revolution. Write an integral for the volume of this solid. Compute this integral and show that its value is $\pi \log\,(25/8)$.

6. A function F is defined by the following indefinite integral:

$$F(x) = \int_1^x \frac{e^t}{t}\, dt \qquad \text{if} \quad x > 0\;.$$

(a) For what values of x is it true that $\log x \le F(x)$?

(b) Prove that $\int_1^x e^t/(t + a)\, dt = e^{-a}[F(x + a) - F(1 + a)]$.

(c) In a similar way, express the following integrals in terms of F:

$$\int_1^x \frac{e^{at}}{t}\, dt, \qquad \int_1^x \frac{e^t}{t^2}\, dt, \qquad \int_1^x e^{1/t}\, dt\;.$$

7. In each case, give an example of a continuous function f satisfying the conditions stated for all real x, or else explain why there is no such function:

(a) $\int_0^x f(t)\, dt = e^x$.

(b) $\int_0^x f(t)\, dt = 1 - 2^{x^2}$.   [$2^{x^2}$ means $2^{(x^2)}$.]

(c) $\int_0^x f(t)\, dt = f^2(x) - 1$.

8. If $f(x + y) = f(x)f(y)$ for all x and y and if $f(x) = 1 + xg(x)$, where $g(x) \to 1$ as $x \to 0$, prove that (a) $f'(x)$ exists for every x, and (b) $f(x) = e^x$.

9. Given a function g which has a derivative $g'(x)$ for every real x and which satisfies the following equations:

$$g'(0) = 2 \qquad \text{and} \qquad g(x + y) = e^y g(x) + e^x g(y) \qquad \text{for all } x \text{ and } y\;.$$

(a) Show that $g(2x) = 2e^x g(x)$ and find a similar formula for $g(3x)$.

(b) Generalize (a) by finding a formula relating $g(nx)$ to $g(x)$, valid for every positive integer n. Prove your result by induction.

(c) Show that $g(0) = 0$ and find the limit of $g(h)/h$ as $h \to 0$.

(d) There is a constant C such that $g'(x) = g(x) + Ce^x$ for all x. Prove this statement and find the value of C. [*Hint:* Use the definition of the derivative $g'(x)$.]

10. A periodic function with period a satisfies $f(x + a) = f(x)$ for all x in its domain. What can you conclude about a function which has a derivative everywhere and satisfies an equation of the form

$$f(x + a) = bf(x)$$

for all x, where a and b are positive constants?

11. Use logarithmic differentiation to derive the formulas for differentiation of products and quotients from the corresponding formulas for sums and differences.

12. Let $A = \int_0^1 e^t/(t + 1)\, dt$. Express the values of the following integrals in terms of A:

(a) $\displaystyle\int_{a-1}^{a} \frac{e^{-t}}{t - a - 1}\, dt.$

(c) $\displaystyle\int_0^1 \frac{e^t}{(t + 1)^2}\, dt.$

(b) $\displaystyle\int_0^1 \frac{te^{t^2}}{t^2 + 1}\, dt.$

(d) $\displaystyle\int_0^1 e^t \log (1 + t)\, dt.$

13. Let $p(x) = c_0 + c_1 x + c_2 x^2$ and let $f(x) = e^x p(x)$.

(a) Show that $f^{(n)}(0)$, the nth derivative of f at 0, is $c_0 + nc_1 + n(n - 1)c_2$.

(b) Solve the problem when p is a polynomial of degree 3.

(c) Generalize to a polynomial of degree m.

14. Let $f(x) = x \sin ax$. Show that $f^{(2n)}(x) = (-1)^n(a^{2n}x \sin ax - 2na^{2n-1} \cos ax)$.

15. Prove that

$$\sum_{k=0}^{n} (-1)^k \binom{n}{k} \frac{1}{k + m + 1} = \sum_{k=0}^{m} (-1)^k \binom{m}{k} \frac{1}{k + n + 1}.$$

[*Hint:* $1/(k + m + 1) = \int_0^1 t^{k+m}\, dt.$]

16. Let $F(x) = \int_0^x f(t)\, dt$. Determine a formula (or formulas) for computing $F(x)$ for all real x if f is defined as follows:

(a) $f(t) = (t + |t|)^2$.

(c) $f(t) = e^{-|t|}$.

(b) $f(t) = \begin{cases} 1 - t^2 & \text{if } |t| \le 1, \\ 1 - |t| & \text{if } |t| > 1. \end{cases}$

(d) $f(t) = $ the maximum of 1 and t^2.

17. A solid of revolution is generated by rotating the graph of a continuous function f around the interval $[0, a]$ on the x-axis. If, for every $a > 0$, the volume is $a^2 + a$, find the function f.

18. Let $f(x) = e^{-2x}$ for all x. Denote by $S(t)$ the ordinate set of f over the interval $[0, t]$, where $t > 0$. Let $A(t)$ be the area of $S(t)$, $V(t)$ the volume of the solid obtained by rotating $S(t)$ about the x-axis, and $W(t)$ the volume of the solid obtained by rotating $S(t)$ about the y-axis. Compute the following: (a) $A(t)$; (b) $V(t)$; (c) $W(t)$; (d) $\lim_{t \to 0} V(t)/A(t)$.

19. Let c be the number such that $\sinh c = \frac{3}{4}$. (Do not attempt to compute c.) In each case find all those x (if any exist) satisfying the given equation. Express your answers in terms of $\log 2$ and $\log 3$.

(a) $\log (e^x + \sqrt{e^{2x} + 1}) = c.$

(b) $\log (e^x - \sqrt{e^{2x} - 1}) = c.$

20. Determine whether each of the following statements is true or false. Prove each true statement.

(a) $2^{\log 5} = 5^{\log 2}.$

(c) $\displaystyle\sum_{k=1}^{n} k^{-1/2} < 2\sqrt{n}$ for every $n \ge 1$.

(b) $\log_2 5 = \dfrac{\log_3 5}{\log_2 3}.$

(d) $1 + \sinh x \le \cosh x$ for every x.

In Exercises 21 through 24, establish each inequality by examining the sign of the derivative of an appropriate function.

21. $\dfrac{2}{\pi} x < \sin x < x$ if $0 < x < \dfrac{\pi}{2}$.

22. $\dfrac{1}{x + \frac{1}{2}} < \log\left(1 + \dfrac{1}{x}\right) < \dfrac{1}{x}$ if $x > 0$.

23. $x - \dfrac{x^3}{6} < \sin x < x$ if $x > 0$.

24. $(x^b + y^b)^{1/b} < (x^a + y^a)^{1/a}$ if $x > 0, y > 0$, and $0 < a < b$.

25. Show that
   (a) $\int_0^x e^{-t}\, t\, dt = e^{-x}(e^x - 1 - x)$.

   (b) $\displaystyle\int_0^x e^{-t} t^2\, dt = 2! e^{-x}\left(e^x - 1 - x - \dfrac{x^2}{2!}\right)$.

   (c) $\displaystyle\int_0^x e^{-t} t^3\, dt = 3! e^{-x}\left(e^x - 1 - x - \dfrac{x^2}{2!} - \dfrac{x^3}{3!}\right)$.

   (d) Guess the generalization suggested and prove it by induction.

26. If a, b, a_1, b_1 are given, with $ab \neq 0$, show that there exist constants A, B, C such that

$$\int \frac{a_1 \sin x + b_1 \cos x}{a \sin x + b \cos x}\, dx = Ax + B \log |a \sin x + b \cos x| + C .$$

[*Hint:* Show that A and B exist such that

$$a_1 \sin x + b_1 \cos x = A(a \sin x + b \cos x) + B(a \cos x - b \sin x).]$$

27. In each case, find a function f satisfying the given conditions.
   (a) $f'(x^2) = 1/x$ for $x > 0$, $f(1) = 1$.
   (b) $f'(\sin^2 x) = \cos^2 x$ for all x, $f(1) = 1$.
   (c) $f'(\sin x) = \cos^2 x$ for all x, $f(1) = 1$.

   (d) $f'(\log x) = \begin{cases} 1 & \text{for} \ \ 0 < x \le 1, \\ x & \text{for} \ \ x > 1, \end{cases}$ $f(0) = 0$.

28. A function, called the *integral logarithm* and denoted by Li, is defined as follows:

$$\text{Li}(x) = \int_2^x \frac{dt}{\log t} \quad \text{if} \ \ x \ge 2 .$$

This function occurs in analytic number theory where it is proved that $\text{Li}(x)$ is a very good approximation to the number of primes $\le x$. Derive the following properties of $\text{Li}(x)$:

(a) $\text{Li}(x) = \dfrac{x}{\log x} + \displaystyle\int_2^x \frac{dt}{\log^2 t} - \dfrac{2}{\log 2}$.

(b) $\text{Li}(x) = \dfrac{x}{\log x} + \displaystyle\sum_{k=1}^{n-1} \frac{k!\, x}{\log^{k+1} x} + n! \int_2^x \frac{dt}{\log^{n+1} t} + C_n$,

where C_n is a constant (depending on n). Find this constant.
(c) Show that there is a constant b such that $\int_b^{\log x} e^t/t\, dt = \text{Li}(x)$ and find the value of b.
(d) Express $\int_c^x e^{2t}/(t - 1)\, dt$ in terms of the integral logarithm, where $c = 1 + \frac{1}{2} \log 2$.

(e) Let $f(x) = e^4 \operatorname{Li}(e^{2x-4}) - e^2 \operatorname{Li}(e^{2x-2})$ if $x > 3$. Show that

$$f'(x) = \frac{e^{2x}}{x^2 - 3x + 2} \,.$$

29. Let $f(x) = \log |x|$ if $x < 0$. Show that f has an inverse, and denote this inverse by g. What is the domain of g? Find a formula for computing $g(y)$ for each y in the domain of g. Sketch the graph of g.

30. Let $f(x) = \int_0^x (1 + t^3)^{-1/2} \, dt$ if $x \geq 0$. (Do not attempt to evaluate this integral.)

    (a) Show that f is strictly increasing on the nonnegative real axis.

    (b) Let g denote the inverse of f. Show that the second derivative of g is proportional to g^2 [that is, $g''(y) = cg^2(y)$ for each y in the domain of g] and find the constant of proportionality.

7

POLYNOMIAL APPROXIMATIONS TO FUNCTIONS

7.1 Introduction

Polynomials are among the simplest functions that occur in analysis. They are pleasant to work with in numerical computations because their values may be found by performing a finite number of multiplications and additions. In Chapter 6 we showed that the logarithm function can be approximated by polynomials that enable us to compute logarithms to any desired degree of accuracy. In this chapter we will show that many other functions, such as the exponential and trigonometric functions, can also be approximated by polynomials. If the difference between a function and its polynomial approximation is sufficiently small, then we can, for practical purposes, compute with the polynomial in place of the original function.

There are many ways to approximate a given function f by polynomials, depending on what use is to be made of the approximation. In this chapter we shall be interested in obtaining a polynomial which agrees with f and some of its derivatives at a given point. We begin our discussion with a simple example.

Suppose f is the exponential function, $f(x) = e^x$. At the point $x = 0$, the function f and all its derivatives have the value 1. The linear polynomial

$$g(x) = 1 + x$$

also has $g(0) = 1$ and $g'(0) = 1$, so it agrees with f and its first derivative at 0. Geometrically, this means the graph of g is the tangent line of f at the point $(0, 1)$, as shown in Figure 7.1.

If we approximate f by a quadratic polynomial Q which agrees with f and its first two derivatives at 0, we might expect a better approximation to f than the linear function g, at least near the point $(0, 1)$. The polynomial

$$Q(x) = 1 + x + \tfrac{1}{2}x^2$$

has $Q(0) = Q'(0) = 1$ and $Q''(0) = f''(0) = 1$. Figure 7.1 shows that the graph of Q approximates the curve $y = e^x$ more closely than the line $y = 1 + x$ near the point $(0, 1)$. We can improve further the accuracy of the approximation by using polynomials which agree with f in the third and higher derivatives as well. It is easy to verify that the polynomial

$$(7.1) \qquad P(x) = \sum_{k=0}^{n} \frac{x^k}{k!} = 1 + x + \frac{x^2}{2!} + \cdots + \frac{x^n}{n!}$$

272

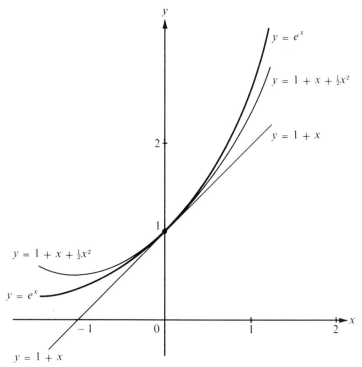

FIGURE 7.1   Polynomial approximations to the curve $y = e^x$ near $(0, 1)$.

agrees with the exponential function and its first n derivatives at the point $x = 0$. Of course, before we can use such polynomials to compute approximate values for the exponential function, we need some information about the error made in the approximation. Rather than discuss this particular example in more detail, we turn now to the general theory.

7.2 The Taylor polynomials generated by a function

Suppose f has derivatives up to order n at the point $x = 0$, where $n \geq 1$, and let us try to find a polynomial P which agrees with f and its first n derivatives at 0. There are $n + 1$ conditions to be satisfied, namely

$$(7.2) \qquad P(0) = f(0), \qquad P'(0) = f'(0), \qquad \ldots, \qquad P^{(n)}(0) = f^{(n)}(0),$$

so we try a polynomial of degree n, say

$$(7.3) \qquad P(x) = c_0 + c_1 x + c_2 x^2 + \cdots + c_n x^n,$$

with $n + 1$ coefficients to be determined. We shall use the conditions in (7.2) to determine these coefficients in succession.

First, we put $x = 0$ in (7.3) and we find $P(0) = c_0$, so $c_0 = f(0)$. Next, we differentiate both sides of (7.3) and then substitute $x = 0$ once more to find $P'(0) = c_1$; hence $c_1 = f'(0)$.

If we differentiate (7.3) again and put $x = 0$, we find that $P''(0) = 2c_2$, so $c_2 = f''(0)/2$. After differentiating k times, we find that $P^{(k)}(0) = k!\,c_k$, and this gives us the formula

$$(7.4) \qquad\qquad c_k = \frac{f^{(k)}(0)}{k!}$$

for $k = 0, 1, 2, \ldots, n$. [When $k = 0$, we interpret $f^{(0)}(0)$ to mean $f(0)$.] This argument proves that if a polynomial of degree $\leq n$ exists which satisfies (7.2), then its coefficients are necessarily given by (7.4). (The degree of P will be equal to n if and only if $f^{(n)}(0) \neq 0$.) Conversely, it is easy to verify that the polynomial P with coefficients given by (7.4) satisfies (7.2), and therefore we have the following theorem.

THEOREM 7.1.   *Let f be a function with derivatives of order n at the point $x = 0$. Then there exists one and only one polynomial P of degree $\leq n$ which satisfies the $n + 1$ conditions*

$$P(0) = f(0), \qquad P'(0) = f'(0), \qquad \ldots, \qquad P^{(n)}(0) = f^{(n)}(0).$$

This polynomial is given by the formula

$$P(x) = \sum_{k=0}^{n} \frac{f^{(k)}(0)}{k!}\, x^k.$$

In the same way, we may show that there is one and only one polynomial of degree $\leq n$ which agrees with f and its first n derivatives at a point $x = a$. In fact, instead of (7.3), we may write P in powers of $x - a$ and proceed as before. If we evaluate the derivatives at a in place of 0, we are led to the polynomial

$$(7.5) \qquad\qquad P(x) = \sum_{k=0}^{n} \frac{f^{(k)}(a)}{k!}\, (x - a)^k.$$

This is the one and only polynomial of degree $\leq n$ which satisfies the conditions

$$P(a) = f(a), \qquad P'(a) = f'(a), \qquad \ldots, \qquad P^{(n)}(a) = f^{(n)}(a),$$

and it is referred to as a *Taylor polynomial* in honor of the English mathematician Brook Taylor (1685–1731). More precisely, we say that the polynomial in (7.5) is the *Taylor polynomial of degree n generated by f at the point a*.

It is convenient to have a notation that indicates the dependence of the Taylor polynomial P on f and n. We shall indicate this dependence by writing $P = T_n f$ or $P = T_n(f)$. The symbol T_n is called the *Taylor operator* of degree n. When this operator is applied to a function f, it produces a new function $T_n f$, the Taylor polynomial of degree n. The value of this function at x is denoted by $T_n f(x)$ or by $T_n[f(x)]$. If we also wish to indicate the dependence on a, we write $T_n f(x; a)$ instead of $T_n f(x)$.

EXAMPLE 1. When f is the exponential function, $f(x) = E(x) = e^x$, we have $E^{(k)}(x) = e^x$ for all k, so $E^{(k)}(0) = e^0 = 1$, and the Taylor polynomial of degree n generated by E at 0 is given by the formula

$$T_n E(x) = T_n(e^x) = \sum_{k=0}^{n} \frac{x^k}{k!} = 1 + x + \frac{x^2}{2!} + \cdots + \frac{x^n}{n!}.$$

If we want a polynomial which agrees with E and its derivatives at the point $a = 1$, we have $E^{(k)}(1) = e$ for all k, so (7.5) gives us

$$T_n E(x; 1) = \sum_{k=0}^{n} \frac{e}{k!} (x - 1)^k.$$

EXAMPLE 2. When $f(x) = \sin x$, we have $f'(x) = \cos x$, $f''(x) = -\sin x$, $f'''(x) = -\cos x$, $f^{(4)}(x) = \sin x$, etc., so $f^{(2n+1)}(0) = (-1)^n$ and $f^{(2n)}(0) = 0$. Thus only odd powers of x appear in the Taylor polynomials generated by the sine function at 0. The Taylor polynomial of degree $2n + 1$ has the form

$$T_{2n+1}(\sin x) = x - \frac{x^3}{3!} + \frac{x^5}{5!} - \frac{x^7}{7!} + \cdots + (-1)^n \frac{x^{2n+1}}{(2n + 1)!}.$$

EXAMPLE 3. Arguing as in Example 2, we find that the Taylor polynomials generated by the cosine function at 0 contain only even powers of x. The polynomial of degree $2n$ is given by

$$T_{2n}(\cos x) = 1 - \frac{x^2}{2!} + \frac{x^4}{4!} - \frac{x^6}{6!} + \cdots + (-1)^n \frac{x^{2n}}{(2n)!}.$$

Note that each Taylor polynomial $T_{2n}(\cos x)$ is the derivative of the Taylor polynomial $T_{2n+1}(\sin x)$. This is due to the fact that the cosine itself is the derivative of the sine. In the next section we learn that certain relations which hold between functions are transmitted to their Taylor polynomials.

7.3 Calculus of Taylor polynomials

If a function f has derivatives of order n at a point a, we can always form its Taylor polynomial $T_n f$ by the formula

$$T_n f(x) = \sum_{k=0}^{n} \frac{f^{(k)}(a)}{k!} (x - a)^k.$$

Sometimes the calculation of the derivatives $f^{(k)}(a)$ may become lengthy, so it is desirable to have alternate methods for determining Taylor polynomials. The next theorem describes properties of the Taylor operator that often enable us to obtain new Taylor polynomials from given ones. In this theorem it is understood that all Taylor polynomials are generated at a common point a.

THEOREM 7.2.   *The Taylor operator T_n has the following properties:*

(a) *Linearity property. If c_1 and c_2 are constants, then*

$$T_n(c_1 f + c_2 g) = c_1 T_n(f) + c_2 T_n(g) \, .$$

(b) *Differentiation property. The derivative of a Taylor polynomial of f is a Taylor polynomial of f'; in fact, we have*

$$(T_n f)' = T_{n-1}(f') \, .$$

(c) *Integration property. An indefinite integral of a Taylor polynomial of f is a Taylor polynomial of an indefinite integral of f. More precisely, if $g(x) = \int_a^x f(t) \, dt$, then we have*

$$T_{n+1} g(x) = \int_a^x T_n f(t) \, dt \, .$$

Proof. Each statement (a), (b), or (c), is an equation involving two polynomials of the same degree. To prove each statement we simply observe that the polynomial which appears on the left has the same value and the same derivatives at the point a as the one which appears on the right. Then we invoke the uniqueness property of Theorem 7.1. Note that differentiation of a polynomial lowers its degree, whereas integration increases its degree.

The next theorem tells us what happens when we replace x by cx in a Taylor polynomial.

THEOREM 7.3.   SUBSTITUTION PROPERTY.   *Let $g(x) = f(cx)$, where c is a constant. Then we have*

$$T_n g(x; a) = T_n f(cx; ca) \, .$$

In particular, when $a = 0$, we have $T_n g(x) = T_n f(cx)$.

Proof. Since $g(x) = f(cx)$, the chain rule gives us

$$g'(x) = cf'(cx), \qquad g''(x) = c^2 f''(cx), \qquad \dots, \qquad g^{(k)}(x) = c^k f^{(k)}(cx) \, .$$

Hence we obtain

$$T_n g(x; a) = \sum_{k=0}^{n} \frac{g^{(k)}(a)}{k!} (x - a)^k = \sum_{k=0}^{n} \frac{f^{(k)}(ca)}{k!} (cx - ca)^k = T_n f(cx; ca) \, .$$

EXAMPLES.   Replacing x by $-x$ in the Taylor polynomial for e^x, we find that

$$T_n(e^{-x}) = 1 - x + \frac{x^2}{2!} - \frac{x^3}{3!} + \cdots + (-1)^n \frac{x^n}{n!} \, .$$

Since $\cosh x = \frac{1}{2} e^x + \frac{1}{2} e^{-x}$, we may use the linearity property to obtain

$$T_{2n}(\cosh x) = \tfrac{1}{2} T_{2n}(e^x) + \tfrac{1}{2} T_{2n}(e^{-x}) = 1 + \frac{x^2}{2!} + \frac{x^4}{4!} + \cdots + \frac{x^{2n}}{(2n)!} \, .$$

The differentiation property gives us

$$T_{2n-1}(\sinh x) = x + \frac{x^3}{3!} + \frac{x^5}{5!} + \cdots + \frac{x^{2n-1}}{(2n-1)!}\,.$$

The next theorem is also useful in simplifying calculations of Taylor polynomials.

THEOREM 7.4. *Let P_n be a polynomial of degree $n \geq 1$. Let f and g be two functions with derivatives of order n at 0 and assume that*

$$(7.6) \qquad\qquad f(x) = P_n(x) + x^n g(x)\,,$$

where $g(x) \to 0$ as $x \to 0$. Then P_n is the Taylor polynomial generated by f at 0.

Proof. Let $h(x) = f(x) - P_n(x) = x^n g(x)$. By differentiating the product $x^n g(x)$ repeatedly, we see that h and its first n derivatives are 0 at $x = 0$. Therefore, f agrees with P_n and its first n derivatives at 0, so $P_n = T_n f$, as asserted.

EXAMPLES. From the algebraic identity

$$(7.7) \qquad\qquad \frac{1}{1-x} = 1 + x + x^2 + \cdots + x^n + \frac{x^{n+1}}{1-x}\,,$$

valid for all $x \neq 1$, we see that (7.6) is satisfied with $f(x) = 1/(1 - x)$, $P_n(x) = 1 + x + \cdots + x^n$, and $g(x) = x/(1 - x)$. Since $g(x) \to 0$ as $x \to 0$, Theorem 7.4 tells us that

$$T_n\left(\frac{1}{1-x}\right) = 1 + x + x^2 + \cdots + x^n.$$

Integration of this relation gives us the further Taylor polynomial

$$T_{n+1}[-\log(1-x)] = x + \frac{x^2}{2} + \frac{x^3}{3} + \cdots + \frac{x^{n+1}}{n+1}\,.$$

In (7.7) we may replace x by $-x^2$ to get

$$\frac{1}{1+x^2} = 1 - x^2 + x^4 - \cdots + (-1)^n x^{2n} - (-1)^n \frac{x^{2n+1}}{1+x^2}\,.$$

Applying Theorem 7.4 once more, we find that

$$T_{2n}\left(\frac{1}{1+x^2}\right) = \sum_{k=0}^{n}(-1)^k x^{2k}\,.$$

Integration of this relation leads to the formula

$$T_{2n+1}(\arctan x) = \sum_{k=0}^{n}(-1)^k \frac{x^{2k+1}}{2k+1}\,.$$

7.4 Exercises

1. Draw graphs of the Taylor polynomials $T_3(\sin x) = x - x^3/3!$ and $T_5(\sin x) = x - x^3/3! + x^5/5!$. Pay careful attention to the points where the curves cross the x-axis. Compare these graphs with that of $f(x) = \sin x$.

2. Do the same as in Exercise 1 for the Taylor polynomials $T_2(\cos x), T_4(\cos x)$, and $f(x) = \cos x$.

In Exercises 3 through 10, obtain the Taylor polynomials $T_n f(x)$ as indicated. In each case, it is understood that $f(x)$ is defined for all x for which $f(x)$ is meaningful. Theorems 7.2, 7.3, and 7.4 will help simplify the computations in many cases.

3. $T_n(a^x) = \displaystyle\sum_{k=0}^{n} \frac{(\log a)^k}{k!} x^k.$

6. $T_n[\log(1 + x)] = \displaystyle\sum_{k=1}^{n} \frac{(-1)^{k+1} x^k}{k}.$

4. $T_n\left(\dfrac{1}{1 + x}\right) = \displaystyle\sum_{k=0}^{n} (-1)^k x^k.$

7. $T_{2n+1}\left(\log \sqrt{\dfrac{1 + x}{1 - x}}\right) = \displaystyle\sum_{k=0}^{n} \frac{x^{2k+1}}{2k + 1}.$

5. $T_{2n+1}\left(\dfrac{x}{1 - x^2}\right) = \displaystyle\sum_{k=0}^{n} x^{2k+1}.$

8. $T_n\left(\dfrac{1}{2 - x}\right) = \displaystyle\sum_{k=0}^{n} \frac{x^k}{2^{k+1}}.$

9. $T_n[(1 + x)^\alpha] = \displaystyle\sum_{k=0}^{n} \binom{\alpha}{k} x^k,$ where $\binom{\alpha}{k} = \dfrac{\alpha(\alpha - 1) \cdots (\alpha - k + 1)}{k!}.$

10. $T_{2n}(\sin^2 x) = \displaystyle\sum_{k=1}^{n} (-1)^{k+1} \frac{2^{2k-1}}{(2k)!} x^{2k}.$ [*Hint:* $\cos 2x = 1 - 2 \sin^2 x.$]

7.5 Taylor's formula with remainder

We turn now to a discussion of the error in the approximation of a function f by its Taylor polynomial $T_n f$ at a point a. The error is defined to be the difference $E_n(x) = f(x) - T_n f(x)$. Thus, if f has a derivative of order n at a, we may write

(7.8)
$$f(x) = \sum_{k=0}^{n} \frac{f^{(k)}(a)}{k!} (x - a)^k + E_n(x).$$

This is known as *Taylor's formula with remainder* $E_n(x)$; it is useful whenever we can estimate the size of $E_n(x)$. We shall express the error as an integral and then estimate the size of the integral. To illustrate the principal ideas, we consider first the error arising from a linear approximation.

THEOREM 7.5. *Assume f has a continuous second derivative f'' in some neighborhood of a. Then, for every x in this neighborhood, we have*

$$f(x) = f(a) + f'(a)(x - a) + E_1(x),$$

where

$$E_1(x) = \int_a^x (x - t) f''(t)\, dt.$$

Proof. From the definition of the error we may write

$$E_1(x) = f(x) - f(a) - f'(a)(x - a) = \int_a^x f'(t)\, dt - f'(a) \int_a^x dt = \int_a^x [f'(t) - f'(a)]\, dt\,.$$

The last integral may be written as $\int_a^x u\, dv$, where $u = f'(t) - f'(a)$, and $v = t - x$. Now $du/dt = f''(t)$ and $dv/dt = 1$, so the formula for integration by parts gives us

$$E_1(x) = \int_a^x u\, dv = uv \Big|_a^x - \int_a^x (t - x) f''(t)\, dt = \int_a^x (x - t) f''(t)\, dt\,,$$

since $u = 0$ when $t = a$, and $v = 0$ when $t = x$. This proves the theorem.

The corresponding result for a polynomial approximation of degree n is given by the following.

THEOREM 7.6. *Assume f has a continuous derivative of order $n + 1$ in some interval containing a. Then, for every x in this interval, we have the Taylor formula*

$$f(x) = \sum_{k=0}^n \frac{f^{(k)}(a)}{k!} (x - a)^k + E_n(x)\,,$$

where

$$E_n(x) = \frac{1}{n!} \int_a^x (x - t)^n f^{(n+1)}(t)\, dt\,.$$

Proof. The theorem is proved by induction on n. We have already proved it for $n = 1$. Now we assume it is true for some n and prove it for $n + 1$. We write Taylor's formula (7.8) with $n + 1$ and with n and subtract to get

$$E_{n+1}(x) = E_n(x) - \frac{f^{(n+1)}(a)}{(n+1)!} (x - a)^{n+1}\,.$$

Now we use the integral for $E_n(x)$ and note that $(x - a)^{n+1}/(n + 1) = \int_a^x (x - t)^n\, dt$ to obtain

$$E_{n+1}(x) = \frac{1}{n!} \int_a^x (x - t)^n f^{(n+1)}(t)\, dt - \frac{f^{(n+1)}(a)}{n!} \int_a^x (x - t)^n\, dt$$

$$= \frac{1}{n!} \int_a^x (x - t)^n [f^{(n+1)}(t) - f^{(n+1)}(a)]\, dt\,.$$

The last integral may be written in the form $\int_a^x u\, dv$, where $u = f^{(n+1)}(t) - f^{(n+1)}(a)$ and $v = -(x - t)^{n+1}/(n + 1)$. Integrating by parts and noting that $u = 0$ when $t = a$, and that $v = 0$ when $t = x$, we find that

$$E_{n+1}(x) = \frac{1}{n!} \int_a^x u\, dv = -\frac{1}{n!} \int_a^x v\, du = \frac{1}{(n + 1)!} \int_a^x (x - t)^{n+1} f^{(n+2)}(t)\, dt\,.$$

This completes the inductive step from n to $n + 1$, so the theorem is true for all $n \geq 1$.

7.6 Estimates for the error in Taylor's formula

Since the error $E_n(x)$ in Taylor's formula has been expressed as an integral involving the $(n+1)$st derivative of f, we need some further information about $f^{(n+1)}$ before we can estimate the size of $E_n(x)$. If upper and lower bounds for $f^{(n+1)}$ are known, we can deduce corresponding upper and lower bounds for $E_n(x)$, as described in the next theorem.

THEOREM 7.7.   *If the $(n+1)$st derivative of f satisfies the inequalities*

$$(7.9) \qquad\qquad m \leq f^{(n+1)}(t) \leq M$$

for all t in some interval containing a, then for every x in this interval we have the following estimates:

$$(7.10) \qquad m \frac{(x-a)^{n+1}}{(n+1)!} \leq E_n(x) \leq M \frac{(x-a)^{n+1}}{(n+1)!} \quad \text{if} \quad x > a,$$

and

$$(7.11) \qquad m \frac{(a-x)^{n+1}}{(n+1)!} \leq (-1)^{n+1} E_n(x) \leq M \frac{(a-x)^{n+1}}{(n+1)!} \quad \text{if} \quad x < a.$$

Proof.   Assume first that $x > a$. Then the integral for $E_n(x)$ is extended over the interval $[a, x]$. For each t in this interval we have $(x - t)^n \geq 0$, so the inequalities in (7.9) give us

$$m \frac{(x-t)^n}{n!} \leq \frac{(x-t)^n}{n!} f^{(n+1)}(t) \leq M \frac{(x-t)^n}{n!} .$$

Integrating from a to x, we find that

$$(7.12) \qquad \frac{m}{n!} \int_a^x (x-t)^n \, dt \leq E_n(x) \leq \frac{M}{n!} \int_a^x (x-t)^n \, dt .$$

The substitution $u = x - t$, $du = -dt$ gives us

$$\int_a^x (x-t)^n \, dt = \int_0^{x-a} u^n \, du = \frac{(x-a)^{n+1}}{n+1} ,$$

so (7.12) reduces to (7.10).

If $x < a$, the integration takes place over the interval $[x, a]$. For each t in this interval we have $t \geq x$, so $(-1)^n (x - t)^n = (t - x)^n \geq 0$. Therefore, we may multiply the inequalities (7.9) by the nonnegative factor $(-1)^n (x - t)^n / n!$ and integrate from x to a to obtain (7.11).

EXAMPLE 1. If $f(x) = e^x$ and $a = 0$, we have the formula

$$e^x = \sum_{k=0}^n \frac{x^k}{k!} + E_n(x) .$$

Since $f^{(n+1)}(x) = e^x$, the derivative $f^{(n+1)}$ is monotonic increasing on every interval, and therefore satisfies the inequalities $e^b \leq f^{(n+1)}(t) \leq e^c$ on every interval of the form $[b, c]$. In such an interval, the inequalities for $E_n(x)$ of Theorem 7.7 are satisfied with $m = e^b$ and $M = e^c$. In particular, when $b = 0$, we have

$$\frac{x^{n+1}}{(n+1)!} \leq E_n(x) \leq e^c \frac{x^{n+1}}{(n+1)!} \qquad \text{if} \quad 0 < x \leq c.$$

We can use these estimates to calculate the Euler number e. We take $b = 0$, $c = 1$, $x = 1$, and use the inequality $e < 3$ to obtain

(7.13)
$$e = \sum_{k=0}^{n} \frac{1}{k!} + E_n(1), \qquad \text{where} \quad \frac{1}{(n+1)!} \leq E_n(1) < \frac{3}{(n+1)!}.$$

This enables us to compute e to any desired degree of accuracy. For example, if we want the value of e correct to seven decimal places, we choose an n so that $3/(n+1)! < \frac{1}{2}10^{-8}$. We shall see presently that $n = 12$ suffices. A table of values of $1/n!$ may be computed rather quickly because $1/n!$ may be obtained from $1/(n-1)!$ by simply dividing by n. The following table for $3 \leq n \leq 12$ contains these numbers rounded off to nine decimals. The "round-off error" in each case is indicated by a plus or minus sign which tells whether the correct value exceeds or is less than the recorded value. (In any case, this error is less than one-half unit in the last decimal place.)

n	$\dfrac{1}{n!}$	n	$\dfrac{1}{n!}$
3	0.166 666 667 −	8	0.000 024 802 −
4	0.041 666 667 −	9	0.000 002 756 −
5	0.008 333 333 +	10	0.000 000 276 −
6	0.001 388 889 −	11	0.000 000 025 +
7	0.000 198 413 −	12	0.000 000 002 +

The terms corresponding to $n = 0, 1, 2$ have sum $\frac{5}{2}$. Adding this to the sum of the entries in the table (for $n \leq 12$), we obtain a total of 2.718281830. If we take into account the roundoff errors, the *actual* value of this sum may be less than this by as much as $\frac{7}{2}$ of a unit in the last decimal place (due to the seven minus signs) or may exceed this by as much as $\frac{3}{2}$ of a unit in the last place (due to the three plus signs). Call the sum s. Then all we can assert by this calculation is the inequality $2.718281826 < s < 2.718281832$. Now the estimates for the error $E_{12}(1)$ give us $0.000000000 \leq E_{12}(1) < 0.000000001$. Since $e = s + E_{12}(1)$, this calculation leads to the following inequalities for e:

$$2.718281826 < e < 2.718281833.$$

This tells us that the value of e, *correct to seven decimals*, is $e = 2.7182818$, or that the value of e, *rounded off to eight decimals*, is $e = 2.71828183$.

EXAMPLE 2. *Irrationality of e.* We can use the foregoing estimates for the error $E_n(1)$ to prove that e is irrational. First we rewrite the inequalities in (7.13) as follows:

$$\frac{1}{(n+1)!} \le e - \sum_{k=0}^{n} \frac{1}{k!} < \frac{3}{(n+1)!} .$$

Multiplying through by $n!$, we obtain

(7.14)
$$\frac{1}{n+1} \le n!\, e - \sum_{k=0}^{n} \frac{n!}{k!} < \frac{3}{n+1} \le \frac{3}{4}$$

if $n \ge 3$. For every n, the sum on k is an integer. If e were rational, we could choose n so large that $n!\, e$ would also be an integer. But then (7.14) would tell us that the difference of these two integers is a positive number not exceeding $\frac{3}{4}$, which is impossible. Therefore e cannot be rational.

Polynomial approximations often enable us to obtain approximate numerical values for integrals that cannot be evaluated directly in terms of elementary functions. A famous example is the integral

$$f(x) = \int_0^x e^{-t^2}\, dt$$

which occurs in probability theory and in many physical problems. It is known that the function f so defined is not an *elementary function.* That is to say, f cannot be obtained from polynomials, exponentials, logarithms, trigonometric or inverse trigonometric functions in a finite number of steps by using the operations of addition, subtraction, multiplication, division, or composition. Other examples which occur rather frequently in both theory and practice are the integrals

$$\int_0^x \frac{\sin t}{t}\, dt , \qquad \int_0^x \sin(t^2)\, dt , \qquad \int_0^x \sqrt{1 - k^2 \sin^2 t}\, dt .$$

(In the first of these, it is understood that the quotient $(\sin t)/t$ is to be replaced by 1 when $t = 0$. In the third integral, k is a constant, $0 < k < 1$.) We conclude this section with an example which illustrates how Taylor's formula may be used to obtain an accurate estimate of the integral $\int_0^{1/2} e^{-t^2} dt$.

EXAMPLE 3. The Taylor formula for e^x with $n = 4$ gives us

(7.15)
$$e^x = 1 + x + \frac{x^2}{2!} + \frac{x^3}{3!} + \frac{x^4}{4!} + E_4(x) .$$

Suppose now that $x \le 0$. In any interval of the form $[-c, 0]$ we have $e^{-c} \le e^x \le 1$, so we may use the inequalities (7.11) of Theorem 7.7 with $m = e^{-c}$ and $M = 1$ to write

$$0 < (-1)^5 E_4(x) \le \frac{(-x)^5}{5!} \qquad \text{if} \quad x < 0 .$$

In other words, if $x < 0$, then $E_4(x)$ is negative and $\geq x^5/5!$. Replacing x by $-t^2$ in (7.15), we have

$$(7.16) \qquad e^{-t^2} = 1 - t^2 + \frac{t^4}{2!} - \frac{t^6}{3!} + \frac{t^8}{4!} + E_4(-t^2),$$

where $-t^{10}/5! \leq E_4(-t^2) < 0$. If $0 \leq t \leq \frac{1}{2}$, we find that $t^{10}/5! \leq (\frac{1}{2})^{10}/5! < 0.000\ 009$. Thus, if we integrate (7.16) from 0 to $\frac{1}{2}$, we obtain

$$\int_0^{1/2} e^{-t^2}\,dt = \frac{1}{2} - \frac{1}{3 \cdot 2^3} + \frac{1}{5 \cdot 2^5 \cdot 2!} - \frac{1}{7 \cdot 2^7 \cdot 3!} + \frac{1}{9 \cdot 2^9 \cdot 4!} - \theta,$$

where $0 < \theta \leq 0.000\ 0045$. Rounding off to four decimals, we find $\int_0^{1/2} e^{-t^2}\,dt = 0.4613$.

*7.7 Other forms of the remainder in Taylor's formula

We have expressed the error in Taylor's formula as an integral,

$$E_n(x) = \frac{1}{n!} \int_a^x (x - t)^n f^{(n+1)}(t)\,dt.$$

It can also be expressed in many other forms. Since the factor $(x - t)^n$ in the integrand never changes sign in the interval of integration, and since $f^{(n+1)}$ is continuous on this interval, the weighted mean-value theorem for integrals (Theorem 3.16) gives us

$$\int_a^x (x - t)^n f^{(n+1)}(t)\,dt = f^{(n+1)}(c) \int_a^x (x - t)^n\,dt = f^{(n+1)}(c)\frac{(x - a)^{n+1}}{n + 1},$$

where c lies in the closed interval joining a and x. Therefore, the error can be written as

$$E_n(x) = \frac{f^{(n+1)}(c)}{(n + 1)!}(x - a)^{n+1}.$$

This is called Lagrange's form of the remainder. It resembles the earlier terms in Taylor's formula, except that the derivative $f^{(n+1)}(c)$ is evaluated at some unknown point c rather than at a. The point c depends on x and on n, as well as on f.

Using a different type of argument, we can drop the continuity requirement on $f^{(n+1)}$ and derive Lagrange's formula and other forms of the remainder under a weaker hypothesis. Suppose that $f^{(n+1)}$ exists in some open interval (h, k) containing the point a, and assume that $f^{(n)}$ is continuous in the closed interval $[h, k]$. Choose any $x \neq a$ in $[h, k]$. For simplicity, say $x > a$. Keep x fixed and define a new function F on the interval $[a, x]$ as follows:

$$F(t) = f(t) + \sum_{k=1}^{n} \frac{f^{(k)}(t)}{k!}(x - t)^k.$$

Note that $F(x) = f(x)$ and $F(a) = T_n f(x; a)$, so $F(x) - F(a) = E_n(x)$. The function F is continuous in the closed interval $[a, x]$ and has a derivative in the open interval (a, x). If we compute $F'(t)$, keeping in mind that each term of the sum defining $F(t)$ is a product, we find that all terms cancel except one, and we are left with the equation

$$F'(t) = \frac{(x - t)^n}{n!} f^{(n+1)}(t).$$

Now let G be any function that is continuous on $[a, x]$ and differentiable on (a, x). Then we can apply Cauchy's mean-value formula (Theorem 4.6) to write

$$G'(c)[F(x) - F(a)] = F'(c)[G(x) - G(a)],$$

for some c in the open interval (a, x). If G' is nonzero in (a, x), this gives the following formula for the error $E_n(x)$:

$$E_n(x) = \frac{F'(c)}{G'(c)} [G(x) - G(a)].$$

We can express the error in various forms by different choices of G. For example, taking $G(t) = (x - t)^{n+1}$, we obtain Lagrange's form,

$$E_n(x) = \frac{f^{(n+1)}(c)}{(n + 1)!} (x - a)^{n+1}, \qquad \text{where} \quad a < c < x.$$

Taking $G(t) = x - t$, we obtain another formula, called Cauchy's form of the remainder,

$$E_n(x) = \frac{f^{(n+1)}(c)}{n!} (x - c)^n (x - a), \qquad \text{where} \quad a < c < x.$$

If $G(t) = (x - t)^p$, where $p \geq 1$, we obtain the formula

$$E_n(x) = \frac{f^{(n+1)}(c)}{n! \, p} (x - c)^{n+1-p} (x - a)^p, \qquad \text{where} \quad a < c < x.$$

7.8 Exercises

Examples of Taylor's formula with remainder are given in Exercises 1, 2, and 3. In each case prove that the error satisfies the given inequalities.

1. $\sin x = \displaystyle\sum_{k=1}^{n} \frac{(-1)^{k-1} x^{2k-1}}{(2k - 1)!} + E_{2n}(x), \qquad |E_{2n}(x)| \leq \dfrac{|x|^{2n+1}}{(2n + 1)!}.$

2. $\cos x = \displaystyle\sum_{k=0}^{n} \frac{(-1)^k x^{2k}}{(2k)!} + E_{2n+1}(x), \qquad |E_{2n+1}(x)| \leq \dfrac{|x|^{2n+2}}{(2n + 2)!}.$

3. $\arctan x = \displaystyle\sum_{k=0}^{n-1} \frac{(-1)^k x^{2k+1}}{2k + 1} + E_{2n}(x), \qquad |E_{2n}(x)| \leq \dfrac{x^{2n+1}}{2n + 1} \qquad \text{if} \quad 0 \leq x \leq 1.$

4. (a) Obtain the number $r = \sqrt{15} - 3$ as an approximation to the nonzero root of the equation $x^2 = \sin x$ by using the cubic Taylor polynomial approximation to $\sin x$.
   (b) Show that the approximation in part (a) satisfies the inequality

$$|\sin r - r^2| < \frac{1}{200},$$

given that $\sqrt{15} - 3 < 0.9$. Is the difference $(\sin r - r^2)$ positive or negative? Give full details of your reasoning.

5. (a) Use the cubic Taylor polynomial approximation to $\arctan x$ to obtain the number $r = (\sqrt{21} - 3)/2$ as an approximation to the nonzero root of the equation $\arctan x = x^2$.
   (b) Given that $\sqrt{21} < 4.6$ and that $2^{16} = 65536$, prove that the approximation in part (a) satisfies the inequality

$$|r^2 - \arctan r| < \frac{7}{100}.$$

Is the difference $(r^2 - \arctan r)$ positive or negative? Give full details of your reasoning.

6. Prove that $\displaystyle\int_0^1 \frac{1 + x^{30}}{1 + x^{60}}\, dx = 1 + \frac{c}{31},$ where $0 < c < 1$.

7. Prove that $0.493948 < \displaystyle\int_0^{1/2} \frac{1}{1 + x^4}\, dx < 0.493958.$

8. (a) If $0 \le x \le \frac{1}{2}$, show that $\sin x = x - x^3/3! + r(x)$, where $|r(x)| \le (\frac{1}{2})^5/5!$.
   (b) Use the estimate in part (a) to find an approximate value for the integral $\int_0^{\sqrt{2}/2} \sin (x^2)\, dx$. Make sure you give an estimate for the error.

9. Use the first three nonzero terms of Taylor's formula for $\sin x$ to find an approximate value for the integral $\int_0^1 (\sin x)/x\, dx$ and give an estimate for the error. [It is to be understood that the quotient $(\sin x)/x$ is equal to 1 when $x = 0$.]

10. This exercise outlines a method for computing π, using Taylor's formula for $\arctan x$ given in Exercise 3. It is based on the fact that π is nearly 3.2, so $\frac{1}{4}\pi$ is nearly 0.8 or $\frac{4}{5}$, and this is nearly 4 arctan $\frac{1}{5}$. Let $\alpha = \arctan \frac{1}{5}$, $\beta = 4\alpha - \frac{1}{4}\pi$.
    (a) Use the identity $\tan(A + B) = (\tan A + \tan B)/(1 - \tan A \tan B)$ with $A = B = \alpha$ and then again with $A = B = 2\alpha$ to get $\tan 2\alpha = \frac{5}{12}$ and $\tan 4\alpha = \frac{120}{119}$. Then use the identity once more with $A = 4\alpha$, $B = -\frac{1}{4}\pi$ to obtain $\tan \beta = \frac{1}{239}$. This yields the following remarkable identity discovered in 1706 by John Machin (1680–1751):

$$\pi = 16 \arctan \tfrac{1}{5} - 4 \arctan \tfrac{1}{239}.$$

(b) Use the Taylor polynomial $T_{11}(\arctan x)$ with $x = \frac{1}{5}$ to show that

$$3.158328934 < 16 \arctan \tfrac{1}{5} < 3.158328972.$$

(c) Use the Taylor polynomial $T_3(\arctan x)$ with $x = \frac{1}{239}$ to show that

$$-0.016736309 < -4 \arctan \tfrac{1}{239} < -0.016736300.$$

(d) Use parts (a), (b) and (c) to show that the value of π, correct to seven decimals, is 3.1415926.

7.9   Further remarks on the error in Taylor's formula.   The o-notation

If f has a continuous $(n + 1)$st derivative in some interval containing a point a, we may write Taylor's formula in the form

$$(7.17) \qquad f(x) = \sum_{k=0}^{n} \frac{f^{(k)}(a)}{k!} (x - a)^k + E_n(x) \,.$$

Suppose we restrict x to lie in some closed interval $[a - c, a + c]$ about a, in which $f^{(n+1)}$ is continuous.   Then $f^{(n+1)}$ is bounded on this interval and hence satisfies an inequality of the form

$$|f^{(n+1)}(t)| \leq M \,,$$

where $M > 0$.   Hence, by Theorem 7.7, we have the error estimate

$$|E_n(x)| \leq M \, \frac{|x - a|^{n+1}}{(n + 1)!}$$

for each x in $[a - c, a + c]$.   If we keep $x \neq a$ and divide this inequality by $|x - a|^n$, we find that

$$0 \leq \left| \frac{E_n(x)}{(x - a)^n} \right| \leq \frac{M}{(n + 1)!} |x - a| \,.$$

If now we let $x \to a$, we see that $E_n(x)/(x - a)^n \to 0$.   We describe this by saying that the error $E_n(x)$ is of smaller order than $(x - a)^n$ as $x \to a$.

In other words, under the conditions stated, $f(x)$ may be approximated near a by a polynomial in $(x - a)$ of degree n, and the error in this approximation is of smaller order than $(x - a)^n$ as $x \to a$.

A special notation, introduced in 1909 by E. Landau,† is particularly appropriate when used in connection with Taylor's formula.   This is called the o-notation (the little-oh notation) and it is defined as follows.

DEFINITION.   *Assume $g(x) \neq 0$ for all $x \neq a$ in some interval containing a.   The notation*

$$f(x) = o(g(x)) \qquad as \quad x \to a$$

means that

$$\lim_{x \to a} \frac{f(x)}{g(x)} = 0 \,.$$

The symbol $f(x) = o(g(x))$ is read "$f(x)$ is little-oh of $g(x)$," or "$f(x)$ is of smaller order than $g(x)$," and it is intended to convey the idea that for x near a, $f(x)$ is small compared with $g(x)$.

---

† Edmund Landau (1877–1938) was a famous German mathematician who made many important contributions to mathematics.   He is best known for his lucid books in analysis and in the theory of numbers.

EXAMPLE 1. $f(x) = o(1)$ as $x \to a$ means that $f(x) \to 0$ as $x \to a$.

EXAMPLE 2. $f(x) = o(x)$ as $x \to 0$ means that $\dfrac{f(x)}{x} \to 0$ as $x \to 0$.

An equation of the form $f(x) = h(x) + o(g(x))$ is understood to mean that $f(x) - h(x) = o(g(x))$ or, in other words, $[f(x) - h(x)]/g(x) \to 0$ as $x \to a$.

EXAMPLE 3. We have $\sin x = x + o(x)$ because $\dfrac{\sin x - x}{x} = \dfrac{\sin x}{x} - 1 \to 0$ as $x \to 0$.

The foregoing remarks concerning the error in Taylor's formula can now be expressed in the *o*-notation. We may write

$$f(x) = \sum_{k=0}^{n} \frac{f^{(k)}(a)}{k!} (x - a)^k + o((x - a)^n) \qquad \text{as} \quad x \to a ,$$

whenever the derivative $f^{(n+1)}$ is continuous in some closed interval containing the point a. This expresses, in a brief way, the fact that the error term is small compared to $(x - a)^n$ when x is near a. In particular, from the discussion of earlier sections, we have the following examples of Taylor's formula expressed in the *o*-notation:

$$\frac{1}{1 - x} = 1 + x + x^2 + \cdots + x^n + o(x^n) \qquad \text{as} \quad x \to 0 .$$

$$\log(1 + x) = x - \frac{x^2}{2} + \frac{x^3}{3} - \frac{x^4}{4} + \cdots + (-1)^{n-1} \frac{x^n}{n} + o(x^n) \qquad \text{as} \quad x \to 0 .$$

$$e^x = 1 + x + \frac{x^2}{2!} + \cdots + \frac{x^n}{n!} + o(x^n) \qquad \text{as} \quad x \to 0 .$$

$$\sin x = x - \frac{x^3}{3!} + \frac{x^5}{5!} - \frac{x^7}{7!} + \cdots + (-1)^{n-1} \frac{x^{2n-1}}{(2n - 1)!} + o(x^{2n}) \qquad \text{as} \quad x \to 0 .$$

$$\cos x = 1 - \frac{x^2}{2!} + \frac{x^4}{4!} - \frac{x^6}{6!} + \cdots + (-1)^n \frac{x^{2n}}{(2n)!} + o(x^{2n+1}) \qquad \text{as} \quad x \to 0 .$$

$$\arctan x = x - \frac{x^3}{3} + \frac{x^5}{5} - \frac{x^7}{7} + \cdots + (-1)^{n-1} \frac{x^{2n-1}}{2n - 1} + o(x^{2n}) \qquad \text{as} \quad x \to 0 .$$

In calculations involving Taylor approximations, it often becomes necessary to combine several terms involving the *o*-symbol. A few simple rules for manipulating *o*-symbols are discussed in the next theorem. These cover most situations that arise in practice.

THEOREM 7.8.   ALGEBRA OF o-SYMBOLS.   *As $x \to a$, we have the following:*

(a) $o(g(x)) \pm o(g(x)) = o(g(x))$.

(b) $o(cg(x)) = o(g(x))$ *if $c \neq 0$.*

(c) $f(x) \cdot o(g(x)) = o(f(x)g(x))$.

(d) $o(o(g(x))) = o(g(x))$.

(e) $\dfrac{1}{1 + g(x)} = 1 - g(x) + o(g(x))$ *if $g(x) \to 0$ as $x \to a$.*

Proof.   The statement in part (a) is understood to mean that if $f_1(x) = o(g(x))$ and if $f_2(x) = o(g(x))$, then $f_1(x) \pm f_2(x) = o(g(x))$. But since we have

$$\frac{f_1(x) \pm f_2(x)}{g(x)} = \frac{f_1(x)}{g(x)} \pm \frac{f_2(x)}{g(x)} ,$$

each term on the right tends to 0 as $x \to a$, so part (a) is proved. The statements in (b), (c), and (d) are proved in a similar way.

To prove (e), we use the algebraic identity

$$\frac{1}{1 + u} = 1 - u + u \frac{u}{1 + u}$$

with u replaced by $g(x)$ and then note that $\dfrac{g(x)}{1 + g(x)} \to 0$ as $x \to a$.

EXAMPLE 1. Prove that $\tan x = x + \frac{1}{3}x^3 + o(x^3)$ as $x \to 0$.

Solution.   We use the Taylor approximations for the sine and cosine. From part (e) of Theorem 7.8, with $g(x) = -\frac{1}{2}x^2 + o(x^3)$, we have

$$\frac{1}{\cos x} = \frac{1}{1 - \frac{1}{2}x^2 + o(x^3)} = 1 + \frac{1}{2}x^2 + o(x^2)   \text{ as }   x \to 0 .$$

Therefore, we have

$$\tan x = \frac{\sin x}{\cos x} = \left(x - \frac{1}{6}x^3 + o(x^4) \right)\left(1 + \frac{1}{2}x^2 + o(x^2) \right) = x + \frac{1}{3}x^3 + o(x^3) .$$

EXAMPLE 2. Prove that $(1 + x)^{1/x} = e \cdot \left(1 - \dfrac{x}{2} + \dfrac{11x^2}{24} + o(x^2) \right)$ as $x \to 0$.

Solution.   Since $(1 + x)^{1/x} = e^{(1/x)\log(1+x)}$, we begin with a polynomial approximation to $\log (1 + x)$. Taking a cubic approximation, we have

$$\log (1 + x) = x - \frac{x^2}{2} + \frac{x^3}{3} + o(x^3) ,   \frac{\log (1 + x)}{x} = 1 - \frac{x}{2} + \frac{x^2}{3} + o(x^2) ,$$

and so we obtain

(7.18) $$(1 + x)^{1/x} = \exp(1 - x/2 + x^2/3 + o(x^2)) = e \cdot e^u,$$

where $u = -x/2 + x^2/3 + o(x^2)$. But as $u \to 0$, we have $e^u = 1 + u + \frac{1}{2}u^2 + o(u^2)$, so we obtain

$$e^u = 1 - \frac{x}{2} + \frac{x^2}{3} + o(x^2) + \frac{1}{2}\left(-\frac{x}{2} + \frac{x^2}{3} + o(x^2)\right)^2 + o(x^2) = 1 - \frac{x}{2} + \frac{11x^2}{24} + o(x^2).$$

When we use this in Equation (7.18), we obtain the desired formula.

7.10 Applications to indeterminate forms

We have already illustrated how polynomial approximations are used in the computation of function values. They can also be used as an aid in the calculation of limits. We illustrate with some examples.

EXAMPLE 1. If a and b are positive numbers, determine the limit

$$\lim_{x \to 0} \frac{a^x - b^x}{x}.$$

Solution. We cannot solve this problem by computing the limit of the numerator and denominator separately, because the denominator tends to 0 and the quotient theorem on limits is not applicable. The numerator in this case also tends to 0 and the quotient is said to assume the "*indeterminate form* 0/0" as $x \to 0$. Taylor's formula and the o-notation often enable us to calculate the limit of an indeterminate form like this one very simply. The idea is to approximate the numerator $a^x - b^x$ by a polynomial in x, then divide by x and let $x \to 0$. We could apply Taylor's formula directly to $f(x) = a^x - b^x$ but, since $a^x = e^{x \log a}$ and $b^x = e^{x \log b}$, it is simpler in this case to use the polynomial approximations already derived for the exponential function. If we begin with the linear approximation

$$e^t = 1 + t + o(t) \qquad \text{as} \quad t \to 0$$

and replace t by $x \log a$ and $x \log b$, respectively, we find

$$a^x = 1 + x \log a + o(x) \qquad \text{and} \qquad b^x = 1 + x \log b + o(x) \qquad \text{as} \quad x \to 0.$$

Here we have used the fact that $o(x \log a) = o(x)$ and $o(x \log b) = o(x)$. If now we subtract and note that $o(x) - o(x) = o(x)$, we find $a^x - b^x = x(\log a - \log b) + o(x)$. Dividing by x and using the relation $o(x)/x = o(1)$, we obtain

$$\frac{a^x - b^x}{x} = \log \frac{a}{b} + o(1) \to \log \frac{a}{b} \qquad \text{as} \quad x \to 0.$$

EXAMPLE 2. Prove that $\lim_{x \to 0} \frac{1}{x}\left(\cot x - \frac{1}{x}\right) = -\frac{1}{3}$.

Solution. We use Example 1 of Section 7.9, and Theorem 7.8(e) to write

$$\cot x = \frac{1}{\tan x} = \frac{1}{x + \frac{1}{3}x^3 + o(x^3)} = \frac{1}{x} \frac{1}{1 + \frac{1}{3}x^2 + o(x^2)}$$

$$= \frac{1}{x}\left(1 - \frac{1}{3}x^2 + o(x^2)\right) = \frac{1}{x} - \frac{1}{3}x + o(x).$$

Hence, we have

$$\frac{1}{x}\left(\cot x - \frac{1}{x}\right) = -\frac{1}{3} + o(1) \to -\frac{1}{3} \quad \text{as} \quad x \to 0 .$$

EXAMPLE 3. Prove that $\lim_{x \to 0} \dfrac{\log (1 + ax)}{x} = a$ for every real a.

Solution. If $a = 0$, the result holds trivially. If $a \neq 0$, we use the linear approximation $\log (1 + x) = x + o(x)$. Replacing x by ax, we obtain $\log (1 + ax) = ax + o(ax) = ax + o(x)$. Dividing by x and letting $x \to 0$, we obtain the limit a.

EXAMPLE 4. Prove that for every real a, we have

(7.19) $$\lim_{x \to 0} (1 + ax)^{1/x} = e^a .$$

Solution. We simply note that $(1 + ax)^{1/x} = e^{(1/x)\log(1+ax)}$ and use the result of Example 3 along with the continuity of the exponential function.

Replacing ax by y in (7.19), we find another important limit relation:

$$\lim_{y \to 0} (1 + y)^{a/y} = e^a .$$

Sometimes these limit relations are taken as the starting point for the theory of the exponential function.

7.11 Exercises

1. Find a quadratic polynomial $P(x)$ such that $2^x = P(x) + o(x^2)$ as $x \to 0$.
2. Find a cubic polynomial $P(x)$ such that $x \cos x = P(x) + o((x - 1)^3)$ as $x \to 1$.
3. Find the polynomial $P(x)$ of smallest degree such that $\sin (x - x^2) = P(x) + o(x^6)$ as $x \to 0$.
4. Find constants a, b, c such that $\log x = a + b(x - 1) + c(x - 1)^2 + o((x - 1)^2)$ as $x \to 1$.
5. Recall that $\cos x = 1 - \frac{1}{2}x^2 + o(x^3)$ as $x \to 0$. Use this to prove that $x^{-2}(1 - \cos x) \to \frac{1}{2}$ as $x \to 0$. In a similar way, find the limit of $x^{-4}(1 - \cos 2x - 2x^2)$ as $x \to 0$.

Assume also that $g'(x) \neq 0$ for each x in (a, b). If the limit

(7.21)
$$\lim_{x \to a+} \frac{f'(x)}{g'(x)}$$

exists and has the value L, say, then the limit

(7.22)
$$\lim_{x \to a+} \frac{f(x)}{g(x)}$$

also exists and has the value L.

Note that the limits in (7.20), (7.21), and (7.22) are "right-handed." There is, of course, a similar theorem in which the hypotheses are satisfied in some open interval of the form (b, a) and all the limits are "left-handed." Also, by combining the two "one-sided" theorems, there follows a "two-sided" result of the same kind in which $x \to a$ in an unrestricted fashion.

Before we discuss the proof of Theorem 7.9, we shall illustrate the use of this theorem in a number of examples.

EXAMPLE 1. We shall use L'Hôpital's rule to obtain the familiar formula

(7.23)
$$\lim_{x \to 0} \frac{\sin x}{x} = 1 .$$

Here $f(x) = \sin x$ and $g(x) = x$. The quotient of derivatives is $f'(x)/g'(x) = (\cos x)/1$ and this tends to 1 as $x \to 0$. By Theorem 7.9 the limit in (7.23) also exists and equals 1.

EXAMPLE 2. To determine the limit

$$\lim_{x \to 0} \frac{x - \tan x}{x - \sin x}$$

by L'Hôpital's rule, we let $f(x) = x - \tan x$, $g(x) = x - \sin x$, and we find that

(7.24)
$$\frac{f'(x)}{g'(x)} = \frac{1 - \sec^2 x}{1 - \cos x} .$$

Although this, too, assumes the form 0/0 as $x \to 0$, we may remove the indeterminacy at this stage by algebraic means. If we write

$$1 - \sec^2 x = 1 - \frac{1}{\cos^2 x} = \frac{\cos^2 x - 1}{\cos^2 x} = - \frac{(1 + \cos x)(1 - \cos x)}{\cos^2 x} ,$$

the quotient in (7.24) becomes

$$\frac{f'(x)}{g'(x)} = - \frac{1 + \cos x}{\cos^2 x} ,$$

and this approaches -2 as $x \to 0$. Notice that the indeterminacy disappeared when we canceled the common factor $1 - \cos x$. Canceling common factors usually tends to simplify the work in problems of this kind.

When the quotient of derivatives $f'(x)/g'(x)$ also assumes the indeterminate form $0/0$, we may try L'Hôpital's rule again. In the next example, the indeterminacy is removed after two applications of the rule.

EXAMPLE 3. For any real number c, we have

$$\lim_{x \to 1} \frac{x^c - cx + c - 1}{(x - 1)^2} = \lim_{x \to 1} \frac{cx^{c-1} - c}{2(x - 1)} = \lim_{x \to 1} \frac{c(c - 1)x^{c-2}}{2} = \frac{c(c - 1)}{2}.$$

In this sequence of equations it is understood that the existence of each limit implies that of the preceding and also their equality.

The next example shows that L'Hôpital's rule is not infallible.

EXAMPLE 4. Let $f(x) = e^{-1/x}$ if $x \neq 0$, and let $g(x) = x$. The quotient $f(x)/g(x)$ assumes the indeterminate form $0/0$ as $x \to 0+$, and one application of L'Hôpital's rule leads to the quotient

$$\frac{f'(x)}{g'(x)} = \frac{(1/x^2)e^{-1/x}}{1} = \frac{e^{-1/x}}{x^2}.$$

This, too, is indeterminate as $x \to 0+$, and if we differentiate numerator and denominator we obtain $(1/x^2)e^{-1/x}/(2x) = e^{-1/x}/(2x^3)$. After n steps we are led to the quotient $e^{-1/x}/(n!\, x^{n+1})$, so the indeterminacy never disappears by this method.

EXAMPLE 5. When using L'Hôpital's rule repeatedly, some care is needed to make certain that the quotient under consideration actually assumes an indeterminate form. A common type of error is illustrated by the following calculation:

$$\lim_{x \to 1} \frac{3x^2 - 2x - 1}{x^2 - x} = \lim_{x \to 1} \frac{6x - 2}{2x - 1} = \lim_{x \to 1} \frac{6}{2} = 3.$$

The first step is correct but the second is not. The quotient $(6x - 2)/(2x - 1)$ is not indeterminate as $x \to 1$. The correct limit, 4, is obtained by substituting 1 for x in $(6x - 2)/(2x - 1)$.

EXAMPLE 6. Sometimes the work can be shortened by a change of variable. For example, we could apply L'Hôpital's rule directly to calculate the limit

$$\lim_{x \to 0+} \frac{\sqrt{x}}{1 - e^{2\sqrt{x}}},$$

but we may avoid differentiation of square roots by writing $t = \sqrt{x}$ and noting that

$$\lim_{x \to 0+} \frac{\sqrt{x}}{1 - e^{2\sqrt{x}}} = \lim_{t \to 0+} \frac{t}{1 - e^{2t}} = \lim_{t \to 0+} \frac{1}{-2e^{2t}} = -\frac{1}{2}.$$

We turn now to the proof of Theorem 7.9.

Proof. We make use of Cauchy's mean-value formula (Theorem 4.6 of Section 4.14) applied to a closed interval having a as its left endpoint. Since the functions f and g may not be defined at a, we introduce two new functions that *are* defined there. Let

$$F(x) = f(x) \quad \text{if} \quad x \neq a \,, \qquad F(a) = 0 \,,$$

$$G(x) = g(x) \quad \text{if} \quad x \neq a \,, \qquad G(a) = 0 \,.$$

Both F and G are continuous at a. In fact, if $a < x < b$, both functions F and G are continuous on the *closed interval* $[a, x]$ and have derivatives everywhere in the *open interval* (a, x). Therefore Cauchy's formula is applicable to the interval $[a, x]$ and we obtain

$$[F(x) - F(a)]G'(c) = [G(x) - G(a)]F'(c) \,,$$

where c is some point satisfying $a < c < x$. Since $F(a) = G(a) = 0$, this becomes

$$f(x)g'(c) = g(x)f'(c) \,.$$

Now $g'(c) \neq 0$ [since, by hypothesis, g' is never zero in (a, b)] and also $g(x) \neq 0$. In fact, if we had $g(x) = 0$ then we would have $G(x) = G(a) = 0$ and, by Rolle's theorem, there would be a point x_1 between a and x where $G'(x_1) = 0$, contradicting the hypothesis that g' is never zero in (a, b). Therefore we may divide by $g'(c)$ and $g(x)$ to obtain

$$\frac{f(x)}{g(x)} = \frac{f'(c)}{g'(c)} \,.$$

As $x \to a$, the point $c \to a$ (since $a < c < x$) and the quotient on the right approaches L [by (7.21)]. Hence, $f(x)/g(x)$ also approaches L and the theorem is proved.

7.13 Exercises

Evaluate the limits in Exercises 1 through 12.

1. $\displaystyle\lim_{x \to 2} \frac{3x^2 + 2x - 16}{x^2 - x - 2}$.

2. $\displaystyle\lim_{x \to 3} \frac{x^2 - 4x + 3}{2x^2 - 13x + 21}$.

3. $\displaystyle\lim_{x \to 0} \frac{\sinh x - \sin x}{x^3}$.

4. $\displaystyle\lim_{x \to 0} \frac{(2 - x)e^x - x - 2}{x^3}$.

5. $\displaystyle\lim_{x \to 0} \frac{\log (\cos ax)}{\log (\cos bx)}$.

6. $\displaystyle\lim_{x \to 0+} \frac{x - \sin x}{(x \sin x)^{3/2}}$.

7. $\displaystyle\lim_{x \to a+} \frac{\sqrt{x} - \sqrt{a} + \sqrt{x - a}}{\sqrt{x^2 - a^2}}$.

8. $\displaystyle\lim_{x \to 1+} \frac{x^x - x}{1 - x + \log x}$.

9. $\displaystyle\lim_{x \to 0} \frac{\arcsin 2x - 2 \arcsin x}{x^3}$.

10. $\displaystyle\lim_{x \to 0} \frac{x \cot x - 1}{x^2}$.

11. $\displaystyle\lim_{x \to 1} \frac{\sum_{k=1}^{n} x^k - n}{x - 1}$.

12. $\displaystyle\lim_{x \to 0+} \frac{1}{x\sqrt{x}} \left(a \arctan \frac{\sqrt{x}}{a} - b \arctan \frac{\sqrt{x}}{b} \right)$.

13. Determine the limit of the quotient

$$\frac{(\sin 4x)(\sin 3x)}{x \sin 2x}$$

as $x \to 0$ and also as $x \to \frac{1}{2}\pi$.

14. For what values of the constants a and b is

$$\lim_{x \to 0} (x^{-3} \sin 3x + ax^{-2} + b) = 0 ?$$

15. Find constants a and b such that $\lim_{x \to 0} \dfrac{1}{bx - \sin x} \displaystyle\int_0^x \frac{t^2\,dt}{\sqrt{a+t}} = 1$.

16. A circular arc of radius 1 subtends an angle of x radians, $0 < x < \frac{1}{2}\pi$, as shown in Figure 7.2. The point C is the intersection of the two tangent lines at A and B. Let $T(x)$ be the area of

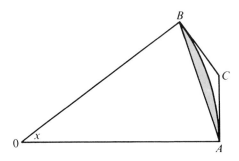

FIGURE 7.2   Exercise 16.

triangle ABC and let $S(x)$ be the area of the shaded region. Compute the following: (a) $T(x)$; (b) $S(x)$; (c) the limit of $T(x)/S(x)$ as $x \to 0+$.

17. The current $I(t)$ flowing in a certain electrical circuit at time t is given by

$$I(t) = \frac{E}{R}\,(1 - e^{-Rt/L}),$$

where E, R, and L are positive numbers. Determine the limiting value of $I(t)$ as $R \to 0+$.

18. A weight hangs by a spring and is caused to vibrate by a sinusoidal force. Its displacement $f(t)$ at time t is given by an equation of the form

$$f(t) = \frac{A}{c^2 - k^2}\,(\sin kt - \sin ct),$$

where A, c, and k are positive constants, with $c \neq k$. Determine the limiting value of the displacement as $c \to k$.

7.14   The symbols $+\infty$ and $-\infty$.   Extension of L'Hôpital's rule

L'Hôpital's rule may be extended in several ways. First of all, we may wish to consider the quotient $f(x)/g(x)$ as x increases without bound. It is convenient to have a short descriptive symbolism to express the fact that we are allowing x to increase indefinitely. For this purpose, mathematicians use the special symbol $+\infty$, called "plus infinity." Although we shall not attach any meaning to the symbol $+\infty$ *by itself*, we shall give precise definitions of various statements involving this symbol.

One of these statements is written as follows:

$$\lim_{x \to +\infty} f(x) = A \,,$$

and is read "The limit of $f(x)$, as x tends to plus infinity, is A." The idea we are trying to express here is that the function values $f(x)$ can be made arbitrarily close to the real number A by taking x large enough. To make this statement mathematically precise, we must explain what is meant by "arbitrarily close" and by "large enough." This is done by means of the following definition:

DEFINITION. *The symbolism*

$$\lim_{x \to +\infty} f(x) = A$$

means that for every number $\epsilon > 0$, there is another number $M > 0$ (which may depend on ϵ) such that

$$|f(x) - A| < \epsilon \qquad whenever \quad x > M \,.$$

Calculations involving limits as $x \to +\infty$ may be reduced to a more familiar case. We simply replace x by $1/t$ (that is, let $t = 1/x$) and note that $t \to 0$ through positive values as $x \to +\infty$. More precisely, we introduce a new function F, where

(7.25)
$$F(t) = f\left(\frac{1}{t}\right) \qquad \text{if} \quad t \neq 0 \,,$$

and simply observe that the two statements

$$\lim_{x \to +\infty} f(x) = A \qquad \text{and} \qquad \lim_{t \to 0+} F(t) = A$$

mean exactly the same thing. The proof of this equivalence requires only the definitions of the two limit symbols and is left as an exercise.

When we are interested in the behavior of $f(x)$ for large *negative* x, we introduce the symbol $-\infty$ ("minus infinity") and write

$$\lim_{x \to -\infty} f(x) = A$$

to mean: For every $\epsilon > 0$, there is an $M > 0$ such that

$$|f(x) - A| < \epsilon \qquad whenever \quad x < -M.$$

If F is defined by (7.25), it is easy to verify that the two statements

$$\lim_{x \to -\infty} f(x) = A \qquad \text{and} \qquad \lim_{t \to 0-} F(t) = A$$

are equivalent.

In view of the above remarks, it is not surprising to find that all the usual rules for calculating with limits (as stated in Theorem 3.1 of Section 3.4) also apply to limits as $x \to \pm\infty$. The same is true of L'Hôpital's rule which may be extended as follows:

THEOREM 7.10. *Assume that f and g have derivatives $f'(x)$ and $g'(x)$ for all x greater than a certain fixed $M > 0$. Suppose that*

$$\lim_{x \to +\infty} f(x) = 0 \qquad \text{and} \qquad \lim_{x \to +\infty} g(x) = 0 ,$$

and that $g'(x) \neq 0$ for $x > M$. If $f'(x)/g'(x)$ tends to a limit as $x \to +\infty$, then $f(x)/g(x)$ also tends to a limit and the two limits are equal. In other words,

(7.26) $$\lim_{x \to +\infty} \frac{f'(x)}{g'(x)} = L \qquad \text{implies} \qquad \lim_{x \to +\infty} \frac{f(x)}{g(x)} = L .$$

Proof.   Let $F(t) = f(1/t)$ and $G(t) = g(1/t)$. Then $f(x)/g(x) = F(t)/G(t)$ if $t = 1/x$, and $t \to 0+$ as $x \to +\infty$. Since $F(t)/G(t)$ assumes the indeterminate form $0/0$ as $t \to 0+$, we examine the quotient of derivatives $F'(t)/G'(t)$. By the chain rule, we have

$$F'(t) = \frac{-1}{t^2} f'\left(\frac{1}{t}\right) \qquad \text{and} \qquad G'(t) = \frac{-1}{t^2} g'\left(\frac{1}{t}\right) .$$

Also, $G'(t) \neq 0$ if $0 < t < 1/M$. When $x = 1/t$ and $x > M$, we have $F'(t)/G'(t) = f'(x)/g'(x)$ since the common factor $-1/t^2$ cancels. Therefore, if $f'(x)/g'(x) \to L$ as $x \to +\infty$, then $F'(t)/G'(t) \to L$ as $t \to 0+$ and hence, by Theorem 7.9, $F(t)/G(t) \to L$. Since $F(t)/G(t) = f(x)/g(x)$ this proves (7.26).

There is, of course, a result analogous to Theorem 7.10 in which we consider limits as $x \to -\infty$.

7.15 Infinite limits

In the foregoing section we used the notation $x \to +\infty$ to convey the idea that x takes on arbitrarily large positive values. We also write

(7.27) $$\lim_{x \to a} f(x) = +\infty$$

or, alternatively,

(7.28) $$f(x) \to +\infty \qquad \text{as} \quad x \to a$$

to indicate that $f(x)$ takes arbitrarily large values as x approaches a. The precise meaning of these symbols is given in the following definition.

DEFINITION. *The symbolism in (7.27) or in (7.28) means that to every positive number M (no matter how large), there corresponds another positive number δ (which may depend on M) such that*

$$f(x) > M \qquad whenever \quad 0 < |x - a| < \delta \,.$$

If $f(x) > M$ whenever $0 < x - a < \delta$, we write

$$\lim_{x \to a+} f(x) = +\infty \,,$$

and we say that $f(x)$ tends to plus infinity as x approaches a from the right. If $f(x) > M$ whenever $0 < a - x < \delta$, we write

$$\lim_{x \to a-} f(x) = +\infty \,,$$

and we say that $f(x)$ tends to plus infinity as x approaches a from the left.

The symbols

$$\lim_{x \to a} f(x) = -\infty \,, \qquad \lim_{x \to a+} f(x) = -\infty \,, \qquad and \qquad \lim_{x \to a-} f(x) = -\infty$$

are similarly defined, the only difference being that we replace $f(x) > M$ by $f(x) < -M$. Examples are shown in Figure 7.3.

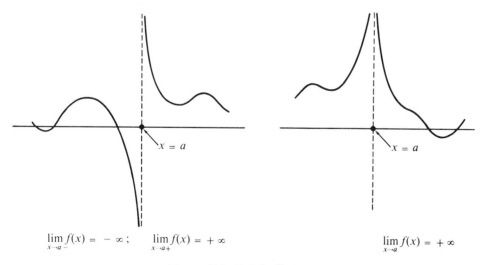

$$\lim_{x \to a-} f(x) = -\infty \,; \qquad \lim_{x \to a+} f(x) = +\infty \qquad\qquad \lim_{x \to a} f(x) = +\infty$$

FIGURE 7.3 Infinite limits.

It is also convenient to extend the definitions of these symbols further to cover the cases when $x \to \pm\infty$. Thus, for example, we write

$$\lim_{x \to +\infty} f(x) = +\infty$$

if, for every positive number M, there exists another positive number X such that $f(x) > M$ whenever $x > X$.

The reader should have no difficulty in formulating similar definitions for the symbols

$$\lim_{x \to -\infty} f(x) = +\infty , \qquad \lim_{x \to +\infty} f(x) = -\infty , \qquad \text{and} \qquad \lim_{x \to -\infty} f(x) = -\infty .$$

EXAMPLES. In Chapter 6 we proved that the logarithm function is increasing and unbounded on the positive real axis. We may express this fact briefly by writing

(7.29) $$\lim_{x \to +\infty} \log x = +\infty .$$

We also proved in Chapter 6 that $\log x < 0$ when $0 < x < 1$ and that the logarithm has no lower bound in the interval $(0, 1)$. Therefore, we may also write $\lim_{x \to 0+} \log x = -\infty$.

From the relation that holds between the logarithm and the exponential function it is easy to prove that

(7.30) $$\lim_{x \to +\infty} e^x = +\infty \qquad \text{and} \qquad \lim_{x \to -\infty} e^x = 0 \qquad (\text{or} \qquad \lim_{x \to +\infty} e^{-x} = 0) .$$

Using these results it is not difficult to show that for $\alpha > 0$ we have

$$\lim_{x \to +\infty} x^\alpha = +\infty \qquad \text{and} \qquad \lim_{x \to +\infty} \frac{1}{x^\alpha} = 0 .$$

The idea is to write $x^\alpha = e^{\alpha \log x}$ and use (7.30) together with (7.29). The formulas in (7.30) also give us the relations

$$\lim_{x \to 0-} e^{-1/x} = +\infty \qquad \text{and} \qquad \lim_{x \to 0+} e^{-1/x} = 0 .$$

The proofs of these statements make good exercises for testing a reader's understanding of limit symbols involving $\pm\infty$.

7.16 The behavior of $\log x$ and e^x for large x

Infinite limits lead to new types of indeterminate forms. For example, we may have a quotient $f(x)/g(x)$ where both $f(x) \to +\infty$ and $g(x) \to +\infty$ as $x \to a$ (or as $x \to \pm\infty$). In this case, we say that the quotient $f(x)/g(x)$ assumes the indeterminate form ∞/∞. There are various extensions of L'Hôpital's rule that often help to determine the behavior of a quotient when it assumes the indeterminate form ∞/∞. However, we shall not discuss these extensions because most examples that occur in practice can be treated by use of the following theorem which describes the behavior of the logarithm and the exponential for large values of x.

THEOREM 7.11. *If $a > 0$ and $b > 0$, we have*

$$(7.31) \qquad \lim_{x \to +\infty} \frac{(\log x)^b}{x^a} = 0$$

and

$$(7.32) \qquad \lim_{x \to +\infty} \frac{x^b}{e^{ax}} = 0 .$$

Proof. We prove (7.31) first and then use it to derive (7.32). A simple proof of (7.31) may be given directly from the definition of the logarithm as an integral. If $c > 0$ and $t \geq 1$, we have $t^{-1} \leq t^{c-1}$. Hence, if $x > 1$, we may write

$$0 < \log x = \int_1^x \frac{1}{t} \, dt \leq \int_1^x t^{c-1} \, dt = \frac{x^c - 1}{c} < \frac{x^c}{c} .$$

Therefore, we have

$$0 < \frac{(\log x)^b}{x^a} < \frac{x^{bc-a}}{c^b} \qquad \text{for every } c > 0 .$$

If we choose $c = \frac{1}{2}a/b$, then $x^{bc-a} = x^{-a/2}$ which tends to 0 as $x \to +\infty$. This proves (7.31). To prove (7.32), we make the change of variable $t = e^x$. Then $x = \log t$, and hence $x^b/e^{ax} = (\log t)^b/t^a$. But $t \to +\infty$ as $x \to +\infty$, so (7.32) follows from (7.31).

With a natural extension of the o-notation, we can write the limit relations just proved in the form

$$(\log x)^b = o(x^a) \qquad \text{as} \quad x \to +\infty ,$$

and

$$x^b = o(e^{ax}) \qquad \text{as} \quad x \to +\infty .$$

In other words, no matter how large b may be and no matter how small a may be (as long as both are positive), $(\log x)^b$ tends to infinity more slowly than x^a. Also, x^b tends to infinity more slowly than e^{ax}.

EXAMPLE 1. In Example 4 of Section 7.12 we showed that the behavior of $e^{-1/x}/x$ for x near 0 could not be decided by any number of applications of L'Hôpital's rule for $0/0$. However, if we write $t = 1/x$, this quotient becomes t/e^t and it assumes the indeterminate form ∞/∞ as $t \to +\infty$. Theorem 7.11 tells us that

$$\lim_{t \to +\infty} \frac{t}{e^t} = 0 .$$

Therefore, $e^{-1/x}/x \to 0$ as $x \to 0+$ or, in other words, $e^{-1/x} = o(x)$ as $x \to 0+$.

There are other indeterminate forms besides $0/0$ and ∞/∞. Some of these, denoted by the symbols $0 \cdot \infty$, 0^0, and ∞^0, are illustrated by the examples given below. In examples like these, algebraic manipulation often enables us to reduce the problem to an indeterminate form of the type $0/0$ or ∞/∞ which may be handled by L'Hôpital's rule, by polynomial approximation, or by Theorem 7.11.

EXAMPLE 2. $(0 \cdot \infty)$. Prove that $\lim_{x \to 0+} x^\alpha \log x = 0$ for each fixed $\alpha > 0$.

Solution. Writing $t = 1/x$, we find that $x^\alpha \log x = -(\log t)/t^\alpha$ and, by (7.31), this tends to 0 as $t \to +\infty$.

EXAMPLE 3. (0^0). Show that $\lim_{x \to 0+} x^x = 1$.

Solution. Since $x^x = e^{x \log x}$, by continuity of the exponential function we have

$$\lim_{x \to 0+} x^x = \exp\left(\lim_{x \to 0+} x \log x\right),$$

if the last limit exists. But by Example 2 we know that $x \log x \to 0$ as $x \to 0+$, and hence $x^x \to e^0 = 1$.

EXAMPLE 4. (∞^0). Show that $\lim_{x \to +\infty} x^{1/x} = 1$.

Solution. Put $t = 1/x$ and use the result of Example 3.

In Section 7.10 we proved the limit relations

(7.33) $\lim_{x \to 0} (1 + ax)^{1/x} = e^a$ and $\lim_{x \to 0} (1 + x)^{a/x} = e^a$.

Each of these is an indeterminate form of the type 1^∞. We may replace x by $1/x$ in these formulas and obtain, respectively,

$$\lim_{x \to +\infty} \left(1 + \frac{a}{x}\right)^x = e^a \quad \text{and} \quad \lim_{x \to +\infty} \left(1 + \frac{1}{x}\right)^{ax} = e^a,$$

both of which are valid for all real a.

The relations (7.33) and those in Examples 2, 3, and 4 are all of the type $f(x)^{g(x)}$. These are usually dealt with by writing

$$f(x)^{g(x)} = e^{g(x) \log f(x)}$$

and then treating the exponent $g(x) \log f(x)$ by one of the methods discussed earlier.

7.17 Exercises

Evaluate the limits in Exercises 1 through 25. The letters a and b denote positive constants.

1. $\lim\limits_{x \to 0} \dfrac{e^{-1/x^2}}{x^{1000}}$.

2. $\lim\limits_{x \to +\infty} \dfrac{\sin (1/x)}{\arctan (1/x)}$.

3. $\lim\limits_{x \to \frac{1}{2}\pi} \dfrac{\tan 3x}{\tan x}$.

4. $\lim\limits_{x \to +\infty} \dfrac{\log(a + be^x)}{\sqrt{a + bx^2}}$.

5. $\lim\limits_{x \to +\infty} x^4 \left(\cos \dfrac{1}{x} - 1 + \dfrac{1}{2x^2} \right) . = \dfrac{1}{24}$

6. $\lim\limits_{x \to \pi} \dfrac{\log |\sin x|}{\log |\sin 2x|}$.

7. $\lim\limits_{x \to \frac{1}{2}-} \dfrac{\log (1 - 2x)}{\tan \pi x}$.

8. $\lim\limits_{x \to +\infty} \dfrac{\cosh (x + 1)}{e^x}$.

9. $\lim\limits_{x \to +\infty} \dfrac{a^x}{x^b}, \qquad a > 1$.

10. $\lim\limits_{x \to \frac{1}{2}\pi} \dfrac{\tan x - 5}{\sec x + 4}$.

11. $\lim\limits_{x \to 0+} \dfrac{1}{\sqrt{x}} \left(\dfrac{1}{\sin x} - \dfrac{1}{x} \right)$.

12. $\lim\limits_{x \to +\infty} x^{1/4} \sin (1/\sqrt{x})$.

13. $\lim\limits_{x \to +\infty} (x^2 - \sqrt{x^4 - x^2 + 1}). = \dfrac{1}{2}$

14. $\lim\limits_{x \to 0+} \left[\dfrac{\log x}{(1 + x)^2} - \log\left(\dfrac{x}{1 + x}\right) \right]$.

15. $\lim\limits_{x \to 1-} (\log x) \log (1 - x)$.

16. $\lim\limits_{x \to 0+} x^{(x^x - 1)}$.

17. $\lim\limits_{x \to 0+} [x^{(x^x)} - 1]$.

18. $\lim\limits_{x \to 0-} (1 - 2^x)^{\sin x}$.

19. $\lim\limits_{x \to 0+} x^{1/\log x}$.

20. $\lim\limits_{x \to 0+} (\cot x)^{\sin x}$.

21. $\lim\limits_{x \to \frac{1}{4}\pi} (\tan x)^{\tan 2x}$.

22. $\lim\limits_{x \to 0+} \left(\log \dfrac{1}{x} \right)^x$.

23. $\lim\limits_{x \to 0+} x^{e/(1+\log x)}$.

24. $\lim\limits_{x \to 1} (2 - x)^{\tan(\pi x/2)}$.

25. $\lim\limits_{x \to 0} \left(\dfrac{1}{\log (x + \sqrt{1 + x^2})} - \dfrac{1}{\log 1(+ x)} \right) . = -\dfrac{1}{2}$

26. Find c so that

$$\lim\limits_{x \to +\infty} \left(\dfrac{x + c}{x - c} \right)^x = 4.$$

27. Prove that $(1 + x)^c = 1 + cx + o(x)$ as $x \to 0$. Use this to compute the limit of

$$\{(x^4 + x^2)^{1/2} - x^2\} \qquad \text{as } x \to +\infty.$$

28. For a certain value of c, the limit

$$\lim\limits_{x \to +\infty} \{(x^5 + 7x^4 + 2)^c - x\}$$

is finite and nonzero. Determine this c and compute the value of the limit.

29. Let $g(x) = xe^{x^2}$ and let $f(x) = \int_1^x g(t)(t + 1/t)\, dt$. Compute the limit of $f''(x)/g''(x)$ as $x \to +\infty$.

30. Let $g(x) = x^c e^{2x}$ and let $f(x) = \int_0^x e^{2t}(3t^2 + 1)^{1/2}\, dt$. For a certain value of c, the limit of $f'(x)/g'(x)$ as $x \to +\infty$ is finite and nonzero. Determine c and compute the value of the limit.

31. Let $f(x) = e^{-1/x^2}$ if $x \neq 0$, and let $f(0) = 0$.
    (a) Prove that for every $m > 0$, $f(x)/x^m \to 0$ as $x \to 0$.
    (b) Prove that for $x \neq 0$ the nth derivative of f has the form $f^{(n)}(x) = f(x)P(1/x)$, where $P(t)$ is a polynomial in t.
    (c) Prove that $f^{(n)}(0) = 0$ for all $n \geq 1$. This shows that every Taylor polynomial generated by f at 0 is the zero polynomial.

32. An amount of P dollars is deposited in a bank which pays interest at a rate r per year, compounded m times a year. (For example, $r = 0.06$ when the annual rate is 6%.) (a) Prove that the total amount of principal plus interest at the end of n years is $P(1 + r/m)^{mn}$. If r and n are kept fixed, this amount approaches the limit Pe^{rn} as $m \to +\infty$. This motivates the following definition: We say that money grows at an annual rate r when compounded continuously if the amount $f(t)$ after t years is $f(0)e^{rt}$, where t is any nonnegative real number. Approximately how long does it take for a bank account to double in value if it receives interest at an annual rate of 6% compounded (b) continuously? (c) four times a year?

8

INTRODUCTION TO DIFFERENTIAL EQUATIONS

8.1 Introduction

A large variety of scientific problems arise in which one tries to determine something from its rate of change. For example, we could try to compute the position of a moving particle from a knowledge of its velocity or acceleration. Or a radioactive substance may be disintegrating at a known rate and we may be required to determine the amount of material present after a given time. In examples like these, we are trying to determine an *unknown function* from prescribed information expressed in the form of an equation involving at least one of the derivatives of the unknown function. These equations are called *differential equations*, and their study forms one of the most challenging branches of mathematics.

Differential equations are classified under two main headings: *ordinary* and *partial*, depending on whether the unknown is a function of just *one* variable or of *two or more* variables. A simple example of an ordinary differential equation is the relation

$$(8.1) \qquad\qquad f'(x) = f(x)$$

which is satisfied, in particular, by the exponential function, $f(x) = e^x$. We shall see presently that every solution of (8.1) must be of the form $f(x) = Ce^x$, where C may be any constant.

On the other hand, an equation like

$$\frac{\partial^2 f(x, y)}{\partial x^2} + \frac{\partial^2 f(x, y)}{\partial y^2} = 0$$

is an example of a partial differential equation. This particular one, called *Laplace's equation*, appears in the theory of electricity and magnetism, fluid mechanics, and elsewhere. It has many different kinds of solutions, among which are $f(x, y) = x + 2y$, $f(x, y) = e^x \cos y$, and $f(x, y) = \log (x^2 + y^2)$.

The study of differential equations is one part of mathematics that, perhaps more than any other, has been directly inspired by mechanics, astronomy, and mathematical physics. Its history began in the 17th century when Newton, Leibniz, and the Bernoullis solved some simple differential equations arising from problems in geometry and mechanics.

These early discoveries, beginning about 1690, gradually led to the development of a now-classic "bag of tricks" for solving certain special kinds of differential equations. Although these special tricks are applicable in relatively few cases, they do enable us to solve many differential equations that arise in mechanics and geometry, so their study is of practical importance. Some of these special methods and some of the problems which they help us solve are discussed near the end of this chapter.

Experience has shown that it is difficult to obtain mathematical theories of much generality about solutions of differential equations, except for a few types. Among these are the so-called *linear* differential equations which occur in a great variety of scientific problems. The simplest types of linear differential equations and some of their applications are also discussed in this introductory chapter. A more thorough study of linear equations is carried out in Volume II.

8.2   Terminology and notation

When we work with a differential equation such as (8.1), it is customary to write y in place of $f(x)$ and y' in place of $f'(x)$, the higher derivatives being denoted by y'', y''', etc. Of course, other letters such as u, v, z, etc. are also used instead of y. By the *order* of an equation is meant the order of the highest derivative which appears. For example, (8.1) is a first-order equation which may be written as $y' = y$. The differential equation $y' = x^3 y + \sin(xy'')$ is one of second order.

In this chapter we shall begin our study with first-order equations which can be solved for y' and written as follows:

$$(8.2) \qquad\qquad y' = f(x, y),$$

where the expression $f(x, y)$ on the right has various special forms. A differentiable function $y = Y(x)$ will be called a *solution* of (8.2) on an interval I if the function Y and its derivative Y' satisfy the relation

$$Y'(x) = f[x, Y(x)]$$

for every x in I. The simplest case occurs when $f(x, y)$ is independent of y. In this case, (8.2) becomes

$$(8.3) \qquad\qquad y' = Q(x),$$

say, where Q is assumed to be a given function defined on some interval I. To solve the differential equation (8.3) means to find a primitive of Q. The second fundamental theorem of calculus tells us how to do it when Q is continuous on an open interval I. We simply integrate Q and add any constant. Thus, every solution of (8.3) is included in the formula

$$(8.4) \qquad\qquad y = \int Q(x)\, dx + C,$$

where C is any constant (usually called an arbitrary constant of integration). The differential equation (8.3) has infinitely many solutions, one for each value of C.

If it is not possible to evaluate the integral in (8.4) in terms of familiar functions, such as polynomials, rational functions, trigonometric and inverse trigonometric functions, logarithms, and exponentials, still we consider the differential equation as having been solved if the solution can be expressed in terms of integrals of known functions. In actual practice, there are various methods for obtaining approximate evaluations of integrals which lead to useful information about the solution. Automatic high-speed computing machines are often designed with this kind of problem in mind.

EXAMPLE. *Linear motion determined from the velocity.* Suppose a particle moves along a straight line in such a way that its velocity at time t is 2 sin t. Determine its position at time t.

Solution. If $Y(t)$ denotes the position at time t measured from some starting point, then the derivative $Y'(t)$ represents the velocity at time t. We are given that

$$Y'(t) = 2 \sin t.$$

Integrating, we find that

$$Y(t) = 2 \int \sin t \, dt + C = -2 \cos t + C.$$

This is all we can deduce about $Y(t)$ from a knowledge of the velocity alone; some other piece of information is needed to fix the position function. We can determine C if we know the value of Y at some particular instant. For example, if $Y(0) = 0$, then $C = 2$ and the position function is $Y(t) = 2 - 2 \cos t$. But if $Y(0) = 2$, then $C = 4$ and the position function is $Y(t) = 4 - 2 \cos t$.

In some respects the example just solved is typical of what happens in general. Somewhere in the process of solving a first-order differential equation, an integration is required to remove the derivative y' and in this step an arbitrary constant C appears. The way in which the arbitrary constant C enters into the solution will depend on the nature of the given differential equation. It may appear as an additive constant, as in Equation (8.4), but it is more likely to appear in some other way. For example, when we solve the equation $y' = y$ in Section 8.3, we shall find that every solution has the form $y = Ce^x$.

In many problems it is necessary to select from the collection of all solutions one having a prescribed value at some point. The prescribed value is called an *initial condition*, and the problem of determining such a solution is called an *initial-value problem*. This terminology originated in mechanics where, as in the above example, the prescribed value represents the displacement at some initial time.

We shall begin our study of differential equations with an important special case.

8.3 A first-order differential equation for the exponential function

The exponential function is equal to its own derivative, and the same is true of any constant multiple of the exponential. It is easy to show that these are the only functions that satisfy this property on the whole real axis.

THEOREM 8.1. *If C is a given real number, there is one and only one function f which satisfies the differential equation*

$$f'(x) = f(x)$$

for all real x and which also satisfies the initial condition $f(0) = C$. This function is given by the formula

$$f(x) = Ce^x.$$

Proof. It is easy to verify that the function $f(x) = Ce^x$ satisfies both the given differential equation and the given initial condition. Now we must show that this is the *only* solution.

Let $y = g(x)$ be any solution of this initial-value problem:

$$g'(x) = g(x) \qquad \text{for all } x, \qquad g(0) = C.$$

We wish to show that $g(x) = Ce^x$ or that $g(x)e^{-x} = C$. We consider the function $h(x) = g(x)e^{-x}$ and show that its derivative is always zero. The derivative of h is given by

$$h'(x) = g'(x)e^{-x} - g(x)e^{-x} = e^{-x}[g'(x) - g(x)] = 0.$$

Hence, by the zero-derivative theorem, h is constant. But $g(0) = C$ so $h(0) = g(0)e^0 = C$. . Hence, we have $h(x) = C$ for all x which means that $g(x) = Ce^x$, as required.

Theorem 8.1 is an example of an existence-uniqueness theorem. It tells us that the given initial-value problem *has* a solution (existence) and that it has *only one* solution (uniqueness). The object of much of the research in the theory of differential equations is to discover existence and uniqueness theorems for wide classes of equations.

We discuss next an important type which includes both the differential equation $y' = Q(x)$ and the equation $y' = y$ as special cases.

8.4 First-order linear differential equations

A differential equation of the form

$$(8.5) \qquad \qquad y' + P(x)y = Q(x),$$

where P and Q are given functions, is called a *first-order linear* differential equation. The terms involving the unknown function y and its derivative y' appear as a linear combination of y and y'. The functions P and Q are assumed to be continuous on some open interval I. We seek all solutions y defined on I.

First we consider the special case in which the right member, $Q(x)$, is identically zero. The equation

$$(8.6) \qquad \qquad y' + P(x)y = 0$$

is called the *homogeneous* or *reduced* equation corresponding to (8.5). We will show how to solve the homogeneous equation and then use the result to help us solve the non-homogeneous equation (8.5).

If y is nonzero on I, Equation (8.6) is equivalent to the equation

$$(8.7) \qquad \qquad \frac{y'}{y} = -P(x).$$

That is, every nonzero y which satisfies (8.6) also satisfies (8.7) and vice versa. Now suppose y is a positive function satisfying (8.7). Since the quotient y'/y is the derivative of $\log y$, Equation (8.7) becomes $D \log y = -P(x)$, from which we find $\log y = -\int P(x) \, dx + C$, so we have

$$(8.8) \qquad y = e^{-A(x)}, \qquad \text{where} \quad A(x) = \int P(x) \, dx - C.$$

In other words, if there is a positive solution of (8.6), it must necessarily have the form (8.8) for some C. But now it is easy to verify that every function in (8.8) is a solution of the homogeneous equation (8.6). In fact, we have

$$y' = -e^{-A(x)}A'(x) = -P(x)e^{-A(x)} = -P(x)y.$$

Thus, we have found all positive solutions of (8.6). But now it is easy to describe all solutions. We state the result as an existence-uniqueness theorem.

THEOREM 8.2. *Assume P is continuous on an open interval I. Choose any point a in I and let b be any real number. Then there is one and only one function $y = f(x)$ which satisfies the initial-value problem*

$$(8.9) \qquad y' + P(x)y = 0, \qquad \text{with} \quad f(a) = b,$$

on the interval I. This function is given by the formula

$$(8.10) \qquad f(x) = be^{-A(x)}, \qquad \text{where} \quad A(x) = \int_a^x P(t) \, dt.$$

Proof. Let f be defined by (8.10). Then $A(a) = 0$ so $f(a) = be^0 = b$. Differentiation shows that f satisfies the differential equation in (8.9), so f is a solution of the initial-value problem. Now we must show that it is the only solution.

Let g be an arbitrary solution. We wish to show that $g(x) = be^{-A(x)}$ or that $g(x)e^{A(x)} = b$. Therefore it is natural to introduce $h(x) = g(x)e^{A(x)}$. The derivative of h is given by

$$(8.11) \qquad h'(x) = g'(x)e^{A(x)} + g(x)e^{A(x)}A'(x) = e^{A(x)}[g'(x) + P(x)g(x)].$$

Now since g satisfies the differential equation in (8.9), we have $g'(x) + P(x)g(x) = 0$ everywhere on I, so $h'(x) = 0$ for all x in I. This means that h is constant on I. Hence, we have $h(x) = h(a) = g(a)e^{A(a)} = g(a) = b$. In other words, $g(x)e^{A(x)} = b$, so $g(x) = be^{-A(x)}$, which shows that $g = f$. This completes the proof.

The last part of the foregoing proof suggests a method for solving the nonhomogeneous differential equation in (8.5). Suppose that g is any function satisfying (8.5), and let $h(x) = g(x)e^{A(x)}$ where, as above, $A(x) = \int_a^x P(t) \, dt$. Then Equation (8.11) is again valid, but since g satisfies (8.5), the formula for $h'(x)$ gives us

$$h'(x) = e^{A(x)}Q(x).$$

Now we may invoke the second fundamental theorem to write

$$h(x) = h(a) + \int_a^x e^{A(t)}Q(t)\,dt \ .$$

Hence, since $h(a) = g(a)$, every solution g of (8.5) has the form

(8.12) $$g(x) = e^{-A(x)}h(x) = g(a)e^{-A(x)} + e^{-A(x)}\int_a^x Q(t)e^{A(t)}\,dt \ .$$

Conversely, by direct differentiation of (8.12), it is easy to verify that each such g is a solution of (8.5), so we have found *all* solutions. We state the result as follows.

THEOREM 8.3.   *Assume P and Q are continuous on an open interval I. Choose any point a in I and let b be any real number. Then there is one and only one function $y = f(x)$ which satisfies the initial-value problem*

$$y' + P(x)y = Q(x), \qquad \text{with}\ \ f(a) = b \ ,$$

on the interval I. This function is given by the formula

$$f(x) = be^{-A(x)} + e^{-A(x)}\int_a^x Q(t)e^{A(t)}\,dt \ ,$$

where $A(x) = \int_a^x P(t)\,dt$.

Up to now the word "interval" has meant a bounded interval of the form (a, b), $[a, b]$, $[a, b)$, or $(a, b]$, with $a < b$. It is convenient to consider also unbounded intervals. They are denoted by the symbols $(a, +\infty)$, $(-\infty, a)$, $[a, +\infty)$ and $(-\infty, a]$, and they are defined as follows:

$$(a, +\infty) = \{x \mid x > a\} \ , \qquad (-\infty, a) = \{x \mid x < a\} \ ,$$

$$[a, +\infty) = \{x \mid x \geq a\} \ , \qquad (-\infty, a] = \{x \mid x \leq a\} \ .$$

In addition, it is convenient to refer to the collection of *all* real numbers as the interval $(-\infty, +\infty)$. Thus, when we discuss a differential equation or its solution over an interval I, it will be understood that I is one of the nine types just described.

EXAMPLE.   Find all solutions of the first-order differential equation $xy' + (1 - x)y = e^{2x}$ on the interval $(0, +\infty)$.

Solution. First we transform the equation to the form $y' + P(x)y = Q(x)$ by dividing through by x. This gives us

$$y' + \left(\frac{1}{x} - 1\right)y = \frac{e^{2x}}{x} \ ,$$

so $P(x) = 1/x - 1$ and $Q(x) = e^{2x}/x$. Since P and Q are continuous on the interval $(0, +\infty)$, there is a unique solution $y = f(x)$ satisfying any given initial condition of the form $f(a) = b$. We shall express all solutions in terms of the initial value at the point $a = 1$. In other words, given any real number b, we will determine all solutions for which $f(1) = b$.

First we compute

$$A(x) = \int_1^x P(t)\, dt = \int_1^x \left(\frac{1}{t} - 1 \right) dt = \log x - (x - 1).$$

Hence we have $e^{-A(x)} = e^{x-1-\log x} = e^{x-1}/x$, and $e^{A(t)} = te^{1-t}$, so Theorem 8.3 tells us that the solution is given by the formula

$$f(x) = b\,\frac{e^{x-1}}{x} + \frac{e^{x-1}}{x} \int_1^x \frac{e^{2t}}{t} te^{1-t}\, dt = b\,\frac{e^{x-1}}{x} + \frac{e^x}{x} \int_1^x e^t\, dt$$

$$= b\,\frac{e^{x-1}}{x} + \frac{e^x}{x}(e^x - e) = b\,\frac{e^{x-1}}{x} + \frac{e^{2x}}{x} - \frac{e^{x+1}}{x}.$$

We can also write this in the form

$$f(x) = \frac{e^{2x} + Ce^x}{x},$$

where $C = be^{-1} - e$. This gives all solutions on the interval $(0, +\infty)$.

It may be of interest to study the behavior of the solutions as $x \to 0$. If we approximate the exponential by its linear Taylor polynomial, we find that $e^{2x} = 1 + 2x + o(x)$ and $e^x = 1 + x + o(x)$ as $x \to 0$, so we have

$$f(x) = \frac{(1 + C) + (2 + C)x + o(x)}{x} = \frac{1 + C}{x} + (2 + C) + o(1).$$

Therefore, only the solution with $C = -1$ tends to a finite limit as $x \to 0$, this limit being 1.

8.5 Exercises

In each of Exercises 1 through 5, solve the initial-value problem on the specified interval.

1. $y' - 3y = e^{2x}$ on $(-\infty, +\infty)$, with $y = 0$ when $x = 0$.
2. $xy' - 2y = x^5$ on $(0, +\infty)$, with $y = 1$ when $x = 1$.
3. $y' + y \tan x = \sin 2x$ on $(-\frac{1}{2}\pi, \frac{1}{2}\pi)$, with $y = 2$ when $x = 0$.
4. $y' + xy = x^3$ on $(-\infty, +\infty)$, with $y = 0$ when $x = 0$.
5. $\dfrac{dx}{dt} + x = e^{2t}$ on $(-\infty, +\infty)$, with $x = 1$ when $t = 0$.
6. Find all solutions of $y' \sin x + y \cos x = 1$ on the interval $(0, \pi)$. Prove that exactly one of these solutions has a finite limit as $x \to 0$, and another has a finite limit as $x \to \pi$.
7. Find all solutions of $x(x + 1)y' + y = x(x + 1)^2 e^{-x^2}$ on the interval $(-1, 0)$. Prove that all solutions approach 0 as $x \to -1$, but that only one of them has a finite limit as $x \to 0$.
8. Find all solutions of $y' + y \cot x = 2 \cos x$ on the interval $(0, \pi)$. Prove that exactly one of these is also a solution on $(-\infty, +\infty)$.

9. Find all solutions of $(x - 2)(x - 3)y' + 2y = (x - 1)(x - 2)$ on each of the following intervals: (a) $(-\infty, 2)$; (b) $(2, 3)$; (c) $(3, +\infty)$. Prove that all solutions tend to a finite limit as $x \to 2$, but that none has a finite limit as $x \to 3$.

10. Let $s(x) = (\sin x)/x$ if $x \neq 0$, and let $s(0) = 1$. Define $T(x) = \int_0^x s(t)\,dt$. Prove that the function $f(x) = xT(x)$ satisfies the differential equation $xy' - y = x \sin x$ on the interval $(-\infty, +\infty)$ and find all solutions on this interval. Prove that the differential equation has no solution satisfying the initial condition $f(0) = 1$, and explain why this does not contradict Theorem 8.3.

11. Prove that there is exactly one function f, continuous on the positive real axis, such that

$$f(x) = 1 + \frac{1}{x} \int_1^x f(t)\,dt$$

for all $x > 0$ and find this function.

12. The function f defined by the equation

$$f(x) = xe^{(1-x^2)/2} - xe^{-x^2/2} \int_1^x t^{-2}e^{t^2/2}\,dt$$

for $x > 0$ has the properties that (i) it is continuous on the positive real axis, and (ii) it satisfies the equation

$$f(x) = 1 - x \int_1^x f(t)\,dt$$

for all $x > 0$. Find all functions with these two properties.

The Bernoulli equation. A differential equation of the form $y' + P(x)y = Q(x)y^n$, where n is not 0 or 1, is called a *Bernoulli equation.* This equation is nonlinear because of the presence of y^n. The next exercise shows that it can always be transformed into a linear first-order equation for a new unknown function v, where $v = y^k$, $k = 1 - n$.

13. Let k be a nonzero constant. Assume P and Q are continuous on an interval I. If $a \in I$ and if b is any real number, let $v = g(x)$ be the unique solution of the initital-value problem $v' + kP(x)v = kQ(x)$ on I, with $g(a) = b$. If $n \neq 1$ and $k = 1 - n$, prove that a function $y = f(x)$, which is not identically zero on I, is a solution of the initial-value problem

$$y' + P(x)y = Q(x)y^n \quad \text{on} \quad I, \quad \text{with} \quad f(a)^k = b$$

if and only if the kth power of f is equal to g on I.

In each of Exercises 14 through 17, solve the initial-value problem on the specified interval.

14. $y' - 4y = 2e^x y^{1/2}$ on $(-\infty, +\infty)$, with $y = 2$ when $x = 0$.

15. $y' - y = -y^2(x^2 + x + 1)$ on $(-\infty, +\infty)$, with $y = 1$ when $x = 0$.

16. $xy' - 2y = 4x^3 y^{1/2}$ on $(-\infty, +\infty)$, with $y = 0$ when $x = 1$.

17. $xy' + y = y^2 x^2 \log x$ on $(0, +\infty)$, with $y = \frac{1}{2}$ when $x = 1$.

18. $2xyy' + (1 + x)y^2 = e^x$ on $(0, +\infty)$, with (a) $y = \sqrt{e}$ when $x = 1$; (b) $y = -\sqrt{e}$ when $x = 1$; (c) a finite limit as $x \to 0$.

19. An equation of the form $y' + P(x)y + Q(x)y^2 = R(x)$ is called a *Riccati equation.* (There is no known method for solving the general Riccati equation.) Prove that if u is a known solution of this equation, then there are further solutions of the form $y = u + 1/v$, where v satisfies a first-order linear equation.

20. The Riccati equation $y' + y + y^2 = 2$ has two constant solutions. Start with each of these and use Exercise 19 to find further solutions as follows: (a) If $-2 \leq b < 1$, find a solution on $(-\infty, +\infty)$ for which $y = b$ when $x = 0$. (b) If $b \geq 1$ or $b < -2$, find a solution on the interval $(-\infty, +\infty)$ for which $y = b$ when $x = 0$.

8.6 Some physical problems leading to first-order linear differential equations

In this section we will discuss various physical problems that can be formulated mathematically as differential equations. In each case, the differential equation represents an idealized simplification of the physical problem and is called a *mathematical model* of the problem. The differential equation occurs as a translation of some physical law, such as Newton's second law of motion, a "conservation" law, etc. Our purpose here is not to justify the choice of the mathematical model but rather to deduce logical consequences from it. Each model is only an approximation to reality, and its justification properly belongs to the science from which the problem emanates. If intuition or experimental evidence agrees with the results deduced mathematically, then we feel that the model is a useful one. If not, we try to find a more suitable model.

EXAMPLE 1. *Radioactive decay.* Although various radioactive elements show marked differences in their rates of decay, they all seem to share a common property—the rate at which a given substance decomposes at any instant is proportional to the amount present at that instant. If we denote by $y = f(t)$ the amount present at time t, the derivative $y' = f'(t)$ represents the rate of change of y at time t, and the "law of decay" states that

$$y' = -ky,$$

where k is a positive constant (called the *decay constant*) whose actual value depends on the particular element that is decomposing. The minus sign comes in because y decreases as t increases, and hence y' is always negative. The differential equation $y' = -ky$ is the mathematical model used for problems concerning radioactive decay. Every solution $y = f(t)$ of this differential equation has the form

(8.13) $$f(t) = f(0)e^{-kt}.$$

Therefore, to determine the amount present at time t, we need to know the initial amount $f(0)$ and the value of the decay constant k.

It is interesting to see what information can be deduced from (8.13), without knowing the exact value of $f(0)$ or of k. First we observe that there is no finite time t at which $f(t)$ will be zero because the exponential e^{-kt} never vanishes. Therefore, it is not useful to study the "total lifetime" of a radioactive substance. However, it is possible to determine the time required for any particular *fraction* of a sample to decay. The fraction $\frac{1}{2}$ is usually chosen for convenience and the time T at which $f(T)/f(0) = \frac{1}{2}$ is called the *half-life* of the substance. This can be determined by solving the equation $e^{-kT} = \frac{1}{2}$ for T. Taking logarithms, we get $-kT = -\log 2$ or $T = (\log 2)/k$. This equation relates the half-life to the decay constant. Since we have

$$\frac{f(t + T)}{f(t)} = \frac{f(0)e^{-k(t+T)}}{f(0)e^{-kt}} = e^{-kT} = \frac{1}{2},$$

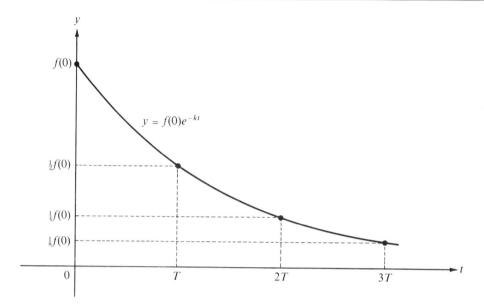

FIGURE 8.1   Radioactive decay with half-life T.

we see that the half-life is the same for every sample of a given material. Figure 8.1 illustrates the general shape of a radioactive decay curve.

EXAMPLE 2. *Falling body in a resisting medium.* A body of mass m is dropped from rest from a great height in the earth's atmosphere. Assume that it falls in a straight line and that the only forces acting on it are the earth's gravitational attraction (mg, where g is the acceleration due to gravity, assumed to be constant) and a resisting force (due to air resistance) which is proportional to its velocity. It is required to discuss the resulting motion.

Let $s = f(t)$ denote the distance the body has fallen at time t and let $v = s' = f'(t)$ denote its velocity. The assumption that it falls from rest means that $f'(0) = 0$.

There are two forces acting on the body, a downward force mg (due to its weight) and an upward force $-kv$ (due to air resistance), where k is some positive constant. Newton's second law states that the net sum of the forces acting on the body at any instant is equal to the product of its mass m and its acceleration. If we denote the acceleration at time t by a, then $a = v' = s''$ and Newton's law gives us the equation

$$ma = mg - kv .$$

This can be considered as a second-order differential equation for the displacement s or as a first-order equation for the velocity v. As a first-order equation for v, it is linear and can be written in the form

$$v' + \frac{k}{m} v = g .$$

This equation is the mathematical model of the problem. Since $v = 0$ when $t = 0$, the unique solution of the differential equation is given by the formula

$$(8.14) \qquad v = e^{-kt/m} \int_0^t g e^{ku/m} \, du = \frac{mg}{k} \left(1 - e^{-kt/m} \right).$$

Note that $v \to mg/k$ as $t \to +\infty$. If we differentiate Equation (8.14), we find that the acceleration at every instant is $a = g e^{-kt/m}$. Note that $a \to 0$ as $t \to +\infty$. Interpreted physically, this means that the air resistance tends to balance out the force of gravity.

Since $v = s'$, Equation (8.14) is itself a differential equation for the displacement s, and it may be integrated directly to give

$$s = \frac{mg}{k} t + \frac{gm^2}{k^2} e^{-kt/m} + C.$$

Since $s = 0$ when $t = 0$, we find that $C = -gm^2/k^2$ and the equation of motion becomes

$$s = \frac{mg}{k} t + \frac{gm^2}{k^2} (e^{-kt/m} - 1).$$

If the initial velocity is v_0 when $t = 0$, formula (8.14) for the velocity at time t must be replaced by

$$v = \frac{mg}{k} (1 - e^{-kt/m}) + v_0 e^{-kt/m}.$$

It is interesting to note that for *every* initial velocity (positive, negative, or zero), the limiting velocity, as t increases without bound, is mg/k, a number independent of v_0. The reader should convince himself, on physical grounds, that this seems reasonable.

EXAMPLE 3. *A cooling problem.* The rate at which a body changes temperature is proportional to the difference between its temperature and that of the surrounding medium. (This is called *Newton's law of cooling.*) If $y = f(t)$ is the (unknown) temperature of the body at time t and if $M(t)$ denotes the (known) temperature of the surrounding medium, Newton's law leads to the differential equation

$$(8.15) \qquad y' = -k[y - M(t)] \qquad \text{or} \qquad y' + ky = kM(t),$$

where k is a positive constant. This first-order linear equation is the mathematical model we use for cooling problems. The unique solution of the equation satisfying the initial condition $f(a) = b$ is given by the formula

$$(8.16) \qquad f(t) = b e^{-kt} + e^{-kt} \int_a^t k M(u) e^{ku} \, du.$$

Consider now a specific problem in which a body cools from $200°$ to $100°$ in 40 minutes while immersed in a medium whose temperature is kept constant, say $M(t) = 10°$. If we measure t in minutes and $f(t)$ in degrees, we have $f(0) = 200$ and Equation (8.16) gives us

(8.17) $$f(t) = 200e^{-kt} + 10ke^{-kt} \int_0^t e^{ku}\,du$$

$$= 200e^{-kt} + 10(1 - e^{-kt}) = 10 + 190e^{-kt}.$$

We can compute k from the information that $f(40) = 100$. Putting $t = 40$ in (8.17), we find $90 = 190e^{-40k}$, so $-40k = \log(90/190)$, $k = \frac{1}{40}(\log 19 - \log 9)$.

Next, let us compute the time required for this same material to cool from $200°$ to $100°$ if the temperature of the medium is kept at $5°$. Then Equation (8.16) is valid with the same constant k but with $M(u) = 5$. Instead of (8.17), we get the formula

$$f(t) = 5 + 195e^{-kt}.$$

To find the time t for which $f(t) = 100$, we get $95 = 195e^{-kt}$, so $-kt = \log(95/195) = \log(19/39)$, and hence

$$t = \frac{1}{k}(\log 39 - \log 19) = 40\,\frac{\log 39 - \log 19}{\log 19 - \log 9}.$$

From a four-place table of natural logarithms, we find $\log 39 = 3.6636$, $\log 19 = 2.9444$, and $\log 9 = 2.1972$ so, with slide-rule accuracy, we get $t = 40(0.719)/(0.747) = 38.5$ minutes.

The differential equation in (8.15) tells us that the rate of cooling decreases considerably as the temperature of the body begins to approach the temperature of the medium. To illustrate, let us find the time required to cool the same substance from $100°$ to $10°$ with the medium kept at $5°$. The calculation leads to $\log(5/95) = -kt$, or

$$t = \frac{1}{k}\log 19 = 40\,\frac{\log 19}{\log 19 - \log 9} = \frac{40(2.944)}{0.747} = 158 \text{ minutes}.$$

Note that the temperature drop from $100°$ to $10°$ takes more than four times as long as the change from $200°$ to $100°$.

EXAMPLE 4. *A dilution problem.* A tank contains 100 gallons of brine whose concentration is 2.5 pounds of salt per gallon. Brine containing 2 pounds of salt per gallon runs into the tank at a rate of 5 gallons per minute and the mixture (kept uniform by stirring) runs out at the same rate. Find the amount of salt in the tank at every instant.

Let $y = f(t)$ denote the number of pounds of salt in the tank at time t minutes after mixing begins. There are two factors which cause y to change, the incoming brine which brings salt in at a rate of 10 pounds per minute and the outgoing mixture which removes salt at a rate of $5(y/100)$ pounds per minute. (The fraction $y/100$ represents the concentration at time t.) Hence the differential equation is

$$y' = 10 - \tfrac{1}{20}y \qquad \text{or} \qquad y' + \tfrac{1}{20}y = 10.$$

This linear equation is the mathematical model for our problem. Since $y = 250$ when

$t = 0$, the unique solution is given by the formula

$$(8.18) \qquad y = 250e^{-t/20} + e^{-t/20} \int_0^t 10e^{u/20}\, du = 200 + 50e^{-t/20}.$$

This equation shows that $y > 200$ for all t and that $y \to 200$ as t increases without bound. Hence, the minimum salt content is 200 pounds. (This could also have been guessed from the statement of the problem.) Equation (8.18) can be solved for t in terms of y to yield

$$t = 20 \log \left(\frac{50}{y - 200} \right).$$

This enables us to find the time at which the salt content will be a given amount y, provided that $200 < y < 250$.

EXAMPLE 5. *Electric circuits.* Figure 8.2(a), page 318, shows an electric circuit which has an electromotive force, a resistor, and an inductor connected in series. The electromotive force produces a voltage which causes an electric current to flow in the circuit. If the reader is not familiar with electric circuits, he should not be concerned. For our purposes, all we need to know about the circuit is that the voltage, denoted by $V(t)$, and the current, denoted by $I(t)$, are functions of time t related by a differential equation of the form

$$(8.19) \qquad LI'(t) + RI(t) = V(t).$$

Here L and R are assumed to be positive constants. They are called, respectively, the *inductance* and *resistance* of the circuit. The differential equation is a mathematical formulation of a conservation law known as *Kirchhoff's voltage law*, and it serves as a mathematical model for the circuit.

Those readers unfamiliar with circuits may find it helpful to think of the current as being analogous to water flowing in a pipe. The electromotive force (usually a battery or a generator) is analogous to a pump which causes the water to flow; the resistor is analogous to friction in the pipe, which tends to oppose the flow; and the inductance is a stabilizing influence which tends to oppose sudden changes in the current due to sudden changes in the voltage.

The usual type of question concerning such circuits is this: If a given voltage $V(t)$ is impressed on the circuit, what is the resulting current $I(t)$? Since we are dealing with a first-order linear differential equation, the solution is a routine matter. If $I(0)$ denotes the initial current at time $t = 0$, the equation has the solution

$$I(t) = I(0)e^{-Rt/L} + e^{-Rt/L} \int_0^t \frac{V(x)}{L} e^{Rx/L}\, dx.$$

An important special case occurs when the impressed voltage is constant, say $V(t) = E$ for all t. In this case, the integration is easy to perform and we are led to the formula

$$I(t) = \frac{E}{R} + \left(I(0) - \frac{E}{R} \right) e^{-Rt/L}.$$

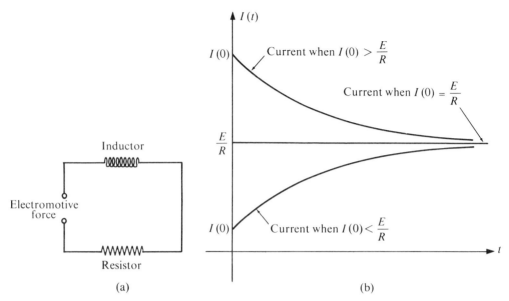

FIGURE 8.2   (a) Diagram for a simple series circuit.   (b) The current resulting from
a constant impressed voltage E.

This shows that the nature of the solution depends on the relation between the initial current $I(0)$ and the quotient E/R. If $I(0) = E/R$, the exponential term is not present and the current is constant, $I(t) = E/R$. If $I(0) > E/R$, the coefficient of the exponential term is positive and the current decreases to the limiting value E/R as $t \to +\infty$. If $I(0) < E/R$, the current increases to the limiting value E/R. The constant E/R is called the *steady-state current*, and the exponential term $[I(0) - E/R]e^{-Rt/L}$ is called the *transient current*. Examples are illustrated in Figure 8.2(b).

The foregoing examples illustrate the unifying power and practical utility of differential equations. They show how several different types of physical problems may lead to exactly the same type of differential equation.

The differential equation in (8.19) is of special interest because it suggests the possibility of attacking a wide variety of physical problems by electrical means. For example, suppose a physical problem leads to a differential equation of the form

$$y' + ay = Q,$$

where a is a positive constant and Q is a known function. We can try to construct an electric circuit with inductance L and resistance R in the ratio $R/L = a$ and then try to impress a voltage LQ on the circuit. We would then have an electric circuit with exactly the same mathematical model as the physical problem. Thus, we can hope to get numerical data about the solution of the physical problem by making measurements of current in the electric circuit. This idea has been used in practice and has led to the development of the *analog computer*.

8.7 Exercises

In the following exercises, use an appropriate first-order differential equation as a mathematical model of the problem.

1. The half-life for radium is approximately 1600 years. Find what percentage of a given quantity of radium disintegrates in 100 years.

2. If a strain of bacteria grows at a rate proportional to the amount present and if the population doubles in one hour, by how much will it increase at the end of two hours?

3. Denote by $y = f(t)$ the amount of a substance present at time t. Assume it disintegrates at a rate proportional to the amount present. If n is a positive integer, the number T for which $f(T) = f(0)/n$ is called the $1/n$th life of the substance.
   (a) Prove that the $1/n$th life is the same for every sample of a given material, and compute T in terms of n and the decay constant k.
   (b) If a and b are given, prove that f can be expressed in the form

$$f(t) = f(a)^{w(t)} f(b)^{1-w(t)}$$

and determine $w(t)$. This shows that the amount present at time t is a weighted geometric mean of the amounts present at two instants $t = a$ and $t = b$.

4. A man wearing a parachute jumps from a great height. The combined weight of man and parachute is 192 pounds. Let $v(t)$ denote his speed (in feet per second) at time t seconds after falling. During the first 10 seconds, before the parachute opens, assume the air resistance is $\frac{3}{4}v(t)$ pounds. Thereafter, while the parachute is open, assume the resistance is $12v(t)$ pounds. Assume the acceleration of gravity is 32 ft/sec^2 and find explicit formulas for the speed $v(t)$ at time t. (You may use the approximation $e^{-5/4} = 37/128$ in your calculations.)

5. Refer to Example 2 of Section 8.6. Use the chain rule to write

$$\frac{dv}{dt} = \frac{ds}{dt}\frac{dv}{ds} = v\frac{dv}{ds}$$

and thus show that the differential equation in the example can be expressed as follows:

$$\frac{ds}{dv} = \frac{bv}{c - v},$$

where $b = m/k$ and $c = gm/k$. Integrate this equation to express s in terms of v. Check your result with the formulas for v and s derived in the example.

6. Modify Example 2 of Section 8.6 by assuming the air resistance is proportional to v^2. Show that the differential equation can be put in each of the following forms:

$$\frac{ds}{dv} = \frac{m}{k}\frac{v}{c^2 - v^2}; \qquad \frac{dt}{dv} = \frac{m}{k}\frac{1}{c^2 - v^2},$$

where $c = \sqrt{mg/k}$. Integrate each of these and obtain the following formulas for v:

$$v^2 = \frac{mg}{k}(1 - e^{-2ks/m}); \qquad v = c\frac{e^{bt} - e^{-bt}}{e^{bt} + e^{-bt}} = c \tanh bt,$$

where $b = \sqrt{kg/m}$. Determine the limiting value of v as $t \to +\infty$.

7. A body in a room at 60° cools from 200° to 120° in half an hour.
   (a) Show that its temperature after t minutes is $60 + 140e^{-kt}$, where $k = (\log 7 - \log 3)/30$.
   (b) Show that the time t required to reach a temperature of T degrees is given by the formula $t = [\log 140 - \log (T - 60)]/k$, where $60 < T \le 200$.
   (c) Find the time at which the temperature is 90°.
   (d) Find a formula for the temperature of the body at time t if the room temperature is not kept constant but falls at a rate of 1° each ten minutes. Assume the room temperature is 60° when the body temperature is 200°.

8. A thermometer has been stored in a room whose temperature is 75°. Five minutes after being taken outdoors it reads 65°. After another five minutes, it reads 60°. Compute the outdoor temperature.

9. In a tank are 100 gallons of brine containing 50 pounds of dissolved salt. Water runs into the tank at the rate of 3 gallons per minute, and the concentration is kept uniform by stirring. How much salt is in the tank at the end of one hour if the mixture runs out at a rate of 2 gallons per minute?

10. Refer to Exercise 9. Suppose the bottom of the tank is covered with a mixture of salt and insoluble material. Assume that the salt dissolves at a rate proportional to the difference between the concentration of the solution and that of a saturated solution (3 pounds of salt per gallon), and that if the water were fresh 1 pound of salt would dissolve per minute. How much salt will be in solution at the end of one hour?

11. Consider an electric circuit like that in Example 5 of Section 8.6. Assume the electromotive force is an alternating current generator which produces a voltage $V(t) = E \sin \omega t$, where E and ω are positive constants (ω is the Greek letter *omega*). If $I(0) = 0$, prove that the current has the form

$$I(t) = \frac{E}{\sqrt{R^2 + \omega^2 L^2}} \sin (\omega t - \alpha) + \frac{E \omega L}{R^2 + \omega^2 L^2} e^{-Rt/L},$$

where α depends only on ω, L, and R. Show that $\alpha = 0$ when $L = 0$.

12. Refer to Example 5 of Section 8.6. Assume the impressed voltage is a step function defined as follows: $E(t) = E$ if $a \le t \le b$, where $a > 0$; $E(t) = 0$ for all other t. If $I(0) = 0$ prove that the current is given by the following formulas: $I(t) = 0$ if $t \le a$;

$$I(t) = \frac{E}{R}(1 - e^{-R(t-a)/L}) \quad \text{if} \quad a \le t \le b; \qquad I(t) = \frac{E}{R} e^{-Rt/L} (e^{Rb/L} - e^{Ra/L}) \quad \text{if} \quad t \ge b.$$

Make a sketch indicating the nature of the graph of I.

Population growth. In a study of the growth of a population (whether human, animal, or bacterial), the function which counts the number x of individuals present at time t is necessarily a *step function* taking on only integer values. Therefore the true *rate of growth* dx/dt is zero (when t lies in an open interval where x is constant), or else the derivative dx/dt does not exist (when x jumps from one integer to another). Nevertheless, useful information can often be obtained if we assume that the population x is a continuous function of t with a continuous derivative dx/dt at each instant. We then postulate various "laws of growth" for the population, depending on the factors in the environment which may stimulate or hinder growth.

For example, if environment has little or no effect, it seems reasonable to assume that the rate of growth is proportional to the amount present. The simplest kind of growth law takes the form

(8.20)
$$\frac{dx}{dt} = kx,$$

where k is a constant that depends on the particular kind of population. Conditions may develop which cause the factor k to change with time, and the growth law (8.20) can be generalized as follows:

$$(8.21) \qquad \frac{dx}{dt} = k(t)x.$$

If, for some reason, the population cannot exceed a certain maximum M (for example, because the food supply may be exhausted), we may reasonably suppose that the rate of growth is jointly proportional to both x and $M - x$. Thus we have a second type of growth law:

$$(8.22) \qquad \frac{dx}{dt} = kx(M - x),$$

where, as in (8.21), k may be constant or, more generally, k may change with time. Technological improvements may tend to increase or decrease the value of M slowly, and hence we can generalize (8.22) even further by allowing M to change with time.

13. Express x as a function of t for each of the "growth laws" in (8.20) and (8.22) (with k and M both constant). Show that the result for (8.22) can be expressed as follows:

$$(8.23) \qquad x = \frac{M}{1 + e^{-\alpha(t-t_1)}},$$

where α is a constant and t_1 is the time at which $x = M/2$.

14. Assume the growth law in formula (8.23) of Exercise 13, and suppose a census is taken at three equally spaced times t_1, t_2, t_3, the resulting numbers being x_1, x_2, x_3. Show that this suffices to determine M and that, in fact, we have

$$(8.24) \qquad M = x_2 \frac{x_3(x_2 - x_1) - x_1(x_3 - x_2)}{x_2^2 - x_1 x_3}.$$

15. Derive a formula that generalizes (8.23) of Exercise 13 for the growth law (8.22) when k is not necessarily constant. Express the result in terms of the time t_0 for which $x = M/2$.

16. The Census Bureau reported the following population figures (in millions) for the United States at ten-year intervals from 1790 to 1950: 3.9, 5.3, 7.2, 9.6, 12.9, 17, 23, 31, 39, 50, 63, 76, 92, 108, 122, 135, 150.
    (a) Use Equation (8.24) to determine a value of M on the basis of the census figures for 1790, 1850, and 1910.
    (b) Same as (a) for the years 1910, 1930, 1950.
    (c) On the basis of your calculations in (a) and (b), would you be inclined to accept or reject the growth law (8.23) for the population of the United States?

17. (a) Plot a graph of $\log x$ as a function of t, where x denotes the population figures quoted in Exercise 16. Use this graph to show that the growth law (8.20) was very nearly satisfied from 1790 to 1910. Determine a reasonable average value of k for this period.
    (b) Determine a reasonable average value of k for the period from 1920 to 1950, assume that the growth law (8.20) will hold for this k, and predict the United States population for the years 2000 and 2050.

18. The presence of toxins in a certain medium destroys a strain of bacteria at a rate jointly proportional to the number of bacteria present and to the amount of toxin. If there were no

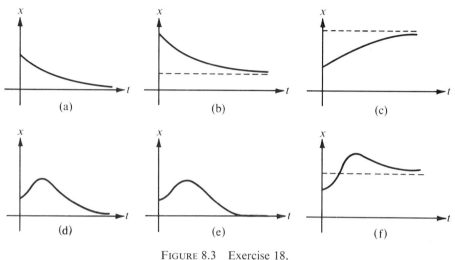

FIGURE 8.3   Exercise 18.

toxins present, the bacteria would grow at a rate proportional to the amount present. Let x denote the number of living bacteria present at time t. Assume that the amount of toxin is increasing at a constant rate and that the production of toxin begins at time $t = 0$. Set up a differential equation for x. Solve the differential equation. One of the curves shown in Figure 8.3 best represents the general behavior of x as a function of t. State your choice and explain your reasoning.

8.8 Linear equations of second order with constant coefficients

A differential equation of the form

$$y'' + P_1(x)y' + P_2(x)y = R(x)$$

is said to be a *linear equation of second order*. The functions P_1 and P_2 which multiply the unknown function y and its derivative y' are called the *coefficients* of the equation.

For first-order linear equations, we proved an existence-uniqueness theorem and determined all solutions by an explicit formula. Although there is a corresponding existence-uniqueness theorem for the general second-order linear equation, there is no explicit formula which gives all solutions, except in some special cases. A study of the general linear equation of second order is undertaken in Volume II. Here we treat only the case in which the coefficients P_1 and P_2 are constants. When the right-hand member $R(x)$ is identically zero, the equation is said to be *homogeneous*.

The homogeneous linear equation with constant coefficients was the first differential equation of a general type to be completely solved. A solution was first published by Euler in 1743. Apart from its historical interest, this equation arises in a great variety of applied problems, so its study is of practical importance. Moreover, we can give explicit formulas for all the solutions.

Consider a homogeneous linear equation with constant coefficients which we write as follows:

$$y'' + ay' + by = 0 .$$

We seek solutions on the entire real axis $(-\infty, +\infty)$. One solution is the constant function $y = 0$. This is called the *trivial* solution. We are interested in finding nontrivial solutions, and we begin our study with some special cases for which nontrivial solutions can be found by inspection. In all these cases, the coefficient of y' is zero, and the equation has the form $y'' + by = 0$. We shall find that solving this special equation is tantamount to solving the general case.

8.9 Existence of solutions of the equation $y'' + by = 0$

EXAMPLE 1. *The equation $y'' = 0$.* Here both coefficients a and b are zero, and we can easily determine all solutions. Assume y is any function satisfying $y'' = 0$ on $(-\infty, +\infty)$. Then its derivative y' is constant, say $y' = c_1$. Integrating this relation, we find that y necessarily has the form

$$y = c_1 x + c_2 ,$$

where c_1 and c_2 are constants. Conversely, for any choice of constants c_1 and c_2, the linear polynomial $y = c_1 x + c_2$ satisfies $y'' = 0$, so we have found all solutions in this case.

Next we assume that $b \neq 0$ and treat separately the cases $b < 0$ and $b > 0$.

EXAMPLE 2. *The equation $y'' + by = 0$, where $b < 0$.* Since $b < 0$, we can write $b = -k^2$, where $k > 0$, and the differential equation takes the form

$$y'' = k^2 y .$$

One obvious solution is $y = e^{kx}$, and another is $y = e^{-kx}$. From these we can obtain further solutions by constructing linear combinations of the form

$$y = c_1 e^{kx} + c_2 e^{-kx},$$

where c_1 and c_2 are arbitrary constants. It will be shown presently, in Theorem 8.6, that *all* solutions are included in this formula.

EXAMPLE 3. *The equation $y'' + by = 0$, where $b > 0$.* Here we can write $b = k^2$, where $k > 0$, and the differential equation takes the form

$$y'' = -k^2 y .$$

Again we obtain some solutions by inspection. One solution is $y = \cos kx$, and another is $y = \sin kx$. From these we get further solutions by forming linear combinations,

$$y = c_1 \cos kx + c_2 \sin kx ,$$

where c_1 and c_2 are arbitrary constants. Theorem 8.6 will show that this formula includes all solutions.

8.10   Reduction of the general equation to the special case $y'' + by = 0$

The problem of solving a second-order linear equation with constant coefficients can be reduced to that of solving the special cases just discussed. There is a method for doing this that also applies to more general equations. The idea is to consider three functions y, u, and v such that $y = uv$. Differentiation gives us $y' = uv' + u'v$, and $y'' = uv'' + 2u'v' + u''v$. Now we express the combination $y'' + ay' + by$ in terms of u and v. We have

$$(8.25) \qquad y'' + ay' + by = uv'' + 2u'v' + u''v + a(uv' + u'v) + buv$$

$$= (v'' + av' + bv)u + (2v' + av)u' + vu''.$$

Next we choose v to make the coefficient of u' zero. This requires that $v' = -av/2$, so we may choose $v = e^{-ax/2}$. For this v we have $v'' = -av'/2 = a^2v/4$, and the coefficient of u in (8.25) becomes

$$v'' + av' + bv = \frac{a^2v}{4} - \frac{a^2v}{2} + bv = \frac{4b - a^2}{4}\,v\,.$$

Thus, Equation (8.25) reduces to

$$y'' + ay' + by = \left(u'' + \frac{4b - a^2}{4}\,u\right)v\,.$$

Since $v = e^{-ax/2}$, the function v is never zero, so y satisfies the differential equation $y'' + ay' + by = 0$ if and only if u satisfies $u'' + \frac{1}{4}(4b - a^2)u = 0$. Thus, we have proved the following theorem.

THEOREM 8.4.   *Let y and u be two functions such that $y = ue^{-ax/2}$. Then, on the interval $(-\infty, +\infty)$, y satisfies the differential equation $y'' + ay' + by = 0$ if and only if u satisfies the differential equation*

$$u'' + \frac{4b - a^2}{4}\,u = 0\,.$$

This theorem reduces the study of the equation $y'' + ay' + by = 0$ to the special case $y'' + by = 0$. We have exhibited nontrivial solutions of this equation but, except for the case $b = 0$, we have not yet shown that we have found *all* solutions.

8.11   Uniqueness theorem for the equation $y'' + by = 0$

The problem of determining all solutions of the equation $y'' + by = 0$ can be solved with the help of the following *uniqueness theorem*.

THEOREM 8.5.   *Assume two functions f and g satisfy the differential equation $y'' + by = 0$ on $(-\infty, +\infty)$. Assume also that f and g satisfy the initial conditions*

$$f(0) = g(0)\,, \qquad f'(0) = g'(0)\,.$$

Then $f(x) = g(x)$ for all x.

Proof. Let $h(x) = f(x) - g(x)$. We wish to prove that $h(x) = 0$ for all x. We shall do this by expressing h in terms of its Taylor polynomial approximations.

First we note that h is also a solution of the differential equation $y'' + by = 0$ and satisfies the initial conditions $h(0) = 0$, $h'(0) = 0$. Now every function y satisfying the differential equation has derivatives of every order on $(-\infty, +\infty)$ and they can be computed by repeated differentiation of the differential equation. For example, since $y'' = -by$, we have $y''' = -by'$, and $y^{(4)} = -by'' = b^2 y$. By induction we find that the derivatives of even order are given by

$$y^{(2n)} = (-1)^n b^n y \,,$$

while those of odd order are $y^{(2n-1)} = (-1)^{n-1} b^{n-1} y'$. Since $h(0)$ and $h'(0)$ are both 0, it follows that all derivatives $h^{(n)}(0)$ are zero. Therefore, each Taylor polynomial generated by h at 0 has all its coefficients zero.

Now we apply Taylor's formula with remainder (Theorem 7.6), using a polynomial approximation of odd degree $2n - 1$, and we find that

$$h(x) = E_{2n-1}(x) \,,$$

where $E_{2n-1}(x)$ is the error term in Taylor's formula. To complete the proof, we show that the error can be made arbitrarily small by taking n large enough.

We use Theorem 7.7 to estimate the size of the error term. For this we need estimates for the size of the derivative $h^{(2n)}$. Consider any finite closed interval $[-c, c]$, where $c > 0$. Since h is continuous on this interval, it is bounded there, say $|h(x)| \le M$ on $[-c, c]$. Since $h^{(2n)}(x) = (-1)^n b^n h(x)$, we have the estimate $|h^{(2n)}(x)| \le M |b|^n$ on $[-c, c]$. Theorem 7.7 gives us $|E_{2n-1}(x)| \le M |b|^n x^{2n}/(2n)!$ so, on the interval $[-c, c]$, we have the estimate

$$(8.26) \qquad 0 \le |h(x)| \le \frac{M |b|^n x^{2n}}{(2n)!} \le \frac{M |b|^n c^{2n}}{(2n)!} = \frac{M A^{2n}}{(2n)!} \,,$$

where $A = |b|^{1/2} c$. Now we show that $A^m/m!$ tends to 0 as $m \to +\infty$. This is obvious if $0 \le A \le 1$. If $A > 1$, we may write

$$\frac{A^m}{m!} = \frac{A}{1} \cdot \frac{A}{2} \cdots \frac{A}{k} \cdot \frac{A}{k+1} \cdots \frac{A}{m} \le \frac{A^k}{k!} \left(\frac{A}{k+1} \right)^{m-k} \,,$$

where $k < m$. If we choose k to be the greatest integer $\le A$, then $A < k + 1$ and the last factor tends to 0 as $m \to +\infty$. Hence $A^m/m!$ tends to 0 as $m \to \infty$, so inequality (8.26) shows that $h(x) = 0$ for every x in $[-c, c]$. But, since c is arbitrary, it follows that $h(x) = 0$ for all real x. This completes the proof.

Note: Theorem 8.5 tells us that two solutions of the differential equation $y'' + by = 0$ which have the same value and the same derivative at 0 must agree everywhere. The choice of the point 0 is not essential. The same argument shows that the theorem is also true if 0 is replaced by an arbitrary point c. In the foregoing proof, we simply use Taylor polynomial approximations at c instead of at 0.

8.12   Complete solution of the equation $y'' + by = 0$

The uniqueness theorem enables us to characterize all solutions of the differential equation $y'' + by = 0$.

THEOREM 8.6.   *Given a real number b, define two functions u_1 and u_2 on $(-\infty, +\infty)$ as follows:*
   (a) *If $b = 0$, let $u_1(x) = 1$, $u_2(x) = x$.*
   (b) *If $b < 0$, write $b = -k^2$ and define $u_1(x) = e^{kx}$, $u_2(x) = e^{-kx}$.*
   (c) *If $b > 0$, write $b = k^2$ and define $u_1(x) = \cos kx$, $u_2(x) = \sin kx$.*
Then every solution of the differential equation $y'' + by = 0$ on $(-\infty, +\infty)$ has the form

$$(8.27) \qquad\qquad y = c_1 u_1(x) + c_2 u_2(x),$$

where c_1 and c_2 are constants.

Proof. We proved in Section 8.9 that for each choice of constants c_1 and c_2 the function y given in (8.27) is a solution of the equation $y'' + by = 0$. Now we show that all solutions have this form. The case $b = 0$ was settled in Section 8.9, so we may assume that $b \neq 0$.
   The idea of the proof is this: Let $y = f(x)$ be any solution of $y'' + by = 0$. If we can show that constants c_1 and c_2 exist satisfying the pair of equations

$$(8.28) \qquad c_1 u_1(0) + c_2 u_2(0) = f(0), \qquad c_1 u_1'(0) + c_2 u_2'(0) = f'(0),$$

then both f and $c_1 u_1 + c_2 u_2$ are solutions of the differential equation $y'' + by = 0$ having the same value and the same derivative at 0. By the uniqueness theorem, it follows that $f = c_1 u_1 + c_2 u_2$.
   In case (b), we have $u_1(x) = e^{kx}$, $u_2(x) = e^{-kx}$, so $u_1(0) = u_2(0) = 1$ and $u_1'(0) = k$, $u_2'(0) = -k$. Thus the equations in (8.28) become $c_1 + c_2 = f(0)$, and $c_1 - c_2 = f'(0)/k$. They have the solution $c_1 = \frac{1}{2}f(0) + \frac{1}{2}f'(0)/k$, $c_2 = \frac{1}{2}f(0) - \frac{1}{2}f'(0)/k$.
   In case (c), we have $u_1(x) = \cos kx$, $u_2(x) = \sin kx$, so $u_1(0) = 1$, $u_2(0) = 0$, $u_1'(0) = 0$, $u_2'(0) = k$, and the solutions are $c_1 = f(0)$, and $c_2 = f'(0)/k$. Since c_1 and c_2 always exist to satisfy (8.28), the proof is complete.

8.13   Complete solution of the equation $y'' + ay' + by = 0$

Theorem 8.4 tells us that y satisfies the differential equation $y'' + ay' + by = 0$ if and only if u satisfies $u'' + \frac{1}{4}(4b - a^2)u = 0$, where $y = e^{-ax/2}u$. From Theorem 8.6 we know that the nature of each solution u depends on the algebraic sign of the coefficient of u, that is, on the algebraic sign of $4b - a^2$ or, alternatively, of $a^2 - 4b$. We call the number $a^2 - 4b$ the *discriminant* of the differential equation $y'' + ay' + by = 0$ and denote it by d. When we combine the results of Theorem 8.4 and 8.6 we obtain the following.

THEOREM 8.7.   *Let $d = a^2 - 4b$ be the discriminant of the linear differential equation $y'' + ay' + by = 0$. Then every solution of this equation on $(-\infty, +\infty)$ has the form*

$$(8.29) \qquad\qquad y = e^{-ax/2}[c_1 u_1(x) + c_2 u_2(x)],$$

where c_1 and c_2 are constants, and the functions u_1 and u_2 are determined according to the algebraic sign of the discriminant as follows:

(a) *If $d = 0$, then $u_1(x) = 1$ and $u_2(x) = x$.*

(b) *If $d > 0$, then $u_1(x) = e^{kx}$ and $u_2(x) = e^{-kx}$, where $k = \frac{1}{2}\sqrt{d}$.*

(c) *If $d < 0$, then $u_1(x) = \cos kx$ and $u_2(x) = \sin kx$, where $k = \frac{1}{2}\sqrt{-d}$.*

Note: In case (b), where the discriminant d is positive, the solution y in (8.29) is a linear combination of two exponential functions,

$$y = e^{-ax/2}(c_1 e^{kx} + c_2 e^{-kx}) = c_1 e^{r_1 x} + c_2 e^{r_2 x},$$

where

$$r_1 = -\frac{a}{2} + k = \frac{-a + \sqrt{d}}{2}, \qquad r_2 = -\frac{a}{2} - k = \frac{-a - \sqrt{d}}{2}.$$

The two numbers r_1 and r_2 have sum $r_1 + r_2 = -a$ and product $r_1 r_2 = \frac{1}{4}(a^2 - d) = b$. Therefore, they are the roots of the quadratic equation

$$r^2 + ar + b = 0.$$

This is called the *characteristic equation* associated with the differential equation

$$y'' + ay' + by = 0.$$

The number $d = a^2 - 4b$ is also called the discriminant of this quadratic equation; its algebraic sign determines the nature of the roots. If $d \geq 0$, the quadratic equation has real roots given by $(-a \pm \sqrt{d})/2$. If $d < 0$, the quadratic equation has no real roots but it does have *complex* roots r_1 and r_2. The definition of the exponential function can be extended so that $e^{r_1 x}$ and $e^{r_2 x}$ are meaningful when r_1 and r_2 are complex numbers. This extension, described in Chapter 9, is made in such a way that the linear combination in (8.29) can also be written as a linear combination of $e^{r_1 x}$ and $e^{r_2 x}$, when r_1 and r_2 are complex.

We conclude this section with some miscellaneous remarks. Since all the solutions of the differential equation $y'' + ay' + by = 0$ are contained in formula (8.29), the linear combination on the right is often called the *general solution* of the differential equation. Any solution obtained by specializing the constants c_1 and c_2 is called a *particular solution*. For example, taking $c_1 = 1$, $c_2 = 0$, and then $c_1 = 0$, $c_2 = 1$, we obtain the two particular solutions

$$v_1 = e^{-ax/2}u_1(x), \qquad v_2 = e^{-ax/2}u_2(x).$$

These two solutions are of special importance because linear combinations of them give us all solutions. Any pair of solutions with this property is called a *basis* for the set of all solutions.

A differential equation always has more than one basis. For example, the equation $y'' = 9y$ has the basis $v_1 = e^{3x}$, $v_2 = e^{-3x}$. But it also has the basis $w_1 = \cosh 3x$, $w_2 = \sinh 3x$. In fact, since $e^{3x} = w_1 + w_2$ and $e^{-3x} = w_1 - w_2$, every linear combination of e^{3x} and e^{-3x} is also a linear combination of w_1 and w_2. Hence, the pair w_1, w_2 is another basis.

It can be shown that any pair of solutions v_1 and v_2 of a differential equation $y'' + ay' + by = 0$ will be a basis if the ratio v_2/v_1 is not constant. Although we shall not need this fact, we mention it here because it is important in the theory of second-order linear equations with nonconstant coefficients. A proof is outlined in Exercise 23 of Section 8.14.

8.14 Exercises

Find all solutions of the following differential equations on $(-\infty, +\infty)$.

1. $y'' - 4y = 0$.
2. $y'' + 4y = 0$.
3. $y'' - 4y' = 0$.
4. $y'' + 4y' = 0$.
5. $y'' - 2y' + 3y = 0$.
6. $y'' + 2y' - 3y = 0$.
7. $y'' - 2y' + 2y = 0$.
8. $y'' - 2y' + 5y = 0$.
9. $y'' + 2y' + y = 0$.
10. $y'' - 2y' + y = 0$.

In Exercises 11 through 14, find the particular solution satisfying the given initial conditions.

11. $2y'' + 3y' = 0$, with $y = 1$ and $y' = 1$ when $x = 0$.
12. $y'' + 25y = 0$, with $y = -1$ and $y' = 0$ when $x = 3$.
13. $y'' - 4y' - y = 0$, with $y = 2$ and $y' = -1$ when $x = 1$.
14. $y'' + 4y' + 5y = 0$, with $y = 2$ and $y' = y''$ when $x = 0$.
15. The graph of a solution u of the differential equation $y'' - 4y' + 29y = 0$ intersects the graph of a solution v of the equation $y'' + 4y' + 13y = 0$ at the origin. The two curves have equal slopes at the origin. Determine u and v if $u'(\frac{1}{2}\pi) = 1$.
16. The graph of a solution u of the differential equation $y'' - 3y' - 4y = 0$ intersects the graph of a solution v of the equation $y'' + 4y' - 5y = 0$ at the origin. Determine u and v if the two curves have equal slopes at the origin and if

$$\lim_{x \to +\infty} \frac{v(x)^4}{u(x)} = \frac{5}{6}.$$

17. Find all values of the constant k such that the differential equation $y'' + ky = 0$ has a non-trivial solution $y = f_k(x)$ for which $f_k(0) = f_k(1) = 0$. For each permissible value of k, determine the corresponding solution $y = f_k(x)$. Consider both positive and negative values of k.
18. If (a, b) is a given point in the plane and if m is a given real number, prove that the differential equation $y'' + k^2 y = 0$ has exactly one solution whose graph passes through (a, b) and has the slope m there. Discuss also the case $k = 0$.
19. (a) Let (a_1, b_1) and (a_2, b_2) be two points in the plane such that $a_1 - a_2 \neq n\pi$, where n is an integer. Prove that there is exactly one solution of the differential equation $y'' + y = 0$ whose graph passes through these two points.
    (b) Is the statement in part (a) ever true if $a_1 - a_2$ is a multiple of π?
    (c) Generalize the result in part (a) for the equation $y'' + k^2 y = 0$. Discuss also the case $k = 0$.
20. In each case, find a linear differential equation of second order satisfied by u_1 and u_2.
    (a) $u_1(x) = e^x$, $u_2(x) = e^{-x}$.
    (b) $u_1(x) = e^{2x}$, $u_2(x) = xe^{2x}$.
    (c) $u_1(x) = e^{-x/2} \cos x$, $u_2(x) = e^{-x/2} \sin x$.
    (d) $u_1(x) = \sin(2x + 1)$, $u_2(x) = \sin(2x + 2)$.
    (e) $u_1(x) = \cosh x$, $u_2(x) = \sinh x$.

The Wronskian. Given two functions u_1 and u_2, the function W defined by $W(x) = u_1(x)u_2'(x) - u_2(x)u_1'(x)$ is called their *Wronskian*, after J. M. H. Wronski (1778–1853). The following exercises are concerned with properties of the Wronskian.

21. (a) If the Wronskian $W(x)$ of u_1 and u_2 is zero for all x in an open interval I, prove that the quotient u_2/u_1 is constant on I. In other words, if u_2/u_1 is not constant on I, then $W(c) \neq 0$ for at least one c in I.
    (b) Prove that the derivative of the Wronskian is $W' = u_1 u_2'' - u_2 u_1''$.

22. Let W be the Wronskian of two solutions u_1, u_2 of the differential equation $y'' + ay' + by = 0$, where a and b are constants.

(a) Prove that W satisfies the first-order equation $W' + aW = 0$ and hence $W(x) = W(0)e^{-ax}$. This formula shows that if $W(0) \neq 0$, then $W(x) \neq 0$ for all x.

(b) Assume u_1 is not identically zero. Prove that $W(0) = 0$ if and only if u_2/u_1 is constant.

23. Let v_1 and v_2 be any two solutions of the differential equation $y'' + ay' + by = 0$ such that v_2/v_1 is not constant.

(a) Let $y = f(x)$ be any solution of the differential equation. Use properties of the Wronskian to prove that constants c_1 and c_2 exist such that

$$c_1 v_1(0) + c_2 v_2(0) = f(0) , \qquad c_1 v_1'(0) + c_2 v_2'(0) = f'(0) .$$

(b) Prove that every solution has the form $y = c_1 v_1 + c_2 v_2$. In other words, v_1 and v_2 form a basis for the set of all solutions.

8.15 Nonhomogeneous linear equations of second order with constant coefficients

We turn now to a discussion of nonhomogeneous equations of the form

(8.30) $$y'' + ay' + by = R ,$$

where the coefficients a and b are constants but the right-hand member R is any function continuous on $(-\infty, +\infty)$. The discussion may be simplified by the use of operator notation. For any function f with derivatives f' and f'', we may define an operator L which transforms f into another function $L(f)$ defined by the equation

$$L(f) = f'' + af' + bf .$$

In operator notation, the differential equation (8.30) is written in the simpler form

$$L(y) = R .$$

It is easy to verify that $L(y_1 + y_2) = L(y_1) + L(y_2)$, and that $L(cy) = cL(y)$ for every constant c. Therefore, for every pair of constants c_1 and c_2, we have

$$L(c_1 y_1 + c_2 y_2) = c_1 L(y_1) + c_2 L(y_2) .$$

This is called the *linearity property* of the operator L.

Now suppose y_1 and y_2 are any two solutions of the equation $L(y) = R$. Since $L(y_1) = L(y_2) = R$, linearity gives us

$$L(y_2 - y_1) = L(y_2) - L(y_1) = R - R = 0 ,$$

so $y_2 - y_1$ is a solution of the homogeneous equation $L(y) = 0$. Therefore, we must have $y_2 - y_1 = c_1 v_1 + c_2 v_2$, where $c_1 v_1 + c_2 v_2$ is the general solution of the homogeneous equation, or

$$y_2 = c_1 v_1 + c_2 v_2 + y_1 .$$

This equation must be satisfied by *every* pair of solutions y_1 and y_2 of the nonhomogeneous equation $L(y) = R$. Therefore, if we can determine *one particular solution* y_1 of the non-homogeneous equation, *all* solutions are contained in the formula

$$(8.31) \qquad\qquad y = c_1 v_1 + c_2 v_2 + y_1 \,,$$

where c_1 and c_2 are arbitrary constants. Each such y is clearly a solution of $L(y) = R$ because $L(c_1 v_1 + c_2 v_2 + y_1) = L(c_1 v_1 + c_2 v_2) + L(y_1) = 0 + R = R$. Since all solutions of $L(y) = R$ are found in (8.31), the linear combination $c_1 v_1 + c_2 v_2 + y_1$ is called the *general solution* of (8.30). Thus, we have proved the following theorem.

THEOREM 8.8.   *If y_1 is a particular solution of the nonhomogeneous equation $L(y) = R$, the general solution is obtained by adding to y_1 the general solution of the corresponding homogeneous equation $L(y) = 0$.*

Theorem 8.7 tells us how to find the general solution of the homogeneous equation $L(y) = 0$. It has the form $y = c_1 v_1 + c_2 v_2$, where

$$(8.32) \qquad v_1(x) = e^{-ax/2} u_1(x) \,, \qquad v_2(x) = e^{-ax/2} u_2(x) \,,$$

the functions u_1 and u_2 being determined by the discriminant of the equation, as described in Theorem 8.7. Now we show that v_1 and v_2 can be used to construct a particular solution y_1 of the nonhomogeneous equation $L(y) = R$.

The construction involves a function W defined by the equation

$$W(x) = v_1(x) v_2'(x) - v_2(x) v_1'(x) \,.$$

This is called the *Wronskian* of v_1 and v_2 ; some of its properties are described in Exercises 21 and 22 of Section 8.14. We shall need the property that $W(x)$ is never zero. This can be proved by the methods outlined in the exercises or it can be verified directly for the particular functions v_1 and v_2 given in (8.32).

THEOREM 8.9.   *Let v_1 and v_2 be the solutions of the equation $L(y) = 0$ given by (8.32), where $L(y) = y'' + ay' + by$. Let W denote the Wronskian of v_1 and v_2. Then the nonhomogeneous equation $L(y) = R$ has a particular solution y_1 given by the formula*

$$y_1(x) = t_1(x) v_1(x) + t_2(x) v_2(x) \,,$$

where

$$(8.33) \qquad t_1(x) = -\int v_2(x) \frac{R(x)}{W(x)} \, dx \,, \qquad t_2(x) = \int v_1(x) \frac{R(x)}{W(x)} \, dx \,.$$

Proof. Let us try to find functions t_1 and t_2 such that the combination $y_1 = t_1 v_1 + t_2 v_2$ will satisfy the equation $L(y_1) = R$. We have

$$y' = t_1 v_1' + t_2 v_2' + (t_1' v_1 + t_2' v_2) \,,$$

$$y_1'' = t_1 v_1'' + t_2 v_2'' + (t_1' v_1' + t_2' v_2') + (t_1' v_1 + t_2' v_2)' \,.$$

When we form the linear combination $L(y_1) = y_1'' + ay_1' + by_1$, the terms involving t_1 and t_2 drop out because of the relations $L(v_1) = L(v_2) = 0$. The remaining terms give us the relation

$$L(y_1) = (t_1'v_1' + t_2'v_2') + (t_1'v_1 + t_2'v_2)' + a(t_1'v_1 + t_2'v_2).$$

We want to choose t_1 and t_2 so that $L(y_1) = R$. We can satisfy this equation if we choose t_1 and t_2 so that

$$t_1'v_1 + t_2'v_2 = 0 \qquad \text{and} \qquad t_1'v_1' + t_2'v_2' = R.$$

This is a pair of algebraic equations for t_1' and t_2'. The determinant of the system is the Wronskian of v_1 and v_2. Since this is never zero, the system has a solution given by

$$t_1' = -v_2 R/W \qquad \text{and} \qquad t_2' = v_1 R/W.$$

Integrating these relations, we obtain Equation (8.33), thus completing the proof.

The method by which we obtained the solution y_1 is sometimes called *variation of parameters*. It was first used by Johann Bernoulli in 1697 to solve linear equations of first order, and then by Lagrange in 1774 to solve linear equations of second order.

Note: Since the functions t_1 and t_2 in Theorem 8.9 are expressed as indefinite integrals, each of them is determined only to within an additive constant. If we add a constant c_1 to t_1 and a constant c_2 to t_2 we change the function y_1 to a new function $y_2 = y_1 + c_1 v_1 + c_2 v_2$. By linearity, we have

$$L(y_2) = L(y_1) + L(c_1 v_2 + c_2 v_2) = L(y_1),$$

so the new function y_2 is also a particular solution of the nonhomogeneous equation.

EXAMPLE 1. Find the general solution of the equation $y'' + y = \tan x$ on $(-\pi/2, \pi/2)$.

Solution. The functions v_1 and v_2 of Equation (8.32) are given by

$$v_1(x) = \cos x, \qquad v_2(x) = \sin x.$$

Their Wronskian is $W(x) = v_1(x)v_2'(x) - v_2(x)v_1'(x) = \cos^2 x + \sin^2 x = 1$. Therefore Equation (8.33) gives us

$$t_1(x) = -\int \sin x \tan x \, dx = \sin x - \log |\sec x + \tan x|,$$

and

$$t_2(x) = \int \cos x \tan x \, dx = \int \sin x \, dx = -\cos x.$$

Thus, a particular solution of the nonhomogeneous equation is

$$y_1 = t_1(x)v_1(x) + t_2(x)v_2(x) = \sin x \cos x - \cos x \log |\sec x + \tan x| - \sin x \cos x$$

$$= -\cos x \log |\sec x + \tan x|.$$

By Theorem 8.8, its general solution is

$$y = c_1 \cos x + c_2 \sin x - \cos x \log |\sec x + \tan x| \, .$$

Although Theorem 8.9 provides a general method for determining a particular solution of $L(y) = R$, special methods are available that are often easier to apply when the function R has certain special forms. In the next section we describe a method that works when R is a polynomial or a polynomial times an exponential.

8.16 Special methods for determining a particular solution of the nonhomogeneous equation $y'' + ay' + by = R$

CASE 1. The right-hand member R is a polynomial of degree n. If $b \neq 0$, we can always find a polynomial of degree n that satisfies the equation. We try a polynomial of the form

$$y_1(x) = \sum_{k=0}^{n} a_k x^k$$

with undetermined coefficients. Substituting in the differential equation $L(y) = R$ and equating coefficients of like powers of x, we may determine $a_n, a_{n-1}, \ldots, a_1, a_0$ in succession. The method is illustrated by the following example.

EXAMPLE 1. Find the general solution of the equation $y'' + y = x^3$.

Solution. The general solution of the homogeneous equation $y'' + y = 0$ is given by $y = c_1 \cos x + c_2 \sin x$. To this we must add one particular solution of the nonhomogeneous equation. Since the right member is a cubic polynomial and since the coefficient of y is nonzero, we try to find a particular solution of the form $y_1(x) = Ax^3 + Bx^2 + Cx + D$. Differentiating twice, we find that $y''(x) = 6Ax + 2B$. The differential equation leads to the relation

$$(6Ax + 2B) + (Ax^3 + Bx^2 + Cx + D) = x^3 \, .$$

Equating coefficients of like powers of x, we obtain $A = 1$, $B = 0$, $C = -6$, and $D = 0$, so a particular solution is $y_1(x) = x^3 - 6x$. Thus, the general solution is

$$y = c_1 \cos x + c_2 \sin x + x^3 - 6x \, .$$

It may be of interest to compare this method with variation of parameters. Equation (8.33) gives us

$$t_1(x) = - \int x^3 \sin x \, dx = -(3x^3 - 6) \sin x + (x^3 - 6x) \cos x$$

and

$$t_2(x) = \int x^3 \cos x \, dx = (3x^2 - 6) \cos x + (x^3 - 6x) \sin x \, .$$

When we form the combination $t_1 v_1 + t_2 v_2$, we find the particular solution $y_1(x) = x^3 - 6x$, as before. In this case, the use of variation of parameters required the evaluation of the integrals $\int x^3 \sin x \, dx$ and $\int x^3 \cos x \, dx$. With the method of undetermined coefficients, no integration is required.

If the coefficient b is zero, the equation $y'' + ay' = R$ cannot be satisfied by a polynomial of degree n, but it can be satisfied by a polynomial of degree $n + 1$ if $a \neq 0$. If both a and b are zero, the equation becomes $y'' = R$; its general solution is a polynomial of degree $n + 2$ obtained by two successive integrations.

CASE 2. *The right-hand member has the form* $R(x) = p(x)e^{mx}$, *where p is a polynomial of degree n, and m is constant.*

In this case the change of variable $y = u(x)e^{mx}$ transforms the differential equation $y'' + ay' + by = R$ to a new equation,

$$u'' + (2m + a)u' + (m^2 + am + b)u = p \, .$$

This is the type discussed in Case 1 so it always has a polynomial solution u_1. Hence, the original equation has a particular solution of the form $y_1 = u_1(x)e^{mx}$, where u_1 is a polynomial. If $m^2 + am + b \neq 0$, the degree of u_1 is the same as the degree of p. If $m^2 + am + b = 0$ but $2m + a \neq 0$, the degree of u_1 is one greater than that of p. If both $m^2 + am + b = 0$ and $2m + a = 0$, the degree of u_1 is two greater than that of p.

EXAMPLE 2. Find a particular solution of the equation $y'' + y = xe^{3x}$.

Solution. The change of variable $y = ue^{3x}$ leads to the new equation $u'' + 6u' + 10u = x$. Trying $u_1(x) = Ax + B$, we find the particular solution $u_1(x) = (5x - 3)/50$, so a particular solution of the original equation is $y_1 = e^{3x}(5x - 3)/50$.

The method of undetermined coefficients can also be used if R has the form $R(x) = p(x)e^{mx} \cos \alpha x$, or $R(x) = p(x)e^{mx} \sin \alpha x$, where p is a polynomial and m and α are constants. In either case, there is always a particular solution of the form $y_1(x) = e^{mx}[q(x) \cos \alpha x + r(x) \sin \alpha x]$, where q and r are polynomials.

8.17 Exercises

Find the general solution of each of the differential equations in Exercises 1 through 17. If the solution is not valid over the entire real axis, describe an interval over which it is valid.

1. $y'' - y = x$.
2. $y'' - y' = x^2$.
3. $y'' + y' = x^2 + 2x$.
4. $y'' - 2y' + 3y = x^3$.
5. $y'' - 5y' + 4y = x^2 - 2x + 1$.
6. $y'' + y' - 6y = 2x^3 + 5x^2 - 7x + 2$.
7. $y'' - 4y = e^{2x}$.
8. $y'' + 4y = e^{-2x}$.
9. $y'' + y' - 2y = e^x$.
10. $y'' + y' - 2y = e^{2x}$.
11. $y'' + y' - 2y = e^x + e^{2x}$.
12. $y'' - 2y' + y = x + 2x \, e^x$.
13. $y'' + 2y' + y = e^{-x}/x^2$.
14. $y'' + y = \cot^2 x$.
15. $y'' - y = 2/(1 + e^x)$.
16. $y'' + y' - 2y = e^x/(1 + e^x)$.
17. $y'' + 6y' + 9y = f(x)$, where $f(x) = 1$ for $1 \le x \le 2$, and $f(x) = 0$ for all other x.
18. If k is a nonzero constant, prove that the equation $y'' - k^2 y = R(x)$ has a particular solution y_1 given by

$$y_1 = \frac{1}{k} \int_0^x R(t) \sinh k(x - t) \, dt \, .$$

Find the general solution of the equation $y'' - 9y = e^{3x}$.

19. If k is a nonzero constant, prove that the equation $y'' + k^2 y = R(x)$ has a particular solution y_1 given by

$$y_1 = \frac{1}{k} \int_0^x R(t) \sin k(x - t) \, dt \, .$$

Find the general solution of the equation $y'' + 9y = \sin 3x$.

In each of Exercises 20 through 25, determine the general solution.

20. $y'' + y = \sin x$.
21. $y'' + y = \cos x$.
22. $y'' + 4y = 3x \cos x$.

23. $y'' + 4y = 3x \sin x$.
24. $y'' - 3y' = 2e^{2x} \sin x$.
25. $y'' + y = e^{2x} \cos 3x$.

8.18 Examples of physical problems leading to linear second-order equations with constant coefficients

EXAMPLE 1. *Simple harmonic motion.* Suppose a particle is constrained to move in a straight line with its acceleration directed toward a fixed point of the line and proportional to the displacement from that point. If we take the origin as the fixed point and let y be the displacement at time x, then the acceleration y'' must be negative when y is positive, and positive when y is negative. Therefore we can write $y'' = -k^2 y$, or

$$y'' + k^2 y = 0 \, ,$$

where k^2 is a positive constant. This is called the differential equation of *simple harmonic motion*. It is often used as the mathematical model for the motion of a point on a vibrating mechanism such as a plucked string or a vibrating tuning fork. The same equation arises in electric circuit theory where it is called the equation of the harmonic oscillator.

Theorem 8.6 tells us that all solutions have the form

(8.34) $y = A \sin kx + B \cos kx \, ,$

where A and B are arbitrary constants. We can express the solutions in terms of the sine or cosine alone. For example, we can introduce new constants C and α, where

$$C = \sqrt{A^2 + B^2} \quad \text{and} \quad \alpha = \arctan \frac{B}{A} \, ,$$

then we have (see Figure 8.4) $A = C \cos \alpha$, $B = C \sin \alpha$, and Equation (8.34) becomes

$$y = C \cos \alpha \sin kx + C \sin \alpha \cos kx = C \sin (kx + \alpha) \, .$$

When the solution is written in this way, the constants C and α have a simple geometric interpretation (see Figure 8.5). The extreme values of y, which occur when $\sin (kx + \alpha) = \pm 1$, are $\pm C$. When $x = 0$, the initial displacement is $C \sin \alpha$. As x increases, the particle oscillates between the extreme values $+C$ and $-C$ with period $2\pi/k$. The angle $kx + \alpha$ is called the *phase angle* and α itself is called the initial value of the phase angle.

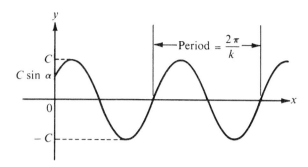

FIGURE 8.4   FIGURE 8.5   Simple harmonic motion.

EXAMPLE 2. *Damped vibrations.* If a particle undergoing simple harmonic motion is suddenly subjected to an external force proportional to its velocity, the new motion satisfies a differential equation of the form

$$y'' + 2cy' + k^2 y = 0 ,$$

where c and k^2 are constants, $c \neq 0$, $k > 0$. If $c > 0$, we will show that all solutions tend to zero as $x \to +\infty$. In this case, the differential equation is said to be *stable*. The external force causes *damping* of the motion. If $c < 0$, we will show that some solutions have arbitrarily large absolute values as $x \to +\infty$. In this case, the equation is said to be *unstable*.

Since the discriminant of the equation is $d = (2c)^2 - 4k^2 = 4(c^2 - k^2)$, the nature of the solutions is determined by the relative sizes of c^2 and k^2. The three cases $d = 0$, $d > 0$, and $d < 0$ may be analyzed as follows:

(a) *Zero discriminant:* $c^2 = k^2$. In this case, all solutions have the form

$$y = e^{-cx}(A + Bx).$$

If $c > 0$, all solutions tend to 0 as $x \to +\infty$. This case is referred to as *critical damping*. If $B \neq 0$, each solution will change sign exactly once because of the linear factor $A + Bx$. An example is shown in Figure 8.6(a). If $c < 0$, each nontrivial solution tends to $+\infty$ or to $-\infty$ as $x \to +\infty$.

(b) *Positive discriminant:* $c^2 > k^2$. By Theorem 8.7 all solutions have the form

$$y = e^{-cx}(Ae^{hx} + Be^{-hx}) = Ae^{(h-c)x} + Be^{-(h+c)x} ,$$

where $h = \frac{1}{2}\sqrt{d} = \sqrt{c^2 - k^2}$. Since $h^2 = c^2 - k^2$, we have $h^2 - c^2 < 0$ so $(h - c)(h + c) < 0$. Therefore, the numbers $h - c$ and $h + c$ have opposite signs. If $c > 0$, then $h + c$ is positive so $h - c$ is negative, and hence both exponentials $e^{(h-c)x}$ and $e^{-(h+c)x}$ tend to zero as $x \to +\infty$. In this case, referred to as *overcritical damping*, all solutions tend to 0 for large x. An example is shown in Figure 8.6(a). Each solution can change sign at most once.

If $c < 0$, then $h - c$ is positive but $h + c$ is negative. Thus, both exponentials $e^{(h-c)x}$

and $e^{-(h+c)x}$ tend to $+\infty$ for large x, so again there are solutions with arbitrarily large absolute values.

(c) *Negative discriminant:* $c^2 < k^2$. In this case, all solutions have the form

$$y = Ce^{-cx} \sin(hx + \alpha),$$

where $h = \frac{1}{2}\sqrt{-d} = \sqrt{k^2 - c^2}$. If $c > 0$, every nontrivial solution oscillates, but the amplitude of the oscillation decreases to 0 as $x \to +\infty$. This case is called *undercritical damping* and is illustrated in Figure 8.6(b). If $c < 0$, all nontrivial solutions take arbitrarily large positive and negative values as $x \to +\infty$.

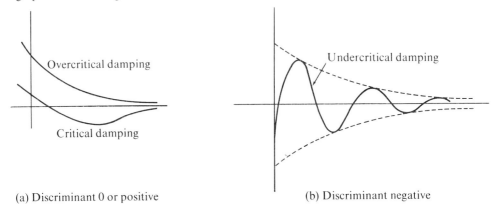

(a) Discriminant 0 or positive   (b) Discriminant negative

FIGURE 8.6   Damped vibrations occurring as solutions of $y'' + 2cy' + k^2y = 0$, with $c > 0$, and discriminant $4(c^2 - k^2)$.

EXAMPLE 3. *Electric circuits.* If we insert a capacitor in the electric circuit of Example 5 in Section 8.6, the differential equation which serves as a model for this circuit is given by

$$LI'(t) + RI(t) + \frac{1}{C}\int I(t)\,dt = V(t),$$

where C is a positive constant called the *capacitance*. Differentiation of this equation gives a second-order linear equation of the form

$$LI''(t) + RI'(t) + \frac{1}{C}I(t) = V'(t).$$

If the impressed voltage $V(t)$ is constant, the right member is zero and the equation takes the form

$$I''(t) + \frac{R}{L}I'(t) + \frac{1}{LC}I(t) = 0.$$

This is the same type of equation analyzed in Example 2 except that $2c$ is replaced by R/L, and k^2 is replaced by $1/(LC)$. In this case, the coefficient c is positive so the equation is always stable. In other words, the current $I(t)$ always tends to 0 as $t \to +\infty$. The terminology of Example 2 is also used here. The current is said to be critically damped when the discriminant is zero $(CR^2 = 4L)$, overcritically damped when the discriminant is positive $(CR^2 > 4L)$, and undercritically damped when the discriminant is negative $(CR^2 < 4L)$.

EXAMPLE 4. *Motion of a rocket with variable mass.* A rocket is propelled by burning fuel in a combustion chamber, allowing the products of combustion to be expelled backward. Assume the rocket starts from rest and moves vertically upward along a straight line. Designate the altitude of the rocket at time t by $r(t)$, the mass of the rocket (including fuel) by $m(t)$, and the velocity of the exhaust matter, relative to the rocket, by $c(t)$. In the absence of external forces, the equation

$$(8.35) \qquad m(t)r''(t) = m'(t)c(t)$$

is used as a mathematical model for discussing the motion. The left member, $m(t)r''(t)$, is the product of the mass of the rocket and its acceleration. The right member, $m'(t)c(t)$, is the accelerating force on the rocket caused by the thrust developed by the rocket engine. In the examples to be considered here, $m(t)$ and $c(t)$ are known or can be prescribed in terms of $r(t)$ or its derivative $r'(t)$ (the velocity of the rocket). Equation (8.35) then becomes a second-order differential equation for the position function r.

If external forces are also present, such as gravitational attraction, then, instead of (8.35), we use the equation

$$(8.36) \qquad m(t)r''(t) = m'(t)c(t) + F(t) ,$$

where $F(t)$ represents the sum of all external forces acting on the rocket at time t.

Before we consider a specific example, we will give an argument which may serve to motivate the Equation (8.35). For this purpose we consider first a rocket that fires its exhaust matter intermittently, like bullets from a gun. Specifically, we consider a time interval $[t, t + h]$, where h is a small positive number; we assume that some exhaust matter is expelled at time t, and that no further exhaust matter is expelled in the half-open interval $(t, t + h]$. On the basis of this assumption, we obtain a formula whose limit, as $h \to 0$, is Equation (8.35).

Just before the exhaust material is expelled at time t, the rocket has mass $m(t)$ and velocity $v(t)$. At the end of the time interval $[t, t + h]$, the rocket has mass $m(t + h)$ and velocity $v(t + h)$. The mass of the expelled matter is $m(t) - m(t + h)$, and its velocity during the interval is $v(t) + c(t)$, since $c(t)$ is the velocity of the exhaust relative to the rocket. Just before the exhaust material is expelled at time t, the rocket is a system with momentum $m(t)v(t)$. At time $t + h$, this system consists of two parts, a rocket with momentum $m(t + h)v(t + h)$ and exhaust matter with momentum $[m(t) - m(t + h)][v(t) + c(t)]$. The law of conservation of momentum states that the momentum of the new system must be equal to that of the old. Therefore, we have

$$m(t)v(t) = m(t + h)v(t + h) + [m(t) - m(t + h)][v(t) + c(t)] ,$$

from which we obtain

$$m(t + h)[v(t + h) - v(t)] = [m(t + h) - m(t)]c(t) .$$

Dividing by h and letting $h \to 0$, we find that

$$m(t)v'(t) = m'(t)c(t),$$

which is equivalent to Equation (8.35).

Consider a special case in which the rocket starts from rest with an initial weight of w pounds (including b pounds of fuel) and moves vertically upward along a straight line. Assume the fuel is consumed at a constant rate of k pounds per second and that the products of combustion are discharged directly backward with a constant speed of c feet per second relative to the rocket. Assume the only external force acting on the rocket is the earth's gravitational attraction. We want to know how high the rocket will travel before all its fuel is consumed.

Since all the fuel is consumed when $kt = b$, we restrict t to the interval $0 \le t \le b/k$. The only external force acting on the rocket is $-m(t)g$, the velocity $c(t) = -c$, so Equation (8.36) becomes

$$m(t)r''(t) = -m'(t)c - m(t)g .$$

The weight of the rocket at time t is $w - kt$, and its mass $m(t)$ is $(w - kt)/g$; hence we have $m'(t) = -k/g$ and the foregoing equation becomes

$$r''(t) = -\frac{m'(t)}{m(t)} c - g = \frac{kc}{w - kt} - g .$$

Integrating, and using the initial condition $r'(0) = 0$, we find

$$r'(t) = -c \log \frac{w - kt}{w} - gt .$$

Integrating again and using the initial condition $r(0) = 0$, we obtain the relation

$$r(t) = \frac{c(w - kt)}{k} \log \frac{w - kt}{w} - \frac{1}{2} gt^2 + ct .$$

All the fuel is consumed when $t = b/k$. At that instant the altitude is

(8.37) $$r\left(\frac{b}{k}\right) = \frac{c(w - b)}{k} \log \frac{w - b}{w} - \frac{1}{2} \frac{gb^2}{k^2} + \frac{cb}{k} .$$

This formula is valid if $b < w$. For some rockets, the weight of the carrier is negligible compared to the weight of the fuel, and it is of interest to consider the limiting case $b = w$. We cannot put $b = w$ in (8.37) because of the presence of the term $\log (w - b)/w$. However, if we let $b \to w$, the first term in (8.37) is an indeterminate form with limit 0. Therefore, when $b \to w$, the limiting value of the right member of (8.37) is

$$\lim_{b \to w} r\left(\frac{b}{k}\right) = -\frac{1}{2} \frac{gw^2}{k^2} + \frac{cw}{k} = -\frac{1}{2} gT^2 + cT,$$

where $T = w/k$ is the time required for the entire weight w to be consumed.

8.19 Exercises

In Exercises 1 through 5, a particle is assumed to be moving in simple harmonic motion, according to the equation $y = C \sin(kx + \alpha)$. The *velocity* of the particle is defined to be the derivative y'. The *frequency* of the motion is the reciprocal of the period. (Period $= 2\pi/k$; frequency $= k/2\pi$.) The frequency represents the number of cycles completed in unit time, provided $k > 0$.

1. Find the amplitude C if the frequency is $1/\pi$ and if the initial values of y and y' (when $x = 0$) are 2 and 4, respectively.
2. Find the velocity when y is zero, given that the amplitude is 7 and the frequency is 10.
3. Show that the equation of motion can also be written as follows:

$$y = A \cos(mx + \beta).$$

Find equations that relate the constants A, m, β, and C, k, α.
4. Find the equation of motion given that $y = 3$ and $y' = 0$ when $x = 0$ and that the period is $\frac{1}{2}$.
5. Find the amplitude of the motion if the period is 2π and the velocity is $\pm v_0$ when $y = y_0$.
6. A particle undergoes simple harmonic motion. Initially its displacement is 1, its velocity is 2 and its acceleration is -12. Compute its displacement and acceleration when the velocity is $\sqrt{8}$.
7. For a certain positive number k, the differential equation of simple harmonic motion $y'' + k^2 y = 0$ has solutions of the form $y = f(x)$ with $f(0) = f(3) = 0$ and $f(x) < 0$ for all x in the open interval $0 < x < 3$. Compute k and find all solutions.
8. The current $I(t)$ at time t flowing in an electric circuit obeys the differential equation $I''(t) + I(t) = G(t)$, where G is a step function given by $G(t) = 1$ if $0 \le t \le 2\pi$, $G(t) = 0$ for all other t. Determine the solution which satisfies the initial conditions $I(0) = 0$, $I'(0) = 1$.
9. The current $I(t)$ at time t flowing in an electric circuit obeys the differential equation

$$I''(t) + RI'(t) + I(t) = \sin \omega t,$$

where R and ω are positive constants. The solution can be expressed in the form $I(t) = F(t) + A \sin(\omega t + \alpha)$, where $F(t) \to 0$ as $t \to +\infty$, and A and α are constants depending on R and ω, with $A > 0$. If there is a value of ω which makes A as large as possible, then $\omega/(2\pi)$ is called a *resonance frequency* of the circuit.
   (a) Find all resonance frequencies when $R = 1$.
   (b) Find those values of R for which the circuit will have a resonance frequency.
10. A spaceship is returning to earth. Assume that the only external force acting on it is the action of gravity, and that it falls along a straight line toward the center of the earth. The effect of gravity is partly overcome by firing a rocket directly downward. The rocket fuel is consumed at a constant rate of k pounds per second and the exhaust material has a constant speed of c feet per second relative to the rocket. Find a formula for the distance the spaceship falls in time t if it starts from rest at time $t = 0$ with an initial weight of w pounds.
11. A rocket of initial weight w pounds starts from rest in free space (no external forces) and moves along a straight line. The fuel is consumed at a constant rate of k pounds per second and the products of combustion are discharged directly backward at a constant speed of c feet per second relative to the rocket. Find the distance traveled at time t.
12. Solve Exercise 11 if the initial speed of the rocket is v_0 and if the products of combustion are fired at such a speed that the discharged material remains at rest in space.

8.20 Remarks concerning nonlinear differential equations

Since second-order linear differential equations with constant coefficients occur in such a wide variety of scientific problems, it is indeed fortunate that we have systematic methods for solving these equations. Many nonlinear equations also arise naturally from both physical and geometrical problems, but there is no comprehensive theory comparable to that for linear equations. In the introduction to this chapter we mentioned a classic "bag of tricks" that has been developed for treating many special cases of nonlinear equations. We conclude this chapter with a discussion of some of these tricks and some of the problems they help to solve. We shall consider only first-order equations which can be solved for the derivative y' and expressed in the form

$$(8.38) \qquad\qquad y' = f(x, y) .$$

We recall that a solution of (8.38) on an interval I is any function, say $y = Y(x)$, which is differentiable on I and satisfies the relation $Y'(x) = f[x, Y(x)]$ for all x in I. In the linear case, we proved an existence-uniqueness theorem which tells us that one and only one solution exists satisfying a prescribed initial condition. Moreover, we have an explicit formula for determining this solution.

This is not typical of the general case. A nonlinear equation may have *no* solution satisfying a given initial condition, or it may have *more than one*. For example, the equation $(y')^2 - xy' + y + 1 = 0$ has no solution with $y = 0$ when $x = 0$, since this would require that $(y')^2 = -1$ when $x = 0$. On the other hand, the equation $y' = 3y^{2/3}$ has two distinct solutions, $Y_1(x) = 0$ and $Y_2(x) = x^3$, satisfying the initial condition $y = 0$ when $x = 0$.

Thus, the study of nonlinear equations is more difficult because of the possible non-existence or nonuniqueness of solutions. Also, even when solutions exist, it may not be possible to determine them explicitly in terms of familiar functions. Sometimes we can eliminate the derivative y' from the differential equation and arrive at a relation of the form

$$F(x, y) = 0$$

satisfied by some, or perhaps all, solutions. If this equation can be solved for y in terms of x, we get an explicit formula for the solution. More often than not, however, the equation is too complicated to solve for y. For example, in a later section we shall study the differential equation

$$y' = \frac{y - x}{y + x} ,$$

and we shall find that every solution necessarily satisfies the relation

$$(8.39) \qquad\qquad \frac{1}{2} \log (x^2 + y^2) + \arctan \frac{y}{x} + C = 0$$

for some constant C. It would be hopeless to try to solve this equation for y in terms of x. In a case like this, we say that the relation (8.39) is an *implicit formula* for the solutions. It is common practice to say that the differential equation has been "solved" or "integrated" when we arrive at an implicit formula such as $F(x, y) = 0$ in which no derivatives of the unknown function appear. Sometimes this formula reveals useful information about the solutions. On the other hand, the reader should realize that such an implicit relation may be less helpful than the differential equation itself for studying properties of the solutions.

In the next section we show how qualitative information about the solutions can often be obtained directly from the differential equation without a knowledge of explicit or implicit formulas for the solutions.

8.21 Integral curves and direction fields

Consider a differential equation of first order, say $y' = f(x, y)$, and suppose some of the solutions satisfy an implicit relation of the form

$$(8.40) \qquad F(x, y, C) = 0 \, ,$$

where C denotes a constant. If we introduce a rectangular coordinate system and plot all the points (x, y) whose coordinates satisfy (8.40) for a particular C, we obtain a curve called an *integral curve* of the differential equation. Different values of C usually give different integral curves, but all of them share a common geometric property. The differential equation $y' = f(x, y)$ relates the slope y' at each point (x, y) of the curve to the coordinates x and y. As C takes on all its values, the collection of integral curves obtained is called a *one-parameter family* of curves.

For example, when the differential equation is $y' = 3$, integration gives us $y = 3x + C$, and the integral curves form a family of straight lines, all having slope 3. The arbitrary constant C represents the y-intercept of these lines.

If the differential equation is $y' = x$, integration yields $y = \frac{1}{2}x^2 + C$, and the integral curves form a family of parabolas as shown in Figure 8.7. Again, the constant C tells us where the various curves cross the y-axis. Figure 8.8 illustrates the family of exponential

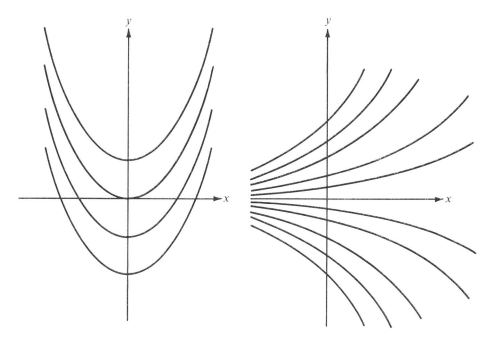

FIGURE 8.7   Integral curves of the differential equation $y' = x$.

FIGURE 8.8   Integral curves of the differential equation $y' = y$.

curves, $y = Ce^x$, which are integral curves of the differential equation $y' = y$. Once more, C represents the y-intercept. In this case, C is also equal to the slope of the curve at the point where it crosses the y-axis.

A family of nonparallel straight lines is shown in Figure 8.9. These are integral curves of the differential equation

(8.41)
$$y = x\frac{dy}{dx} - \frac{1}{4}\left(\frac{dy}{dx}\right)^2,$$

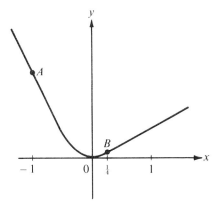

FIGURE 8.9   Integral curves of the differential
equation $y = x\dfrac{dy}{dx} - \dfrac{1}{4}\left(\dfrac{dy}{dx}\right)^2$.

FIGURE 8.10   A solution of Equation (8.41) that is not a member of the family in Equation (8.42).

and a one-parameter family of solutions is given by

(8.42)
$$y = Cx - \tfrac{1}{4}C^2 .$$

This family is one which possesses an *envelope*, that is, a curve having the property that at each of its points it is tangent to one of the members of the family.† The envelope here is $y = x^2$ and its graph is indicated by the dotted curve in Figure 8.9. The envelope of a family of integral curves is itself an integral curve because the slope and coordinates at a point of the envelope are the same as those of one of the integral curves of the family. In this example, it is easy to verify directly that $y = x^2$ is a solution of (8.41). Note that this particular solution is not a member of the family in (8.42). Further solutions, not members of the family, may be obtained by piecing together members of the family with portions of the envelope. An example is shown in Figure 8.10. The tangent line at A comes from taking $C = -2$ in (8.42) and the tangent at B comes from $C = \frac{1}{2}$. The resulting solution, $y = f(x)$, is given as follows:

$$f(x) = \begin{cases} -2x - 1 & \text{if } x \le -1 , \\ x^2 & \text{if } -1 \le x \le \frac{1}{4} , \\ \frac{1}{2}x - \frac{1}{16} & \text{if } x \ge \frac{1}{4} . \end{cases}$$

† And conversely, each member of the family is tangent to the envelope.

This function has a derivative and satisfies the differential equation in (8.41) for every real x. It is clear that an infinite number of similar examples could be constructed in the same way. This example shows that it may not be easy to exhibit all possible solutions of a differential equation.

Sometimes it is possible to find a first-order differential equation satisfied by all members of a one-parameter family of curves. We illustrate with two examples.

EXAMPLE 1. Find a first-order differential equation satisfied by all circles with center at the origin.

Solution. A circle with center at the origin and radius C satisfies the equation $x^2 + y^2 = C^2$. As C varies over all positive numbers, we obtain every circle with center at the origin. To find a first-order differential equation having these circles as integral curves, we simply differentiate the Cartesian equation to obtain $2x + 2yy' = 0$. Thus, each circle satisfies the differential equation $y' = -x/y$.

EXAMPLE 2. Find a first-order differential equation for the family of all circles passing through the origin and having their centers on the x-axis.

Solution. If the center of a circle is at $(C, 0)$ and if it passes through the origin, the theorem of Pythagoras tells us that each point (x, y) on the circle satisfies the Cartesian equation $(x - C)^2 + y^2 = C^2$, which can be written as

$$(8.43) \qquad\qquad x^2 + y^2 - 2Cx = 0 .$$

To find a differential equation having these circles as integral curves, we differentiate (8.43) to obtain $2x + 2yy' - 2C = 0$, or

$$(8.44) \qquad\qquad x + yy' = C .$$

Since this equation contains C, it is satisfied only by that circle in (8.43) corresponding to the same C. To obtain one differential equation satisfied by all the curves in (8.43), we must eliminate C. We could differentiate (8.44) to obtain $1 + yy'' + (y')^2 = 0$. This is a second-order differential equation satisfied by all the curves in (8.43). We can obtain a first-order equation by eliminating C algebraically from (8.43) and (8.44). Substituting $x + yy'$ for C in (8.43), we obtain $x^2 + y^2 - 2x(x + yy')$, a first-order equation which can be solved for y' and written as $y' = (y^2 - x^2)/(2xy)$.

Figure 8.11 illustrates what is called a *direction field* of a differential equation. This is simply a collection of short line segments drawn tangent to the various integral curves. The particular example shown in Figure 8.11 is a direction field of the equation $y' = y$.

A direction field can be constructed without solving the differential equation. Choose a point, say (a, b), and compute the number $f(a, b)$ obtained by substituting in the right-hand side of the differential equation $y' = f(x, y)$. If there is an integral curve through this point, its slope there must be equal to $f(a, b)$. Therefore, if we draw a short line segment through (a, b) having this slope, it will be part of a direction field of the differential equation. By drawing several of these line segments, we can get a fair idea of the general behavior of the

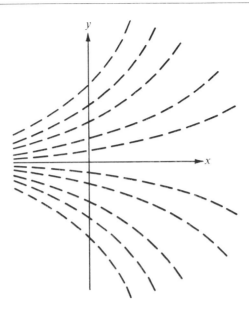

FIGURE 8.11   A direction field for the differential equation $y' = y$.

integral curves. Sometimes such qualitative information about the solution may be all that is needed. Notice that different points $(0, b)$ on the y-axis yield different integral curves. This gives us a geometric reason for expecting an arbitrary constant to appear when we integrate a first-order equation.

8.22   Exercises

In Exercises 1 through 12, find a first-order differential equation having the given family of curves as integral curves.

1. $2x + 3y = C.$
2. $y = Ce^{-2x}.$
3. $x^2 - y^2 = C.$
4. $xy = C.$
5. $y^2 = Cx.$
6. $x^2 + y^2 + 2Cy = 1.$
7. $y = C(x - 1)e^x.$
8. $y^4(x + 2) = C(x - 2).$
9. $y = C \cos x.$
10. $\arctan y + \arcsin x = C.$
11. All circles through the points $(1, 0)$ and $(-1, 0)$.
12. All circles through the points $(1, 1)$ and $(-1, -1)$.

In the construction of a direction field of a differential equation, sometimes the work may be speeded considerably if we first locate those points at which the slope y' has a constant value C. For each C, these points lie on a curve called an *isocline*.

13. Plot the isoclines corresponding to the constant slopes $\frac{1}{2}$, 1, $\frac{3}{2}$, and 2 for the differential equation $y' = x^2 + y^2$. With the aid of the isoclines, construct a direction field for the equation and try to determine the shape of the integral curve passing through the origin.

14. Show that the isoclines of the differential equation $y' = x + y$ form a one-parameter family of straight lines. Plot the isoclines corresponding to the constant slopes 0, $\pm\frac{1}{2}$, ± 1, $\pm\frac{3}{2}$, ± 2. With the aid of the isoclines, construct a direction field and sketch the integral curve passing through the origin. One of the integral curves is also an isocline; find this curve.

15. Plot a number of isoclines and construct a direction field for the equation

$$y = x\frac{dy}{dx} + \left(\frac{dy}{dx}\right)^2.$$

If you draw the direction field carefully, you should be able to determine a one-parameter family of solutions of this equation from the appearance of the direction field.

8.23 First-order separable equations

A first-order differential equation of the form $y' = f(x, y)$ in which the right member $f(x, y)$ splits into a product of two factors, one depending on x alone and the other depending on y alone, is said to be a *separable equation*. Examples are $y' = x^3$, $y' = y$, $y' = \sin y \log x$, $y' = x/\tan y$, etc. Thus each separable equation can be expressed in the form

$$y' = Q(x)R(y),$$

where Q and R are given functions. When $R(y) \neq 0$, we can divide by $R(y)$ and rewrite this differential equation in the form

$$A(y)y' = Q(x),$$

where $A(y) = 1/R(y)$. The next theorem tells us how to find an implicit formula satisfied by every solution of such an equation.

THEOREM 8.10. *Let* $y = Y(x)$ *be any solution of the separable differential equation*

$$(8.45) \qquad A(y)y' = Q(x)$$

such that Y' *is continuous on an open interval* I. *Assume that both* Q *and the composite function* $A \circ Y$ *are continuous on* I. *Let* G *be any primitive of* A, *that is, any function such that* $G' = A$. *Then the solution* Y *satisfies the implicit formula*

$$(8.46) \qquad G(y) = \int Q(x)\, dx + C$$

for some constant C. *Conversely, if* y *satisfies* (8.46) *then* y *is a solution of* (8.45).

Proof. Since Y is a solution of (8.45), we must have

$$(8.47) \qquad A[Y(x)]\, Y'(x) = Q(x)$$

for each x in I. Since $G' = A$, this equation becomes

$$G'[Y(x)]\, Y'(x) = Q(x).$$

But, by the chain rule, the left member is the derivative of the composite function $G \circ Y$.

Therefore $G \circ Y$ is a primitive of Q, which means that

$$(8.48) \qquad\qquad G[Y(x)] = \int Q(x)\,dx + C$$

for some constant C. This is the relation (8.46). Conversely, if $y = Y(x)$ satisfies (8.46), differentiation gives us (8.47), which shows that Y is a solution of the differential equation (8.45).

Note: The implicit formula (8.46) can also be expressed in terms of A. From (8.47) we have

$$\int A[Y(x)]\,Y'(x)\,dx = \int Q(x)\,dx + C\,.$$

If we make the substitution $y = Y(x)$, $dy = Y'(x)\,dx$ in the integral on the left, the equation becomes

$$(8.49) \qquad\qquad \int A(y)\,dy = \int Q(x)\,dx + C\,.$$

Since the indefinite integral $\int A(y)\,dy$ represents any primitive of A, Equation (8.49) is an alternative way of writing (8.46).

In practice, formula (8.49) is obtained directly from (8.45) by a mechanical process. In the differential equation (8.45) we write dy/dx for the derivative y' and then treat dy/dx as a fraction to obtain the relation $A(y)\,dy = Q(x)\,dx$. Now we simply attach integral signs to both sides of this equation and add the constant C to obtain (8.49). The justification for this mechanical process is provided by Theorem 8.10. This process is another example illustrating the effectiveness of the Leibniz notation.

EXAMPLE. The nonlinear equation $xy' + y = y^2$ is separable since it can be written in the form

$$(8.50) \qquad\qquad \frac{y'}{y(y-1)} = \frac{1}{x}\,,$$

provided that $y(y - 1) \neq 0$ and $x \neq 0$. Now the two constant functions $y = 0$ and $y = 1$ are clearly solutions of $xy' + y = y^2$. The remaining solutions, if any exist, satisfy (8.50) and, hence, by Theorem 8.10 they also satisfy

$$\int \frac{dy}{y(y-1)} = \int \frac{dx}{x} + K$$

for some constant K. Since the integrand on the left is $1/(y - 1) - 1/y$, when we integrate, we find that

$$\log|y - 1| - \log|y| = \log|x| + K\,.$$

This gives us $|(y - 1)/y| = |x|\,e^K$ or $(y - 1)/y = Cx$ for some constant C. Solving for y, we obtain the explicit formula

$$(8.51) \qquad\qquad y = \frac{1}{1 - Cx}\,.$$

Theorem 8.10 tells us that for any choice of C this y is a solution; therefore, in this example we have determined all solutions: the constant functions $y = 0$ and $y = 1$ and all the functions defined by (8.51). Note that the choice $C = 0$ gives the constant solution $y = 1$.

8.24 Exercises

In Exercises 1 through 12, assume solutions exist and find an implicit formula satisfied by the solutions.

1. $y' = x^3/y^2$.
2. $\tan x \cos y = -y' \tan y$.
3. $(x + 1)y' + y^2 = 0$.
4. $y' = (y - 1)(y - 2)$.
5. $y\sqrt{1 - x^2}\, y' = x$.
6. $(x - 1)y' = xy$.

7. $(1 - x^2)^{1/2}y' + 1 + y^2 = 0$.
8. $xy(1 + x^2)y' - (1 + y^2) = 0$.
9. $(x^2 - 4)y' = y$.
10. $xyy' = 1 + x^2 + y^2 + x^2y^2$.
11. $yy' = e^{x+2y} \sin x$.
12. $x\, dx + y\, dy = xy(x\, dy - y\, dx)$.

In Exercises 13 through 16, find functions f, continuous on the whole real axis, which satisfy the conditions given. When it is easy to enumerate all of them, do so; in any case, find as many as you can.

13. $f(x) = 2 + \int_1^x f(t)\, dt$.
14. $f(x)f'(x) = 5x$, $\quad f(0) = 1$.
15. $f'(x) + 2xe^{f(x)} = 0$, $\quad f(0) = 0$.
16. $f^2(x) + [f'(x)]^2 = 1$. $\quad$ *Note:* $f(x) = -1$ is one solution.
17. A nonnegative function f, continuous on the whole real axis, has the property that its ordinate set over an arbitrary interval has an area proportional to the length of the interval. Find f.
18. Solve Exercise 17 if the area is proportional to the difference of the function values at the end-points of the interval.
19. Solve Exercise 18 when "difference" is replaced by "sum."
20. Solve Exercise 18 when "difference" is replaced by "product."

8.25 Homogeneous first-order equations

We consider now a special kind of first-order equation,

$$(8.52) \qquad\qquad y' = f(x, y),$$

in which the right-hand side has a special property known as *homogeneity*. This means that

$$(8.53) \qquad\qquad f(tx, ty) = f(x, y)$$

for all x, y, and all $t \neq 0$. In other words, replacement of x by tx and y by ty has no effect on the value of $f(x, y)$. Equations of the form (8.52) which have this property are called *homogeneous* (sometimes called *homogeneous of degree zero*). Examples are the following:

$$y' = \frac{y - x}{y + x}, \qquad y' = \left(\frac{x^2 + y^2}{xy}\right)^3, \qquad y' = \frac{x}{y}\sin\frac{x^2 + y^2}{x^2 - y^2}, \qquad y' = \log x - \log y.$$

If we use (8.53) with $t = 1/x$, the differential equation in (8.52) becomes

$$(8.54) \qquad\qquad y' = f\left(1, \frac{y}{x}\right).$$

The appearance of the quotient y/x on the right suggests that we introduce a new unknown function v where $v = y/x$. Then $y = vx$, $y' = v'x + v$, and this substitution transforms (8.54) into

$$v'x + v = f(1, v) \qquad \text{or} \qquad x\frac{dv}{dx} = f(1, v) - v \,.$$

This last equation is a first-order separable equation for v. We may use Theorem 8.10 to obtain an implicit formula for v and then replace v by y/x to obtain an implicit formula for y.

EXAMPLE. Solve the differential equation $y' = (y - x)/(y + x)$.

Solution. We rewrite the equation as follows:

$$y' = \frac{y/x - 1}{y/x + 1} \,.$$

The substitution $v = y/x$ transforms this into

$$x\frac{dv}{dx} = \frac{v - 1}{v + 1} - v = -\frac{1 + v^2}{v + 1} \,.$$

Applying Theorem 8.10, we get

$$\int \frac{v}{1 + v^2}\, dv + \int \frac{1}{1 + v^2}\, dv = -\int \frac{dx}{x} + C \,.$$

Integration yields

$$\tfrac{1}{2} \log (1 + v^2) + \arctan v = -\log |x| + C \,.$$

Replacing v by y/x, we have

$$\tfrac{1}{2} \log (x^2 + y^2) - \tfrac{1}{2} \log x^2 + \arctan \frac{y}{x} = -\log |x| + C \,,$$

and since $\log x^2 = 2 \log |x|$, this simplifies to

$$\tfrac{1}{2} \log (x^2 + y^2) + \arctan \frac{y}{x} = C \,.$$

There are some interesting geometric properties possessed by the solutions of a homogeneous equation $y' = f(x, y)$. First of all, it is easy to show that straight lines through the origin are isoclines of the equation. We recall that an isocline of $y' = f(x, y)$ is a curve along which the slope y' is constant. This property is illustrated in Figure 8.12 which shows a direction field of the differential equation $y' = -2y/x$. The isocline corresponding to slope c has the equation $-2y/x = c$, or $y = -\frac{1}{2}cx$ and is therefore a line of slope $-\frac{1}{2}c$ through the origin. To prove the property in general, consider a line of slope m through the origin. Then $y = mx$ for all (x, y) on this line; in particular, the point $(1, m)$ is on the line. Suppose now, for the sake of simplicity, that there is an integral curve through each point of the line $y = mx$. The slope of the integral curve through a point (a, b) on this line is $f(a, b) = f(a, ma)$. If $a \neq 0$, we may use the homogeneity property in (8.53) to

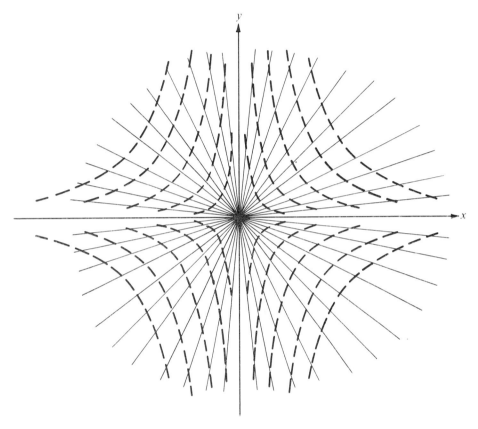

FIGURE 8.12   A direction field for the differential equation $y' = -2y/x$. The isoclines are straight lines through the origin.

write $f(a, ma) = f(1, m)$. In other words, if $(a, b) \neq (0, 0)$, the integral curve through (a, b) has the same slope as the integral curve through $(1, m)$. Therefore the line $y = mx$ is an isocline, as asserted. (It can also be shown that these are the only isoclines of a homogeneous equation.)

This property of the isoclines suggests a property of the integral curves known as *invariance under similarity transformations*. We recall that a similarity transformation carries a set S into a new set kS obtained by multiplying the coordinates of each point of S by a constant factor $k > 0$. Every line through the origin remains fixed under a similarity transformation. Therefore, the isoclines of a homogeneous equation do not change under a similarity transformation; hence the appearance of the direction field does not change either. This suggests that similarity transformations carry integral curves into integral curves. To prove this analytically, let us assume that S is an integral curve described by an explicit formula of the form

(8.55) $y = F(x)$.

To say that S is an integral curve of $y' = f(x, y)$ means that we have

(8.56) $F'(x) = f(x, F(x))$

for all x under consideration. Now choose any point (x, y) on kS. Then the point $(x/k, y/k)$ lies on S and hence its coordinates satisfy (8.55), so we have $y/k = F(x/k)$ or $y = kF(x/k)$. In other words, the curve kS is described by the equation $y = G(x)$, where $G(x) = kF(x/k)$. Note that the derivative of G is given by

$$G'(x) = kF'\left(\frac{x}{k}\right) \cdot \frac{1}{k} = F'\left(\frac{x}{k}\right).$$

To prove that kS is an integral curve of $y' = f(x, y)$ it will suffice to show that $G'(x) = f(x, G(x))$ or, what is the same thing, that

(8.57) $F'\left(\dfrac{x}{k}\right) = f\left(x, kF\left(\dfrac{x}{k}\right)\right)$.

But if we replace x by x/k in Equation (8.56) and then use the homogeneity property with $t = k$, we obtain

$$F'\left(\frac{x}{k}\right) = f\left(\frac{x}{k}, F\left(\frac{x}{k}\right)\right) = f\left(x, kF\left(\frac{x}{k}\right)\right),$$

and this proves (8.57). In other words, we have shown that kS is an integral curve whenever S is. A simple example in which this geometric property is quite obvious is the homogeneous equation $y' = -x/y$ whose integral curves form a one-parameter family of concentric circles given by the equation $x^2 + y^2 = C$.

It can also be shown that if the integral curves of a first-order equation $y' = f(x, y)$ are invariant under similarity transformations, then the differential equation is necessarily homogeneous.

8.26 Exercises

1. Show that the substitution $y = x/v$ transforms a homogeneous equation $y' = f(x, y)$ into a first-order equation for v which is separable. Sometimes this substitution leads to integrals that are easier to evaluate than those obtained by the substitution $y = xv$ discussed in the text.

Integrate the differential equations in Exercises 2 through 11.

2. $y' = \dfrac{-x}{y}$.

3. $y' = 1 + \dfrac{y}{x}$.

4. $y' = \dfrac{x^2 + 2y^2}{xy}$.

5. $(2y^2 - x^2)y' + 3xy = 0$.

6. $xy' = y - \sqrt{x^2 + y^2}$.

9. $y' = \dfrac{y(x^2 + xy + y^2)}{x(x^2 + 3xy + y^2)}$.

7. $x^2 y' + xy + 2y^2 = 0$.

10. $y' = \dfrac{y}{x} + \sin\dfrac{y}{x}$.

8. $y^2 + (x^2 - xy + y^2)y' = 0$.

11. $x(y + 4x)y' + y(x + 4y) = 0$.

8.27   Some geometrical and physical problems leading to first-order equations

We discuss next some examples of geometrical and physical problems that lead to first-order differential equations that are either separable or homogeneous.

Orthogonal trajectories. Two curves are said to intersect *orthogonally* at a point if their tangent lines are perpendicular at that point. A curve which intersects every member of a family of curves orthogonally is called an orthogonal trajectory for the family. Figure 8.13 shows some examples. Problems involving orthogonal trajectories are of importance in both pure and applied mathematics. For example, in the theory of fluid flow, two orthogonal families of curves are called the *equipotential lines* and the *stream lines*, respectively. In the theory of heat, they are known as *isothermal lines* and *lines of flow*.

Suppose a given family of curves satisfies a first-order differential equation, say

(8.58) $$y' = f(x, y).$$

The number $f(x, y)$ is the slope of an integral curve passing through (x, y). The slope of each orthogonal trajectory through this point is the negative reciprocal $-1/f(x, y)$, so the orthogonal trajectories satisfy the differential equation

(8.59) $$y' = -\frac{1}{f(x, y)}.$$

If (8.58) is separable, then (8.59) is also separable. If (8.58) is homogeneous, then (8.59) is also homogeneous.

EXAMPLE 1.   Find the orthogonal trajectories of the family of all circles through the origin with their centers on the x-axis.

Solution.   In Example 2 of Section 8.21 we found that this family is given by the Cartesian equation $x^2 + y^2 - 2Cx = 0$ and that it satisfies the differential equation $y' = (y^2 - x^2)/(2xy)$. Replacing the right member by its negative reciprocal, we find that the orthogonal trajectories satisfy the differential equation

$$y' = \frac{2xy}{x^2 - y^2}.$$

This homogeneous equation may be integrated by the substitution $y = vx$, and it leads to the family of integral curves

$$x^2 + y^2 - 2Cy = 0.$$

This is a family of circles passing through the origin and having their centers on the y-axis. Examples are shown in Figure 8.13.

Pursuit problems. A point Q is constrained to move along a prescribed plane curve C_1. Another point P in the same plane "pursues" the point Q. That is, P moves in such a manner that its direction of motion is always toward Q. The point P thereby traces out another curve C_2 called a *curve of pursuit*. An example is shown in Figure 8.14 where C_1 is

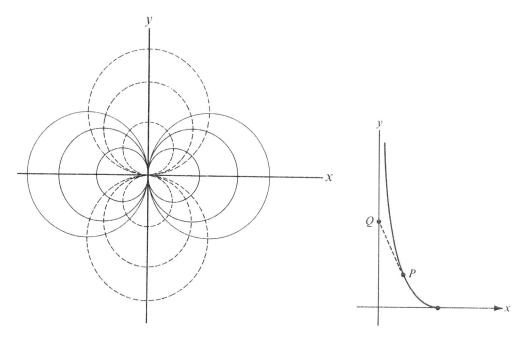

FIGURE 8.13   Orthogonal circles.

FIGURE 8.14   The tractrix as a curve of pursuit. The distance from P to Q is constant.

the y-axis. In a typical problem of pursuit we seek to determine the curve C_2 when the curve C_1 is known and some additional piece of information is given concerning P and Q, for example, a relation between their positions or their velocities.

When we say that the direction of motion of P is always toward Q, we mean that the tangent line of C_2 through P passes through Q. Therefore, if we denote by (x, y) the rectangular coordinates of P at a given instant, and by (X, Y) those of Q at the same instant, we must have

(8.60)
$$y' = \frac{Y - y}{X - x}.$$

The additional piece of information usually enables us to consider X and Y as known functions of x and y, in which case Equation (8.60) becomes a first-order differential equation for y. Now we consider a specific example in which this equation is separable.

EXAMPLE 2. A point Q moves on a straight line C_1, and a point P pursues Q in such a way that the distance from P to Q has a constant value $k > 0$. If P is initially not on C_1, find the curve of pursuit.

Solution. We take C_1 to be the y-axis and place P initially at the point $(k, 0)$. Since the distance from P to Q is k, we must have $(X - x)^2 + (Y - y)^2 = k^2$. But $X = 0$ on C_1, so we have $Y - y = \sqrt{k^2 - x^2}$, and the differential equation (8.60) becomes

$$y' = \frac{\sqrt{k^2 - x^2}}{-x}.$$

Integrating this equation with the help of the substitution $x = k \cos t$ and using the fact that $y = 0$ when $x = k$, we obtain the relation

$$y = k \log \frac{k + \sqrt{k^2 - x^2}}{x} - \sqrt{k^2 - x^2}.$$

The curve of pursuit in this example is called a *tractrix;* it is shown in Figure 8.14.

Flow of fluid through an orifice. Suppose we are given a tank (not necessarily cylindrical) containing a fluid. The fluid flows from the tank through a sharp-edged orifice. If there were no friction (and hence no loss of energy) the speed of the jet would be equal to $\sqrt{2gy}$ feet per second, where y denotes the height (in feet) of the surface above the orifice.† (See Figure 8.15.) If A_0 denotes the area (in square feet) of the orifice, then $A_0 \sqrt{2gy}$ represents the number of cubic feet per second of fluid flowing from the orifice. Because of friction, the jet stream contracts somewhat and the actual rate of discharge is more nearly $cA_0\sqrt{2gy}$, where c is an experimentally determined number called the *discharge coefficient.* For ordinary sharp-edged orifices, the approximate value of c is 0.60. Using this and taking $g = 32$, we find that the speed of the jet is $4.8\sqrt{y}$ feet per second, and therefore the rate of discharge of volume is $4.8A_0\sqrt{y}$ cubic feet per second.

Let $V(y)$ denote the volume of the fluid in the tank when the height of the fluid is y. If the cross-sectional area of the tank at the height u is $A(u)$, then we have $V(y) = \int_0^y A(u)\, du$, from which we obtain $dV/dy = A(y)$. The argument in the foregoing paragraph tells us that the rate of change of volume with respect to time is $dV/dt = -4.8A_0\sqrt{y}$ cubic feet per second, the minus sign coming in because the volume is decreasing. By the chain rule we have

$$\frac{dV}{dt} = \frac{dV}{dy}\frac{dy}{dt} = A(y)\frac{dy}{dt}.$$

Combining this with the equation $dV/dt = -4.8A_0\sqrt{y}$, we obtain the differential equation

$$A(y)\frac{dy}{dt} = -4.8A_0\sqrt{y}.$$

---

† If a particle of mass m falls freely through a distance y and reaches a speed v, its kinetic energy $\frac{1}{2}mv^2$ must be equal to the potential energy mgy (the work done in lifting it up a distance y). Solving for v, we get $v = \sqrt{2gy}$.

This separable differential equation is used as the mathematical model for problems concerning fluid flow through an orifice. The height y of the surface is related to the time t by an equation of the form

(8.61) $$\int \frac{A(y)}{\sqrt{y}}\, dy = -4.8 A_0 \int dt + C .$$

Area $= A(y)$

y

FIGURE 8.15   Flow of fluid through an orifice.

EXAMPLE 3. Consider a specific case in which the cross-sectional area of the tank is constant, say $A(y) = A$ for all y, and suppose the level of the fluid is lowered from 10 feet to 9 feet in 10 minutes (600 seconds). These data can be combined with Equation (8.61) to give us

$$-\int_{10}^{9} \frac{dy}{\sqrt{y}} = k \int_{0}^{600} dt ,$$

where $k = 4.8 A_0 / A$. Using this, we can determine k and we find that

$$\frac{\sqrt{10} - \sqrt{9}}{\frac{1}{2}} = 600k \qquad \text{or} \qquad k = \frac{\sqrt{10} - 3}{300} .$$

Now we can compute the time required for the level to fall from one given value to any other. For example, if at time t_1 the level is 7 feet and at time t_2 it is 1 foot (t_1, t_2 measured in minutes, say), then we must have

$$-\int_7^1 \frac{dy}{\sqrt{y}} = k \int_{60t_1}^{60t_2} dt \, ,$$

which yields

$$t_2 - t_1 = \frac{2(\sqrt{7}-1)}{60k} = 10\,\frac{\sqrt{7}-1}{\sqrt{10}-3} = \frac{10(\sqrt{7}-1)(\sqrt{10}+3)}{10-9} = (10)(1.645)(6.162)$$

$$= 101.3 \text{ min.}$$

8.28 Miscellaneous review exercises

In each of Exercises 1 through 10 find the orthogonal trajectories of the given family of curves.

1. $2x + 3y = C$.
2. $xy = C$.
3. $x^2 + y^2 + 2Cy = 1$.
4. $y^2 = Cx$.
5. $x^2 y = C$.
6. $y = Ce^{-2x}$.
7. $x^2 - y^2 = C$.
8. $y = C \cos x$.
9. All circles through the points $(1, 0)$ and $(-1, 0)$.
10. All circles through the points $(1, 1)$ and $(-1, -1)$.
11. A point Q moves upward along the positive y-axis. A point P, initially at $(1, 0)$, pursues Q in such a way that its distance from the y-axis is $\frac{1}{2}$ the distance of Q from the origin. Find a Cartesian equation for the path of pursuit.
12. Solve Exercise 11 when the fraction $\frac{1}{2}$ is replaced by an arbitrary positive number k.
13. A curve with Cartesian equation $y = f(x)$ passes through the origin. Lines drawn parallel to the coordinate axes through an arbitrary point of the curve form a rectangle with two sides on the axes. The curve divides every such rectangle into two regions A and B, one of which has an area equal to n times the other. Find the function f.
14. Solve Exercise 13 if the two regions A and B have the property that, when rotated about the x-axis, they sweep out solids one of which has a volume n times that of the other.
15. The graph of a nonnegative differentiable function f passes through the origin and through the point $(1, 2/\pi)$. If, for every $x > 0$, the ordinate set of f above the interval $[0, x]$ sweeps out a solid of volume $x^2 f(x)$ when rotated about the x-axis, find the function f.
16. A nonnegative differentiable function f is defined on the closed interval $[0, 1]$ with $f(1) = 0$. For each a, $0 < a < 1$, the line $x = a$ cuts the ordinate set of f into two regions having areas A and B, respectively, A being the area of the leftmost region. If $A - B = 2f(a) + 3a + b$, where b is a constant independent of a, find the function f and the constant b.
17. The graph of a function f passes through the two points $P_0 = (0, 1)$ and $P_1 = (1, 0)$. For every point $P = (x, y)$ on the graph, the curve lies above the chord $P_0 P$, and the area $A(x)$ of the region between the curve and the chord PP_0 is equal to x^3. Determine the function f.
18. A tank with vertical sides has a square cross-section of area 4 square feet. Water is leaving the tank through an orifice of area 5/3 square inches. If the water level is initially 2 feet above the orifice, find the time required for the level to drop 1 foot.
19. Refer to the preceding problem. If water also flows into the tank at the rate of 100 cubic inches per second, show that the water level approaches the value $(25/24)^2$ feet above the orifice, regardless of the initial water level.
20. A tank has the shape of a right circular cone with its vertex up. Find the time required to empty a liquid from the tank through an orifice in its base. Express your result in terms of the dimensions of the cone and the area A_0 of the orifice.

21. The equation $xy'' - y' + (1 - x)y = 0$ possesses a solution of the form $y = e^{mx}$, where m is constant. Determine this solution explicitly.

22. Solve the differential equation $(x + y^3) + 6xy^2y' = 0$ by making a suitable change of variable which converts it into a linear equation.

23. Solve the differential equation $(1 + y^2e^{2x})y' + y = 0$ by introducing a change of variable of the form $y = ue^{mx}$, where m is constant and u is a new unknown function.

24. (a) Given a function f which satisfies the relations

$$2f'(x) = f\left(\frac{1}{x}\right) \quad \text{if} \quad x > 0, \quad f(1) = 2,$$

let $y = f(x)$ and show that y satisfies a differential equation of the form

$$x^2y'' + axy' + by = 0,$$

where a and b are constants. Determine a and b.
(b) Find a solution of the form $f(x) = Cx^n$.

25. (a) Let u be a nonzero solution of the second-order equation

$$y'' + P(x)y' + Q(x)y = 0.$$

Show that the substitution $y = uv$ converts the equation

$$y'' + P(x)y' + Q(x)y = R(x)$$

into a first-order linear equation for v'.
(b) Obtain a nonzero solution of the equation $y'' - 4y' + x^2(y' - 4y) = 0$ by inspection and use the method of part (a) to find a solution of

$$y'' - 4y' + x^2(y' - 4y) = 2xe^{-x^3/3}$$

such that $y = 0$ and $y' = 4$ when $x = 0$.

26. Scientists at the Ajax Atomics Works isolated one gram of a new radioactive element called Deteriorum. It was found to decay at a rate proportional to the *square* of the amount present. After one year, $\frac{1}{2}$ gram remained.
(a) Set up and solve the differential equation for the mass of Deteriorum remaining at time t.
(b) Evaluate the decay constant in units of $\text{gm}^{-1} \, yr^{-1}$.

27. In the preceding problem, suppose the word *square* were replaced by *square root*, the other data remaining the same. Show that in this case the substance would decay entirely within a finite time, and find this time.

28. At the beginning of the Gold Rush, the population of Coyote Gulch, Arizona was 365. From then on, the population would have grown by a factor of e each year, except for the high rate of "accidental" death, amounting to one victim per day among every 100 citizens. By solving an appropriate differential equation determine, as functions of time, (a) the actual population of Coyote Gulch t years from the day the Gold Rush began, and (b) the cumulative number of fatalities.

29. With what speed should a rocket be fired upward so that it never returns to earth? (Neglect all forces except the earth's gravitational attraction.)

30. Let $y = f(x)$ be that solution of the differential equation

$$y' = \frac{2y^2 + x}{3y^2 + 5}$$

which satisfies the initial condition $f(0) = 0$. (Do not attempt to solve this differential equation.)
(a) The differential equation shows that $f'(0) = 0$. Discuss whether f has a relative maximum or minimum or neither at 0.
(b) Notice that $f'(x) \geq 0$ for each $x \geq 0$ and that $f'(x) \geq \frac{2}{3}$ for each $x \geq \frac{10}{3}$. Exhibit two positive numbers a and b such that $f(x) > ax - b$ for each $x \geq \frac{10}{3}$.
(c) Show that $x/y^2 \to 0$ as $x \to +\infty$. Give full details of your reasoning.
(d) Show that y/x tends to a finite limit as $x \to +\infty$ and determine this limit.

31. Given a function f which satisfies the differential equation

$$xf''(x) + 3x[f'(x)]^2 = 1 - e^{-x}$$

for all real x. (Do not attempt to solve this differential equation.)
(a) If f has an extremum at a point $c \neq 0$, show that this extremum is a minimum.
(b) If f has an extremum at 0, is it a maximum or a minimum? Justify your conclusion.
(c) If $f(0) = f'(0) = 0$, find the *smallest* constant A such that $f(x) \leq Ax^2$ for all $x \geq 0$.

9

COMPLEX NUMBERS

9.1 Historical introduction

The quadratic equation $x^2 + 1 = 0$ has no solution in the real-number system because there is no real number whose square is -1. New types of numbers, called *complex numbers*, have been introduced to provide solutions to such equations. In this brief chapter we discuss complex numbers and show that they are important in solving algebraic equations and that they have an impact on differential and integral calculus.

As early as the 16th century, a symbol $\sqrt{-1}$ was introduced to provide solutions of the quadratic equation $x^2 + 1 = 0$. This symbol, later denoted by the letter i, was regarded as a fictitious or imaginary number which could be manipulated algebraically like an ordinary real number, except that its square was -1. Thus, for example, the quadratic polynomial $x^2 + 1$ was factored by writing $x^2 + 1 = x^2 - i^2 = (x - i)(x + i)$, and the solutions of the equation $x^2 + 1 = 0$ were exhibited as $x = \pm i$, without any concern regarding the meaning or validity of such formulas. Expressions such as $2 + 3i$ were called complex numbers, and they were used in a purely formal way for nearly 300 years before they were described in a manner that would be considered satisfactory by present-day standards.

Early in the 19th century, Karl Friedrich Gauss (1777–1855) and William Rowan Hamilton (1805–1865) independently and almost simultaneously proposed the idea of defining complex numbers as ordered pairs (a, b) of real numbers endowed with certain special properties. This idea is widely accepted today and is described in the next section.

9.2 Definitions and field properties

DEFINITION. *If a and b are real numbers, the pair (a, b) is called a complex number, provided that equality, addition, and multiplication of pairs is defined as follows:*
  (a) *Equality:* $(a, b) = (c, d)$ *means* $a = c$ *and* $b = d$.
  (b) *Sum:* $(a, b) + (c, d) = (a + c, b + d)$.
  (c) *Product:* $(a, b)(c, d) = (ac - bd, ad + bc)$.

The definition of equality tells us that the pair (a, b) is to be regarded as an *ordered* pair. Thus, the complex number $(2, 3)$ is not equal to the complex number $(3, 2)$. The numbers

358

a and *b* are called *components* of (a, b). The first component, *a*, is also called the *real part* of the complex number; the second component, *b*, is called the *imaginary part*.

Note that the symbol $i = \sqrt{-1}$ does not appear anywhere in this definition. Presently we shall introduce *i* as a particular complex number which has all the algebraic properties ascribed to the fictitious symbol $\sqrt{-1}$ by the early mathematicians. However, before we do this, we will discuss the basic properties of the operations just defined.

THEOREM 9.1. *The operations of addition and multiplication of complex numbers satisfy the commutative, associative and distributive laws. That is, if x, y, and z are arbitrary complex numbers, we have the following.*

    Commutative laws: $x + y = y + x, \qquad xy = yx$.
    Associative laws: $x + (y + z) = (x + y) + z, \qquad x(yz) = (xy)z$.
    Distributive law: $x(y + z) = xy + xz$.

Proof. All these laws are easily verified directly from the definition of sum and product. For example, to prove the associative law for multiplication, we write $x = (x_1, x_2)$, $y = (y_1, y_2)$, $z = (z_1, z_2)$ and note that

$$x(yz) = (x_1, x_2)(y_1z_1 - y_2z_2, y_1z_2 + y_2z_1)$$

$$= (x_1(y_1z_1 - y_2z_2) - x_2(y_1z_2 + y_2z_1), x_1(y_1z_2 + y_2z_1) + x_2(y_1z_1 - y_2z_2))$$

$$= ((x_1y_1 - x_2y_2)z_1 - (x_1y_2 + x_2y_1)z_2, (x_1y_2 + x_2y_1)z_1 + (x_1y_1 - x_2y_2)z_2)$$

$$= (x_1y_1 - x_2y_2, x_1y_2 + x_2y_1)(z_1, z_2) = (xy)z .$$

The commutative and distributive laws may be similarly proved.

Theorem 9.1 shows that the set of all complex numbers satisfies the first three field axioms for the real number system, as given in Section I 3.2. Now we will show that Axioms 4, 5, and 6 are also satisfied.

Since $(0, 0) + (a, b) = (a, b)$ for all complex numbers (a, b), the complex number $(0, 0)$ is an identity element for addition. It is called the zero complex number. Similarly, the complex number $(1, 0)$ is an identity for multiplication because

$$(a, b)(1, 0) = (a, b)$$

for all (a, b). Thus, Axiom 4 is satisfied with $(0, 0)$ as the identity for addition and $(1, 0)$ as the identity for multiplication.

To verify Axiom 5, we simply note that $(-a, -b) + (a, b) = (0, 0)$, so $(-a, -b)$ is the negative of (a, b). We write $-(a, b)$ for $(-a, -b)$.

Finally, we show that each nonzero complex number has a reciprocal relative to the identity element $(1, 0)$. That is, if $(a, b) \neq (0, 0)$, there is a complex number (c, d) such that

$$(a, b)(c, d) = (1, 0) .$$

In fact, this equation is equivalent to the pair of equations

$$ac - bd = 1, \qquad ad + bc = 0 ,$$

which has the unique solution

(9.1)
$$c = \frac{a}{a^2 + b^2}, \qquad d = \frac{-b}{a^2 + b^2}.$$

The condition $(a, b) \neq (0, 0)$ ensures that $a^2 + b^2 \neq 0$, so the reciprocal is well defined. We write $(a, b)^{-1}$ or $1/(a, b)$ for the reciprocal of (a, b). Thus, we have

(9.2)
$$\frac{1}{(a, b)} = \left(\frac{a}{a^2 + b^2}, \frac{-b}{a^2 + b^2} \right) \qquad \text{if} \quad (a, b) \neq (0, 0).$$

The foregoing discussion shows that the set of all complex numbers satisfies the six field axioms for the real-number system. Therefore, all the laws of algebra deducible from the field axioms also hold for complex numbers. In particular, Theorems I.1 through I.15 of Section I 3.2 are all valid for complex numbers as well as for real numbers. Theorem I.8 tells us that quotients of complex numbers exist. That is, if (a, b) and (c, d) are two complex numbers with $(a, b) \neq (0, 0)$, then there is exactly one complex number (x, y) such that $(a, b)(x, y) = (c, d)$. In fact, we have $(x, y) = (c, d)(a, b)^{-1}$.

9.3   The complex numbers as an extension of the real numbers

Let $\mathbf{C}$ denote the set of all complex numbers. Consider the subset $\mathbf{C}_0$ of $\mathbf{C}$ consisting of all complex numbers of the form $(a, 0)$, that is, all complex numbers with zero imaginary part. The sum or product of two members of $\mathbf{C}_0$ is again in $\mathbf{C}_0$. In fact, we have

(9.3) $(a, 0) + (b, 0) = (a + b, 0)$ and $(a, 0)(b, 0) = (ab, 0).$

This shows that we can add or multiply two numbers in $\mathbf{C}_0$ by adding or multiplying the real parts alone. Or, in other words, with respect to addition and multiplication, the numbers in $\mathbf{C}_0$ act exactly as though they were real numbers. The same is true for subtraction and division, since $-(a, 0) = (-a, 0)$ and $(b, 0)^{-1} = (b^{-1}, 0)$ if $b \neq 0$. For this reason, we ordinarily make no distinction between the real number x and the complex number $(x, 0)$ whose real part is x; we agree to identify x and $(x, 0)$, and we write $x = (x, 0)$. In particular, we write $0 = (0, 0)$, $1 = (1, 0)$, $-1 = (-1, 0)$, and so on. Thus, we can think of the complex number system as an extension of the real number system.

The relation between $\mathbf{C}_0$ and the real-number system can be described in a slightly different way. Let $\mathbf{R}$ denote the set of all real numbers, and let f denote the function which maps each real number x onto the complex number $(x, 0)$. That is, if $x \in \mathbf{R}$, let

$$f(x) = (x, 0).$$

The function f so defined has domain $\mathbf{R}$ and range $\mathbf{C}_0$, and it maps distinct elements of $\mathbf{R}$ onto distinct elements of $\mathbf{C}_0$. Because of these properties, f is said to establish a *one-to-one correspondence* between $\mathbf{R}$ and $\mathbf{C}_0$. The operations of addition and multiplication are preserved under this correspondence. That is, we have

$$f(a + b) = f(a) + f(b) \qquad \text{and} \qquad f(ab) = f(a)f(b),$$

these equations being merely a restatement of (9.3). Since $\mathbf{R}$ satisfies the six field axioms, the same is true of $\mathbf{C}_0$. The two fields $\mathbf{R}$ and $\mathbf{C}_0$ are said to be *isomorphic*; the function f which relates them as described above is called an *isomorphism*. As far as the algebraic operations of addition and multiplication are concerned, we make no distinction between isomorphic fields. That is why we identify the real number x with the complex number $(x, 0)$. The complex-number system $\mathbf{C}$ is called an *extension* of the real-number system $\mathbf{R}$ because it contains a subset $\mathbf{C}_0$ which is isomorphic to $\mathbf{R}$.

The field $\mathbf{C}_0$ can also be *ordered* in such a way that the three order axioms of Section I 3.4 are satisfied. In fact, we simply define $(x, 0)$ to be positive if and only if $x > 0$. It is trivial to verify that Axioms 7, 8, and 9 are satisfied, so $\mathbf{C}_0$ is an *ordered* field. The isomorphism f described above also preserves order since it maps the positive elements of $\mathbf{R}$ onto the positive elements of $\mathbf{C}_0$.

9.4 The imaginary unit i

Complex numbers have some algebraic properties not possessed by real numbers. For example, the quadratic equation $x^2 + 1 = 0$, which has no solution among the real numbers, can now be solved with the use of complex numbers. In fact, the complex number $(0, 1)$ is a solution, since we have

$$(0, 1)^2 = (0, 1)(0, 1) = (0 \cdot 0 - 1 \cdot 1, 0 \cdot 1 + 1 \cdot 0) = (-1, 0) = -1 .$$

The complex number $(0, 1)$ is denoted by i and is called the *imaginary unit*. It has the property that its square is -1, $i^2 = -1$. The reader can easily verify that $(-i)^2 = -1$, so $x = -i$ is another solution of the equation $x^2 + 1 = 0$.

Now we can relate the ordered-pair idea with the notation used by the early mathematicians. First we note that the definition of multiplication of complex numbers gives us $(b, 0)(0, 1) = (0, b)$, and hence we have

$$(a, b) = (a, 0) + (0, b) = (a, 0) + (b, 0)(0, 1) .$$

Therefore, if we write $a = (a, 0)$, $b = (b, 0)$, and $i = (0, 1)$, we get $(a, b) = a + bi$. In other words, we have proved the following.

THEOREM 9.2. *Every complex number (a, b) can be expressed in the form $(a, b) = a + bi$.*

The advantage of this notation is that it aids us in algebraic manipulations of formulas involving addition and multiplication. For example, if we multiply $a + bi$ by $c + di$, using the distributive and associative laws, and replace i^2 by -1, we find that

$$(a + bi)(c + di) = ac - bd + (ad + bc)i ,$$

which, of course, is in agreement with the definition of multiplication. Similarly, to compute the reciprocal of a nonzero complex number $a + bi$, we may write

$$\frac{1}{a + bi} = \frac{a - bi}{(a + bi)(a - bi)} = \frac{a - bi}{a^2 + b^2} = \frac{a}{a^2 + b^2} - \frac{bi}{a^2 + b^2} .$$

This formula is in agreement with that given in (9.2).

By the introduction of complex numbers, we have gained much more than the ability to solve the simple quadratic equation $x^2 + 1 = 0$. Consider, for example, the quadratic equation $ax^2 + bx + c = 0$, where a, b, c are real and $a \neq 0$. By completing the square, we may write this equation in the form

$$\left(x + \frac{b}{2a}\right)^2 + \frac{4ac - b^2}{4a^2} = 0.$$

If $4ac - b^2 \leq 0$, the equation has the real roots $(-b \pm \sqrt{b^2 - 4ac})/(2a)$. If $4ac - b^2 > 0$, the left member is positive for every real x and the equation has no real roots. In this case, however, there are two complex roots, given by the formulas

(9.4) $\qquad r_1 = -\dfrac{b}{2a} + i\,\dfrac{\sqrt{4ac - b^2}}{2a}$ $\qquad$ and $\qquad$ $r_2 = -\dfrac{b}{2a} - i\,\dfrac{\sqrt{4ac - b^2}}{2a}.$

In 1799, Gauss proved that every polynomial equation of the form

$$a_0 + a_1 x + a_2 x^2 + \cdots + a_n x^n = 0,$$

where a_0, a_1, $\ldots$, a_n are arbitrary real numbers, with $a_n \neq 0$, has a solution among the complex numbers if $n \geq 1$. Moreover, even if the coefficients a_0, a_1, $\ldots$, a_n are complex, a solution exists in the complex-number system. This fact is known as the *fundamental theorem of algebra*.[†] It shows that there is no need to construct numbers more general than complex numbers to solve polynomial equations with complex coefficients.

9.5 Geometric interpretation. Modulus and argument

Since a complex number (x, y) is an ordered pair of real numbers, it may be represented geometrically by a point in the plane, or by an arrow or geometric vector from the origin to the point (x, y), as shown in Figure 9.1. In this context, the xy-plane is often referred to as the complex plane. The x-axis is called the real axis; the y-axis is the imaginary axis. It is customary to use the words *complex number* and *point* interchangeably. Thus, we refer to the point z rather than the point corresponding to the complex number z.

The operations of addition and subtraction of complex numbers have a simple geometric interpretation. If two complex numbers z_1 and z_2 are represented by arrows from the origin to z_1 and z_2, respectively, then the sum $z_1 + z_2$ is determined by the *parallelogram law*. The arrow from the origin to $z_1 + z_2$ is a diagonal of the parallelogram determined by 0, z_1, and z_2, as illustrated by the example in Figure 9.2. The other diagonal is related to the difference of z_1 and z_2. The arrow from z_1 to z_2 is parallel to and equal in length to the arrow from 0 to $z_2 - z_1$; the arrow in the opposite direction, from z_2 to z_1, is related in the same way to $z_1 - z_2$.

---

† A proof of the fundamental theorem of algebra can be found in almost any book on the theory of functions of a complex variable. For example, see K. Knopp, *Theory of Functions*, Dover Publications, New York, 1945, or E. Hille, *Analytic Function Theory*, Vol. I, Blaisdell Publishing Co., 1959. A more elementary proof is given in O. Schreier and E. Sperner, *Introduction to Modern Algebra and Matrix Theory*, Chelsea Publishing Company, New York, 1951.

If $(x, y) \neq (0, 0)$, we can express x and y in polar coordinates,

$$x = r \cos \theta, \qquad y = r \sin \theta,$$

and we obtain

(9.5) $$x + iy = r (\cos \theta + i \sin \theta).$$

The positive number r, which represents the distance of (x, y) from the origin, is called the *modulus* or *absolute value* of $x + iy$ and is denoted by $|x + iy|$. Thus, we have

$$|x + iy| = \sqrt{x^2 + y^2}.$$

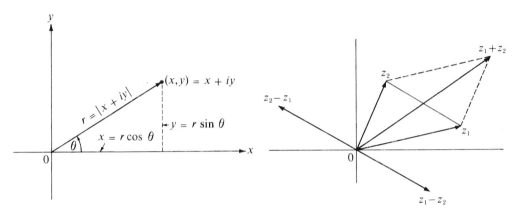

FIGURE 9.1   Geometric representation of the complex number $x + iy$.

FIGURE 9.2   Addition and subtraction of complex numbers represented geometrically by the parallelogram law.

The polar angle θ is called an *argument* of $x + iy$. We say *an* argument rather than *the* argument because for a given point (x, y) the angle θ is determined only up to multiples of 2π. Sometimes it is desirable to assign a unique argument to a complex number. This may be done by restricting θ to lie in a half-open interval of length 2π. The intervals $[0, 2\pi)$ and $(-\pi, \pi]$ are commonly used for this purpose. We shall use the interval $(-\pi, \pi]$ and refer to the corresponding θ as the *principal argument* of $x + iy$; we denote this θ by $\arg(x + iy)$. Thus, if $x + iy \neq 0$ and $r = |x + iy|$, we define $\arg(x + iy)$ to be the unique real θ satisfying the conditions

$$x = r \cos \theta, \qquad y = r \sin \theta, \qquad -\pi < \theta \leq \pi.$$

For the zero complex number, we assign the modulus 0 and agree that any real θ may be used as an argument.

Since the absolute value of a complex number z is simply the length of a line segment, it is not surprising to find that it has the usual properties of absolute values of real numbers. For example, we have

$$|z| > 0 \quad \text{if} \quad z \neq 0, \quad \text{and} \quad |z_1 - z_2| = |z_2 - z_1|.$$

Geometrically, the absolute value $|z_1 - z_2|$ represents the distance between the points z_1 and z_2 in the complex plane. The triangle inequality

$$|z_1 + z_2| \leq |z_1| + |z_2|$$

is also valid. In addition, we have the following formulas for absolute values of products and quotients of complex numbers:

(9.6) $$|z_1 z_2| = |z_1| \, |z_2|$$

and

$$\left| \frac{z_1}{z_2} \right| = \frac{|z_1|}{|z_2|} \quad \text{if} \quad z_2 \neq 0 \,.$$

If we write $z_1 = a + bi$ and $z_2 = c + di$, we obtain (9.6) at once from the identity

$$(ac - bd)^2 + (bc + ad)^2 = (a^2 + b^2)(c^2 + d^2) \,.$$

The formula for $|z_1/z_2|$ follows from (9.6) if we write z_1 as a product,

$$z_1 = z_2 \frac{z_1}{z_2} \,.$$

If $z = x + iy$, the *complex conjugate* of z is the complex number $\bar{z} = x - iy$. Geometrically, $\bar{z}$ represents the reflection of z through the real axis. The definition of conjugate implies that

$$\overline{z_1 + z_2} = \bar{z}_1 + \bar{z}_2 \,, \qquad \overline{z_1 z_2} = \bar{z}_1 \bar{z}_2 \,, \qquad \overline{z_1/z_2} = \bar{z}_1/\bar{z}_2 \,, \qquad z\bar{z} = |z|^2 \,.$$

The verification of these properties is left as an exercise for the reader.

If a quadratic equation with real coefficients has no real roots, its complex roots, given by (9.4), are conjugates. Conversely, if r_1 and r_2 are complex conjugates, say $r_1 = \alpha + i\beta$ and $r_2 = \alpha - i\beta$, where α and β are real, then r_1 and r_2 are roots of a quadratic equation with real coefficients. In fact, we have

$$r_1 + r_2 = 2\alpha \quad \text{and} \quad r_1 r_2 = \alpha^2 + \beta^2 \,,$$

so

$$(x - r_1)(x - r_2) = x^2 - (r_1 + r_2)x + r_1 r_2 \,,$$

and the quadratic equation in question is

$$x^2 - 2\alpha x + \alpha^2 + \beta^2 = 0 \,.$$

9.6 Exercises

1. Express the following complex numbers in the form $a + bi$.
   (a) $(1 + i)^2$.
   (b) $1/i$.
   (c) $1/(1 + i)$.
   (d) $(2 + 3i)(3 - 4i)$.
   (e) $(1 + i)/(1 - 2i)$.
   (f) $i^5 + i^{16}$.
   (g) $1 + i + i^2 + i^3$.
   (h) $\frac{1}{2}(1 + i)(1 + i^{-8})$.

2. Compute the absolute values of the following complex numbers.
   (a) $1 + i$.
   (b) $3 + 4i$.
   (c) $(1 + i)/(1 - i)$.
   (d) $1 + i + i^2$.
   (e) $i^7 + i^{10}$.
   (f) $2(1 - i) + 3(2 + i)$.

3. Compute the modulus and principal argument of each of the following complex numbers.
   (a) $2i$.
   (b) $-3i$.
   (c) -1.
   (d) 1.
   (e) $-3 + \sqrt{3}\, i$.
   (f) $(1 + i)/\sqrt{2}$.
   (g) $(-1 + i)^3$.
   (h) $(-1 - i)^3$.
   (i) $1/(1 + i)$.
   (j) $1/(1 + i)^2$.

4. In each case, determine all real numbers x and y which satisfy the given relation.
   (a) $x + iy = x - iy$.
   (b) $x + iy = |x + iy|$.
   (c) $|x + iy| = |x - iy|$.
   (d) $(x + iy)^2 = (x - iy)^2$.
   (e) $\dfrac{x + iy}{x - iy} = x - iy$.
   (f) $\displaystyle\sum_{k=0}^{100} i^k = x + iy$.

5. Make a sketch showing the set of all z in the complex plane which satisfy each of the following conditions.
   (a) $|z| < 1$.
   (b) $z + \bar{z} = 1$.
   (c) $z - \bar{z} = i$.
   (d) $|z - 1| = |z + 1|$.
   (e) $|z - i| = |z + i|$.
   (f) $z + \bar{z} = |z|^2$.

6. Let f be a polynomial with real coefficients.
   (a) Show that $\overline{f(z)} = f(\bar{z})$ for every complex z.
   (b) Use part (a) to deduce that the nonreal zeros of f (if any exist) must occur in pairs of conjugate complex numbers.

7. Prove that an ordering relation cannot be introduced in the complex number system so that all three order axioms of Section I3.4 are satisfied.

   [*Hint:* Assume that such an ordering can be introduced and try to decide whether the imaginary unit i is positive or negative.]

8. Define the following "pseudo-ordering" among the complex numbers. If $z = x + iy$, we say that z is positive if and only if $x > 0$. Which of the order axioms of Section I3.4 are satisfied with this definition of positive?

9. Solve Exercise 8 if the pseudo-ordering is defined as follows: We say that z is positive if and only if $|z| > 0$.

10. Solve Exercise 8 if the pseudo-ordering is defined as follows: If $z = x + iy$, we say that z is positive if and only if $x > y$.

11. Make a sketch showing the set of all complex z which satisfy each of the following conditions.
    (a) $|2z + 3| < 1$.
    (b) $|z + 1| < |z - 1|$.
    (c) $|z - i| \le |z + i|$.
    (d) $|z| \le |2z + 1|$.

12. Let $w = (az + b)/(cz + d)$, where a, b, c, and d are real. Prove that

$$w - \bar{w} = (ad - bc)(z - \bar{z})/|cz + d|^2 .$$

If $ad - bc > 0$, prove that the imaginary parts of z and w have the same sign.

9.7   Complex exponentials

We wish now to extend the definition of e^x so that it becomes meaningful when x is replaced by any complex number z. We wish this extension to be such that the law of exponents, $e^a e^b = e^{a+b}$, will be valid for all complex a and b. And, of course, we want e^z to agree with the usual exponential when z is real. There are several equivalent ways to carry out this extension. Before we state the definition of e^z that we have chosen, we shall give a heuristic discussion which will serve as motivation for this definition.

If we write $z = x + iy$, then, if the law of exponents is to be valid for complex numbers, we must have

$$e^z = e^{x+iy} = e^x e^{iy}\,.$$

Since e^x has already been defined when x is real, our task is to arrive at a reasonable definition for e^{iy} when y is real. Now, if e^{iy} is to be a complex number, we may write

$$(9.7)\qquad\qquad\qquad e^{iy} = A(y) + iB(y)\,,$$

where A and B are real-valued functions to be determined. Let us differentiate both sides of Equation (9.7), assuming A and B are differentiable, and treating the complex number i as though it were a real number. Then we get

$$(9.8)\qquad\qquad\qquad ie^{iy} = A'(y) + iB'(y)\,.$$

Differentiating once more, we find that

$$-e^{iy} = A''(y) + iB''(y)\,.$$

Comparison of this equation with (9.7) shows that A and B must satisfy the equations

$$A''(y) = -A(y)\qquad\text{and}\qquad B''(y) = -B(y)\,.$$

In other words, each of the functions A and B is a solution of the differential equation $f'' + f = 0$. From the work of Chapter 8, we know that this equation has exactly one solution with specified initial values $f(0)$ and $f'(0)$. If we put $y = 0$ in (9.7) and (9.8) and use the fact that $e^0 = 1$, we find that A and B have the initial values

$$A(0) = 1,\qquad A'(0) = 0,\qquad\text{and}\qquad B(0) = 0,\qquad B'(0) = 1\,.$$

By the uniqueness theorem for second-order differential equations with constant coefficients, we must have

$$A(y) = \cos y\qquad\text{and}\qquad B(y) = \sin y\,.$$

In other words, if e^{iy} is to be a complex number with the properties just described, then we must have $e^{iy} = \cos y + i \sin y$. This discussion serves to motivate the following definition.

DEFINITION. *If $z = x + iy$, we define e^z to be the complex number given by the equation*

(9.9) $$e^z = e^x(\cos y + i \sin y).$$

Note that $e^z = e^x$ when $y = 0$; hence this exponential agrees with the usual exponential when z is real. Now we shall use this definition to deduce the law of exponents.

THEOREM 9.3. *If a and b are complex numbers, we have*

(9.10) $$e^a e^b = e^{a+b}.$$

Proof. Writing $a = x + iy$ and $b = u + iv$, we have

$$e^a = e^x(\cos y + i \sin y), \qquad e^b = e^u(\cos v + i \sin v),$$

so

$$e^a e^b = e^x e^u[\cos y \cos v - \sin y \sin v + i(\cos y \sin v + \sin y \cos v)].$$

Now we use the addition formulas for $\cos (y + v)$ and $\sin (y + v)$ and the law of exponents for real exponentials, and we see that the foregoing equation becomes

(9.11) $$e^a e^b = e^{x+u}[\cos (y + v) + i \sin (y + v)].$$

Since $a + b = (x + u) + i(y + v)$, the right member of (9.11) is e^{a+b}. This proves (9.10).

THEOREM 9.4. *Every complex number $z \neq 0$ can be expressed in the form*

(9.12) $$z = re^{i\theta},$$

where $r = |z|$ and $\theta = \arg (z) + 2n\pi$, n being any integer. This representation is called the polar form of z.

Proof. If $z = x + iy$, the polar-coordinate representation (9.5) gives us

$$z = r(\cos \theta + i \sin \theta),$$

where $r = |z|$ and $\theta = \arg (z) + 2n\pi$, n being any integer. But if we take $x = 0$ and $y = \theta$ in (9.9), we obtain the formula

$$e^{i\theta} = \cos \theta + i \sin \theta,$$

which proves (9.12).

The representation of complex numbers in the polar form (9.12) is especially useful in connection with multiplication and division of complex numbers. For example, if $z_1 = r_1 e^{i\theta}$ and $z_2 = r_2 e^{i\phi}$, we have

(9.13) $$z_1 z_2 = r_1 e^{i\theta} r_2 e^{i\phi} = r_1 r_2 e^{i(\theta+\phi)}.$$

Therefore the product of the moduli, r_1r_2, is the modulus of the product z_1z_2, in agreement with Equation (9.6), and the sum of the arguments, $\theta + \phi$, is an admissible argument for the product z_1z_2.

When $z = re^{i\theta}$, repeated application of (9.13) gives us the formula

$$z^n = r^n e^{in\theta} = r^n(\cos n\theta + i \sin n\theta),$$

valid for any nonnegative integer n. This formula is also valid for negative integers n if we define z^{-m} to be $(z^{-1})^m$ when m is a positive integer.

Similarly, we have

$$\frac{z_1}{z_2} = \frac{r_1 e^{i\theta}}{r_2 e^{i\phi}} = \frac{r_1}{r_2} e^{i(\theta - \phi)},$$

so the modulus of z_1/z_2 is r_1/r_2 and the difference $\theta - \phi$ is an admissible argument for z_1/z_2.

9.8   Complex-valued functions

A function f whose values are complex numbers is called a complex-valued function. If the domain of f is a set of real numbers, f is called a complex-valued function of a real variable. If the domain is a set of complex numbers, f is called a complex-valued function of a complex variable, or more simply, a function of a complex variable. An example is the exponential function, defined by the equation

$$f(z) = e^z$$

for all complex z. Most of the familiar elementary functions of calculus, such as the exponential, the logarithm, and the trigonometric functions, can be extended to become functions of a complex variable. (See Exercises 9 and 10 in Section 9.10.) In this more general framework many new properties and interrelationships are often revealed. For example, the complex exponential function is periodic. In fact, if $z = x + iy$ and if n is any integer, we have

$$e^{z+2n\pi i} = e^x[\cos (y + 2n\pi) + i \sin (y + 2n\pi)] = e^x(\cos y + i \sin y) = e^z .$$

Thus we see that $f(z + 2n\pi i) = f(z)$, so f has the period $2\pi i$. This property of the exponential function is revealed only when we study the exponential as a function of a complex variable.

The first systematic treatment of the differential and integral calculus of functions of a complex variable was given by Cauchy early in the 19th century. Since then the theory has developed into one of the most important and interesting branches of mathematics. It has become an indispensable tool for physicists and engineers and has connections in nearly every branch of pure mathematics. A discussion of this theory will not be given here. We shall discuss only the rudiments of the calculus of complex-valued functions of a real variable.

Suppose f is a complex-valued function defined on some interval I of real numbers. For each x in I, the function value $f(x)$ is a complex number, so we can write

$$f(x) = u(x) + iv(x),$$

where $u(x)$ and $v(x)$ are real. This equation determines two real-valued functions u and v called, respectively, the real and imaginary parts of f; we write the equation more briefly as $f = u + iv$. Concepts such as continuity, differentiation, and integration of f may be defined in terms of the corresponding concepts for u and v, as described in the following definition.

DEFINITION. *If $f = u + iv$, we say f is continuous at a point if both u and v are continuous at that point. The derivative of f is defined by the equation*

$$f'(x) = u'(x) + iv'(x)$$

whenever both derivatives $u'(x)$ and $v'(x)$ exist. Similarly, we define the integral of f by the equation

$$\int_a^b f(x)\, dx = \int_a^b u(x)\, dx + i \int_a^b v(x)\, dx$$

whenever both integrals on the right exist.

In view of this definition, it is not surprising to find that many of the theorems of differential and integral calculus are also valid for complex-valued functions. For example, the rules for differentiating sums, products, and quotients (Theorem 4.1) are valid for complex functions. The first and second fundamental theorems of calculus (Theorems 5.1 and 5.3) as well as the zero-derivative theorem (Theorem 5.2) also hold for complex functions. To illustrate the ease with which these theorems can be proved, we consider the zero-derivative theorem:

If $f'(x) = 0$ for all x on an open interval I, then f is constant on I.

Proof. Write $f = u + iv$. Since $f' = u' + iv'$, the statement $f' = 0$ on I means that both u' and v' are zero on I. Hence, by Theorem 5.2, both u and v are constant on I. Therefore f is constant on I.

9.9 Examples of differentiation and integration formulas

In this section we discuss an important example of a complex-valued function of a real variable, namely the function f defined for all real x by the equation

$$f(x) = e^{tx},$$

where t is a fixed complex number. When t is real, the derivative of this function is given by the formula $f'(x) = te^{tx}$. Now we prove that this formula is also valid for complex t.

THEOREM 9.5.   *If $f(x) = e^{tx}$ for all real x and a fixed complex t, then $f'(x) = te^{tx}$.*

Proof. Write $t = \alpha + i\beta$, where α and β are real. From the definition of the complex exponential, we have

$$f(x) = e^{tx} = e^{\alpha x + i\beta x} = e^{\alpha x} \cos \beta x + ie^{\alpha x} \sin \beta x \,.$$

Therefore, the real and imaginary parts of f are given by

(9.14) $$u(x) = e^{\alpha x} \cos \beta x \quad \text{and} \quad v(x) = e^{\alpha x} \sin \beta x \,.$$

These functions are differentiable for all x and their derivatives are given by the formulas

$$u'(x) = \alpha e^{\alpha x} \cos \beta x - \beta e^{\alpha x} \sin \beta x \,, \qquad v'(x) = \alpha e^{\alpha x} \sin \beta x + \beta e^{\alpha x} \cos \beta x \,.$$

Since $f'(x) = u'(x) + iv'(x)$, we have

$$f'(x) = \alpha e^{\alpha x}(\cos \beta x + i \sin \beta x) + i\beta e^{\alpha x}(\cos \beta x + i \sin \beta x)$$
$$= (\alpha + i\beta)e^{(\alpha + i\beta)x} = te^{tx} \,.$$

This completes the proof.

Theorem 9.5 has some interesting consequences. For example, if we adopt the Leibniz notation for indefinite integrals, we can restate Theorem 9.5 in the form

(9.15) $$\int e^{tx} \, dx = \frac{e^{tx}}{t}$$

when $t \neq 0$. If we let $t = \alpha + i\beta$ and equate the real and imaginary parts of Equation (9.15), we obtain the integration formulas

$$\int e^{\alpha x} \cos \beta x \, dx = \frac{e^{\alpha x}(\alpha \cos \beta x + \beta \sin \beta x)}{\alpha^2 + \beta^2}$$

and

$$\int e^{\alpha x} \sin \beta x \, dx = \frac{e^{\alpha x}(\alpha \sin \beta x - \beta \cos \beta x)}{\alpha^2 + \beta^2} \,,$$

which are valid if α and β are not both zero.

Another consequence of Theorem 9.5 is the connection between complex exponentials and second-order linear differential equations with constant coefficients.

THEOREM 9.6.   *Consider the differential equation*

(9.16) $$y'' + ay' + by = 0 \,,$$

where a and b are real constants. The real and imaginary parts of the function f defined on

$(-\infty, +\infty)$ *by the equation* $f(x) = e^{tx}$ *are solutions of the differential equation* (9.16) *if and only if t is a root of the characteristic equation*

$$t^2 + at + b = 0 .$$

Proof. Let $L(y) = y'' + ay' + by$. Since $f'(x) = te^{tx}$, we also have $f''(x) = t^2 e^{tx}$, so $L(f) = e^{tx}(t^2 + at + b)$. But e^{tx} is never zero since $e^{tx}e^{-tx} = e^0 = 1$. Hence, $L(f) = 0$ if and only if $t^2 + at + b = 0$. But if we write $f = u + iv$, we find $L(f) = L(u) + iL(v)$, and hence $L(f) = 0$ if and only if both $L(u) = 0$ and $L(v) = 0$. This completes the proof.

Note: If $t = \alpha + i\beta$, the real and imaginary parts of f are given by (9.14). If the characteristic equation has two distinct roots, real or complex, the linear combination

$$y = c_1 u(x) + c_2 v(x)$$

is the general solution of the differential equation. This agrees with the results proved in Theorem 8.7.

Further examples of complex functions are discussed in the next set of exercises.

9.10 Exercises

1. Express each of the following complex numbers in the form $a + bi$.
   (a) $e^{\pi i/2}$.
   (b) $2e^{-\pi i/2}$.
   (c) $3e^{\pi i}$.
   (d) $-e^{-\pi i}$.
   (e) $i + e^{2\pi i}$.
   (f) $e^{\pi i/4}$.
   (g) $e^{\pi i/4} - e^{-\pi i/4}$.
   (h) $\dfrac{1 - e^{\pi i/2}}{1 + e^{\pi i/2}}$.

2. In each case, find all real x and y that satisfy the given relation.
   (a) $x + iy = xe^{iy}$.
   (b) $x + iy = ye^{ix}$.
   (c) $e^{x+iy} = -1$.
   (d) $\dfrac{1 + i}{1 - i} = xe^{iy}$.

3. (a) Prove that $e^z \neq 0$ for all complex z.
   (b) Find all complex z for which $e^z = 1$.

4. (a) If θ is real, show that

$$\cos \theta = \frac{e^{i\theta} + e^{-i\theta}}{2} \qquad \text{and} \qquad \sin \theta = \frac{e^{i\theta} - e^{-i\theta}}{2i} .$$

   (b) Use the formulas in (a) to deduce the identities

$$\cos^2 \theta = \tfrac{1}{2}(1 + \cos 2\theta), \qquad \sin^2 \theta = \tfrac{1}{2}(1 - \cos 2\theta) .$$

5. (a) Prove *DeMoivre's theorem*,

$$(\cos \theta + i \sin \theta)^n = \cos n\theta + i \sin n\theta ,$$

   valid for every real θ and every positive integer n.
   (b) Take $n = 3$ in part (a) and deduce the trigonometric identities

$$\sin 3\theta = 3 \cos^2 \theta \sin \theta - \sin^3 \theta, \qquad \cos 3\theta = \cos^3 \theta - 3 \cos \theta \sin^2 \theta .$$

6. Prove that every trigonometric sum of the form

$$S_n(x) = \tfrac{1}{2}a_0 + \sum_{k=1}^{n} (a_k \cos kx + b_k \sin kx)$$

can be expressed as a sum of complex exponentials,

$$S_n(x) = \sum_{k=-n}^{n} c_k e^{ikx},$$

where $c_k = \tfrac{1}{2}(a_k - ib_k)$ for $k = 1, 2, \ldots, n$. Determine corresponding formulas for c_{-k}.

7. (a) If m and n are integers, prove that

$$\int_0^{2\pi} e^{inx} e^{-imx} \, dx = \begin{cases} 0 & \text{if } m \neq n, \\ 2\pi & \text{if } m = n. \end{cases}$$

(b) Use part (a) to deduce the orthogonality relations for the sine and cosine (m and n are integers, $m^2 \neq n^2$):

$$\int_0^{2\pi} \sin nx \cos mx \, dx = \int_0^{2\pi} \sin nx \sin mx \, dx = \int_0^{2\pi} \cos nx \cos mx \, dx = 0,$$

$$\int_0^{2\pi} \sin^2 nx \, dx = \int_0^{2\pi} \cos^2 nx \, dx = \pi \qquad \text{if } n \neq 0.$$

8. Given a complex number $z \neq 0$. Write $z = re^{i\theta}$, where $\theta = \arg(z)$. Let $z_1 = Re^{i\alpha}$, where $R = r^{1/n}$ and $\alpha = \theta/n$, and let $\epsilon = e^{2\pi i/n}$, where n is a positive integer.
(a) Show that $z_1^n = z$; that is, z_1 is an nth root of z.
(b) Show that z has exactly n distinct nth roots,

$$z_1, \epsilon z_1, \epsilon^2 z_1, \ldots, \epsilon^{n-1} z_1,$$

and that they are equally spaced on a circle of radius R.
(c) Determine the three cube roots of i.
(d) Determine the four fourth roots of i.
(e) Determine the four fourth roots of $-i$.

9. The definitions of the sine and cosine functions can be extended to the complex plane as follows:

$$\cos z = \frac{e^{iz} + e^{-iz}}{2}, \qquad \sin z = \frac{e^{iz} - e^{-iz}}{2i}.$$

When z is real, these formulas agree with the ordinary sine and cosine functions. (See Exercise 4.) Use these formulas to deduce the following properties of complex sines and cosines. Here u, v, and z denote complex numbers, with $z = x + iy$.
(a) $\sin(u + v) = \sin u \cos v + \cos u \sin v$.
(b) $\cos(u + v) = \cos u \cos v - \sin u \sin v$.
(c) $\sin^2 z + \cos^2 z = 1$.
(d) $\cos(iy) = \cosh y, \qquad \sin(iy) = i \sinh y$.
—(e) $\cos z = \cos x \cosh y - i \sin x \sinh y$.
—(f) $\sin z = \sin x \cosh y + i \cos x \sinh y$.

10. If z is a nonzero complex number, we define Log z, the complex logarithm of z, by the equation

$$\text{Log } z = \log |z| + i \arg(z) .$$

When z is real and positive, this formula agrees with the ordinary logarithm. Use this formula to deduce the following properties of complex logarithms.
   (a) $\text{Log} (-1) = \pi i,$ $\text{Log} (i) = \pi i/2.$
   (b) $\text{Log} (z_1 z_2) = \text{Log } z_1 + \text{Log } z_2 + 2n\pi i,$ where n is an integer.
   (c) $\text{Log} (z_1/z_2) = \text{Log } z_1 - \text{Log } z_2 + 2n\pi i,$ where n is an integer.
   (d) $e^{\text{Log } z} = z.$

11. If w and z are complex numbers, $z \neq 0$, we define z^w by the equation

$$z^w = e^{w \, \text{Log } z} ,$$

where Log z is defined as in Exercise 10.
   (a) Compute 1^i, i^i, and $(-1)^i$.
   (b) Prove that $z^a z^b = z^{a+b}$ if a, b, and z are complex, $z \neq 0$.
   (c) Note that the equation

(9.17) $$(z_1 z_2)^w = z_1^w z_2^w$$

is violated when $z_1 = z_2 = -1$ and $w = i$. What conditions on z_1 and z_2 are necessary for Equation (9.17) to hold for all complex w?

In Exercises 12 through 15, L denotes the linear operator defined by $L(y) = y'' + ay' + by$, where a and b are real constants.

12. Prove that if R is a complex-valued function, say $R(x) = P(x) + iQ(x)$, then a complex-valued function $f(x) = u(x) + iv(x)$ satisfies the differential equation $L(y) = R(x)$ on an interval I if and only if u and v satisfy the equations $L(u) = P(x)$ and $L(v) = Q(x)$ on I.

13. If A is complex and ω is real, prove that the differential equation $L(y) = Ae^{i\omega x}$ has a complex-valued solution of the form $y = Be^{i\omega x}$, provided that either $b \neq \omega^2$ or $a\omega \neq 0$. Express the complex number B in terms of a, b, A, and ω.

14. Assume c is real and $b \neq \omega^2$. Use the results of Exercise 13 to prove that the differential equation $L(y) = c \cos \omega x$ has a particular solution of the form $y = A \cos (\omega x + \alpha)$, where

$$A = \frac{c}{\sqrt{(b - \omega^2)^2 + a^2\omega^2}} \quad \text{and} \quad \tan \alpha = \frac{a\omega}{b - \omega^2} .$$

15. Assume c is real and $b \neq \omega^2$. Prove that the differential equation $L(y) = c \sin \omega x$ has a particular solution of the form $y = A \sin (\omega x + \alpha)$ and express A and α in terms of a, b, c, and ω.

10

SEQUENCES, INFINITE SERIES,
IMPROPER INTEGRALS

10.1 Zeno's paradox

The principal subject matter of this chapter had its beginning nearly 2400 years ago when the Greek philosopher Zeno of Elea (495–435 B.C.) precipitated a crisis in ancient mathematics by setting forth a number of ingenious paradoxes. One of these, often called the *racecourse paradox*, may be described as follows:

> A runner can never reach the end of a racecourse because he must cover half of any distance before he covers the whole. That is to say, having covered the first half he still has the second half before him. When half of this is covered, one-fourth yet remains. When half of this one-fourth is covered, there remains one-eighth, and so on, *ad infinitum*.

Zeno was referring, of course, to an idealized situation in which the runner is to be thought of as a particle or point moving from one end of a line segment to the other. We can formulate the paradox in another way. Assume that the runner starts at the point marked 1 in Figure 10.1 and runs toward the goal marked 0. The positions labeled $\frac{1}{2}$, $\frac{1}{4}$, $\frac{1}{8}$, etc., indicate the fraction of the course yet to be covered when these points are reached. These fractions, each of which is half the previous one, subdivide the whole course into an endless number of smaller portions. A positive amount of time is required to cover each portion separately, and the time required for the whole course is the sum total of all these amounts. To say that the runner can never reach the goal is to say that he never arrives there in a finite length of time; or, in other words, that the sum of an endless number of positive time intervals cannot possibly be finite.

This assertion was rejected 2000 years after Zeno's time when the theory of infinite series was created. In the 17th and 18th centuries, mathematicians began to realize that it *is* possible to extend the ideas of ordinary addition from *finite* collections of numbers to *infinite* collections so that sometimes infinitely many positive numbers have a finite "sum." To see how this extension might come about and to get an idea of some of the difficulties that might be encountered in making the extension, let us analyze Zeno's paradox in more detail.

Suppose the aforementioned runner travels at a *constant speed* and suppose it takes him T minutes to cover the first half of the course. The next quarter of the course will take

$T/2$ minutes, the next eighth will take $T/4$ minutes, and, in general, the portion from $1/2^n$ to $1/2^{n+1}$ will take $T/2^n$ minutes. The "sum" of all these time intervals may be indicated symbolically by writing the following expression:

$$(10.1) \qquad T + \frac{T}{2} + \frac{T}{4} + \cdots + \frac{T}{2^n} + \cdots .$$

This is an example of what is known as an *infinite series*, and the problem here is to decide whether there is some reasonable way to assign a number which may be called the *sum* of this series.

Our physical experience tells us that a runner who travels at a constant speed should reach his goal in twice the time it takes for him to reach the halfway point. Since it takes

FIGURE 10.1 The racecourse paradox.

T minutes to cover half the course, it should require $2T$ minutes for the whole course. This line of reasoning strongly suggests that we should assign the "sum" $2T$ to the series in (10.1), and it leads us to expect that the equation

$$(10.2) \qquad T + \frac{T}{2} + \frac{T}{4} + \cdots + \frac{T}{2^n} + \cdots = 2T$$

should be "true" in some sense.

The theory of infinite series tells us exactly how to interpret this equation. The idea is this: First we add a *finite number* of the terms, say the first n, and denote their sum by s_n. Thus we have

$$(10.3) \qquad s_n = T + \frac{T}{2} + \frac{T}{4} + \cdots + \frac{T}{2^{n-1}} .$$

This is called the nth *partial sum* of the series. Now we study the behavior of s_n as n takes larger and larger values. In particular, we try to determine whether the partial sums s_n approach a finite limit as n increases without bound.

In this example it is easy to see that $2T$ is the limiting value of the partial sums. In fact, if we calculate a few of these partial sums, we find that

$$s_1 = T, \qquad s_2 = T + \frac{T}{2} = \frac{3}{2}T, \qquad s_3 = T + \frac{T}{2} + \frac{T}{4} = \frac{7}{4}T,$$

$$s_4 = T + \frac{T}{2} + \frac{T}{4} + \frac{T}{8} = \frac{15}{8}T.$$

Now, observe that these results may be expressed as follows:

$$s_1 = (2 - 1)T, \qquad s_2 = (2 - \tfrac{1}{2})T, \qquad s_3 = (2 - \tfrac{1}{4})T, \qquad s_4 = (2 - \tfrac{1}{8})T.$$

This leads us to conjecture the following general formula:

(10.4) $$s_n = \left(2 - \frac{1}{2^{n-1}}\right)T \qquad \text{for all positive integers } n.$$

Formula (10.4) is easily verified by induction. Since $1/2^{n-1} \to 0$ as n increases indefinitely, this shows that $s_n \to 2T$. Therefore, Equation (10.2) is "true" if we interpret it to mean that $2T$ is the *limit* of the partial sums s_n. This limit process seems to invalidate the assertion that the sum of an infinite number of time intervals can never be finite.

Now we shall give an argument which lends considerable support to Zeno's point of view. Suppose we make a small but important change in the foregoing analysis of the racecourse paradox. Instead of assuming that the speed of the runner is constant, let us suppose that his speed gradually decreases in such a way that he requires T minutes to go from 1 to 1/2, $T/2$ minutes to go from 1/2 to 1/4, $T/3$ minutes to go from 1/4 to 1/8, and, in general, T/n minutes to go from $1/2^{n-1}$ to $1/2^n$. The "total time" for the course may now be represented by the following infinite series:

(10.5) $$T + \frac{T}{2} + \frac{T}{3} + \cdots + \frac{T}{n} + \cdots.$$

In this case, our physical experience does not suggest any natural or obvious "sum" to assign to this series, and hence we must rely entirely on mathematical analysis to deal with this example.

Let us proceed as before and introduce the partial sums s_n. That is, let

(10.6) $$s_n = T + \frac{T}{2} + \frac{T}{3} + \cdots + \frac{T}{n}.$$

Our object is to decide what happens to s_n for larger and larger values of n. These partial sums are not as easy to study as those in (10.3) because there is no simple formula analogous to (10.4) for simplifying the expression on the right of (10.6). Nevertheless, it is easy to obtain an *estimate* for the size of s_n if we compare the partial sum with an appropriate integral.

Figure 10.2 shows the graph of the function $f(x) = 1/x$ for $x > 0$. (The scale is distorted along the y-axis.) The rectangles shown there have a total area equal to the sum

(10.7) $$1 + \frac{1}{2} + \frac{1}{3} + \cdots + \frac{1}{n}.$$

The area of the shaded region is $\int_1^{n+1} x^{-1}\, dx = \log(n + 1)$. Since this area cannot exceed the sum of the areas of the rectangles, we have the inequality

(10.8) $$1 + \frac{1}{2} + \frac{1}{3} + \cdots + \frac{1}{n} \geq \log(n + 1).$$

Multiplying both sides by T, we obtain $s_n \geq T \log (n + 1)$. In other words, if the runner's speed decreases in the manner described above, the time required to reach the point $1/2^n$ is at least $T \log (n + 1)$ minutes. Since $\log (n + 1)$ increases without bound as n increases, we must agree with Zeno and conclude that the runner cannot reach his goal in any finite time.

The general theory of infinite series makes a distinction between series like (10.1) whose partial sums tend to a finite limit, and those like (10.5) whose partial sums have no finite

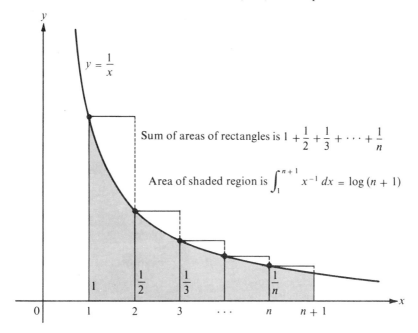

FIGURE 10.2   Geometric meaning of the inequality $1 + 1/2 + \cdots + 1/n \geq \log (n + 1)$.

limit. The former are called *convergent*, the latter *divergent*. Early investigators in the field paid little or no attention to questions of convergence or divergence. They treated infinite series as though they were ordinary finite sums, subject to the usual laws of algebra, not realizing that these laws cannot be universally extended to infinite series. Therefore, it is not surprising that some of the results they obtained were later shown to be incorrect. Fortunately, many of the early pioneers possessed unusual intuition and skill which prevented them from arriving at too many false conclusions, even though they could not justify all their methods. Foremost among these men was Leonard Euler who discovered one beautiful formula after another and at the same time used infinite series as a unifying idea to bring together many branches of mathematics, hitherto unrelated. The great quantity of Euler's work that has survived the test of history is a tribute to his remarkable instinct for what is mathematically correct.

The widespread use of infinite series began late in the 17th century, nearly fifty years before Euler was born, and coincided with the early development of the integral calculus. Nicholas Mercator (1620–1687) and William Brouncker (1620–1684) discovered an infinite series for the logarithm in 1668 while attempting to calculate the area of a hyperbolic segment. Shortly thereafter, Newton discovered the *binomial series*. This discovery proved to be a landmark in the history of mathematics. A special case of the binomial series is the now-familiar *binomial theorem* which states that

$$(1 + x)^n = \sum_{k=0}^{n} \binom{n}{k} x^k,$$

where x is an arbitrary real number, n is a nonnegative integer, and $\binom{n}{k}$ is the binomial coefficient. Newton found that this formula could be extended from *integer* values of the exponent n to arbitrary *real* values of n by replacing the finite sum on the right by a suitable infinite series, although he gave no proof of this fact. Actually, a careful treatment of the binomial series raises some rather delicate questions of convergence that could not have been answered in Newton's time.

Shortly after Euler's death in 1783, the flood of new discoveries began to recede and the formal period in the history of series came to a close. A new and more critical period began in 1812 when Gauss published a celebrated memoir which contained, for the first time in history, a thorough and rigorous treatment of the convergence of a particular infinite series. A few years later Cauchy introduced an analytic definition of the limit concept in his treatise *Cours d'analyse algébrique* (published in 1821) and laid the foundations of the modern theory of convergence and divergence. The rudiments of that theory are discussed in the sections that follow.

10.2 Sequences

In everyday usage of the English language, the words "sequence" and "series" are synonyms, and they are used to suggest a succession of things or events arranged in some order. In mathematics these words have special technical meanings. The word "sequence" is employed as in the common use of the term to convey the idea of a set of things arranged in order, but the word "series" is used in a somewhat different sense. The concept of a sequence will be discussed in this section, and series will be defined in Section 10.5.

If for every positive integer n there is associated a real or complex number a_n, then the ordered set

$$a_1, a_2, a_3, \ldots, a_n, \ldots$$

is said to define an infinite sequence. The important thing here is that each member of the set has been labeled with an integer so that we may speak of the *first term a_1*, the *second term a_2*, and, in general, the *nth term a_n*. Each term a_n has a successor a_{n+1} and hence there is no "last" term.

The most common examples of sequences can be constructed if we give some rule or formula for describing the nth term. Thus, for example, the formula $a_n = 1/n$ defines a sequence whose first five terms are

$$1, \tfrac{1}{2}, \tfrac{1}{3}, \tfrac{1}{4}, \tfrac{1}{5}.$$

Sometimes two or more formulas may be employed as, for example,

$$a_{2n-1} = 1, \qquad a_{2n} = 2n^2,$$

the first few terms in this case being

$$1, 2, 1, 8, 1, 18, 1, 32, 1 .$$

Another common way to define a sequence is by a set of instructions which explains how to carry on after a given start. Thus we may have

$$a_1 = a_2 = 1, \qquad a_{n+1} = a_n + a_{n-1} \qquad \text{for } n \geq 2 .$$

This particular rule is known as a *recursion* formula, and it defines a famous sequence whose terms are called the *Fibonacci†* *numbers*. The first few terms are

$$1, 1, 2, 3, 5, 8, 13, 21, 34 .$$

In any sequence the essential thing is that there be some function *f* defined on the positive integers such that $f(n)$ is the *n*th term of the sequence for each $n = 1, 2, 3, \ldots$. In fact, this is probably the most convenient way to state a technical definition of sequence.

DEFINITION. *A function f whose domain is the set of all positive integers* $1, 2, 3, \ldots$ *is called an infinite sequence. The function value* $f(n)$ *is called the nth term of the sequence.*

The *range* of the function (that is, the set of function values) is usually displayed by writing the terms in order, thus:

$$f(1), f(2), f(3), \ldots, f(n), \ldots$$

For brevity, the notation $\{f(n)\}$ is used to denote the sequence whose *n*th term is $f(n)$. Very often the dependence on *n* is denoted by using subscripts, and we write a_n, s_n, x_n, u_n, or something similar instead of $f(n)$. Unless otherwise specified, all sequences in this chapter are assumed to have real or complex terms.

The main question we are concerned with here is to decide whether or not the terms $f(n)$ tend to a finite limit as *n* increases indefinitely. To treat this problem, we must extend the limit concept to sequences. This is done as follows.

DEFINITION. *A sequence* $\{f(n)\}$ *is said to have a limit L if, for every positive number* ϵ, *there is another positive number N (which may depend on ϵ) such that*

$$|f(n) - L| < \epsilon \qquad \text{for all } n \geq N .$$

In this case, we say the sequence $\{f(n)\}$ *converges to L and we write*

$$\lim_{n \to \infty} f(n) = L, \qquad \text{or} \qquad f(n) \to L \qquad \text{as} \quad n \to \infty .$$

A sequence which does not converge is called divergent.

In this definition the function values $f(n)$ and the limit *L* may be real or complex numbers. If *f* and *L* are complex, we may decompose them into their real and imaginary parts, say $f = u + iv$ and $L = a + ib$. Then we have $f(n) - L = u(n) - a + i[v(n) - b]$. The

---

† Fibonacci, also known as Leonardo of Pisa (*circa* 1175–1250), encountered this sequence in a problem concerning the offspring of rabbits.

inequalities

$$|u(n) - a| \leq |f(n) - L| \qquad \text{and} \qquad |v(n) - b| \leq |f(n) - L|$$

show that the relation $f(n) \to L$ implies $u(n) \to a$ and $v(n) \to b$ as $n \to \infty$. Conversely, the inequality

$$|f(n) - L| \leq |u(n) - a| + |v(n) - b|$$

shows that the two relations $u(n) \to a$ and $v(n) \to b$ imply $f(n) \to L$ as $n \to \infty$. In other words, a complex-valued sequence f converges if and only if both the real part u and the imaginary part v converge separately, in which case we have

$$\lim_{n \to \infty} f(n) = \lim_{n \to \infty} u(n) + i \lim_{n \to \infty} v(n) .$$

It is clear that any function defined for all positive real x may be used to construct a sequence by restricting x to take only *integer* values. This explains the strong analogy between the definition just given and the one in Section 7.14 for more general functions. The analogy carries over to *infinite limits* as well, and we leave it for the reader to define the symbols

$$\lim_{n \to \infty} f(n) = +\infty \qquad \text{and} \qquad \lim_{n \to \infty} f(n) = -\infty$$

as was done in Section 7.15 when f is real-valued. If f is complex, we write $f(n) \to \infty$ as $n \to \infty$ if $|f(n)| \to +\infty$.

The phrase "convergent sequence" is used only for a sequence whose limit is *finite*. A sequence with an infinite limit is said to diverge. There are, of course, divergent sequences that do not have infinite limits. Examples are defined by the following formulas:

$$f(n) = (-1)^n , \qquad f(n) = \sin \frac{n\pi}{2} , \qquad f(n) = (-1)^n \left(1 + \frac{1}{n}\right) , \qquad f(n) = e^{\pi i n/2} .$$

The basic rules for dealing with limits of sums, products, etc., also hold for limits of convergent sequences. The reader should have no difficulty in formulating these theorems for himself. Their proofs are somewhat similar to those given in Section 3.5.

The convergence or divergence of many sequences may be determined by using properties of familiar functions that are defined for all positive x. We mention a few important examples of real-valued sequences whose limits may be found directly or by using some of the results derived in Chapter 7.

(10.9)
$$\lim_{n \to \infty} \frac{1}{n^\alpha} = 0 \qquad \text{if} \quad \alpha > 0 .$$

(10.10)
$$\lim_{n \to \infty} x^n = 0 \qquad \text{if} \quad |x| < 1 .$$

(10.11)
$$\lim_{n \to \infty} \frac{(\log n)^a}{n^b} = 0 \qquad \text{for all } a > 0, b > 0 .$$

(10.12)
$$\lim_{n \to \infty} n^{1/n} = 1 .$$

(10.13)
$$\lim_{n \to \infty} \left(1 + \frac{a}{n}\right)^n = e^a \qquad \text{for all real } a .$$

10.3   Monotonic sequences of real numbers

A sequence $\{f(n)\}$ is said to be *increasing* if

$$f(n) \leq f(n+1) \qquad \text{for all } n \geq 1 \, .$$

We indicate this briefly by writing $f(n) \nearrow$. If, on the other hand, we have

$$f(n) \geq f(n+1) \qquad \text{for all } n \geq 1 \, ,$$

we call the sequence *decreasing* and write $f(n) \searrow$. A sequence is called *monotonic* if it is increasing or if it is decreasing.

Monotonic sequences are pleasant to work with because their convergence or divergence is particularly easy to determine. In fact, we have the following simple criterion.

THEOREM 10.1.   *A monotonic sequence converges if and only if it is bounded.*

> *Note:*   A sequence $\{f(n)\}$ is called *bounded* if there exists a positive number M such that $|f(n)| \leq M$ for all n. A sequence that is not bounded is called *unbounded.*

Proof. It is clear that an unbounded sequence cannot converge. Therefore, all we need to prove is that a bounded monotonic sequence must converge.

Assume $f(n) \nearrow$ and let L denote the least upper bound of the set of function values. (Since the sequence is bounded, it has a least upper bound by Axiom 10 of the real-number

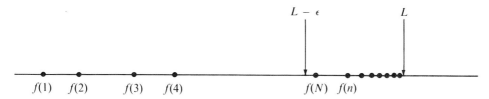

FIGURE 10.3   A bounded increasing sequence converges to its least upper bound.

system.) Then $f(n) \leq L$ for all n, and we shall prove that the sequence converges to L.

Choose any positive number ϵ. Since $L - \epsilon$ cannot be an upper bound for *all* numbers $f(n)$, we must have $L - \epsilon < f(N)$ for some N. (This N may depend on ϵ.) If $n \geq N$, we have $f(N) \leq f(n)$ since $f(n) \nearrow$. Hence, we have $L - \epsilon < f(n) \leq L$ for all $n \geq N$, as illustrated in Figure 10.3. From these inequalities we find that

$$0 \leq L - f(n) < \epsilon \qquad \text{for all } n \geq N$$

and this means that the sequence converges to L, as asserted.

If $f(n) \searrow$, the proof is similar, the limit in this case being the greatest lower bound of the set of function values.

10.4 Exercises

In Exercises 1 through 22, a sequence $\{f(n)\}$ is defined by the formula given. In each case, (a) determine whether the sequence converges or diverges, and (b) find the limit of each convergent sequence. In some cases it may be helpful to replace the integer n by an arbitrary positive real x and to study the resulting function of x by the methods of Chapter 7. You may use formulas (10.9) through (10.13) listed at the end of Section 10.2.

1. $f(n) = \dfrac{n}{n+1} - \dfrac{n+1}{n}$.

2. $f(n) = \dfrac{n^2}{n+1} - \dfrac{n^2+1}{n}$.

3. $f(n) = \cos\dfrac{n\pi}{2}$.

4. $f(n) = \dfrac{n^2 + 3n - 2}{5n^2}$.

5. $f(n) = \dfrac{n}{2^n}$.

6. $f(n) = 1 + (-1)^n$.

7. $f(n) = \dfrac{1 + (-1)^n}{n}$.

8. $f(n) = \dfrac{(-1)^n}{n} + \dfrac{1 + (-1)^n}{2}$.

9. $f(n) = 2^{1/n}$.

10. $f(n) = n^{(-1)^n}$.

11. $f(n) = \dfrac{n^{2/3}\sin(n!)}{n+1}$.

12. $f(n) = \dfrac{3^n + (-2)^n}{3^{n+1} + (-2)^{n+1}}$.

13. $f(n) = \sqrt{n+1} - \sqrt{n}$.

14. $f(n) = na^n$,   where $|a| < 1$.

15. $f(n) = \dfrac{\log_a n}{n}$, $a > 1$.

16. $f(n) = \dfrac{100{,}000n}{1 + n^2}$.

17. $f(n) = \left(1 + \dfrac{2}{n}\right)^n$.

18. $f(n) = 1 + \dfrac{n}{n+1}\cos\dfrac{n\pi}{2}$.

19. $f(n) = \left(1 + \dfrac{i}{2}\right)^{-n}$.

20. $f(n) = e^{-\pi in/2}$.

21. $f(n) = \dfrac{1}{n}e^{-\pi in/2}$.

22. $f(n) = ne^{-\pi in/2}$.

Each of the sequences $\{a_n\}$ in Exercises 23 through 28 is convergent. Therefore, for every preassigned $\epsilon > 0$, there exists an integer N (depending on ϵ) such that $|a_n - L| < \epsilon$ if $n \geq N$, where $L = \lim_{n\to\infty} a_n$. In each case, determine a value of N that is suitable for each of the following values of ϵ: $\epsilon = 1, 0.1, 0.01, 0.001, 0.0001$.

23. $a_n = \dfrac{1}{n}$.

24. $a_n = \dfrac{n}{n+1}$.

25. $a_n = \dfrac{(-1)^{n+1}}{n}$.

26. $a_n = \dfrac{1}{n!}$.

27. $a_n = \dfrac{2n}{n^3 + 1}$.

28. $a_n = (-1)^n\left(\dfrac{9}{10}\right)^n$.

29. Prove that a sequence cannot converge to two different limits.

30. Assume $\lim_{n\to\infty} a_n = 0$. Use the definition of limit to prove that $\lim_{n\to\infty} a_n^2 = 0$.

31. If $\lim_{n\to\infty} a_n = A$ and $\lim_{n\to\infty} b_n = B$, use the definition of limit to prove that we have $\lim_{n\to\infty}(a_n + b_n) = A + B$, and $\lim_{n\to\infty}(ca_n) = cA$, where c is a constant.

32. From the results of Exercises 30 and 31, prove that if $\lim_{n\to\infty} a_n = A$ then $\lim_{n\to\infty} a_n^2 = A^2$. Then use the identity $2a_nb_n = (a_n + b_n)^2 - a_n^2 - b_n^2$ to prove that $\lim_{n\to\infty}(a_nb_n) = AB$ if $\lim_{n\to\infty} a_n = A$ and $\lim_{n\to\infty} b_n = B$.

33. If α is a real number and n a nonnegative integer, the binomial coefficient $\binom{\alpha}{n}$ is defined by the equation

$$\binom{\alpha}{n} = \frac{\alpha(\alpha - 1)(\alpha - 2) \cdots (\alpha - n + 1)}{n!}.$$

(a) When $\alpha = -\frac{1}{2}$, show that

$$\binom{\alpha}{1} = -\frac{1}{2}, \quad \binom{\alpha}{2} = \frac{3}{8}, \quad \binom{\alpha}{3} = -\frac{5}{16}, \quad \binom{\alpha}{4} = \frac{35}{128}, \quad \binom{\alpha}{5} = -\frac{63}{256}.$$

(b) Let $a_n = (-1)^n \binom{-1/2}{n}$. Prove that $a_n > 0$ and that $a_{n+1} < a_n$.

34. Let f be a real-valued function that is monotonic increasing and bounded on the interval $[0, 1]$. Define two sequences $\{s_n\}$ and $\{t_n\}$ as follows:

$$s_n = \frac{1}{n} \sum_{k=0}^{n-1} f\left(\frac{k}{n}\right), \qquad t_n = \frac{1}{n} \sum_{k=1}^{n} f\left(\frac{k}{n}\right).$$

(a) Prove that $s_n \leq \int_0^1 f(x)\, dx \leq t_n$ and that $0 \leq \int_0^1 f(x)\, dx - s_n \leq \frac{f(1) - f(0)}{n}$.

(b) Prove that both sequences $\{s_n\}$ and $\{t_n\}$ converge to the limit $\int_0^1 f(x)\, dx$.

(c) State and prove a corresponding result for the interval $[a, b]$.

35. Use Exercise 34 to establish the following limit relations:

(a) $\displaystyle \lim_{n \to \infty} \frac{1}{n} \sum_{k=1}^{n} \left(\frac{k}{n}\right)^2 = \frac{1}{3}$.

(b) $\displaystyle \lim_{n \to \infty} \sum_{k=1}^{n} \frac{1}{n + k} = \log 2$.

(c) $\displaystyle \lim_{n \to \infty} \sum_{k=1}^{n} \frac{n}{n^2 + k^2} = \frac{\pi}{4}$.

(d) $\displaystyle \lim_{n \to \infty} \sum_{k=1}^{n} \frac{1}{\sqrt{n^2 + k^2}} = \log(1 + \sqrt{2})$.

(e) $\displaystyle \lim_{n \to \infty} \sum_{k=1}^{n} \frac{1}{n} \sin \frac{k\pi}{n} = \frac{2}{\pi}$.

(f) $\displaystyle \lim_{n \to \infty} \sum_{k=1}^{n} \frac{1}{n} \sin^2 \frac{k\pi}{n} = \frac{1}{2}$.

10.5 Infinite series

From a given sequence of real or complex numbers, we can always generate a *new* sequence by adding together successive terms. Thus, if the given sequence has the terms

$$a_1, a_2, \ldots, a_n, \ldots,$$

we may form, in succession, the "partial sums"

$$s_1 = a_1, \qquad s_2 = a_1 + a_2, \qquad s_3 = a_1 + a_2 + a_3,$$

and so on, the partial sum s_n of the first n terms being defined as follows:

(10.14) $$s_n = a_1 + a_2 + \cdots + a_n = \sum_{k=1}^{n} a_k.$$

The sequence $\{s_n\}$ of partial sums is called an *infinite series*, or simply a *series*, and is also denoted by the following symbols:

(10.15) $a_1 + a_2 + a_3 + \cdots, \qquad a_1 + a_2 + \cdots + a_n + \cdots, \qquad \sum_{k=1}^{\infty} a_k .$

For example, the series $\sum_{k=1}^{\infty} 1/k$ represents the sequence $\{s_n\}$ for which

$$s_n = \sum_{k=1}^{n} \frac{1}{k} .$$

The symbols in (10.15) are intended to remind us that the sequence of partial sums $\{s_n\}$ is obtained from the sequence $\{a_n\}$ by addition of successive terms.

If there is a real or complex number S such that

$$\lim_{n \to \infty} s_n = S ,$$

we say that the series $\sum_{k=1}^{\infty} a_k$ is *convergent* and has the *sum S*, in which case we write

$$\sum_{k=1}^{\infty} a_k = S .$$

If $\{s_n\}$ diverges, we say that the series $\sum_{k=1}^{\infty} a_k$ *diverges* and has no sum.

EXAMPLE 1. THE HARMONIC SERIES. In the discussion of Zeno's paradox, we showed that the partial sums s_n of the series $\sum_{k=1}^{\infty} 1/k$ satisfy the inequality

$$s_n = \sum_{k=1}^{n} \frac{1}{k} \geq \log (n + 1) .$$

Since $\log (n + 1) \to \infty$ as $n \to \infty$, the same is true of s_n, and hence the series $\sum_{k=1}^{\infty} 1/k$ diverges. This series is called the *harmonic series*.

EXAMPLE 2. In the discussion of Zeno's paradox, we also encountered the partial sums of the series $1 + \frac{1}{2} + \frac{1}{4} + \cdots$, given by the formula

$$\sum_{k=1}^{n} \frac{1}{2^{k-1}} = 2 - \frac{1}{2^{n-1}} ,$$

which is easily proved by induction. As $n \to \infty$, these partial sums approach the limit 2, and hence the series converges and has sum 2. We may indicate this by writing

(10.16) $1 + \frac{1}{2} + \frac{1}{4} + \cdots = 2 .$

The reader should realize that the word "sum" is used here in a very special sense. The sum of a convergent series is not obtained by ordinary addition but rather as the *limit of the sequence of partial sums.* Also, the reader should note that for a convergent series, the symbol $\sum_{k=1}^{\infty} a_k$ is used to denote both the *series* and its *sum*, even though the two are conceptually distinct. The sum represents a *number* and it is not capable of being convergent or divergent. Once the distinction between a series and its sum has been realized, the use of one symbol to represent both should cause no confusion.

As in the case of finite summation notation, the letter k used in the symbol $\sum_{k=1}^{\infty} a_k$ is a "dummy index" and may be replaced by any other convenient symbol. The letters n, m, and r are commonly used for this purpose. Sometimes it is desirable to start the summation from $k = 0$ or from $k = 2$ or from some other value of k. Thus, for example, the series in (10.16) could be written as $\sum_{k=0}^{\infty} 1/2^k$. In general, if $p \geq 0$, we define the symbol $\sum_{k=p}^{\infty} a_k$ to mean the same as $\sum_{k=1}^{\infty} b_k$, where $b_k = a_{p+k-1}$. Thus $b_1 = a_p$, $b_2 = a_{p+1}$, etc. When there is no danger of confusion or when the starting point is unimportant, we write $\sum a_k$ instead of $\sum_{k=p}^{\infty} a_k$.

It is easy to prove that the two series $\sum_{k=1}^{\infty} a_k$ and $\sum_{k=p}^{\infty} a_k$ both converge or both diverge. Suppose we let $s_n = a_1 + \cdots + a_n$ and $t_n = a_p + a_{p+1} + \cdots + a_{p+n-1}$. If $p = 0$, we have $t_{n+1} = a_0 + s_n$, so if $s_n \to S$ as $n \to \infty$, then $t_n \to a_0 + S$ and, conversely, if $t_n \to T$ as $n \to \infty$, then $s_n \to T - a_0$. Therefore, both series converge or both diverge when $p = 0$. The same holds true if $p \geq 1$. For $p = 1$, we have $s_n = t_n$, and for $p > 1$, we have $t_n = s_{n+p-1} - s_{p-1}$, and again it follows that the sequences $\{s_n\}$ and $\{t_n\}$ both converge or both diverge. This is often described by saying that a finite number of terms may be omitted or added at the beginning of a series without affecting its convergence or divergence.

10.6 The linearity property of convergent series

Ordinary finite sums have the following important properties:

(10.17) $$\sum_{k=1}^{n}(a_k + b_k) = \sum_{k=1}^{n} a_k + \sum_{k=1}^{n} b_k \qquad \text{(additive property)}$$

and

(10.18) $$\sum_{k=1}^{n}(ca_k) = c\sum_{k=1}^{n} a_k \qquad \text{(homogeneous property)} .$$

The next theorem provides a natural extension of these properties to convergent infinite series and thereby justifies many algebraic manipulations in which convergent series are treated as though they were finite sums. Both additivity and homogeneity may be combined into one property called *linearity* which may be described as follows:

THEOREM 10.2. *Let $\sum a_n$ and $\sum b_n$ be convergent infinite series of complex terms and let α and β be complex constants. Then the series $\sum (\alpha a_n + \beta b_n)$ also converges, and its sum is given by the equation*

(10.19) $$\sum_{n=1}^{\infty}(\alpha a_n + \beta b_n) = \alpha \sum_{n=1}^{\infty} a_n + \beta \sum_{n=1}^{\infty} b_n .$$

Proof. Using (10.17) and (10.18), we may write

$$(10.20) \qquad \sum_{k=1}^{n}(\alpha a_k + \beta b_k) = \alpha \sum_{k=1}^{n} a_k + \beta \sum_{k=1}^{n} b_k .$$

When $n \to \infty$, the first term on the right of (10.20) tends to $\alpha \sum_{k=1}^{\infty} a_k$ and the second term tends to $\beta \sum_{k=1}^{\infty} b_k$. Therefore the left-hand side tends to their sum, and this proves that the series $\sum (\alpha a_k + \beta b_k)$ converges to the sum indicated by (10.19).

Theorem 10.2 has an interesting corollary which is often used to establish the divergence of a series.

THEOREM 10.3. *If $\sum a_n$ converges and if $\sum b_n$ diverges, then $\sum (a_n + b_n)$ diverges.*

Proof. Since $b_n = (a_n + b_n) - a_n$, and since $\sum a_n$ converges, Theorem 10.2 tells us that convergence of $\sum (a_n + b_n)$ implies convergence of $\sum b_n$. Therefore, $\sum (a_n + b_n)$ cannot converge if $\sum b_n$ diverges.

EXAMPLE. The series $\sum (1/k + 1/2^k)$ diverges because $\sum 1/k$ diverges and $\sum 1/2^k$ converges.

If $\sum a_n$ and $\sum b_n$ are *both* divergent, the series $\sum (a_n + b_n)$ may or may not converge. For example, when $a_n = b_n = 1$ for all n, then $\sum (a_n + b_n)$ diverges. But when $a_n = 1$ and $b_n = -1$ for all n, then $\sum (a_n + b_n)$ converges.

10.7 Telescoping series

Another important property of finite sums is the telescoping property which states that

$$(10.21) \qquad \sum_{k=1}^{n}(b_k - b_{k+1}) = b_1 - b_{n+1} .$$

When we try to extend this property to infinite series we are led to consider those series $\sum a_n$ for which each term a_n may be expressed as a difference of the form

$$(10.22) \qquad a_n = b_n - b_{n+1} .$$

These series are known as *telescoping series* and their behavior is characterized by the following theorem.

THEOREM 10.4. *Let $\{a_n\}$ and $\{b_n\}$ be two sequences of complex numbers such that*

$$(10.23) \qquad a_n = b_n - b_{n+1} \qquad for \qquad n = 1, 2, 3, \ldots .$$

Then the series $\sum a_n$ converges if and only if the sequence $\{b_n\}$ converges, in which case we have

$$(10.24) \qquad \sum_{n=1}^{\infty} a_n = b_1 - L , \qquad where \qquad L = \lim_{n \to \infty} b_n .$$

Proof. Let s_n denote the nth partial sum of $\sum a_n$. Then we have

$$s_n = \sum_{k=1}^{n} a_k = \sum_{k=1}^{n} (b_k - b_{k+1}) = b_1 - b_{n+1},$$

because of (10.21). Therefore, both sequences $\{s_n\}$ and $\{b_n\}$ converge or both diverge. Moreover, if $b_n \to L$ as $n \to \infty$, then $s_n \to b_1 - L$, and this proves (10.24).

Note: Every series is telescoping because we can always satisfy (10.22) if we first choose b_1 to be arbitrary and then choose $b_{n+1} = b_1 - s_n$ for $n \geq 1$, where $s_n = a_1 + \cdots + a_n$.

EXAMPLE 1. Let $a_n = 1/(n^2 + n)$. Then we have

$$a_n = \frac{1}{n(n+1)} = \frac{1}{n} - \frac{1}{n+1},$$

and hence (10.23) holds with $b_n = 1/n$. Since $b_1 = 1$ and $L = 0$, we obtain

$$\sum_{n=1}^{\infty} \frac{1}{n(n+1)} = 1.$$

EXAMPLE 2. If x is not a negative integer, we have the decomposition

$$\frac{1}{(n+x)(n+x+1)(n+x+2)} = \frac{1}{2}\left(\frac{1}{(n+x)(n+x+1)} - \frac{1}{(n+x+1)(n+x+2)}\right)$$

for each integer $n \geq 1$. Therefore, by the telescoping property, the following series converges and has the sum indicated:

$$\sum_{n=1}^{\infty} \frac{1}{(n+x)(n+x+1)(n+x+2)} = \frac{1}{2(x+1)(x+2)}.$$

EXAMPLE 3. Since $\log [n/(n+1)] = \log n - \log (n+1)$, and since $\log n \to \infty$ as $n \to \infty$, the series $\sum \log [n/(n+1)]$ diverges.

Note: Telescoping series illustrate an important difference between finite sums and infinite series. If we write (10.21) in extended form, it becomes

$$(b_1 - b_2) + (b_2 - b_3) + \cdots + (b_n - b_{n+1}) = b_1 - b_{n+1}$$

which can be verified by merely removing parentheses and canceling. Suppose now we perform the same operations on the infinite series

$$(b_1 - b_2) + (b_2 - b_3) + (b_3 - b_4) + \cdots.$$

We leave b_1, cancel b_2, cancel b_3, and so on. For each $n > 1$, at some stage we cancel b_n. Thus every b_n cancels with the exception of b_1. This leads us to the conclusion that the sum of the series is b_1. Because of Theorem 10.4, this conclusion is false unless $\lim_{n \to \infty} b_n = 0$. This shows that parentheses cannot always be removed in an infinite series as they can in a finite sum. (See also Exercise 24 in Section 10.9.)

10.8   The geometric series

The telescoping property of finite sums may be used to study a very important example known as the *geometric series*. This series is generated by successive addition of the terms in a geometric progression and has the form $\sum x^n$, where the nth term x^n is the nth power of a fixed real or complex number x. It is convenient to start this series with $n = 0$, with the understanding that the initial term, x^0, is equal to 1.

Let s_n denote the nth partial sum of this series, so that

$$s_n = 1 + x + x^2 + \cdots + x^{n-1}.$$

If $x = 1$, each term on the right is 1 and $s_n = n$. In this case, the series diverges since $s_n \to \infty$ as $n \to \infty$. If $x \neq 1$, we may simplify the sum for s_n by writing

$$(1 - x)s_n = (1 - x)\sum_{k=0}^{n-1} x^k = \sum_{k=0}^{n-1}(x^k - x^{k+1}) = 1 - x^n,$$

since the last sum telescopes. Dividing by $1 - x$, we obtain the formula

$$s_n = \frac{1 - x^n}{1 - x} = \frac{1}{1 - x} - \frac{x^n}{1 - x} \qquad \text{if} \quad x \neq 1.$$

This shows that the behavior of s_n for large n depends entirely on the behavior of x^n. When $|x| < 1$, then $x^n \to 0$ as $n \to \infty$, and the series converges to the sum $1/(1 - x)$.

Since $s_{n+1} - s_n = x^n$, convergence of $\{s_n\}$ implies $x^n \to 0$ as $n \to \infty$. Therefore, if $|x| \geq 1$ the sequence $\{s_n\}$ diverges since x^n does not tend to 0 in this case. Thus we have proved the following theorem.

THEOREM 10.5.   *If x is complex, with $|x| < 1$, the geometric series $\sum_{n=0}^{\infty} x^n$ converges and has sum $1/(1 - x)$. That is to say, we have*

(10.25) $\qquad 1 + x + x^2 + \cdots + x^n + \cdots = \dfrac{1}{1 - x} \qquad \text{if} \quad |x| < 1.$

If $|x| \geq 1$, the series diverges.

The geometric series, with $|x| < 1$, is one of those rare examples whose sum we are able to determine by finding first a simple formula for its partial sums. (A special case with $x = \frac{1}{2}$ was encountered in Section 10.1 in connection with Zeno's paradox.) The real importance of this series lies in the fact that it may be used as a starting point for determining the sums of a large number of other interesting series. For example, if we assume $|x| < 1$ and replace x by x^2 in (10.25), we obtain the formula

(10.26) $\qquad 1 + x^2 + x^4 + \cdots + x^{2n} + \cdots = \dfrac{1}{1 - x^2} \qquad \text{if} \quad |x| < 1.$

Notice that this series contains those terms of (10.25) with *even* exponents. To find the sum of the odd powers alone, we need only multiply both sides of (10.26) by x to obtain

$$(10.27) \qquad x + x^3 + x^5 + \cdots + x^{2n+1} + \cdots = \frac{x}{1 - x^2} \qquad \text{if} \quad |x| < 1 .$$

If we replace x by $-x$ in (10.25), we find that

$$(10.28) \qquad 1 - x + x^2 - x^3 + \cdots + (-1)^n x^n + \cdots = \frac{1}{1 + x} \qquad \text{if} \quad |x| < 1 .$$

Replacing x by x^2 in (10.28), we find that

$$(10.29) \qquad 1 - x^2 + x^4 - x^6 + \cdots + (-1)^n x^{2n} + \cdots = \frac{1}{1 + x^2} \qquad \text{if} \quad |x| < 1 .$$

Multiplying both sides of (10.29) by x, we obtain

$$(10.30) \quad x - x^3 + x^5 - x^7 + \cdots + (-1)^n x^{2n+1} + \cdots = \frac{x}{1 + x^2} \qquad \text{if} \quad |x| < 1 .$$

If we replace x by $2x$ in (10.26), we find that

$$1 + 4x^2 + 16x^4 + \cdots + 4^n x^{2n} + \cdots = \frac{1}{1 - 4x^2} ,$$

which is valid if $|2x| < 1$ or, what is the same thing, if $|x| < \frac{1}{2}$. It is clear that many other examples may be constructed by similar means.

All these series have the special form

$$\sum_{n=0}^{\infty} a_n x^n$$

and are known as *power series*. The numbers $a_0 , a_1 , a_2 , \ldots$, which may be real or complex, are called *coefficients* of the power series. The geometric series is an example with all coefficients equal to 1. If x and all the coefficients are real, the series is called a *real* power series. We shall find later, when we discuss the general theory of real power series, that it is permissible to differentiate and to integrate both sides of each of the Equations (10.25) through (10.30), treating the left-hand members as though they were ordinary finite sums. These operations lead to many remarkable new formulas. For example, differentiation of (10.25) gives us

$$(10.31) \qquad 1 + 2x + 3x^2 + \cdots + nx^{n-1} + \cdots = \frac{1}{(1 - x)^2} \qquad \text{if} \quad |x| < 1 ,$$

whereas integration of (10.28) yields the interesting formula

$$(10.32) \qquad x - \frac{x^2}{2} + \frac{x^3}{3} - \frac{x^4}{4} + \cdots + \frac{(-1)^n x^{n+1}}{n+1} + \cdots = \log(1+x)$$

which expresses the logarithm as a power series. This is the discovery of Mercator and Brouncker (1668) that we mentioned earlier. Although each of the Equations (10.25) through (10.31) is valid for x in the open interval $-1 < x < +1$, it turns out that the logarithmic series in (10.32) is valid at the endpoint $x = +1$ as well.

Another important example, which may be obtained by integration of (10.29), is the following power-series expansion for the inverse tangent, discovered in 1671 by James Gregory (1638–1675):

$$(10.33) \qquad x - \frac{x^3}{3} + \frac{x^5}{5} - \frac{x^7}{7} + \cdots + \frac{(-1)^n x^{2n+1}}{2n+1} + \cdots = \arctan x .$$

Gregory's series converges for each complex x with $|x| < 1$ and also for $x = \pm 1$. When x is real, the series agrees with the inverse tangent function introduced in Chapter 6. The series can be used to extend the definition of the arctangent function from real values of x to complex x with $|x| < 1$.

Many of the other elementary functions of calculus, such as the sine, cosine, and exponential, may also be represented by power series. This is not too surprising, in view of Taylor's formula which tells us that any function may be approximated by a Taylor polynomial in x of degree $\leq n$ if it has derivatives of order $n + 1$ in some neighborhood of the origin. In the examples given above, the partial sums of the power series are precisely the Taylor polynomials. When a function f has derivatives of every order in a neighborhood of the origin, then for every positive integer n Taylor's formula leads to an equation of the form

$$(10.34) \qquad\qquad f(x) = \sum_{k=0}^{n} a_k x^k + E_n(x) ,$$

where the finite sum $\sum_{k=0}^{n} a_k x^k$ is a Taylor polynomial of degree $\leq n$ and $E_n(x)$ is the error for this approximation. If, now, we keep x fixed and let n increase without bound in (10.34) the Taylor polynomials give rise to a power series, namely $\sum_{k=0}^{\infty} a_k x^k$, where each coefficient a_k is determined as follows:

$$a_k = \frac{f^{(k)}(0)}{k!} .$$

If, for some x, the error $E_n(x)$ tends to 0 as $n \to \infty$, then for this x we may let $n \to \infty$ in (10.34) to obtain

$$f(x) = \lim_{n \to \infty} \sum_{k=0}^{n} a_k x^k + \lim_{n \to \infty} E_n(x) = \sum_{k=0}^{\infty} a_k x^k .$$

In other words, the power series in question converges to $f(x)$. If x is a point for which $E_n(x)$ does not tend to 0 as $n \to \infty$, then the partial sums will not approach $f(x)$. Conditions on f for guaranteeing that $E_n(x) \to 0$ will be discussed later in Section 11.10.

To lay a better foundation for the general theory of power series, we turn next to certain general questions related to the convergence and divergence of arbitrary series. We shall return to the subject of power series in Chapter 11.

10.9 Exercises

Each of the series in Exercises 1 through 10 is a telescoping series, or a geometric series, or some related series whose partial sums may be simplified. In each case, prove that the series converges and has the sum indicated.

1. $\displaystyle\sum_{n=1}^{\infty} \frac{1}{(2n-1)(2n+1)} = \frac{1}{2}$.

2. $\displaystyle\sum_{n=1}^{\infty} \frac{2}{3^{n-1}} = 3$.

3. $\displaystyle\sum_{n=2}^{\infty} \frac{1}{n^2 - 1} = \frac{3}{4}$.

4. $\displaystyle\sum_{n=1}^{\infty} \frac{2^n + 3^n}{6^n} = \frac{3}{2}$.

5. $\displaystyle\sum_{n=1}^{\infty} \frac{\sqrt{n+1} - \sqrt{n}}{\sqrt{n^2 + n}} = 1$.

6. $\displaystyle\sum_{n=1}^{\infty} \frac{n}{(n+1)(n+2)(n+3)} = \frac{1}{4}$.

7. $\displaystyle\sum_{n=1}^{\infty} \frac{2n+1}{n^2(n+1)^2} = 1$.

8. $\displaystyle\sum_{n=1}^{\infty} \frac{2^n + n^2 + n}{2^{n+1}n(n+1)} = 1$.

9. $\displaystyle\sum_{n=1}^{\infty} \frac{(-1)^{n-1}(2n+1)}{n(n+1)} = 1$.

10. $\displaystyle\sum_{n=2}^{\infty} \frac{\log\left[(1 + 1/n)^n(1+n)\right]}{(\log n^n)[\log(n+1)^{n+1}]} = \log_2 \sqrt{e}$.

Power series for $\log(1 + x)$ and $\arctan x$ were obtained in Section 10.8 by performing various operations on the geometric series. In a similar manner, without attempting to justify the steps, obtain the formulas in Exercises 11 through 19. They are all valid at least for $|x| < 1$. (The theoretical justification is provided in Section 11.8.)

11. $\displaystyle\sum_{n=1}^{\infty} nx^n = \frac{x}{(1-x)^2}$.

12. $\displaystyle\sum_{n=1}^{\infty} n^2 x^n = \frac{x^2 + x}{(1-x)^3}$.

13. $\displaystyle\sum_{n=1}^{\infty} n^3 x^n = \frac{x^3 + 4x^2 + x}{(1-x)^4}$.

14. $\displaystyle\sum_{n=1}^{\infty} n^4 x^n = \frac{x^4 + 11x^3 + 11x^2 + x}{(1-x)^5}$.

15. $\displaystyle\sum_{n=1}^{\infty} \frac{x^n}{n} = \log \frac{1}{1-x}$.

16. $\displaystyle\sum_{n=1}^{\infty} \frac{x^{2n-1}}{2n-1} = \frac{1}{2} \log \frac{1+x}{1-x}$.

17. $\displaystyle\sum_{n=0}^{\infty} (n+1)x^n = \frac{1}{(1-x)^2}$.

18. $\displaystyle\sum_{n=0}^{\infty} \frac{(n+1)(n+2)}{2!} x^n = \frac{1}{(1-x)^3}$.

19. $\displaystyle\sum_{n=0}^{\infty} \frac{(n+1)(n+2)(n+3)}{3!} x^n = \frac{1}{(1-x)^4}$.

20. The results of Exercises 11 through 14 suggest that there exists a general formula of the form

$$\sum_{n=1}^{\infty} n^k x^n = \frac{P_k(x)}{(1-x)^{k+1}},$$

where $P_k(x)$ is a polynomial of degree k, the term of lowest degree being x and that of highest degree being x^k. Prove this by induction, without attempting to justify the formal manipulations with the series.

21. The results of Exercises 17 through 19 suggest the more general formula

$$\sum_{n=0}^{\infty} \binom{n+k}{k} x^n = \frac{1}{(1-x)^{k+1}}, \quad \text{where} \quad \binom{n+k}{k} = \frac{(n+1)(n+2)\cdots(n+k)}{k!}.$$

Prove this by induction, without attempting to justify the formal manipulations with the series.

22. Given that $\sum_{n=0}^{\infty} x^n/n! = e^x$ for all x, find the sums of the following series, assuming it is permissible to operate on infinite series as though they were finite sums.

(a) $\displaystyle\sum_{n=2}^{\infty} \frac{n-1}{n!}$.

(b) $\displaystyle\sum_{n=2}^{\infty} \frac{n+1}{n!}$.

(c) $\displaystyle\sum_{n=2}^{\infty} \frac{(n-1)(n+1)}{n!}$.

23. (a) Given that $\sum_{n=0}^{\infty} x^n/n! = e^x$ for all x, show that

$$\sum_{n=1}^{\infty} \frac{n^2 x^n}{n!} = (x^2 + x)e^x,$$

assuming it is permissible to operate on these series as though they were finite sums.

(b) The sum of the series $\sum_{n=1}^{\infty} n^3/n!$ is ke, where k is a positive integer. Find the value of k. Do not attempt to justify formal manipulations.

24. Two series $\sum_{n=1}^{\infty} a_n$ and $\sum_{n=1}^{\infty} b_n$ are called *identical* if $a_n = b_n$ for each $n \geq 1$. For example, the series

$$0 + 0 + 0 + \cdots \quad \text{and} \quad (1-1) + (1-1) + (1-1) + \cdots$$

are identical, but the series

$$1 + 1 + 1 + \cdots \quad \text{and} \quad 1 + 0 + 1 + 0 + 1 + 0 + \cdots$$

are not identical. Determine whether or not the series are identical in each of the following pairs:

(a) $1 - 1 + 1 - 1 + \cdots$ and $(2-1) - (3-2) + (4-3) - (5-4) + \cdots$.

(b) $1 - 1 + 1 - 1 + \cdots$ and $(1-1) + (1-1) + (1-1) + (1-1) + \cdots$.

(c) $1 - 1 + 1 - 1 + \cdots$ and $1 + (-1+1) + (-1+1) + (-1+1) + \cdots$.

(d) $1 + \frac{1}{2} + \frac{1}{4} + \frac{1}{8} + \cdots$ and $1 + (1 - \frac{1}{2}) + (\frac{1}{2} - \frac{1}{4}) + (\frac{1}{4} - \frac{1}{8}) + \cdots$.

25. (a) Use (10.26) to prove that

$$1 + 0 + x^2 + 0 + x^4 + \cdots = \frac{1}{1-x^2} \quad \text{if} \quad |x| < 1.$$

Note that, according to the definition given in Exercise 24, this series is not identical to the one in (10.26) if $x \neq 0$.

(b) Apply Theorem 10.2 to the result in part (a) and to (10.25) to deduce (10.27).

(c) Show that Theorem 10.2 when applied directly to (10.25) and (10.26) does not yield (10.27). Instead, it yields the formula $\sum_{n=1}^{\infty} (x^n - x^{2n}) = x/(1 - x^2)$, valid for $|x| < 1$.

*10.10 Exercises on decimal expansions

Decimal representations of real numbers were introduced in Section I3.15. It was shown there that every positive real x has a decimal representation of the form

$$x = a_0 . a_1 a_2 a_3 \ldots ,$$

where $0 \le a_k \le 9$ for each $k \ge 1$. The number x is related to the digits $a_0 , a_1 , a_2 , \ldots$ by the inequalities

(10.35) $$a_0 + \frac{a_1}{10} + \cdots + \frac{a_n}{10^n} \le x < a_0 + \frac{a_1}{10} + \cdots + \frac{a_{n-1}}{10^{n-1}} + \frac{a_n + 1}{10^n} .$$

If we let $s_n = \sum_{k=0}^{n} a_k/10^k$, and if we subtract s_n from each member of (10.35), we obtain

$$0 \le x - s_n < 10^{-n}.$$

This shows that $s_n \to x$ as $n \to \infty$, and hence x is given by the convergent series

(10.36) $$x = \sum_{k=0}^{\infty} \frac{a_k}{10^k} .$$

Each of the infinite decimal expansions in Exercises 1 through 5 is understood to be repeated indefinitely as suggested. In each case, express the decimal as an infinite series, find the sum of the series, and thereby express x as a quotient of two integers.

1. $x = 0.4444\ldots.$
2. $x = 0.51515151\ldots.$
3. $x = 2.02020202\ldots.$
4. $x = 0.123123123123\ldots.$
5. $x = 0.142857142857142857142857\ldots.$
6. Prove that every repeating decimal represents a rational number.
7. If a number has a decimal expansion which ends in zeros, such as $\frac{1}{8} = 0.1250000\ldots$, then this number can also be written as a decimal which ends in nines if we decrease the last nonzero digit by one unit. For example, $\frac{1}{8} = 0.1249999\ldots.$ Use infinite series to prove this statement.

The decimal representation in (10.36) may be generalized by replacing the integer 10 by any other integer $b > 1$. If $x > 0$, let a_0 denote the greatest integer in x; assuming that $a_0 , a_1 , \ldots , a_{n-1}$ have been defined, let a_n denote the largest integer such that

$$\sum_{k=0}^{n} \frac{a_k}{b^k} \le x .$$

The following exercises refer to the sequence of integers $a_0 , a_1 , a_2 , \ldots$ so obtained.

8. Show that $0 \le a_k \le b - 1$ for each $k \ge 1$.
9. Describe a geometric method for obtaining the numbers $a_0 , a_1 , a_2 , \ldots.$
10. Show that the series $\sum_{k=0}^{\infty} a_k/b^k$ converges and has sum x. This provides a decimal expansion of x in the scale of b. Important special cases, other than $b = 10$, are the *binary scale*, $b = 2$, and the *duodecimal scale*, $b = 12$.

10.11   Tests for convergence

In theory, the convergence or divergence of a particular series $\sum a_n$ is decided by examining its partial sums s_n to see whether or not they tend to a finite limit as $n \to \infty$. In some special cases, such as the geometric series, the sums defining s_n may be simplified to the point where it becomes a simple matter to determine their behavior for large n. However, in the majority of cases there is no nice formula for simplifying s_n and the convergence or divergence may be rather difficult to establish in a straightforward manner. Early investigators in the subject, notably Cauchy and his contemporaries, realized this difficulty and they developed a number of "convergence tests" that by-passed the need for an explicit knowledge of the partial sums. A few of the simplest and most useful of these tests will be discussed in this chapter, but first we want to make some general remarks about the nature of these tests.

Convergence tests may be broadly classified into three categories: (i) *sufficient* conditions; (ii) *necessary* conditions; (iii) *necessary and sufficient* conditions. A test of type (i) may be expressed symbolically as follows:

"If C is satisfied, then $\sum a_n$ converges,"

where C stands for the condition in question. Tests of type (ii) have the form

"If $\sum a_n$ converges, then C is satisfied,"

whereas those of type (iii) may be written thus:

"$\sum a_n$ converges if and only if C is satisfied."

We shall see presently that there are tests of type (ii) that are not of type (i) (and vice versa). Beginners often use such tests incorrectly by failing to realize the difference between a *necessary* condition and a *sufficient* condition. Therefore the reader should make an effort to keep this distinction in mind when using a particular test in practice.

The simplest of all convergence tests gives a *necessary* condition for convergence and may be stated as follows.

THEOREM 10.6.   *If the series* $\sum a_n$ *converges, then its nth term tends to* 0; *that is,*

(10.37)
$$\lim_{n \to \infty} a_n = 0.$$

Proof. Let $s_n = a_1 + a_2 + \cdots + a_n$. Then $a_n = s_n - s_{n-1}$. As $n \to \infty$, both s_n and s_{n-1} tend to the same limit and hence $a_n \to 0$. This proves the theorem.

This is an example of a test of type (ii) which is not of type (i). Condition (10.37) is *not* sufficient for convergence. For example, when $a_n = 1/n$, the condition $a_n \to 0$ is satisfied but the series $\sum 1/n$ diverges. The real usefulness of this test is that it gives us a *sufficient* condition for *divergence*. That is, if the terms a_n of a series $\sum a_n$ do *not* tend to zero, then the series must diverge. This statement is logically equivalent to Theorem 10.6.

10.12   Comparison tests for series of nonnegative terms

In this section we shall be concerned with series having *nonnegative terms*, that is, series of the form $\sum a_n$, where each $a_n \geq 0$. Since the partial sums of such series are monotonic increasing, we may use Theorem 10.1 to obtain the following *necessary and sufficient condition* for convergence.

THEOREM 10.7. *Assume that $a_n \geq 0$ for each $n \geq 1$. Then the series $\sum a_n$ converges if and only if the sequence of its partial sums is bounded above.*

If the partial sums are bounded above by a number M, say, then the sum of the series cannot exceed M.

EXAMPLE 1. Theorem 10.7 may be used to establish the convergence of the series $\sum_{n=1}^{\infty} 1/n!$. We estimate the partial sums from above by using the inequality

$$\frac{1}{k!} \leq \frac{1}{2^{k-1}},$$

which is obviously true for all $k \geq 1$ since $k!$ consists of $k-1$ factors, each ≥ 2. Therefore we have

$$\sum_{k=1}^{n} \frac{1}{k!} \leq \sum_{k=1}^{n} \frac{1}{2^{k-1}} = \sum_{k=0}^{n-1} \left(\frac{1}{2}\right)^k \leq \sum_{k=0}^{\infty} \left(\frac{1}{2}\right)^k = 2,$$

the last series being a geometric series. The series $\sum_{n=1}^{\infty} 1/n!$ is therefore convergent and has a sum ≤ 2. We shall see later that the sum of this series is $e - 1$, where e is the Euler number.

The convergence of the foregoing example was established by comparing the terms of the given series with those of a series known to converge. This idea may be pursued further to yield a number of tests known as *comparison tests*.

THEOREM 10.8. COMPARISON TEST. *Assume $a_n \geq 0$ and $b_n \geq 0$ for all $n \geq 1$. If there exists a positive constant c such that*

(10.38) $a_n \leq cb_n$

for all n, then convergence of $\sum b_n$ implies convergence of $\sum a_n$.

Note: The conclusion may also be formulated as follows: "Divergence of $\sum a_n$ implies divergence of $\sum b_n$." This statement is logically equivalent to Theorem 10.8. When the inequality (10.38) is satisfied, we say that the series $\sum b_n$ *dominates* the series $\sum a_n$.

Proof. Let $s_n = a_1 + \cdots + a_n$, $t_n = b_1 + \cdots + b_n$. Then (10.38) implies $s_n \leq ct_n$. If $\sum b_n$ converges, its partial sums are bounded, say by M. Then $s_n \leq cM$, and hence $\sum a_n$ is also convergent since its partial sums are bounded by cM. This completes the proof.

Omitting a finite number of terms at the beginning of a series does not affect its convergence or divergence. Therefore Theorem 10.8 still holds true if the inequality (10.38) is valid only for all $n \geq N$ for some N.

THEOREM 10.9. LIMIT COMPARISON TEST. *Assume that $a_n > 0$ and $b_n > 0$ for all $n \geq 1$, and suppose that*

$$(10.39) \qquad \lim_{n \to \infty} \frac{a_n}{b_n} = 1 \, .$$

Then $\sum a_n$ converges if and only if $\sum b_n$ converges.

Proof. There exists an N such that $n \geq N$ implies $\frac{1}{2} < a_n/b_n < \frac{3}{2}$. Therefore $b_n < 2a_n$ and $a_n < \frac{3}{2} b_n$ for all $n \geq N$, and the theorem follows by applying Theorem 10.8 twice.

Note that Theorem 10.9 also holds if $\lim_{n \to \infty} a_n/b_n = c$, provided that $c > 0$, because we then have $\lim_{n \to \infty} a_n/(cb_n) = 1$ and we may compare $\sum a_n$ with $\sum (cb_n)$. However, if $\lim_{n \to \infty} a_n/b_n = 0$, we conclude only that convergence of $\sum b_n$ implies convergence of $\sum a_n$.

DEFINITION. *Two sequences $\{a_n\}$ and $\{b_n\}$ of complex numbers are said to be asymptotically equal if*

$$\lim_{n \to \infty} \frac{a_n}{b_n} = 1 \, .$$

This relation is often indicated symbolically by writing

$$(10.40) \qquad a_n \sim b_n \qquad \text{as} \quad n \to \infty \, .$$

The notation $a_n \sim b_n$ is read "a_n is asymptotically equal to b_n," and it is intended to suggest that a_n and b_n behave in essentially the same way for large n. Using this terminology, we may state the limit comparison test in the following manner.

THEOREM 10.10. *Two series $\sum a_n$ and $\sum b_n$ with terms that are positive and asymptotically equal converge together or they diverge together.*

EXAMPLE 2. THE RIEMANN ZETA-FUNCTION. In Example 1 of Section 10.7, we proved that $\sum 1/(n^2 + n)$ is a convergent telescoping series. If we use this as a comparison series, it follows that $\sum 1/n^2$ is convergent, since $1/n^2 \sim 1/(n^2 + n)$ as $n \to \infty$. Also, $\sum 1/n^2$ dominates $\sum 1/n^s$ for $s \geq 2$, and therefore $\sum 1/n^s$ converges for every real $s \geq 2$. We shall prove in the next section that this series also converges for every $s > 1$. Its sum, denoted by $\zeta(s)$ (ζ is the Greek letter zeta), defines an important function in analysis known as the *Riemann zeta-function:*

$$\zeta(s) = \sum_{n=1}^{\infty} \frac{1}{n^s} \qquad \text{if} \quad s > 1 \, .$$

Euler discovered many beautiful formulas involving $\zeta(s)$. In particular, he found that $\zeta(2) = \pi^2/6$, a result which is not easy to derive at this stage.

EXAMPLE 3. Since $\sum 1/n$ diverges, every series having positive terms asymptotically equal to $1/n$ must also diverge. For example, this is true of the two series

$$\sum_{n=1}^{\infty} \frac{1}{\sqrt{n(n+10)}} \qquad \text{and} \qquad \sum_{n=1}^{\infty} \sin \frac{1}{n}.$$

The relation $\sin 1/n \sim 1/n$ follows from the fact that $(\sin x)/x \to 1$ as $x \to 0$.

10.13 The integral test

To use comparison tests effectively, we must have at our disposal some examples of series of known behavior. The geometric series and the zeta-function are useful for this purpose. New examples can be obtained very simply by applying the *integral test*, first proved by Cauchy in 1837.

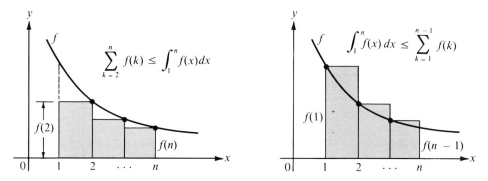

FIGURE 10.4   Proof of the integral test.

THEOREM 10.11.   INTEGRAL TEST.   *Let f be a positive decreasing function, defined for all real $x \geq 1$. For each $n \geq 1$, let*

$$s_n = \sum_{k=1}^{n} f(k) \qquad \text{and} \qquad t_n = \int_{1}^{n} f(x)\, dx.$$

Then both sequences $\{s_n\}$ and $\{t_n\}$ converge or both diverge.

Proof. By comparing f with appropriate step functions as suggested in Figure 10.4, we obtain the inequalities

$$\sum_{k=2}^{n} f(k) \leq \int_{1}^{n} f(x)\, dx \leq \sum_{k=1}^{n-1} f(k)$$

or $s_n - f(1) \leq t_n \leq s_{n-1}$. Since both sequences $\{s_n\}$ and $\{t_n\}$ are monotonic increasing, these inequalities show that both are bounded above or both are unbounded. Therefore, both sequences converge or both diverge, as asserted.

EXAMPLE 1. The integral test enables us to prove that

$$\sum_{n=1}^{\infty} \frac{1}{n^s} \qquad \text{converges if and only if} \quad s > 1 .$$

Taking $f(x) = x^{-s}$, we have

$$t_n = \int_1^n \frac{1}{x^s}\, dx = \begin{cases} \dfrac{n^{1-s} - 1}{1 - s} & \text{if} \quad s \neq 1 , \\[2mm] \log n & \text{if} \quad s = 1 . \end{cases}$$

When $s > 1$ the term $n^{1-s} \to 0$ as $n \to \infty$ and hence $\{t_n\}$ converges. By the integral test, this implies convergence of the series for $s > 1$.

When $s \le 1$, then $t_n \to \infty$ and the series diverges. The special case $s = 1$ (the *harmonic series*) was discussed earlier in Section 10.5. Its divergence was known to Leibniz.

EXAMPLE 2. The same method may be used to prove that

$$\sum_{n=2}^{\infty} \frac{1}{n(\log n)^s} \qquad \text{converges if and only if} \quad s > 1 .$$

(We start the sum with $n = 2$ to avoid n for which $\log n$ may be zero.)

The corresponding integral in this case is

$$t_n = \int_2^n \frac{1}{x(\log x)^s}\, dx = \begin{cases} \dfrac{(\log n)^{1-s} - (\log 2)^{1-s}}{1 - s} & \text{if} \quad s \neq 1 , \\[2mm] \log\,(\log n) - \log\,(\log 2) & \text{if} \quad s = 1 . \end{cases}$$

Thus $\{t_n\}$ converges if and only if $s > 1$, and hence, by the integral test, the same holds true for the series in question.

10.14   Exercises

Test the following series for convergence or divergence. In each case, give a reason for your decision.

1. $\displaystyle\sum_{n=1}^{\infty} \frac{n}{(4n-3)(4n-1)} .$

2. $\displaystyle\sum_{n=1}^{\infty} \frac{\sqrt{2n-1}\,\log\,(4n+1)}{n(n+1)} .$

3. $\displaystyle\sum_{n=1}^{\infty} \frac{n+1}{2^n} .$

4. $\displaystyle\sum_{n=1}^{\infty} \frac{n^2}{2^n} .$

5. $\displaystyle\sum_{n=1}^{\infty} \frac{|\sin nx|}{n^2} .$

6. $\displaystyle\sum_{n=1}^{\infty} \frac{2 + (-1)^n}{2^n} .$

7. $\displaystyle\sum_{n=1}^{\infty} \frac{n!}{(n+2)!} .$

8. $\displaystyle\sum_{n=2}^{\infty} \frac{\log n}{n\sqrt{n+1}} .$

9. $\displaystyle\sum_{n=1}^{\infty} \frac{1}{\sqrt{n(n+1)}}$.

10. $\displaystyle\sum_{n=1}^{\infty} \frac{1 + \sqrt{n}}{(n+1)^3 - 1}$.

11. $\displaystyle\sum_{n=2}^{\infty} \frac{1}{(\log n)^s}$.

12. $\displaystyle\sum_{n=1}^{\infty} \frac{|a_n|}{10^n}$, $\quad |a_n| < 10$.

13. $\displaystyle\sum_{n=1}^{\infty} \frac{1}{1000n + 1}$.

14. $\displaystyle\sum_{n=1}^{\infty} \frac{n \cos^2 (n\pi/3)}{2^n}$.

15. $\displaystyle\sum_{n=3}^{\infty} \frac{1}{n \log n (\log \log n)^s}$.

16. $\displaystyle\sum_{n=1}^{\infty} n e^{-n^2}$.

17. $\displaystyle\sum_{n=1}^{\infty} \int_0^{1/n} \frac{\sqrt{x}}{1 + x^2} \, dx$.

18. $\displaystyle\sum_{n=1}^{\infty} \int_n^{n+1} e^{-\sqrt{x}} \, dx$.

19. Assume f is a nonnegative increasing function defined for all $x \geq 1$. Use the method suggested by the proof of the integral test to show that

$$\sum_{k=1}^{n-1} f(k) \leq \int_1^n f(x) \, dx \leq \sum_{k=2}^n f(k) .$$

Take $f(x) = \log x$ and deduce the inequalities

(10.41) $e \, n^n \, e^{-n} < n! < e \, n^{n+1} e^{-n}$.

These give a rough estimate of the order of magnitude of $n!$. From (10.41), we may write

$$\frac{e^{1/n}}{e} < \frac{(n!)^{1/n}}{n} < \frac{e^{1/n} \, n^{1/n}}{e} .$$

Letting $n \to \infty$, we find that

$$\frac{(n!)^{1/n}}{n} \to \frac{1}{e} \quad \text{or} \quad (n!)^{1/n} \sim \frac{n}{e} \quad \text{as} \quad n \to \infty .$$

10.15   The root test and the ratio test for series of nonnegative terms

Using the geometric series $\sum x^n$ as a comparison series, Cauchy developed two useful tests known as the *root test* and the *ratio test*.

If $\sum a_n$ is a series whose terms (from some point on) satisfy an inequality of the form

(10.42) $0 \leq a_n \leq x^n,$ where $0 < x < 1 ,$

a direct application of the comparison test (Theorem 10.8) tells us that $\sum a_n$ converges. The inequalities in (10.42) are equivalent to

(10.43) $0 \leq a_n^{1/n} \leq x ;$

hence the name *root test*.

If the sequence $\{a_n^{1/n}\}$ is convergent, the test may be restated in a somewhat more useful form that makes no reference to the number x.

THEOREM 10.12.   ROOT TEST.   *Let $\sum a_n$ be a series of nonnegative terms such that*

$$a_n^{1/n} \to R \qquad as \quad n \to \infty \, .$$

(a) *If $R < 1$, the series converges.*
(b) *If $R > 1$, the series diverges.*
(c) *If $R = 1$, the test is inconclusive.*

Proof. Assume $R < 1$ and choose x so that $R < x < 1$. Then (10.43) must be satisfied for all $n \geq N$ for some N. Hence, $\sum a_n$ converges by the comparison test. This proves (a).

To prove (b), we observe that $R > 1$ implies $a_n > 1$ for infinitely many values of n and hence a_n cannot tend to 0. Therefore, by Theorem 10.6, $\sum a_n$ diverges. This proves (b).

To prove (c), consider the two examples in which $a_n = 1/n$ and $a_n = 1/n^2$. In both cases $R = 1$ since $n^{1/n} \to 1$ as $n \to \infty$ [see Equation (10.12) of Section 10.2], but $\sum 1/n$ diverges whereas $\sum 1/n^2$ converges.

EXAMPLE 1. The root test makes it easy to determine the convergence of the series $\sum_{n=3}^{\infty} (\log n)^{-n}$ since

$$a_n^{1/n} = \frac{1}{\log n} \to 0 \qquad as \quad n \to \infty \, .$$

EXAMPLE 2. Applying the root test to $\sum [n/(n+1)]^{n^2}$, we find that

$$a_n^{1/n} = \left(\frac{n}{n+1} \right)^n = \frac{1}{(1 + 1/n)^n} \to \frac{1}{e} \qquad as \qquad n \to \infty,$$

by Equation (10.13) of Section 10.2. Since $1/e < 1$, the series converges.

A slightly different use of the comparison test yields the ratio test.

THEOREM 10.13.   RATIO TEST.   *Let $\sum a_n$ be a series of positive terms such that*

$$\frac{a_{n+1}}{a_n} \to L \qquad as \quad n \to \infty \, .$$

(a) *If $L < 1$, the series converges.*
(b) *If $L > 1$, the series diverges.*
(c) *If $L = 1$, the test is inconclusive.*

Proof. Assume $L < 1$ and choose x so that $L < x < 1$. Then there must be an N such that $a_{n+1}/a_n < x$ for all $n \geq N$. This implies

$$\frac{a_{n+1}}{x^{n+1}} < \frac{a_n}{x^n} \qquad \text{for all } n \geq N \, .$$

In other words, the sequence $\{a_n/x^n\}$ is decreasing for $n \geq N$. In particular, when $n \geq N$, we must have $a_n/x^n \leq a_N/x^N$, or, in other words,

$$a_n \leq cx^n, \qquad \text{where} \quad c = \frac{a_N}{x^N}.$$

Therefore $\sum a_n$ is dominated by the convergent series $\sum x^n$. This proves (a).

To prove (b), we simply observe that $L > 1$ implies $a_{n+1} > a_n$ for all $n \geq N$ for some N, and hence a_n cannot approach 0.

Finally, (c) is proved by using the same examples as in Theorem 10.12.

Warning. If the test ratio a_{n+1}/a_n is always less than 1, it does not necessarily follow that the *limit* L will be less than 1. For example, the harmonic series, which diverges, has test ratio $n/(n + 1)$ which is always less than 1 but the limit L equals 1. On the other hand, for divergence it is sufficient that the test ratio be greater than 1 for all sufficiently large n because for such n we have $a_{n+1} > a_n$ and a_n cannot approach 0.

EXAMPLE 3. We may establish the convergence of the series $\sum n!/n^n$ by the ratio test. The ratio of consecutive terms is

$$\frac{a_{n+1}}{a_n} = \frac{(n + 1)!}{(n + 1)^{n+1}} \cdot \frac{n^n}{n!} = \left(\frac{n}{n + 1}\right)^n = \frac{1}{(1 + 1/n)^n} \to \frac{1}{e} \qquad \text{as} \quad n \to \infty,$$

by formula (10.13) of Section 10.2. Since $1/e < 1$, the series converges. In particular, this implies that the general term of the series tends to 0; that is,

$$(10.44) \qquad \qquad \frac{n!}{n^n} \to 0 \qquad \text{as} \quad n \to \infty.$$

This is often described by saying that n^n "grows faster" than $n!$ for large n. Also, with a natural extension of the o-notation, we can write (10.44) as follows: $n! = o(n^n)$ as $n \to \infty$.

Note: The relation (10.44) may also be proved directly by writing

$$\frac{n!}{n^n} = \frac{1}{n} \cdot \frac{2}{n} \cdots \frac{k}{n} \cdot \frac{k + 1}{n} \cdots \frac{n}{n},$$

where $k = n/2$ if n is even, and $k = (n - 1)/2$ if n is odd. If $n \geq 2$, the product of the first k factors on the right does not exceed $(\frac{1}{2})^k$, and each of the remaining factors does not exceed 1. Since $(\frac{1}{2})^k \to 0$ as $n \to \infty$, this proves (10.44). Relation (10.44) also follows from (10.41).

The reader should realize that both the root test and the ratio test are, in reality, special cases of the comparison test. In both tests when we have case (a), convergence is deduced from the fact that the series in question can be dominated by a suitable geometric series $\sum x^n$. The usefulness of these tests in practice is that a knowledge of a particular comparison series $\sum x^n$ is not explicitly required. Further convergence tests may be deduced by using the comparison test in other ways. Two important examples known as *Raabe's test* and *Gauss' test* are described in Exercises 16 and 17 of Section 10.16. These are often helpful when the ratio test fails.

10.16   Exercises

Test the following series for convergence or divergence and give a reason for your decision in each case.

1. $\displaystyle\sum_{n=1}^{\infty} \frac{(n!)^2}{(2n)!}$.

8. $\displaystyle\sum_{n=1}^{\infty} (n^{1/n} - 1)^n$.

2. $\displaystyle\sum_{n=1}^{\infty} \frac{(n!)^2}{2^{n^2}}$.

9. $\displaystyle\sum_{n=1}^{\infty} e^{-n^2}$.

3. $\displaystyle\sum_{n=1}^{\infty} \frac{2^n n!}{n^n}$.

10. $\displaystyle\sum_{n=1}^{\infty} \left(\frac{1}{n} - e^{-n^2} \right)$.

4. $\displaystyle\sum_{n=1}^{\infty} \frac{3^n n!}{n^n}$.

11. $\displaystyle\sum_{n=1}^{\infty} \frac{(1000)^n}{n!}$.

5. $\displaystyle\sum_{n=1}^{\infty} \frac{n!}{3^n}$.

12. $\displaystyle\sum_{n=1}^{\infty} \frac{n^{n+1/n}}{(n + 1/n)^n}$.

6. $\displaystyle\sum_{n=1}^{\infty} \frac{n!}{2^{2n}}$.

13. $\displaystyle\sum_{n=1}^{\infty} \frac{n^3[\sqrt{2} + (-1)^n]^n}{3^n}$.

7. $\displaystyle\sum_{n=2}^{\infty} \frac{1}{(\log n)^{1/n}}$.

14. $\displaystyle\sum_{n=1}^{\infty} r^n |\sin nx|,\qquad r > 0$.

15. Let $\{a_n\}$ and $\{b_n\}$ be two sequences with $a_n > 0$ and $b_n > 0$ for all $n \geq N$, and let $c_n = b_n - b_{n+1}a_{n+1}/a_n$. Prove that:

   (a) If there is a positive constant r such that $c_n \geq r > 0$ for all $n \geq N$, then $\sum a_n$ converges.

   [*Hint:*   Show that $\sum_{k=N}^{n} a_k \leq a_N b_N / r$.]

   (b) If $c_n \leq 0$ for $n \geq N$ and if $\sum 1/b_n$ diverges, then $\sum a_n$ diverges.

   [*Hint:*   Show that $\sum a_n$ dominates $\sum 1/b_n$.]

16. Let $\sum a_n$ be a series of positive terms. Prove *Raabe's test*: If there is an $r > 0$ and an $N \geq 1$ such that

$$\frac{a_{n+1}}{a_n} \leq 1 - \frac{1}{n} - \frac{r}{n} \qquad \text{for all } n \geq N ,$$

then $\sum a_n$ converges. The series $\sum a_n$ diverges if

$$\frac{a_{n+1}}{a_n} \geq 1 - \frac{1}{n} \qquad \text{for all } n \geq N .$$

   [*Hint:*   Use Exercise 15 with $b_{n+1} = n$.]

17. Let $\sum a_n$ be a series of positive terms. Prove *Gauss' test*: If there is an $N \geq 1$, an $s > 1$, and an $M > 0$ such that

$$\frac{a_{n+1}}{a_n} = 1 - \frac{A}{n} + \frac{f(n)}{n^s} \qquad \text{for } n \geq N ,$$

where $|f(n)| \leq M$ for all n, then $\sum a_n$ converges if $A > 1$ and diverges if $A \leq 1$.

   [*Hint:*   If $A \neq 1$, use Exercise 16. If $A = 1$, use Exercise 15 with $b_{n+1} = n \log n$.]

18. Use Gauss' test (in Exercise 17) to prove that the series

$$\sum_{n=1}^{\infty} \left(\frac{1 \cdot 3 \cdot 5 \cdots (2n-1)}{2 \cdot 4 \cdot 6 \cdots (2n)} \right)^{k}$$

converges if $k > 2$ and diverges if $k \le 2$. For this example the ratio test fails.

10.17 Alternating series

Up to now we have been concerned largely with series of nonnegative terms. We wish to turn our attention next to series whose terms may be positive or negative. The simplest examples occur when the terms alternate in sign. These are called *alternating series* and they have the form

(10.45) $$\sum_{n=1}^{\infty} (-1)^{n-1} a_n = a_1 - a_2 + a_3 - a_4 + \cdots + (-1)^{n-1} a_n + \cdots,$$

where each $a_n > 0$.

Examples of alternating series were known to many early investigators. We have already mentioned the logarithmic series

$$\log (1 + x) = x - \frac{x^2}{2} + \frac{x^3}{3} - \frac{x^4}{4} + \cdots + (-1)^{n-1} \frac{x^n}{n} + \cdots.$$

As we shall prove later on, this series converges and has the sum $\log (1 + x)$ whenever $-1 < x \le 1$. For positive x, it is an alternating series. In particular, when $x = 1$ we obtain the formula

(10.46) $$\log 2 = 1 - \frac{1}{2} + \frac{1}{3} - \frac{1}{4} + \cdots + \frac{(-1)^{n-1}}{n} + \cdots,$$

which tells us that the alternating harmonic series has the sum $\log 2$. This result is of special interest in view of the fact that the harmonic series $\sum 1/n$ diverges.

Closely related to (10.46) is the interesting formula

(10.47) $$\frac{\pi}{4} = 1 - \frac{1}{3} + \frac{1}{5} - \frac{1}{7} + \cdots + \frac{(-1)^{n-1}}{2n-1} + \cdots$$

discovered by James Gregory in 1671. Leibniz rediscovered this result in 1673 while computing the area of a unit circular disk.

Both series in (10.46) and in (10.47) are alternating series of the form (10.45) in which the sequence $\{a_n\}$ decreases monotonically to zero. Leibniz noticed, in 1705, that this simple property of the a_n implies the convergence of *any* alternating series.

THEOREM 10.14.   LEIBNIZ'S RULE.   *If $\{a_n\}$ is a monotonic decreasing sequence with limit 0, then the alternating series $\sum_{n=1}^{\infty} (-1)^{n-1} a_n$ converges. If S denotes its sum and s_n its nth partial sum, we also have the inequalities*

$$(10.48) \qquad\qquad 0 < (-1)^n(S - s_n) < a_{n+1} \qquad \text{for each } n \geq 1 \, .$$

The inequalities in (10.48) provide a useful way to estimate the error in approximating the sum S by any partial sum s_n. The first inequality tells us that the error, $S - s_n$, has the sign $(-1)^n$, which is the same as the sign of the first neglected term, $(-1)^n a_{n+1}$. The second inequality states that the absolute value of this error is less than that of the first neglected term.

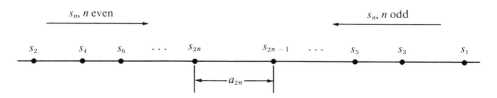

FIGURE 10.5   Proof of Leibniz's rule for alternating series.

Proof. The idea of the proof of Leibniz's rule is quite simple and is illustrated in Figure 10.5. The partial sums s_{2n} (consisting of an even number of terms) form an increasing sequence because $s_{2n+2} - s_{2n} = a_{2n+1} - a_{2n+2} > 0$. Similarly, the partial sums s_{2n-1} form a decreasing sequence. Both sequences are bounded below by s_2 and above by s_1. Therefore, each sequence $\{s_{2n}\}$ and $\{s_{2n-1}\}$, being monotonic and bounded, converges to a limit, say $s_{2n} \to S'$, and $s_{2n-1} \to S''$. But $S' = S''$ because

$$S' - S'' = \lim_{n \to \infty} s_{2n} - \lim_{n \to \infty} s_{2n-1} = \lim_{n \to \infty} (s_{2n} - s_{2n-1}) = \lim_{n \to \infty} (-a_{2n}) = 0 \, .$$

If we denote this common limit by S, it is clear that the series converges and has sum S. To derive the inequalities in (10.48) we argue as follows: Since $s_{2n} \nearrow$ and $s_{2n-1} \searrow$, we have

$$s_{2n} < s_{2n+2} \leq S \qquad \text{and} \qquad S \leq s_{2n+1} < s_{2n-1} \qquad \text{for all } n \geq 1 \, .$$

Therefore we have the inequalities

$$0 < S - s_{2n} \leq s_{2n+1} - s_{2n} = a_{2n+1} \qquad \text{and} \qquad 0 < s_{2n-1} - S \leq s_{2n-1} - s_{2n} = a_{2n} \, ,$$

which, taken together, yield (10.48). This completes the proof.

EXAMPLE 1. Since $1/n \searrow$ and $1/n \to 0$ as $n \to \infty$, the convergence of the alternating harmonic series $1 - \frac{1}{2} + \frac{1}{3} - \frac{1}{4} + \cdots$ is an immediate consequence of Leibniz's rule. The sum of this series is computed below in Example 4.

EXAMPLE 2. The alternating series $\sum (-1)^n (\log n)/n$ converges. To prove this using Leibniz's rule, we must show that $(\log n)/n \to 0$ as $n \to \infty$ and that $(\log n)/n \searrow$. The first statement follows from Equation (10.11) of Section 10.2. To prove the second statement, we note that the function f for which

$$f(x) = \frac{\log x}{x} \qquad \text{when} \quad x > 0$$

has the derivative $f'(x) = (1 - \log x)/x^2$. When $x > e$, this is negative and f is monotonic decreasing. In particular, $f(n + 1) < f(n)$ for $n \geq 3$.

EXAMPLE 3. An important limit relation may be derived as a consequence of Leibniz's rule. Let

$$a_1 = 1, \qquad a_2 = \int_1^2 \frac{dx}{x}, \qquad a_3 = \tfrac{1}{2}, \qquad a_4 = \int_2^3 \frac{dx}{x}, \qquad \dots ,$$

where, in general,

$$a_{2n-1} = \frac{1}{n} \qquad \text{and} \qquad a_{2n} = \int_n^{n+1} \frac{dx}{x} \qquad \text{for} \quad n = 1, 2, 3, \dots .$$

It is easy to verify that $a_n \to 0$ as $n \to \infty$ and that $a_n \searrow$. Hence the series $\sum (-1)^{n-1} a_n$ converges. Denote its sum by C and its nth partial sum by s_n. The $(2n - 1)$st partial sum may be expressed as follows:

$$s_{2n-1} = 1 - \int_1^2 \frac{dx}{x} + \frac{1}{2} - \int_2^3 \frac{dx}{x} + \cdots + \frac{1}{n-1} - \int_{n-1}^n \frac{dx}{x} + \frac{1}{n}$$

$$= 1 + \frac{1}{2} + \cdots + \frac{1}{n} - \int_1^n \frac{dx}{x} = 1 + \frac{1}{2} + \cdots + \frac{1}{n} - \log n .$$

Since $s_{2n-1} \to C$ as $n \to \infty$, we obtain the following limit formula:

$$(10.49) \qquad \lim_{n \to \infty} \left(1 + \frac{1}{2} + \cdots + \frac{1}{n} - \log n \right) = C .$$

The number C defined by this limit is called *Euler's constant* (sometimes denoted by γ). Like π and e, this number appears in many analytic formulas. Its value, correct to ten decimals, is 0.5772156649. An interesting problem, unsolved to this time, is to decide whether Euler's constant is rational or irrational.

Relation (10.49) can also be expressed as follows:

$$(10.50) \qquad \sum_{k=1}^{n} \frac{1}{k} = \log n + C + o(1) \qquad \text{as} \quad n \to \infty .$$

From this it follows that the ratio $(1 + \tfrac{1}{2} + \cdots + 1/n)/\log n \to 1$ as $n \to \infty$, so the partial sums of the harmonic series are asymptotically equal to $\log n$. That is, we have

$$\sum_{k=1}^{n} \frac{1}{k} \sim \log n \qquad \text{as} \quad n \to \infty .$$

The relation (10.50) not only explains why the harmonic series diverges, but it also gives us some concrete idea of the rate of growth of its partial sums. In the next example we use this relation to prove that the alternating harmonic series has the sum log 2.

EXAMPLE 4. Let $s_m = \sum_{k=1}^{m} (-1)^{k-1}/k$. We know that s_m tends to a limit as $m \to \infty$, and we shall prove now that this limit is log 2. When m is even, say $m = 2n$, we may separate the positive and negative terms to obtain

$$s_{2n} = \sum_{k=1}^{n} \frac{1}{2k-1} - \sum_{k=1}^{n} \frac{1}{2k} = \left(\sum_{k=1}^{2n} \frac{1}{k} - \sum_{k=1}^{n} \frac{1}{2k} \right) - \sum_{k=1}^{n} \frac{1}{2k} = \sum_{k=1}^{2n} \frac{1}{k} - \sum_{k=1}^{n} \frac{1}{k}.$$

Applying (10.50) to each sum on the extreme right, we obtain

$$s_{2n} = (\log 2n + C + o(1)) - (\log n + C + o(1)) = \log 2 + o(1),$$

so $s_{2n} \to \log 2$ as $n \to \infty$. This proves that the sum of the alternating harmonic series is log 2.

10.18 Conditional and absolute convergence

Although the alternating harmonic series $\sum (-1)^{n-1}/n$ is convergent, the series obtained by replacing each term by its absolute value is divergent. This shows that, in general, convergence of $\sum a_n$ does not imply convergence of $\sum |a_n|$. In the other direction, we have the following theorem.

THEOREM 10.15.   *Assume $\sum |a_n|$ converges.   Then $\sum a_n$ also converges, and we have*

(10.51)
$$\left| \sum_{n=1}^{\infty} a_n \right| \leq \sum_{n=1}^{\infty} |a_n|.$$

Proof.   Assume first that the terms a_n are real. Let $b_n = a_n + |a_n|$. We shall prove that $\sum b_n$ converges. It then follows (by Theorem 10.2) that $\sum a_n$ converges because $a_n = b_n - |a_n|$.

Since b_n is either 0 or $2 |a_n|$, we have $0 \leq b_n \leq 2 |a_n|$, and hence $\sum |a_n|$ dominates $\sum b_n$. Therefore $\sum b_n$ converges and, as already mentioned, this implies convergence of $\sum a_n$.

Now suppose the terms a_n are complex, say $a_n = u_n + iv_n$, where u_n and v_n are real. Since $|u_n| \leq |a_n|$, convergence of $\sum |a_n|$ implies convergence of $\sum |u_n|$ and this, in turn, implies convergence of $\sum u_n$, since the u_n are real. Similarly, $\sum v_n$ converges. By linearity, the series $\sum (u_n + iv_n)$ converges.

To prove (10.51), we note that $|\sum_{k=1}^{n} a_k| \leq \sum_{k=1}^{n} |a_k|$, and then we let $n \to \infty$.

DEFINITION.   *A series $\sum a_n$ is called absolutely convergent if $\sum |a_n|$ converges.   It is called conditionally convergent if $\sum a_n$ converges but $\sum |a_n|$ diverges.*

If $\sum a_n$ and $\sum b_n$ are absolutely convergent, then so is the series $\sum (\alpha a_n + \beta b_n)$ for every choice of α and β. This follows at once from the inequalities

$$\sum_{n=1}^{M} |\alpha a_n + \beta b_n| \leq |\alpha| \sum_{n=1}^{M} |a_n| + |\beta| \sum_{n=1}^{M} |b_n| \leq |\alpha| \sum_{n=1}^{\infty} |a_n| + |\beta| \sum_{n=1}^{\infty} |b_n| ,$$

which show that the partial sums of $\sum |\alpha a_n + \beta b_n|$ are bounded.

10.19 The convergence tests of Dirichlet and Abel

The convergence tests of the earlier sections that were developed for series of nonnegative terms may also be used to test *absolute* convergence of a series with arbitrary complex terms. In this section we discuss two tests that are often useful for determining convergence when the series might not converge absolutely. Both tests make use of an algebraic identity known as the *Abel partial summation formula*, named in honor of the Norwegian mathematician Niels Henrik Abel (1802–1829). Abel's formula is analogous to the formula for integration by parts and may be described as follows.

THEOREM 10.16. ABEL'S PARTIAL SUMMATION FORMULA. *Let $\{a_n\}$ and $\{b_n\}$ be two sequences of complex numbers, and let*

$$A_n = \sum_{k=1}^{n} a_k .$$

Then we have the identity

(10.52)
$$\sum_{k=1}^{n} a_k b_k = A_n b_{n+1} + \sum_{k=1}^{n} A_k (b_k - b_{k+1}) .$$

Proof. If we define $A_0 = 0$, then $a_k = A_k - A_{k-1}$ for each $k = 1, 2, \ldots, n$, so we have

$$\sum_{k=1}^{n} a_k b_k = \sum_{k=1}^{n} (A_k - A_{k-1}) b_k = \sum_{k=1}^{n} A_k b_k - \sum_{k=1}^{n} A_k b_{k+1} + A_n b_{n+1} ,$$

which gives us (10.52).

If we let $n \to \infty$ in (10.52), we see that the series $\sum a_k b_k$ converges if both the series $\sum A_k(b_k - b_{k+1})$ and the sequence $\{A_n b_{n+1}\}$ converge. The next two tests give sufficient conditions for these to converge.

THEOREM 10.17. DIRICHLET'S TEST. *Let $\sum a_n$ be a series of complex terms whose partial sums form a bounded sequence. Let $\{b_n\}$ be a decreasing sequence which converges to 0. Then the series $\sum a_n b_n$ converges.*

Proof. Using the notation of Theorem 10.16, there is an $M > 0$ such that $|A_n| \leq M$ for all n. Therefore $A_n b_{n+1} \to 0$ as $n \to \infty$. To establish convergence of $\sum a_n b_n$, we need only show that the series $\sum A_k(b_k - b_{k+1})$ is convergent. Since $b_n \searrow$, we have the inequality

$$|A_k(b_k - b_{k+1})| \leq M(b_k - b_{k+1}) .$$

But the series $\sum (b_k - b_{k+1})$ is a convergent telescoping series which dominates

$$\sum A_k(b_k - b_{k+1}) \, .$$

This implies absolute convergence and hence convergence of $\sum A_k(b_k - b_{k+1})$.

THEOREM 10.18. ABEL'S TEST. *Let $\sum a_n$ be a convergent series of complex terms and let $\{b_n\}$ be a monotonic convergent sequence of real terms. Then the series $\sum a_n b_n$ converges.*

Proof. Again we use the notation of Theorem 10.16. Convergence of $\sum a_n$ implies convergence of the sequence $\{A_n\}$ and hence of the sequence $\{A_n b_{n+1}\}$. Also, $\{A_n\}$ is a bounded sequence. The rest of the proof is similar to that of Dirichlet's test.

To use Dirichlet's test effectively, we need some examples of series having bounded partial sums. Of course, every *convergent* series has this property. An important example of a divergent series with bounded partial sums is the geometric series $\sum x^n$, where x is a complex number with $|x| = 1$ but $x \neq 1$. The next theorem gives an upper bound for the partial sums of this series. When $|x| = 1$, we may write $x = e^{2i\theta}$, where θ is real, and we have the following.

THEOREM 10.19. *For every real θ not an integer multiple of π, we have the identity*

(10.53)
$$\sum_{k=1}^{n} e^{2ik\theta} = \frac{\sin n\theta}{\sin \theta} \, e^{i(n+1)\theta} ,$$

from which we obtain the estimate

(10.54)
$$\left| \sum_{k=1}^{n} e^{2ik\theta} \right| \leq \frac{1}{|\sin \theta|} \, .$$

Proof. If $x \neq 1$, the partial sums of the geometric series are given by

$$\sum_{k=1}^{n} x^k = x \frac{x^n - 1}{x - 1} \, .$$

Writing $x = e^{2i\theta}$ in this formula, where θ is real but not an integer multiple of π, we find

$$\sum_{k=1}^{n} e^{2ik\theta} = e^{2i\theta} \frac{e^{2in\theta} - 1}{e^{2i\theta} - 1} = \frac{e^{in\theta} - e^{-in\theta}}{e^{i\theta} - e^{-i\theta}} e^{i(n+1)\theta} = \frac{\sin n\theta}{\sin \theta} e^{i(n+1)\theta} \, .$$

This proves (10.53). To deduce (10.54), we simply note that $|\sin n\theta| \leq 1$ and $|e^{i(n+1)\theta}| = 1$.

EXAMPLES. Assume $\{b_n\}$ is any decreasing sequence of real numbers with limit 0. Taking $a_n = x^n$ in Dirichlet's test, where x is complex, $|x| = 1$, $x \neq 1$, we find that the series

$$(10.55) \qquad\qquad \sum_{n=1}^{\infty} b_n x^n$$

converges. Note that Leibniz's rule for alternating series is merely the special case in which $x = -1$. If we write $x = e^{i\theta}$, where θ is real but not an integer multiple of 2π, and consider the real and imaginary parts of (10.55), we deduce that the two trigonometric series

$$\sum_{n=1}^{\infty} b_n \cos n\theta \qquad \text{and} \qquad \sum_{n=1}^{\infty} b_n \sin n\theta$$

converge. In particular, when $b_n = n^{-\alpha}$, where $\alpha > 0$, we find the following series converge:

$$\sum_{n=1}^{\infty} \frac{e^{in\theta}}{n^{\alpha}}, \qquad \sum_{n=1}^{\infty} \frac{\cos n\theta}{n^{\alpha}}, \qquad \sum_{n=1}^{\infty} \frac{\sin n\theta}{n^{\alpha}}.$$

When $\alpha > 1$, they converge absolutely since they are dominated by $\sum n^{-\alpha}$.

10.20 Exercises

In Exercises 1 through 32, determine convergence or divergence of the given series. In case of convergence, determine whether the series converges absolutely or conditionally.

1. $\displaystyle\sum_{n=1}^{\infty} \frac{(-1)^{n+1}}{\sqrt{n}}$.

2. $\displaystyle\sum_{n=1}^{\infty} (-1)^n \frac{\sqrt{n}}{n + 100}$.

3. $\displaystyle\sum_{n=1}^{\infty} \frac{(-1)^{n-1}}{n^s}$.

4. $\displaystyle\sum_{n=1}^{\infty} (-1)^n \left(\frac{1 \cdot 3 \cdot 5 \cdots (2n - 1)}{2 \cdot 4 \cdot 6 \cdots (2n)} \right)^3$.

5. $\displaystyle\sum_{n=1}^{\infty} \frac{(-1)^{n(n-1)/2}}{2^n}$.

6. $\displaystyle\sum_{n=1}^{\infty} (-1)^n \left(\frac{2n + 100}{3n + 1} \right)^n$.

7. $\displaystyle\sum_{n=2}^{\infty} \frac{(-1)^n}{\sqrt{n} + (-1)^n}$.

8. $\displaystyle\sum_{n=1}^{\infty} \frac{(-1)^n}{\sqrt[n]{n}}$.

9. $\displaystyle\sum_{n=1}^{\infty} (-1)^n \frac{n^2}{1 + n^2}$.

10. $\displaystyle\sum_{n=1}^{\infty} \frac{(-1)^n}{\log (e^n + e^{-n})}$.

11. $\displaystyle\sum_{n=1}^{\infty} \frac{(-1)^n}{n \log^2 (n + 1)}$.

12. $\displaystyle\sum_{n=1}^{\infty} \frac{(-1)^n}{\log (1 + 1/n)}$.

13. $\displaystyle\sum_{n=1}^{\infty} \frac{(-1)^n n^{37}}{(n + 1)!}$.

14. $\displaystyle\sum_{n=1}^{\infty} (-1)^n \int_n^{n+1} \frac{e^{-x}}{x} \, dx$.

15. $\displaystyle\sum_{n=1}^{\infty} \sin (\log n)$.

16. $\displaystyle\sum_{n=1}^{\infty} \log \left(n \sin \frac{1}{n} \right)$.

17. $\displaystyle\sum_{n=1}^{\infty} (-1)^n \left(1 - n \sin \frac{1}{n}\right)$.

18. $\displaystyle\sum_{n=1}^{\infty} (-1)^n \left(1 - \cos \frac{1}{n}\right)$.

19. $\displaystyle\sum_{n=1}^{\infty} (-1)^n \arctan \frac{1}{2n + 1}$.

20. $\displaystyle\sum_{n=1}^{\infty} (-1)^n \left(\frac{\pi}{2} - \arctan (\log n)\right)$.

21. $\displaystyle\sum_{n=1}^{\infty} \log \left(1 + \frac{1}{|\sin n|}\right)$.

22. $\displaystyle\sum_{n=2}^{\infty} \sin \left(n\pi + \frac{1}{\log n}\right)$.

23. $\displaystyle\sum_{n=1}^{\infty} \frac{1}{n(1 + 1/2 + \cdots + 1/n)}$.

24. $\displaystyle\sum_{n=1}^{\infty} (-1)^n \left[e - \left(1 + \frac{1}{n}\right)^n\right]$.

25. $\displaystyle\sum_{n=2}^{\infty} \frac{(-1)^n}{(n + (-1)^n)^s}$.

26. $\displaystyle\sum_{n=1}^{\infty} (-1)^{n(n-1)/2} \left(\frac{n^{100}}{2^n}\right)$.

27. $\displaystyle\sum_{n=1}^{\infty} a_n$, where $a_n = \begin{cases} 1/n & \text{if } n \text{ is a square,} \\ 1/n^2 & \text{otherwise.} \end{cases}$

28. $\displaystyle\sum_{n=1}^{\infty} a_n$, where $a_n = \begin{cases} 1/n^2 & \text{if } n \text{ is odd,} \\ -1/n & \text{if } n \text{ is even.} \end{cases}$

29. $\displaystyle\sum_{n=1}^{\infty} \left(\sin \frac{1}{n}\right)^{3/2}$.

30. $\displaystyle\sum_{n=1}^{\infty} \frac{\sin (1/n)}{n}$.

31. $\displaystyle\sum_{n=1}^{\infty} \left(1 - n \sin \frac{1}{n}\right)$.

32. $\displaystyle\sum_{n=1}^{\infty} \frac{1 - n \sin (1/n)}{n}$.

In Exercises 33 through 46, describe the set of all complex z for which the series converges.

33. $\displaystyle\sum_{n=1}^{\infty} n^n z^n$.

34. $\displaystyle\sum_{n=1}^{\infty} \frac{(-1)^n z^{3n}}{n!}$.

35. $\displaystyle\sum_{n=0}^{\infty} \frac{z^n}{3^n}$.

36. $\displaystyle\sum_{n=1}^{\infty} \frac{z^n}{n^n}$.

37. $\displaystyle\sum_{n=1}^{\infty} \frac{(-1)^n}{z + n}$.

38. $\displaystyle\sum_{n=1}^{\infty} \frac{z^n}{\sqrt{n}} \log \frac{2n + 1}{n}$.

39. $\displaystyle\sum_{n=1}^{\infty} \left(1 + \frac{1}{5n + 1}\right)^{n^2} |z|^{17n}$.

40. $\displaystyle\sum_{n=0}^{\infty} \frac{(z - 1)^n}{(n + 2)!}$.

41. $\displaystyle\sum_{n=1}^{\infty} \frac{(-1)^n (z - 1)^n}{n}$.

42. $\displaystyle\sum_{n=1}^{\infty} \frac{(2z + 3)^n}{n \log (n + 1)}$.

43. $\displaystyle\sum_{n=1}^{\infty} \frac{(-1)^n}{2n - 1} \left(\frac{1 - z}{1 + z}\right)^n$.

44. $\displaystyle\sum_{n=1}^{\infty} \left(\frac{z}{2z + 1}\right)^n$.

45. $\displaystyle\sum_{n=1}^{\infty} \frac{n}{n + 1} \left(\frac{z}{2z + 1}\right)^n$.

46. $\displaystyle\sum_{n=1}^{\infty} \frac{1}{(1 + |z|^2)^n}$.

In Exercises 47 and 48, determine the set of real x for which the given series converges.

47. $\displaystyle\sum_{n=1}^{\infty} (-1)^n \frac{2^n \sin^{2n} x}{n}$.

48. $\displaystyle\sum_{n=1}^{\infty} \frac{2^n \sin^n x}{n^2}$.

In Exercises 49 through 52, the series are assumed to have real terms.

49. If $a_n > 0$ and $\sum a_n$ converges, prove that $\sum 1/a_n$ diverges.

50. If $\sum |a_n|$ converges, prove that $\sum a_n^2$ converges. Give a counterexample in which $\sum a_n^2$ converges but $\sum |a_n|$ diverges.

51. Given a convergent series $\sum a_n$, where each $a_n \geq 0$. Prove that $\sum \sqrt{a_n}\, n^{-p}$ converges if $p > \frac{1}{2}$. Give a counterexample for $p = \frac{1}{2}$.

52. Prove or disprove the following statements:
    (a) If $\sum a_n$ converges absolutely, then so does $\sum a_n^2/(1 + a_n^2)$.
    (b) If $\sum a_n$ converges absolutely, and if no $a_n = -1$, then $\sum a_n/(1 + a_n)$ converges absolutely.

⋆10.21 Rearrangements of series

The order of the terms in a finite sum can be rearranged without affecting the value of the sum. In 1833 Cauchy made the surprising discovery that this is not always true for infinite series. For example, consider the alternating harmonic series

(10.56)
$$1 - \tfrac{1}{2} + \tfrac{1}{3} - \tfrac{1}{4} + \tfrac{1}{5} - \tfrac{1}{6} + - \cdots = \log 2 .$$

The convergence of this series to the sum $\log 2$ was shown in Section 10.17. If we rearrange the terms of this series, taking alternately two positive terms followed by one negative term, we get a new series which can be designated as follows:

(10.57)
$$1 + \tfrac{1}{3} - \tfrac{1}{2} + \tfrac{1}{5} + \tfrac{1}{7} - \tfrac{1}{4} + \tfrac{1}{9} + \tfrac{1}{11} - \tfrac{1}{6} + + - \cdots .$$

Each term which occurs in the alternating harmonic series occurs exactly once in this rearrangement, and vice versa. But we can easily prove that this new series has a sum greater than $\log 2$. We proceed as follows:

Let t_n denote the nth partial sum of (10.57). If n is a multiple of 3, say $n = 3m$, the partial sum t_{3m} contains $2m$ positive terms and m negative terms and is given by

$$t_{3m} = \sum_{k=1}^{2m} \frac{1}{2k-1} - \sum_{k=1}^{m} \frac{1}{2k} = \left(\sum_{k=1}^{4m} \frac{1}{k} - \sum_{k=1}^{2m} \frac{1}{2k} \right) - \frac{1}{2} \sum_{k=1}^{m} \frac{1}{k} = \sum_{k=1}^{4m} \frac{1}{k} - \frac{1}{2} \sum_{k=1}^{2m} \frac{1}{k} - \frac{1}{2} \sum_{k=1}^{m} \frac{1}{k} .$$

In each of the last three sums, we use the asymptotic relation

$$\sum_{k=1}^{n} \frac{1}{k} = \log n + C + o(1) \qquad \text{as} \quad n \to \infty ,$$

to obtain

$$t_{3m} = (\log 4m + C + o(1)) - \tfrac{1}{2}(\log 2m + C + o(1)) - \tfrac{1}{2}(\log m + C + o(1))$$

$$= \tfrac{3}{2} \log 2 + o(1) .$$

Thus $t_{3m} \to \frac{3}{2} \log 2$ as $m \to \infty$. But $t_{3m+1} = t_{3m} + 1/(4m + 1)$ and $t_{3m-1} = t_{3m} - 1/(2m)$, so t_{3m+1} and t_{3m-1} have the same limit as t_{3m} when $m \to \infty$. Therefore, every partial sum t_n has the limit $\frac{3}{2} \log 2$ as $n \to \infty$, so the sum of the series in (10.57) is $\frac{3}{2} \log 2$.

The foregoing example shows that rearrangement of the terms of a convergent series may alter its sum. We shall prove next that this can happen only if the given series is *conditionally* convergent. That is, rearrangement of an absolutely convergent series does not alter its sum. Before we prove this, we will explain more precisely what is meant by a rearrangement.

DEFINITION. *Let* $\mathbf{P} = \{1, 2, 3, \ldots\}$ *denote the set of positive integers. Let f be a function whose domain is* $\mathbf{P}$ *and whose range is* $\mathbf{P}$*, and assume f has the following property:*

$$m \neq n \quad \text{implies} \quad f(m) \neq f(n) \,.$$

Such a function f is called a permutation of $\mathbf{P}$*, or a one-to-one mapping of* $\mathbf{P}$ *onto itself. If* $\sum a_n$ *and* $\sum b_n$ *are two series such that for every* $n \geq 1$ *we have*

$$b_n = a_{f(n)}$$

for some permutation f, then the series $\sum b_n$ *is said to be a rearrangement of* $\sum a_n$.

EXAMPLE. If $\sum a_n$ denotes the alternating harmonic series in (10.56) and if $\sum b_n$ denotes the series in (10.57), we have $b_n = a_{f(n)}$, where f is the permutation defined by the formulas

$$f(3n + 1) = 4n + 1 \,, \quad f(3n + 2) = 4n + 3 \,, \quad f(3n + 3) = 2n + 2 \,.$$

THEOREM 10.20. *Let* $\sum a_n$ *be an absolutely convergent series having sum S. Then every rearrangement of* $\sum a_n$ *also converges absolutely and has sum S.*

Proof. Let $\sum b_n$ be a rearrangement, say $b_n = a_{f(n)}$. First we note that $\sum b_n$ converges absolutely because $\sum |b_n|$ is a series of nonnegative terms whose partial sums are bounded above by $\sum |a_n|$.

To prove that $\sum b_n$ also has sum S, we introduce

$$B_n = \sum_{k=1}^{n} b_k \,, \quad A_n = \sum_{k=1}^{n} a_k \,, \quad A_n^* = \sum_{k=1}^{n} |a_k| \,, \quad \text{and} \quad S^* = \sum_{k=1}^{\infty} |a_k| \,.$$

Now $A_n \to S$ and $A_n^* \to S^*$ as $n \to \infty$. Therefore, given any $\epsilon > 0$, there is an N such that

$$|A_N - S| < \frac{\epsilon}{2} \quad \text{and} \quad |A_N^* - S^*| < \frac{\epsilon}{2} \,.$$

For this N we can choose M so that

$$\{1, 2, \ldots, N\} \subseteq \{f(1), f(2), \ldots, f(M)\} \,.$$

This is possible because the range of f includes all the positive integers. If $n \geq M$, we have

$$(10.58) \quad |B_n - S| = |B_n - A_N + A_N - S| \leq |B_n - A_N| + |A_N - S| \leq |B_n - A_N| + \frac{\epsilon}{2}.$$

But we also have

$$|B_n - A_N| = \left| \sum_{k=1}^{n} b_k - \sum_{k=1}^{N} a_k \right| = \left| \sum_{k=1}^{n} a_{f(k)} - \sum_{k=1}^{N} a_k \right|.$$

The terms $a_1, \ldots, a_N$ cancel in the subtraction, so we have

$$|B_n - A_N| \leq |a_{N+1}| + |a_{N+2}| + \cdots = |A_N^* - S^*| < \frac{\epsilon}{2}.$$

Combining this with (10.58), we see that $|B_n - S| < \epsilon$ for all $n \geq M$, which means that $B_n \to S$ as $n \to \infty$. This proves that the rearranged series $\sum b_n$ has sum S.

The hypothesis of absolute convergence in Theorem 10.20 is essential. Riemann discovered that a conditionally convergent series of real terms can always be rearranged to give a series which converges to any preassigned sum. Riemann's argument is based on a special property of conditionally convergent series of real terms. Such a series $\sum a_n$ has infinitely many positive terms and infinitely many negative terms. Consider the two new series $\sum a_n^+$ and $\sum a_n^-$ obtained by taking the positive terms alone and the negative terms alone. More specifically, define a_n^+ and a_n^- as follows:

$$(10.59) \qquad\qquad a_n^+ = \frac{a_n + |a_n|}{2}, \qquad a_n^- = \frac{a_n - |a_n|}{2}.$$

If a_n is positive, then $a_n^+ = a_n$ and $a_n^- = 0$; if a_n is negative, then $a_n^- = a_n$ and $a_n^+ = 0$. The two new series $\sum a_n^+$ and $\sum a_n^-$ are related to the given series $\sum a_n$ as follows.

THEOREM 10.21.   *Given a series $\sum a_n$ of real terms, define a_n^+ and a_n^- by (10.59).*
(a) *If $\sum a_n$ is conditionally convergent, both $\sum a_n^+$ and $\sum a_n^-$ diverge.*
(b) *If $\sum a_n$ is absolutely convergent, both $\sum a_n^+$ and $\sum a_n^-$ converge, and we have*

$$(10.60) \qquad\qquad \sum_{n=1}^{\infty} a_n = \sum_{n=1}^{\infty} a_n^+ + \sum_{n=1}^{\infty} a_n^-.$$

Proof.   To prove part (a), we note that $\sum \frac{1}{2} a_n$ converges and $\sum \frac{1}{2} |a_n|$ diverges. Therefore, by the linearity property (Theorem 10.3) $\sum a_n^+$ diverges and $\sum a_n^-$ diverges. To prove part (b), we note that both $\sum \frac{1}{2} a_n$ and $\sum \frac{1}{2} |a_n|$ converge, so by the linearity property (Theorem 10.2) both $\sum a_n^+$ and $\sum a_n^-$ converge. Since $a_n = a_n^+ + a_n^-$, we also obtain (10.60).

Now we can easily prove Riemann's rearrangement theorem.

THEOREM 10.22.   *Let $\sum a_n$ be a conditionally convergent series of real terms, and let S be a given real number. Then there is a rearrangement $\sum b_n$ of $\sum a_n$ which converges to the sum S.*

Proof. Define a_n^+ and a_n^- as indicated in (10.59). Both series $\sum a_n^+$ and $\sum a_n^-$ diverge since $\sum a_n$ is conditionally convergent. We rearrange $\sum a_n$ as follows:

Take, in order, just enough positive terms a_n^+ so that their sum exceeds S. If p_1 positive terms are required, we have

$$\sum_{n=1}^{p_1} a_n > S \qquad \text{but} \qquad \sum_{n=1}^{q} a_n \le S \qquad \text{if} \quad q < p_1 .$$

This is always possible since the partial sums of $\sum a_n^+$ tend to $+\infty$. To this sum we add just enough negative terms a_n^-, say n_1 negative terms, so that the resulting sum is less than S. This is possible since the partial sums of a_n^- tend to $-\infty$. Thus, we have

$$\sum_{n=1}^{p_1} a_n^+ + \sum_{n=1}^{n_1} a_n^- < S \qquad \text{but} \qquad \sum_{n=1}^{p_1} a_n^+ + \sum_{n=1}^{m} a_n^- \ge S \qquad \text{if} \quad m < n_1 .$$

Now we repeat the process, adding just enough new positive terms to make the sum exceed S, and then just enough new negative terms to make the sum less than S. Continuing in this way, we obtain a rearrangement $\sum b_n$. Each partial sum of $\sum b_n$ differs from S by at most one term a_n^+ or a_n^-. But $a_n \to 0$ as $n \to \infty$ since $\sum a_n$ converges, so the partial sums of $\sum b_n$ tend to S. This proves that the rearranged series $\sum b_n$ converges and has sum S, as asserted.

10.22 Miscellaneous review exercises

1. (a) Let $a_n = \sqrt{n+1} - \sqrt{n}$. Compute $\lim_{n \to \infty} a_n$.
   (b) Let $a_n = (n+1)^c - n^c$, where c is real. Determine those c for which the sequence $\{a_n\}$ converges and those for which it diverges. In case of convergence, compute the limit of the sequence. Remember that c can be positive, negative, or zero.
2. (a) If $0 < x < 1$, prove that $(1 + x^n)^{1/n}$ approaches a limit as $n \to \infty$ and compute this limit.
   (b) Given $a > 0$, $b > 0$, compute $\lim_{n \to \infty} (a^n + b^n)^{1/n}$.
3. A sequence $\{a_n\}$ is defined recursively in terms of a_1 and a_2 by the formula

$$a_{n+1} = \frac{a_n + a_{n-1}}{2} \qquad \text{for} \quad n \ge 2 .$$

   (a) Assuming that $\{a_n\}$ converges, compute the limit of the sequence in terms of a_1 and a_2 . The result is a weighted arithmetic mean of a_1 and a_2 .
   (b) Prove that for every choice of a_1 and a_2 the sequence $\{a_n\}$ converges. You may assume that $a_1 < a_2$. [*Hint:* Consider $\{a_{2n}\}$ and $\{a_{2n+1}\}$ separately.]
4. A sequence $\{x_n\}$ is defined by the following recursion formula:

$$x_1 = 1, \qquad x_{n+1} = \sqrt{1 + x_n} .$$

   Prove that the sequence converges and find its limit.
5. A sequence $\{x_n\}$ is defined by the following recursion formula:

$$x_0 = 1, \qquad x_1 = 1, \qquad \frac{1}{x_{n+2}} = \frac{1}{x_{n+1}} + \frac{1}{x_n} .$$

   Prove that the sequence converges and find its limit.

6. Let $\{a_n\}$ and $\{b_n\}$ be two sequences such that for each n we have

$$e^{a_n} = a_n + e^{b_n}$$

(a) Show that $a_n > 0$ implies $b_n > 0$.
(b) If $a_n > 0$ for all n and if $\sum a_n$ converges, show that $\sum (b_n/a_n)$ converges.

In Exercises 7 through 11, test the given series for convergence.

7. $\sum_{n=1}^{\infty} (\sqrt{1 + n^2} - n)$.

8. $\sum_{n=1}^{\infty} n^s(\sqrt{n + 1} - 2\sqrt{n} + \sqrt{n - 1})$.

9. $\sum_{n=2}^{\infty} \frac{1}{(\log n)^{\log n}}$.

10. $\sum_{n=1}^{\infty} \frac{1}{n^{1+1/n}}$.

11. $\sum_{n=1}^{\infty} a_n$, where $a_n = 1/n$ if n is odd, $a_n = 1/n^2$ if n is even.
12. Show that the infinite series

$$\sum_{n=0}^{\infty} (\sqrt{n^a + 1} - \sqrt{n^a})$$

converges for $a > 2$ and diverges for $a = 2$.
13. Given $a_n > 0$ for each n. For each of the following statements, give a proof or exhibit a counterexample.
(a) If $\sum_{n=1}^{\infty} a_n$ diverges, then $\sum_{n=1}^{\infty} a_n^2$ diverges.
(b) If $\sum_{n=1}^{\infty} a_n^2$ converges, then $\sum_{n=1}^{\infty} a_n/n$ converges.
14. Find all real c for which the series $\sum_{n=1}^{\infty} (n!)^c/(3n)!$ converges.
15. Find all integers $a \geq 1$ for which the series $\sum_{n=1}^{\infty} (n!)^3/(an)!$ converges.
16. Let $n_1 < n_2 < n_3 < \cdots$ denote those positive integers that do not involve the digit 0 in their decimal representations. Thus $n_1 = 1$, $n_2 = 2, \ldots, n_9 = 9$, $n_{10} = 11, \ldots, n_{18} = 19$, $n_{19} = 21$, etc. Show that the series of reciprocals $\sum_{k=1}^{\infty} 1/n_k$ converges and has a sum less than 90.

[*Hint:* Dominate the series by $9 \sum_{n=0}^{\infty} (9/10)^n$.]

17. If a is an arbitrary real number, let $s_n(a) = 1^a + 2^a + \cdots + n^a$. Determine the following limit:

$$\lim_{n \to \infty} \frac{s_n(a + 1)}{ns_n(a)}.$$

(Consider both positive and negative a, as well as $a = 0$.)
18. (a) If p and q are fixed integers, $p \geq q \geq 1$, show that

$$\lim_{n \to \infty} \sum_{k=qn}^{pn} \frac{1}{k} = \log \frac{p}{q}.$$

(b) The following series is a rearrangement of the alternating harmonic series in which there appear, alternately, three positive terms followed by two negative terms:

$$1 + \tfrac{1}{3} + \tfrac{1}{5} - \tfrac{1}{2} - \tfrac{1}{4} + \tfrac{1}{7} + \tfrac{1}{9} + \tfrac{1}{11} - \tfrac{1}{6} - \tfrac{1}{8} + + + - - \cdots.$$

Show that the series converges and has sum $\log 2 + \tfrac{1}{2} \log \tfrac{3}{2}$.

[*Hint:* Consider the partial sum s_{5n} and use part (a).]

(c) Rearrange the alternating harmonic series, writing alternately p positive terms followed by q negative terms. Then use part (a) to show that this rearranged series converges and has sum $\log 2 + \frac{1}{2} \log (p/q)$.

10.23 Improper integrals

The concept of an integral $\int_a^b f(x)\, dx$ was introduced in Chapter 1 under the restriction that the function f is *defined and bounded* on a *finite interval* $[a, b]$. The scope of integration theory may be extended by relaxing these restrictions.

To begin with, we may study the behavior of $\int_a^b f(x)\, dx$ as $b \to +\infty$. This leads to the notion of an *infinite integral* (also called an *improper integral of the first kind*) denoted by the symbol $\int_a^\infty f(x)\, dx$. Another extension is obtained if we keep the interval $[a, b]$ finite and allow f to become unbounded at one or more points. The new integrals so obtained (by a suitable limit process) are called *improper integrals of the second kind*. To distinguish the integrals of Chapter 1 from improper integrals, the former are often called "proper" integrals.

Many important functions in analysis appear as improper integrals of one kind or another, and a detailed study of such functions is ordinarily undertaken in courses in advanced calculus. We shall be concerned here only with the most elementary aspects of the theory. In fact, we shall merely state some definitions and theorems and give some examples.

It will be evident presently that the definitions pertaining to improper integrals bear a strong resemblance to those for infinite series. Therefore it is not surprising that many of the elementary theorems on series have direct analogs for improper integrals.

If the proper integral $\int_a^b f(x)\, dx$ exists for every $b \geq a$, we may define a new function I as follows:

$$I(b) = \int_a^b f(x)\, dx \qquad \text{for each } b \geq a \,.$$

The function I defined in this way is called an *infinite integral*, or an *improper integral of the first kind*, and it is denoted by the symbol $\int_a^\infty f(x)\, dx$. The integral is said to *converge* if the limit

$$(10.61) \qquad\qquad \lim_{b \to +\infty} I(b) = \lim_{b \to +\infty} \int_a^b f(x)\, dx$$

exists and is finite. Otherwise, the integral $\int_a^\infty f(x)\, dx$ is said to *diverge*. If the limit in (10.61) exists and equals A, the number A is called the *value* of the integral, and we write

$$\int_a^\infty f(x)\, dx = A \,.$$

These definitions are similar to those given for infinite series. The function values $I(b)$ play the role of the "partial sums" and may be referred to as "partial integrals." Note that the symbol $\int_a^\infty f(x)\, dx$ is used both for the integral and for the value of the integral when the integral converges. (Compare with the remarks near the end of Section 10.5.)

EXAMPLE 1. The improper integral $\int_1^\infty x^{-s}\,dx$ converges if $s > 1$ and diverges if $s \le 1$. To prove this, we note that

$$I(b) = \int_1^b x^{-s}\,dx = \begin{cases} \dfrac{b^{1-s} - 1}{1 - s} & \text{if } s \ne 1\,, \\[2mm] \log b & \text{if } s = 1\,. \end{cases}$$

Therefore $I(b)$ tends to a finite limit if and only if $s > 1$, in which case the limit is

$$\int_1^\infty x^{-s}\,dx = \frac{1}{s-1}\,.$$

The behavior of this integral is analogous to that of the series for the zeta-function, $\zeta(s) = \sum_{n=1}^\infty n^{-s}$.

EXAMPLE 2. The integral $\int_0^\infty \sin x\,dx$ diverges because

$$I(b) = \int_0^b \sin x\,dx = 1 - \cos b\,,$$

and this does not tend to a limit as $b \to +\infty$.

Infinite integrals of the form $\int_{-\infty}^b f(x)\,dx$ are similarly defined. Also, if $\int_{-\infty}^c f(x)\,dx$ and $\int_c^\infty f(x)\,dx$ are *both convergent* for some c, we say that the integral $\int_{-\infty}^\infty f(x)\,dx$ is convergent, and its value is defined to be the sum

(10.62) $$\int_{-\infty}^\infty f(x)\,dx = \int_{-\infty}^c f(x)\,dx + \int_c^\infty f(x)\,dx\,.$$

(It is easy to show that the choice of c is unimportant.) The integral $\int_{-\infty}^\infty f(x)\,dx$ is said to diverge if at least one of the integrals on the right of (10.62) is divergent.

EXAMPLE 3. The integral $\int_{-\infty}^\infty e^{-a|x|}\,dx$ converges if $a > 0$, for if $b > 0$, we have

$$\int_0^b e^{-a|x|}\,dx = \int_0^b e^{-ax}\,dx = \frac{e^{-ab} - 1}{-a} \to \frac{1}{a} \qquad \text{as} \quad b \to \infty\,.$$

Hence $\int_0^\infty e^{-a|x|}\,dx$ converges and has the value $1/a$. Also, if $b > 0$, we have

$$\int_{-b}^0 e^{-a|x|}\,dx = \int_{-b}^0 e^{ax}\,dx = -\int_b^0 e^{-at}\,dt = \int_0^b e^{-at}\,dt\,.$$

Therefore $\int_{-\infty}^0 e^{-a|x|}\,dx$ also converges and has the value $1/a$. Hence we have $\int_{-\infty}^\infty e^{-a|x|}\,dx = 2/a$. Note, however, that the integral $\int_{-\infty}^\infty e^{-ax}\,dx$ *diverges* because $\int_{-\infty}^0 e^{-ax}\,dx$ diverges.

As in the case of series, we have various convergence tests for improper integrals. The simplest of these refers to a positive integrand.

THEOREM 10.23.   *Assume that the proper integral $\int_a^b f(x)\,dx$ exists for each $b \geq a$ and suppose that $f(x) \geq 0$ for all $x \geq a$. Then $\int_a^\infty f(x)\,dx$ converges if and only if there is a constant $M > 0$ such that*

$$\int_a^b f(x)\,dx \leq M \qquad for\ every\ b \geq a\ .$$

This theorem forms the basis for the following comparison tests.

THEOREM 10.24.   *Assume the proper integral $\int_a^b f(x)\,dx$ exists for each $b \geq a$ and suppose that $0 \leq f(x) \leq g(x)$ for all $x \geq a$, where $\int_a^\infty g(x)\,dx$ converges. Then $\int_a^\infty f(x)\,dx$ also converges and*

$$\int_a^\infty f(x)\,dx \leq \int_a^\infty g(x)\,dx\ .$$

Note: The integral $\int_a^\infty g(x)\,dx$ is said to *dominate* the integral $\int_a^\infty f(x)\,dx$.

THEOREM 10.25.   LIMIT COMPARISON TEST.   *Assume both proper integrals $\int_a^b f(x)\,dx$ and $\int_a^b g(x)\,dx$ exist for each $b \geq a$, where $f(x) \geq 0$ and $g(x) > 0$ for all $x \geq a$. If*

(10.63) $$\lim_{x \to +\infty} \frac{f(x)}{g(x)} = c\ , \qquad where\ \ c \neq 0\ ,$$

then both integrals $\int_a^\infty f(x)\,dx$ and $\int_a^\infty g(x)\,dx$ converge or both diverge.

Note: If the limit in (10.63) is 0, we can conclude only that convergence of $\int_a^\infty g(x)\,dx$ implies convergence of $\int_a^\infty f(x)\,dx$.

The proofs of Theorem 10.23 through 10.25 are similar to the corresponding results for series and are left as exercises.

EXAMPLE 4.   For each real s, the integral $\int_1^\infty e^{-x}x^s\,dx$ converges. This is seen by comparison with $\int_1^\infty x^{-2}\,dx$ since $e^{-x}x^s/x^{-2} \to 0$ as $x \to +\infty$.

Improper integrals of the second kind may be introduced as follows: Suppose f is defined on the half-open interval $(a, b]$, and assume that the integral $\int_x^b f(t)\,dt$ exists for each x satisfying $a < x \leq b$. Define a new function I as follows:

$$I(x) = \int_x^b f(t)\,dt \qquad if\ \ a < x \leq b\ .$$

The function I so defined is called an *improper integral of the second kind* and is denoted by the symbol $\int_{a+}^b f(t)\,dt$. The integral is said to *converge* if the limit

(10.64) $$\lim_{x \to a+} I(x) = \lim_{x \to a+} \int_x^b f(t)\,dt$$

exists and is finite. Otherwise, the integral $\int_{a+}^b f(t)\,dt$ is said to *diverge*. If the limit in (10.64) exists and equals A, the number A is called the *value* of the integral, and we write

$$\int_{a+}^b f(t)\,dt = A\ .$$

EXAMPLE 5. Let $f(t) = t^{-s}$ if $t > 0$. If $b > 0$ and $x > 0$, we have

$$I(x) = \int_x^b t^{-s}\, dt = \begin{cases} \dfrac{b^{1-s} - x^{1-s}}{1-s} & \text{if } s \neq 1, \\[2mm] \log b - \log x & \text{if } s = 1. \end{cases}$$

When $x \to 0+$, $I(x)$ tends to a finite limit if and only if $s < 1$. Hence the integral $\int_{0+}^b t^{-s}\, dt$ converges if $s < 1$ and diverges if $s \geq 1$.

This example may be dealt with in another way. If we introduce the substitution $t = 1/u$, $dt = -u^{-2}\, du$, we obtain

$$\int_x^b t^{-s}\, dt = \int_{1/b}^{1/x} u^{s-2}\, du .$$

When $x \to 0+$, $1/x \to +\infty$ and hence $\int_{0+}^b t^{-s}\, dt = \int_{1/b}^\infty u^{s-2}\, du$, provided the last integral converges. By Example 1, this converges if and only if $s - 2 < -1$, which means $s < 1$.

The foregoing example illustrates a remarkable geometric fact. Consider the function f defined by the equation $f(x) = x^{-3/4}$ if $0 < x \leq 1$. The integral $\int_{0+}^1 f(x)\, dx$ converges, but the integral $\int_{0+}^1 \pi f^2(x)\, dx$ diverges. Geometrically, this means that the ordinate set of f has a finite area, but the solid obtained by rotating this ordinate set about the x-axis has an infinite volume.

Improper integrals of the form $\int_a^{b-} f(t)\, dt$ are defined in a similar fashion. If the two integrals $\int_{a+}^c f(t)\, dt$ and $\int_c^{b-} f(t)\, dt$ *both converge*, we write

$$\int_{a+}^{b-} f(t)\, dt = \int_{a+}^c f(t)\, dt + \int_c^{b-} f(t)\, dt .$$

Note: Some authors write $\int_a^b$ where we have written $\int_{a+}^{b-}$.

The definition can be extended (in an obvious way) to cover the case of any finite number of summands. For example, if f is undefined at two points $c < d$ interior to an interval $[a, b]$, we say the improper integral $\int_a^b f(t)\, dt$ converges and has the value $\int_a^{c-} f(t)\, dt + \int_{c+}^{d-} f(t)\, dt + \int_{d+}^b f(t)\, dt$, provided that each of these integrals converges. Furthermore, we can consider "mixed" combinations such as $\int_{a+}^b f(t)\, dt + \int_b^\infty f(t)\, dt$ which we write as $\int_{a+}^\infty f(t)\, dt$, or mixed combinations of the form $\int_a^{b-} f(t)\, dt + \int_{b+}^c f(t)\, dt + \int_c^\infty f(t)\, dt$ which we write simply as $\int_a^\infty f(t)\, dt$.

EXAMPLE 6. *The gamma function.* If $s > 0$ the integral $\int_{0+}^\infty e^{-t} t^{s-1}\, dt$ converges. This must be interpreted as a sum, say

(10.65) $$\int_{0+}^1 e^{-t} t^{s-1}\, dt + \int_1^\infty e^{-t} t^{s-1}\, dt .$$

The second integral converges for all real s, by Example 4. To test the first integral we put $t = 1/u$ and note that

$$\int_x^1 e^{-t} t^{s-1}\, dt = \int_1^{1/x} e^{-1/u} u^{-s-1}\, du .$$

But $\int_1^\infty e^{-1/u} u^{-s-1}\, du$ converges for $s > 0$ by comparison with $\int_1^\infty u^{-s-1}\, du$. Therefore the integral $\int_{0+}^1 e^{-t} t^{s-1}\, dt$ converges for $s > 0$. When $s > 0$, the sum in (10.65) is denoted by $\Gamma(s)$. The function Γ so defined is called the *gamma function*, first introduced by Euler in 1729. It has the interesting property that $\Gamma(n + 1) = n!$ when n is any integer ≥ 0. (See Exercise 19 of Section 10.24 for an outline of the proof.)

The convergence tests given in Theorems 10.23 through 10.25 have straightforward analogs for improper integrals of the second kind. The reader should have no difficulty in formulating these tests for himself.

10.24   Exercises

In each of Exercises 1 through 10, test the improper integral for convergence.

1. $\displaystyle\int_0^\infty \frac{x}{\sqrt{x^4 + 1}}\, dx.$

2. $\displaystyle\int_{-\infty}^\infty e^{-x^2}\, dx.$

3. $\displaystyle\int_0^\infty \frac{1}{\sqrt{x^3 + 1}}\, dx.$

4. $\displaystyle\int_0^\infty \frac{1}{\sqrt{e^x}}\, dx.$

5. $\displaystyle\int_{0+}^\infty \frac{e^{-\sqrt{x}}}{\sqrt{x}}\, dx.$

6. $\displaystyle\int_{0+}^1 \frac{\log x}{\sqrt{x}}\, dx.$

7. $\displaystyle\int_{0+}^{1-} \frac{\log x}{1 - x}\, dx.$

8. $\displaystyle\int_{-\infty}^\infty \frac{x}{\cosh x}\, dx.$

9. $\displaystyle\int_{0+}^{1-} \frac{dx}{\sqrt{x} \log x}.$

10. $\displaystyle\int_2^\infty \frac{dx}{x\,(\log x)^s}.$

11. For a certain real C the integral

$$\int_2^\infty \left(\frac{Cx}{x^2 + 1} - \frac{1}{2x + 1} \right) dx$$

converges. Determine C and evaluate the integral.

12. For a certain real C, the integral

$$\int_1^\infty \left(\frac{x}{2x^2 + 2C} - \frac{C}{x + 1} \right) dx$$

converges. Determine C and evaluate the integral.

13. For a certain real C, the integral

$$\int_0^\infty \left(\frac{1}{\sqrt{1 + 2x^2}} - \frac{C}{x + 1} \right) dx$$

converges. Determine C and evaluate the integral.

14. Find the values of a and b such that

$$\int_1^\infty \left(\frac{2x^2 + bx + a}{x(2x + a)} - 1 \right) dx = 1 .$$

15. For what values of the constants a and b will the following limit exist and be equal to 1 ?

$$\lim_{p \to +\infty} \int_{-p}^{p} \frac{x^3 + ax^2 + bx}{x^2 + x + 1} \, dx .$$

16. (a) Prove that

$$\lim_{h \to 0+} \left(\int_{-1}^{-h} \frac{dx}{x} + \int_{h}^{1} \frac{dx}{x} \right) = 0 \quad \text{and that} \quad \lim_{h \to +\infty} \int_{-h}^{h} \sin x \, dx = 0 .$$

(b) Do the following improper integrals converge or diverge ?

$$\int_{-1}^{1} \frac{dx}{x} \; ; \qquad \int_{-\infty}^{\infty} \sin x \, dx .$$

17. (a) Prove that the integral $\int_{0+}^{1} (\sin x)/x \, dx$ converges.
(b) Prove that $\lim_{x \to 0+} x \int_{x}^{1} (\cos t)/t^2 \, dt = 1$.
(c) Does the integral $\int_{0+}^{1} (\cos t)/t^2 \, dt$ converge or diverge ?

18. (a) If f is monotonic decreasing for all $x \geq 1$ and if $f(x) \to 0$ as $x \to +\infty$, prove that the integral $\int_{1}^{\infty} f(x) \, dx$ and the series $\sum f(n)$ both converge or both diverge.

[*Hint:* Recall the proof of the integral test.]

(b) Give an example of a nonmonotonic f for which the series $\sum f(n)$ converges and the integral $\int_{1}^{\infty} f(x) \, dx$ diverges.

19. Let $\Gamma(s) = \int_{0+}^{\infty} t^{s-1} e^{-t} \, dt$, if $s > 0$. (The gamma function.) Use integration by parts to show $\Gamma(s + 1) = s\Gamma(s)$. Then use induction to prove that $\Gamma(n + 1) = n!$ if n is a positive integer.

Each of Exercises 20 through 25 contains a statement, not necessarily true, about a function f defined for all $x \geq 1$. In each of these exercises, n denotes a positive integer, and I_n denotes the integral $\int_{1}^{n} f(x) \, dx$, which is always assumed to exist. For each statement either give a proof or provide a counterexample.

20. If f is monotonic decreasing and if $\lim_{n \to \infty} I_n$ exists, then the integral $\int_{1}^{\infty} f(x) \, dx$ converges.
21. If $\lim_{x \to \infty} f(x) = 0$ and $\lim_{n \to \infty} I_n = A$, then $\int_{1}^{\infty} f(x) \, dx$ converges and has the value A.
22. If the sequence $\{I_n\}$ converges, then the integral $\int_{1}^{\infty} f(x) \, dx$ converges.
23. If f is positive and if $\lim_{n \to \infty} I_n = A$, then $\int_{1}^{\infty} f(x) \, dx$ converges and has the value A.
24. Assume $f'(x)$ exists for each $x \geq 1$ and suppose there is a constant $M > 0$ such that $|f'(x)| \leq M$ for all $x \geq 1$. If $\lim_{n \to \infty} I_n = A$, then the integral $\int_{1}^{\infty} f(x) \, dx$ converges and has the value A.
25. If $\int_{1}^{\infty} f(x) \, dx$ converges, then $\lim_{x \to \infty} f(x) = 0$.

11

SEQUENCES AND SERIES OF FUNCTIONS

11.1 Pointwise convergence of sequences of functions

In Chapter 10 we discussed sequences whose terms were real or complex numbers. Now we wish to consider sequences $\{f_n\}$ whose terms are real- or complex-valued *functions* having a common domain on the real line or in the complex plane. For each x in the domain, we can form another sequence $\{f_n(x)\}$ of numbers whose terms are the corresponding function values. Let S denote the set of points x for which this sequence converges. The function f defined on S by the equation

$$f(x) = \lim_{n \to \infty} f_n(x) \qquad \text{if} \quad x \in S \,,$$

is called the *limit function* of the sequence $\{f_n\}$, and we say that the sequence $\{f_n\}$ *converges pointwise* to f on the set S.

The study of such sequences is concerned primarily with the following type of question: If each term of a sequence $\{f_n\}$ has a certain property, such as continuity, differentiability, or integrability, to what extent is this property transferred to the limit function? For example, if each function f_n is continuous at a point x, is the limit function f also continuous at x? The following example shows that, in general, it is not.

EXAMPLE 1. *A sequence of continuous functions with a discontinuous limit function.* Let $f_n(x) = x^n$ if $0 \le x \le 1$. The graphs of a few terms are shown in Figure 11.1. The sequence $\{f_n\}$ converges pointwise on the closed interval $[0, 1]$, and its limit function f is given by the formula

$$f(x) = \lim_{n \to \infty} x^n = \begin{cases} 0 & \text{if} \quad 0 \le x < 1 \,, \\ 1 & \text{if} \quad x = 1 \,. \end{cases}$$

Note that the limit function f is discontinuous at 1, although each term of the sequence is continuous in the entire interval $[0, 1]$.

EXAMPLE 2. *A sequence for which* $\lim_{n \to \infty} \int_a^b f_n(x)\, dx \neq \int_a^b \lim_{n \to \infty} f_n(x)\, dx$. Let $f_n(x) = nx(1 - x^2)^n$ for $0 \le x \le 1$. In this example, the sequence $\{f_n\}$ converges pointwise to a limit function f which is 0 everywhere in the closed interval $[0, 1]$. A few terms of the sequence are shown in Figure 11.2. The integral of f_n over the interval $[0, 1]$ is given by

$$\int_0^1 f_n(x)\, dx = n \int_0^1 x(1 - x^2)^n\, dx = -\frac{n}{2} \frac{(1 - x^2)^{n+1}}{n + 1} \bigg|_0^1 = \frac{n}{2(n + 1)}.$$

Therefore we have $\lim_{n \to \infty} \int_0^1 f_n(x)\, dx = \frac{1}{2}$, but $\int_0^1 \lim_{n \to \infty} f_n(x)\, dx = 0$. In other words, the limit of the integrals is not equal to the integral of the limit. This example shows that

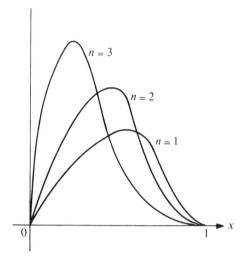

FIGURE 11.1   A sequence of continuous functions with a discontinuous limit function.

FIGURE 11.2   A sequence of functions for which $f_n \to 0$ on the interval $[0, 1]$ but $\int_0^1 f_n \to \frac{1}{2}$ as $n \to \infty$.

the two operations of "limit" and "integration" cannot always be interchanged. (See also Exercises 17 and 18 in Section 11.7.)

George G. Stokes (1819–1903), Phillip L. v. Seidel (1821–1896), and Karl Weierstrass were the first to realize that some extra condition is needed to justify interchanging these operations. In 1848, Stokes and Seidel (independently and almost simultaneously) introduced a concept now known as *uniform convergence* and showed that for a uniformly convergent sequence the operations of limit and integration could be interchanged. Weierstrass later showed that the concept is of great importance in advanced analysis. We shall introduce the concept in the next section and show its relation to continuity and to integration.

11.2   Uniform convergence of sequences of functions

Let $\{f_n\}$ be a sequence which converges pointwise on a set S to a limit function f. By the definition of limit, this means that for each x in S and for each $\epsilon > 0$ there is an integer N, which depends on both x and ϵ, such that $|f_n(x) - f(x)| < \epsilon$ whenever $n \geq N$. If the same N serves equally well for *all* points x in S, then the convergence is said to be *uniform* on S. That is, we have the following.

DEFINITION. *A sequence of functions $\{f_n\}$ is said to converge uniformly to f on a set S if for every $\epsilon > 0$ there is an N (depending only on ϵ) such that $n \geq N$ implies*

$$|f_n(x) - f(x)| < \epsilon \qquad \text{for all } x \text{ in } S.$$

We denote this symbolically by writing

$$f_n \to f \quad \text{uniformly on } S.$$

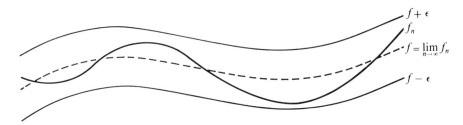

FIGURE 11.3   Geometric meaning of uniform convergence. If $n \geq N$, the entire graph of each f_n lies within a distance ϵ from the graph of the limit function f.

When the functions f_n are real-valued, there is a simple geometric interpretation of uniform convergence. The inequality $|f_n(x) - f(x)| < \epsilon$ is equivalent to the pair of inequalities

$$f(x) - \epsilon < f_n(x) < f(x) + \epsilon.$$

If these hold for all $n \geq N$ and every x in S, then the entire graph of f_n above S lies within a band of height 2ϵ situated symmetrically about the graph of f, as indicated in Figure 11.3.

11.3   Uniform convergence and continuity

Now we prove that uniform convergence transmits continuity from the individual terms of the sequence $\{f_n\}$ to the limit function f.

THEOREM 11.1   *Assume $f_n \to f$ uniformly on an interval S. If each function f_n is continuous at a point p in S, then the limit function f is also continuous at p.*

Proof. We will show that for every $\epsilon > 0$ there is a neighborhood $N(p)$ such that $|f(x) - f(p)| < \epsilon$ whenever $x \in N(p) \cap S$. If $\epsilon > 0$ is given, there is an integer N such that $n \geq N$ implies

$$|f_n(x) - f(x)| < \frac{\epsilon}{3} \qquad \text{for all } x \text{ in } S.$$

Since f_N is continuous at p, there is a neighborhood $N(p)$ such that

$$|f_N(x) - f_N(p)| < \frac{\epsilon}{3} \qquad \text{for all } x \text{ in } N(p) \cap S.$$

Therefore, for all x in $N(p) \cap S$, we have

$$|f(x) - f(p)| = |f(x) - f_N(x) + f_N(x) - f_N(p) + f_N(p) - f(p)|$$
$$\leq |f(x) - f_N(x)| + |f_N(x) - f_N(p)| + |f_N(p) - f(p)| \, .$$

Since each term on the right is $< \epsilon/3$, we find $|f(x) - f(p)| < \epsilon$, which completes the proof.

The foregoing theorem has an important application to infinite series of functions. If the function values $f_n(x)$ are partial sums of other functions, say

$$f_n(x) = \sum_{k=1}^{n} u_k(x) \, ,$$

and if $f_n \to f$ pointwise on S, then we have

$$f(x) = \lim_{n \to \infty} f_n(x) = \sum_{k=1}^{\infty} u_k(x)$$

for each x in S. In this case, the series $\sum u_k$ is said to converge pointwise to the sum function f. If $f_n \to f$ uniformly on S, we say the series $\sum u_k$ converges uniformly to f. If each term u_k is continuous at a point p in S, then each partial sum f_n is also continuous at p so, from Theorem 11.1, we obtain the following corollary.

THEOREM 11.2.   *If a series of functions* $\sum u_k$ *converges uniformly to a sum function f on a set S, and if each term u_k is continuous at a point p in S, then the sum f is also continuous at p.*

Note: We can also express this result symbolically by writing

$$\lim_{x \to p} \sum_{k=1}^{\infty} u_k(x) = \sum_{k=1}^{\infty} \lim_{x \to p} u_k(x) \, .$$

We describe this by saying that for a uniformly convergent series we may interchange the limit symbol with the summation symbol, or that we can pass to the limit term by term.

11.4 Uniform convergence and integration

The next theorem shows that uniform convergence allows us to interchange the integration symbol with the limit symbol.

THEOREM 11.3.   *Assume $f_n \to f$ uniformly on an interval $[a, b]$, and assume that each function f_n is continuous on $[a, b]$. Define a new sequence $\{g_n\}$ by the equation*

$$g_n(x) = \int_a^x f_n(t) \, dt \qquad if \quad x \in [a, b] \, ,$$

and let

$$g(x) = \int_a^x f(t)\,dt\,.$$

Then $g_n \to g$ *uniformly on* $[a, b]$. *In symbols, we have*

$$\lim_{n \to \infty} \int_a^x f_n(t)\,dt = \int_a^x \lim_{n \to \infty} f_n(t)\,dt\,.$$

Proof. The proof is very simple. Given $\epsilon > 0$, there is an integer N such that $n \geq N$ implies

$$|f_n(t) - f(t)| < \frac{\epsilon}{b - a} \qquad \text{for all } t \text{ in } [a, b]\,.$$

Hence, if $x \in [a, b]$ and if $n \geq N$, we have

$$|g_n(x) - g(x)| = \left| \int_a^x (f_n(t) - f(t))\,dt \right| \leq \int_a^b |f_n(t) - f(t)|\,dt < \int_a^b \frac{\epsilon}{b - a}\,dt = \epsilon\,,$$

so $g_n \to g$ uniformly on $[a, b]$.

Again, as a corollary, we have a corresponding result for infinite series.

THEOREM 11.4.   *Assume that a series of functions* $\sum u_k$ *converges uniformly to a sum function* f *on an interval* $[a, b]$, *where each* u_k *is continuous on* $[a, b]$. *If* $x \in [a, b]$, *define*

$$g_n(x) = \sum_{k=1}^n \int_a^x u_k(t)\,dt \qquad and \qquad g(x) = \int_a^x f(t)\,dt\,.$$

Then $g_n \to g$ *uniformly on* $[a, b]$. *In other words, we have*

$$\lim_{n \to \infty} \sum_{k=1}^n \int_a^x u_k(t)\,dt = \int_a^x \lim_{n \to \infty} \sum_{k=1}^n u_k(t)\,dt$$

or

$$\sum_{k=1}^{\infty} \int_a^x u_k(t)\,dt = \int_a^x \sum_{k=1}^{\infty} u_k(t)\,dt\,.$$

Proof. Apply Theorem 11.3 to the sequence of partial sums $\{f_n\}$ given by

$$f_n(t) = \sum_{k=1}^n u_k(t)\,,$$

and note that $\int_a^x f_n(t)\,dt = \sum_{k=1}^n \int_a^x u_k(t)\,dt$.

Theorem 11.4 is often described by saying that a uniformly convergent series may be integrated term by term.

11.5 A sufficient condition for uniform convergence

Weierstrass developed a useful test for showing that certain series are uniformly convergent. The test is applicable whenever the given series can be dominated by a convergent series of positive constants.

THEOREM 11.5. THE WEIERSTRASS M-TEST. *Given a series of functions $\sum u_n$ which converges pointwise to a function f on a set S. If there is a convergent series of positive constants $\sum M_n$ such that*

$$0 \leq |u_n(x)| \leq M_n \qquad \text{for every } n \geq 1 \text{ and every } x \text{ in } S \, ,$$

then the series $\sum u_n$ converges uniformly on S.

Proof. The comparison test shows that the series $\sum u_n(x)$ converges absolutely for each x in S. For each x in S, we have

$$\left| f(x) - \sum_{k=1}^{n} u_k(x) \right| = \left| \sum_{k=n+1}^{\infty} u_k(x) \right| \leq \sum_{k=n+1}^{\infty} |u_k(x)| \leq \sum_{k=n+1}^{\infty} M_k \, .$$

Since the series $\sum M_k$ converges, for every $\epsilon > 0$ there is an integer N such that $n \geq N$ implies

$$\sum_{k=n+1}^{\infty} M_k < \epsilon \, .$$

This shows that

$$\left| f(x) - \sum_{k=1}^{n} u_k(x) \right| < \epsilon$$

for all $n \geq N$ and every x in S. Therefore, the series $\sum u_n$ converges uniformly to f on S.

Term-by-term differentiation of an arbitrary series of functions is even less promising than term-by-term integration. For example, the series $\sum_{n=1}^{\infty} (\sin nx)/n^2$ converges for all real x because it is dominated by $\sum 1/n^2$. Moreover, the convergence is uniform on the whole real axis. However, the series obtained by differentiating term by term is $\sum (\cos nx)/n$, and this *diverges* when $x = 0$. This example shows that term-by-term differentiation may destroy convergence, even though the original series is uniformly convergent. Therefore, the problem of justifying the interchange of the operations of differentiation and summation is, in general, more serious than in the case of integration. We mention this example so the reader may realize that familiar manipulations with finite sums do not always carry over to infinite series, even if the series involved are uniformly convergent. We turn next to special series of functions, known as power series, which can be manipulated in many respects as though they were finite sums.

11.6 Power series. Circle of convergence

An infinite series of the form

$$\sum_{n=0}^{\infty} a_n(z - a)^n = a_0 + a_1(z - a) + \cdots + a_n(z - a)^n + \cdots$$

is called a power series in $z - a$. The numbers z, a, and the coefficients a_n are complex. With each power series there is associated a circle, called the *circle of convergence*, such that the series converges absolutely for every z interior to this circle, and diverges for every z outside this circle. The center of the circle is at a and its radius r is called the *radius of*

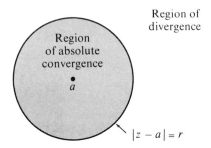

FIGURE 11.4   The circle of convergence of a power series.

convergence. (See Figure 11.4.) In extreme cases, the circle may shrink to the single point a, in which case $r = 0$, or it may consist of the entire complex plane, in which case we say that $r = +\infty$. The existence of the circle of convergence is shown in Theorem 11.7.

The behavior of the series at the boundary points of the circle cannot be predicted in advance. Examples show that there may be convergence at none, some, or all the boundary points.

For many power series that occur in practice, the radius of convergence can be determined by using either the ratio test or the root test, as in the following examples.

EXAMPLE 1. To find the radius of convergence of the power series $\sum z^n/n!$, we apply the ratio test. If $z \neq 0$, the ratio of consecutive terms has absolute value

$$\left| \frac{z^{n+1}}{(n + 1)!} \frac{n!}{z^n} \right| = \frac{|z|}{n + 1} \, .$$

Since this ratio tends to 0 as $n \to \infty$, we conclude that the series converges absolutely for all complex $z \neq 0$. It also converges for $z = 0$, so the radius of convergence is $+\infty$.

Since the general term of a convergent series must tend to 0, the result of the foregoing example proves that

$$\lim_{n \to \infty} \frac{z^n}{n!} = 0$$

for every complex z. That is, $n!$ "grows faster" than the nth power of any fixed complex number z as $n \to \infty$.

EXAMPLE 2. To test the series $\sum n^2 3^n z^n$, we use the root test. We have

$$(n^2 3^n |z|^n)^{1/n} = 3 |z| n^{2/n} \to 3 |z| \qquad \text{as} \quad n \to \infty ,$$

since $n^{2/n} = (n^{1/n})^2$ and $n^{1/n} \to 1$ as $n \to \infty$. Therefore, the series converges absolutely if $|z| < \frac{1}{3}$ and diverges if $|z| > \frac{1}{3}$. The radius of convergence is $\frac{1}{3}$. This particular power series diverges at every boundary point because, if $|z| = \frac{1}{3}$, the general term has absolute value n^2.

EXAMPLE 3. For each of the series $\sum z^n/n$ and $\sum z^n/n^2$, the ratio test tells us that the radius of convergence is 1. The first series diverges at the boundary point $z = 1$ but converges at all other boundary points (see Section 10.19). The second series converges at every boundary point since it is dominated by $\sum 1/n^2$.

We conclude this section with a proof that every power series has a circle of convergence. The proof is based on the following theorem.

THEOREM 11.6. *Assume the power series $\sum a_n z^n$ converges for a particular $z \neq 0$, say for $z = z_1$. Then we have:*

(a) *The series converges absolutely for every z with $|z| < |z_1|$.*

(b) *The series converges uniformly on every circular disk with center at 0 and radius $R < |z_1|$.*

Proof. Since $\sum a_n z_1^n$ converges, its general term tends to 0 as $n \to \infty$. In particular, $|a_n z_1^n| < 1$ from some point on, say for $n \geq N$. Let S be a circular disk of radius R, where $0 < R < |z_1|$. If $z \in S$ and $n \geq N$, we have $|z| \leq R$ and

$$|a_n z^n| = |a_n z_1^n| \left| \frac{z}{z_1} \right|^n < \left| \frac{z}{z_1} \right|^n \leq \left| \frac{R}{z_1} \right|^n = t^n , \qquad \text{where} \quad t = \left| \frac{R}{z_1} \right| .$$

Since $0 < t < 1$, the series $\sum a_n z^n$ is dominated by the convergent geometric series $\sum t^n$. By Weierstrass' M-test, the series $\sum a_n z^n$ converges uniformly on S. This proves (b). The argument also shows that the series $\sum a_n z^n$ converges absolutely for each z in S. But since each z with $|z| < |z_1|$ lies in some circular disk S with radius $R < |z_1|$, this also proves part (a).

THEOREM 11.7. EXISTENCE OF A CIRCLE OF CONVERGENCE. *Assume that the power series $\sum a_n z^n$ converges for at least one $z \neq 0$, say for $z = z_1$, and that it diverges for at least one z, say for $z = z_2$. Then there exists a positive real number r such that the series converges absolutely if $|z| < r$ and diverges if $|z| > r$.*

Proof. Let A denote the set of all positive numbers $|z|$ for which the power series $\sum a_n z^n$ converges. The set A is not empty since, by hypothesis, it contains $|z_1|$. Also, no number in A can exceed $|z_2|$ (because of Theorem 11.6). Hence, $|z_2|$ is an upper bound for A. Since A is a nonempty set of positive numbers that is bounded above, it has a least upper bound which we denote by r. It is clear that $r > 0$ since $r \geq |z_1|$. Because of Theorem 11.6, no number in A can exceed r. Therefore, the series diverges if $|z| > r$. But it is easy to prove that the series converges *absolutely* if $|z| < r$. If $|z| < r$, there is a positive number x in A such that $|z| < x < r$. By Theorem 11.6, the series $\sum a_n z^n$ converges absolutely. This completes the proof.

There is, of course, a corresponding theorem for power series in $z - a$ which may be deduced from the case just treated by introducing the change of variable $Z = z - a$. The circle of convergence has its center at a, as shown in Figure 11.4.

11.7 Exercises

In Exercises 1 through 16, determine the radius of convergence r of the given power series. In Exercises 1 through 10, test for convergence at the boundary points if r is finite.

1. $\displaystyle\sum_{n=0}^{\infty} \frac{z^n}{2^n}$.

2. $\displaystyle\sum_{n=0}^{\infty} \frac{z^n}{(n+1)2^n}$.

3. $\displaystyle\sum_{n=0}^{\infty} \frac{(z+3)^n}{(n+1)2^n}$.

4. $\displaystyle\sum_{n=1}^{\infty} \frac{(-1)^n 2^{2n} z^{2n}}{2n}$.

5. $\displaystyle\sum_{n=1}^{\infty} [1 - (-2)^n]z^n$.

6. $\displaystyle\sum_{n=1}^{\infty} \frac{n! z^n}{n^n}$.

7. $\displaystyle\sum_{n=0}^{\infty} \frac{(-1)^n (z+1)^n}{n^2 + 1}$.

8. $\displaystyle\sum_{n=0}^{\infty} a^{n^2} z^n$, $0 < a < 1$.

9. $\displaystyle\sum_{n=1}^{\infty} \frac{(n!)^2}{(2n)!} z^n$.

10. $\displaystyle\sum_{n=1}^{\infty} \frac{3^{\sqrt{n}} z^n}{n}$.

11. $\displaystyle\sum_{n=1}^{\infty} \left(\frac{1 \cdot 3 \cdot 5 \cdots (2n-1)}{2 \cdot 4 \cdot 6 \cdots (2n)}\right)^3 z^n$.

12. $\displaystyle\sum_{n=1}^{\infty} \left(1 + \frac{1}{n}\right)^{n^2} z^n$.

13. $\displaystyle\sum_{n=0}^{\infty} (\sin an)z^n$, $a > 0$.

14. $\displaystyle\sum_{n=0}^{\infty} (\sinh an)z^n$, $a > 0$.

15. $\displaystyle\sum_{n=1}^{\infty} \frac{z^n}{a^n + b^n}$, $a > 0, b > 0$.

16. $\displaystyle\sum_{n=1}^{\infty} \left(\frac{a^n}{n} + \frac{b^n}{n^2}\right) z^n$, $a > 0, b > 0$.

17. If $f_n(x) = nxe^{-nx^2}$ for $n = 1, 2, \ldots$ and x real, show that

$$\lim_{n \to \infty} \int_0^1 f_n(x)\, dx \neq \int_0^1 \lim_{n \to \infty} f_n(x)\, dx .$$

This example shows that the operations of integration and limit cannot always be interchanged.

18. Let $f_n(x) = (\sin nx)/n$, and for each fixed real x let $f(x) = \lim_{n \to \infty} f_n(x)$. Show that

$$\lim_{n \to \infty} f_n'(0) \neq f'(0) .$$

This example shows that the operations of differentiation and limit cannot always be interchanged.

19. Show that the series $\sum_{n=1}^{\infty}(\sin nx)/n^2$ converges for every real x, and denote its sum by $f(x)$. Prove that f is continuous on $[0, \pi]$, and use Theorem 11.4 to prove that

$$\int_0^\pi f(x)\,dx = 2\sum_{n=1}^{\infty}\frac{1}{(2n-1)^3}\,.$$

20. It is known that

$$\sum_{n=1}^{\infty}\frac{\cos nx}{n^2} = \frac{x^2}{4} - \frac{\pi x}{2} + \frac{\pi^2}{6} \qquad \text{if} \quad 0 \le x \le 2\pi\,.$$

Use this formula and Theorem 11.4 to deduce the following formulas:

(a) $\displaystyle\sum_{n=1}^{\infty}\frac{1}{n^2} = \frac{\pi^2}{6}$;

(b) $\displaystyle\sum_{n=1}^{\infty}\frac{(-1)^{n+1}}{(2n-1)^3} = \frac{\pi^3}{32}\,.$

11.8 Properties of functions represented by real power series

In this section we restrict ourselves to *real* power series, that is series of the form $\sum a_n(z-a)^n$ in which z, a, and the coefficients a_n are all real numbers. We also write x in place of z. The interior of the circle of convergence intersects the real axis along an interval $(a-r, a+r)$ symmetrically located about a; we refer to this as the *interval of convergence* of the real power series $\sum a_n(x-a)^n$. The number r is called the radius of convergence. (See Figure 11.5.)

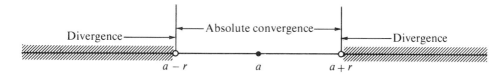

FIGURE 11.5   The interval of convergence of a real power series.

Each real power series defines a sum function whose value at each x in the interval of convergence is given by

$$f(x) = \sum_{n=0}^{\infty} a_n(x-a)^n\,.$$

The series is said to *represent the function f* in the interval of convergence, and it is called the *power-series expansion* of f about a.

There are two basic problems about power-series expansions that concern us here:

(1) Given the series, to find properties of the sum function f.

(2) Given a function f, to find whether or not it may be represented by a power series. It turns out that only rather special functions possess power-series expansions. Nevertheless, the class of such functions includes most examples that arise in practice, and hence their study is of great importance. We turn now to a discussion of question (1).

Theorem 11.6 tells us that the power series converges absolutely for each x in the open interval $(a - r, a + r)$, and that it converges uniformly on every closed subinterval $[a - R, a + R]$, where $0 < R < r$. Since each term of the power series is continuous on the whole real axis, it follows from Theorem 11.2 that the sum function f is continuous on every closed subinterval $[a - R, a + R]$, and hence on the open interval $(a - r, a + r)$. Also, Theorem 11.4 tells us that we can integrate the power series term by term on every closed subinterval $[a - R, a + R]$. These properties of functions represented by power series are stated formally in the following theorem.

THEOREM 11.8.   *Assume a function f is represented by the power series*

$$(11.1) \qquad\qquad f(x) = \sum_{n=0}^{\infty} a_n(x - a)^n$$

in an open interval $(a - r, a + r)$. Then f is continuous on this interval, and its integral over any closed subinterval may be computed by integrating the series term by term. In particular, for every x in $(a - r, a + r)$, we have

$$\int_a^x f(t)\, dt = \sum_{n=0}^{\infty} a_n \int_a^x (t - a)^n\, dt = \sum_{n=0}^{\infty} \frac{a_n}{n + 1} (x - a)^{n+1} .$$

Theorem 11.8 also shows that the radius of convergence of the integrated series is at least as large as that of the original series. We will prove presently that both series have exactly the same radius of convergence. First we show that a power series may be differentiated term by term within its interval of convergence.

THEOREM 11.9.   *Let f be represented by the power series* (11.1) *in the interval of convergence $(a - r, a + r)$. Then we have:*
    (a) *The differentiated series $\sum_{n=1}^{\infty} na_n(x - a)^{n-1}$ also has radius of convergence r.*
    (b) *The derivative $f'(x)$ exists for each x in the interval of convergence and is given by*

$$f'(x) = \sum_{n=1}^{\infty} na_n(x - a)^{n-1} .$$

Proof.   For simplicity, in the proof we assume that $a = 0$. First we prove that the differentiated series converges absolutely in the interval $(-r, r)$. Choose any positive x such that $0 < x < r$, and let h be a small positive number such that $0 < x < x + h < r$. Then the series for $f(x)$ and for $f(x + h)$ are each absolutely convergent. Hence, we may write

$$(11.2) \qquad\qquad \frac{f(x + h) - f(x)}{h} = \sum_{n=0}^{\infty} a_n \frac{(x + h)^n - x^n}{h} .$$

The series on the right is absolutely convergent since it is a linear combination of absolutely convergent series. Now we apply the mean-value theorem to write

$$(x + h)^n - x^n = hnc_n^{n-1} ,$$

where $x < c_n < x + h$. Hence, the series in (11.2) is identical to the series

(11.3)
$$\sum_{n=1}^{\infty} n a_n c_n^{n-1}$$

which must be absolutely convergent, since that in Equation (11.2) is. The series (11.3) is no longer a power series, but it dominates the power series $\sum n a_n x^{n-1}$, so this latter series must be absolutely convergent for this x. This proves that the radius of convergence of the differentiated series $\sum n a_n x^{n-1}$ is at least as large as r. On the other hand, the radius of convergence of the differentiated series cannot exceed r because the differentiated series dominates the original series $\sum a_n x^n$. This proves part (a).

To prove part (b), let g be the sum function of the differentiated series,

$$g(x) = \sum_{n=1}^{\infty} n a_n x^{n-1} \, .$$

Applying Theorem 11.8 to g, we may integrate term by term in the interval of convergence to obtain

$$\int_0^x g(t) \, dt = \sum_{n=1}^{\infty} a_n x^n = f(x) - a_0 \, .$$

Since g is continuous, the first fundamental theorem of calculus tells us that $f'(x)$ exists and equals $g(x)$ for each x in the interval of convergence. This proves (b).

    Note: Since every power series $\sum a_n(x - a)^n$ can be obtained by differentiating its integrated series, $\sum a_n(x - a)^{n+1}/(n + 1)$, Theorem 11.9 tells us that both these series have the same radius of convergence.

Theorems 11.8 and 11.9 justify the formal manipulations of Section 10.8 where we obtained various power-series expansions using term-by-term differentiation and integration of the geometric series. In particular, these theorems establish the validity of the expansions

$$\log (1 + x) = \sum_{n=0}^{\infty} \frac{(-1)^n x^{n+1}}{n + 1} \qquad \text{and} \qquad \arctan x = \sum_{n=0}^{\infty} \frac{(-1)^n x^{2n+1}}{2n + 1} \, ,$$

whenever x is in the open interval $-1 < x < 1$.

As a further consequence of Theorem 11.9, we conclude that the sum function of a power series has derivatives of *every* order and they may be obtained by repeated term-by-term differentiation of the power series. If $f(x) = \sum a_n(x - a)^n$ and if we differentiate this formula k times and then put $x = a$ in the result, we find that $f^{(k)}(a) = k! a_k$, so the kth coefficient a_k is given by the formula

$$a_k = \frac{f^{(k)}(a)}{k!} \qquad \text{for} \quad k = 1, 2, 3, \dots \, .$$

This formula also holds for $k = 0$ if we interpret $f^{(0)}(a)$ to mean $f(a)$. Thus, the power-series expansion of f has the form

(11.4)
$$f(x) = \sum_{k=0}^{\infty} \frac{f^{(k)}(a)}{k!} (x - a)^k .$$

This property can be formulated as a *uniqueness theorem* for power-series expansions.

THEOREM 11.10.   *If two power series $\sum a_n(x - a)^n$ and $\sum b_n(x - a)^n$ have the same sum function f in some neighborhood of the point a, then the two series are equal term by term; in fact, we have $a_n = b_n = f^{(n)}(a)/n!$ for each $n \geq 0$.*

Equation (11.4) also shows that the partial sums of a power series are simply the Taylor polynomials of the sum function at a. In other words, if a function f is representable by a power series in an interval $(a - r, a + r)$, then the sequence of Taylor polynomials $\{T_n f(x; a)\}$ generated by f at a converges pointwise in this interval to the sum function f. Moreover, the convergence is uniform in every closed subinterval of the interval of convergence.

11.9   The Taylor's series generated by a function

We turn now to the second problem raised at the beginning of the foregoing section. That is, given a function f, to find whether or not it has a power series expansion in some open interval about a point a.

We know from what was just proved that such a function must necessarily have derivatives of every order in some open interval about a and that the coefficients of its power-series expansion are given by Equation (11.4). Suppose, then, that we start with a function f having derivatives of every order in an open interval about a. We call such a function *infinitely differentiable* in this interval. Then we can certainly *form* the power series

(11.5)
$$\sum_{k=0}^{\infty} \frac{f^{(k)}(a)}{k!} (x - a)^k .$$

This is called the *Taylor's series generated by f at a*. We now ask two questions: Does this series converge for any x other than $x = a$? If so, is its sum equal to $f(x)$? Surprisingly enough, the answer to both questions is, in general, "no." The series may or may not converge for $x \neq a$ and, if it does converge, its sum may or may not be $f(x)$. An example where the series converges to a sum different from $f(x)$ is given in Exercise 24 in Section 11.13.

A necessary and sufficient condition for answering both questions in the affirmative can be given by using Taylor's formula with remainder, which provides a *finite* expansion of the form

(11.6)
$$f(x) = \sum_{k=0}^{n} \frac{f^{(k)}(a)}{k!} (x - a)^k + E_n(x) .$$

The finite sum is the Taylor polynomial of degree n generated by f at a, and $E_n(x)$ is the error made in approximating f by its Taylor polynomial. If we let $n \to \infty$ in (11.6), we see that the power series (11.5) will converge to $f(x)$ if and only if the error term tends to 0. In the next section we discuss a useful *sufficient condition* for the error term to tend to 0.

11.10   A sufficient condition for convergence of a Taylor's series

In Theorem 7.6 we proved that the error term in Taylor's formula could be expressed as an integral,

$$(11.7) \qquad\qquad E_n(x) = \frac{1}{n!} \int_a^x (x - t)^n f^{(n+1)}(t) \, dt$$

in any interval about a in which $f^{(n+1)}$ is continuous. Therefore, if f is infinitely differentiable, we always have this representation of the error so the Taylor's series converges to $f(x)$ if and only if this integral tends to 0 as $n \to \infty$.

The integral can be put into a slightly more useful form by a change of variable. We write

$$t = x + (a - x)u, \qquad dt = -(x - a) \, du,$$

and note that u varies from 1 to 0 as t varies from a to x. Therefore, the integral in (11.7) becomes

$$(11.8) \qquad\qquad E_n(x) = \frac{(x - a)^{n+1}}{n!} \int_0^1 u^n f^{(n+1)}[x + (a - x)u] \, du.$$

This form of the error enables us to give the following sufficient condition for convergence of a Taylor's series.

THEOREM 11.11.   *Assume f is infinitely differentiable in an open interval $I = (a - r, a + r)$, and assume that there is a positive constant A such that*

$$(11.9) \qquad\qquad |f^{(n)}(x)| \le A^n \qquad for \quad n = 1, 2, 3, \dots,$$

and every x in I. Then the Taylor's series generated by f at a converges to $f(x)$ for each x in I.

Proof.   Using the inequality (11.9) in the integral formula (11.8), we obtain the estimate

$$0 \le |E_n(x)| \le \frac{|x - a|^{n+1}}{n!} A^{n+1} \int_0^1 u^n \, du = \frac{|x - a|^{n+1} A^{n+1}}{(n + 1)!} = \frac{B^{n+1}}{(n + 1)!},$$

where $B = A |x - a|$. But for every B, $B^n/n!$ tends to 0 as $n \to \infty$, so $E_n(x) \to 0$ for each x in I.

11.11   Power-series expansions for the exponential and trigonometric functions

The sine and cosine functions and all their derivatives are bounded by 1 over the entire real axis. Therefore, inequality (11.9) holds with $A = 1$ if $f(x) = \sin x$ or if $f(x) = \cos x$, and we have the power-series expansions

$$\sin x = x - \frac{x^3}{3!} + \frac{x^5}{5!} - \frac{x^7}{7!} + \cdots + (-1)^{n-1} \frac{x^{2n-1}}{(2n-1)!} + \cdots,$$

$$\cos x = 1 - \frac{x^2}{2!} + \frac{x^4}{4!} - \frac{x^6}{6!} + \cdots + (-1)^n \frac{x^{2n}}{(2n)!} + \cdots,$$

valid for every real x. For the exponential function, $f(x) = e^x$, we have $f^{(n)}(x) = e^x$ for all x, so in any finite interval $(-r, r)$ we have $e^x \le e^r$. Therefore, (11.9) is satisfied with $A = e^r$. Since r is arbitrary, this shows that the following power-series expansion is valid for all real x:

$$e^x = 1 + x + \frac{x^2}{2!} + \cdots + \frac{x^n}{n!} + \cdots.$$

The foregoing power-series expansions for the sine and cosine can be used as the starting point for a completely analytic treatment of the trigonometric functions. If we use these series as *definitions* of the sine and cosine, it is possible to derive all the familiar algebraic and analytic properties of the trigonometric functions from these series alone. For example, the series immediately give us the formulas

$$\sin 0 = 0, \quad \cos 0 = 1, \quad \sin (-x) = -\sin x, \quad \cos (-x) = \cos x,$$

$$D \sin x = \cos x, \quad D \cos x = -\sin x.$$

The addition formulas may be derived by the following simple device: Let u and v be new functions defined by the equations

$$u(x) = \sin (x + a) - \sin x \cos a - \cos x \sin a,$$

$$v(x) = \cos (x + a) - \cos x \cos a + \sin x \sin a,$$

where a is a fixed real number, and let $f(x) = [u(x)]^2 + [v(x)]^2$. Then it is easy to verify that $u'(x) = v(x)$ and $v'(x) = -u(x)$, and so $f'(x) = 0$ for all x. Therefore, f is a constant and, since $f(0) = 0$, we must have $f(x) = 0$ for all x. This implies $u(x) = v(x) = 0$ for all x or, in other words,

$$\sin (x + a) = \sin x \cos a + \cos x \sin a,$$

$$\cos (x + a) = \cos x \cos a - \sin x \sin a.$$

The number π may be introduced as the smallest positive x such that $\sin x = 0$ (such an x can be shown to exist) and then it can be shown that the sine and cosine are periodic with period 2π, that $\sin (\frac{1}{2}\pi) = 1$, and that $\cos (\frac{1}{2}\pi) = 0$. The details, which we shall not present here, may be found in the book *Theory and Application of Infinite Series* by K. Knopp (New York: Hafner, 1951).

*11.12 Bernstein's theorem

Theorem 11.11 shows that the Taylor's series of a function f converges if the nth derivative $f^{(n)}$ grows no faster than the nth power of some positive number. Another sufficient condition for convergence was formulated by the Russian mathematician Sergei N. Bernstein (1880–).

THEOREM 11.12. BERNSTEIN'S THEOREM. *Assume f and all its derivatives are nonnegative on a closed interval* $[0, r]$. *That is, assume that*

$$f(x) \geq 0 \qquad and \qquad f^{(n)}(x) \geq 0$$

for each x in $[0, r]$ and each $n = 1, 2, 3, \ldots$. Then, if $0 \leq x < r$, the Taylor's series

$$\sum_{k=0}^{\infty} \frac{f^{(k)}(0)}{k!} x^k$$

converges to $f(x)$.

Proof. The result holds trivially for $x = 0$, so we assume that $0 < x < r$. We use Taylor's formula with remainder to write

(11.10)
$$f(x) = \sum_{k=0}^{n} \frac{f^{(k)}(0)}{k!} x^k + E_n(x) .$$

We will prove that the error term satisfies the inequalities

(11.11)
$$0 \leq E_n(x) \leq \left(\frac{x}{r}\right)^{n+1} f(r) .$$

This, in turn, shows that $E_n(x) \to 0$ as $n \to \infty$ since the quotient $(x/r)^{n+1} \to 0$ when $0 < x < r$.

To prove (11.11), we use the integral form of the error as given in Equation (11.8) with $a = 0$:

$$E_n(x) = \frac{x^{n+1}}{n!} \int_0^1 u^n f^{(n+1)}(x - xu) \, du .$$

This formula is valid for each x in the closed interval $[0, r]$. If $x \neq 0$, let

$$F_n(x) = \frac{E_n(x)}{x^{n+1}} = \frac{1}{n!} \int_0^1 u^n f^{(n+1)}(x - xu) \, du .$$

The function $f^{(n+1)}$ is monotonic increasing in the interval $[0, r]$ since its derivative is nonnegative. Therefore, we have

$$f^{(n+1)}(x - xu) = f^{(n+1)}[x(1 - u)] \leq f^{(n+1)}[r(1 - u)]$$

if $0 \le u \le 1$, which implies that $F_n(x) \le F_n(r)$ if $0 < x \le r$. In other words, we have $E_n(x)/x^{n+1} \le E_n(r)/r^{n+1}$ or

$$(11.12) \qquad\qquad E_n(x) \le \left(\frac{x}{r}\right)^{n+1} E_n(r) \,.$$

Setting $x = r$ in Equation (11.10), we see that $E_n(r) \le f(r)$ because each term in the sum is nonnegative. Using this in (11.12), we obtain (11.11) which, in turn, completes the proof.

11.13 Exercises

For each of the power series in Exercises 1 through 10 determine the set of all real x for which the series converges and compute the sum of the series. The power-series expansions given earlier in the text may be used whenever it is convenient to do so.

1. $\displaystyle\sum_{n=0}^{\infty} (-1)^n x^{2n}.$

6. $\displaystyle\sum_{n=1}^{\infty} \frac{2^n x^n}{n}\,.$

2. $\displaystyle\sum_{n=0}^{\infty} \frac{x^n}{3^{n+1}}\,.$

7. $\displaystyle\sum_{n=0}^{\infty} \frac{(-1)^n}{2n+1}\left(\frac{x}{2}\right)^{2n}.$

3. $\displaystyle\sum_{n=0}^{\infty} n x^n.$

8. $\displaystyle\sum_{n=0}^{\infty} \frac{(-1)^n x^{3n}}{n!}\,.$

4. $\displaystyle\sum_{n=0}^{\infty} (-1)^n n x^n.$

9. $\displaystyle\sum_{n=0}^{\infty} \frac{x^n}{(n+3)!}\,.$

5. $\displaystyle\sum_{n=0}^{\infty} (-2)^n \frac{n+2}{n+1} x^n.$

10. $\displaystyle\sum_{n=0}^{\infty} \frac{(x-1)^n}{(n+2)!}\,.$

Each of the functions in Exercises 11 through 21 has a power-series representation in powers of x. Assume the existence of the expansion, verify that the coefficients have the form given, and show that the series converges for the values of x indicated. The expansions given earlier in the text may be used whenever it is convenient to do so.

11. $a^x = \displaystyle\sum_{n=0}^{\infty} \frac{(\log a)^n}{n!} x^n, \qquad a > 0 \qquad$ (all x).   [*Hint:* $a^x = e^{x \log a}.$]

12. $\sinh x = \displaystyle\sum_{n=0}^{\infty} \frac{x^{2n+1}}{(2n+1)!} \qquad$ (all x).

13. $\sin^2 x = \displaystyle\sum_{n=1}^{\infty} (-1)^{n+1} \frac{2^{2n-1}}{(2n)!} x^{2n} \qquad$ (all x).   [*Hint:* $\cos 2x = 1 - 2\sin^2 x.$]

14. $\dfrac{1}{2-x} = \displaystyle\sum_{n=0}^{\infty} \frac{x^n}{2^{n+1}} \qquad$ ($|x| < 2$).

15. $e^{-x^2} = \displaystyle\sum_{n=0}^{\infty} \frac{(-1)^n x^{2n}}{n!} \qquad$ (all x).

16. $\sin^3 x = \dfrac{3}{4} \displaystyle\sum_{n=1}^{\infty} (-1)^{n+1} \frac{3^{2n}-1}{(2n+1)!} x^{2n+1} \qquad$ (all x).

17. $\log \sqrt{\dfrac{1+x}{1-x}} = \displaystyle\sum_{n=0}^{\infty} \dfrac{x^{2n+1}}{2n+1}$ $(|x| < 1)$.

18. $\dfrac{x}{1+x-2x^2} = \dfrac{1}{3}\displaystyle\sum_{n=1}^{\infty} [1 - (-2)^n]x^n$ $(|x| < \frac{1}{2})$.

   [*Hint:* $3x/(1 + x - 2x^2) = 1/(1 - x) - 1/(1 + 2x)$.]

19. $\dfrac{12 - 5x}{6 - 5x - x^2} = \displaystyle\sum_{n=0}^{\infty}\left(1 + \dfrac{(-1)^n}{6^n}\right)x^n$ $(|x| < 1)$.

20. $\dfrac{1}{x^2 + x + 1} = \dfrac{2}{\sqrt{3}}\displaystyle\sum_{n=0}^{\infty} \sin\dfrac{2\pi(n+1)}{3} x^n$ $(|x| < 1)$.

   [*Hint:* $x^3 - 1 = (x - 1)(x^2 + x + 1)$.]

21. $\dfrac{x}{(1 - x)(1 - x^2)} = \dfrac{1}{2}\displaystyle\sum_{n=1}^{\infty}\left(n + \dfrac{1 - (-1)^n}{2}\right)x^n$ $(|x| < 1)$.

22. Determine the coefficient a_{98} in the power-series expansion $\sin(2x + \frac{1}{4}\pi) = \sum_{n=0}^{\infty} a_n x^n$.

23. Let $f(x) = (2 + x^2)^{5/2}$.   Determine the coefficients $a_0, a_1, \ldots, a_4$ in the Taylor's series generated by f at 0.

24. Let $f(x) = e^{-1/x^2}$ if $x \neq 0$, and let $f(0) = 0$.

   (a) Show that f has derivatives of every order everywhere on the real axis.

   (b) Show that $f^{(n)}(0) = 0$ for all $n \geq 1$.   This example shows that the Taylor's series generated by f about the point 0 converges everywhere on the real axis, but that it represents f *only* at the origin.

11.14   Power series and differential equations

Power series sometimes enable us to obtain solutions of differential equations when other methods fail.   A systematic discussion of the use of power series in the theory of linear second-order differential equations is given in Volume II.   Here we illustrate with an example some of the ideas and techniques involved.

Consider the second-order differential equation

(11.13) $(1 - x^2)y'' = -2y$.

Assume there exists a solution, say $y = f(x)$, which may be represented by a power-series expansion in some neighborhood of the origin, say

(11.14) $y = \displaystyle\sum_{n=0}^{\infty} a_n x^n$.

The first thing we do is determine the coefficients $a_0, a_1, a_2, \ldots$.

One way to proceed is this: Differentiating (11.14) twice, we obtain

$$y'' = \sum_{n=2}^{\infty} n(n - 1)a_n x^{n-2}.$$

Multiplying by $1 - x^2$, we find that

(11.15) $$(1 - x^2)y'' = \sum_{n=2}^{\infty} n(n - 1)a_n x^{n-2} - \sum_{n=2}^{\infty} n(n - 1)a_n x^n$$

$$= \sum_{n=0}^{\infty} (n + 2)(n + 1)a_{n+2} x^n - \sum_{n=0}^{\infty} n(n - 1)a_n x^n$$

$$= \sum_{n=0}^{\infty} [(n + 2)(n + 1)a_{n+2} - n(n - 1)a_n]x^n .$$

Substituting each of the series (11.14) and (11.15) in the differential equation, we obtain an equation involving two power series, valid in some neighborhood of the origin. By the uniqueness theorem, these power series must be equal term by term. Therefore we may equate coefficients of x^n and obtain the relation

$$(n + 2)(n + 1)a_{n+2} - n(n - 1)a_n = -2a_n$$

or, what amounts to the same thing,

$$a_{n+2} = \frac{n^2 - n - 2}{(n + 2)(n + 1)} a_n = \frac{n - 2}{n + 2} a_n .$$

This relation enables us to determine $a_2 , a_4 , a_6 , \ldots$ successively in terms of a_0. Similarly, we can compute $a_3 , a_5 , a_7 , \ldots$ in terms of a_1. For the coefficients with even subscripts, we find that

$$a_2 = -a_0 , \qquad a_4 = 0 \cdot a_2 = 0 , \qquad a_6 = a_8 = a_{10} = \cdots = 0 .$$

The odd coefficients are

$$a_3 = \frac{1 - 2}{1 + 2} a_1 = \frac{-1}{3} a_1 , \qquad a_5 = \frac{3 - 2}{3 + 2} a_2 = \frac{1}{5} \cdot \frac{(-1)}{3} a_1 ,$$

$$a_7 = \frac{5 - 2}{5 + 2} a_5 = \frac{3}{7} \cdot \frac{1}{5} \cdot \frac{(-1)}{3} a_1 = \frac{-1}{7 \cdot 5} a_1$$

and, in general,

$$a_{2n+1} = \frac{2n - 3}{2n + 1} a_{2n-1} = \frac{2n - 3}{2n + 1} \cdot \frac{2n - 5}{2n - 1} \cdot \frac{2n - 7}{2n - 3} \cdot \ldots \cdot \frac{3}{7} \cdot \frac{1}{5} \cdot \frac{(-1)}{3} a_1 .$$

When the common factors are canceled, this simplifies to

$$a_{2n+1} = \frac{-1}{(2n + 1)(2n - 1)} a_1 .$$

Therefore, the series for y can be written as follows:

$$y = a_0(1 - x^2) - a_1 \sum_{n=0}^{\infty} \frac{1}{(2n + 1)(2n - 1)} x^{2n+1} .$$

The ratio test may be used to verify the convergence of this series for $|x| < 1$. The work just carried out shows that the series actually satisfies the differential equation in (11.13), where a_0 and a_1 may be thought of as arbitrary constants. The reader should note that in this particular example the polynomial which multiplies a_0 is itself a solution of (11.13), and the series which multiplies a_1 is another solution.

The procedure just described is called the *method of undetermined coefficients*. Another way to find these coefficients is to use the formula

$$a_n = \frac{f^{(n)}(0)}{n!} \quad \text{if} \quad y = f(x).$$

Sometimes the higher derivatives of y at the origin can be computed directly from the differential equation. For example, setting $x = 0$ in (11.13), we immediately obtain

$$f''(0) = -2f(0) = -2a_0,$$

and hence we have

$$a_2 = \frac{f''(0)}{2!} = -a_0.$$

To find the higher derivatives, we differentiate the differential equation to obtain

(11.16) $$(1 - x^2)y''' - 2xy'' = -2y'.$$

Putting $x = 0$, we see that $f'''(0) = -2f'(0) = -2a_1$, and hence $a_3 = f'''(0)/3! = -a_1/3$. Differentiation of (11.16) leads to the equation

$$(1 - x^2)y^{(4)} - 4xy''' = 0.$$

When $x = 0$, this yields $f^{(4)}(0) = 0$, and hence $a_4 = 0$. Repeating the process once more, we find

$$(1 - x^2)y^{(5)} - 6xy^{(4)} - 4y''' = 0,$$

$$f^{(5)}(0) = 4f'''(0) = -8a_1, \qquad a_5 = \frac{f^{(5)}(0)}{5!} = -\frac{a_1}{15}.$$

It is clear that the process may be continued as long as desired.

11.15 The binomial series

We can also use our knowledge of differential equations to determine the sums of certain power series. For example, we shall use the existence-uniqueness theorem for first-order linear differential equations to prove that the binomial series expansion

(11.17) $$(1 + x)^\alpha = \sum_{n=0}^{\infty} \binom{\alpha}{n} x^n$$

is valid in the interval $|x| < 1$. Here the exponent α is an arbitrary real number and $\binom{\alpha}{n}$ denotes the binomial coefficient defined by

(11.18)
$$\binom{\alpha}{n} = \frac{\alpha(\alpha - 1) \cdots (\alpha - n + 1)}{n!}.$$

When α is a nonnegative integer, all but a finite number of the coefficients $\binom{\alpha}{n}$ are zero, and the series reduces to a polynomial of degree α, giving us the familiar binomial theorem. To prove (11.17) for an arbitrary real α, we first use the ratio test to find that the series converges absolutely in the open interval $-1 < x < 1$. Then we define a function f by means of the equation

(11.19)
$$f(x) = \sum_{n=0}^{\infty} \binom{\alpha}{n} x^n \qquad \text{if} \quad |x| < 1.$$

We then show that f is a solution of the linear differential equation

(11.20)
$$y' - \frac{\alpha}{x + 1} y = 0$$

and satisfies the initial condition $f(0) = 1$. Theorem 8.3 tells us that in any interval not containing the point $x = -1$ there is only one solution of this differential equation with $y = 1$ when $x = 0$. Since $y = (1 + x)^\alpha$ is such a solution, it follows that $f(x) = (1 + x)^\alpha$ if $-1 < x < 1$.

Therefore, to prove (11.17) we need only show that f satisfies the differential equation (11.20). For this purpose, we require the following property of the binomial coefficients:

$$(n + 1)\binom{\alpha}{n + 1} = (\alpha - n)\binom{\alpha}{n}.$$

This property, which is an immediate consequence of the definition in (11.18), holds for every real α and every integer $n \geq 0$. It can also be expressed in the form

(11.21)
$$(n + 1)\binom{\alpha}{n + 1} + n\binom{\alpha}{n} = \alpha\binom{\alpha}{n}.$$

Differentiation of (11.19) gives us

$$f'(x) = \sum_{n=1}^{\infty} n\binom{\alpha}{n} x^{n-1} = \sum_{n=0}^{\infty} (n + 1)\binom{\alpha}{n + 1} x^n,$$

from which we find that

$$(1 + x)f'(x) = \sum_{n=0}^{\infty} \left\{ (n + 1)\binom{\alpha}{n + 1} + n\binom{\alpha}{n} \right\} x^n = \alpha \sum_{n=0}^{\infty} \binom{\alpha}{n} x^n = \alpha f(x),$$

because of (11.21). This shows that f satisfies the differential equation (11.20) and this, in turn, proves (11.17).

11.16   Exercises

1. The differential equation $(1 - x^2)y'' - 2xy' + 6y = 0$ has a power-series solution $f(x) = \sum_{n=0}^{\infty} a_n x^n$ with $f(0) = 1$ and $f'(0) = 0$. Use the method of undetermined coefficients to obtain a recursion formula relating a_{n+2} to a_n. Determine a_n explicitly for each n and find the sum of the series.

2. Do the same as in Exercise 1 for the differential equation $(1 - x^2)y'' - 2xy' + 12y = 0$ and the initial conditions $f(0) = 0, f'(0) = 2$.

In each of Exercises 3 through 9, the power series is used to define the function f. Determine the interval of convergence in each case and show that f satisfies the differential equation indicated, where $y = f(x)$. In Exercises 6 through 9, solve the differential equation and thereby obtain the sum of the series.

3. $f(x) = \sum_{n=0}^{\infty} \dfrac{x^{4n}}{(4n)!}$; $\dfrac{d^4 y}{dx^4} = y$.

4. $f(x) = \sum_{n=0}^{\infty} \dfrac{x^n}{(n!)^2}$; $xy'' + y' - y = 0$.

5. $f(x) = 1 + \sum_{n=1}^{\infty} \dfrac{1 \cdot 4 \cdot 7 \cdots (3n - 2)}{(3n)!} x^{3n}$; $y'' = x^a y + b$.   (Find a and b.)

6. $f(x) = \sum_{n=0}^{\infty} \dfrac{x^{2n}}{n!}$; $y' = 2xy$.

8. $f(x) = \sum_{n=0}^{\infty} \dfrac{(-1)^n 2^{2n} x^{2n}}{(2n)!}$; $y'' + 4y = 0$.

7. $f(x) = \sum_{n=2}^{\infty} \dfrac{x^n}{n!}$; $y' = x + y$.

9. $f(x) = x + \sum_{n=0}^{\infty} \dfrac{(3x)^{2n+1}}{(2n + 1)!}$; $y'' = 9(y - x)$.

10. The functions J_0 and J_1 defined by the series

$$J_0(x) = \sum_{n=0}^{\infty} (-1)^n \frac{x^{2n}}{(n!)^2 2^{2n}}, \qquad J_1(x) = \sum_{n=0}^{\infty} (-1)^n \frac{x^{2n+1}}{n!(n + 1)! 2^{2n+1}}$$

are called *Bessel functions of the first kind* of orders zero and one, respectively. These functions arise in many problems in pure and applied mathematics. Show (a) both series converge for all real x; (b) $J_0'(x) = -J_1(x)$; (c) $j_0'(x) = j_1'(x)$, where $j_0(x) = xJ_0(x)$ and $j_1(x) = xJ_1(x)$.

11. The differential equation

$$x^2 y'' + xy' + (x^2 - n^2)y = 0$$

is called *Bessel's equation*. Show that J_0 and J_1 (as defined in Exercise 10) are solutions when $n = 0$ and 1, respectively.

In each of Exercises 12, 13, and 14, assume the given differential equation has a power-series solution and find the first four nonzero terms.

12. $y' = x^2 + y^2$, with $y = 1$ when $x = 0$.

13. $y' = 1 + xy^2$, with $y = 0$ when $x = 0$.

14. $y' = x + y^2$, with $y = 0$ when $x = 0$.

In Exercises 15, 16, and 17, assume the given differential equation has a power-series solution of the form $y = \sum a_n x^n$, and determine the nth coefficient a_n.

15. $y' = \alpha y$.   16. $y'' = xy$.   17. $y'' + xy' + y = 0$.

18. Let $f(x) = \sum_{n=0}^{\infty} a_n x^n$, where $a_0 = 1$ and the remaining coefficients are determined by the identity

$$e^{-2x} = \sum_{n=0}^{\infty} \{2a_n + (n+1)a_{n+1}\}x^n.$$

Compute a_1, a_2, a_3, and find the sum of the series for $f(x)$.

19. Let $f(x) = \sum_{n=0}^{\infty} a_n x^n$, where the coefficients a_n are determined by the relation

$$\cos x = \sum_{n=0}^{\infty} a_n(n+2)x^n.$$

Compute a_5, a_6, and $f(\pi)$.

20. (a) Show that the first six terms of the binomial series for $(1-x)^{-1/2}$ are:

$$1 + \frac{1}{2}x + \frac{3}{8}x^2 + \frac{5}{16}x^3 + \frac{35}{128}x^4 + \frac{63}{256}x^5.$$

(b) Let a_n denote the nth term of this series when $x = 1/50$, and let r_n denote the remainder after n terms; that is, for $n \geq 0$ let

$$r_n = a_{n+1} + a_{n+2} + a_{n+3} + \cdots.$$

Show that $0 < r_n < a_n/49$.

[*Hint:* Show that $a_{n+1} < a_n/50$, and dominate r_n by a suitable geometric series.]

(c) Verify the identity

$$\sqrt{2} = \frac{7}{5}\left(1 - \frac{1}{50}\right)^{-1/2}$$

and use it to compute the first ten correct decimals of $\sqrt{2}$.

[*Hint:* Use parts (a) and (b), retain twelve decimals during the calculations, and take into account round-off errors.]

21. (a) Show that

$$\sqrt{3} = \frac{1732}{1000}\left(1 - \frac{176}{3,000,000}\right)^{-1/2}.$$

(b) Proceed as suggested in Exercise 20 and compute the first fifteen correct decimals of $\sqrt{3}$.

22. Integrate the binomial series for $(1-x^2)^{-1/2}$ and thereby obtain the power-series expansion

$$\arcsin x = x + \sum_{n=1}^{\infty} \frac{1 \cdot 3 \cdot 5 \cdots (2n-1)}{2 \cdot 4 \cdot 6 \cdots (2n)} \frac{x^{2n+1}}{2n+1} \qquad (|x| < 1).$$

12

VECTOR ALGEBRA

12.1 Historical introduction

In the foregoing chapters we have presented many of the basic concepts of calculus and have illustrated their use in solving a few relatively simple geometrical and physical problems. Further applications of the calculus require a deeper knowledge of analytic geometry than has been presented so far, and therefore we turn our attention to a more detailed investigation of some fundamental geometric ideas.

As we have pointed out earlier in this book, calculus and analytic geometry were intimately related throughout their historical development. Every new discovery in one subject led to an improvement in the other. The problem of drawing tangents to curves resulted in the discovery of the derivative; that of area led to the integral; and partial derivatives were introduced to investigate curved surfaces in space. Along with these accomplishments came other parallel developments in mechanics and mathematical physics. In 1788 Lagrange published his masterpiece *Mécanique analytique* (Analytical Mechanics) which showed the great flexibility and tremendous power attained by using analytical methods in the study of mechanics. Later on, in the 19th century, the Irish mathematician William Rowan Hamilton (1805–1865) introduced his *Theory of Quaternions*, a new method and a new point of view that contributed much to the understanding of both algebra and physics. The best features of quaternion analysis and Cartesian geometry were later united, largely through the efforts of J. W. Gibbs (1839–1903) and O. Heaviside (1850–1925), and a new subject called *vector algebra* sprang into being. It was soon realized that vectors are the ideal tools for the exposition and simplification of many important ideas in geometry and physics. In this chapter we propose to discuss the elements of vector algebra. Applications to analytic geometry are given in Chapter 13. In Chapter 14 vector algebra is combined with the methods of calculus, and applications are given to both geometry and mechanics.

There are essentially three different ways to introduce vector algebra: *geometrically*, *analytically*, and *axiomatically*. In the geometric approach, vectors are represented by directed line segments, or arrows. Algebraic operations on vectors, such as addition, subtraction, and multiplication by real numbers, are defined and studied by geometric methods.

In the analytic approach, vectors and vector operations are described entirely in terms of *numbers*, called *components*. Properties of the vector operations are then deduced from corresponding properties of numbers. The analytic description of vectors arises naturally from the geometric description as soon as a coordinate system is introduced.

In the axiomatic approach, no attempt is made to describe the nature of a vector or of the algebraic operations on vectors. Instead, vectors and vector operations are thought of as *undefined concepts* of which we know nothing except that they satisfy a certain set of axioms. Such an algebraic system, with appropriate axioms, is called a *linear space* or a *linear vector space*. Examples of linear spaces occur in all branches of mathematics, and we will study many of them in Chapter 15. The algebra of directed line segments and the algebra of vectors described by components are merely two examples of linear spaces.

The study of vector algebra from the axiomatic point of view is perhaps the most mathematically satisfactory approach to use since it furnishes a description of vectors that is free of coordinate systems and free of any particular geometric representation. This study is carried out in detail in Chapter 15. In this chapter we base our treatment on the analytic approach, and we also use directed line segments to interpret many of the results geometrically. When possible, we give proofs by coordinate-free methods. Thus, this chapter serves to provide familiarity with important concrete examples of vector spaces, and it also motivates the more abstract approach in Chapter 15.

12.2 The vector space of *n*-tuples of real numbers

The idea of using a number to locate a point on a line was known to the ancient Greeks. In 1637 Descartes extended this idea, using a *pair* of numbers (a_1, a_2) to locate a point in the plane, and a *triple* of numbers (a_1, a_2, a_3) to locate a point in space. The 19th century mathematicians A. Cayley (1821–1895) and H. G. Grassmann (1809–1877) realized that there is no need to stop with three numbers. One can just as well consider a *quadruple* of numbers (a_1, a_2, a_3, a_4) or, more generally, an *n-tuple* of real numbers

$$(a_1, a_2, \ldots, a_n)$$

for any integer $n \geq 1$. Such an *n*-tuple is called an *n-dimensional point* or an *n-dimensional vector*, the individual numbers $a_1, a_2, \ldots, a_n$ being referred to as *coordinates* or *components* of the vector. The collection of all *n*-dimensional vectors is called *the vector space of n-tuples*, or simply *n-space*. We denote this space by V_n.

The reader may well ask at this stage why we are interested in spaces of dimension greater than three. One answer is that many problems which involve a large number of simultaneous equations are more easily analyzed by introducing vectors in a suitable *n*-space and replacing all these equations by a single vector equation. Another advantage is that we are able to deal in one stroke with many properties common to 1-space, 2-space, 3-space, etc., that is, properties independent of the dimensionality of the space. This is in keeping with the spirit of modern mathematics which favors the development of comprehensive methods for attacking problems on a wide front.

Unfortunately, the geometric pictures which are a great help in motivating and illustrating vector concepts when $n = 1, 2$, and 3 are not available when $n > 3$; therefore, the study of vector algebra in higher-dimensional spaces must proceed entirely by analytic means.

In this chapter we shall usually denote vectors by capital letters $A, B, C, \ldots$, and components by the corresponding small letters $a, b, c, \ldots$. Thus, we write

$$A = (a_1, a_2, \ldots, a_n).$$

To convert V_n into an algebraic system, we introduce *equality* of vectors and two vector operations called *addition* and *multiplication by scalars*. The word "scalar" is used here as a synonym for "real number."

DEFINITION. *Two vectors A and B in V_n are called equal whenever they agree in their respective components. That is, if $A = (a_1, a_2, \ldots, a_n)$ and $B = (b_1, b_2, \ldots, b_n)$, the vector equation $A = B$ means exactly the same as the n scalar equations*

$$a_1 = b_1, \qquad a_2 = b_2, \qquad \ldots, \qquad a_n = b_n.$$

The sum $A + B$ is defined to be the vector obtained by adding corresponding components:

$$A + B = (a_1 + b_1, a_2 + b_2, \ldots, a_n + b_n).$$

If c is a scalar, we define cA or Ac to be the vector obtained by multiplying each component of A by c:

$$cA = (ca_1, ca_2, \ldots, ca_n).$$

From this definition it is easy to verify the following properties of these operations.

THEOREM 12.1. *Vector addition is commutative,*

$$A + B = B + A,$$

and associative,

$$A + (B + C) = (A + B) + C.$$

Multiplication by scalars is associative,

$$c(dA) = (cd)A$$

and satisfies the two distributive laws

$$c(A + B) = cA + cB, \qquad and \qquad (c + d)A = cA + dA.$$

Proofs of these properties follow quickly from the definition and are left as exercises for the reader.

The vector with all components 0 is called the *zero vector* and is denoted by O. It has the property that $A + O = A$ for every vector A; in other words, O is an identity element for vector addition. The vector $(-1)A$ is also denoted by $-A$ and is called the *negative* of A. We also write $A - B$ for $A + (-B)$ and call this the *difference* of A and B. The equation $(A + B) - B = A$ shows that subtraction is the inverse of addition. Note that $0A = O$ and that $1A = A$.

The reader may have noticed the similarity between vectors in 2-space and complex numbers. Both are defined as ordered pairs of real numbers and both are added in exactly the same way. Thus, as far as addition is concerned, complex numbers and two-dimensional vectors are algebraically indistinguishable. They differ only when we introduce multiplication.

Multiplication of complex numbers gives the complex-number system the field properties also possessed by the real numbers. It can be shown (although the proof is difficult) that except for $n = 1$ and 2, it is not possible to introduce multiplication in V_n so as to satisfy all the field properties. However, special products can be introduced in V_n which do not satisfy *all* the field properties. For example, in Section 12.5 we shall discuss the *dot product* of two vectors in V_n. The result of this multiplication is a scalar, not a vector. Another product, called the *cross product*, is discussed in Section 13.9. This multiplication is applicable only in the space V_3. The result is always a vector, but the cross product is not commutative.

12.3   Geometric interpretation for $n \leq 3$

Although the foregoing definitions are completely divorced from geometry, vectors and vector operations have an interesting geometric interpretation for spaces of dimension three or less. We shall draw pictures in 2-space to illustrate these concepts and ask the reader to produce the corresponding visualizations for himself in 3-space and in 1-space.

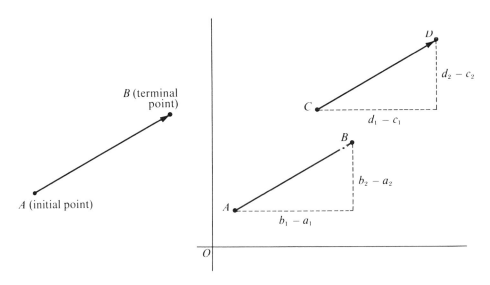

FIGURE 12.1   The geometric vector $\overrightarrow{AB}$ from A to B.

FIGURE 12.2 $\overrightarrow{AB}$ and $\overrightarrow{CD}$ are equivalent because $B - A = D - C$.

A pair of points A and B is called a *geometric vector* if one of the points, say A, is called the *initial point* and the other, B, the *terminal point*, or *tip*. We visualize a geometric vector as an arrow from A to B, as shown in Figure 12.1, and denote it by the symbol $\overrightarrow{AB}$.

Geometric vectors are especially convenient for representing certain physical quantities such as force, displacement, velocity, and acceleration, which possess both magnitude and direction. The length of the arrow is a measure of the magnitude and the arrowhead indicates the required direction.

Suppose we introduce a coordinate system with origin O. Figure 12.2 shows two geometric vectors $\overrightarrow{AB}$ and $\overrightarrow{CD}$ with $B - A = D - C$. In terms of components, this means that we have

$$b_1 - a_1 = d_1 - c_1 \qquad \text{and} \qquad b_2 - a_2 = d_2 - c_2 \,.$$

By comparison of the congruent triangles in Figure 12.2, we see that the two arrows representing $\overrightarrow{AB}$ and $\overrightarrow{CD}$ have equal lengths, are parallel, and point in the same direction. We call such geometric vectors *equivalent*. That is, we say $\overrightarrow{AB}$ is equivalent to $\overrightarrow{CD}$ whenever

(12.1) $$B - A = D - C \,.$$

Note that the four points A, B, C, D are vertices of a parallelogram. (See Figure 12.3.) Equation (12.1) can also be written in the form $A + D = B + C$ which tells us that *opposite vertices of the parallelogram have the same sum*. In particular, if one of the vertices, say A, is the origin O, as in Figure 12.4, the geometric vector from O to the opposite vertex D corresponds to the vector sum $D = B + C$. This is described by saying that vector addition corresponds geometrically to addition of geometric vectors by the *parallelogram law*. The importance of vectors in physics stems from the remarkable fact that many physical quantities (such as force, velocity, and acceleration) combine by the parallelogram law.

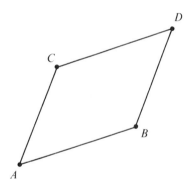

FIGURE 12.3 Opposite vertices of a parallelogram have the same sum:
$$A + D = B + C.$$

FIGURE 12.4 Vector addition interpreted geometrically by the parallelogram law.

For simplicity in notation, we shall use the same symbol to denote a point in V_n (when $n \leq 3$) and the geometric vector from the origin to this point. Thus, we write A instead of $\overrightarrow{OA}$, B instead of $\overrightarrow{OB}$, and so on. Sometimes we also write A in place of any geometric vector equivalent to $\overrightarrow{OA}$. For example, Figure 12.5 illustrates the geometric meaning of vector subtraction. Two geometric vectors are labeled as $B - A$, but these geometric vectors are equivalent. They have the same length and the same direction.

Figure 12.6 illustrates the geometric meaning of multiplication by scalars. If $B = cA$, the geometric vector B has length $|c|$ times the length of A; it points in the same direction as A if c is positive, and in the opposite direction if c is negative.

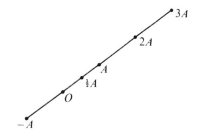

FIGURE 12.5   Geometric meaning of subtraction of   FIGURE 12.6   Multiplication of
vectors.   vectors by scalars.

The geometric interpretation of vectors in V_n for $n \leq 3$ suggests a way to define parallelism in a general n-space.

DEFINITION.   *Two vectors A and B in V_n are said to have the same direction if $B = cA$ for some positive scalar c, and the opposite direction if $B = cA$ for some negative c. They are called parallel if $B = cA$ for some nonzero c.*

Note that this definition makes every vector have the same direction as itself—a property which we surely want.   Note also that this definition ascribes the following properties to the zero vector: The zero vector is the only vector having the same direction as its negative and therefore the only vector having the opposite direction to itself.   The zero vector is the only vector parallel to the zero vector.

12.4   Exercises

1. Let $A = (1, 3, 6)$, $B = (4, -3, 3)$, and $C = (2, 1, 5)$ be three vectors in V_3. Determine the components of each of the following vectors: (a) $A + B$; (b) $A - B$; (c) $A + B - C$; (d) $7A - 2B - 3C$; (e) $2A + B - 3C$.
2. Draw the geometric vectors from the origin to the points $A = (2, 1)$ and $B = (1, 3)$.   On the same figure, draw the geometric vector from the origin to the point $C = A + tB$ for each of the following values of t: $t = \frac{1}{3}$; $t = \frac{1}{2}$; $t = \frac{3}{4}$; $t = 1$; $t = 2$; $t = -1$; $t = -2$.
3. Solve Exercise 2 if $C = tA + B$.
4. Let $A = (2, 1)$, $B = (1, 3)$, and $C = xA + yB$, where x and y are scalars.
   (a) Draw the geometric vector from the origin to C for each of the following pairs of values of x and y: $x = y = \frac{1}{2}$; $x = \frac{1}{4}$, $y = \frac{3}{4}$; $x = \frac{1}{3}$, $y = \frac{2}{3}$; $x = 2$, $y = -1$; $x = 3$, $y = -2$; $x = -\frac{1}{2}$, $y = \frac{3}{2}$; $x = -1$, $y = 2$.
   (b) What do you think is the set of points C obtained as x and y run through all real numbers such that $x + y = 1$? (Just make a guess and show the locus on the figure.   No proof is required.)
   (c) Make a guess for the set of all points C obtained as x and y range independently over the intervals $0 \leq x \leq 1$, $0 \leq y \leq 1$, and make a sketch of this set.
   (d) What do you think is the set of all C obtained if x ranges through the interval $0 \leq x \leq 1$ and y ranges through all real numbers?
   (e) What do you think is the set if x and y both range over all real numbers?
5. Let $A = (2, 1)$ and $B = (1, 3)$.   Show that every vector $C = (c_1, c_2)$ in V_2 can be expressed in the form $C = xA + yB$.   Express x and y in terms of c_1 and c_2.

6. Let $A = (1, 1, 1)$, $B = (0, 1, 1)$, and $C = (1, 1, 0)$ be three vectors in V_3 and let $D = xA + yB + zC$, where x, y, z are scalars.
   (a) Determine the components of D.
   (b) If $D = O$, prove that $x = y = z = 0$.
   (c) Find x, y, z such that $D = (1, 2, 3)$.

7. Let $A = (1, 1, 1)$, $B = (0, 1, 1)$ and $C = (2, 1, 1)$ be three vectors in V_3, and let $D = xA + yB + zC$, where $x, y,$ and z are scalars.
   (a) Determine the components of D.
   (b) Find $x, y,$ and z, not all zero, such that $D = O$.
   (c) Prove that no choice of x, y, z makes $D = (1, 2, 3)$.

8. Let $A = (1, 1, 1, 0)$, $B = (0, 1, 1, 1)$, $C = (1, 1, 0, 0)$ be three vectors in V_4, and let $D = xA + yB + zC$, where $x, y,$ and z are scalars.
   (a) Determine the components of D.
   (b) If $D = O$, prove that $x = y = z = 0$.
   (c) Find $x, y,$ and z such that $D = (1, 5, 3, 4)$.
   (d) Prove that no choice of x, y, z makes $D = (1, 2, 3, 4)$.

9. In V_n, prove that two vectors parallel to the same vector are parallel to each other.

10. Given four nonzero vectors A, B, C, D in V_n such that $C = A + B$ and A is parallel to D. Prove that C is parallel to D if and only if B is parallel to D.

11. (a) Prove, for vectors in V_n, the properties of addition and multiplication by scalars given in Theorem 12.1.
    (b) By drawing geometric vectors in the plane, illustrate the geometric meaning of the two distributive laws $(c + d)A = cA + dA$ and $c(A + B) = cA + cB$.

12. If a quadrilateral $OABC$ in V_2 is a parallelogram having A and C as opposite vertices, prove that $A + \frac{1}{2}(C - A) = \frac{1}{2}B$. What geometrical theorem about parallelograms can you deduce from this equation?

12.5 The dot product

We introduce now a new kind of multiplication called the dot product or scalar product of two vectors in V_n.

DEFINITION. *If $A = (a_1, \ldots, a_n)$ and $B = (b_1, \ldots, b_n)$ are two vectors in V_n, their dot product is denoted by $A \cdot B$ and is defined by the equation*

$$A \cdot B = \sum_{k=1}^{n} a_k b_k .$$

Thus, to compute $A \cdot B$ we multiply corresponding components of A and B and then add all the products. This multiplication has the following algebraic properties.

THEOREM 12.2. *For all vectors A, B, C in V_n and all scalars c, we have the following properties:*

(a) $A \cdot B = B \cdot A$ (*commutative law*),
(b) $A \cdot (B + C) = A \cdot B + A \cdot C$ (*distributive law*),
(c) $c(A \cdot B) = (cA) \cdot B = A \cdot (cB)$ (*homogeneity*),
(d) $A \cdot A > 0$ if $A \neq O$ (*positivity*),
(e) $A \cdot A = 0$ if $A = O$.

Proof. The first three properties are easy consequences of the definition and are left as exercises. To prove the last two, we use the relation $A \cdot A = \sum a_k^2$. Since each term is nonnegative, the sum is nonnegative. Moreover, the sum is zero if and only if each term in the sum is zero and this can happen only if $A = O$.

The dot product has an interesting geometric interpretation which will be described in Section 12.9. Before we discuss this, however, we mention an important inequality concerning dot products that is fundamental in vector algebra.

THEOREM 12.3.   THE CAUCHY–SCHWARZ INEQUALITY.   *If A and B are vectors in V_n, we have*

(12.2) $(A \cdot B)^2 \leq (A \cdot A)(B \cdot B)$.

Moreover, the equality sign holds if and only if one of the vectors is a scalar multiple of the other.

Proof. Expressing each member of (12.2) in terms of components, we obtain

$$\left(\sum_{k=1}^{n} a_k b_k \right)^2 \leq \left(\sum_{k=1}^{n} a_k^2 \right) \left(\sum_{k=1}^{n} b_k^2 \right).$$

which is the inequality proved earlier in Theorem I.41.

We shall present another proof of (12.2) that makes no use of components. Such a proof is of interest because it shows that the Cauchy–Schwarz inequality is a consequence of the five properties of the dot product listed in Theorem 12.2 and does not depend on the particular definition that was used to deduce these properties.

To carry out this proof, we notice first that (12.2) holds trivially if either A or B is the zero vector. Therefore, we may assume that both A and B are nonzero. Let C be the vector

$$C = xA - yB, \qquad \text{where} \quad x = B \cdot B \quad \text{and} \quad y = A \cdot B.$$

Properties (d) and (e) imply that $C \cdot C \geq 0$. When we translate this in terms of x and y, it will yield (12.2). To express $C \cdot C$ in terms of x and y, we use properties (a), (b) and (c) to obtain

$$C \cdot C = (xA - yB) \cdot (xA - yB) = x^2(A \cdot A) - 2xy(A \cdot B) + y^2(B \cdot B).$$

Using the definitions of x and y and the inequality $C \cdot C \geq 0$, we get

$$(B \cdot B)^2(A \cdot A) - 2(A \cdot B)^2(B \cdot B) + (A \cdot B)^2(B \cdot B) \geq 0.$$

Property (d) implies $B \cdot B > 0$ since $B \neq O$, so we may divide by $(B \cdot B)$ to obtain

$$(B \cdot B)(A \cdot A) - (A \cdot B)^2 \geq 0,$$

which is (12.2). This proof also shows that the equality sign holds in (12.2) if and only if $C = O$. But $C = O$ if and only if $xA = yB$. This equation holds, in turn, if and only if one of the vectors is a scalar multiple of the other.

The Cauchy–Schwarz inequality has important applications to the properties of the *length* or *norm* of a vector, a concept which we discuss next.

12.6 Length or norm of a vector

Figure 12.7 shows the geometric vector from the origin to a point $A = (a_1, a_2)$ in the plane. From the theorem of Pythagoras, we find that the length of A is given by the formula

$$\text{length of } A = \sqrt{a_1^2 + a_2^2}.$$

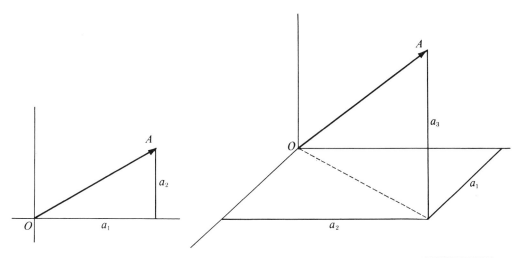

FIGURE 12.7   In V_2, the length   FIGURE 12.8   In V_3, the length of A is $\sqrt{a_1^2 + a_2^2 + a_3^2}$.
of A is $\sqrt{a_1^2 + a_2^2}$.

A corresponding picture in 3-space is shown in Figure 12.8. Applying the theorem of Pythagoras twice, we find that the length of a geometric vector A in 3-space is given by

$$\text{length of } A = \sqrt{a_1^2 + a_2^2 + a_3^2}.$$

Note that in either case the length of A is given by $(A \cdot A)^{1/2}$, the square root of the dot product of A with itself. This formula suggests a way to introduce the concept of length in n-space.

DEFINITION.   *If A is a vector in V_n, its length or norm is denoted by $\|A\|$ and is defined by the equation*

$$\|A\| = (A \cdot A)^{1/2}.$$

The fundamental properties of the dot product lead to corresponding properties of norms.

THEOREM 12.4.   *If A is a vector in V_n and if c is a scalar, we have the following properties:*
(a) $\|A\| > 0$ *if* $A \neq O$ (*positivity*),
(b) $\|A\| = 0$ *if* $A = O$,
(c) $\|cA\| = |c| \, \|A\|$ (*homogeneity*).

Proof. Properties (a) and (b) follow at once from properties (d) and (e) of Theorem 12.2. To prove (c), we use the homogeneity property of dot products to obtain

$$\|cA\| = (cA \cdot cA)^{1/2} = (c^2 A \cdot A)^{1/2} = (c^2)^{1/2}(A \cdot A)^{1/2} = |c|\,\|A\|\,.$$

The Cauchy–Schwarz inequality can also be expressed in terms of norms. It states that

$$(12.3) \qquad\qquad (A \cdot B)^2 \leq \|A\|^2\,\|B\|^2\,.$$

Taking the positive square root of each member, we can also write the Cauchy–Schwarz inequality in the equivalent form

$$(12.4) \qquad\qquad |A \cdot B| \leq \|A\|\,\|B\|\,.$$

Now we shall use the Cauchy–Schwarz inequality to deduce the triangle inequality.

THEOREM 12.5.   TRIANGLE INEQUALITY.   *If A and B are vectors in V_n, we have*

$$\|A + B\| \leq \|A\| + \|B\|\,.$$

Moreover, the equality sign holds if and only if $A = O$, or $B = O$, or $B = cA$ for some $c > 0$.

Proof. To avoid square roots, we write the triangle inequality in the equivalent form

$$(12.5) \qquad\qquad \|A + B\|^2 \leq (\|A\| + \|B\|)^2\,.$$

The left member of (12.5) is

$$\|A + B\|^2 = (A + B) \cdot (A + B) = A \cdot A + 2A \cdot B + B \cdot B = \|A\|^2 + 2A \cdot B + \|B\|^2,$$

whereas the right member is

$$(\|A\| + \|B\|)^2 = \|A\|^2 + 2\|A\|\,\|B\| + \|B\|^2\,.$$

Comparing these two formulas, we see that (12.5) holds if and only if we have

$$(12.6) \qquad\qquad A \cdot B \leq \|A\|\,\|B\|\,.$$

But $A \cdot B \leq |A \cdot B|$ so (12.6) follows from the Cauchy–Schwarz inequality, as expressed in (12.4). This proves that the triangle inequality is a consequence of the Cauchy–Schwarz inequality.

The converse statement is also true. That is, if the triangle inequality holds then (12.6) also holds for A and for $-A$, from which we obtain (12.3). If equality holds in (12.5), then $A \cdot B = \|A\|\,\|B\|$, so $B = cA$ for some scalar c. Hence $A \cdot B = c\|A\|^2$ and $\|A\|\,\|B\| = |c|\,\|A\|^2$. If $A \neq O$ this implies $c = |c| \geq 0$. If $B \neq O$ then $B = cA$ with $c > 0$.

The triangle inequality is illustrated geometrically in Figure 12.9. It states that the length of one side of a triangle does not exceed the sum of the lengths of the other two sides.

12.7 Orthogonality of vectors

In the course of the proof of the triangle inequality (Theorem 12.5), we obtained the formula

(12.7) $$\|A + B\|^2 = \|A\|^2 + \|B\|^2 + 2A \cdot B$$

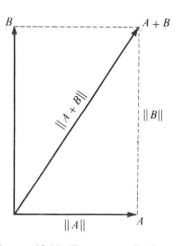

FIGURE 12.9 Geometric meaning of the triangle inequality:

$$\|A + B\| \le \|A\| + \|B\|.$$

FIGURE 12.10 Two perpendicular vectors satisfy the Pythagorean identity:

$$\|A + B\|^2 = \|A\|^2 + \|B\|^2.$$

which is valid for any two vectors A and B in V_n. Figure 12.10 shows two perpendicular geometric vectors in the plane. They determine a right triangle whose legs have lengths $\|A\|$ and $\|B\|$ and whose hypotenuse has length $\|A + B\|$. The theorem of Pythagoras states that

$$\|A + B\|^2 = \|A\|^2 + \|B\|^2.$$

Comparing this with (12.7), we see that $A \cdot B = 0$. In other words, the dot product of two perpendicular vectors in the plane is zero. This property motivates the definition of perpendicularity of vectors in V_n.

DEFINITION. *Two vectors A and B in V_n are called perpendicular or orthogonal if $A \cdot B = 0$.*

Equation (12.7) shows that two vectors A and B in V_n are orthogonal if and only if $\|A + B\|^2 = \|A\|^2 + \|B\|^2$. This is called the Pythagorean identity in V_n.

12.8   Exercises

1. Let $A = (1, 2, 3, 4)$, $B = (-1, 2, -3, 0)$, and $C = (0, 1, 0, 1)$ be three vectors in V_4. Compute each of the following dot products:
   (a) $A \cdot B$;   (b) $B \cdot C$;   (c) $A \cdot C$;   (d) $A \cdot (B + C)$;   (e) $(A - B) \cdot C$.

2. Given three vectors $A = (2, 4, -7)$, $B = (2, 6, 3)$, and $C = (3, 4, -5)$. In each of the following there is only one way to insert parentheses to obtain a meaningful expression. Insert parentheses and perform the indicated operations.
   (a) $A \cdot BC$;   (b) $A \cdot B + C$;   (c) $A + B \cdot C$;   (d) $AB \cdot C$;   (e) $A/B \cdot C$.

3. Prove or disprove the following statement about vectors in V_n: If $A \cdot B = A \cdot C$ and $A \ne O$, then $B = C$.

4. Prove or disprove the following statement about vectors in V_n: If $A \cdot B = 0$ for every B, then $A = O$.

5. If $A = (2, 1, -1)$ and $B = (1, -1, 2)$, find a nonzero vector C in V_3 such that $A \cdot C = B \cdot C = 0$.

6. If $A = (1, -2, 3)$ and $B = (3, 1, 2)$, find scalars x and y such that $C = xA + yB$ is a nonzero vector with $C \cdot B = 0$.

7. If $A = (2, -1, 2)$ and $B = (1, 2, -2)$, find two vectors C and D in V_3 satisfying all the following conditions: $A = C + D$, $B \cdot D = 0$, C parallel to B.

8. If $A = (1, 2, 3, 4, 5)$ and $B = (1, \frac{1}{2}, \frac{1}{3}, \frac{1}{4}, \frac{1}{5})$, find two vectors C and D in V_5 satisfying all the following conditions: $B = C + 2D$, $D \cdot A = 0$, C parallel to A.

9. Let $A = (2, -1, 5)$, $B = (-1, -2, 3)$, and $C = (1, -1, 1)$ be three vectors in V_3. Calculate the norm of each of the following vectors:
   (a) $A + B$;   (b) $A - B$;   (c) $A + B - C$;   (d) $A - B + C$.

10. In each case, find a vector B in V_2 such that $B \cdot A = 0$ and $\|B\| = \|A\|$ if:
    (a) $A = (1, 1)$;   (b) $A = (1, -1)$;   (c) $A = (2, -3)$;   (d) $A = (a, b)$.

11. Let $A = (1, -2, 3)$ and $B = (3, 1, 2)$ be two vectors in V_3. In each case, find a vector C of length 1 parallel to:
    (a) $A + B$;   (b) $A - B$;   (c) $A + 2B$;   (d) $A - 2B$;   (e) $2A - B$.

12. Let $A = (4, 1, -3)$, $B = (1, 2, 2)$, $C = (1, 2, -2)$, $D = (2, 1, 2)$, and $E = (2, -2, -1)$ be vectors in V_3. Determine all orthogonal pairs.

13. Find all vectors in V_2 that are orthogonal to A and have the same length as A if:
    (a) $A = (1, 2)$;   (b) $A = (1, -2)$;   (c) $A = (2, -1)$;   (d) $A = (-2, 1)$.

14. If $A = (2, -1, 1)$ and $B = (3, -4, -4)$, find a point C in 3-space such that A, B, and C are the vertices of a right triangle.

15. If $A = (1, -1, 2)$ and $B = (2, 1, -1)$, find a nonzero vector C in V_3 orthogonal to A and B.

16. Let $A = (1, 2)$ and $B = (3, 4)$ be two vectors in V_2. Find vectors P and Q in V_2 such that $A = P + Q$, P is parallel to B, and Q is orthogonal to B.

17. Solve Exercise 16 if the vectors are in V_4, with $A = (1, 2, 3, 4)$ and $B = (1, 1, 1, 1)$.

18. Given vectors $A = (2, -1, 1)$, $B = (1, 2, -1)$, and $C = (1, 1, -2)$ in V_3. Find every vector D of the form $xB + yC$ which is orthogonal to A and has length 1.

19. Prove that for two vectors A and B in V_n we have the identity

$$\|A + B\|^2 - \|A - B\|^2 = 4A \cdot B,$$

and hence $A \cdot B = 0$ if and only if $\|A + B\| = \|A - B\|$. When this is interpreted geometrically in V_2, it states that the diagonals of a parallelogram are of equal length if and only if the parallelogram is a rectangle.

20. Prove that for any two vectors A and B in V_n we have

$$\|A + B\|^2 + \|A - B\|^2 = 2\|A\|^2 + 2\|B\|^2.$$

What geometric theorem about the sides and diagonals of a parallelogram can you deduce from this identity?

21. The following theorem in geometry suggests a vector identity involving three vectors A, B, and C. Guess the identity and prove that it holds for vectors in V_n. This provides a proof of the theorem by vector methods.

"The sum of the squares of the sides of any quadrilateral exceeds the sum of the squares of the diagonals by four times the square of the length of the line segment which connects the midpoints of the diagonals."

22. A vector A in V_n has length 6. A vector B in V_n has the property that for every pair of scalars x and y the vectors $xA + yB$ and $4yA - 9xB$ are orthogonal. Compute the length of B and the length of $2A + 3B$.

23. Given two vectors $A = (1, 2, 3, 4, 5)$ and $B = (1, \frac{1}{2}, \frac{1}{3}, \frac{1}{4}, \frac{1}{5})$ in V_5. Find two vectors C and D satisfying the following three conditions: C is parallel to A, D is orthogonal to A, and $B = C + D$.

24. Given two nonperpendicular vectors A and B in V_n, prove that there exist vectors C and D in V_n satisfying the three conditions in Exercise 23 and express C and D in terms of A and B.

25. Prove or disprove each of the following statements concerning vectors in V_n:

(a) If A is orthogonal to B, then $\|A + xB\| \geq \|A\|$ for all real x.

(b) If $\|A + xB\| \geq \|A\|$ for all real x, then A is orthogonal to B.

12.9 Projections. Angle between vectors in *n*-space

The dot product of two vectors in V_2 has an interesting geometric interpretation. Figure 12.11(a) shows two nonzero geometric vectors A and B making an angle θ with each other. In this example, we have $0 < \theta < \frac{1}{2}\pi$. Figure 12.11(b) shows the same vector A and two perpendicular vectors whose sum is A. One of these, tB, is a scalar multiple of B which we call the *projection of A along B*. In this example, t is positive since $0 < \theta < \frac{1}{2}\pi$.

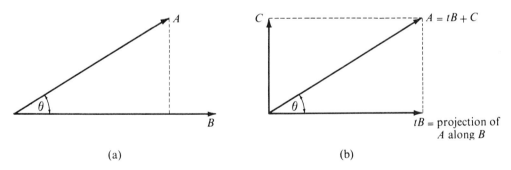

(a)   (b)

FIGURE 12.11   The vector tB is the projection of A along B.

We can use dot products to express t in terms of A and B. First we write $tB + C = A$ and then take the dot product of each member with B to obtain

$$tB \cdot B + C \cdot B = A \cdot B.$$

But $C \cdot B = 0$, because C was drawn perpendicular to B. Therefore $tB \cdot B = A \cdot B$, so we have

(12.8)
$$t = \frac{A \cdot B}{B \cdot B} = \frac{A \cdot B}{\|B\|^2}.$$

On the other hand, the scalar *t* bears a simple relation to the angle θ. From Figure 12.11(b), we see that

$$\cos \theta = \frac{\|tB\|}{\|A\|} = \frac{t \|B\|}{\|A\|}.$$

Using (12.8) in this formula, we find that

(12.9)
$$\cos \theta = \frac{A \cdot B}{\|A\| \|B\|}$$

or

$$A \cdot B = \|A\| \|B\| \cos \theta.$$

In other words, the dot product of two nonzero vectors *A* and *B* in V_2 is equal to the product of three numbers: the length of *A*, the length of *B*, and the cosine of the angle between *A* and *B*.

Equation (12.9) suggests a way to define the concept of angle in V_n. The Cauchy–Schwarz inequality, as expressed in (12.4), shows that the quotient on the right of (12.9) has absolute value ≤ 1 for any two nonzero vectors in V_n. In other words, we have

$$-1 \leq \frac{A \cdot B}{\|A\| \|B\|} \leq 1.$$

Therefore, there is exactly one real θ in the interval $0 \leq \theta \leq \pi$ such that (12.9) holds. We define the angle between *A* and *B* to be this θ. The foregoing discussion is summarized in the following definition.

DEFINITION. *Let A and B be two vectors in* V_n, *with* $B \neq O$. *The vector tB, where*

$$t = \frac{A \cdot B}{B \cdot B},$$

is called the projection of A along B. If both A and B are nonzero, the angle θ between A and B is defined by the equation

$$\theta = \arccos \frac{A \cdot B}{\|A\| \|B\|}.$$

Note: The arc cosine function restricts θ to the interval $0 \leq \theta \leq \pi$. Note also that $\theta = \frac{1}{2}\pi$ when $A \cdot B = 0$.

12.10 The unit coordinate vectors

In Chapter 9 we learned that every complex number (a, b) can be expressed in the form $a + bi$, where *i* denotes the complex number $(0, 1)$. Similarly, every vector (a, b) in V_2 can be expressed in the form

$$(a, b) = a(1, 0) + b(0, 1).$$

The two vectors $(1, 0)$ and $(0, 1)$ which multiply the components a and b are called *unit coordinate vectors*. We now introduce the corresponding concept in V_n.

DEFINITION. *In V_n, the n vectors $E_1 = (1, 0, \ldots, 0)$, $E_2 = (0, 1, 0, \ldots, 0), \ldots, E_n = (0, 0, \ldots, 0, 1)$ are called the unit coordinate vectors. It is understood that the kth component of E_k is 1 and all other components are 0.*

The name "unit vector" comes from the fact that each vector E_k has length 1. Note that these vectors are mutually orthogonal, that is, the dot product of any two distinct vectors is zero,

$$E_k \cdot E_j = 0 \qquad \text{if} \quad k \neq j.$$

THEOREM 12.6. *Every vector $X = (x_1, \ldots, x_n)$ in V_n can be expressed in the form*

$$X = x_1 E_1 + \cdots + x_n E_n = \sum_{k=1}^{n} x_k E_k.$$

Moreover, this representation is unique. That is, if

$$X = \sum_{k=1}^{n} x_k E_k \qquad and \qquad X = \sum_{k=1}^{n} y_k E_k,$$

then $x_k = y_k$ for each $k = 1, 2, \ldots, n$.

Proof. The first statement follows immediately from the definition of addition and multiplication by scalars. The uniqueness property follows from the definition of vector equality.

A sum of the type $\sum c_i A_i$ is called a *linear combination* of the vectors $A_1, \ldots, A_n$. Theorem 12.6 tells us that every vector in V_n can be expressed as a linear combination of the unit coordinate vectors. We describe this by saying that the unit coordinate vectors $E_1, \ldots, E_n$ *span* the space V_n. We also say they span V_n *uniquely* because each representation of a vector as a linear combination of $E_1, \ldots, E_n$ is unique. Some collections of vectors other than $E_1, \ldots, E_n$ also span V_n uniquely, and in Section 12.12 we turn to the study of such collections.

In V_2 the unit coordinate vectors E_1 and E_2 are often denoted, respectively, by the symbols $\boldsymbol{i}$ and $\boldsymbol{j}$ in bold-face italic type. In V_3 the symbols $\boldsymbol{i}, \boldsymbol{j}$, and $\boldsymbol{k}$ are also used in place of E_1, E_2, E_3. Sometimes a bar or arrow is placed over the symbol, for example, $\bar{i}$ or $\vec{i}$. The geometric meaning of Theorem 12.6 is illustrated in Figure 12.12 for $n = 3$.

When vectors are expressed as linear combinations of the unit coordinate vectors, algebraic manipulations involving vectors can be performed by treating the sums $\sum x_k E_k$ according to the usual rules of algebra. The various components can be recognized at any stage in the calculation by collecting the coefficients of the unit coordinate vectors. For example, to add two vectors, say $A = (a_1, \ldots, a_n)$ and $B = (b_1, \ldots, b_n)$, we write

$$A = \sum_{k=1}^{n} a_k E_k, \qquad B = \sum_{k=1}^{n} b_k E_k,$$

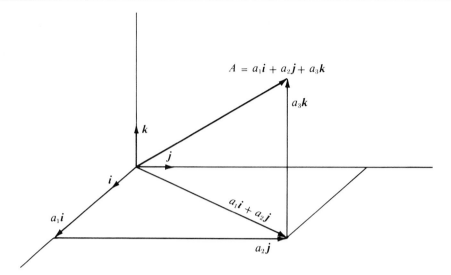

FIGURE 12.12   A vector A in V_3 expressed as a linear combination of $\boldsymbol{i}, \boldsymbol{j}, \boldsymbol{k}$.

and apply the linearity property of finite sums to obtain

$$A + B = \sum_{k=1}^{n} a_k E_k + \sum_{k=1}^{n} b_k E_k = \sum_{k=1}^{n} (a_k + b_k)E_k .$$

The coefficient of E_k on the right is the kth component of the sum $A + B$.

12.11   Exercises

1. Determine the projection of A along B if $A = (1, 2, 3)$ and $B = (1, 2, 2)$.
2. Determine the projection of A along B if $A = (4, 3, 2, 1)$ and $B = (1, 1, 1, 1)$.
3. (a) Let $A = (6, 3, -2)$, and let a, b, c denote the angles between A and the unit coordinate vectors $\boldsymbol{i}, \boldsymbol{j}, \boldsymbol{k}$, respectively. Compute $\cos a$, $\cos b$, and $\cos c$. These are called the direction cosines of A.
   (b) Find all vectors in V_3 of length 1 parallel to A.
4. Prove that the angle between the two vectors $A = (1, 2, 1)$ and $B = (2, 1, -1)$ is twice that between $C = (1, 4, 1)$ and $D = (2, 5, 5)$.
5. Use vector methods to determine the cosines of the angles of the triangle in 3-space whose vertices are at the points $(2, -1, 1)$, $(1, -3, -5)$, and $(3, -4, -4)$.
6. Three vectors A, B, C in V_3 satisfy all the following properties:

$$\|A\| = \|C\| = 5, \qquad \|B\| = 1, \qquad \|A - B + C\| = \|A + B + C\|.$$

   If the angle between A and B is $\pi/8$, find the angle between B and C.
7. Given three nonzero vectors A, B, C in V_n. Assume that the angle between A and C is equal to the angle between B and C. Prove that C is orthogonal to the vector $\|B\| A - \|A\| B$.
8. Let θ denote the angle between the following two vectors in V_n: $A = (1, 1, \ldots, 1)$ and $B = (1, 2, \ldots, n)$. Find the limiting value of θ as $n \to \infty$.
9. Solve Exercise 8 if $A = (2, 4, 6, \ldots, 2n)$ and $B = (1, 3, 5, \ldots, 2n - 1)$.

10. Given vectors $A = (\cos\theta, -\sin\theta)$ and $B = (\sin\theta, \cos\theta)$ in V_2.
    (a) Prove that A and B are orthogonal vectors of length 1. Make a sketch showing A and B when $\theta = \pi/6$.
    (b) Find all vectors (x, y) in V_2 such that $(x, y) = xA + yB$. Be sure to consider all possible values of θ.

11. Use vector methods to prove that the diagonals of a rhombus are perpendicular.

12. By forming the dot product of the two vectors $(\cos a, \sin a)$ and $(\cos b, \sin b)$, deduce the trigonometric identity $\cos(a - b) = \cos a \cos b + \sin a \sin b$.

13. If θ is the angle between two nonzero vectors A and B in V_n, prove that

$$\|A - B\|^2 = \|A\|^2 + \|B\|^2 - 2\|A\|\,\|B\|\cos\theta.$$

When interpreted geometrically in V_2, this is the law of cosines of trigonometry.

14. Suppose that instead of defining the dot product of two vectors $A = (a_1, \ldots, a_n)$ and $B = (b_1, \ldots, b_n)$ by the formula $A \cdot B = \sum_{k=1}^{n} a_k b_k$, we used the following definition:

$$A \cdot B = \sum_{k=1}^{n} |a_k b_k|.$$

Which of the properties of Theorem 12.2 are valid with this definition? Is the Cauchy–Schwarz inequality valid with this definition?

15. Suppose that in V_2 we define the dot product of two vectors $A = (a_1, a_2)$ and $B = (b_1, b_2)$ by the formula

$$A \cdot B = 2a_1 b_1 + a_2 b_2 + a_1 b_2 + a_2 b_1.$$

Prove that all the properties of Theorem 12.2 are valid with this definition of dot product. Is the Cauchy–Schwarz inequality still valid?

16. Solve Exercise 15 if the dot product of two vectors $A = (a_1, a_2, a_3)$ and $B = (b_1, b_2, b_3)$ in V_3 is defined by the formula $A \cdot B = 2a_1 b_1 + a_2 b_2 + a_3 b_3 + a_1 b_3 + a_3 b_1$.

17. Suppose that instead of defining the norm of a vector $A = (a_1, \ldots, a_n)$ by the formula $(A \cdot A)^{1/2}$, we used the following definition:

$$\|A\| = \sum_{k=1}^{n} |a_k|.$$

    (a) Prove that this definition of norm satisfies all the properties in Theorems 12.4 and 12.5.
    (b) Use this definition in V_2 and describe on a figure the set of all points (x, y) of norm 1.
    (c) Which of the properties of Theorems 12.4 and 12.5 would hold if we used the definition

$$\|A\| = \left|\sum_{k=1}^{n} a_k\right|?$$

18. Suppose that the norm of a vector $A = (a_1, \ldots, a_n)$ were defined by the formula

$$\|A\| = \max_{1 \le k \le n} |a_k|,$$

where the symbol on the right means the maximum of the n numbers $|a_1|, |a_2|, \ldots, |a_n|$.
    (a) Which of the properties of Theorems 12.4 and 12.5 are valid with this definition?
    (b) Use this definition of norm in V_2 and describe on a figure the set of all points (x, y) of norm 1.

19. If $A = (a_1, \ldots, a_n)$ is a vector in V_n, define two norms as follows:

$$\|A\|_1 = \sum_{k=1}^{n} |a_k| \qquad \text{and} \qquad \|A\|_2 = \max_{1 \le k \le n} |a_k|.$$

Prove that $\|A\|_2 \le \|A\| \le \|A\|_1$. Interpret this inequality geometrically in the plane.

20. If A and B are two points in n-space, the distance from A to B is denoted by $d(A, B)$ and is defined by the equation $d(A, B) = \|A - B\|$. Prove that distance has the following properties:
   (a) $d(A, B) = d(B, A)$.   (b) $d(A, B) = 0$ if and only if $A = B$.
   (c) $d(A, B) \le d(A, C) + d(C, B)$.

12.12   The linear span of a finite set of vectors

Let $S = \{A_1, \ldots, A_k\}$ be a nonempty set consisting of k vectors in V_n, where k, the number of vectors, may be less than, equal to, or greater than n, the dimension of the space. If a vector X in V_n can be represented as a linear combination of $A_1, \ldots, A_k$, say

$$X = \sum_{i=1}^{k} c_i A_i,$$

then the set S is said to *span* the vector X.

DEFINITION.   *The set of all vectors spanned by S is called the linear span of S and is denoted by* $L(S)$.

In other words, the linear span of S is simply the set of all possible linear combinations of vectors in S. Note that linear combinations of vectors in $L(S)$ are again in $L(S)$. We say that S *spans the whole space* V_n if $L(S) = V_n$.

EXAMPLE 1. Let $S = \{A_1\}$. Then $L(S)$ consists of all scalar multiples of A_1.

EXAMPLE 2. Every set $S = \{A_1, \ldots, A_k\}$ spans the zero vector since $O = 0A_1 + \cdots + 0A_k$. This representation, in which all the coefficients $c_1, \ldots, c_k$ are zero, is called the *trivial representation* of the zero vector. However, there may be nontrivial linear combinations that represent O. For example, suppose one of the vectors in S is a scalar multiple of another, say $A_2 = 2A_1$. Then we have many nontrivial representations of O, for example

$$O = 2tA_1 - tA_2 + 0A_3 + \cdots + 0A_k,$$

where t is any nonzero scalar.

We are especially interested in sets S that span vectors in exactly one way.

DEFINITION.   *A set* $S = \{A_1, \ldots, A_k\}$ *of vectors in* V_n *is said to span X uniquely if S spans X and if*

$$(12.10) \qquad X = \sum_{i=1}^{k} c_i A_i \qquad and \qquad X = \sum_{i=1}^{k} d_i A_i \qquad implies \quad c_i = d_i \quad for\ all\ i.$$

In the two sums appearing in (12.10), it is understood that the vectors $A_1, \ldots, A_k$ are written in the same order. It is also understood that the implication (12.10) is to hold for a fixed but arbitrary ordering of the vectors $A_1, \ldots, A_k$.

THEOREM 12.7. *A set S spans every vector in L(S) uniquely if and only if S spans the zero vector uniquely.*

Proof. If S spans every vector in $L(S)$ uniquely, then it certainly spans O uniquely. To prove the converse, assume S spans O uniquely and choose any vector X in $L(S)$. Suppose S spans X in two ways, say

$$X = \sum_{i=1}^{k} c_i A_i \qquad \text{and} \qquad X = \sum_{i=1}^{k} d_i A_i .$$

By subtraction, we find that $O = \sum_{i=1}^{k} (c_i - d_i) A_i$. But since S spans O uniquely, we must have $c_i - d_i = 0$ for all i, so S spans X uniquely.

12.13 Linear independence

Theorem 12.7 demonstrates the importance of sets that span the zero vector uniquely. Such sets are distinguished with a special name.

DEFINITION. *A set $S = \{A_1, \ldots, A_k\}$ which spans the zero vector uniquely is said to be a linearly independent set of vectors. Otherwise, S is called linearly dependent.*

In other words, *independence* means that S spans O with only the trivial representation:

$$\sum_{i=1}^{k} c_i A_i = O \qquad \text{implies all } c_i = 0 .$$

Dependence means that S spans O in some nontrivial way. That is, for some choice of scalars $c_1, \ldots, c_k$, we have

$$\sum_{i=1}^{k} c_i A_i = O \qquad \text{but not all } c_i \text{ are zero} .$$

Although dependence and independence are properties of *sets* of vectors, it is common practice to also apply these terms to the vectors themselves. For example, the vectors in a linearly independent set are often called linearly independent vectors. We also agree to call the empty set linearly independent.

The following examples may serve to give further insight into the meaning of dependence and independence.

EXAMPLE 1. If a subset T of a set S is dependent, then S itself is dependent, because if T spans O nontrivially, then so does S. This is logically equivalent to the statement that every subset of an independent set is independent.

EXAMPLE 2. The n unit coordinate vectors $E_1, \ldots, E_n$ in V_n span O uniquely so they are linearly independent.

EXAMPLE 3. Any set containing the zero vector is dependent. For example, if $A_1 = O$, we have the nontrivial representation $O = 1A_1 + 0A_2 + \cdots + 0A_k$.

EXAMPLE 4. The set $S = \{i, j, i + j\}$ of vectors in V_2 is linearly dependent because we have the nontrivial representation of the zero vector

$$O = i + j + (-1)(i + j).$$

In this example the subset $T = \{i, j\}$ is linearly independent. The third vector, $i + j$, is in the linear span of T. The next theorem shows that if we adjoin to i and j any vector in the linear span of T, we get a dependent set.

THEOREM 12.8.   *Let* $S = \{A_1, \ldots, A_k\}$ *be a linearly independent set of* k *vectors in* V_n, *and let* $L(S)$ *be the linear span of* S. *Then, every set of* $k + 1$ *vectors in* $L(S)$ *is linearly dependent.*

Proof.   The proof is by induction on k, the number of vectors in S. First suppose $k = 1$. Then, by hypothesis, S consists of one vector, say A_1, where $A_1 \neq O$ since S is independent. Now take any two distinct vectors B_1 and B_2 in $L(S)$. Then each is a scalar multiple of A_1, say $B_1 = c_1 A_1$ and $B_2 = c_2 A_1$, where c_1 and c_2 are not both zero. Multiplying B_1 by c_2 and B_2 by c_1 and subtracting, we find that

$$c_2 B_1 - c_1 B_2 = O.$$

This is a nontrivial representation of O so B_1 and B_2 are dependent. This proves the theorem when $k = 1$.

Now we assume that the theorem is true for $k - 1$ and prove that it is also true for k. Take any set of $k + 1$ vectors in $L(S)$, say $T = \{B_1, B_2, \ldots, B_{k+1}\}$. We wish to prove that T is linearly dependent. Since each B_i is in $L(S)$, we may write

(12.11) $$B_i = \sum_{j=1}^{k} a_{ij} A_j$$

for each $i = 1, 2, \ldots, k + 1$. We examine all the scalars a_{i1} that multiply A_1 and split the proof into two cases according to whether all these scalars are 0 or not.

CASE 1. $a_{i1} = 0$ *for every* $i = 1, 2, \ldots, k + 1$. In this case the sum in (12.11) does not involve A_1 so each B_i in T is in the linear span of the set $S' = \{A_2, \ldots, A_k\}$. But S' is linearly independent and consists of $k - 1$ vectors. By the induction hypothesis, the theorem is true for $k - 1$ so the set T is dependent. This proves the theorem in Case 1.

CASE 2. Not all the scalars a_{i1} *are zero.* Let us assume that $a_{11} \neq 0$. (If necessary, we can renumber the B's to achieve this.) Taking $i = 1$ in Equation (12.11) and multiplying both members by c_i , where $c_i = a_{i1}/a_{11}$, we get

$$c_i B_1 = a_{i1} A_1 + \sum_{j=2}^{k} c_i a_{1j} A_j .$$

From this we subtract Equation (12.11) to get

$$c_i B_1 - B_i = \sum_{j=2}^{k} (c_i a_{1j} - a_{ij}) A_j ,$$

for $i = 2, \ldots, k + 1$. This equation expresses each of the k vectors $c_i B_1 - B_i$ as a linear combination of $k - 1$ linearly independent vectors $A_2, \ldots, A_k$. By the induction hypothesis, the k vectors $c_i B_1 - B_i$ must be dependent. Hence, for some choice of scalars $t_2, \ldots, t_{k+1}$, not all zero, we have

$$\sum_{i=2}^{k+1} t_i (c_i B_1 - B_i) = O ,$$

from which we find

$$\left(\sum_{i=2}^{k+1} t_i c_i \right) B_1 - \sum_{i=2}^{k+1} t_i B_i = O .$$

But this is a nontrivial linear combination of $B_1, \ldots, B_{k+1}$ which represents the zero vector, so the vectors $B_1, \ldots, B_{k+1}$ must be dependent. This completes the proof.

We show next that the concept of orthogonality is intimately related to linear independence.

DEFINITION. *A set $S = \{A_1, \ldots, A_k\}$ of vectors in V_n is called an orthogonal set if $A_i \cdot A_j = 0$ whenever $i \neq j$. In other words, any two distinct vectors in an orthogonal set are perpendicular.*

THEOREM 12.9. *Any orthogonal set $S = \{A_1, \ldots, A_k\}$ of nonzero vectors in V_n is linearly independent. Moreover, if S spans a vector X, say*

$$(12.12) \qquad X = \sum_{i=1}^{k} c_i A_i ,$$

then the scalar multipliers $c_1, \ldots, c_k$ are given by the formulas

$$(12.13) \qquad c_j = \frac{X \cdot A_j}{A_j \cdot A_j} \quad for \quad j = 1, 2, \ldots, k .$$

Proof. First we prove that S is linearly independent. Assume that $\sum_{i=1}^{k} c_i A_i = O$. Taking the dot product of each member with A_1 and using the fact that $A_1 \cdot A_i = 0$ for each $i \neq 1$, we find $c_1(A_1 \cdot A_1) = 0$. But $(A_1 \cdot A_1) \neq 0$ since $A_1 \neq O$, so $c_1 = 0$. Repeating this argument with A_1 replaced by A_j, we find that each $c_j = 0$. Therefore S spans O uniquely so S is linearly independent.

Now suppose that S spans X as in Equation (12.12). Taking the dot product of X with A_j as above, we find that $c_j(A_j \cdot A_j) = X \cdot A_j$ from which we obtain (12.13).

If all the vectors $A_1, \ldots, A_k$ in Theorem 12.9 have norm 1, the formula for the multipliers simplifies to

$$c_j = X \cdot A_j.$$

An orthogonal set of vectors $\{A_1, \ldots, A_k\}$, each of which has norm 1, is called an *orthonormal* set. The unit coordinate vectors $E_1, \ldots, E_n$ are an example of an orthonormal set.

12.14 Bases

It is natural to study sets of vectors that span every vector in V_n uniquely. Such sets are called *bases* for V_n.

DEFINITION. *A set $S = \{A_1, \ldots, A_k\}$ of vectors in V_n is called a basis for V_n if S spans every vector in V_n uniquely. If, in addition, S is orthogonal, then S is called an orthogonal basis.*

Thus, a basis is a linearly independent set which spans the whole space V_n. The set of unit coordinate vectors is an example of a basis. This particular basis is also an orthogonal basis. Now we prove that every basis contains the same number of elements.

THEOREM 12.10. *In a given vector space V_n, bases have the following properties:*
(a) *Every basis contains exactly n vectors.*
(b) *Any set of linearly independent vectors is a subset of some basis.*
(c) *Any set of n linearly independent vectors is a basis.*

Proof. The unit coordinate vectors $E_1, \ldots, E_n$ form one basis for V_n. If we prove that any two bases contain the same number of vectors we obtain (a).

Let S and T be two bases, where S has k vectors and T has r vectors. If $r > k$, then T contains at least $k + 1$ vectors in $L(S)$, since $L(S) = V_n$. Therefore, because of Theorem 12.8, T must be linearly dependent, contradicting the assumption that T is a basis. This means we cannot have $r > k$, so we must have $r \le k$. Applying the same argument with S and T interchanged, we find that $k \le r$. Hence, $k = r$ so part (a) is proved.

To prove (b), let $S = \{A_1, \ldots, A_k\}$ be any linearly independent set of vectors in V_n. If $L(S) = V_n$, then S is a basis. If not, then there is some vector X in V_n which is not in $L(S)$. Adjoin this vector to S and consider the new set $S' = \{A_1, \ldots, A_k, X\}$. If this set were dependent, there would be scalars $c_1, \ldots, c_{k+1}$, not all zero, such that

$$\sum_{i=1}^{k} c_i A_i + c_{k+1} X = O.$$

But $c_{k+1} \ne 0$ since $A_1, \ldots, A_k$ are independent. Hence, we could solve this equation for

X and find that $X \in L(S)$, contradicting the fact that X is not in $L(S)$. Therefore, the set S' is linearly independent but contains $k + 1$ vectors. If $L(S') = V_n$, then S' is a basis and, since S is a subset of S', part (b) is proved. If S' is not a basis, we may argue with S' as we did with S, getting a new set S'' which contains $k + 2$ vectors and is linearly independent. If S'' is a basis, then part (b) is proved. If not, we repeat the process. We must arrive at a basis in a finite number of steps, otherwise we would eventually obtain an independent set with $n + 1$ vectors, contradicting Theorem 12.8. Therefore part (b) is proved.

Finally, we use (a) and (b) to prove (c). Let S be any linearly independent set consisting of n vectors. By part (b), S is a subset of some basis, say B. But by (a) the basis B has exactly n elements, so $S = B$.

12.15 Exercises

1. Let i and j denote the unit coordinate vectors in V_2. In each case find scalars x and y such that $x(i - j) + y(i + j)$ is equal to
   (a) i; (b) j; (c) $3i - 5j$; (d) $7i + 5j$.
2. If $A = (1, 2)$, $B = (2, -4)$, and $C = (2, -3)$ are three vectors in V_2, find scalars x and y such that $C = xA + yB$. How many such pairs x, y are there?
3. If $A = (2, -1, 1)$, $B = (1, 2, -1)$, and $C = (2, -11, 7)$ are three vectors in V_3, find scalars x and y such that $C = xA + yB$.
4. Prove that Exercise 3 has no solution if C is replaced by the vector $(2, 11, 7)$.
5. Let A and B be two nonzero vectors in V_n.
   (a) If A and B are parallel, prove that A and B are linearly dependent.
   (b) If A and B are not parallel, prove that A and B are linearly independent.
6. If (a, b) and (c, d) are two vectors in V_2, prove that they are linearly independent if and only if $ad - bc \neq 0$.
7. Find all real t for which the two vectors $(1 + t, 1 - t)$ and $(1 - t, 1 + t)$ in V_2 are linearly independent.
8. Let i, j, k be the unit coordinate vectors in V_3. Prove that the four vectors $i, j, k, i + j + k$ are linearly dependent, but that any three of them are linearly independent.
9. Let i and j be the unit coordinate vectors in V_2 and let $S = \{i, i + j\}$.
   (a) Prove that S is linearly independent.
   (b) Prove that j is in the linear span of S.
   (c) Express $3i - 4j$ as a linear combination of i and $i + j$.
   (d) Prove that $L(S) = V_2$.
10. Consider the three vectors $A = i$, $B = i + j$, and $C = i + j + 3k$ in V_3.
    (a) Prove that the set $\{A, B, C\}$ is linearly independent.
    (b) Express each of j and k as a linear combination of A, B, and C.
    (c) Express $2i - 3j + 5k$ as a linear combination of A, B, and C.
    (d) Prove that $\{A, B, C\}$ is a basis for V_3.
11. Let $A = (1, 2)$, $B = (2, -4)$, $C = (2, -3)$, and $D = (1, -2)$ be four vectors in V_2. Display all nonempty subsets of $\{A, B, C, D\}$ which are linearly independent.
12. Let $A = (1, 1, 1, 0)$, $B = (0, 1, 1, 1)$ and $C = (1, 1, 0, 0)$ be three vectors in V_4.
    (a) Determine whether A, B, C are linearly dependent or independent.
    (b) Exhibit a nonzero vector D such that A, B, C, D are dependent.
    (c) Exhibit a vector E such that A, B, C, E are independent.
    (d) Having chosen E in part (c), express the vector $X = (1, 2, 3, 4)$ as a linear combination of A, B, C, E.
13. (a) Prove that the following three vectors in V_3 are linearly independent: $(\sqrt{3}, 1, 0), (1, \sqrt{3}, 1),$ $(0, 1, \sqrt{3})$.

(b) Prove that the following three are dependent: $(\sqrt{2}, 1, 0), (1, \sqrt{2}, 1), (0, 1, \sqrt{2})$.

(c) Find all real t for which the following three vectors in V_3 are dependent: $(t, 1, 0), (1, t, 1)$, $(0, 1, t)$.

14. Consider the following sets of vectors in V_4. In each case, find a linearly independent subset containing as many vectors as possible.

(a) $\{(1, 0, 1, 0), \ (1, 1, 1, 1), \ (0, 1, 0, 1), \ (2, 0, -1, 0)\}$.

(b) $\{(1, 1, 1, 1), \ (1, -1, 1, 1), \ (1, -1, -1, 1), \ (1, -1, -1, -1)\}$.

(c) $\{(1, 1, 1, 1), \ (0, 1, 1, 1), \ (0, 0, 1, 1), \ (0, 0, 0, 1)\}$.

15. Given three linearly independent vectors A, B, C in V_n. Prove or disprove each of the following statements.

(a) $A + B, B + C, A + C$ are linearly independent.

(b) $A - B, B + C, A + C$ are linearly independent.

16. (a) Prove that a set S of three vectors in V_3 is a basis for V_3 if and only if its linear span $L(S)$ contains the three unit coordinate vectors $i, j,$ and k.

(b) State and prove a generalization of part (a) for V_n.

17. Find two bases for V_3 containing the two vectors $(0, 1, 1)$ and $(1, 1, 1)$.

18. Find two bases for V_4 having only the two vectors $(0, 1, 1, 1)$ and $(1, 1, 1, 1)$ in common.

19. Consider the following sets of vectors in V_3:

$$S = \{(1, 1, 1), (0, 1, 2), (1, 0, -1)\}, \qquad T = \{(2, 1, 0), (2, 0, -2)\}, \qquad U = \{(1, 2, 3), (1, 3, 5)\}.$$

(a) Prove that $L(T) \subseteq L(S)$.

(b) Determine all inclusion relations that hold among the sets $L(S), L(T),$ and $L(U)$.

20. Let A and B denote two finite subsets of vectors in a vector space V_n, and let $L(A)$ and $L(B)$ denote their linear spans. Prove each of the following statements.

(a) If $A \subseteq B$, then $L(A) \subseteq L(B)$.

(b) $L(A \cap B) \subseteq L(A) \cap L(B)$.

(c) Give an example in which $L(A \cap B) \neq L(A) \cap L(B)$.

12.16 The vector space $V_n(\mathbf{C})$ of n-tuples of complex numbers

In Section 12.2 the vector space V_n was defined to be the collection of all n-tuples of real numbers. Equality, vector addition, and multiplication by scalars were defined in terms of the components as follows: If $A = (a_1, \ldots, a_n)$ and $B = (b_1, \ldots, b_n)$, then

$$A = B \qquad \text{means} \qquad a_i = b_i \qquad \text{for each } i = 1, 2, \ldots, n,$$

$$A + B = (a_1 + b_1, \ldots, a_n + b_n), \qquad cA = (ca_1, \ldots, ca_n).$$

If all the scalars a_i, b_i and c in these relations are replaced by *complex* numbers, the new algebraic system so obtained is called *complex vector space* and is denoted by $V_n(\mathbf{C})$. Here $\mathbf{C}$ is used to remind us that the scalars are complex.

Since complex numbers satisfy the same field properties as real numbers, all theorems about real vector space V_n that use only the field properties of the real numbers are also valid for $V_n(\mathbf{C})$, provided all the scalars are allowed to be complex. In particular, those theorems in this chapter that involve only vector addition and multiplication by scalars are also valid for $V_n(\mathbf{C})$.

This extension is not made simply for the sake of generalization. Complex vector spaces arise naturally in the theory of linear differential equations and in modern quantum mechanics, so their study is of considerable importance. Fortunately, many of the theorems about real vector space V_n carry over without change to $V_n(\mathbf{C})$. Some small changes have to be made, however, in those theorems that involve dot products. In proving that the dot product $A \cdot A$ of a nonzero vector with itself is positive, we used the fact that a sum of squares of real numbers is positive. Since a sum of squares of complex numbers can be negative, we must modify the definition of $A \cdot B$ if we wish to retain the positivity property. For $V_n(\mathbf{C})$, we use the following definition of dot product.

DEFINITION. *If $A = (a_1, \ldots, a_n)$ and $B = (b_1, \ldots, b_n)$ are two vectors in $V_n(\mathbf{C})$, we define their dot product $A \cdot B$ by the formula*

$$A \cdot B = \sum_{k=1}^{n} a_k \bar{b}_k \, ,$$

where $\bar{b}_k$ is the complex conjugate of b_k .

Note that this definition agrees with the one given earlier for V_n because $\bar{b}_k = b_k$ when b_k is real. The fundamental properties of the dot product, corresponding to those in Theorem 12.2, now take the following form.

THEOREM 12.11. *For all vectors A, B, C in $V_n(\mathbf{C})$ and all complex scalars c, we have*
  (a) $A \cdot B = \overline{B \cdot A}$,
  (b) $A \cdot (B + C) = A \cdot B + A \cdot C$,
  (c) $c(A \cdot B) = (cA) \cdot B = A \cdot (\bar{c}B)$,
  (d) $A \cdot A > 0$ *if* $A \neq O$,
  (e) $A \cdot A = 0$ *if* $A = O$.

All these properties are easy consequences of the definition and their proofs are left as exercises. The reader should note that conjugation takes place in property (a) when the order of the factors is reversed. Also, conjugation of the scalar multiplier occurs in property (c) when the scalar c is moved from one side of the dot to the other.

The Cauchy–Schwarz inequality now takes the form

(12.14) $$|A \cdot B|^2 \leq (A \cdot A)(B \cdot B) \, .$$

The proof is similar to that given for Theorem 12.3. We consider the vector $C = xA - yB$, where $x = B \cdot B$ and $y = A \cdot B$, and compute $C \cdot C$. The inequality $C \cdot C \geq 0$ leads to (12.14). Details are left as an exercise for the reader.

Since the dot product of a vector with itself is nonnegative, we can introduce the norm of a vector in $V_n(\mathbf{C})$ by the usual formula,

$$\|A\| = (A \cdot A)^{1/2} \, .$$

The fundamental properties of norms, as stated in Theorem 12.4, are also valid without change for $V_n(\mathbf{C})$. The triangle inequality, $\|A + B\| \leq \|A\| + \|B\|$, also holds in $V_n(\mathbf{C})$.

Orthogonality of vectors in $V_n(\mathbf{C})$ is defined by the relation $A \cdot B = 0$. As in the real case, two vectors A and B in $V_n(\mathbf{C})$ are orthogonal if and only if they satisfy the Pythagorean identity, $\|A + B\|^2 = \|A\|^2 + \|B\|^2$.

The concepts of linear span, linear independence, linear dependence, and basis, are defined for $V_n(\mathbf{C})$ exactly as in the real case. Theorems 12.7 through 12.10 and their proofs are all valid without change for $V_n(\mathbf{C})$.

12.17 Exercises

1. Let $A = (1, i)$, $B = (i, -i)$, and $C = (2i, 1)$ be three vectors in $V_2(\mathbf{C})$. Compute each of the following dot products:
   (a) $A \cdot B$;   (b) $B \cdot A$;   (c) $(iA) \cdot B$;   (d) $A \cdot (iB)$;   (e) $(iA) \cdot (iB)$;
   (f) $B \cdot C$;   (g) $A \cdot C$;   (h) $(B + C) \cdot A$;   (i) $(A - C) \cdot B$;
   (j) $(A - iB) \cdot (A + iB)$.

2. If $A = (2, 1, -i)$ and $B = (i, -1, 2i)$, find a nonzero vector C in $V_3(\mathbf{C})$ orthogonal to both A and B.

3. Prove that for any two vectors A and B in $V_n(\mathbf{C})$, we have the identity

$$\|A + B\|^2 = \|A\|^2 + \|B\|^2 + A \cdot B + \overline{A \cdot B} \,.$$

4. Prove that for any two vectors A and B in $V_n(\mathbf{C})$, we have the identity

$$\|A + B\|^2 - \|A - B\|^2 = 2(A \cdot B + \overline{A \cdot B}) \,.$$

5. Prove that for any two vectors A and B in $V_n(\mathbf{C})$, we have the identity

$$\|A + B\|^2 + \|A - B\|^2 = 2 \|A\|^2 + 2 \|B\|^2 \,.$$

6. (a) Prove that for any two vectors A and B in $V_n(\mathbf{C})$, the sum $\overline{A \cdot B} + A \cdot B$ is real.
   (b) If A and B are nonzero vectors in $V_n(\mathbf{C})$, prove that

$$-2 \leq \frac{A \cdot B + \overline{A \cdot B}}{\|A\| \, \|B\|} \leq 2 \,.$$

7. We define the angle θ between two nonzero vectors A and B in $V_n(\mathbf{C})$ by the equation

$$\theta = \arccos \frac{\tfrac{1}{2}(A \cdot B + \overline{A \cdot B})}{\|A\| \, \|B\|} \,.$$

The inequality in Exercise 6 shows that there is always a unique angle θ in the closed interval $0 \leq \theta \leq \pi$ satisfying this equation. Prove that we have

$$\|A - B\|^2 = \|A\|^2 + \|B\|^2 - 2 \|A\| \, \|B\| \cos \theta \,.$$

8. Use the definition in Exercise 7 to compute the angle between the following two vectors in $V_5(\mathbf{C})$: $A = (1, 0, i, i, i)$, and $B = (i, i, i, 0, i)$.

9. (a) Prove that the following three vectors form a basis for $V_3(\mathbf{C})$: $A = (1, 0, 0)$, $B = (0, i, 0)$, $C = (1, 1, i)$.
   (b) Express the vector $(5, 2 - i, 2i)$ as a linear combination of A, B, C.

10. Prove that the basis of unit coordinate vectors $E_1, \ldots, E_n$ in V_n is also a basis for $V_n(\mathbf{C})$.

13

APPLICATIONS OF VECTOR ALGEBRA
TO ANALYTIC GEOMETRY

13.1 Introduction

This chapter discusses applications of vector algebra to the study of lines, planes, and conic sections. In Chapter 14 vector algebra is combined with the methods of calculus, and further applications are given to the study of curves and to some problems in mechanics.

The study of geometry as a deductive system, as conceived by Euclid around 300 B.C., begins with a set of axioms or postulates which describe properties of points and lines. The concepts "point" and "line" are taken as primitive notions and remain undefined. Other concepts are defined in terms of points and lines, and theorems are systematically deduced from the axioms. Euclid listed ten axioms from which he attempted to deduce all his theorems. It has since been shown that these axioms are not adequate for the theory. For example, in the proof of his very first theorem Euclid made a tacit assumption concerning the intersection of two circles that is not covered by his axioms. Since then other lists of axioms have been formulated that do give all of Euclid's theorems. The most famous of these is a list given by the German mathematician David Hilbert (1862–1943) in his now classic *Grundlagen der Geometrie*, published in 1899. (An English translation exists: *The Foundations of Geometry*, Open Court Publishing Co., 1947.) This work, which went through seven German editions in Hilbert's lifetime, is said to have inaugurated the abstract mathematics of the twentieth century.

Hilbert starts his treatment of plane geometry with five undefined concepts: *point, line, on* (a relation holding between a point and a line), *between* (a relation between a point and a pair of points), and *congruence* (a relation between pairs of points). He then gives fifteen axioms from which he develops all of plane Euclidean geometry. His treatment of solid geometry is based on twenty-one axioms involving six undefined concepts.

The approach in analytic geometry is somewhat different. We define concepts such as point, line, on, between, etc., but we do so in terms of real numbers, which are left undefined. The resulting mathematical structure is called an *analytic model* of Euclidean geometry. In this model, properties of real numbers are used to deduce Hilbert's axioms. We shall not attempt to describe all of Hilbert's axioms. Instead, we shall merely indicate how the primitive concepts may be defined in terms of numbers and give a few proofs to illustrate the methods of analytic geometry.

13.2 Lines in *n*-space

In this section we use real numbers to define the concepts of *point*, *line*, and *on*. The definitions are formulated to fit our intuitive ideas about three-dimensional Euclidean geometry, but they are meaningful in *n*-space for any $n \geq 1$.

A point is simply a vector in V_n, that is, an ordered *n*-tuple of real numbers; we shall use the words "point" and "vector" interchangeably. The vector space V_n is called an analytic model of *n*-dimensional Euclidean space or simply *Euclidean n-space*. To define "line," we employ the algebraic operations of addition and multiplication by scalars in V_n.

DEFINITION. *Let P be a given point and A a given nonzero vector. The set of all points of the form P + tA, where t runs through all real numbers, is called a line through P parallel to A. We denote this line by L(P; A) and write*

$$L(P; A) = \{P + tA \mid t \ real\} \quad or, more\ briefly, \quad L(P; A) = \{P + tA\}.$$

A point Q is said to be on the line L(P; A) if Q ∈ L(P; A).

In the symbol $L(P; A)$, the point P which is written first is on the line since it corresponds to $t = 0$. The second point, A, is called a *direction vector* for the line. The line $L(O; A)$ through the origin O is the linear span of A; it consists of all scalar multiples of A. The line through P parallel to A is obtained by adding P to each vector in the linear span of A.

Figure 13.1 shows the geometric interpretation of this definition in V_3. Each point $P + tA$ can be visualized as the tip of a geometric vector drawn from the origin. As t varies over all the real numbers, the corresponding point $P + tA$ traces out a line through P parallel to the vector A. Figure 13.1 shows points corresponding to a few values of t on both lines $L(P; A)$ and $L(O; A)$.

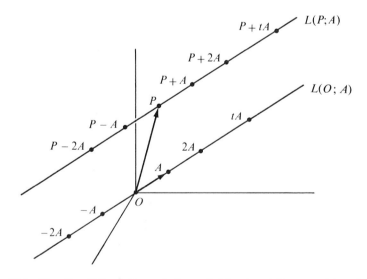

FIGURE 13.1   The line $L(P; A)$ through P parallel to A and its geometric relation to the line $L(O; A)$ through O parallel to A.

13.3 Some simple properties of straight lines

First we show that the direction vector A which occurs in the definition of $L(P; A)$ can be replaced by any vector parallel to A. (We recall that two vectors A and B are called parallel if $A = cB$ for some nonzero scalar c.)

THEOREM 13.1. *Two lines $L(P; A)$ and $L(P; B)$ through the same point P are equal if and only if the direction vectors A and B are parallel.*

Proof. Assume first that $L(P; A) = L(P; B)$. Take a point on $L(P; A)$ other than P, for example, $P + A$. This point is also on $L(P; B)$ so $P + A = P + cB$ for some scalar c. Hence, we have $A = cB$ and $c \neq 0$ since $A \neq O$. Therefore, A and B are parallel.

Now we prove the converse. Assume A and B are parallel, say $A = cB$ for some $c \neq 0$. If Q is on $L(P; A)$, then we have $Q = P + tA = P + t(cB) = P + (ct)B$, so Q is on $L(P; B)$. Therefore $L(P; A) \subseteq L(P; B)$. Similarly, $L(P; B) \subseteq L(P; A)$, so $L(P; A) = L(P; B)$.

Next we show that the point P which occurs in the definition of $L(P; A)$ can be replaced by any other point Q on the same line.

THEOREM 13.2. *Two lines $L(P; A)$ and $L(Q; A)$ with the same direction vector A are equal if and only if Q is on $L(P; A)$.*

Proof. Assume $L(P; A) = L(Q; A)$. Since Q is on $L(Q; A)$, Q is also on $L(P; A)$. To prove the converse, assume that Q is on $L(P; A)$, say $Q = P + cA$. We wish to prove that $L(P; A) = L(Q; A)$. If $X \in L(P; A)$, then $X = P + tA$ for some t. But $P = Q - cA$, so $X = Q - cA + tA = Q + (t - c)A$, and hence X is also on $L(Q; A)$. Therefore $L(P; A) \subseteq L(Q; A)$. Similarly, we find $L(Q; A) \subseteq L(P; A)$, so the two lines are equal.

One of Euclid's famous postulates is the *parallel postulate* which is logically equivalent to the statement that "through a given point there exists one and only one line parallel to a given line." We shall deduce this property as an easy consequence of Theorem 13.1. First we need to define parallelism of lines.

DEFINITION. *Two lines $L(P; A)$ and $L(Q; B)$ are called parallel if their direction vectors A and B are parallel.*

THEOREM 13.3. *Given a line L and a point Q not on L, then there is one and only one line L' containing Q and parallel to L.*

Proof. Suppose the given line has direction vector A. Consider the line $L' = L(Q; A)$. This line contains Q and is parallel to L. Theorem 13.1 tells us that this is the only line with these two properties.

Note: For a long time mathematicians suspected that the parallel postulate could be deduced from the other Euclidean postulates, but all attempts to prove this resulted in failure. Then in the early 19th century the mathematicians Karl F. Gauss (1777–1855),

J. Bolyai (1802–1860), and N. I. Lobatchevski (1793–1856) became convinced that the parallel postulate could not be derived from the others and proceeded to develop non-Euclidean geometries, that is to say, geometries in which the parallel postulate does not hold. The work of these men inspired other mathematicians and scientists to enlarge their points of view about "accepted truths" and to challenge other axioms that had been considered sacred for centuries.

It is also easy to deduce the following property of lines which Euclid stated as an axiom.

THEOREM 13.4. *Two distinct points determine a line. That is, if $P \neq Q$, there is one and only one line containing both P and Q. It can be described as the set $\{P + t(Q - P)\}$.*

Proof. Let L be the line through P parallel to $Q - P$, that is, let

$$L = L(P; Q - P) = \{P + t(Q - P)\}.$$

This line contains both P and Q (take $t = 0$ to get P and $t = 1$ to get Q). Now let L' be any line containing both P and Q. We shall prove that $L' = L$. Since L' contains P, we have $L' = L(P; A)$ for some $A \neq O$. But L' also contains Q so $P + cA = Q$ for some c. Hence we have $Q - P = cA$, where $c \neq 0$ since $Q \neq P$. Therefore $Q - P$ is parallel to A so, by Theorem 13.2, we have $L' = L(P; A) = L(P; Q - P) = L$.

EXAMPLE. Theorem 13.4 gives us an easy way to test if a point Q is on a given line $L(P; A)$. It tells us that Q is on $L(P; A)$ if and only if $Q - P$ is parallel to A. For example, consider the line $L(P; A)$, where $P = (1, 2, 3)$ and $A = (2, -1, 5)$. To test if the point $Q = (1, 1, 4)$ is on this line, we examine $Q - P = (0, -1, 1)$. Since $Q - P$ is not a scalar multiple of A, the point $(1, 1, 4)$ is not on this line. On the other hand, if $Q = (5, 0, 13)$, we find that $Q - P = (4, -2, 10) = 2A$, so this Q is on the line.

Linear dependence of two vectors in V_n can be expressed in geometric language.

THEOREM 13.5. *Two vectors A and B in V_n are linearly dependent if and only if they lie on the same line through the origin.*

Proof. If either A or B is zero, the result holds trivially. If both are nonzero, then A and B are dependent if and only if $B = tA$ for some scalar t. But $B = tA$ if and only if B lies on the line through the origin parallel to A.

13.4 Lines and vector-valued functions

The concept of a line can be related to the function concept. The correspondence which associates to each real t the vector $P + tA$ on the line $L(P; A)$ is an example of a function whose domain is the set of real numbers and whose range is the line $L(P; A)$. If we denote the function by the symbol X, then the function value $X(t)$ at t is given by the equation

(13.1) $$X(t) = P + tA.$$

We call this a vector-valued function of a real variable.

The function point of view is important because, as we shall see in Chapter 14, it provides a natural method for describing more general space curves as well.

The scalar t in Equation (13.1) is often called a *parameter*, and Equation (13.1) is called a *vector parametric equation* or, simply a *vector equation* of the line. Occasionally it is convenient to think of the line as the track of a moving particle, in which case the parameter t is referred to as *time* and the vector $X(t)$ is called the *position vector*.

Note that two points $X(a)$ and $X(b)$ on a given line $L(P; A)$ are equal if and only if we have $P + aA = P + bA$, or $(a - b)A = O$. Since $A \neq O$, this last relation holds if and only if $a = b$. Thus, distinct values of the parameter t lead to distinct points on the line.

Now consider three distinct points on a given line, say $X(a)$, $X(b)$, and $X(c)$, where $a > b$. We say that $X(c)$ is *between* $X(a)$ and $X(b)$ if c is between a and b, that is, if $a < c < b$.

Congruence can be defined in terms of norms. A pair of points P, Q is called *congruent* to another pair P', Q' if $\|P - Q\| = \|P' - Q'\|$. The norm $\|P - Q\|$ is also called the distance between P and Q.

This completes the definitions of the concepts of *point*, *line*, *on*, *between*, and *congruence* in our analytic model of Euclidean n-space. We conclude this section with some further remarks concerning parametric equations for lines in 3-space.

If a line passes through two distinct points P and Q, we can use $Q - P$ for the direction vector A in Equation (13.1); the vector equation of the line then becomes

$$X(t) = P + t(Q - P) \qquad \text{or} \qquad X(t) = tQ + (1 - t)P.$$

Vector equations can also be expressed in terms of components. For example, if we write $P = (p, q, r)$, $A = (a, b, c)$, and $X(t) = (x, y, z)$, Equation (13.1) is equivalent to the three scalar equations

(13.2) $$x = p + ta, \qquad y = q + tb, \qquad z = r + tc.$$

These are called *scalar parametric equations* or simply *parametric equations* for the line; they are useful in computations involving components. The vector equation is simpler and more natural for studying general properties of lines.

If all the vectors are in 2-space, only the first two parametric equations in (13.2) are needed. In this case, we can eliminate t from the two parametric equations to obtain the relation

(13.3) $$b(x - p) - a(y - q) = 0,$$

which is called a *Cartesian equation* for the line. If $a \neq 0$, this can be written in the *point-slope form*

$$y - q = \frac{b}{a}(x - p).$$

The point (p, q) is on the line; the number b/a is the slope of the line.

The Cartesian equation (13.3) can also be written in terms of dot products. If we let $N = (b, -a)$, $X = (x, y)$, and $P = (p, q)$, Equation (13.3) becomes

$$(X - P) \cdot N = 0 \qquad \text{or} \qquad X \cdot N = P \cdot N.$$

The vector N is perpendicular to the direction vector A since $N \cdot A = ba - ab = 0$; the vector N is called a *normal vector* to the line. The line consists of all points X satisfying the relation $(X - P) \cdot N = 0$.

The geometric meaning of this relation is shown in Figure 13.2. The points P and X are on the line and the normal vector N is orthogonal to $X - P$. The figure suggests that among all points X on the line, the smallest length $\|X\|$ occurs when X is the projection of P along N. We now give an algebraic proof of this fact.

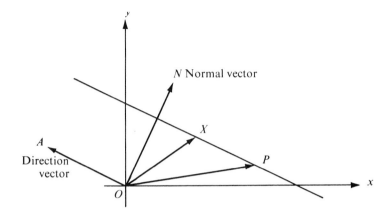

FIGURE 13.2   A line in the xy-plane through P with normal vector N. Each point X on the line satisfies $(X - P) \cdot N = 0$.

THEOREM 13.6.   *Let L be the line in V_2 consisting of all points X satisfying*

$$X \cdot N = P \cdot N,$$

where P is on the line and N is a nonzero vector normal to the line. Let

$$d = \frac{|P \cdot N|}{\|N\|}.$$

Then every X on L has length $\|X\| \geq d$. Moreover, $\|X\| = d$ if and only if X is the projection of P along N:

$$X = tN, \qquad where \quad t = \frac{P \cdot N}{N \cdot N}.$$

Proof. If $X \in L$, we have $X \cdot N = P \cdot N$. By the Cauchy–Schwarz inequality, we have

$$|P \cdot N| = |X \cdot N| \leq \|X\| \, \|N\|,$$

which implies $\|X\| \geq |P \cdot N|/\|N\| = d$. The equality sign holds if and only if $X = tN$ for some scalar t, in which case $P \cdot N = X \cdot N = tN \cdot N$, so $t = P \cdot N/N \cdot N$. This completes the proof.

In the same way we can prove that if Q is a given point in V_2 not on the line L, then for all X on L the smallest value of $\|X - Q\|$ is $|(P - Q) \cdot N|/\|N\|$, and this occurs when $X - Q$ is the projection of $P - Q$ along the normal vector N. The number

$$\frac{|(P - Q) \cdot N|}{\|N\|}$$

is called the *distance from the point Q to the line L*. The reader should illustrate these concepts on a figure similar to that in Figure 13.2.

13.5 Exercises

1. A line L in V_2 contains the two points $P = (-3, 1)$ and $Q = (1, 1)$. Determine which of the following points are on L. (a) $(0, 0)$; (b) $(0, 1)$; (c) $(1, 2)$; (d) $(2, 1)$; (e) $(-2, 1)$.

2. Solve Exercise 1 if $P = (2, -1)$ and $Q = (-4, 2)$.

3. A line L in V_3 contains the point $P = (-3, 1, 1)$ and is parallel to the vector $(1, -2, 3)$. Determine which of the following points are on L. (a) $(0, 0, 0)$; (b) $(2, -1, 4)$; (c) $(-2, -1, 4)$; (d) $(-4, 3, -2)$; (e) $(2, -9, 16)$.

4. A line L contains the two points $P = (-3, 1, 1)$ and $Q = (1, 2, 7)$. Determine which of the following points are on L. (a) $(-7, 0, 5)$; (b) $(-7, 0, -5)$; (c) $(-11, 1, 11)$; (d) $(-11, -1, 11)$; (e) $(-1, \frac{3}{2}, 4)$; (f) $(-\frac{5}{3}, \frac{4}{3}, 3)$; (g) $(-1, \frac{3}{2}, -4)$.

5. In each case, determine if all three points P, Q, R lie on a line.
   (a) $P = (2, 1, 1)$, $Q = (4, 1, -1)$, $R = (3, -1, 1)$.
   (b) $P = (2, 2, 3)$, $Q = (-2, 3, 1)$, $R = (-6, 4, 1)$.
   (c) $P = (2, 1, 1)$, $Q = (-2, 3, 1)$, $R = (5, -1, 1)$.

6. Among the following eight points, the three points A, B, and C lie on a line. Determine all subsets of three or more points which lie on a line: $A = (2, 1, 1)$, $B = (6, -1, 1)$, $C = (-6, 5, 1)$, $D = (-2, 3, 1)$, $E = (1, 1, 1)$, $F = (-4, 4, 1)$, $G = (-13, 9, 1)$, $H = (14, -6, 1)$.

7. A line through the point $P = (1, 1, 1)$ is parallel to the vector $A = (1, 2, 3)$. Another line through $Q = (2, 1, 0)$ is parallel to the vector $B = (3, 8, 13)$. Prove that the two lines intersect and determine the point of intersection.

8. (a) Prove that two lines $L(P; A)$ and $L(Q; B)$ in V_n intersect if and only if $P - Q$ is in the linear span of A and B.
   (b) Determine whether or not the following two lines in V_3 intersect:

   $$L = \{(1, 1, -1) + t(-2, 1, 3)\}, \qquad L' = \{(3, -4, 1) + t(-1, 5, 2)\}.$$

9. Let $X(t) = P + tA$ be an arbitrary point on the line $L(P; A)$, where $P = (1, 2, 3)$ and $A = (1, -2, 2)$, and let $Q = (3, 3, 1)$.
   (a) Compute $\|Q - X(t)\|^2$, the square of the distance between Q and $X(t)$.
   (b) Prove that there is exactly one point $X(t_0)$ for which the distance $\|Q - X(t)\|$ is a minimum, and compute this minimum distance.
   (c) Prove that $Q - X(t_0)$ is orthogonal to A.

10. Let Q be a point not on the line $L(P; A)$ in V_n.
   (a) Let $f(t) = \|Q - X(t)\|^2$, where $X(t) = P + tA$. Prove that $f(t)$ is a quadratic polynomial in t and that this polynomial takes on its minimum value at exactly one t, say at $t = t_0$.
   (b) Prove that $Q - X(t_0)$ is orthogonal to A.

11. Given two parallel lines $L(P; A)$ and $L(Q; A)$ in V_n. Prove that either $L(P; A) = L(Q; A)$ or the intersection $L(P; A) \cap L(Q; A)$ is empty.

12. Given two lines $L(P; A)$ and $L(Q; B)$ in V_n which are not parallel. Prove that the intersection is either empty or consists of exactly one point.

13.6 Planes in Euclidean *n*-space

A line in *n*-space was defined to be a set of the form $\{P + tA\}$ obtained by adding to a given point P all vectors in the linear span of a nonzero vector A. A plane is defined in a similar fashion except that we add to P all vectors in the linear span of two linearly independent vectors A and B. To make certain that V_n contains two linearly independent vectors, we assume at the outset that $n \geq 2$. Most of our applications will be concerned with the case $n = 3$.

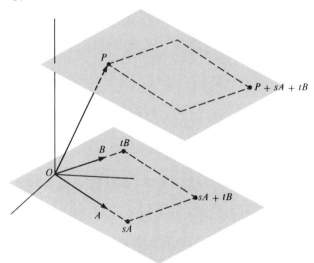

FIGURE 13.3 The plane through P spanned by A and B, and its geometric relation to the plane through O spanned by A and B.

DEFINITION. *A set M of points in V_n is called a plane if there is a point P and two linearly independent vectors A and B such that*

$$M = \{P + sA + tB \mid s, t \text{ real}\}.$$

We shall denote the set more briefly by writing $M = \{P + sA + tB\}$. Each point of M is said to be *on* the plane. In particular, taking $s = t = 0$, we see that P is on the plane. The set $\{P + sA + tB\}$ is also called the plane through P spanned by A and B. When P is the origin, the plane is simply the linear span of A and B. Figure 13.3 shows a plane in V_3 through the origin spanned by A and B and also a plane through a nonzero point P spanned by the same two vectors.

Now we shall deduce some properties of planes analogous to the properties of lines given in Theorems 13.1 through 13.4. The first of these shows that the vectors A and B in the definition of the plane $\{P + sA + tB\}$ can be replaced by any other pair which has the same linear span.

THEOREM 13.7. *Two planes $M = \{P + sA + tB\}$ and $M' = \{P + sC + tD\}$ through the same point P are equal if and only if the linear span of A and B is equal to the linear span of C and D.*

Proof. If the linear span of A and B is equal to that of C and D, then it is clear that $M = M'$. Conversely, assume that $M = M'$. Plane M contains both $P + A$ and $P + B$. Since both these points are also on M', each of A and B must be in the linear span of C and D. Similarly, each of C and D is in the linear span of A and B. Therefore the linear span of A and B is equal to that of C and D.

The next theorem shows that the point P which occurs in the definition of the plane $\{P + sA + tB\}$ can be replaced by any other point Q on the same plane.

THEOREM 13.8. *Two planes $M = \{P + sA + tB\}$ and $M' = \{Q + sA + tB\}$ spanned by the same vectors A and B are equal if and only if Q is on M.*

Proof. If $M = M'$, then Q is certainly on M. To prove the converse, assume Q is on M, say $Q = P + aA + bB$. Take any point X in M. Then $X = P + sA + tB$ for some scalars s and t. But $P = Q - aA - bB$, so $X = Q + (s - a)A + (t - b)B$. Therefore X is in M', so $M \subseteq M'$. Similarly, we find that $M' \subseteq M$, so the two planes are equal.

Euclid's parallel postulate (Theorem 13.3) has an analog for planes. Before we state this theorem we need to define parallelism of two planes. The definition is suggested by the geometric representation in Figure 13.3.

DEFINITION. *Two planes $M = \{P + sA + tB\}$ and $M' = \{Q + sC + tD\}$ are said to be parallel if the linear span of A and B is equal to the linear span of C and D. We also say that a vector X is parallel to the plane M if X is in the linear span of A and B.*

THEOREM 13.9. *Given a plane M and a point Q not on M, there is one and only one plane M' which contains Q and is parallel to M.*

Proof. Let $M = \{P + sA + tB\}$ and consider the plane $M' = \{Q + sA + tB\}$. This plane contains Q and is spanned by the same vectors A and B which span M. Therefore M' is parallel to M. If M'' is another plane through Q parallel to M, then

$$M'' = \{Q + sC + tD\}$$

where the linear span of C and D is equal to that of A and B. By Theorem 13.7, we must have $M'' = M'$. Therefore M' is the only plane through Q which is parallel to M.

Theorem 13.4 tells us that two distinct points determine a line. The next theorem shows that three distinct points determine a plane, provided that the three points are not collinear.

THEOREM 13.10. *If P, Q, and R are three points not on the same line, then there is one and only one plane M containing these three points. It can be described as the set*

(13.4) $$M = \{P + s(Q - P) + t(R - P)\}.$$

Proof. We assume first that one of the points, say P, is the origin. Then Q and R are not on the same line through the origin so they are linearly independent. Therefore, they span a plane through the origin, say the plane

$$M' = \{sQ + tR\}.$$

This plane contains all three points O, Q, and R.

Now we prove that M' is the only plane which contains all three points O, Q, and R. Any other plane through the origin has the form

$$M'' = \{sA + tB\},$$

where A and B are linearly independent. If M'' contains Q and R, we have

(13.5) $$Q = aA + bB, \qquad R = cA + dB,$$

for some scalars a, b, c, d. Hence, every linear combination of Q and R is also a linear combination of A and B, so $M' \subseteq M''$.

To prove that $M'' \subseteq M'$, it suffices to prove that each of A and B is a linear combination of Q and R. Multiplying the first equation in (13.5) by d and the second by b and subtracting, we eliminate B and get

$$(ad - bc)A = dQ - bR.$$

Now $ad - bc$ cannot be zero, otherwise Q and R would be dependent. Therefore we can divide by $ad - bc$ and express A as a linear combination of Q and R. Similarly, we can express B as a linear combination of Q and R, so we have $M'' \subseteq M'$. This proves the theorem when one of the three points P, Q, R is the origin.

To prove the theorem in the general case, let M be the set in (13.4), and let $C = Q - P$, $D = R - P$. First we show that C and D are linearly independent. If not we would have $D = tC$ for some scalar t, giving us $R - P = t(Q - P)$, or $R = P + t(Q - P)$, contradicting the fact that P, Q, R are not on the same line. Therefore the set M is a plane through P spanned by the linearly independent pair C and D. This plane contains all three points P, Q, and R (take $s = 1$, $t = 0$ to get Q, and $s = 0$, $t = 1$ to get R). Now we must prove that this is the only plane containing P, Q, and R.

Let M' be any plane containing P, Q, and R. Since M' is a plane containing P, we have

$$M' = \{P + sA + tB\}$$

for some linearly independent pair A and B. Let $M'_0 = \{sA + tB\}$ be the plane through the origin spanned by the same pair A and B. Clearly, M' contains a vector X if and only if M'_0 contains $X - P$. Since M' contains Q and R, the plane M'_0 contains $C = Q - P$ and $D = R - P$. But we have just shown that there is one and only one plane containing O, C, and D since C and D are linearly independent. Therefore $M'_0 = \{sC + tD\}$, so $M' = \{P + sC + tD\} = M$. This completes the proof.

In Theorem 13.5 we proved that two vectors in V_n are linearly dependent if and only if they lie on a line through the origin. The next theorem is the corresponding result for three vectors.

THEOREM 13.11. *Three vectors A, B, C in V_n are linearly dependent if and only if they lie on the same plane through the origin.*

Proof. Assume A, B, C are dependent. Then we can express one of the vectors as a linear combination of the other two, say $C = sA + tB$. If A and B are independent, they span a plane through the origin and C is on this plane. If A and B are dependent, then A, B, and C lie on a line through the origin, and hence they lie on any plane through the origin which contains all three points A, B, and C.

To prove the converse, assume that A, B, C lie on the same plane through the origin, say the plane M. If A and B are dependent, then A, B, and C are dependent, and there is nothing more to prove. If A and B are independent, they span a plane M' through the origin. By Theorem 13.10, there is one and only one plane through O containing A and B. Therefore $M' = M$. Since C is on this plane, we must have $C = sA + tB$, so A, B, and C are dependent.

13.7 Planes and vector-valued functions

The correspondence which associates to each pair of real numbers s and t the vector $P + sA + tB$ on the plane $M = \{P + sA + tB\}$ is another example of a vector-valued function. In this case, the domain of the function is the set of all pairs of real numbers (s, t) and its range is the plane M. If we denote the function by X and the function values by $X(s, t)$, then for each pair (s, t) we have

$$(13.6) \qquad\qquad X(s, t) = P + sA + tB.$$

We call X a vector-valued function of two real variables. The scalars s and t are called parameters, and the equation (13.6) is called a parametric or vector equation of the plane. This is analogous to the representation of a line by a vector-valued function of one real variable. The presence of two parameters in Equation (13.6) gives the plane a two-dimensional quality. When each vector is in V_3 and is expressed in terms of its components, say

$$P = (p_1, p_2, p_3), \qquad A = (a_1, a_2, a_3), \qquad B = (b_1, b_2, b_3), \qquad \text{and} \qquad X(s, t) = (x, y, z),$$

the vector equation (13.6) can be replaced by three scalar equations,

$$x = p_1 + sa_1 + tb_1, \qquad y = p_2 + sa_2 + tb_2, \qquad z = p_3 + sa_3 + tb_3.$$

The parameters s and t can always be eliminated from these three equations to give one linear equation of the form $ax + by + cz = d$, called a Cartesian equation of the plane. We illustrate with an example.

EXAMPLE. Let $M = \{P + sA + tB\}$,   where $P = (1, 2, 3)$, $A = (1, 2, 1)$,   and $B = (1, -4, -1)$. The corresponding vector equation is

$$X(s, t) = (1, 2, 3) + s(1, 2, 1) + t(1, -4, -1).$$

From this we obtain the three scalar parametric equations

$$x = 1 + s + t, \qquad y = 2 + 2s - 4t, \qquad z = 3 + s - t.$$

To obtain a Cartesian equation, we rewrite the first and third equations in the form $x - 1 = s + t$, $z - 3 = s - t$. Adding and then subtracting these equations, we find that $2s = x + z - 4$, $2t = x - z + 2$. Substituting in the equation for y, we are led to the Cartesian equation $x + y - 3z = -6$. We shall return to a further study of linear Cartesian equations in Section 13.16.

13.8   Exercises

1. Let $M = \{P + sA + tB\}$, where $P = (1, 2, -3)$, $A = (3, 2, 1)$, and $B = (1, 0, 4)$. Determine which of the following points are on M.
   (a) $(1, 2, 0)$;   (b) $(1, 2, 1)$;   (c) $(6, 4, 6)$;   (d) $(6, 6, 6)$;   (e) $(6, 6, -5)$.
2. The three points $P = (1, 1, -1)$, $Q = (3, 3, 2)$, and $R = (3, -1, -2)$ determine a plane M. Determine which of the following points are on M.
   (a) $(2, 2, \frac{1}{2})$;   (b) $(4, 0, -\frac{1}{2})$;   (c) $(-3, 1, -3)$;   (d) $(3, 1, 3)$;   (e) $(0, 0, 0)$.
3. Determine scalar parametric equations for each of the following planes.
   (a) The plane through $(1, 2, 1)$ spanned by the vectors $(0, 1, 0)$ and $(1, 1, 4)$.
   (b) The plane through $(1, 2, 1)$, $(0, 1, 0)$, and $(1, 1, 4)$.
4. A plane M has scalar parametric equations

$$x = 1 + s - 2t, \qquad y = 2 + s + 4t, \qquad z = 2s + t.$$

   (a) Determine which of the following points are on M: $(0, 0, 0)$, $(1, 2, 0)$, $(2, -3, -3)$.
   (b) Find vectors P, A, and B such that $M = \{P + sA + tB\}$.
5. Let M be the plane determined by three points P, Q, R not on the same line.
   (a) If p, q, r are three scalars such that $p + q + r = 1$, prove that $pP + qQ + rR$ is on M.
   (b) Prove that every point on M has the form $pP + qQ + rR$, where $p + q + r = 1$.
6. Determine a linear Cartesian equation of the form $ax + by + cz = d$ for each of the following planes.
   (a) The plane through $(2, 3, 1)$ spanned by $(3, 2, 1)$ and $(-1, -2, -3)$.
   (b) The plane through $(2, 3, 1)$, $(-2, -1, -3)$, and $(4, 3, -1)$.
   (c) The plane through $(2, 3, 1)$ parallel to the plane through the origin spanned by $(2, 0, -2)$ and $(1, 1, 1)$.
7. A plane M has the Cartesian equation $3x - 5y + z = 9$.
   (a) Determine which of the following points are on M: $(0, -2, -1)$, $(-1, -2, 2)$, $(3, 1, -5)$.
   (b) Find vectors P, A, and B such that $M = \{P + sA + tB\}$.
8. Consider the two planes $M = \{P + sA + tB\}$ and $M' = \{Q + sC + tD\}$, where $P = (1, 1, 1)$, $A = (2, -1, 3)$, $B = (-1, 0, 2)$, $Q = (2, 3, 1)$, $C = (1, 2, 3)$, and $D = (3, 2, 1)$. Find two distinct points on the intersection $M \cap M'$.
9. Given a plane $M = \{P + sA + tB\}$, where $P = (2, 3, 1)$, $A = (1, 2, 3)$, and $B = (3, 2, 1)$, and another plane M' with Cartesian equation $x - 2y + z = 0$.
   (a) Determine whether M and M' are parallel.

(b) Find two points on the intersection $M' \cap M''$ if M'' has the Cartesian equation

$$x + 2y + z = 0 .$$

10. Let L be the line through $(1, 1, 1)$ parallel to the vector $(2, -1, 3)$, and let M be the plane through $(1, 1, -2)$ spanned by the vectors $(2, 1, 3)$ and $(0, 1, 1)$. Prove that there is one and only one point on the intersection $L \cap M$ and determine this point.

11. A line with direction vector X is said to be parallel to a plane M if X is parallel to M. Let L be the line through $(1, 1, 1)$ parallel to the vector $(2, -1, 3)$. Determine whether L is parallel to each of the following planes.
    (a) The plane through $(1, 1, -2)$ spanned by $(2, 1, 3)$ and $(\frac{3}{4}, 1, 1)$.
    (b) The plane through $(1, 1, -2)$, $(3, 5, 2)$, and $(2, 4, -1)$.
    (c) The plane with Cartesian equation $x + 2y + 3z = -3$.

12. Two distinct points P and Q lie on a plane M. Prove that every point on the line through P and Q also lies on M.

13. Given the line L through $(1, 2, 3)$ parallel to the vector $(1, 1, 1)$, and given a point $(2, 3, 5)$ which is not on L. Find a Cartesian equation for the plane M through $(2, 3, 5)$ which contains every point on L.

14. Given a line L and a point P not on L. Prove that there is one and only one plane through P which contains every point on L.

13.9 The cross product

In many applications of vector algebra to problems in geometry and mechanics it is helpful to have an easy method for constructing a vector perpendicular to each of two given vectors A and B. This is accomplished by means of the cross product $A \times B$ (read "A cross B") which is defined as follows:

DEFINITION.   *Let $A = (a_1, a_2, a_3)$ and $B = (b_1, b_2, b_3)$ be two vectors in V_3. Their cross product $A \times B$ (in that order) is defined to be the vector*

$$A \times B = (a_2 b_3 - a_3 b_2 ,\, a_3 b_1 - a_1 b_3 ,\, a_1 b_2 - a_2 b_1) .$$

The following properties are easily deduced from this definition.

THEOREM 13.12.   *For all vectors A, B, C in V_3 and for all real c we have:*
(a) $A \times B = -(B \times A)$ (*skew symmetry*),
(b) $A \times (B + C) = (A \times B) + (A \times C)$ (*distributive law*),
(c) $c(A \times B) = (cA) \times B$,
(d) $A \cdot (A \times B) = 0$ (*orthogonality to A*),
(e) $B \cdot (A \times B) = 0$ (*orthogonality to B*),
(f) $\|A \times B\|^2 = \|A\|^2 \|B\|^2 - (A \cdot B)^2$ (*Lagrange's identity*),
(g) $A \times B = O$ *if and only if A and B are linearly dependent.*

Proof.   Parts (a), (b), and (c) follow quickly from the definition and are left as exercises for the reader. To prove (d), we note that

$$A \cdot (A \times B) = a_1(a_2 b_3 - a_3 b_2) + a_2(a_3 b_1 - a_1 b_3) + a_3(a_1 b_2 - a_2 b_1) = 0 .$$

Part (e) follows in the same way, or it can be deduced from (a) and (d). To prove (f), we write

$$\|A \times B\|^2 = (a_2 b_3 - a_3 b_2)^2 + (a_3 b_1 - a_1 b_3)^2 + (a_1 b_2 - a_2 b_1)^2$$

and

$$\|A\|^2 \|B\|^2 - (A \cdot B)^2 = (a_1^2 + a_2^2 + a_3^2)(b_1^2 + b_2^2 + b_3^2) - (a_1 b_1 + a_2 b_2 + a_3 b_3)^2$$

and then verify by brute force that the two right-hand members are identical.

Property (f) shows that $A \times B = O$ if and only if $(A \cdot B)^2 = \|A\|^2 \|B\|^2$. By the Cauchy-Schwarz inequality (Theorem 12.3), this happens if and only if one of the vectors is a scalar multiple of the other. In other words, $A \times B = O$ if and only if A and B are linearly dependent, which proves (g).

EXAMPLES. Both (a) and (g) show that $A \times A = O$. From the definition of cross product we find that

$$i \times j = k, \quad j \times k = i, \quad k \times i = j.$$

The cross product is *not* associative. For example, we have

$$i \times (i \times j) = i \times k = -j \quad \text{but} \quad (i \times i) \times j = O \times j = O.$$

The next theorem describes two more fundamental properties of the cross product.

THEOREM 13.13. *Let A and B be linearly independent vectors in V_3. Then we have the following:*
   (a) *The vectors A, B, A × B are linearly independent.*
   (b) *Every vector N in V_3 orthogonal to both A and B is a scalar multiple of A × B.*

Proof. Let $C = A \times B$. Then $C \neq O$ since A and B are linearly independent. Given scalars a, b, c such that $aA + bB + cC = O$, we take the dot product of each member with C and use the relations $A \cdot C = B \cdot C = 0$ to find $c = 0$. This gives $aA + bB = O$, so $a = b = 0$ since A and B are independent. This proves (a).

Let N be any vector orthogonal to both A and B, and let $C = A \times B$. We shall prove that

$$(N \cdot C)^2 = (N \cdot N)(C \cdot C).$$

Then from the Cauchy–Schwarz inequality (Theorem 12.3) it follows that N is a scalar multiple of C.

Since A, B, and C are linearly independent, we know, by Theorem 12.10(c), that they span V_3. In particular, they span N, so we can write

$$N = aA + bB + cC$$

for some scalars a, b, c. This gives us

$$N \cdot N = N \cdot (aA + bB + cC) = c\, N \cdot C$$

since $N \cdot A = N \cdot B = 0$. Also, since $C \cdot A = C \cdot B = 0$, we have

$$C \cdot N = C \cdot (aA + bB + cC) = cC \cdot C.$$

Therefore, $(N \cdot N)(C \cdot C) = (cN \cdot C)(C \cdot C) = (N \cdot C)(cC \cdot C) = (N \cdot C)^2$, which completes the proof.

Theorem 13.12 helps us visualize the cross product geometrically. From properties (d) and (e), we know that $A \times B$ is perpendicular to both A and B. When the vector $A \times B$ is represented geometrically by an arrow, the direction of the arrow depends on the relative

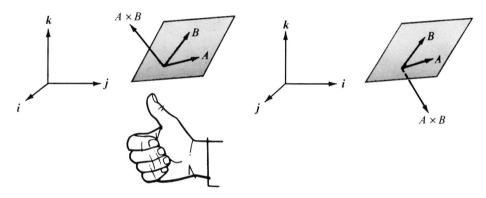

(a) A right-handed coordinate system   (b) A left-handed coordinate system

FIGURE 13.4   Illustrating the relative positions of A, B, and $A \times B$.

positions of the three unit coordinate vectors. If i, j, and k are arranged as shown in Figure 13.4(a), they are said to form a *right-handed coordinate system*. In this case, the direction of $A \times B$ is determined by the "right-hand rule." That is to say, when A is rotated into B in such a way that the fingers of the right hand point in the direction of rotation, then the thumb indicates the direction of $A \times B$ (assuming, for the sake of the discussion, that the thumb is perpendicular to the other fingers). In a left-handed coordinate system, as shown in Figure 13.4(b), the direction of $A \times B$ is reversed and may be determined by a corresponding left-hand rule.

The length of $A \times B$ has an interesting geometric interpretation. If A and B are nonzero vectors making an angle θ with each other, where $0 \le \theta \le \pi$, we may write $A \cdot B = \|A\| \|B\| \cos \theta$ in property (f) of Theorem 13.12 to obtain

$$\|A \times B\|^2 = \|A\|^2 \|B\|^2 (1 - \cos^2 \theta) = \|A\|^2 \|B\|^2 \sin^2 \theta ,$$

from which we find

$$\|A \times B\| = \|A\| \|B\| \sin \theta .$$

Since $\|B\| \sin \theta$ is the altitude of the parallelogram determined by A and B (see Figure 13.5), we see that *the length of $A \times B$ is equal to the area of this parallelogram.*

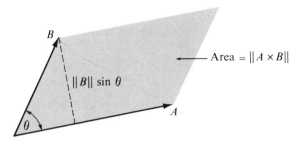

FIGURE 13.5   The length of $A \times B$ is the area of the parallelogram determined by A and B.

13.10   The cross product expressed as a determinant

The formula which defines the cross product can be put in a more compact form with the aid of determinants. If a, b, c, d are four numbers, the difference $ad - bc$ is often denoted by the symbol

$$\begin{vmatrix} a & b \\ c & d \end{vmatrix}$$

and is called a *determinant* (of order two). The numbers a, b, c, d are called its *elements*, and they are said to be arranged in two horizontal *rows*, a, b and c, d, and in two vertical *columns*, a, c and b, d. Note that an interchange of two rows or of two columns only changes the sign of the determinant. For example, since $ad - bc = -(bc - ad)$, we have

$$\begin{vmatrix} a & b \\ c & d \end{vmatrix} = - \begin{vmatrix} b & a \\ d & c \end{vmatrix}.$$

If we express each of the components of the cross product as a determinant of order two, the formula defining $A \times B$ becomes

$$A \times B = \left(\begin{vmatrix} a_2 & a_3 \\ b_2 & b_3 \end{vmatrix}, \begin{vmatrix} a_3 & a_1 \\ b_3 & b_1 \end{vmatrix}, \begin{vmatrix} a_1 & a_2 \\ b_1 & b_2 \end{vmatrix} \right).$$

This can also be expressed in terms of the unit coordinate vectors i, j, k as follows:

(13.7) $$A \times B = \begin{vmatrix} a_2 & a_3 \\ b_2 & b_3 \end{vmatrix} i + \begin{vmatrix} a_3 & a_1 \\ b_3 & b_1 \end{vmatrix} j + \begin{vmatrix} a_1 & a_2 \\ b_1 & b_2 \end{vmatrix} k .$$

Determinants of order three are written with three rows and three columns and they may be defined in terms of second-order determinants by the formula

(13.8) $$\begin{vmatrix} a_1 & a_2 & a_3 \\ b_1 & b_2 & b_3 \\ c_1 & c_2 & c_3 \end{vmatrix} = a_1 \begin{vmatrix} b_2 & b_3 \\ c_2 & c_3 \end{vmatrix} - a_2 \begin{vmatrix} b_1 & b_3 \\ c_1 & c_3 \end{vmatrix} + a_3 \begin{vmatrix} b_1 & b_2 \\ c_1 & c_2 \end{vmatrix}.$$

This is said to be an "expansion" of the determinant along its first row. Note that the determinant on the right that multiplies a_1 may be obtained from that on the left by deleting the row and column in which a_1 appears. The other two determinants on the right are obtained similarly.

Determinants of order greater than three are discussed in Volume II. Our only purpose in introducing determinants of order two and three at this stage is to have a useful device for writing certain formulas in a compact form that makes them easier to remember.

Determinants are meaningful if the elements in the first row are vectors. For example, if we write the determinant

$$\begin{vmatrix} i & j & k \\ a_1 & a_2 & a_3 \\ b_1 & b_2 & b_3 \end{vmatrix}$$

and "expand" this according to the rule prescribed in (13.8), we find that the result is equal to the right member of (13.7). In other words, we may write the definition of the cross product $A \times B$ in the following compact form:

$$A \times B = \begin{vmatrix} i & j & k \\ a_1 & a_2 & a_3 \\ b_1 & b_2 & b_3 \end{vmatrix}.$$

For example, to compute the cross product of $A = 2i - 8j + 3k$ and $B = 4j + 3k$, we write

$$A \times B = \begin{vmatrix} i & j & k \\ 2 & -8 & 3 \\ 0 & 4 & 3 \end{vmatrix} = \begin{vmatrix} -8 & 3 \\ 4 & 3 \end{vmatrix} i - \begin{vmatrix} 2 & 3 \\ 0 & 3 \end{vmatrix} j + \begin{vmatrix} 2 & -8 \\ 0 & 4 \end{vmatrix} k = -36i - 6j + 8k$$

13.11 Exercises

1. Let $A = -i + 2k$, $B = 2i + j - k$, $C = i + 2j + 2k$. Compute each of the following vectors in terms of i, j, k:
   (a) $A \times B$;   (d) $A \times (C \times A)$;   (g) $(A \times C) \times B$;
   (b) $B \times C$;   (e) $(A \times B) \times C$;   (h) $(A + B) \times (A - C)$;
   (c) $C \times A$;   (f) $A \times (B \times C)$;   (i) $(A \times B) \times (A \times C)$.

2. In each case find a vector of length 1 in V_3 orthogonal to both A and B:
   (a) $A = i + j + k$, $B = 2i + 3j - k$;
   (b) $A = 2i - 3j + 4k$, $B = -i + 5j + 7k$;
   (c) $A = i - 2j + 3k$, $B = -3i + 2j - k$.

3. In each case use the cross product to compute the area of the triangle with vertices A, B, C:
   (a) $A = (0, 2, 2)$, $B = (2, 0, -1)$, $C = (3, 4, 0)$;
   (b) $A = (-2, 3, 1)$, $B = (1, -3, 4)$, $C = (1, 2, 1)$;
   (c) $A = (0, 0, 0)$, $B = (0, 1, 1)$, $C = (1, 0, 1)$.

4. If $A = 2i + 5j + 3k$, $B = 2i + 7j + 4k$, and $C = 3i + 3j + 6k$, express the cross product $(A - C) \times (B - A)$ in terms of i, j, k.

5. Prove that $\|A \times B\| = \|A\| \|B\|$ if and only if A and B are orthogonal.

6. Given two linearly independent vectors A and B in V_3. Let $C = (B \times A) - B$.
   (a) Prove that A is orthogonal to $B + C$.

(b) Prove that the angle θ between B and C satisfies $\frac{1}{2}\pi < \theta < \pi$.

(c) If $\|B\| = 1$ and $\|B \times A\| = 2$, compute the length of C.

7. Let A and B be two orthogonal vectors in V_3, each having length 1.

(a) Prove that A, B, $A \times B$ is an orthonormal basis for V_3.

(b) Let $C = (A \times B) \times A$. Prove that $\|C\| = 1$.

(c) Draw a figure showing the geometric relation between A, B, and $A \times B$, and use this figure to obtain the relations

$$(A \times B) \times A = B, \qquad (A \times B) \times B = -A.$$

(d) Prove the relations in part (c) algebraically.

8. (a) If $A \times B = O$ and $A \cdot B = 0$, then at least one of A or B is zero. Prove this statement and give its geometric interpretation.

(b) Given $A \neq O$. If $A \times B = A \times C$ and $A \cdot B = A \cdot C$, prove that $B = C$.

9. Let $A = 2i - j + 2k$ and $C = 3i + 4j - k$.

(a) Find a vector B such that $A \times B = C$. Is there more than one solution?

(b) Find a vector B such that $A \times B = C$ and $A \cdot B = 1$. Is there more than one solution?

10. Given a nonzero vector A and a vector C orthogonal to A, both vectors in V_3. Prove that there is exactly one vector B such that $A \times B = C$ and $A \cdot B = 1$.

11. Three vertices of a parallelogram are at the points $A = (1, 0, 1)$, $B = (-1, 1, 1)$, $C = (2, -1, 2)$.

(a) Find all possible points D which can be the fourth vertex of the parallelogram.

(b) Compute the area of triangle ABC.

12. Given two nonparallel vectors A and B in V_3 with $A \cdot B = 2$, $\|A\| = 1$, $\|B\| = 4$. Let $C = 2(A \times B) - 3B$. Compute $A \cdot (B + C)$, $\|C\|$, and the cosine of the angle θ between B and C.

13. Given two linearly independent vectors A and B in V_3. Determine whether each of the following statements is true or false.

(a) $A + B$, $A - B$, $A \times B$ are linearly independent.

(b) $A + B$, $A + (A \times B)$, $B + (A \times B)$ are linearly independent.

(c) A, B, $(A + B) \times (A - B)$ are linearly independent.

14. (a) Prove that three vectors A, B, C in V_3 lie on a line if and only if $(B - A) \times (C - A) = O$.

(b) If $A \neq B$, prove that the line through A and B consists of the set of all vectors P such that $(P - A) \times (P - B) = O$.

15. Given two orthogonal vectors A, B in V_3, each of length 1. Let P be a vector satisfying the equation $P \times B = A - P$. Prove each of the following statements.

(a) P is orthogonal to B and has length $\frac{1}{2}\sqrt{2}$.

(b) P, B, $P \times B$ form a basis for V_3.

(c) $(P \times B) \times B = -P$.

(d) $P = \frac{1}{2}A - \frac{1}{2}(A \times B)$.

13.12 The scalar triple product

The dot and cross products can be combined to form the *scalar triple product* $A \cdot B \times C$, which can only mean $A \cdot (B \times C)$. Since this is a dot product of two vectors, its value is a scalar. We can compute this scalar by means of determinants. Write $A = (a_1, a_2, a_3)$, $B = (b_1, b_2, b_3)$, $C = (c_1, c_2, c_3)$ and express $B \times C$ according to Equation (13.7). Forming the dot product with A, we obtain

$$A \cdot B \times C = a_1 \begin{vmatrix} b_2 & b_3 \\ c_2 & c_3 \end{vmatrix} + a_2 \begin{vmatrix} b_3 & b_1 \\ c_3 & c_1 \end{vmatrix} + a_3 \begin{vmatrix} b_1 & b_2 \\ c_1 & c_2 \end{vmatrix} = \begin{vmatrix} a_1 & a_2 & a_3 \\ b_1 & b_2 & b_3 \\ c_1 & c_2 & c_3 \end{vmatrix}.$$

Thus, $A \cdot B \times C$ is equal to the determinant whose rows are the components of the factors A, B, and C.

In Theorem 13.12 we found that two vectors A and B are linearly dependent if and only if their cross product $A \times B$ is the zero vector. The next theorem gives a corresponding criterion for linear dependence of three vectors.

THEOREM 13.14. *Three vectors A, B, C in V_3 are linearly dependent if and only if*

$$A \cdot B \times C = 0.$$

Proof. Assume first that A, B, and C are dependent. If B and C are dependent, then $B \times C = O$, and hence $A \cdot B \times C = 0$. Suppose, then, that B and C are independent. Since all three are dependent, there exist scalars a, b, c, not all zero, such that $aA + bB + cC = O$. We must have $a \neq 0$ in this relation, otherwise B and C would be dependent. Therefore, we can divide by a and express A as a linear combination of B and C, say $A = tB + sC$. Taking the dot product of each member with $B \times C$, we find

$$A \cdot (B \times C) = tB \cdot B \times C + sC \cdot B \times C = 0,$$

since each of B and C is orthogonal to $B \times C$. Therefore dependence of A, B, and C implies $A \cdot B \times C = 0$.

To prove the converse, assume that $A \cdot B \times C = 0$. If B and C are dependent, then so are A, B, and C, and there is nothing more to prove. Assume then, that B and C are linearly independent. Then, by Theorem 13.13, the three vectors B, C, and $B \times C$ are linearly independent. Hence, they span A so we can write

$$A = aB + bC + c(B \times C)$$

for some scalars a, b, c. Taking the dot product of each member with $B \times C$ and using the fact that $A \cdot (B \times C) = 0$, we find $c = 0$, so $A = aB + bC$. This proves that A, B, and C are linearly dependent.

EXAMPLE. To determine whether the three vectors $(2, 3, -1)$, $(3, -7, 5)$, and $(1, -5, 2)$ are dependent, we form their scalar triple product, expressing it as the determinant

$$\begin{vmatrix} 2 & 3 & -1 \\ 3 & -7 & 5 \\ 1 & -5 & 2 \end{vmatrix} = 2(-14 + 25) - 3(6 - 5) - 1(-15 + 7) = 27.$$

Since the scalar triple product is nonzero, the vectors are linearly independent.

The scalar triple product has an interesting geometric interpretation. Figure 13.6 shows a parallelepiped determined by three geometric vectors A, B, C not in the same plane. Its altitude is $\|C\| \cos \phi$, where ϕ is the angle between $A \times B$ and C. In this figure, $\cos \phi$ is positive because $0 \leq \phi < \frac{1}{2}\pi$. The area of the parallelogram which forms the base is $\|A \times B\|$, and this is also the area of each cross section parallel to the base. Integrating the cross-sectional area from 0 to $\|C\| \cos \phi$, we find that the volume of the parallelepiped is $\|A \times B\|$ ($\|C\|$ cos ϕ), the area of the base times the altitude. But we have

$$\|A \times B\| \,(\|C\| \cos \phi) = (A \times B) \cdot C \,.$$

In other words, the scalar triple product $A \times B \cdot C$ is equal to the volume of the parallelepiped determined by A, B, C. When $\frac{1}{2}\pi < \phi \le \pi$, cos ϕ is negative and the product $A \times B \cdot C$ is the negative of the volume. If A, B, C are on a plane through the origin, they are linearly dependent and their scalar triple product is zero. In this case, the parallelepiped degenerates and has zero volume.

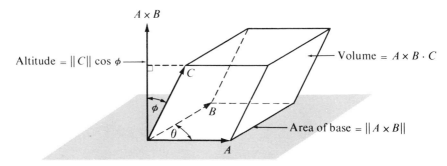

FIGURE 13.6   Geometric interpretation of the scalar triple product as the volume of a parallelepiped.

This geometric interpretation of the scalar triple product suggests certain algebraic properties of this product. For example, a cyclic permutation of the vectors A, B, C leaves the scalar triple product unchanged. By this we mean that

(13.9) $$A \times B \cdot C = B \times C \cdot A = C \times A \cdot B \,.$$

An algebraic proof of this property is outlined in Exercise 7 of Section 13.14. This property implies that the dot and cross are interchangeable in a scalar triple product. In fact, the commutativity of the dot product implies $(B \times C) \cdot A = A \cdot (B \times C)$ and when this is combined with the first equation in (13.9), we find that

(13.10) $$A \times B \cdot C = A \cdot B \times C \,.$$

The scalar triple product $A \cdot B \times C$ is often denoted by the symbol $[ABC]$ without indicating the dot or cross. Because of Equation (13.10), there is no ambiguity in this notation— the product depends only on the order of the factors A, B, C and not on the positions of the dot and cross.

13.13   Cramer's rule for solving a system of three linear equations

The scalar triple product may be used to solve a system of three simultaneous linear equations in three unknowns x, y, z. Suppose the system is written in the form

(13.11)
$$a_1 x + b_1 y + c_1 z = d_1 \,,$$
$$a_2 x + b_2 y + c_2 z = d_2 \,,$$
$$a_3 x + b_3 y + c_3 z = d_3 \,.$$

Let A be the vector with components a_1, a_2, a_3 and define B, C, and D similarly. Then the three equations in (13.11) are equivalent to the single vector equation

$$(13.12) \qquad\qquad xA + yB + zC = D .$$

If we dot multiply both sides of this equation with $B \times C$, writing $[ABC]$ for $A \cdot B \times C$, we find that

$$x[ABC] + y[BBC] + z[CBC] = [DBC] .$$

Since $[BBC] = [CBC] = 0$, the coefficients of y and z drop out and we obtain

$$(13.13) \qquad\qquad x = \frac{[DBC]}{[ABC]} \quad \text{if} \quad [ABC] \neq 0 .$$

A similar argument yields analogous formulas for y and z. Thus we have

$$(13.14) \qquad y = \frac{[ADC]}{[ABC]} \quad \text{and} \quad z = \frac{[ABD]}{[ABC]} \quad \text{if} \quad [ABC] \neq 0 .$$

The condition $[ABC] \neq 0$ means that the three vectors A, B, C are linearly independent. In this case, (13.12) shows that every vector D in 3-space is spanned by A, B, C and the multipliers x, y, z are uniquely determined by the formulas in (13.13) and (13.14). When the scalar triple products that occur in these formulas are written as determinants, the result is known as *Cramer's rule* for solving the system (13.11):

$$x = \frac{\begin{vmatrix} d_1 & b_1 & c_1 \\ d_2 & b_2 & c_2 \\ d_3 & b_3 & c_3 \end{vmatrix}}{\begin{vmatrix} a_1 & b_1 & c_1 \\ a_2 & b_2 & c_2 \\ a_3 & b_3 & c_3 \end{vmatrix}}, \quad y = \frac{\begin{vmatrix} a_1 & d_1 & c_1 \\ a_2 & d_2 & c_2 \\ a_3 & d_3 & c_3 \end{vmatrix}}{\begin{vmatrix} a_1 & b_1 & c_1 \\ a_2 & b_2 & c_2 \\ a_3 & b_3 & c_3 \end{vmatrix}}, \quad z = \frac{\begin{vmatrix} a_1 & b_1 & d_1 \\ a_2 & b_2 & d_2 \\ a_3 & b_3 & d_3 \end{vmatrix}}{\begin{vmatrix} a_1 & b_1 & c_1 \\ a_2 & b_2 & c_2 \\ a_3 & b_3 & c_3 \end{vmatrix}} .$$

If $[ABC] = 0$, then A, B, C lie on a plane through the origin and the system has no solution unless D lies in the same plane. In this latter case, it is easy to show that there are infinitely many solutions of the system. In fact, the vectors A, B, C are linearly dependent so there exist scalars u, v, w not all zero such that $uA + vB + wC = O$. If the triple (x, y, z) satisfies (13.12), then so does the triple $(x + tu, y + tv, z + tw)$ for all real t, since we have

$$(x + tu)A + (y + tv)B + (z + tw)C$$
$$= xA + yB + zC + t(uA + vB + wC) = xA + yB + zC .$$

13.14 Exercises

1. Compute the scalar triple product $A \cdot B \times C$ in each case.
   (a) $A = (3, 0, 0)$, $B = (0, 4, 0)$, $C = (0, 0, 8)$.
   (b) $A = (2, 3, -1)$, $B = (3, -7, 5)$, $C = (1, -5, 2)$.
   (c) $A = (2, 1, 3)$, $B = (-3, 0, 6)$, $C = (4, 5, -1)$.

2. Find all real t for which the three vectors $(1, t, 1)$, $(t, 1, 0)$, $(0, 1, t)$ are linearly dependent.

3. Compute the volume of the parallelepiped determined by the vectors $i + j, j + k, k + i$.

4. Prove that $A \times B = A \cdot (B \times i)i + A \cdot (B \times j)j + A \cdot (B \times k)k$.

5. Prove that $i \times (A \times i) + j \times (A \times j) + k \times (A \times k) = 2A$.

6. (a) Find all vectors $ai + bj + ck$ which satisfy the relation

$$(ai + bj + ck) \cdot k \times (6i + 3j + 4k) = 3 .$$

(b) Find that vector $ai + bj + ck$ of shortest length which satisfies the relation in (a).

7. Use algebraic properties of the dot and cross products to derive the following properties of the scalar triple product.

(a) $(A + B) \cdot (A + B) \times C = 0$.

(b) $A \cdot B \times C = -B \cdot A \times C$. This shows that switching the first two vectors reverses the sign. [*Hint:* Use part (a) and distributive laws.]

(c) $A \cdot B \times C = -A \cdot C \times B$. This shows that switching the second and third vectors reverses the sign. [*Hint:* Use skew-symmetry.]

(d) $A \cdot B \times C = -C \cdot B \times A$. This shows that switching the first and third vectors reverses the sign. [*Hint:* Use (b) and (c).]

Equating the right members of (b), (c), and (d), we find that

$$A \cdot B \times C = B \cdot C \times A = C \cdot A \times B ,$$

which shows that a cyclic permutation of A, B, C leaves their scalar triple product unchanged.

9. This exercise outlines a proof of the vector identity

(13.15) $A \times (B \times C) = (C \cdot A)B - (B \cdot A)C ,$

sometimes referred to as the "cab minus bac" formula. Let $B = (b_1, b_2, b_3)$, $C = (c_1, c_2, c_3)$ and prove that

$$i \times (B \times C) = c_1 B - b_1 C .$$

This proves (13.15) in the special case $A = i$. Prove corresponding formulas for $A = j$ and $A = k$, and then combine them to obtain (13.15).

10. Use the "cab minus bac" formula of Exercise 9 to derive the following vector identities.

(a) $(A \times B) \times (C \times D) = (A \times B \cdot D)C - (A \times B \cdot C)D$.

(b) $A \times (B \times C) + B \times (C \times A) + C \times (A \times B) = O$.

(c) $A \times (B \times C) = (A \times B) \times C$ if and only if $B \times (C \times A) = O$.

(d) $(A \times B) \cdot (C \times D) = (B \cdot D)(A \cdot C) - (B \cdot C)(A \cdot D)$.

11. Four vectors A, B, C, D in V_3 satisfy the relations $A \times C \cdot B = 5$, $A \times D \cdot B = 3$, $C + D = i + 2j + k$, $C - D = i - k$. Compute $(A \times B) \times (C \times D)$ in terms of i, j, k.

12. Prove that $(A \times B) \cdot (B \times C) \times (C \times A) = (A \cdot B \times C)^2$.

13. Prove or disprove the formula $A \times [A \times (A \times B)] \cdot C = -\|A\|^2 A \cdot B \times C$.

14. (a) Prove that the volume of the tetrahedron whose vertices are A, B, C, D is

$$\tfrac{1}{6} |(B - A) \cdot (C - A) \times (D - A)| .$$

(b) Compute this volume when $A = (1, 1, 1)$, $B = (0, 0, 2)$, $C = (0, 3, 0)$, and $D = (4, 0, 0)$.

15. (a) If $B \neq C$, prove that the perpendicular distance from A to the line through B and C is

$$\|(A - B) \times (C - B)\|/\|B - C\| .$$

(b) Compute this distance when $A = (1, -2, -5)$, $B = (-1, 1, 1)$, and $C = (4, 5, 1)$.

16. Heron's formula for computing the area S of a triangle whose sides have lengths a, b, c states that $S = \sqrt{s(s - a)(s - b)(s - c)}$, where $s = (a + b + c)/2$. This exercise outlines a vectorial proof of this formula.

Assume the triangle has vertices at O, A, and B, with $\|A\| = a$, $\|B\| = b$, $\|B - A\| = c$.

(a) Combine the two identities

$$\|A \times B\|^2 = \|A\|^2\|B\|^2 - (A \cdot B)^2, \qquad -2A \cdot B = \|A - B\|^2 - \|A\|^2 - \|B\|^2$$

to obtain the formula

$$4S^2 = a^2b^2 - \tfrac{1}{4}(c^2 - a^2 - b^2)^2 = \tfrac{1}{4}(2ab - c^2 + a^2 + b^2)(2ab + c^2 - a^2 - b^2).$$

(b) Rewrite the formula in part (a) to obtain

$$S^2 = \tfrac{1}{16}(a + b + c)(a + b - c)(c - a + b)(c + a - b),$$

and thereby deduce Heron's formula.

Use Cramer's rule to solve the system of equations in each of Exercises 17, 18, and 19.

17. $x + 2y + 3z = 5$, $\quad 2x - y + 4z = 11$, $\quad -y + z = 3$.
18. $x + y + 2z = 4$, $\quad 3x - y - z = 2$, $\quad 2x + 5y + 3z = 3$.
19. $x + y = 5$, $\quad x + z = 2$, $\quad y + z = 5$.
20. If $P = (1, 1, 1)$ and $A = (2, 1, -1)$, prove that each point (x, y, z) on the line $\{P + tA\}$ satisfies the system of linear equations $x - y + z = 1$, $x + y + 3z = 5$, $3x + y + 7z = 11$.

13.15 Normal vectors to planes

A plane was defined in Section 13.6 as a set of the form $\{P + sA + tB\}$, where A and B are linearly independent vectors. Now we show that planes in V_3 can be described in an entirely different way, using the concept of a normal vector.

DEFINITION. *Let $M = \{P + sA + tB\}$ be the plane through P spanned by A and B. A vector N in V_3 is said to be perpendicular to M if N is perpendicular to both A and B. If, in addition, N is nonzero, then N is called a normal vector to the plane.*

Note: If $N \cdot A = N \cdot B = 0$, then $N \cdot (sA + tB) = 0$, so a vector perpendicular to both A and B is perpendicular to every vector in the linear span of A and B. Also, if N is normal to a plane, so is tN for every real $t \neq 0$.

THEOREM 13.15. *Given a plane $M = \{P + sA + tB\}$ through P spanned by A and B. Let $N = A \times B$. Then we have the following:*

(a) *N is a normal vector to M.*

(b) *M is the set of all X in V_3 satisfying the equation*

(13.16) $$(X - P) \cdot N = 0.$$

Proof. Since M is a plane, A and B are linearly independent, so $A \times B \neq O$. This proves (a) since $A \times B$ is orthogonal to both A and B.

To prove (b), let M' be the set of all X in V_3 satisfying Equation (13.16). If $X \in M$, then $X - P$ is in the linear span of A and B, so $X - P$ is orthogonal to N. Therefore $X \in M'$ which proves that $M \subseteq M'$. Conversely, suppose $X \in M'$. Then X satisfies (13.16). Since A, B, N are linearly independent (Theorem 13.13), they span every vector in V_3 so, in particular, we have

$$X - P = sA + tB + uN$$

for some scalars s, t, u. Taking the dot product of each member with N, we find $u = 0$, so $X - P = sA + tB$. This shows that $X \in M$. Hence, $M' \subseteq M$, which completes the proof of (b).

The geometric meaning of Theorem 13.15 is shown in Figure 13.7. The points P and X are on the plane and the normal vector N is orthogonal to $X - P$. This figure suggests the following theorem.

THEOREM 13.16. *Given a plane M through a point P, and given a nonzero vector N normal to M, let*

(13.17)
$$d = \frac{|P \cdot N|}{\|N\|} \cdot$$

Then every X on M has length $\|X\| \geq d$. Moreover, we have $\|X\| = d$ if and only if X is the projection of P along N:

$$X = tN, \quad \text{where} \quad t = \frac{P \cdot N}{N \cdot N}.$$

Proof. The proof follows from the Cauchy-Schwarz inequality in exactly the same way as we proved Theorem 13.6, the corresponding result for lines in V_2.

By the same argument we find that if Q is a point not on M, then among all points X on M the smallest length $\|X - Q\|$ occurs when $X - Q$ is the projection of $P - Q$ along N. This minimum length is $|(P - Q) \cdot N|/\|N\|$ and is called the *distance from Q to the plane*. The number d in (13.17) is the distance from the origin to the plane.

13.16 Linear Cartesian equations for planes

The results of Theorems 13.15 and 13.16 can also be expressed in terms of components. If we write $N = (a, b, c)$, $P = (x_1, y_1, z_1)$, and $X = (x, y, z)$, Equation (13.16) becomes

(13.18)
$$a(x - x_1) + b(y - y_1) + c(z - z_1) = 0.$$

This is called a Cartesian equation for the plane, and it is satisfied by those and only those points (x, y, z) which lie on the plane. The set of points satisfying (13.18) is not altered if we multiply each of a, b, c by a nonzero scalar t. This simply amounts to a different choice of normal vector in (13.16).

We may transpose the terms not involving x, y, and z, and write (13.18) in the form

(13.19)
$$ax + by + cz = d_1,$$

where $d_1 = ax_1 + by_1 + cz_1$. An equation of this type is said to be *linear* in x, y, and z. We have just shown that every point (x, y, z) on a plane satisfies a linear Cartesian equation (13.19) in which not all three of a, b, c are zero. Conversely, every linear equation with this property represents a plane. (The reader may verify this as an exercise.)

The number d_1 in Equation (13.19) bears a simple relation to the distance d of the plane from the origin. Since $d_1 = P \cdot N$, we have $|d_1| = |P \cdot N| = d\|N\|$. In particular $|d_1| = d$ if the normal N has length 1. The plane passes through the origin if and only if $d_1 = 0$.

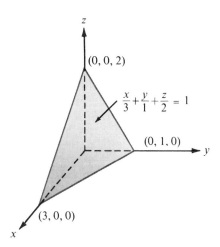

FIGURE 13.7 A plane through P and
X with normal vector N.

FIGURE 13.8 A plane with intercepts
3, 1, 2.

EXAMPLE. The Cartesian equation $2x + 6y + 3z = 6$ represents a plane with normal vector $N = 2i + 6j + 3k$. We rewrite the Cartesian equation in the form

$$\frac{x}{3} + \frac{y}{1} + \frac{z}{2} = 1$$

from which it is apparent that the plane intersects the coordinate axes at the points $(3, 0, 0)$, $(0, 1, 0)$, and $(0, 0, 2)$. The numbers 3, 1, 2 are called, respectively, the x-, y-, and z-*intercepts* of the plane. A knowledge of the intercepts makes it possible to sketch the plane quickly. A portion of the plane is shown in Figure 13.8. Its distance d from the origin is $d = 6/\|N\| = 6/7$.

Two parallel planes will have a common normal N. If $N = (a, b, c)$, the Cartesian equations of two parallel planes can be written as follows:

$$ax + by + cz = d_1, \qquad ax + by + cz = d_2,$$

the only difference being in the right-hand members. The number $|d_1 - d_2|/\|N\|$ is called the perpendicular distance between the two planes, a definition suggested by Theorem 13.16.

Two planes are called perpendicular if a normal of one is perpendicular to a normal of the other. More generally, if the normals of two planes make an angle θ with each other, then we say that θ is an angle between the two planes.

13.17 Exercises

1. Given vectors $A = 2i + 3j - 4k$ and $B = j + k$.
   (a) Find a nonzero vector N perpendicular to both A and B.
   (b) Give a Cartesian equation for the plane through the origin spanned by A and B.
   (c) Give a Cartesian equation for the plane through (1, 2, 3) spanned by A and B.
2. A plane has Cartesian equation $x + 2y - 2z + 7 = 0$. Find the following:
   (a) a normal vector of unit length;
   (b) the intercepts of the plane;
   (c) the distance of the plane from the origin;
   (d) the point Q on the plane nearest the origin.
3. Find a Cartesian equation of the plane which passes through (1, 2, −3) and is parallel to the plane given by $3x - y + 2z = 4$. What is the distance between the two planes?
4. Four planes have Cartesian equations $x + 2y - 2z = 5$, $3x - 6y + 3z = 2$, $2x + y + 2z = -1$, and $x - 2y + z = 7$.
   (a) Show that two of them are parallel and the other two are perpendicular.
   (b) Find the distance between the two parallel planes.
5. The three points (1, 1, −1), (3, 3, 2), and (3, −1, −2) determine a plane. Find (a) a vector normal to the plane; (b) a Cartesian equation for the plane; (c) the distance of the plane from the origin.
6. Find a Cartesian equation for the plane determined by (1, 2, 3), (2, 3, 4), and (−1, 7, −2).
7. Determine an angle between the planes with Cartesian equations $x + y = 1$ and $y + z = 2$.
8. A line parallel to a nonzero vector N is said to be perpendicular to a plane M if N is normal to M. Find a Cartesian equation for the plane through (2, 3, −7), given that the line through (1, 2, 3) and (2, 4, 12) is perpendicular to this plane.
9. Find a vector parametric equation for the line which contains the point (2, 1, −3) and is perpendicular to the plane given by $4x - 3y + z = 5$.
10. A point moves in space in such a way that at time t its position is given by the vector $X(t) = (1 - t)i + (2 - 3t)j + (2t - 1)k$.
    (a) Prove that the point moves along a line. (Call it L.)
    (b) Find a vector N parallel to L.
    (c) At what time does the point strike the plane given by $2x + 3y + 2z + 1 = 0$?
    (d) Find a Cartesian equation for that plane parallel to the one in part (c) which contains the point $X(3)$.
    (e) Find a Cartesian equation for that plane perpendicular to L which contains the point $X(2)$.
11. Find a Cartesian equation for the plane through (1, 1, 1) if a normal vector N makes angles $\frac{1}{3}\pi$, $\frac{1}{4}\pi$, $\frac{1}{3}\pi$, with i, j, k, respectively.
12. Compute the volume of the tetrahedron whose vertices are at the origin and at the points where the coordinate axes intersect the plane given by $x + 2y + 3z = 6$.
13. Find a vector A of length 1 perpendicular to $i + 2j - 3k$ and parallel to the plane with Cartesian equation $x - y + 5z = 1$.
14. Find a Cartesian equation of the plane which is parallel to both vectors $i + j$ and $j + k$ and intersects the x-axis at (2, 0, 0).
15. Find all points which lie on the intersection of the three planes given by $3x + y + z = 5$, $3x + y + 5z = 7$, $x - y + 3z = 3$.
16. Prove that three planes whose normals are linearly independent intersect in one and only one point.

17. A line with direction vector A is said to be parallel to a plane M if A is parallel to M. A line containing $(1, 2, 3)$ is parallel to each of the planes given by $x + 2y + 3z = 4$, $2x + 3y + 4z = 5$. Find a vector parametric equation for this line.

18. Given a line L not parallel to a plane M, prove that the intersection $L \cap M$ contains exactly one point.

19. (a) Prove that the distance from the point (x_0, y_0, z_0) to the plane with Cartesian equation $ax + by + cz + d = 0$ is

$$\frac{|ax_0 + by_0 + cz_0 + d|}{(a^2 + b^2 + c^2)^{1/2}}.$$

(b) Find the point P on the plane given by $5x - 14y + 2z + 9 = 0$ which is nearest to the point $Q = (-2, 15, -7)$.

20. Find a Cartesian equation for the plane parallel to the plane given by $2x - y + 2z + 4 = 0$ if the point $(3, 2, -1)$ is equidistant from both planes.

21. (a) If three points A, B, C determine a plane, prove that the distance from a point Q to this plane is $|(Q - A) \cdot (B - A) \times (C - A)|/\|(B - A) \times (C - A)\|$.

(b) Compute this distance if $Q = (1, 0, 0)$, $A = (0, 1, 1)$, $B = (1, -1, 1)$, and $C = (2, 3, 4)$.

22. Prove that if two planes M and M' are not parallel, their intersection $M \cap M'$ is a line.

23. Find a Cartesian equation for the plane which is parallel to j and which passes through the intersection of the planes described by the equations $x + 2y + 3z = 4$, and $2x + y + z = 2$.

24. Find a Cartesian equation for the plane parallel to the vector $3i - j + 2k$ if it contains every point on the line of intersection of the planes with equations $x + y = 3$ and $2y + 3z = 4$.

13.18 The conic sections

A moving line G which intersects a fixed line A at a given point P, making a constant angle θ with A, where $0 < \theta < \frac{1}{2}\pi$, generates a surface in 3-space called a right circular cone. The line G is called a *generator* of the cone, A is its *axis*, and P its *vertex*. Each of the cones shown in Figure 13.9 has a vertical axis. The upper and lower portions of the cone meeting at the vertex are called *nappes* of the cone. The curves obtained by slicing the cone with a plane not passing through the vertex are called *conic sections*, or simply *conics*. If the cutting plane is parallel to a line of the cone through the vertex, the conic is called a

Parabola   Ellipse   Hyperbola

FIGURE 13.9   The conic sections.

parabola. Otherwise the intersection is called an *ellipse* or a *hyperbola*, according as the plane cuts just one or both nappes. (See Figure 13.9.) The hyperbola consists of two "branches," one on each nappe.

Many important discoveries in both pure and applied mathematics have been related to the conic sections. Appolonius' treatment of conics as early as the 3rd century B.C. was one of the most profound achievements of classical Greek geometry. Nearly 2000 years later, Galileo discovered that a projectile fired horizontally from the top of a tower falls to earth along a parabolic path (if air resistance is neglected and if the motion takes place above a part of the earth that can be regarded as a flat plane). One of the turning points in the history of astronomy occurred around 1600 when Kepler suggested that all planets move in elliptical orbits. Some 80 years later, Newton was able to demonstrate that an elliptical planetary path implies an inverse-square law of gravitational attraction. This led Newton to formulate his famous theory of universal gravitation which has often been referred to as the greatest scientific discovery ever made. Conic sections appear not only as orbits of planets and satellites but also as trajectories of elementary atomic particles. They are used in the design of lenses and mirrors, and in architecture. These examples and many others show that the importance of the conic sections can hardly be overestimated.

There are other equivalent definitions of the conic sections. One of these refers to special points known as *foci* (singular: *focus*). An ellipse may be defined as the set of all points in a plane the sum of whose distances d_1 and d_2 from two fixed points F_1 and F_2 (the foci) is

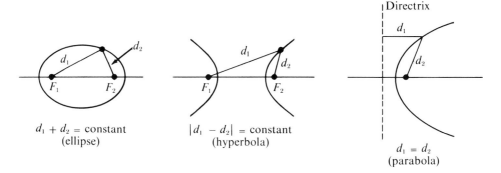

FIGURE 13.10   Focal definitions of the conic sections.

constant. (See Figure 13.10.) If the foci coincide, the ellipse reduces to a circle. A hyperbola is the set of all points for which the difference $|d_1 - d_2|$ is constant. A parabola is the set of all points in a plane for which the distance to a fixed point F (called the focus) is equal to the distance to a given line (called the directrix).

There is a very simple and elegant argument which shows that the focal property of an ellipse is a consequence of its definition as a section of a cone. This proof, which we may refer to as the "ice-cream-cone proof," was discovered in 1822 by a Belgian mathematician, G. P. Dandelin (1794–1847), and makes use of the two spheres S_1 and S_2 which are drawn so as to be tangent to the cutting plane and the cone, as illustrated in Figure 13.11. These spheres touch the cone along two parallel circles C_1 and C_2. We shall prove that the points F_1 and F_2, where the spheres contact the plane, can serve as foci of the ellipse.

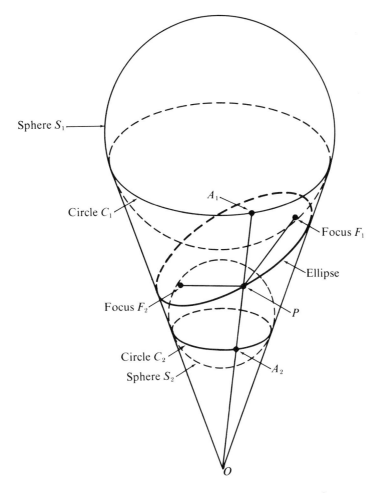

FIGURE 13.11 The ice-cream-cone proof.

Let P be an arbitrary point of the ellipse. The problem is to prove that $\|\overrightarrow{PF_1}\| + \|\overrightarrow{PF_2}\|$ is constant, that is, independent of the choice of P. For this purpose, draw that line on the cone from the vertex O to P and let A_1 and A_2 be its intersections with the circles C_1 and C_2, respectively. Then $\overrightarrow{PF_1}$ and $\overrightarrow{PA_1}$ are two tangents to S_1 from P, and hence $\|\overrightarrow{PF_1}\| = \|\overrightarrow{PA_1}\|$. Similarly $\|\overrightarrow{PF_2}\| = \|\overrightarrow{PA_2}\|$, and therefore we have

$$\|\overrightarrow{PF_1}\| + \|\overrightarrow{PF_2}\| = \|\overrightarrow{PA_1}\| + \|\overrightarrow{PA_2}\| .$$

But $\|\overrightarrow{PA_1}\| + \|\overrightarrow{PA_2}\| = \|\overrightarrow{A_1A_2}\|$, which is the distance between the parallel circles C_1 and C_2 measured along the surface of the cone. This proves that F_1 and F_2 can serve as foci of the ellipse, as asserted.

Modifications of this proof work also for the hyperbola and the parabola. In the case of the hyperbola, the proof employs one sphere in each portion of the cone. For the parabola one sphere tangent to the cutting plane at the focus F is used. This sphere touches the cone along a circle which lies in a plane whose intersection with the cutting plane is the directrix of the parabola. With these hints the reader should be able to show that the focal properties of the hyperbola and parabola may be deduced from their definitions as sections of a cone.

13.19   Eccentricity of conic sections

Another characteristic property of conic sections involves a concept called eccentricity. A conic section can be defined as a curve traced out by a point moving in a plane in such a way that the ratio of its distances from a fixed point and a fixed line is constant. This constant ratio is called the *eccentricity* of the curve and is denoted by e. (This should not be confused with the Euler number e.) The curve is an *ellipse* if $0 < e < 1$, a *parabola* if $e = 1$, and a *hyperbola* if $e > 1$. The fixed point is called a *focus* and the fixed line a *directrix*.

We shall adopt this definition as the basis for our study of the conic sections since it permits a simultaneous treatment of all three types of conics and lends itself to the use of vector methods. In this discussion it is understood that all points and lines are in the same plane.

DEFINITION.   *Given a line L, a point F not on L, and a positive number e. Let $d(X, L)$ denote the distance from a point X to L. The set of all X satisfying the relation*

$$(13.20) \qquad\qquad \|X - F\| = e\, d(X, L)$$

is called a conic section with eccentricity e. The conic is called an ellipse if $e < 1$, a parabola if $e = 1$, and a hyperbola if $e > 1$.

If N is a vector normal to L and if P is any point on L the distance $d(X, L)$ from any point X to L is given by the formula

$$d(X, L) = \frac{|(X - P) \cdot N|}{\|N\|}.$$

When N has length 1, this simplifies to $d(X, L) = |(X - P) \cdot N|$, and the basic equation (13.20) for the conic sections becomes

$$(13.21) \qquad\qquad \|X - F\| = e\,|(X - P) \cdot N|.$$

The line L separates the plane into two parts which we shall arbitrarily label as "positive" and "negative" according to the choice of N. If $(X - P) \cdot N > 0$, we say that X is in the positive half-plane, and if $(X - P) \cdot N < 0$, we say that X is in the negative half-plane. On the line L itself we have $(X - P) \cdot N = 0$. In Figure 13.12 the choice of the normal vector N dictates that points to the right of L are in the positive half-plane and those to the left are in the negative half-plane.

Now we place the focus F in the negative half-plane, as indicated in Figure 13.12, and choose P to be that point on L nearest to F. Then $P - F = dN$, where $|d| = \|P - F\|$ is

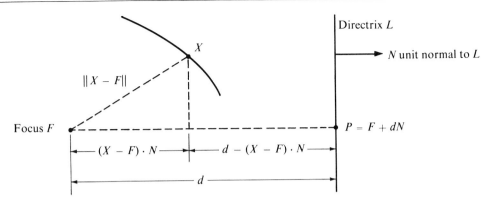

FIGURE 13.12 A conic section with eccentricity e is the set of all X satisfying
$$\|X - F\| = e \, |(X - F) \cdot N - d|.$$

the distance from the focus to the directrix. Since F is in the negative half-plane, we have $(F - P) \cdot N = -d < 0$, so d is positive. Replacing P by $F + dN$ in (13.21), we obtain the following theorem, which is illustrated in Figure 13.12.

THEOREM 13.17. *Let C be a conic section with eccentricity e, focus F, and directrix L at a distance d from F. If N is a unit normal to L and if F is in the negative half-plane determined by N, then C consists of all points X satisfying the equation*

$$(13.22) \qquad\qquad \|X - F\| = e \, |(X - F) \cdot N - d| \, .$$

13.20 Polar equations for conic sections

The equation in Theorem 13.17 can be simplified if we place the focus in a special position. For example, if the focus is at the origin the equation becomes

$$(13.23) \qquad\qquad \|X\| = e \, |X \cdot N - d| \, .$$

This form is especially useful if we wish to express X in terms of polar coordinates. Take the directrix L to be vertical, as shown in Figure 13.13, and let $N = i$. If X has polar coordinates r and θ, we have $\|X\| = r$, $X \cdot N = r \cos\theta$, and Equation (13.23) becomes

$$(13.24) \qquad\qquad r = e \, |r \cos\theta - d| \, .$$

If X lies to the left of the directrix, we have $r \cos\theta < d$, so $|r \cos\theta - d| = d - r \cos\theta$ and (13.24) becomes $r = e(d - r \cos\theta)$, or, solving for r, we obtain

$$(13.25) \qquad\qquad r = \frac{ed}{e \cos\theta + 1} \, .$$

If X lies to the right of the directrix, we have $r \cos \theta > d$, so (13.24) becomes

$$r = e(r \cos \theta - d),$$

giving us

(13.26)
$$r = \frac{ed}{e \cos \theta - 1}.$$

Since $r > 0$, this last equation implies $e > 1$. In other words, there are points to the right of the directrix only for the hyperbola. Thus, we have proved the following theorem which is illustrated in Figure 13.13.

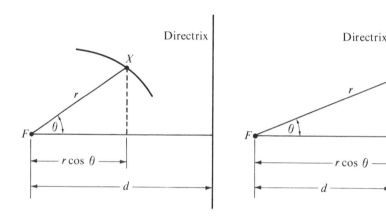

(a) $r \cos \theta < d$ on the ellipse, parabola, and left branch of the hyperbola

(b) $r \cos \theta > d$ on the right branch of the hyperbola

FIGURE 13.13   Conic sections with polar equation $r = e \, |r \cos \theta - d|$. The focus F is at the origin and lies to the left of the directrix.

THEOREM 13.18.   *Let C be a conic section with eccentricity e, with a focus F at the origin, and with a vertical directrix L at a distance d to the right of F. If $0 < e \le 1$, the conic C is an ellipse or a parabola; every point on C lies to the left of L and satisfies the polar equation*

(13.27)
$$r = \frac{ed}{e \cos \theta + 1}.$$

If $e > 1$, the curve is a hyperbola with a branch on each side of L. Points on the left branch satisfy (13.27) and points on the right branch satisfy

(13.28)
$$r = \frac{ed}{e \cos \theta - 1}.$$

Polar equations corresponding to other positions of the directrix are discussed in the next set of exercises.

13.21   Exercises

1. Prove that Equation (13.22) in Theorem 13.17 must be replaced by

$$\|X - F\| = e \,|(X - F) \cdot N + d|$$

  if F is in the positive half-plane determined by N.

2. Let C be a conic section with eccentricity e, with a focus at the origin, and with a vertical directrix L at a distance d to the left of F.

  (a) Prove that if C is an ellipse or parabola, every point of C lies to the right of L and satisfies the polar equation

$$r = \frac{ed}{1 - e \cos \theta}.$$

  (b) Prove that if C is a hyperbola, points on the right branch satisfy the equation in part (a) and points on the left branch satisfy $r = -ed/(1 + e \cos \theta)$. Note that $1 + e \cos \theta$ is always negative in this case.

3. If a conic section has a horizontal directrix at a distance d above a focus at the origin, prove that its points satisfy the polar equations obtained from those in Theorem 13.18 by replacing $\cos \theta$ by $\sin \theta$. What are the corresponding polar equations if the directrix is horizontal and lies below the focus?

Each of Exercises 4 through 9 gives a polar equation for a conic section with a focus F at the origin and a vertical directrix lying to the right of F. In each case, determine the eccentricity e and the distance d from the focus to the directrix. Make a sketch showing the relation of the curve to its focus and directrix.

4. $r = \dfrac{2}{1 + \cos \theta}.$

5. $r = \dfrac{3}{1 + \frac{1}{2} \cos \theta}.$

6. $r = \dfrac{6}{3 + \cos \theta}.$

7. $r = \dfrac{1}{-\frac{1}{2} + \cos \theta}.$

8. $r = \dfrac{4}{1 + 2 \cos \theta}.$

9. $r = \dfrac{4}{1 + \cos \theta}.$

In each of Exercises 10 through 12, a conic section of eccentricity e has a focus at the origin and a directrix with the given Cartesian equation. In each case, compute the distance d from the focus to the directrix and determine a polar equation for the conic section. For a hyperbola, give a polar equation for each branch. Make a sketch showing the relation of the curve to its focus and directrix.

10. $e = \frac{1}{2}$;   directrix: $3x + 4y = 25.$

11. $e = 1$;   directrix: $4x + 3y = 25.$

12. $e = 2$;   directrix: $x + y = 1.$

13. A comet moves in a parabolic orbit with the sun at the focus. When the comet is 10^8 miles from the sun, a vector from the focus to the comet makes an angle of $\pi/3$ with a unit vector N from the focus perpendicular to the directrix, the focus being in the negative half-plane determined by N.

  (a) Find a polar equation for the orbit, taking the origin at the focus, and compute the smallest distance from the comet to the sun.

  (b) Solve part (a) if the focus is in the positive half-plane determined by N.

13.22   Conic sections symmetric about the origin

A set of points is said to be *symmetric about the origin* if $-X$ is in the set whenever X is in the set. We show next that the focus of an ellipse or hyperbola can always be placed so the conic section will be symmetric about the origin. To do this we rewrite the basic equation (13.22) as follows:

$$(13.29) \quad \|X - F\| = e\,|(X - F)\cdot N - d| = e\,|X\cdot N - F\cdot N - d| = |eX\cdot N - a|,$$

where $a = ed + eF\cdot N$. Squaring both members, we obtain

$$(13.30) \qquad \|X\|^2 - 2F\cdot X + \|F\|^2 = e^2(X\cdot N)^2 - 2eaX\cdot N + a^2.$$

If we are to have symmetry about the origin, this equation must also be satisfied when X is replaced by $-X$, giving us

$$(13.31) \qquad \|X\|^2 + 2F\cdot X + \|F\|^2 = e^2(X\cdot N)^2 + 2eaX\cdot N + a^2.$$

Subtracting (13.31) from (13.30), we have symmetry if and only if

$$F\cdot X = eaX\cdot N \qquad \text{or} \qquad (F - eaN)\cdot X = 0.$$

This equation can be satisfied for all X on the curve if and only if F and N are related by the equation

$$(13.32) \qquad\qquad F = eaN, \qquad \text{where} \quad a = ed + eF\cdot N.$$

The relation $F = eaN$ implies $F\cdot N = ea$, giving us $a = ed + e^2a$. If $e = 1$, this last equation cannot be satisfied since d, the distance from the focus to the directrix, is nonzero. This means there is no symmetry about the origin for a parabola. If $e \neq 1$, we can always satisfy the relations in (13.32) by taking

$$(13.33) \qquad\qquad a = \frac{ed}{1 - e^2}, \qquad F = \frac{e^2 d}{1 - e^2}\,N.$$

Note that $a > 0$ if $e < 1$ and $a < 0$ if $e > 1$. Putting $F = eaN$ in (13.30) we obtain the following.

THEOREM 13.19.   *Let C be a conic section with eccentricity $e \neq 1$ and with a focus F at a distance d from a directrix L. If N is a unit normal to L and if $F = eaN$, where $a = ed/(1 - e^2)$, then C is the set of all points X satisfying the equation*

$$(13.34) \qquad\qquad \|X\|^2 + e^2 a^2 = e^2(X\cdot N)^2 + a^2.$$

This equation displays the symmetry about the origin since it is unchanged when X is replaced by $-X$. Because of this symmetry, the ellipse and the hyperbola each have two foci, symmetrically located about the center, and two directrices, also symmetrically located about the center.

Equation (13.34) is satisfied when $X = \pm aN$. These two points are called *vertices* of the conic. The segment joining them is called the *major axis* if the conic is an ellipse, the *transverse axis* if the conic is a hyperbola.

Let N' be a unit vector orthogonal to N. If $X = bN'$, then $X \cdot N = 0$, so Equation (13.34) is satisfied by $X = bN'$ if and only if $b^2 + e^2a^2 = a^2$. This requires $e < 1$, $b^2 = a^2(1 - e^2)$. The segment joining the points $X = \pm bN'$, where $b = a\sqrt{1 - e^2}$ is called the *minor axis* of the ellipse.

> *Note:* If we put $e = 0$ in (13.34), it becomes $\|X\| = a$, the equation of a circle of radius a and center at the origin. In view of (13.33), we can consider such a circle as a limiting case of an ellipse in which $e \to 0$ and $d \to \infty$ in such a way that $ed \to a$.

13.23 Cartesian equations for the conic sections

To obtain Cartesian equations for the ellipse and hyperbola, we simply write (13.34) in terms of the rectangular coordinates of X. Choose $N = i$ (which means the directrices are vertical) and let $X = (x, y)$. Then $\|X\|^2 = x^2 + y^2$, $X \cdot N = x$, and (13.34) becomes $x^2 + y^2 + e^2a^2 = e^2x^2 + a^2$, or $x^2(1 - e^2) + y^2 = a^2(1 - e^2)$, which gives us

$$(13.35) \qquad \frac{x^2}{a^2} + \frac{y^2}{a^2(1 - e^2)} = 1 .$$

This Cartesian equation represents both the ellipse ($e < 1$) and the hyperbola ($e > 1$) and is said to be in *standard form*. The foci are at the points $(ae, 0)$ and $(-ae, 0)$; the directrices are the vertical lines $x = a/e$ and $x = -a/e$.

If $e < 1$, we let $b = a\sqrt{1 - e^2}$ and write the equation of the ellipse in the standard form

$$(13.36) \qquad \frac{x^2}{a^2} + \frac{y^2}{b^2} = 1 .$$

Its foci are located at $(c, 0)$ and $(-c, 0)$, where $c = ae = \sqrt{a^2 - b^2}$. An example is shown in Figure 13.14(a).

If $e > 1$, we let $b = |a|\sqrt{e^2 - 1}$ and write the equation of the hyperbola in the standard form

$$(13.37) \qquad \frac{x^2}{a^2} - \frac{y^2}{b^2} = 1 .$$

Its foci are at the points $(c, 0)$ and $(-c, 0)$, where $c = |a|\, e = \sqrt{a^2 + b^2}$. An example is shown in Figure 13.14(b).

Note: Solving for y in terms of x in (13.37), we obtain two solutions

(13.38)
$$y = \pm \frac{b}{|a|} \sqrt{x^2 - a^2}.$$

For large positive x, the number $\sqrt{x^2 - a^2}$ is nearly equal to x, so the right member of (13.38) is nearly $\pm bx/|a|$. It is easy to prove that the difference between $y_1 = bx/|a|$ and $y_2 = b\sqrt{x^2 - a^2}/|a|$ approaches 0 as $x \to +\infty$. This difference is

$$y_1 - y_2 = \frac{b}{|a|}(x - \sqrt{x^2 - a^2}) = \frac{b}{|a|} \frac{x^2 - (x^2 - a^2)}{x + \sqrt{x^2 - a^2}} = \frac{|a| \, b}{x + \sqrt{x^2 - a^2}} < \frac{|a| \, b}{x},$$

so $y_1 - y_2 \to 0$ as $x \to +\infty$. Therefore, the line $y = bx/|a|$ is an asymptote of the hyperbola. The line $y = -bx/|a|$ is another asymptote. The hyperbola is said to approach these lines asymptotically. The asymptotes are shown in Figure 13.14(b).

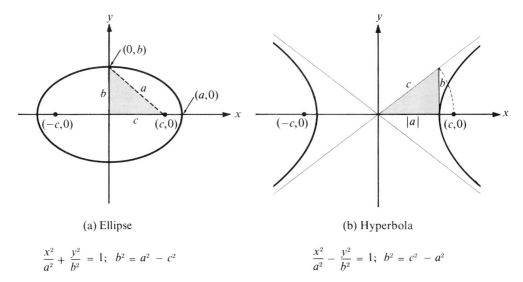

(a) Ellipse

$$\frac{x^2}{a^2} + \frac{y^2}{b^2} = 1; \quad b^2 = a^2 - c^2$$

(b) Hyperbola

$$\frac{x^2}{a^2} - \frac{y^2}{b^2} = 1; \quad b^2 = c^2 - a^2$$

FIGURE 13.14   Conic sections of eccentricity $e \neq 1$, symmetric about the origin. The foci are at $(\pm c, 0)$, where $c = |a| \, e$. The triangles relate a, b, c geometrically.

The Cartesian equation for the ellipse and hyperbola will take a different form if the directrices are not vertical. For example, if the directrices are taken to be horizontal, we may take $N = j$ in Equation (13.34). Since $X \cdot N = X \cdot j = y$, we obtain a Cartesian equation like (13.35), except that x and y are interchanged. The standard form in this case is

(13.39)
$$\frac{y^2}{a^2} + \frac{x^2}{a^2(1 - e^2)} = 1.$$

If the conic is translated by adding a vector $X_0 = (x_0, y_0)$ to each of its points, the center will be at (x_0, y_0) instead of at the origin. The corresponding Cartesian equations may be obtained from (13.35) or (13.39) by replacing x by $x - x_0$ and y by $y - y_0$.

To obtain a Cartesian equation for the parabola, we return to the basic equation (13.20) with $e = 1$. Take the directrix to be the vertical line $x = -c$ and place the focus at $(c, 0)$. If $X = (x, y)$, we have $X - F = (x - c, y)$, and Equation (13.20) gives us $(x - c)^2 + y^2 = |x + c|^2$. This simplifies to the standard form

(13.40)
$$y^2 = 4cx.$$

The point midway between the focus and directrix (the origin in Figure 13.15) is called the *vertex* of the parabola, and the line passing through the vertex and focus is the *axis* of the parabola. The parabola is symmetric about its axis. If $c > 0$, the parabola lies to the right of the y-axis, as in Figure 13.15. When $c < 0$, the curve lies to the left of the y-axis.

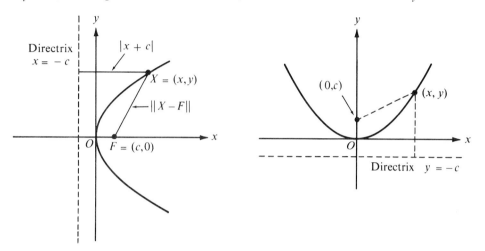

FIGURE 13.15   The parabola $y^2 = 4cx$.   FIGURE 13.16   The parabola $x^2 = 4cy$.

If the axes are chosen so the focus is on the y-axis at the point $(0, c)$ and if the horizontal line $y = -c$ is taken as directrix, the standard form of the Cartesian equation becomes

$$x^2 = 4cy.$$

When $c > 0$ the parabola opens upward as shown in Figure 13.16. When $c < 0$, it opens downward.

If the parabola in Figure 13.15 is translated so that its vertex is at the point (x_0, y_0), the corresponding equation becomes

$$(y - y_0)^2 = 4c(x - x_0).$$

The focus is now at the point $(x_0 + c, y_0)$ and the directrix is the line $x = x_0 - c$. The axis of the parabola is the line $y = y_0$.

Similarly, a translation of the parabola in Figure 13.16 leads to the equation

$$(x - x_0)^2 = 4c(y - y_0),$$

with focus at $(x_0, y_0 + c)$. The line $y = y_0 - c$ is its directrix, the line $x = x_0$ its axis.

The reader may find it amusing to prove that a parabola does not have any asymptotes.

13.24 Exercises

Each of the equations in Exercises 1 through 6 represents an ellipse. Find the coordinates of the center, the foci, and the vertices, and sketch each curve. Also determine the eccentricity.

1. $\dfrac{x^2}{100} + \dfrac{y^2}{36} = 1.$

2. $\dfrac{y^2}{100} + \dfrac{x^2}{36} = 1.$

3. $\dfrac{(x-2)^2}{16} + \dfrac{(y+3)^2}{9} = 1.$

4. $9x^2 + 25y^2 = 25.$

5. $4y^2 + 3x^2 = 1.$

6. $\dfrac{(x+1)^2}{16} + \dfrac{(y+2)^2}{25} = 1.$

In each of Exercises 7 through 12, find a Cartesian equation (in the appropriate standard form) for the ellipse that satisfies the conditions given. Sketch each curve.

7. Center at $(0,0)$, one focus at $(\frac{3}{4}, 0)$, one vertex at $(1,0)$.
8. Center at $(-3, 4)$, semiaxes of lengths 4 and 3, major axis parallel to the x-axis.
9. Same as Exercise 8, except with major axis parallel to the y-axis.
10. Vertices at $(-1, 2)$, $(-7, 2)$, minor axis of length 2.
11. Vertices at $(3, -2)$, $(13, -2)$, foci at $(4, -2)$, $(12, -2)$.
12. Center at $(2, 1)$, major axis parallel to the x-axis, the curve passing through the points $(6, 1)$ and $(2, 3)$.

Each of the equations in Exercises 13 through 18 represents a hyperbola. Find the coordinates of the center, the foci, and the vertices. Sketch each curve and show the positions of the asymptotes. Also, compute the eccentricity.

13. $\dfrac{x^2}{100} - \dfrac{y^2}{64} = 1.$

14. $\dfrac{y^2}{100} - \dfrac{x^2}{64} = 1.$

15. $\dfrac{(x+3)^2}{4} - (y-3)^2 = 1.$

16. $9x^2 - 16y^2 = 144.$

17. $4x^2 - 5y^2 + 20 = 0.$

18. $\dfrac{(x-1)^2}{4} - \dfrac{(y+2)^2}{9} = 1.$

In each of Exercises 19 through 23, find a Cartesian equation (in the appropriate standard form) for the hyperbola which satisfies the conditions given. Sketch each curve and show the positions of the asymptotes.

19. Center at $(0,0)$, one focus at $(4, 0)$, one vertex at $(2, 0)$.
20. Foci at $(0, \pm\sqrt{2})$, vertices at $(0, \pm 1)$.
21. Vertices at $(\pm 2, 0)$, asymptotes $y = \pm 2x$.
22. Center at $(-1, 4)$, one focus at $(-1, 2)$, one vertex at $(-1, 3)$.
23. Center at $(2, -3)$, transverse axis parallel to one of the coordinate axes, the curve passing through $(3, -1)$ and $(-1, 0)$.
24. For what value (or values) of C will the line $3x - 2y = C$ be tangent to the hyperbola $x^2 - 3y^2 = 1$?
25. The asymptotes of a hyperbola are the lines $2x - y = 0$ and $2x + y = 0$. Find a Cartesian equation for the curve if it passes through the point $(3, -5)$.

Each of the equations in Exercises 26 through 31 represents a parabola. Find the coordinates of the vertex, an equation for the directrix, and an equation for the axis. Sketch each of the curves.

26. $y^2 = -8x.$

27. $y^2 = 3x.$

28. $(y-1)^2 = 12x - 6.$

29. $x^2 = 6y.$

30. $x^2 + 8y = 0.$

31. $(x+2)^2 = 4y + 9.$

In each of Exercises 32 through 37, find a Cartesian equation (in appropriate standard form) for the parabola that satisfies the conditions given and sketch the curve.

32. Focus at $(0, -\frac{1}{4})$; equation of directrix, $y = \frac{1}{4}$.
33. Vertex at $(0, 0)$; equation of directrix, $x = -2$.
34. Vertex at $(-4, 3)$; focus at $(-4, 1)$.
35. Focus at $(3, -1)$; equation of directrix, $x = \frac{1}{2}$.
36. Axis is parallel to the y-axis; passes through $(0, 1)$, $(1, 0)$, and $(2, 0)$.
37. Axis is parallel to the x-axis; vertex at $(1, 3)$; passes through $(-1, -1)$.
38. Proceeding directly from the focal definition, find a Cartesian equation for the parabola whose focus is the origin and whose directrix is the line $2x + y = 10$.

13.25 Miscellaneous exercises on conic sections

1. Show that the area of the region bounded by the ellipse $x^2/a^2 + y^2/b^2 = 1$ is ab times the area of a circle of radius 1.

   Note: This statement can be proved from general properties of the integral, without performing any integrations.

2. (a) Show that the volume of the solid of revolution generated by rotating the ellipse $x^2/a^2 + y^2/b^2 = 1$ about its major axis is ab^2 times the volume of a unit sphere.

   Note: This statement can be proved from general properties of the integral, without performing any integrations.

   (b) What is the result if the ellipse is rotated about its minor axis?
3. Find all positive numbers A and B, $A > B$, such that the area of the region enclosed by the ellipse $Ax^2 + By^2 = 3$ is equal to the area of the region enclosed by the ellipse

$$(A + B)x^2 + (A - B)y^2 = 3 .$$

4. A parabolic arch has a base of length b and altitude h. Determine the area of the region bounded by the arch and the base.
5. The region bounded by the parabola $y^2 = 8x$ and the line $x = 2$ is rotated about the x-axis. Find the volume of the solid of revolution so generated.
6. Two parabolas having the equations $y^2 = 2(x - 1)$ and $y^2 = 4(x - 2)$ enclose a plane region R.
   (a) Compute the area of R by integration.
   (b) Find the volume of the solid of revolution generated by revolving R about the x-axis.
   (c) Same as (b), but revolve R about the y-axis.
7. Find a Cartesian equation for the conic section consisting of all points (x, y) whose distance from the point $(0, 2)$ is half the distance from the line $y = 8$.
8. Find a Cartesian equation for the parabola whose focus is at the origin and whose directrix is the line $x + y + 1 = 0$.
9. Find a Cartesian equation for a hyperbola passing through the origin, given that its asymptotes are the lines $y = 2x + 1$ and $y = -2x + 3$.
10. (a) For each $p > 0$, the equation $px^2 + (p + 2)y^2 = p^2 + 2p$ represents an ellipse. Find (in terms of p) the eccentricity and the coordinates of the foci.
    (b) Find a Cartesian equation for the hyperbola which has the same foci as the ellipse of part (a) and which has eccentricity $\sqrt{3}$.
11. In Section 13.22 we proved that a conic symmetric about the origin satisfies the equation $\|X - F\| = |eX \cdot N - a|$, where $a = ed + eF \cdot N$. Use this relation to prove that $\|X - F\| + \|X + F\| = 2a$ if the conic is an ellipse. In other words, the sum of the distances from any point on an ellipse to its foci is constant.

12. Refer to Exercise 11. Prove that on each branch of a hyperbola the difference $\|X - F\| - \|X + F\|$ is constant.

13. (a) Prove that a similarity transformation (replacing x by tx and y by ty) carries an ellipse with center at the origin into another ellipse with the same eccentricity. In other words, similar ellipses have the same eccentricity.
    (b) Prove also the converse. That is, if two concentric ellipses have the same eccentricity and major axes on the same line, then they are related by a similarity transformation.
    (c) Prove results corresponding to (a) and (b) for hyperbolas.

14. Use the Cartesian equation which represents all conics of eccentricity e and center at the origin to prove that these conics are integral curves of the differential equation $y' = (e^2 - 1)x/y$.

> *Note:* Since this is a homogeneous differential equation (Section 8.25), the set of all such conics of eccentricity e is invariant under a similarity transformation. (Compare with Exercise 13.)

15. (a) Prove that the collection of all parabolas is invariant under a similarity transformation. That is, a similarity transformation carries a parabola into a parabola.
    (b) Find all the parabolas similar to $y = x^2$.

16. The line $x - y + 4 = 0$ is tangent to the parabola $y^2 = 16x$. Find the point of contact.

17. (a) Given $a \neq 0$. If the two parabolas $y^2 = 4p(x - a)$ and $x^2 = 4qy$ are tangent to each other, show that the x-coordinate of the point of contact is determined by a alone.
    (b) Find a condition on a, p, and q which expresses the fact that the two parabolas are tangent to each other.

18. Consider the locus of the points P in the plane for which the distance of P from the point $(2, 3)$ is equal to the sum of the distances of P from the two coordinate axes.
    (a) Show that the part of this locus which lies in the first quadrant is part of a hyperbola. Locate the asymptotes and make a sketch.
    (b) Sketch the graph of the locus in the other quadrants.

19. Two parabolas have the same point as focus and the same line as axis, but their vertices lie on opposite sides of the focus. Prove that the parabolas intersect orthogonally (i.e., their tangent lines are perpendicular at the points of intersection).

20. (a) Prove that the Cartesian equation

$$\frac{x^2}{a^2} + \frac{y^2}{a^2 - c^2} = 1$$

represents all conics symmetric about the origin with foci at $(c, 0)$ and $(-c, 0)$.
    (b) Keep c fixed and let S denote the set of all such conics obtained as a^2 varies over all positive numbers $\neq c^2$. Prove that every curve in S satisfies the differential equation

$$xy \left(\frac{dy}{dx}\right)^2 + (x^2 - y^2 - c^2)\frac{dy}{dx} - xy = 0.$$

    (c) Prove that S is self-orthogonal; that is, the set of all orthogonal trajectories of curves in S is S itself. [*Hint:* Replace y' by $-1/y'$ in the differential equation in (b).]

21. Show that the locus of the centers of a family of circles, all of which pass through a given point and are tangent to a given line, is a parabola.

22. Show that the locus of the centers of a family of circles, all of which are tangent (externally) to a given circle and also to a given straight line, is a parabola. (Exercise 21 can be considered to be a special case.)

23. (a) A chord of length $8\,|c|$ is drawn perpendicular to the axis of the parabola $y^2 = 4cx$. Let P and Q be the points where the chord meets the parabola. Show that the vector from O to P is perpendicular to that from O to Q.

(b) The chord of a parabola drawn through the focus and parallel to the directrix is called the *latus rectum*. Show first that the length of the latus rectum is twice the distance from the focus to the directrix, and then show that the tangents to the parabola at both ends of the latus rectum intersect the axis of the parabola on the directrix.

24. Two points P and Q are said to be symmetric with respect to a circle if P and Q are collinear with the center, if the center is not between them, and if the product of their distances from the center is equal to the square of the radius. Given that Q describes the straight line $x + 2y - 5 = 0$, find the locus of the point P symmetric to Q with respect to the circle $x^2 + y^2 = 4$.

14

CALCULUS OF VECTOR-VALUED FUNCTIONS

14.1 Vector-valued functions of a real variable

This chapter combines vector algebra with the methods of calculus and describes some applications to the study of curves and to some problems in mechanics. The concept of a vector-valued function is fundamental in this study.

DEFINITION. *A function whose domain is a set of real numbers and whose range is a subset of n-space V_n is called a vector-valued function of a real variable.*

We have encountered such functions in Chapter 13. For example, the line through a point P parallel to a nonzero vector A is the range of the vector-valued function X given by

$$X(t) = P + tA$$

for all real t.

Vector-valued functions will be denoted by capital letters such as F, G, X, Y, etc., or by small bold-face italic letters f, g, etc. The value of a function F at t is denoted, as usual, by $F(t)$. In the examples we shall study, the domain of F will be an interval which may contain one or both endpoints or which may be infinite.

14.2 Algebraic operations. Components

The usual operations of vector algebra can be applied to combine two vector-valued functions or to combine a vector-valued function with a real-valued function. If F and G are vector-valued functions, and if u is a real-valued function, all having a common domain, we define new functions $F + G$, uF, and $F \cdot G$ by the equations

$$(F + G)(t) = F(t) + G(t), \qquad (uF)(t) = u(t)F(t), \qquad (F \cdot G)(t) = F(t) \cdot G(t).$$

The sum $F + G$ and the product uF are vector valued, whereas the dot product $F \cdot G$ is real valued. If $F(t)$ and $G(t)$ are in 3-space, we can also define the cross product $F \times G$ by the formula

$$(F \times G)(t) = F(t) \times G(t).$$

512

The operation of composition may be applied to combine vector-valued functions with real-valued functions. For example, if F is a vector-valued function whose domain includes the range of a real-valued function u, the composition $G = F \circ u$ is a new vector-valued function defined by the equation

$$G(t) = F[u(t)]$$

for each t in the domain of u.

If a function F has its values in V_n, then each vector $F(t)$ has n components, and we can write

$$F(t) = (f_1(t), f_2(t), \ldots, f_n(t)).$$

Thus, each vector-valued F gives rise to n real-valued functions $f_1, \ldots, f_n$ whose values at t are the components of $F(t)$. We indicate this relation by writing $F = (f_1, \ldots, f_n)$, and we call f_k the kth component of F.

14.3 Limits, derivatives, and integrals

The basic concepts of calculus, such as limit, derivative, and integral, can also be extended to vector-valued functions. We simply express the vector-valued function in terms of its components and perform the operations of calculus on the components.

DEFINITION. *If $F = (f_1, \ldots, f_n)$ is a vector-valued function, we define limit, derivative, and integral by the equations*

$$\lim_{t \to p} F(t) = \left(\lim_{t \to p} f_1(t), \ldots, \lim_{t \to p} f_n(t) \right),$$

$$F'(t) = (f_1'(t), \ldots, f_n'(t)),$$

$$\int_a^b F(t)\, dt = \left(\int_a^b f_1(t)\, dt, \ldots, \int_a^b f_n(t)\, dt \right),$$

whenever the components on the right are meaningful.

We also say that F is *continuous, differentiable,* or *integrable* on an interval if each component of F has the corresponding property on the interval.

In view of these definitions, it is not surprising to find that many of the theorems on limits, continuity, differentiation, and integration of real-valued functions are also valid for vector-valued functions. We state some of the theorems that we use in this chapter.

THEOREM 14.1. *If F, G, and u are differentiable on an interval, then so are $F + G$, uF, and $F \cdot G$, and we have*

$$(F + G)' = F' + G', \qquad (uF)' = u'F + uF', \qquad (F \cdot G)' = F' \cdot G + F \cdot G'.$$

If F and G have values in V_3, we also have

$$(F \times G)' = F' \times G + F \times G'.$$

Proof. To indicate the routine nature of the proofs we discuss the formula for $(uF)'$. The proofs of the others are similar and are left as exercises for the reader.

Writing $F = (f_1, \ldots, f_n)$, we have

$$uF = (uf_1, \ldots, uf_n), \qquad (uF)' = ((uf_1)', \ldots, (uf_n)').$$

But the derivative of the kth component of uF is $(uf_k)' = u'f_k + uf_k'$, so we have

$$(uF)' = u'(f_1, \ldots, f_n) + u(f_1', \ldots, f_n') = u'F + uF'.$$

The reader should note that the differentiation formulas in Theorem 14.1 are analogous to the usual formulas for differentiating a sum or product of real-valued functions. Since the cross product is not commutative, one must pay attention to the order of the factors in the formula for $(F \times G)'$.

The formula for differentiating $F \cdot G$ gives us the following theorem which we shall use frequently.

THEOREM 14.2. *If a vector-valued function is differentiable and has constant length on an open interval* I, *then* $F \cdot F' = 0$ *on* I. *In other words,* $F'(t)$ *is perpendicular to* $F(t)$ *for each* t *in* I.

Proof. Let $g(t) = \|F(t)\|^2 = F(t) \cdot F(t)$. By hypothesis, g is constant on I, and hence $g' = 0$ on I. But since g is a dot product, we have $g' = F' \cdot F + F \cdot F' = 2F \cdot F'$. Therefore we have $F \cdot F' = 0$.

The next theorem deals with composite functions. Its proof follows easily from Theorems 3.5 and 4.2 which contain the corresponding results for real-valued functions.

THEOREM 14.3. *Let* $G = F \circ u$, *where* F *is vector valued and* u *is real valued. If* u *is continuous at* t *and if* F *is continuous at* $u(t)$, *then* G *is continuous at* t. *If the derivatives* $u'(t)$ *and* $F'[u(t)]$ *exist, then* $G'(t)$ *also exists and is given by the chain rule,*

$$G'(t) = F'[u(t)]u'(t).$$

If a vector-valued function F is continuous on a closed interval $[a, b]$, then each component is continuous and hence integrable on $[a, b]$, so F is integrable on $[a, b]$. The next three theorems give basic properties of the integral of vector-valued functions. In each case, the proofs follow at once from the corresponding results for integrals of real-valued functions.

THEOREM 14.4. LINEARITY AND ADDITIVITY. *If the vector-valued functions* F *and* G *are integrable on* $[a, b]$, *so is* $c_1F + c_2G$ *for all* c_1 *and* c_2, *and we have*

$$\int_a^b (c_1F(t) + c_2G(t)) \, dt = c_1 \int_a^b F(t) \, dt + c_2 \int_a^b G(t) \, dt.$$

Also, for each c in [a, b], we have

$$\int_a^b F(t)\, dt = \int_a^c F(t)\, dt + \int_c^b F(t)\, dt\ .$$

THEOREM 14.5. FIRST FUNDAMENTAL THEOREM OF CALCULUS. *Assume F is a vector-valued function continuous on $[a, b]$. If $c \in [a, b]$, define the indefinite integral A to be the vector-valued function given by*

$$A(x) = \int_c^x F(t)\, dt \qquad if \quad a \le x \le b,$$

Then $A'(x)$ exists, and we have $A'(x) = F(x)$ for each x in (a, b).

THEOREM 14.6. SECOND FUNDAMENTAL THEOREM OF CALCULUS. *Assume that the vector-valued function F has a continuous derivative F' on an open interval I. Then, for each choice of c and x in I, we have*

$$F(x) = F(c) + \int_c^x F'(t)\, dt\ .$$

The next theorem is an extension of the property $c\int_a^b F(t)\, dt = \int_a^b cF(t)\, dt$, with multiplication by the scalar c replaced by dot multiplication by a vector C.

THEOREM 14.7. *If $F = (f_1, \ldots, f_n)$ is integrable on $[a, b]$, then for every vector $C = (c_1, \ldots, c_n)$ the dot product $C \cdot F$ is integrable on $[a, b]$, and we have*

$$C \cdot \int_a^b F(t)\, dt = \int_a^b C \cdot F(t)\, dt\ .$$

Proof. Since each component of F is integrable, we have

$$C \cdot \int_a^b F(t)\, dt = \sum_{i=1}^n c_i \int_a^b f_i(t)\, dt = \int_a^b \sum_{i=1}^n c_i f_i(t)\, dt = \int_a^b C \cdot F(t)\, dt\ .$$

Now we use Theorem 14.7 in conjunction with the Cauchy-Schwarz inequality to obtain the following important property of integrals of vector-valued functions.

THEOREM 14.8. *If F and $\|F\|$ are integrable on $[a, b]$ we have*

(14.1) $$\left\| \int_a^b F(t)\, dt \right\| \le \int_a^b \|F(t)\|\, dt\ .$$

Proof. Let $C = \int_a^b F(t)\, dt$. If $C = O$, then (14.1) holds trivially. Assume, then, that $C \ne O$ and apply Theorem 14.7 to get

(14.2) $$\|C\|^2 = C \cdot C = C \cdot \int_a^b F(t)\, dt = \int_a^b C \cdot F(t)\, dt\ .$$

Since the dot product $C \cdot F(t)$ is real valued, we have the inequality

(14.3) $$\int_a^b C \cdot F(t)\, dt \leq \int_a^b |C \cdot F(t)|\, dt \leq \int_a^b \|C\|\ \|F(t)\|\, dt\,,$$

where in the last step we used the Cauchy-Schwarz inequality, $|C \cdot F(t)| \leq \|C\|\ \|F(t)\|$. Combining (14.2) and (14.3), we get

$$\|C\|^2 \leq \|C\| \int_a^b \|F(t)\|\, dt\,.$$

Since $\|C\| > 0$, we can divide by $\|C\|$ to get (14.1).

14.4 Exercises

Compute the derivatives $F'(t)$ and $F''(t)$ for each of the vector-valued functions in Exercises 1 through 6.

1. $F(t) = (t, t^2, t^3, t^4)$.

2. $F(t) = (\cos t, \sin^2 t, \sin 2t, \tan t)$.

3. $F(t) = (\arcsin t, \arccos t)$.

4. $F(t) = 2e^t i + 3e^t j$.

5. $F(t) = \cosh t\, i + \sinh 2t\, j + e^{-3t} k$.

6. $F(t) = \log (1 + t^2)\, i + \arctan t\, j + \dfrac{1}{1 + t^2}\, k$.

7. Let F be the vector-valued function given by

$$F(t) = \frac{2t}{1 + t^2}\, i + \frac{1 - t^2}{1 + t^2}\, j + k\,.$$

Prove that the angle between $F(t)$ and $F'(t)$ is constant, that is, independent of t.

Compute the vector-valued integrals in Exercises 8 through 11.

8. $\displaystyle\int_0^1 (t, \sqrt{t}, e^t)\, dt$.

9. $\displaystyle\int_0^{\pi/4} (\sin t, \cos t, \tan t)\, dt$.

10. $\displaystyle\int_0^1 \left(\frac{e^t}{1 + e^t}\, i + \frac{1}{1 + e^t}\, j \right) dt$.

11. $\displaystyle\int_0^1 (te^t i + t^2 e^t j + te^{-t} k)\, dt$.

12. Compute $A \cdot B$, where $A = 2i - 4j + k$ and $B = \int_0^1 (te^{2t} i + t \cosh 2t\, j + 2te^{-2t} k)\, dt$.

13. Given a nonzero vector B and a vector-valued function F such that $F(t) \cdot B = t$ for all t, and such that the angle between $F'(t)$ and B is constant (independent of t). Prove that $F''(t)$ is orthogonal to $F'(t)$.

14. Given fixed nonzero vectors A and B, let $F(t) = e^{2t} A + e^{-2t} B$. Prove that $F''(t)$ has the same direction as $F(t)$.

15. If $G = F \times F'$, compute G' in terms of F and derivatives of F.

16. If $G = F \cdot F' \times F''$, prove that $G' = F \cdot F' \times F'''$.

17. Prove that $\lim_{t \to p} F(t) = A$ if and only if $\lim_{t \to p} \|F(t) - A\| = 0$.

18. Prove that a vector-valued function F is differentiable on an open interval I if and only if for each t in I we have

$$F'(t) = \lim_{h \to 0} \frac{1}{h} [F(t + h) - F(t)]\,.$$

19. Prove the zero-derivative theorem for vector-valued functions. If $F'(t) = O$ for each t in an open interval I, then there is a vector C such that $F(t) = C$ for all t in I.

20. Given fixed vectors A and B and a vector-valued function F such that $F''(t) = tA + B$, determine $F(t)$ if $F(0) = D$ and $F'(0) = C$.

21. A differential equation of the form $Y'(x) + p(x) Y(x) = Q(x)$, where p is a given real-valued function, Q a given vector-valued function, and Y an unknown vector-valued function, is called a first-order linear vector differential equation. Prove that if p and Q are continuous on an interval I, then for each a in I and each vector B there is one and only one solution Y which satisfies the initial condition $Y(a) = B$, and that this solution is given by the formula

$$Y(t) = Be^{-q(t)} + e^{-q(t)} \int_a^t Q(x)e^{q(x)} \, dx \,,$$

where $q(x) = \int_a^x p(t) \, dt$.

22. A vector-valued function F satisfies the equation $tF'(t) = F(t) + tA$ for each $t \geq 0$, where A is a fixed vector. Compute $F''(1)$ and $F(3)$ in terms of A, if $F(1) = 2A$.

23. Find a vector-valued function F, continuous on the interval $(0, +\infty)$, such that

$$F(x) = xe^x A + \frac{1}{x} \int_1^x F(t) \, dt \,,$$

for all $x > 0$, where A is a fixed nonzero vector.

24. A vector-valued function F, which is never zero and has a continuous derivative $F'(t)$ for all t, is always parallel to its derivative. Prove that there is a constant vector A and a positive real-valued function u such that $F(t) = u(t)A$ for all t.

14.5 Applications to curves. Tangency

Let X be a vector-valued function whose domain is an interval I. As t runs through I, the corresponding function values $X(t)$ run through a set of points which we call the *graph* of the function X. If the function values are in 2-space or in 3-space, we can visualize the graph geometrically. For example, if $X(t) = P + tA$, where P and A are fixed vectors in V_3, with $A \neq O$, the graph of X is a straight line through P parallel to A. A more general function will trace out a more general graph, as suggested by the example in Figure 14.1. If X is continuous on I, such a graph is called a *curve*; more specifically, the curve described by X. Sometimes we say that the curve is described *parametrically* by X. The interval I is called a *parametric interval*; each t in I is called a *parameter*.

Properties of the function X can be used to investigate geometric properties of its graph. In particular, the derivative X' is related to the concept of tangency, as in the case of a real-valued function. We form the difference quotient

(14.4)
$$\frac{X(t + h) - X(t)}{h}$$

and investigate its behavior as $h \to 0$. This quotient is the product of the vector $X(t + h) - X(t)$ by the scalar $1/h$. The numerator, $X(t + h) - X(t)$, illustrated geometrically in Figure 14.2, is parallel to the vector in (14.4). If we express this difference quotient in terms of its components and let $h \to 0$, we find that

$$\lim_{h \to 0} \frac{X(t + h) - X(t)}{h} = X'(t) \,,$$

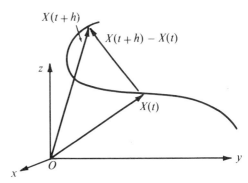

FIGURE 14.1   A curve traced out by a
vector $X(t)$.

FIGURE 14.2   The vector $X(t + h) - X(t)$ is
parallel to $[X(t + h) - X(t)]/h$.

assuming that the derivative $X'(t)$ exists.   The geometric interpretation of this relation
suggests the following definition.

DEFINITION.   *Let C be a curve described by a continuous vector-valued function X.   If
the derivative $X'(t)$ exists and is nonzero, the straight line through $X(t)$ parallel to $X'(t)$ is
called the tangent line to C at $X(t)$.   The vector $X'(t)$ is called a tangent vector to C at $X(t)$.*

EXAMPLE 1.   *Straight line.*   For a line given by $X(t) = P + tA$, where $A \neq O$, we have
$X'(t) = A$, so the tangent line at each point coincides with the graph of X, a property which
we surely want.

EXAMPLE 2.   *Circle.*   If X describes a circle of radius a and center at a point P, then
$\|X(t) - P\| = a$ for each t.   The vector $X(t) - P$ is called a *radius vector;* it may be represented geometrically by an arrow from the center to the point $X(t)$.   Since the radius vector
has constant length, Theorem 14.2 tells us that it is perpendicular to its derivative and hence
perpendicular to the tangent line.   Thus, for a circle, our definition of tangency agrees
with that given in elementary plane geometry.

EXAMPLE 3.   *Invariance under a change of parameter.*   Different functions can have the
same graph.   For example, suppose that X is a continuous vector-valued function defined
on an interval I and suppose that u is a real-valued function that is differentiable with u'
never zero on an interval J, and such that the range of u is I.   Then the function Y defined
on J by the equation

$$Y(t) = X[u(t)]$$

is a continuous vector-valued function having the same graph as X.   Two functions X
and Y so related are called *equivalent*.   They are said to provide different parametric
representations of the same curve.   The function u is said to define a change of parameter.

   The most important geometric concepts associated with a curve are those that remain
invariant under a change of parameter.   For example, it is easy to prove that the tangent

line is invariant. If the derivative $X'[u(t)]$ exists, the chain rule shows that $Y'(t)$ also exists and is given by the formula

$$Y'(t) = X'[u(t)]u'(t).$$

The derivative $u'(t)$ is never zero. If $X'[u(t)]$ is nonzero, then $Y'(t)$ is also nonzero, so $Y'(t)$ is parallel to $X'[u(t)]$. Therefore both representations X and Y lead to the same tangent line at each point of the curve.

EXAMPLE 4. *Reflection properties of the conic sections.* Conic sections have reflection properties often used in the design of optical and acoustical equipment. Light rays emanating from one focus of an elliptical reflector will converge at the other focus, as shown in

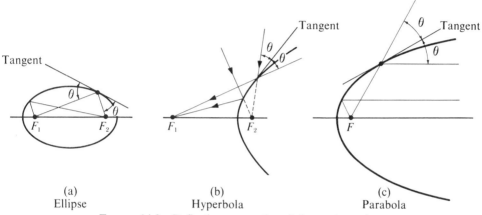

FIGURE 14.3   Reflection properties of the conic sections.

Figure 14.3(a). Light rays directed toward one focus of a hyperbolic reflector will converge at the other focus, as suggested by Figure 14.3(b). In a parabolic reflector, light rays parallel to the axis converge at the focus, as shown in Figure 14.3(c). To establish these reflection properties, we need to prove that in each figure the angles labeled θ are equal. We shall do this for the ellipse and hyperbola and ask the reader to give a proof for the parabola.

Place one focus F_1 at the origin and let u_1 and u_2 be unit vectors having the same directions as X and $X - F_2$, respectively, where X is an arbitrary point on the conic. (See Figure 14.4.) If $d_1 = \|X\|$ and $d_2 = \|X - F_2\|$ are the focal distances between X and the foci F_1 and F_2, respectively, we have

$$X = d_1 u_1 \qquad \text{and} \qquad X = d_2 u_2 + F_2.$$

Now we think of X, u_1, u_2, d_1, and d_2 as functions defined on some interval of real numbers. Their derivatives are related by the equations

(14.5) $$X' = d_1 u_1' + d_1' u_1, \qquad X' = d_2 u_2' + d_2' u_2.$$

Since u_1 and u_2 have constant length, each is perpendicular to its derivative, so Equations (14.5) give us $X' \cdot u_1 = d_1'$ and $X' \cdot u_2 = d_2'$. Adding and subtracting these relations, we find that

(14.6) $X' \cdot (\boldsymbol{u}_1 + \boldsymbol{u}_2) = d_1' + d_2', \qquad X' \cdot (\boldsymbol{u}_1 - \boldsymbol{u}_2) = d_1' - d_2'.$

On the ellipse, $d_1 + d_2$ is constant, so $d_1' + d_2' = 0$. On each branch of the hyperbola,

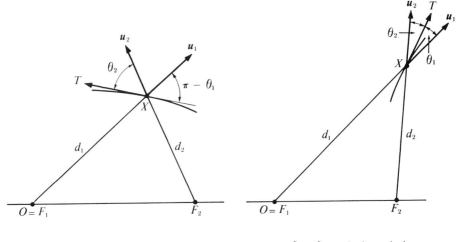

(a) $\theta_2 = \pi - \theta_1$ on the ellipse   (b) $\theta_2 = \theta_1$ on the hyperbola

FIGURE 14.4   Proofs of the reflection properties for the ellipse and hyperbola.

$d_1 - d_2$ is constant, so $d_1' - d_2' = 0$. Therefore, Equations (14.6) give us

$\quad X' \cdot (\boldsymbol{u}_1 + \boldsymbol{u}_2) = 0 \quad$ on the ellipse, $\quad X' \cdot (\boldsymbol{u}_1 - \boldsymbol{u}_2) = 0 \quad$ on the hyperbola.

Let $T = X'/\|X'\|$ be a unit vector having the same direction as X'. Then T is tangent to the conic, and we have

$\quad T \cdot \boldsymbol{u}_2 = -T \cdot \boldsymbol{u}_1 \quad$ on the ellipse, $\quad T \cdot \boldsymbol{u}_2 = T \cdot \boldsymbol{u}_1 \quad$ on the hyperbola.

If θ_1 and θ_2 denote, respectively, the angles that T makes with $\boldsymbol{u}_1$ and $\boldsymbol{u}_2$, where $0 \le \theta_1 \le \pi$ and $0 \le \theta_2 \le \pi$, these last two equations show that

$\quad \cos \theta_2 = -\cos \theta_1 \quad$ on the ellipse, $\quad \cos \theta_2 = \cos \theta_1 \quad$ on the hyperbola.

Hence we have $\theta_2 = \pi - \theta_1$ on the ellipse, and $\theta_2 = \theta_1$ on the hyperbola. These relations between the angles θ_1 and θ_2 give the reflection properties of the ellipse and hyperbola.

14.6   Applications to curvilinear motion. Velocity, speed, and acceleration

Suppose a particle moves in 2-space or in 3-space in such a way that its position at time t relative to some coordinate system is given by a vector $X(t)$. As t varies through a time interval, the path traced out by the particle is simply the graph of X. Thus, the vector-valued function X serves as a natural mathematical model to describe the motion. We call

X the *position function* of the motion. Physical concepts such as velocity, speed, and acceleration can be defined in terms of derivatives of the position function.

In the following discussion we assume that the position function may be differentiated as often as is necessary without saying so each time.

DEFINITION. *Consider a motion described by a vector-valued function X. The derivative $X'(t)$ is called the velocity vector at time t. The length of the velocity vector, $\|X'(t)\|$, is called the speed. The second derivative of the position vector, $X''(t)$, is called the acceleration vector.*

Notation. Sometimes the position function X is denoted by **r**, the velocity vector by **v**, the speed by v, and the acceleration by **a**. Thus, $\boldsymbol{v} = \boldsymbol{r}'$, $v = \|\boldsymbol{v}\|$, and $\boldsymbol{a} = \boldsymbol{v}' = \boldsymbol{r}''$.

If the velocity vector $X'(t)$ is visualized as a geometric vector attached to the curve at $X(t)$, we see that it lies along the tangent line. The use of the word "speed" for the length of the velocity vector will be justified in Section 14.12 where it is shown that the speed is the rate of change of arc length along the curve. This is what the speedometer of an automobile tries to measure. Thus, the length of the velocity vector tells us how fast the particle is moving at every instant, and its direction tells us which way it is going. The velocity will change if we alter either the speed or the direction of the motion (or both). The acceleration vector is a measure of this change. Acceleration causes the effect one feels when an automobile changes its speed or its direction. Unlike the velocity vector, the acceleration vector does not necessarily lie along the tangent line.

EXAMPLE 1. *Linear motion.* Consider a motion whose position vector is given by

$$\boldsymbol{r}(t) = P + f(t)A \,,$$

where P and A are fixed vectors, $A \neq O$. This motion takes place along a line through P parallel to A. The velocity, speed, and acceleration are given by

$$\boldsymbol{v}(t) = f'(t)A \,, \qquad v(t) = \|\boldsymbol{v}(t)\| = |f'(t)|\,\|A\| \,, \qquad \boldsymbol{a}(t) = f''(t)A \,.$$

If $f'(t)$ and $f''(t)$ are nonzero, the acceleration vector is parallel to the velocity.

EXAMPLE 2. *Circular motion.* If a point (x, y) in V_2 is represented by its polar coordinates r and θ, we have

$$x = r \cos \theta \,, \qquad y = r \sin \theta \,.$$

If r is fixed, say $r = a$, and if θ is allowed to vary over any interval of length at least 2π, the corresponding point (x, y) traces out a circle of radius a and center at the origin. If we make θ a function of time t, say $\theta = f(t)$, we have a motion given by the position function

$$\boldsymbol{r}(t) = a \cos f(t)\boldsymbol{i} + a \sin f(t)\boldsymbol{j} \,.$$

The corresponding velocity vector is given by

$$\boldsymbol{v}(t) = \boldsymbol{r}'(t) = -af'(t) \sin f(t)\boldsymbol{i} + af'(t) \cos f(t)\boldsymbol{j} \,,$$

from which we find that the speed at time t is

$$v(t) = \|v(t)\| = a\,|f'(t)|\,.$$

The factor $|f'(t)| = |d\theta/dt|$ is called the *angular speed* of the particle.

An important special case occurs when $\theta = \omega t$, where ω (omega) is a positive constant. In this case, the particle starts at the point $(a, 0)$ at time $t = 0$ and moves counter-clockwise around the circle with constant angular speed ω. The formulas for the position, velocity, and speed become

$$r(t) = a\cos \omega t\,i + a\sin \omega t\,j\,, \qquad v(t) = -\omega a \sin \omega t\,i + \omega a \cos \omega t\,j\,, \qquad v(t) = a\omega\,.$$

The acceleration vector is given by

$$a(t) = -\omega^2 a \cos \omega t\,i - \omega^2 a \sin \omega t\,j = -\omega^2 r(t)\,,$$

which shows that the acceleration is always directed opposite to the position vector. When it is visualized as a geometric vector drawn at the location of the particle, the acceleration vector is directed toward the center of the circle. Because of this, the acceleration is called *centripetal* or "center-seeking," a term originally proposed by Newton.

> *Note:* If a moving particle has mass m, Newton's second law of motion states that the force acting on it (due to its acceleration) is the vector $ma(t)$, mass times acceleration. If the particle moves on a circle with constant angular speed, this is called a centripetal force because it is directed toward the center. This force is exerted by the mechanism that confines the particle to a circular orbit. The mechanism is a *string* in the case of a stone whirling in a slingshot, or *gravitational attraction* in the case of a satellite around the earth. The equal and opposite reaction (due to Newton's third law), that is, the force $-ma(t)$, is said to be *centrifugal* or "center-fleeing."

EXAMPLE 3. *Motion on an ellipse.* Figure 14.5 shows an ellipse with Cartesian equation $x^2/a^2 + y^2/b^2 = 1$, and two concentric circles with radii a and b. The angle θ shown in the figure is called the *eccentric angle*. It is related to the coordinates (x, y) of a point on the ellipse by the equations

$$x = a \cos \theta\,, \qquad y = b \sin \theta\,.$$

As θ varies over an interval of length 2π, the corresponding point (x, y) traces out the ellipse. If we make θ a function of time t, say $\theta = f(t)$, we have a motion given by the position function

$$r(t) = a \cos f(t)i + b \sin f(t)j\,.$$

If $\theta = \omega t$, where ω is a positive constant, the velocity, speed, and acceleration are given by

$$v(t) = \omega(-a \sin \omega t\,i + b \cos \omega t\,j)\,, \qquad v(t) = \omega(a^2 \sin^2 \omega t + b^2 \cos^2 \omega t)^{1/2}\,,$$

$$a(t) = -\omega^2(a \cos \omega t\,i + b \sin \omega t\,j) = -\omega^2 r(t)\,.$$

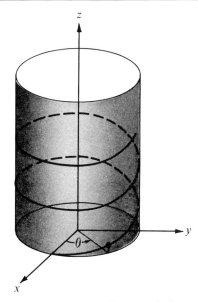

FIGURE 14.5   Motion on an ellipse.   FIGURE 14.6   Motion on a helix.

Thus, when a particle moves on an ellipse in such a way that its eccentric angle changes at a constant rate, the acceleration is centripetal.

EXAMPLE 4. *Motion on a helix.* If a point (x, y, z) revolves around the z-axis at a constant distance a from it and simultaneously moves parallel to the z-axis in such a way that its z-component is proportional to the angle of revolution, the resulting path is called a *circular helix*. An example is shown in Figure 14.6. If θ denotes the angle of revolution, we have

(14.7) $x = a \cos \theta , \qquad y = a \sin \theta , \qquad z = b\theta ,$

where $a > 0$, and $b \neq 0$. When θ varies from 0 to 2π, the x- and y-coordinates return to their original values while z changes from 0 to $2\pi b$. The number $2\pi b$ is often referred to as the *pitch* of the helix.

Now suppose that $\theta = \omega t$, where ω is constant. The motion on the helix is then described by the position vector

$$\boldsymbol{r}(t) = a \cos \omega t \, \boldsymbol{i} + a \sin \omega t \, \boldsymbol{j} + b\omega t \boldsymbol{k} .$$

The corresponding velocity and acceleration vectors are given by

$$\boldsymbol{v}(t) = -\omega a \sin \omega t \, \boldsymbol{i} + \omega a \cos \omega t \, \boldsymbol{j} + b\omega \boldsymbol{k} , \qquad \boldsymbol{a}(t) = -\omega^2 (a \cos \omega t \, \boldsymbol{i} + a \sin \omega t \, \boldsymbol{j}) .$$

Thus, when the acceleration vector is located on the helix, it is parallel to the xy-plane and directed toward the z-axis.

If we eliminate θ from the first two equations in (14.7), we obtain the Cartesian equation $x^2 + y^2 = a^2$ which we recognize as the equation of a circle in the xy-plane. In 3-space, however, this equation represents a surface. A point (x, y, z) satisfies the equation if and only if its distance from the z-axis is equal to a. The set of all such points is a right circular cylinder of radius a with its axis along the z-axis. The helix winds around this cylinder.

14.7 Exercises

In each of Exercises 1 through 6, $r(t)$ denotes the position vector at time t for a particle moving on a space curve. In each case, determine the velocity $v(t)$ and acceleration $a(t)$ in terms of i, j, k; also, compute the speed $v(t)$.

1. $r(t) = (3t - t^3)i + 3t^2j + (3t + t^3)k$.
2. $r(t) = \cos t\, i + \sin t\, j + e^t k$.
3. $r(t) = 3t \cos t\, i + 3t \sin t\, j + 4t k$.
4. $r(t) = (t - \sin t)i + (1 - \cos t)j + 4 \sin \dfrac{t}{2} k$.
5. $r(t) = 3t^2 i + 2t^3 j + 3t k$.
6. $r(t) = t i + \sin t\, j + (1 - \cos t)k$.

7. Consider the helix described by the vector equation $r(t) = a \cos \omega t\, i + a \sin \omega t\, j + b\omega t k$, where ω is a positive constant. Prove that the tangent line makes a constant angle with the z-axis and that the cosine of this angle is $b/\sqrt{a^2 + b^2}$.

8. Referring to the helix in Exercise 7, prove that the velocity v and acceleration a are vectors of constant length, and that

$$\frac{\|v \times a\|}{\|v\|^3} = \frac{a}{a^2 + b^2}\,.$$

9. Referring to Exercise 7, let $u(t)$ denote the unit vector $u(t) = \sin \omega t\, i - \cos \omega t\, j$. Prove that there are two constants A and B such that $v \times a = Au(t) + Bk$, and express A and B in terms of a, b, and ω.

10. Prove that for any motion the dot product of the velocity and acceleration is half the derivative of the square of the speed:

$$v(t) \cdot a(t) = \frac{1}{2}\frac{d}{dt}\, v^2(t)\,.$$

11. Let c be a fixed unit vector. A particle moves in space in such a way that its position vector $r(t)$ satisfies the equation $r(t) \cdot c = e^{2t}$ for all t, and its velocity vector $v(t)$ makes a constant angle θ with c, where $0 < \theta < \frac{1}{2}\pi$.
   (a) Prove that the speed at time t is $2e^{2t}/\cos \theta$.
   (b) Compute the dot product $a(t) \cdot v(t)$ in terms of t and θ.

12. The identity $\cosh^2 \theta - \sinh^2 \theta = 1$ for hyperbolic functions suggests that the hyperbola $x^2/a^2 - y^2/b^2 = 1$ may be represented by the parametric equations $x = a \cosh \theta$, $y = b \sinh \theta$, or what amounts to the same thing, by the vector equation $r = a \cosh \theta\, i + b \sinh \theta\, j$. When $a = b = 1$, the parameter θ may be given a geometric interpretation analogous to that which holds between θ, $\sin \theta$, and $\cos \theta$ in the unit circle shown in Figure 14.7(a). Figure 14.7(b) shows one branch of the hyperbola $x^2 - y^2 = 1$. If the point P has coordinates $x = \cosh \theta$ and $y = \sinh \theta$, prove that θ equals twice the area of the sector OAP shaded in the figure.

   [*Hint:* Let $A(\theta)$ denote the area of sector OAP. Show that

$$A(\theta) = \tfrac{1}{2} \cosh \theta \sinh \theta - \int_1^{\cosh \theta} \sqrt{x^2 - 1}\; dx\,.$$

   Differentiate to get $A'(\theta) = \frac{1}{2}$.]

13. A particle moves along a hyperbola according to the equation $r(t) = a \cosh \omega t\, i + b \sinh \omega t\, j$, where ω is a constant. Prove that the acceleration is centrifugal.

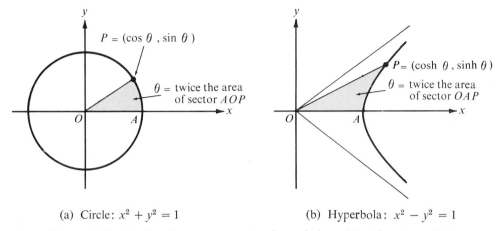

(a) Circle: $x^2 + y^2 = 1$ (b) Hyperbola: $x^2 - y^2 = 1$

FIGURE 14.7   Analogy between parameter for a circle and that for a hyperbola.

14. Prove that the tangent line at a point X of a parabola bisects the angle between the line joining X to the focus and the line through X parallel to the axis. This gives the reflection property of the parabola. (See Figure 14.3.)

15. A particle of mass 1 moves in a plane according to the equation $r(t) = x(t)\mathbf{i} + y(t)\mathbf{j}$. It is attracted toward the origin by a force whose magnitude is four times its distance from the origin. At time $t = 0$, the initial position is $r(0) = 4\mathbf{i}$ and the initial velocity is $v(0) = 6\mathbf{j}$.
    (a) Determine the components $x(t)$ and $y(t)$ explicitly in terms of t.
    (b) The path of the particle is a conic section. Find a Cartesian equation for this conic, sketch the conic, and indicate the direction of motion along the curve.

16. A particle moves along the parabola $x^2 + c(y - x) = 0$ in such a way that the horizontal and vertical components of the acceleration vector are equal. If it takes T units of time to go from the point $(c, 0)$ to the point $(0, 0)$, how much time will it require to go from $(c, 0)$ to the halfway point $(c/2, c/4)$?

17. Suppose a curve C is described by two equivalent functions X and Y, where $Y(t) = X[u(t)]$. Prove that at each point of C the velocity vectors associated with X and Y are parallel, but that the corresponding acceleration vectors need not be parallel.

14.8 The unit tangent, the principal normal, and the osculating plane of a curve

For linear motion the acceleration vector is parallel to the velocity vector. For circular motion with constant angular speed, the acceleration vector is perpendicular to the velocity. In this section we show that for a general motion the acceleration vector is a sum of two perpendicular vectors, one parallel to the velocity and one perpendicular to the velocity. If the motion is not linear, these two perpendicular vectors determine a plane through each point of the curve called the osculating plane.

To study these concepts, we introduce the *unit tangent* vector T. This is another vector-valued function associated with the curve, and it is defined by the equation

$$T(t) = \frac{X'(t)}{\|X'(t)\|}$$

whenever the speed $\|X'(t)\| \neq 0$. Note that $\|T(t)\| = 1$ for all t.

Figure 14.8 shows the position of the unit tangent geometric vector $T(t)$ for various values of t when it is attached to the curve. As the particle moves along the curve, the corresponding vector T, being of constant length, can change only in its direction. The tendency of T to change its direction is measured by its derivative T'. Since T has constant length, Theorem 14.2 tells us that T is perpendicular to its derivative T'.

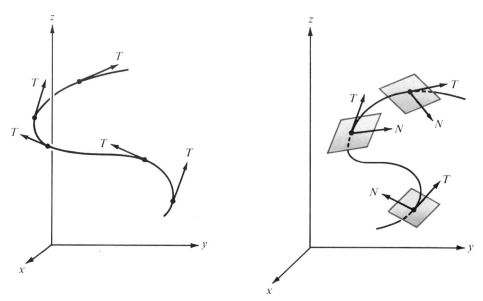

FIGURE 14.8   The unit tangent vector T.   FIGURE 14.9   The osculating plane.

If the motion is linear, then $T' = O$. If $T' \neq O$, the unit vector having the same direction as T' is called the *principal normal* to the curve and it is denoted by N. Thus, N is a new vector-valued function associated with the curve and it is defined by the equation

$$N(t) = \frac{T'(t)}{\|T'(t)\|}, \qquad \text{whenever} \quad \|T'(t)\| \neq 0.$$

When the two unit geometric vectors $T(t)$ and $N(t)$ are attached to the curve at the point $X(t)$, they determine a plane known as the *osculating plane* of the curve. If we choose three values of t, say t_1, t_2, and t_3, and consider the plane determined by the three points $X(t_1)$, $X(t_2)$, $X(t_3)$, it can be shown that the position of the plane approaches the position of the osculating plane at $X(t_1)$ as t_2 and t_3 approach t_1. Because of this, the osculating plane is often called the plane that best fits the curve at each of its points. If the curve itself is a plane curve (not a straight line), the osculating plane coincides with the plane of the curve. In general, however, the osculating plane changes with t. Examples are illustrated in Figure 14.9.

The next theorem shows that the acceleration vector is a sum of two vectors, one parallel to T and one parallel to T'.

THEOREM 14.9.   *For a motion described by a vector-valued function* **r**, *let* $v(t)$ *denote the speed at time* t, $v(t) = \|\mathbf{r}'(t)\|$. *Then the acceleration vector* **a** *is a linear combination of* T *and* T' *given by the formula*

(14.8) $$\mathbf{a}(t) = v'(t)T(t) + v(t)T'(t).$$

If $T'(t) \neq O$, *we also have*

(14.9) $$\mathbf{a}(t) = v'(t)T(t) + v(t)\,\|T'(t)\|\,N(t).$$

   Proof.   The formula defining the unit tangent gives us

$$\mathbf{v}(t) = v(t)T(t).$$

Differentiating this product, we find that

$$\mathbf{a}(t) = v'(t)T(t) + v(t)T'(t),$$

which proves (14.8). To prove (14.9), we use the definition of N to write $T'(t) = \|T'(t)\|\,N(t)$.

   This theorem shows that the acceleration vector always lies in the osculating plane. An example is shown in Figure 14.10. The coefficients of $T(t)$ and $N(t)$ in (14.9) are called, respectively, the *tangential* and *normal components* of the acceleration. A change in speed contributes to the tangential component, whereas a change in direction contributes to the normal component.

   For a plane curve, the length of $T'(t)$ has an interesting geometric interpretation. Since T is a unit vector, we may write

$$T(t) = \cos \alpha(t)\mathbf{i} + \sin \alpha(t)\mathbf{j},$$

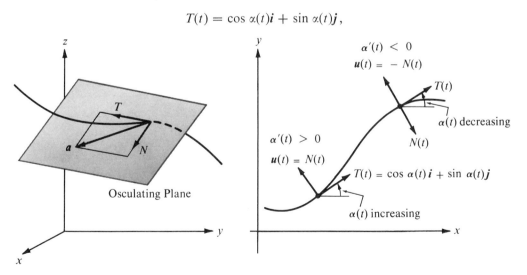

FIGURE 14.10   The acceleration vector lies in the osculating plane

FIGURE 14.11   The angle of inclination of the tangent vector of a plane curve.

where $\alpha(t)$ denotes the angle between the tangent vector and the positive x-axis, as shown in Figure 14.11. Differentiating, we find that

$$T'(t) = -\sin \alpha(t)\,\alpha'(t)\boldsymbol{i} + \cos \alpha(t)\,\alpha'(t)\boldsymbol{j} = \alpha'(t)\boldsymbol{u}(t),$$

where $\boldsymbol{u}(t)$ is a unit vector. Therefore $\|T'(t)\| = |\alpha'(t)|$ and this shows that $\|T'(t)\|$ is a measure of the rate of change of the angle of inclination of the tangent vector. When $\alpha'(t) > 0$, the angle is increasing, and hence $\boldsymbol{u}(t) = N(t)$. When $\alpha'(t) < 0$, the angle is decreasing and, in this case, $\boldsymbol{u}(t) = -N(t)$. The two cases are illustrated in Figure 14.11. Note that the angle of inclination of $\boldsymbol{u}(t)$ is $\alpha(t) + \frac{1}{2}\pi$ since we have

$$\boldsymbol{u}(t) = -\sin \alpha(t)\boldsymbol{i} + \cos \alpha(t)\boldsymbol{j} = \cos\left(\alpha(t) + \frac{\pi}{2}\right)\boldsymbol{i} + \sin\left(\alpha(t) + \frac{\pi}{2}\right)\boldsymbol{j}.$$

14.9 Exercises

Exercises 1 through 6 below refer to the motions described in Exercises 1 through 6, respectively, of Section 14.7. For the value of t specified, (a) express the unit tangent T and the principal normal N in terms of $\boldsymbol{i}, \boldsymbol{j}, \boldsymbol{k}$; (b) express the acceleration $\boldsymbol{a}$ as a linear combination of T and N.

1. $t = 2$.
2. $t = \pi$.
3. $t = 0$.
4. $t = \pi$.
5. $t = 1$.
6. $t = \frac{1}{4}\pi$.

7. Prove that if the acceleration vector is always zero, the motion is linear.
8. Prove that the normal component of the acceleration vector is $\|v \times a\|/\|v\|$.
9. For each of the following statements about a curve traced out by a particle moving in 3-space, either give a proof or exhibit a counter example.
    (a) If the velocity is constant, the curve lies in a plane.
    (b) If the speed is constant, the curve lies in a plane.
    (c) If the acceleration is constant, the curve lies in a plane.
    (d) If the velocity is perpendicular to the acceleration, the curve lies in a plane.
10. A particle of unit mass with position vector $r(t)$ at time t is moving in space under the actions of certain forces.
    (a) Prove that $r \times a = O$ implies $r \times v = c$, where c is a constant vector.
    (b) If $r \times v = c$, where c is a constant vector, prove that the motion takes place in a plane. Consider both $c \neq O$ and $c = O$.
    (c) If the net force acting on the particle is always directed toward the origin, prove that the particle moves in a plane.
    (d) Is $r \times v$ necessarily constant if a particle moves in a plane?
11. A particle moves along a curve in such a way that the velocity vector makes a constant angle with a given unit vector c.
    (a) If the curve lies in a plane containing c, prove that the acceleration vector is either zero or parallel to the velocity.
    (b) Give an example of such a curve (not a plane curve) for which the acceleration vector is never zero nor parallel to the velocity.
12. A particle moves along the ellipse $3x^2 + y^2 = 1$ with position vector $r(t) = f(t)\boldsymbol{i} + g(t)\boldsymbol{j}$. The motion is such that the horizontal component of the velocity vector at time t is $-g(t)$.
    (a) Does the particle move around the ellipse in a clockwise or counterclockwise direction?
    (b) Prove that the vertical component of the velocity vector at time t is proportional to $f(t)$ and find the factor of proportionality.
    (c) How much time is required for the particle to go once around the ellipse?
13. A plane curve C in the first quadrant has a negative slope at each of its points and passes

through the point $(\frac{3}{2}, 1)$. The position vector r from the origin to any point (x, y) on C makes an angle θ with i, and the velocity vector makes an angle ϕ with i, where $0 < \theta < \frac{1}{2}\pi$, and $0 < \phi < \frac{1}{2}\pi$. If $3 \tan \phi = 4 \cot \theta$ at each point of C, find a Cartesian equation for C and sketch the curve.

14. A line perpendicular to the tangent line of a plane curve is called a normal line. If the normal line and a vertical line are drawn at any point of a certain plane curve C, they cut off a segment of length 2 on the x-axis. Find a Cartesian equation for this curve if it passes through the point $(1, 2)$. Two solutions are possible.

15. Given two fixed nonzero vectors A and B making an angle θ with each other, where $0 < \theta < \pi$. A motion with position vector $r(t)$ at time t satisfies the differential equation

$$r'(t) = A \times r(t)$$

and the initial condition $r(0) = B$.
   (a) Prove that the acceleration $a(t)$ is orthogonal to A.
   (b) Prove that the speed is constant and compute this speed in terms of A, B, and θ.
   (c) Make a sketch of the curve, showing its relation to the vectors A and B.

16. This exercise describes how the unit tangent and the principal normal are affected by a change of parameter. Suppose a curve C is described by two equivalent functions X and Y, where $Y(t) = X[u(t)]$. Denote the unit tangent for X by T_X and that for Y by T_Y.
   (a) Prove that at each point of C we have $T_Y(t) = T_X[u(t)]$ if u is strictly increasing, but that $T_Y(t) = -T_X[u(t)]$ if u is strictly decreasing. In the first case, u is said to *preserve orientation*; in the second case, u is said to *reverse orientation*.
   (b) Prove that the corresponding principal normal vectors N_X and N_Y satisfy $N_Y(t) = N_X[u(t)]$ at each point of C. Deduce that the osculating plane is invariant under a change of parameter.

14.10 The definition of arc length

Various parts of calculus and analytic geometry refer to the arc length of a curve. Before we can study the properties of the length of a curve we must agree on a *definition* of arc length. The purpose of this section is to formulate such a definition. This will lead, in a natural way, to the construction of a function (called the arc-length function) which measures the length of the path traced out by a moving particle at every instant of its motion. Some of the basic properties of this function are discussed in Section 14.12. In particular, we shall prove that for most curves that arise in practice this function may be expressed as the integral of the speed.

To arrive at a definition of what we mean by the length of a curve, we proceed as though we had to measure this length with a straight yardstick. First, we mark off a number of points on the curve which we use as vertices of an inscribed polygon. (An example is shown in Figure 14.12.) Then, we measure the total length of this polygon with our yardstick and consider this as an approximation to the length of the curve. We soon observe that some polygons "fit" the curve better than others. In particular, if we start with a polygon P_1, and construct a new inscribed polygon P_2 by adding more vertices to those of P_1, it is clear that the length of P_2 will be larger than that of P_1, as suggested in Figure 14.13. In the same way we can form more and more polygons with successively larger and larger lengths.

On the other hand, our intuition tells us that the length of any inscribed polygon should not exceed that of the curve (since a straight line is the shortest path between two points).

In other words, when we arrive at a definition for the length of a curve, it should be a number which is an *upper bound* to the lengths of all inscribed polygons. Therefore, it certainly seems reasonable to define the length of the curve to be the *least upper bound* of the lengths of all possible inscribed polygons.

For most curves that arise in practice, this definition gives us a useful and reasonable way to assign a length to a curve. Surprisingly enough, however, there are certain pathological cases where this definition is not applicable. There are curves for which there is *no* upper bound to the lengths of the inscribed polygons. (An example is given in Exercise

 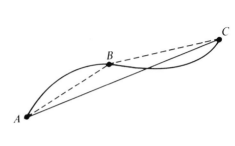

FIGURE 14.12 A curve with an in-   FIGURE 14.13 The polygon *ABC* has a
   scribed polygon.   length greater than the polygon *AC*.

22 in Section 14.13.) Therefore it becomes necessary to classify all curves into two categories: those which have a length, and those which do not. The former are called *rectifiable curves*, the latter, *nonrectifiable*.

To formulate these ideas in analytic terms, we begin with a curve in 3-space or in 2-space described by a vector-valued function r, and we consider the portion of the curve traced out by $r(t)$ as t varies over an interval $[a, b]$. At the outset, we only assume that r is continuous on the parametric interval. Later we shall add further restrictions.

Consider now any partition P of the interval $[a, b]$, say

$$P = \{t_0, t_1, \ldots, t_n\}, \qquad \text{where} \quad a = t_0 < t_1 < \cdots < t_n = b.$$

Denote by $\pi(P)$ the polygon whose vertices are the points $r(t_0), r(t_1), \ldots, r(t_n)$, respectively. (An example with $n = 6$ is shown in Figure 14.14.) The sides of this polygon have lengths

$$\|r(t_1) - r(t_0)\|, \ \|r(t_2) - r(t_1)\|, \ \ldots, \ \|r(t_n) - r(t_{n-1})\| \,.$$

Therefore, the length of the polygon $\pi(P)$, which we denote by $|\pi(P)|$, is the sum

$$|\pi(P)| = \sum_{k=1}^{n} \|r(t_k) - r(t_{k-1})\| \,.$$

DEFINITION. *If there exists a positive number* M *such that*

(14.10) $$|\pi(P)| \leq M$$

for all partitions P of [a, b], then the curve is said to be rectifiable and its arc length, denoted by $\Lambda(a, b)$, is defined to be the least upper bound of the set of all numbers $|\pi(P)|$. If there is no such M, the curve is called nonrectifiable.

Note that if an M exists satisfying (14.10), then, for every partition P, we have

(14.11)
$$|\pi(P)| \le \Lambda(a, b) \le M \, ,$$

since the least upper bound cannot exceed any upper bound.

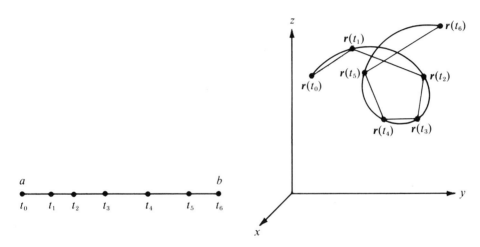

FIGURE 14.14   A partition of $[a, b]$ into six subintervals and the corresponding inscribed polygon.

It is easy to prove that a curve is rectifiable whenever its velocity vector v is continuous on the parametric interval $[a, b]$. In fact, the following theorem tells us that in this case we may use the integral of the speed as an upper bound for all numbers $|\pi(P)|$.

THEOREM 14.10.   *Denote by $v(t)$ the velocity vector of the curve with position vector $r(t)$ and let $v(t) = \|v(t)\|$ denote the speed. If v is continuous on $[a, b]$, the curve is rectifiable and its length $\Lambda(a, b)$ satisfies the inequality*

(14.12)
$$\Lambda(a, b) \le \int_a^b v(t) \, dt \, .$$

Proof.   For each partition P of $[a, b]$, we have

$$|\pi(P)| = \sum_{k=1}^{n} \|r(t_k) - r(t_{k-1})\| = \sum_{k=1}^{n} \left\| \int_{t_{k-1}}^{t_k} r'(t) \, dt \right\|$$

$$= \sum_{k=1}^{n} \left\| \int_{t_{k-1}}^{t_k} v(t) \, dt \right\| \le \sum_{k=1}^{n} \int_{t_{k-1}}^{t_k} \|v(t)\| \, dt = \int_a^b v(t) \, dt \, ,$$

the inequality being a consequence of Theorem 14.8. This shows that we have

$$|\pi(P)| \leq \int_a^b v(t)\,dt$$

for all partitions P, and hence the number $\int_a^b v(t)\,dt$ is an upper bound for the set of all numbers $|\pi(P)|$. This proves that the curve is rectifiable and, at the same time, it tells us that the length $\Lambda(a, b)$ cannot exceed the integral of the speed.

In a later section we shall prove that the inequality in (14.12) is, in fact, an *equality*. The proof of this fact will make use of the *additivity* of arc length, a property described in the next section.

14.11   Additivity of arc length

If a rectifiable curve is cut into two pieces, the length of the whole curve is the sum of the lengths of the two parts. This is another of those "intuitively obvious" statements whose proof is not trivial. This property is called *additivity of arc length* and it may be expressed analytically as follows.

THEOREM 14.11.   *Consider a rectifiable curve of length $\Lambda(a, b)$ traced out by a vector $\mathbf{r}(t)$ as t varies over an interval $[a, b]$. If $a < c < b$, let C_1 and C_2 be the curves traced out by $\mathbf{r}(t)$ as t varies over the intervals $[a, c]$ and $[c, b]$, respectively. Then C_1 and C_2 are also rectifiable and, if $\Lambda(a, c)$ and $\Lambda(c, b)$ denote their respective lengths, we have*

$$\Lambda(a, b) = \Lambda(a, c) + \Lambda(c, b)\,.$$

Proof.   Let P_1 and P_2 be arbitrary partitions of $[a, c]$ and $[c, b]$, respectively. The points in P_1 taken together with those in P_2 give us a new partition P of $[a, b]$ for which we have

(14.13) $|\pi(P_1)| + |\pi(P_2)| = |\pi(P)| \leq \Lambda(a, b)\,.$

This shows that $|\pi(P_1)|$ and $|\pi(P_2)|$ are bounded by $\Lambda(a, b)$, and hence C_1 and C_2 are rectifiable. From (14.13), we also have

$$|\pi(P_1)| \leq \Lambda(a, b) - |\pi(P_2)|\,.$$

Now, keep P_2 fixed and let P_1 vary over all possible partitions of $[a, c]$. Since the number $\Lambda(a, b) - |\pi(P_2)|$ is an upper bound for all numbers $|\pi(P_1)|$, it cannot be less than their least upper bound, which is $\Lambda(a, c)$. Hence, we have $\Lambda(a, c) \leq \Lambda(a, b) - |\pi(P_2)|$ or, what is the same thing,

$$|\pi(P_2)| \leq \Lambda(a, b) - \Lambda(a, c)\,.$$

This shows that $\Lambda(a, b) - \Lambda(a, c)$ is an upper bound for all the sums $|\pi(P_2)|$, and since it cannot be less than their least upper bound, $\Lambda(c, b)$, we have $\Lambda(c, b) \leq \Lambda(a, b) - \Lambda(a, c)$. In other words, we have

(14.14) $\Lambda(a, c) + \Lambda(c, b) \leq \Lambda(a, b)\,.$

Next we prove the reverse inequality. We begin with any partition P of $[a, b]$. If we adjoin the point c to P, we obtain a partition P_1 of $[a, c]$ and a partition P_2 of $[c, b]$ such that

$$|\pi(P)| \le |\pi(P_1)| + |\pi(P_2)| \le \Lambda(a, c) + \Lambda(c, b).$$

This shows that $\Lambda(a, c) + \Lambda(c, b)$ is an upper bound for all numbers $|\pi(P)|$. Since this cannot be less than the least upper bound, we must have

$$\Lambda(a, b) \le \Lambda(a, c) + \Lambda(c, b).$$

This inequality, along with (14.14), implies the additive property.

14.12   The arc-length function

Suppose a curve is the path traced out by a position vector $r(t)$. A natural question to ask is this: How far has the particle moved along the curve at time t? To discuss this question, we introduce the *arc-length function s*, defined as follows:

$$s(t) = \Lambda(a, t) \quad \text{if} \quad t > a, \quad s(a) = 0.$$

The statement $s(a) = 0$ simply means we are assuming the motion begins when $t = a$.

The theorem on additivity enables us to derive some important properties of s. For example, we have the following.

THEOREM 14.12.   *For any rectifiable curve, the arc-length function s is monotonically increasing on $[a, b]$. That is, we have*

(14.15) $$s(t_1) \le s(t_2) \quad \text{if} \quad a \le t_1 < t_2 \le b.$$

Proof. If $a \le t_1 < t_2 \le b$, we have

$$s(t_2) - s(t_1) = \Lambda(a, t_2) - \Lambda(a, t_1) = \Lambda(t_1, t_2),$$

where the last equality comes from additivity. Since $\Lambda(t_1, t_2) \ge 0$, this proves (14.15).

Next we shall prove that the function s has a derivative at each interior point of the parametric interval and that this derivative is equal to the speed of the particle.

THEOREM 14.13.   *Let s denote the arc-length function associated with a curve and let $v(t)$ denote the speed at time t. If v is continuous on $[a, b]$, then the derivative $s'(t)$ exists for each t in (a, b) and is given by the formula*

(14.16) $$s'(t) = v(t).$$

Proof. Define $f(t) = \int_a^t v(u)\, du$. We know that $f'(t) = v(t)$ because of the first fundamental theorem of calculus. We shall prove that $s'(t) = v(t)$. For this purpose we form the difference quotient

(14.17)
$$\left\| \frac{r(t+h) - r(t)}{h} \right\|.$$

Suppose first that $h > 0$. The line segment joining the points $r(t)$ and $r(t+h)$ may be thought of as a polygon approximating the arc joining these two points. Therefore, because of (14.11), we have

$$\| r(t+h) - r(t) \| \leq \Lambda(t, t+h) = s(t+h) - s(t).$$

Using this in (14.17) along with the inequality (14.12) of Theorem 14.10 we have

$$\left\| \frac{r(t+h) - r(t)}{h} \right\| \leq \frac{s(t+h) - s(t)}{h} \leq \frac{1}{h} \int_t^{t+h} v(u) \, du = \frac{f(t+h) - f(t)}{h}.$$

A similar argument shows that these inequalities are also valid for $h < 0$. If we let $h \to 0$, the difference quotient on the extreme left approaches $\| r'(t) \| = v(t)$ and that on the extreme right approaches $f'(t) = v(t)$. It follows that the quotient $[s(t+h) - s(t)]/h$ also approaches $v(t)$. But this means that $s'(t)$ exists and equals $v(t)$, as asserted.

Theorem 14.13 conforms with our intuitive notion of speed as the distance per unit time being covered during the motion.

Using (14.16) along with the second fundamental theorem of calculus, we can compute arc length by integrating the speed. Thus, the distance traveled by a particle during a time interval $[t_1, t_2]$ is

$$s(t_2) - s(t_1) = \int_{t_1}^{t_2} s'(t) \, dt = \int_{t_1}^{t_2} v(t) \, dt.$$

In particular, when $t_1 = a$ and $t_2 = b$, we obtain the following integral for arc length:

$$\Lambda(a, b) = \int_a^b v(t) \, dt.$$

EXAMPLE 1. *Length of a circular arc.* To compute the length of an arc of a circle of radius a, we may imagine a particle moving along the circle according to the equation $r(t) = a \cos t \, i + a \sin t \, j$. The velocity vector is $v(t) = -a \sin t \, i + a \cos t \, j$ and the speed is $v(t) = a$. Integrating the speed over an interval of length θ, we find that the length of arc traced out is $a\theta$. In other words, the length of a circular arc is proportional to the angle it subtends; the constant of proportionality is the radius of the circle. For a unit circle we have $a = 1$, and the arc length is exactly equal to the angular measure.

EXAMPLE 2. *Length of the graph of a real-valued function.* The graph of a real-valued function f defined on an interval $[a, b]$ can be treated as a curve with position vector $r(t)$ given by

$$r(t) = t i + f(t) j.$$

The corresponding velocity vector is $v(t) = i + f'(t) j$, and the speed is

$$v(t) = \| v(t) \| = \sqrt{1 + [f'(t)]^2}.$$

Therefore, the arc length of the graph of f above a subinterval $[a, x]$ is given by the integral

(14.18)
$$s(x) = \int_a^x v(t)\, dt = \int_a^x \sqrt{1 + [f'(t)]^2}\, dt \, .$$

14.13 Exercises

In Exercises 1 through 9, find the length of the path traced out by a particle moving on a curve according to the given equation during the time interval specified in each case.

1. $r(t) = a(1 - \cos t)i + a(t - \sin t)j$, $\quad 0 \le t \le 2\pi$, $\quad a > 0$.

2. $r(t) = e^t \cos t\, i + e^t \sin t\, j$, $\quad 0 \le t \le 2$.

3. $r(t) = a(\cos t + t \sin t)i + a(\sin t - t \cos t)j$, $\quad 0 \le t \le 2\pi$, $\quad a > 0$.

4. $r(t) = \dfrac{c^2}{a} \cos^3 t\, i + \dfrac{c^2}{b} \sin^3 t\, j$, $\quad 0 \le t \le 2\pi$, $\quad c^2 = a^2 - b^2$, $\quad 0 < b < a$.

5. $r(t) = a(\sinh t - t)i + a(\cosh t - 1)j$, $\quad 0 \le t \le T$, $\quad a > 0$.

6. $r(t) = \sin t\, i + t\, j + (1 - \cos t)k$ $\quad (0 \le t \le 2\pi)$.

7. $r(t) = t\, i + 3t^2 j + 6t^3 k$ $\quad (0 \le t \le 2)$.

8. $r(t) = t\, i + \log (\sec t)j + \log (\sec t + \tan t)k$ $\quad (0 \le t \le \frac{1}{4}\pi)$.

9. $r(t) = a \cos \omega t\, i + a \sin \omega t\, j + b\omega k$ $\quad (t_0 \le t \le t_1)$.

10. Find an integral similar to that in (14.18) for the length of the graph of an equation of the form $x = g(y)$, where g has a continuous derivative on an interval $[c, d]$.

11. A curve has the equation $y^2 = x^3$. Find the length of the arc joining $(1, -1)$ to $(1, 1)$.

12. Two points A and B on a unit circle with center at O determine a circular sector AOB. Prove that the arc AB has a length equal to twice the area of the sector.

13. Set up integrals for the lengths of the curves whose equations are (a) $y = e^x$, $0 \le x \le 1$; (b) $x = t + \log t$, $y = t - \log t$, $1 \le t \le e$. Show that the second length is $\sqrt{2}$ times the first one.

14. (a) Set up the integral which gives the length of the curve $y = c \cosh (x/c)$ from $x = 0$ to $x = a$ $(a > 0, c > 0)$.

   (b) Show that c times the length of this curve is equal to the area of the region bounded by $y = c \cosh (x/c)$, the x-axis, the y-axis, and the line $x = a$.

   (c) Evaluate this integral and find the length of the curve when $a = 2$.

15. Show that the length of the curve $y = \cosh x$ joining the points $(0, 1)$ and $(x, \cosh x)$ is $\sinh x$ if $x > 0$.

16. A nonnegative function f has the property that its ordinate set over an arbitrary interval has an area proportional to the arc length of the graph above the interval. Find f.

17. Use the vector equation $r(t) = a \sin t\, i + b \cos t\, j$, where $0 < b < a$, to show that the circumference L of an ellipse is given by the integral

$$L = 4a \int_0^{\pi/2} \sqrt{1 - e^2 \sin^2 t}\, dt \, ,$$

where $e = \sqrt{a^2 - b^2}/a$. (The number e is the eccentricity of the ellipse.) This is a special case of an integral of the form

$$E(k) = \int_0^{\pi/2} \sqrt{1 - k^2 \sin^2 t}\, dt \, ,$$

called an *elliptic integral of the second kind*, where $0 \le k < 1$. The numbers $E(k)$ have been tabulated for various values of k.

18. If $0 < b < 4a$, let $r(t) = a(t - \sin t)\mathbf{i} + a(1 - \cos t)\mathbf{j} + b \sin \frac{1}{2}t\,\mathbf{k}$. Show that the length of the path traced out from $t = 0$ to $t = 2\pi$ is $8aE(k)$, where $E(k)$ has the meaning given in Exercise 17 and $k^2 = 1 - (b/4a)^2$.

19. A particle moves with position vector

$$r(t) = tA + t^2B + 2(\tfrac{2}{3}t)^{3/2}\,A \times B,$$

where A and B are two fixed unit vectors making an angle of $\pi/3$ radians with each other. Compute the speed of the particle at time t and find how long it takes for it to move a distance of 12 units of arc length from the initial position $r(0)$.

20. (a) When a circle rolls (without slipping) along a straight line, a point on the circumference traces out a curve called a *cycloid*. If the fixed line is the x-axis and if the tracing point (x, y) is originally at the origin, show that when the circle rolls through an angle θ we have

$$x = a(\theta - \sin \theta), \qquad y = a(1 - \cos \theta),$$

where a is the radius of the circle. These serve as parametric equations for the cycloid.

(b) Referring to part (a), show that $dy/dx = \cot \frac{1}{2}\theta$ and deduce that the tangent line of the cycloid at (x, y) makes an angle $\frac{1}{2}(\pi - \theta)$ with the x-axis. Make a sketch and show that the tangent line passes through the highest point on the circle.

21. Let C be a curve described by two equivalent functions X and Y, where $Y(t) = X[u(t)]$ for $c \le t \le d$. If the function u which defines the change of parameter has a continuous derivative in $[c, d]$ prove that

$$\int_{u(c)}^{u(d)} \|X'(u)\|\,du = \int_{c}^{d} \|Y'(t)\|\,dt,$$

and deduce that the arc length of C is invariant under such a change of parameter.

22. Consider the plane curve whose vector equation is $r(t) = t\mathbf{i} + f(t)\mathbf{j}$, where

$$f(t) = t \cos\left(\frac{\pi}{2t}\right) \qquad \text{if} \quad t \ne 0, \qquad f(0) = 0.$$

Consider the following partition of the interval $[0, 1]$:

$$P = \left\{0, \frac{1}{2n}, \frac{1}{2n-1}, \ldots, \frac{1}{3}, \frac{1}{2}, 1\right\}.$$

Show that the corresponding inscribed polygon $\pi(P)$ has length

$$|\pi(P)| > 1 + \frac{1}{2} + \frac{1}{3} + \cdots + \frac{1}{2n}$$

and deduce that this curve is nonrectifiable.

14.14 Curvature of a curve

For a straight line the unit tangent vector T does not change its direction, and hence $T' = O$. If the curve is not a straight line, the derivative T' measures the tendency of the tangent to change its direction. The rate of change of the unit tangent *with respect to arc length* is called the *curvature vector* of the curve. We denote this by dT/ds, where s represents arc length. The chain rule, used in conjunction with the relation $s'(t) = v(t)$, tells us that the curvature vector dT/ds is related to the "time" derivative T' by the equation

$$\frac{dT}{ds} = \frac{dt}{ds}\frac{dT}{dt} = \frac{1}{s'(t)} T'(t) = \frac{1}{v(t)} T'(t).$$

Since $T'(t) = \|T'(t)\| N(t)$, we obtain

(14.19)
$$\frac{dT}{ds} = \frac{\|T'(t)\|}{v(t)} N(t),$$

which shows that the curvature vector has the same direction as the principal normal $N(t)$. The scalar factor which multiplies $N(t)$ in (14.19) is a nonnegative number called the *curvature* of the curve at t and it is denoted by $\kappa(t)$ (κ is the Greek letter kappa). Thus the curvature $\kappa(t)$, defined to be the *length of the curvature vector*, is given by the following formula:

(14.20)
$$\kappa(t) = \frac{\|T'(t)\|}{v(t)}.$$

EXAMPLE 1. *Curvature of a circle.* For a circle of radius a, given by $r(t) = a \cos t\, i + a \sin t\, j$, we have $v(t) = -a \sin t\, i + a \cos t\, j$, $v(t) = a$, $T(t) = -\sin t\, i + \cos t\, j$, and $T'(t) = -\cos t\, i - \sin t\, j$. Hence we have $\|T'(t)\| = 1$ so $\kappa(t) = 1/a$. This shows that a circle has constant curvature. The reciprocal of the curvature is the radius of the circle.

When $\kappa(t) \neq 0$, its reciprocal is called the *radius of curvature* and is denoted by $\rho(t)$ (ρ is the Greek letter rho). That circle in the osculating plane with radius $\rho(t)$ and center at the tip of the curvature vector is called the *osculating circle*. It can be shown that the osculating circle is the limiting position of circles passing through three nearby points on the curve as two of the points approach the third. Because of this property, the osculating circle is often called the circle that "best fits the curve" at each of its points.

EXAMPLE 2. *Curvature of a plane curve.* For a plane curve, we have seen that $\|T'(t)\| = |\alpha'(t)|$, where $\alpha(t)$ is the angle the tangent vector makes with the positive x-axis, as shown in Figure 14.11. From the chain rule, we have $\alpha'(t) = d\alpha/dt = (d\alpha/ds)(ds/dt) = v(t)d\alpha/ds$, so Equation (14.20) implies

$$\kappa(t) = \left| \frac{d\alpha}{ds} \right|.$$

In other words, the curvature of a plane curve is the absolute value of the rate of change of α with respect to arc length. It measures the change of direction per unit distance along the curve.

EXAMPLE 3. *Plane curves of constant curvature.* If $d\alpha/ds$ is a nonzero constant, say $d\alpha/ds = a$, then $\alpha = as + b$, where b is a constant. Hence, if we use the arc length s as a parameter, we have $T = \cos(as + b)\mathbf{i} + \sin(as + b)\mathbf{j}$. Integrating, we find that $\mathbf{r} = (1/a)\sin(as + b)\mathbf{i} - (1/a)\cos(as + b)\mathbf{j} + A$, where A is a constant vector. Therefore $\|\mathbf{r} - A\| = 1/|a|$, so the curve is a circle (or an arc of a circle) with center at A and radius $1/|a|$. This proves that a plane curve of constant curvature $\kappa \neq 0$ is a circle (or an arc of a circle) with radius $1/\kappa$.

Now we prove a theorem which relates the curvature to the velocity and acceleration.

THEOREM 14.14. *For any motion with velocity $\mathbf{v}(t)$, speed $v(t)$, acceleration $\mathbf{a}(t)$, and curvature $\kappa(t)$, we have*

$$(14.21) \qquad\qquad \mathbf{a}(t) = v'(t)T(t) + \kappa(t)v^2(t)N(t) .$$

This formula, in turn, implies

$$(14.22) \qquad\qquad \kappa(t) = \frac{\|\mathbf{a}(t) \times \mathbf{v}(t)\|}{v^3(t)} .$$

Proof. To prove (14.21), we rewrite (14.20) in the form $\|T'(t)\| = \kappa(t)v(t)$, which gives us $T'(t) = \kappa(t)v(t)N(t)$. Substituting this expression for $T'(t)$ in Equation (14.8), we obtain (14.21).

To prove (14.22), we form the cross product $\mathbf{a}(t) \times \mathbf{v}(t)$, using (14.21) for $\mathbf{a}(t)$ and the formula $\mathbf{v}(t) = v(t)T(t)$ for the velocity. This gives us

$$(14.23) \qquad\qquad \mathbf{a} \times \mathbf{v} = v'vT \times T + \kappa v^3 N \times T = \kappa v^3 N \times T$$

since $T \times T = O$. If we take the length of each member of (14.23) and note that

$$\|N \times T\| = \|N\| \, \|T\| \sin \tfrac{1}{2}\pi = 1 ,$$

we obtain $\|\mathbf{a} \times \mathbf{v}\| = \kappa v^3$, which proves (14.22).

In practice it is fairly easy to compute the vectors $\mathbf{v}$ and $\mathbf{a}$ (by differentiating the position vector $\mathbf{r}$); hence Equation (14.22) provides a useful method for computing the curvature. This method is usually simpler than determining the curvature from its definition.

For a straight line we have $\mathbf{a} \times \mathbf{v} = O$, so the curvature is everywhere zero. A curve with a small curvature at a point has a large radius of curvature there and hence does not differ much from a straight line in the immediate vicinity of the point. Thus the curvature is a measure of the tendency of a curve to deviate from a straight line.

14.15 Exercises

1. Refer to the curves described in Exercises 1 through 6 of Section 14.9 and in each case determine the curvature $\kappa(t)$ for the value of t indicated.

2. A helix is described by the position function $\mathbf{r}(t) = a\cos\omega t\,\mathbf{i} + a\sin\omega t\,\mathbf{j} + b\omega t\mathbf{k}$. Prove that it has constant curvature $\kappa = a/(a^2 + b^2)$.

3. Two fixed unit vectors A and B make an angle θ with each other, where $0 < \theta < \pi$. A particle moves on a space curve in such a way that its position vector $r(t)$ and velocity $v(t)$ are related by the equation $v(t) = A \times r(t)$. If $r(0) = B$, prove that the curve has constant curvature and compute this curvature in terms of θ.

4. A point moves in space according to the vector equation

$$r(t) = 4 \cos t \, i + 4 \sin t \, j + 4 \cos t \, k \, .$$

(a) Show that the path is an ellipse and find a Cartesian equation for the plane containing this ellipse.

(b) Show that the radius of curvature is $\rho(t) = 2\sqrt{2}\,(1 + \sin^2 t)^{3/2}$.

5. For the curve whose vector equation is $r(t) = e^t i + e^{-t} j + \sqrt{2}\, t\, k$, show that the curvature is $\kappa(t) = \sqrt{2}/(e^t + e^{-t})^2$.

6. (a) For a plane curve described by the equation $r(t) = x(t)i + y(t)j$, show that the curvature is given by the formula

$$\kappa(t) = \frac{|x'(t)y''(t) - y'(t)x''(t)|}{\{[x'(t)]^2 + [y'(t)]^2\}^{3/2}} \, .$$

(b) If a plane curve has the Cartesian equation $y = f(x)$, show that the curvature at the point $(x, f(x))$ is

$$\frac{|f''(x)|}{\{1 + [f'(x)]^2\}^{3/2}} \, .$$

7. If a point moves so that the velocity and acceleration vectors always have constant lengths, prove that the curvature is constant at all points of the path. Express this constant in terms of $\|a\|$ and $\|v\|$.

8. If two plane curves with Cartesian equations $y = f(x)$ and $y = g(x)$ have the same tangent at a point (a, b) and the same curvature at that point, prove that $|f''(a)| = |g''(a)|$.

9. For certain values of the constants a and b, the two curves with Cartesian equations $y = ax(b - x)$ and $(x + 2)y = x$ intersect at only one point P, have a common tangent line at P, and have the same curvature at P.

(a) Find all a and b which satisfy all these conditions.

(b) For each possible choice of a and b satisfying the given conditions, make a sketch of the two curves. Show how they intersect at P.

10. (a) Prove that the radius of curvature of a parabola is smallest at its vertex.

(b) Given two fixed unit vectors A and B making an angle θ with each other, where $0 < \theta < \pi$. The curve with position vector $r(t) = tA + t^2 B$ is a parabola lying in the plane spanned by A and B. Determine (in terms of A, B, and θ) the position vector of the vertex of this parabola. You may use the property of the parabola stated in part (a).

11. A particle moves along a plane curve with constant speed 5. It starts at the origin at time $t = 0$ with initial velocity $5j$, and it never goes to the left of the y-axis. At every instant the curvature of the path is $\kappa(t) = 2t$. Let $\alpha(t)$ denote the angle that the velocity vector makes with the positive x-axis at time t.

(a) Determine $\alpha(t)$ explicitly as a function of t.

(b) Determine the velocity $v(t)$ in terms of i and j.

12. A particle moves along a plane curve with constant speed 2. The motion starts at the origin when $t = 0$ and the initial velocity $v(0)$ is $2i$. At every instant it is known that the curvature $\kappa(t) = 4t$. Find the velocity when $t = \frac{1}{4}\sqrt{\pi}$ if the curve never goes below the x-axis.

14.16   Velocity and acceleration in polar coordinates

Sometimes it is more natural to describe the points on a plane curve by polar coordinates rather than rectangular coordinates. Since the rectangular coordinates (x, y) are related to the polar coordinates r and θ by the equations

$$x = r \cos \theta \,, \qquad y = r \sin \theta \,,$$

FIGURE 14.15   Polar coordinates.

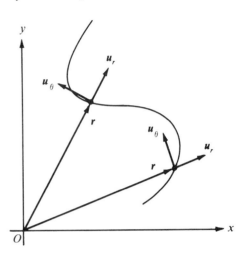

FIGURE 14.16   The unit vectors $\boldsymbol{u}_r$ and $\boldsymbol{u}_\theta$.

the position vector $\boldsymbol{r} = x\boldsymbol{i} + y\boldsymbol{j}$ joining the origin to (x, y) is given by

$$\boldsymbol{r} = r \cos \theta \, \boldsymbol{i} + r \sin \theta \, \boldsymbol{j} = r(\cos \theta \, \boldsymbol{i} + \sin \theta \, \boldsymbol{j}) \,,$$

where $r = \|\boldsymbol{r}\|$. This relation is illustrated in Figure 14.15.

The vector $\cos \theta \, \boldsymbol{i} + \sin \theta \, \boldsymbol{j}$ is a vector of unit length having the same direction as $\boldsymbol{r}$. This unit vector is usually denoted by $\boldsymbol{u}_r$ and the foregoing equation is written as follows:

$$\boldsymbol{r} = r\boldsymbol{u}_r, \qquad \text{where} \quad \boldsymbol{u}_r = \cos \theta \, \boldsymbol{i} + \sin \theta \, \boldsymbol{j} \,.$$

It is convenient to introduce also a unit vector $\boldsymbol{u}_\theta$, perpendicular to $\boldsymbol{u}_r$, which is defined as follows:

$$\boldsymbol{u}_\theta = \frac{d\boldsymbol{u}_r}{d\theta} = -\sin \theta \, \boldsymbol{i} + \cos \theta \, \boldsymbol{j} \,.$$

Note that we have

$$\frac{d\boldsymbol{u}_\theta}{d\theta} = -\cos \theta \, \boldsymbol{i} - \sin \theta \, \boldsymbol{j} = -\boldsymbol{u}_r \,.$$

In the study of plane curves, the two unit vectors $\boldsymbol{u}_r$ and $\boldsymbol{u}_\theta$ play the same roles in polar coordinates as the unit vectors $\boldsymbol{i}$ and $\boldsymbol{j}$ in rectangular coordinates. Figure 14.16 shows the unit vectors $\boldsymbol{u}_r$ and $\boldsymbol{u}_\theta$ attached to a curve at some of its points.

Now suppose the polar coordinates r and θ are functions of t, say $r = f(t)$, $\theta = g(t)$. We shall derive formulas for expressing the velocity and acceleration in terms of $\boldsymbol{u}_r$ and $\boldsymbol{u}_\theta$. For the position vector, we have

$$\boldsymbol{r} = r\boldsymbol{u}_r = f(t)\boldsymbol{u}_r .$$

Since θ depends on the parameter t, the same is true of the unit vector $\boldsymbol{u}_r$ and we must take this into account when we compute the velocity vector. Thus we have

$$\boldsymbol{v} = \frac{d\boldsymbol{r}}{dt} = \frac{d(r\boldsymbol{u}_r)}{dt} = \frac{dr}{dt}\boldsymbol{u}_r + r\frac{d\boldsymbol{u}_r}{dt} .$$

Using the chain rule, we may express $d\boldsymbol{u}_r/dt$ in terms of $\boldsymbol{u}_\theta$ by writing

(14.24)
$$\frac{d\boldsymbol{u}_r}{dt} = \frac{d\theta}{dt}\frac{d\boldsymbol{u}_r}{d\theta} = \frac{d\theta}{dt}\boldsymbol{u}_\theta ,$$

and the equation for the velocity vector becomes

(14.25)
$$\boldsymbol{v} = \frac{dr}{dt}\boldsymbol{u}_r + r\frac{d\theta}{dt}\boldsymbol{u}_\theta .$$

The scalar factors dr/dt and $r\,d\theta/dt$ multiplying $\boldsymbol{u}_r$ and $\boldsymbol{u}_\theta$ are called, respectively, the *radial* and *transverse components* of velocity.

Since $\boldsymbol{u}_r$ and $\boldsymbol{u}_\theta$ are orthogonal unit vectors, we find that

$$\boldsymbol{v} \cdot \boldsymbol{v} = \left(\frac{dr}{dt}\right)^2 + \left(r\frac{d\theta}{dt}\right)^2 ,$$

so the speed v is given by the formula

$$v = \sqrt{\left(\frac{dr}{dt}\right)^2 + \left(r\frac{d\theta}{dt}\right)^2} .$$

Differentiating both sides of (14.25), we find that the acceleration vector is given by

$$\boldsymbol{a} = \left(\frac{d^2 r}{dt^2}\boldsymbol{u}_r + \frac{dr}{dt}\frac{d\boldsymbol{u}_r}{dt}\right) + \left(r\frac{d^2\theta}{dt^2}\boldsymbol{u}_\theta + \frac{dr}{dt}\frac{d\theta}{dt}\boldsymbol{u}_\theta + r\frac{d\theta}{dt}\frac{d\boldsymbol{u}_\theta}{dt}\right) .$$

The derivative $d\boldsymbol{u}_r/dt$ may be expressed in terms of $\boldsymbol{u}_\theta$ by (14.24). We may similarly express the derivative of $\boldsymbol{u}_\theta$ by the equation

$$\frac{d\boldsymbol{u}_\theta}{dt} = \frac{d\theta}{dt}\frac{d\boldsymbol{u}_\theta}{d\theta} = -\frac{d\theta}{dt}\boldsymbol{u}_r .$$

This leads to the following formula which expresses a in terms of its radial and transverse components:

$$(14.26) \qquad a = \left(\frac{d^2r}{dt^2} - r\left(\frac{d\theta}{dt}\right)^2\right)u_r + \left(r\frac{d^2\theta}{dt^2} + 2\frac{dr}{dt}\frac{d\theta}{dt}\right)u_\theta .$$

When $\theta = t$, the curve may be described by the polar equation $r = f(\theta)$. In this case, the formulas for velocity, speed, and acceleration simplify considerably, and we obtain

$$v = \frac{dr}{d\theta}u_r + ru_\theta, \qquad v = \sqrt{\left(\frac{dr}{d\theta}\right)^2 + r^2}, \qquad a = \left(\frac{d^2r}{d\theta^2} - r\right)u_r + 2\frac{dr}{d\theta}u_\theta .$$

14.17 Plane motion with radial acceleration

The acceleration vector is said to be *radial* if the transverse component in Equation (14.26) is always zero. This component is equal to

$$r\frac{d^2\theta}{dt^2} + 2\frac{dr}{dt}\frac{d\theta}{dt} = \frac{1}{r}\frac{d}{dt}\left(r^2\frac{d\theta}{dt}\right).$$

Therefore, the acceleration is radial if and only if $r^2\,d\theta/dt$ is constant.

Plane motion with radial acceleration has an interesting geometric interpretation in terms of area. Denote by $A(t)$ the area of the region swept out by the position vector from a fixed time, say $t = a$, to a later time t. An example is the shaded region shown in Figure 14.17. We shall prove that the time rate of change of this area is exactly equal to $\frac{1}{2}r^2\,d\theta/dt$. That is, we have

$$(14.27) \qquad A'(t) = \frac{1}{2}r^2\frac{d\theta}{dt} .$$

From this it follows that the acceleration vector is radial if and only if the position vector sweeps out area at a constant rate.

To prove (14.27), we assume that it is possible to eliminate t from the two equations $r = f(t)$, $\theta = g(t)$, and thereby express r as a function of θ, say $r = R(\theta)$. This means that there is a real-valued function R such that $R[g(t)] = f(t)$. Then the shaded region in Figure 14.17 is the radial set of R over the interval $[g(a), g(t)]$. By Theorem 2.6, the area of this region is given by the integral

$$A(t) = \frac{1}{2}\int_{g(a)}^{g(t)} R^2(\theta)\,d\theta .$$

Differentiating this integral by the first fundamental theorem of calculus and the chain rule, we find that

$$A'(t) = \frac{1}{2}R^2[g(t)]g'(t) = \frac{1}{2}f^2(t)g'(t) = \frac{1}{2}r^2\frac{d\theta}{dt},$$

which proves (14.27).

14.18 Cylindrical coordinates

If the *x*- and *y*-coordinates of a point $P = (x, y, z)$ in 3-space are replaced by polar coordinates *r* and θ, then the three numbers *r*, θ, *z* are called *cylindrical coordinates* for the point *P*. The nonnegative number *r* now represents the distance from the *z*-axis to the point *P*, as indicated in Figure 14.18. Those points in space for which *r* is constant are at a fixed distance from the *z*-axis and therefore lie on a circular cylinder (hence the name *cylindrical* coordinates).

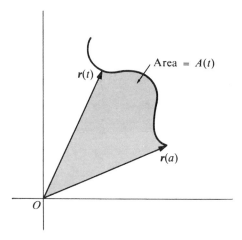

FIGURE 14.17   The position vector sweeps

out area at the rate $A'(t) = \dfrac{1}{2} r^2 \dfrac{d\theta}{dt}$.

FIGURE 14.18   Cylindrical coordinates.

To discuss *space* curves in cylindrical coordinates, the equation for the position vector *r* must be replaced by one of the form

$$r = r u_r + z(t) k .$$

Corresponding formulas for the velocity and acceleration vectors are obtained by merely adding the terms $z'(t)k$ and $z''(t)k$, respectively, to the right-hand members of the two-dimensional formulas in (14.25) and (14.26).

14.19   Exercises

1. A particle moves in a plane so that its position at time *t* has polar coordinates $r = t$, $\theta = t$. Find formulas for the velocity *v*, the acceleration *a*, and the curvature κ at any time *t*.

2. A particle moves in space so that its position at time *t* has cylindrical coordinates $r = t$, $\theta = t$, $z = t$. It traces out a curve called a *conical helix*.
   (a) Find formulas for the velocity *v*, the acceleration *a*, and the curvature κ at time *t*.
   (b) Find a formula for determining the angle between the velocity vector and the generator of the cone at each point of the curve.

3. A particle moves in space so that its position at time *t* has cylindrical coordinates $r = \sin t$, $\theta = t$, $z = \log \sec t$, where $0 \leq t < \frac{1}{2}\pi$.

(a) Show that the curve lies on the cylinder with Cartesian equation $x^2 + (y - \frac{1}{2})^2 = \frac{1}{4}$.

(b) Find a formula (in terms of t) for the angle which the velocity vector makes with $\mathbf{k}$.

4. If a curve is given by a polar equation $r = f(\theta)$, where $a \leq \theta \leq b \leq a + 2\pi$, prove that its arc length is

$$\int_a^b \sqrt{r^2 + \left(\frac{dr}{d\theta}\right)^2}\, d\theta\,.$$

5. The curve described by the polar equation $r = a(1 + \cos\theta)$, where $a > 0$ and $0 \leq \theta \leq 2\pi$, is called a *cardiod*. Draw a graph of the cardiod $r = 4(1 + \cos\theta)$ and compute its arc length.

6. A particle moves along a plane curve whose polar equation is $r = e^{c\theta}$, where c is a constant and θ varies from 0 to 2π.

(a) Make a sketch indicating the general shape of the curve for each of the following values of c: $c = 0$, $c = 1$, $c = -1$.

(b) Let $L(c)$ denote the arc length of the curve and let $a(c)$ denote the area of the region swept out by the position vector as θ varies from 0 to 2π. Compute $L(c)$ and $a(c)$ in terms of c.

7. Sketch the curve whose polar equation is $r = \sin^2\theta$, $0 \leq \theta \leq 2\pi$, and show that it consists of two loops.

(a) Find the area of region enclosed by one loop of the curve.

(b) Compute the length of one loop of the curve.

In each of Exercises 8 through 11, make a sketch of the plane curve having the given polar equation and compute its arc length.

8. $r = \theta$, $0 \leq \theta \leq \pi$.   10. $r = 1 + \cos\theta$, $0 \leq \theta \leq \pi$.

9. $r = e^\theta$, $0 \leq \theta \leq \pi$.   11. $r = 1 - \cos\theta$, $0 \leq \theta \leq 2\pi$.

12. If a curve has the polar equation $r = f(\theta)$, show that its radius of curvature ρ is given by the formula $\rho = (r^2 + r'^2)^{3/2}/|r^2 - rr'' + 2r'^2|$, where $r' = f'(\theta)$ and $r'' = f''(\theta)$.

13. For each of the curves in Exercises 8 through 11, compute the radius of curvature for the value of θ indicated.

(a) Arbitrary θ in Exercise 8.   (c) $\theta = \frac{1}{4}\pi$ in Exercise 10.

(b) Arbitrary θ in Exercise 9.   (d) $\theta = \frac{1}{2}\pi$ in Exercise 11.

14. Let ϕ denote the angle, $0 \leq \phi \leq \pi$, between the position vector and the velocity vector of a curve. If the curve is expressed in polar coordinates, prove that $v \sin\phi = r$ and $v \cos\phi = dr/d\theta$, where v is the speed.

15. A missile is designed to move directly toward its target. Due to mechanical failure, its direction in actual flight makes a fixed angle $\alpha \neq 0$ with the line from the missile to the target. Find the path if it is fired at a fixed target. Discuss how the path varies with α. Does the missile ever reach the target? (Assume the motion takes place in a plane.)

16. Due to a mechanical failure, a ground crew has lost control of a missile recently fired. It is known that the missile will proceed at a constant speed on a straight course of unknown direction. When the missile is 4 miles away, it is sighted for an instant and lost again. Immediately an anti-missile missile is fired with a constant speed three times that of the first missile. What should be the course of the second missile in order for it to overtake the first one? (Assume both missiles move in the same plane.)

17. Prove that if a homogeneous first-order differential equation of the form $y' = f(x, y)$ is rewritten in polar coordinates, it reduces to a separable equation. Use this method to solve $y' = (y - x)/(y + x)$.

18. A particle (moving in space) has velocity vector $\mathbf{v} = \omega\mathbf{k} \times \mathbf{r}$, where ω is a positive constant and $\mathbf{r}$ is the position vector. Prove that the particle moves along a circle with constant angular speed ω. (The angular speed is defined to be $|d\theta/dt|$, where θ is the polar angle at time t.)

19. A particle moves in a plane perpendicular to the z-axis. The motion takes place along a circle with center on this axis.

(a) Show that there is a vector $\omega(t)$ parallel to the z-axis such that

$$v(t) = \omega(t) \times r(t),$$

where $r(t)$ and $v(t)$ denote the position and velocity vectors at time t. The vector $\omega(t)$ is called the *angular velocity* vector and its magnitude $\omega(t) = \|\omega(t)\|$ is called the *angular speed*.

(b) The vector $\alpha(t) = \omega'(t)$ is called the *angular acceleration* vector. Show that the acceleration vector $a(t)$ $[= v'(t)]$ is given by the formula

$$a(t) = [\omega(t) \cdot r(t)]\omega(t) - \omega^2(t)r(t) + \alpha(t) \times r(t).$$

(c) If the particle lies in the xy-plane and if the angular speed $\omega(t)$ is constant, say $\omega(t) = \omega$, prove that the acceleration vector $a(t)$ is centripetal and that, in fact, $a(t) = -\omega^2 r(t)$.

20. A body is said to undergo a *rigid motion* if, for every pair of particles p and q in the body, the distance $\|r_p(t) - r_q(t)\|$ is independent of t, where $r_p(t)$ and $r_q(t)$ denote the position vectors of p and q at time t. Prove that for a rigid motion in which each particle p rotates about the z-axis we have $v_p(t) = \omega(t) \times r_p(t)$, where $\omega(t)$ is the same for each particle, and $v_p(t)$ is the velocity of particle p.

14.20 Applications to planetary motion

By analyzing the voluminous data on planetary motion accumulated up to 1600, the German astronomer Johannes Kepler (1571–1630) tried to discover the mathematical laws governing the motions of the planets. There were six known planets at that time and, according to the Copernican theory, their orbits were thought to lie on concentric spherical shells about the sun. Kepler attempted to show that the radii of these shells were linked up with the five regular solids of geometry. He proposed an ingenious idea that the solar system was designed something like a Chinese puzzle. At the center of the system he placed the sun. Then, in succession, he arranged the six concentric spheres that can be inscribed and circumscribed around the five regular solids—the octahedron, icosahedron, dodecahedron, tetrahedron, and cube, in respective order (from inside out). The innermost sphere, inscribed in the regular octahedron, corresponded to Mercury's path. The next sphere, which circumscribed the octahedron and inscribed the icosahedron, corresponded to the orbit of Venus. Earth's orbit lay on the sphere around the icosahedron and inside the dodecahedron, and so on, the outermost sphere, containing Jupiter's orbit, being circumscribed around the cube. Although this theory seemed correct to within five percent, astronomical observations at that time were accurate to a percentage error much smaller than this, and Kepler finally realized that he had to modify this theory. After much further study it occurred to him that the observed data concerning the orbits corresponded more to *elliptical* paths than the circular paths of the Copernican system. After several more years of unceasing effort, Kepler set forth three famous laws, empirically discovered, which explained all the astronomical phenomena known at that time. They may be stated as follows:

Kepler's first law: Planets move in ellipses with the sun at one focus.

Kepler's second law: The position vector from the sun to a planet sweeps out area at a constant rate.

Kepler's third law: The square of the period of a planet is proportional to the cube of its mean distance from the sun.

> *Note:* By the *period* of a planet is meant the time required to go once around the elliptical orbit. The *mean distance* from the sun is one half the length of the major axis of the ellipse.

The formulation of these laws from a study of astronomical tables was a remarkable achievement. Nearly 50 years later, Newton proved that all three of Kepler's laws are consequences of his own second law of motion and his celebrated universal law of gravitation. In this section we shall use vector methods to show how Kepler's laws may be deduced from Newton's.

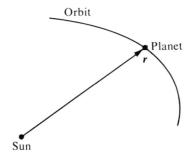

FIGURE 14.19   The position vector from the sun to a planet.

Assume we have a fixed sun of mass M and a moving planet of mass m attracted to the sun by a force F. (We neglect the influence of all other forces.) Newton's second law of motion states that

(14.28) $F = m\mathbf{a}$,

where $\mathbf{a}$ is the acceleration vector of the moving planet. Denote by $\mathbf{r}$ the position vector from the sun to the planet (as in Figure 14.19), let $r = \|\mathbf{r}\|$, and let $\mathbf{u}_r$ be a unit vector with the same direction as $\mathbf{r}$, so that $\mathbf{r} = r\mathbf{u}_r$. The universal law of gravitation states that

$$F = -G\,\frac{mM}{r^2}\,\mathbf{u}_r \,,$$

where G is a constant. Combining this with (14.28), we obtain

(14.29) $$\mathbf{a} = -\,\frac{GM}{r^2}\,\mathbf{u}_r \,,$$

which tells us that the acceleration is *radial*. In a moment we shall prove that the orbit lies in a plane. Once we know this, it follows at once from the results of Section 14.17 that the position vector sweeps out area at a constant rate.

To prove that the path lies in a plane we use the fact that r and a are parallel. If we introduce the velocity vector $v = dr/dt$, we have

$$r \times a = r \times \frac{dv}{dt} + v \times v = r \times \frac{dv}{dt} + \frac{dr}{dt} \times v = \frac{d}{dt}(r \times v) \,.$$

Since $r \times a = O$, this means that $r \times v$ is a constant vector, say $r \times v = c$.

If $c = O$, the position vector r is parallel to v and the motion is along a straight line. Since the path of a planet is not a straight line, we must have $c \neq O$. The relation $r \times v = c$ shows that $r \cdot c = 0$, so the position vector lies in a plane perpendicular to c. Since the acceleration is radial, r sweeps out area at a constant rate. This proves Kepler's second law.

It is easy to prove that this constant rate is exactly half the length of the vector c. In fact, if we use polar coordinates and express the velocity in terms of u_r and u_θ as in Equation (14.25), we find that

$$(14.30) \qquad c = r \times v = (ru_r) \times \left(\frac{dr}{dt} u_r + r \frac{d\theta}{dt} u_\theta \right) = r^2 \frac{d\theta}{dt} u_r \times u_\theta \,,$$

and hence $\|c\| = |r^2 \, d\theta/dt|$. By (14.27) this is equal to $2|A'(t)|$, where $A'(t)$ is the rate at which the radius vector sweeps out area.

Kepler's second law is illustrated in Figure 14.20. The two shaded regions, which are swept out by the position vector in equal time intervals, have equal areas.

We shall prove next that the path is an ellipse. First of all, we form the cross product $a \times c$, using (14.29) and (14.30), and we find that

$$a \times c = \left(-\frac{GM}{r^2} u_r \right) \times \left(r^2 \frac{d\theta}{dt} u_r \times u_\theta \right) = -GM \frac{d\theta}{dt} u_r \times (u_r \times u_\theta) = GM \frac{d\theta}{dt} u_\theta \,.$$

Since $a = dv/dt$ and $u_\theta = du_r/d\theta$, the foregoing equation for $a \times c$ can also be written as follows:

$$\frac{d}{dt}(v \times c) = \frac{d}{dt}(GMu_r) \,.$$

Integration gives us

$$v \times c = GMu_r + b \,,$$

where b is another constant vector. We can rewrite this as follows:

$$(14.31) \qquad v \times c = GM(u_r + e) \,,$$

where $GMe = b$. We shall combine this with (14.30) to eliminate v and obtain an equation for r. For this purpose we dot multiply both sides of (14.30) by c and both sides of (14.31) by r. Equating the two expressions for the scalar triple product $r \cdot v \times c$, we are led to the equation

$$(14.32) \qquad GMr(1 + e \cos \phi) = c^2 \,,$$

where $e = \|e\|$, $c = \|c\|$, and ϕ represents the angle between the constant vector e and the radius vector $\boldsymbol{r}$. (See Figure 14.21.) If we let $d = c^2/(GMe)$, Equation (14.32) becomes

(14.33) $$r = \frac{ed}{e\cos\phi + 1} \qquad \text{or} \qquad r = e(d - r\cos\phi)\,.$$

By Theorem 13.18, this is the polar equation of a conic section with eccentricity e and a focus at the sun. Figure 14.21 shows the directrix drawn perpendicular to $\boldsymbol{e}$ at a distance d from the sun. The distance from the planet to the directrix is $d - r\cos\phi$, and the ratio

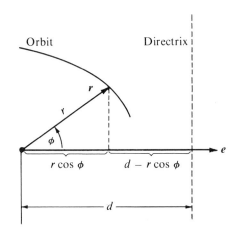

FIGURE 14.20.   Kepler's second law. The
two shaded regions, swept out in equal time
intervals, have equal areas.

FIGURE 14.21.   The ratio $r/(d - r\cos\phi)$
is the eccentricity $e = \|\boldsymbol{e}\|$.

$r/(d - r\cos\phi)$ is the eccentricity e. The conic is an ellipse if $e < 1$, a parabola if $e = 1$, and a hyperbola if $e > 1$. Since planets are known to move on closed paths, the orbit under consideration must be an ellipse. This proves Kepler's first law.

Finally, we deduce Kepler's third law. Suppose the ellipse has major axis of length $2a$ and minor axis of length $2b$. Then the area of the ellipse is πab. Let T be the time it takes for the planet to go once around the ellipse. Since the position vector sweeps out area at the rate $\tfrac{1}{2}c$, we have $\tfrac{1}{2}cT = \pi ab$, or $T = 2\pi ab/c$. We wish to prove that T^2 is proportional to a^3.

From Section 13.22 we have $b^2 = a^2(1 - e^2)$, $ed = a(1 - e^2)$, so

$$c^2 = GMed = GMa(1 - e^2)\,,$$

and hence we have

$$T^2 = \frac{4\pi^2 a^2 b^2}{c^2} = \frac{4\pi^2 a^4 (1 - e^2)}{GMa(1 - e^2)} = \frac{4\pi^2}{GM}\,a^3\,.$$

Since T^2 is a constant times a^3, this proves Kepler's third law.

14.21   Miscellaneous review exercises

1. Let r denote the vector from the origin to an arbitrary point on the parabola $y^2 = x$, let α be the angle that r makes with the tangent line, $0 \le \alpha \le \pi$, and let θ be the angle that r makes with the positive x-axis, $0 \le \theta \le \pi$. Express α in terms of θ.

2. Show that the vector $T = y\mathbf{i} + 2c\mathbf{j}$ is tangent to the parabola $y^2 = 4cx$ at the point (x, y), and that the vector $N = 2c\mathbf{i} - y\mathbf{j}$ is perpendicular to T.

   [*Hint:*   Write a vector equation for the parabola, using y as a parameter.]

3. Prove that an equation of the line of slope m that is tangent to the parabola $y^2 = 4cx$ can be written in the form $y = mx + c/m$. What are the coordinates of the point of contact?

4. (a) Solve Exercise 3 for the parabola $(y - y_0)^2 = 4c(x - x_0)$.
   (b) Solve Exercise 3 for the parabola $x^2 = 4cy$ and, more generally, for the parabola $(x - x_0)^2 = 4c(y - y_0)$.

5. Prove that an equation of the line that is tangent to the parabola $y^2 = 4cx$ at the point (x_1, y_1) can be written in the form $y_1 y = 2c(x + x_1)$.

6. Solve Exercise 5 for each of the parabolas described in Exercise 4.

7. (a) Let P be a point on the parabola $y = x^2$. Let Q be the point of intersection of the normal line at P with the y-axis. What is the limiting position of Q as P tends to the y-axis?
   (b) Solve the same problem for the curve $y = f(x)$, where $f'(0) = 0$.

8. Given that the line $y = c$ intersects the parabola $y = x^2$ at two points. Find the radius of the circle passing through these two points and through the vertex of the parabola. The radius you determine depends on c. What happens to this radius as $c \to 0$?

9. Prove that a point (x_0, y_0) is *inside*, *on*, or *outside* the ellipse $x^2/a^2 + y^2/b^2 = 1$ according as $x_0^2/a^2 + y_0^2/b^2$ is *less than, equal to,* or *greater than* 1.

10. Given an ellipse $x^2/a^2 + y^2/b^2 = 1$. Show that the vectors T and N given by

$$T = -\frac{y}{b^2}\mathbf{i} + \frac{x}{a^2}\mathbf{j}, \qquad N = \frac{x}{a^2}\mathbf{i} + \frac{y}{b^2}\mathbf{j}$$

are, respectively, *tangent* and *normal* to the ellipse when placed at the point (x, y). If the eccentric angle of (x_0, y_0) is θ_0, show that the tangent line at (x_0, y_0) has the Cartesian equation

$$\frac{x}{a}\cos\theta_0 + \frac{y}{b}\sin\theta_0 = 1 .$$

11. Show that the tangent line to the ellipse $x^2/a^2 + y^2/b^2 = 1$ at the point (x_0, y_0) has the equation $x_0 x/a^2 + y_0 y/b^2 = 1$.

12. Prove that the product of the perpendicular distances from the foci of an ellipse to any tangent line is constant, this constant being the square of the length of half the minor axis.

13. Two tangent lines are drawn to the ellipse $x^2 + 4y^2 = 8$, each parallel to the line $x + 2y = 7$. Find the points of tangency.

14. A circle passes through both foci of an ellipse and is tangent to the ellipse at two points. Find the eccentricity of the ellipse.

15. Let V be one of the two vertices of a hyperbola whose transverse axis has length $2a$ and whose eccentricity is 2. Let P be a point on the same branch as V. Denote by A the area of the region bounded by the hyperbola and the line segment VP, and let r be the length of VP.
    (a) Place the coordinate axes in a convenient position and write an equation for the hyperbola.
    (b) Express the area A as an integral and, without attempting to evaluate this integral, show that Ar^{-3} tends to a limit as the point P tends to V. Find this limit.

16. Show that the vectors $T = (y/b^2)\mathbf{i} + (x/a^2)\mathbf{j}$ and $N = (x/a^2)\mathbf{i} - (y/b^2)\mathbf{j}$ are, respectively, tangent and normal to the hyperbola $x^2/a^2 - y^2/b^2 = 1$ if placed at the point (x, y) on the curve.

17. Show that the tangent line to the hyperbola $x^2/a^2 - y^2/b^2 = 1$ at the point(x_0, y_0) is given by the equation $x_0 x/a^2 - y_0 y/b^2 = 1$.

18. The normal line at each point of a curve and the line from that point to the origin form an isosceles triangle whose base is on the x-axis. Show that the curve is a hyperbola.

19. The normal line at a point P of a curve intersects the x-axis at X and the y-axis at Y. Find the curve if each P is the mid-point of the corresponding line segment XY and if the point $(4, 5)$ is on the curve.

20. Prove that the product of the perpendicular distances from an arbitrary point on a hyperbola to its asymptotes is constant.

21. A curve is given by a polar equation $r = f(\theta)$. Find f if an arbitrary arc joining two distinct points of the curve has arc length proportional to (a) the angle subtended at the origin; (b) the difference of the radial distances from the origin to its endpoints; (c) the area of the sector formed by the arc and the radii to its endpoints.

22. If a curve in 3-space is described by a vector-valued function $\mathbf{r}$ defined on a parametric interval $[a, b]$, prove that the scalar triple product $\mathbf{r}'(t) \cdot \mathbf{r}(a) \times \mathbf{r}(b)$ is zero for at least one t in (a, b). Interpret this result geometrically.

15

LINEAR SPACES

15.1 Introduction

Throughout this book we have encountered many examples of mathematical objects that can be added to each other and multiplied by real numbers. First of all, the real numbers themselves are such objects. Other examples are real-valued functions, the complex numbers, infinite series, vectors in n-space, and vector-valued functions. In this chapter we discuss a general mathematical concept, called a *linear space*, which includes all these examples and many others as special cases.

Briefly, a linear space is a set of elements of any kind on which certain operations (called *addition* and *multiplication by numbers*) can be performed. In defining a linear space, we do not specify the nature of the elements nor do we tell how the operations are to be performed on them. Instead, we require that the operations have certain properties which we take as axioms for a linear space. We turn now to a detailed description of these axioms.

15.2 The definition of a linear space

Let V denote a nonempty set of objects, called *elements*. The set V is called a linear space if it satisfies the following ten axioms which we list in three groups.

Closure axioms

AXIOM 1. CLOSURE UNDER ADDITION. *For every pair of elements x and y in V there corresponds a unique element in V called the sum of x and y, denoted by $x + y$.*

AXIOM 2. CLOSURE UNDER MULTIPLICATION BY REAL NUMBERS. *For every x in V and every real number a there corresponds an element in V called the product of a and x, denoted by ax.*

Axioms for addition

AXIOM 3. COMMUTATIVE LAW. *For all x and y in V, we have $x + y = y + x$.*

AXIOM 4. ASSOCIATIVE LAW. *For all $x, y,$ and z in V, we have $(x + y) + z = x + (y + z)$.*

AXIOM 5.   EXISTENCE OF ZERO ELEMENT.   *There is an element in V, denoted by O, such that*

$$x + O = x \qquad for\ all\ x\ in\ V\,.$$

AXIOM 6.   EXISTENCE OF NEGATIVES.   *For every x in V, the element* $(-1)x$ *has the property*

$$x + (-1)x = O\,.$$

Axioms for multiplication by numbers

AXIOM 7.   ASSOCIATIVE LAW.   *For every x in V and all real numbers a and b, we have*

$$a(bx) = (ab)x\,.$$

AXIOM 8.   DISTRIBUTIVE LAW FOR ADDITION IN *V*.   *For all x and y in V and all real a, we have*

$$a(x + y) = ax + ay\,.$$

AXIOM 9.   DISTRIBUTIVE LAW FOR ADDITION OF NUMBERS.   *For all x in V and all real a and b, we have*

$$(a + b)x = ax + bx\,.$$

AXIOM 10.   EXISTENCE OF IDENTITY.   *For every x in V, we have* $1x = x$.

Linear spaces, as defined above, are sometimes called *real* linear spaces to emphasize the fact that we are multiplying the elements of *V* by real numbers. If *real number* is replaced by *complex number* in Axioms 2, 7, 8, and 9, the resulting structure is called a *complex linear space*. Sometimes a linear space is referred to as a *linear vector space* or simply a *vector space*; the numbers used as multipliers are also called *scalars*. A real linear space has real numbers as scalars; a complex linear space has complex numbers as scalars. Although we shall deal primarily with examples of real linear spaces, all the theorems are valid for complex linear spaces as well. When we use the term linear space without further designation, it is to be understood that the space can be real or complex.

15.3   Examples of linear spaces

If we specify the set *V* and tell how to add its elements and how to multiply them by numbers, we get a concrete example of a linear space. The reader can easily verify that each of the following examples satisfies all the axioms for a real linear space.

EXAMPLE 1. Let $V = \mathbf{R}$, the set of all real numbers, and let $x + y$ and ax be ordinary addition and multiplication of real numbers.

EXAMPLE 2. Let $V = \mathbf{C}$, the set of all complex numbers, define $x + y$ to be ordinary addition of complex numbers, and define ax to be multiplication of the complex number x by the real number a. Even though the elements of *V* are complex numbers, this is a real linear space because the scalars are real.

EXAMPLE 3. Let $V = V_n$, the vector space of all n-tuples of real numbers, with addition and multiplication by scalars defined in the usual way in terms of components.

EXAMPLE 4. Let V be the set of all vectors in V_n orthogonal to a given nonzero vector N. If $n = 2$, this linear space is a line through O with N as a normal vector. If $n = 3$, it is a plane through O with N as normal vector.

The following examples are called *function spaces*. The elements of V are real-valued functions, with addition of two functions f and g defined in the usual way:

$$(f + g)(x) = f(x) + g(x)$$

for every real x in the intersection of the domains of f and g. Multiplication of a function f by a real scalar a is defined as follows: af is that function whose value at each x in the domain of f is $af(x)$. The zero element is the function whose values are everywhere zero. The reader can easily verify that each of the following sets is a function space.

EXAMPLE 5. The set of all functions defined on a given interval.

EXAMPLE 6. The set of all polynomials.

EXAMPLE 7. The set of all polynomials of degree $\leq n$, where n is fixed. (Whenever we consider this set it is understood that the zero polynomial is also included.) The set of all polynomials of degree *equal* to n is not a linear space because the closure axioms are not satisfied. For example, the sum of two polynomials of degree n need not have degree n.

EXAMPLE 8. The set of all functions continuous on a given interval. If the interval is $[a, b]$, we denote this space by $C(a, b)$.

EXAMPLE 9. The set of all functions differentiable at a given point.

EXAMPLE 10. The set of all functions integrable on a given interval.

EXAMPLE 11. The set of all functions f defined at 1 with $f(1) = 0$. The number 0 is essential in this example. If we replace 0 by a nonzero number c, we violate the closure axioms.

EXAMPLE 12. The set of all solutions of a homogeneous linear differential equation $y'' + ay' + by = 0$, where a and b are given constants. Here again 0 is essential. The set of solutions of a nonhomogeneous differential equation does not satisfy the closure axioms.

These examples and many others illustrate how the linear space concept permeates algebra, geometry, and analysis. When a theorem is deduced from the axioms of a linear space, we obtain, in one stroke, a result valid for each concrete example. By unifying diverse examples in this way we gain a deeper insight into each. Sometimes special knowledge of one particular example helps to anticipate or interpret results valid for other examples and reveals relationships which might otherwise escape notice.

15.4   Elementary consequences of the axioms

The following theorems are easily deduced from the axioms for a linear space.

THEOREM 15.1.   UNIQUENESS OF THE ZERO ELEMENT.   *In any linear space there is one and only one zero element.*

Proof.   Axiom 5 tells us that there is at least one zero element. Suppose there were two, say O_1 and O_2. Taking $x = O_1$ and $O = O_2$ in Axiom 5, we obtain $O_1 + O_2 = O_1$. Similarly, taking $x = O_2$ and $O = O_1$, we find $O_2 + O_1 = O_2$. But $O_1 + O_2 = O_2 + O_1$ because of the commutative law, so $O_1 = O_2$.

THEOREM 15.2.   UNIQUENESS OF NEGATIVE ELEMENTS.   *In any linear space every element has exactly one negative. That is, for every x there is one and only one y such that $x + y = O$.*

Proof.   Axiom 6 tells us that each x has at least one negative, namely $(-1)x$. Suppose x has two negatives, say y_1 and y_2. Then $x + y_1 = O$ and $x + y_2 = O$. Adding y_2 to both members of the first equation and using Axioms 5, 4, and 3, we find that

$$y_2 + (x + y_1) = y_2 + O = y_2,$$

and

$$y_2 + (x + y_1) = (y_2 + x) + y_1 = O + y_1 = y_1 + O = y_1.$$

Therefore $y_1 = y_2$, so x has exactly one negative, the element $(-1)x$.

Notation.   The negative of x is denoted by $-x$. The difference $y - x$ is defined to be the sum $y + (-x)$.

The next theorem describes a number of properties which govern elementary algebraic manipulations in a linear space.

THEOREM 15.3.   *In a given linear space, let x and y denote arbitrary elements and let a and b denote arbitrary scalars. Then we have the following properties*:
   (a) $0x = O$.
   (b) $aO = O$.
   (c) $(-a)x = -(ax) = a(-x)$.
   (d) *If $ax = O$, then either $a = 0$ or $x = O$.*
   (e) *If $ax = ay$ and $a \neq 0$, then $x = y$.*
   (f) *If $ax = bx$ and $x \neq O$, then $a = b$.*
   (g) $-(x + y) = (-x) + (-y) = -x - y$.
   (h) $x + x = 2x$, $x + x + x = 3x$, *and in general*, $\sum_{i=1}^{n} x = nx$.

We shall prove (a), (b), and (c) and leave the proofs of the other properties as exercises.

Proof of (a).   Let $z = 0x$. We wish to prove that $z = O$. Adding z to itself and using Axiom 9, we find that

$$z + z = 0x + 0x = (0 + 0)x = 0x = z .$$

Now add $-z$ to both members to get $z = O$.

Proof of (b).   Let $z = aO$, add z to itself, and use Axiom 8.

Proof of (c).   Let $z = (-a)x$. Adding z to ax and using Axiom 9, we find that

$$z + ax = (-a)x + ax = (-a + a)x = 0x = O ,$$

so z is the negative of ax, $z = -(ax)$. Similarly, if we add $a(-x)$ to ax and use Axiom 8 and property (b), we find that $a(-x) = -(ax)$.

15.5   Exercises

In Exercises 1 through 28, determine whether each of the given sets is a real linear space, if addition and multiplication by real scalars are defined in the usual way. For those that are not, tell which axioms fail to hold. The functions in Exercises 1 through 17 are real-valued. In Exercises 3, 4, and 5, each function has domain containing 0 and 1. In Exercises 7 through 12, each domain contains all real numbers.

1. All rational functions.
2. All rational functions f/g, with the degree of $f \leq$ the degree of g (including $f = 0$).
3. All f with $f(0) = f(1)$.   8. All even functions.
4. All f with $2f(0) = f(1)$.   9. All odd functions.
5. All f with $f(1) = 1 + f(0)$.   10. All bounded functions.
6. All step functions defined on $[0, 1]$.   11. All increasing functions.
7. All f with $f(x) \to 0$ as $x \to +\infty$.   12. All functions with period 2π.
13. All f integrable on $[0, 1]$ with $\int_0^1 f(x)\, dx = 0$.
14. All f integrable on $[0, 1]$ with $\int_0^1 f(x)\, dx \geq 0$.
15. All f satisfying $f(x) = f(1 - x)$ for all x.
16. All Taylor polynomials of degree $\leq n$ for a fixed n (including the zero polynomial).
17. All solutions of a linear second-order homogeneous differential equation $y'' + P(x)y' + Q(x)y = 0$, where P and Q are given functions, continuous everywhere.
18. All bounded real sequences.   20. All convergent real series.
19. All convergent real sequences.   21. All absolutely convergent real series.
22. All vectors (x, y, z) in V_3 with $z = 0$.
23. All vectors (x, y, z) in V_3 with $x = 0$ or $y = 0$.
24. All vectors (x, y, z) in V_3 with $y = 5x$.
25. All vectors (x, y, z) in V_3 with $3x + 4y = 1$, $z = 0$.
26. All vectors (x, y, z) in V_3 which are scalar multiples of $(1, 2, 3)$.
27. All vectors (x, y, z) in V_3 whose components satisfy a system of three linear equations of the form:

$$a_{11}x + a_{12}y + a_{13}z = 0 , \qquad a_{21}x + a_{22}y + a_{23}z = 0 , \qquad a_{31}x + a_{32}y + a_{33}z = 0 .$$

28. All vectors in V_n that are linear combinations of two given vectors A and B.

29. Let $V = \mathbf{R}^+$, the set of positive real numbers. Define the "sum" of two elements x and y in V to be their product $x \cdot y$ (in the usual sense), and define "multiplication" of an element x in V by a scalar c to be x^c. Prove that V is a real linear space with 1 as the zero element.

30. (a) Prove that Axiom 10 can be deduced from the other axioms.
    (b) Prove that Axiom 10 cannot be deduced from the other axioms if Axiom 6 is replaced by
        Axiom 6′: For every x in V there is an element y in V such that $x + y = O$.

31. Let S be the set of all ordered pairs (x_1, x_2) of real numbers. In each case determine whether or not S is a linear space with the operations of addition and multiplication by scalars defined as indicated. If the set is not a linear space, indicate which axioms are violated.
    (a) $(x_1, x_2) + (y_1, y_2) = (x_1 + y_1, x_2 + y_2)$, $\qquad a(x_1, x_2) = (ax_1, 0)$.
    (b) $(x_1, x_2) + (y_1, y_2) = (x_1 + y_1, 0)$, $\qquad\quad a(x_1, x_2) = (ax_1, ax_2)$.
    (c) $(x_1, x_2) + (y_1, y_2) = (x_1, x_2 + y_2)$, $\qquad\quad a(x_1, x_2) = (ax_1, ax_2)$.
    (d) $(x_1, x_2) + (y_1, y_2) = (|x_1 + x_2|, |y_1 + y_2|)$, $\quad a(x_1, x_2) = (|ax_1|, |ax_2|)$.

32. Prove parts (d) through (h) of Theorem 15.3.

15.6 Subspaces of a linear space

Given a linear space V, let S be a nonempty subset of V. If S is also a linear space, with the same operations of addition and multiplication by scalars, then S is called a *subspace* of V. The next theorem gives a simple criterion for determining whether or not a subset of a linear space is a subspace.

THEOREM 15.4. *Let S be a nonempty subset of a linear space V. Then S is a subspace if and only if S satisfies the closure axioms.*

Proof. If S is a subspace, it satisfies all the axioms for a linear space, and hence, in particular, it satisfies the closure axioms.

Now we show that if S satisfies the closure axioms it satisfies the others as well. The commutative and associative laws for addition (Axioms 3 and 4) and the axioms for multiplication by scalars (Axioms 7 through 10) are automatically satisfied in S because they hold for all elements of V. It remains to verify Axioms 5 and 6, the existence of a zero element in S, and the existence of a negative for each element in S.

Let x be any element of S. (S has at least one element since S is not empty.) By Axiom 2, ax is in S for every scalar a. Taking $a = 0$, it follows that $0x$ is in S. But $0x = O$, by Theorem 15.3(a), so $O \in S$, and Axiom 5 is satisfied. Taking $a = -1$, we see that $(-1)x$ is in S. But $x + (-1)x = O$ since both x and $(-1)x$ are in V, so Axiom 6 is satisfied in S. Therefore S is a subspace of V.

DEFINITION. *Let S be a nonempty subset of a linear space V. An element x in V of the form*

$$x = \sum_{i=1}^{k} c_i x_i,$$

where $x_1, \ldots, x_k$ are all in S and $c_1, \ldots, c_k$ are scalars, is called a finite linear combination of elements of S. The set of all finite linear combinations of elements of S satisfies the closure axioms and hence is a subspace of V. We call this the subspace spanned by S, or the *linear span of S, and denote it by L(S). If S is empty, we define L(S) to be* $\{O\}$, *the set consisting of the zero element alone.*

Different sets may span the same subspace. For example, the space V_2 is spanned by each of the following sets of vectors: $\{i, j\}, \{i, j, i + j\}, \{O, i, -i, j, -j, i + j\}$. The space of all polynomials $p(t)$ of degree $\leq n$ is spanned by the set of $n + 1$ polynomials

$$\{1, t, t^2, \ldots, t^n\}\,.$$

It is also spanned by the set $\{1, t/2, t^2/3, \ldots, t^n/(n + 1)\}$, and by $\{1, (1 + t), (1 + t)^2, \ldots, (1 + t)^n\}$. The space of all polynomials is spanned by the infinite set of polynomials $\{1, t, t^2, \ldots\}$.

A number of questions arise naturally at this point. For example, which spaces can be spanned by a finite set of elements? If a space can be spanned by a finite set of elements, what is the smallest number of elements required? To discuss these and related questions, we introduce the concepts of *dependence, independence, bases,* and *dimension.* These ideas were encountered in Chapter 12 in our study of the vector space V_n. Now we extend them to general linear spaces.

15.7 Dependent and independent sets in a linear space

DEFINITION. *A set S of elements in a linear space V is called dependent if there is a finite set of distinct elements in S, say* $x_1, \ldots, x_k$, *and corresponding set of scalars* $c_1, \ldots, c_k$, *not all zero, such that*

$$\sum_{i=1}^{k} c_i x_i = O\,.$$

The set S is called independent if it is not dependent. In this case, for all choices of distinct elements $x_1, \ldots, x_k$ *in S and scalars* $c_1, \ldots, c_k$,

$$\sum_{i=1}^{k} c_i x_i = O \qquad implies \quad c_1 = c_2 = \cdots = c_k = 0\,.$$

Although dependence and independence are properties of sets of elements, we also apply these terms to the elements themselves. For example, the elements in an independent set are called independent elements.

If S is a finite set, the foregoing definition agrees with that given in Chapter 12 for the space V_n. However, the present definition is not restricted to finite sets.

EXAMPLE 1. If a subset T of a set S is dependent, then S itself is dependent. This is logically equivalent to the statement that every subset of an independent set is independent.

EXAMPLE 2. If one element in S is a scalar multiple of another, then S is dependent.

EXAMPLE 3. If $O \in S$, then S is dependent.

EXAMPLE 4. The empty set is independent.

Many examples of dependent and independent sets of vectors in V_n were discussed in Chapter 12. The following examples illustrate these concepts in function spaces. In each case the underlying linear space V is the set of all real-valued functions defined on the real line.

EXAMPLE 5. Let $u_1(t) = \cos^2 t$, $u_2(t) = \sin^2 t$, $u_3(t) = 1$ for all real t. The Pythagorean identity shows that $u_1 + u_2 - u_3 = O$, so the three functions u_1, u_2, u_3 are dependent.

EXAMPLE 6. Let $u_k(t) = t^k$ for $k = 0, 1, 2, \ldots$, and t real. The set $S = \{u_0, u_1, u_2, \ldots\}$ is independent. To prove this, it suffices to show that for each n the $n + 1$ polynomials $u_0, u_1, \ldots, u_n$ are independent. A relation of the form $\sum c_k u_k = O$ means that

$$(15.1) \qquad \sum_{k=0}^{n} c_k t^k = 0$$

for all real t. When $t = 0$, this gives $c_0 = 0$. Differentiating (15.1) and setting $t = 0$, we find that $c_1 = 0$. Repeating the process, we find that each coefficient c_k is zero.

EXAMPLE 7. If $a_1, \ldots, a_n$ are distinct real numbers, the n exponential functions

$$u_1(x) = e^{a_1 x}, \ldots, u_n(x) = e^{a_n x}$$

are independent. We can prove this by induction on n. The result holds trivially when $n = 1$. Therefore, assume it is true for $n - 1$ exponential functions and consider scalars $c_1, \ldots, c_n$ such that

$$(15.2) \qquad \sum_{k=1}^{n} c_k e^{a_k x} = 0.$$

Let a_M be the largest of the n numbers $a_1, \ldots, a_n$. Multiplying both members of (15.2) by $e^{-a_M x}$, we obtain

$$(15.3) \qquad \sum_{k=1}^{n} c_k e^{(a_k - a_M)x} = 0.$$

If $k \neq M$, the number $a_k - a_M$ is negative. Therefore, when $x \to +\infty$ in Equation (15.3), each term with $k \neq M$ tends to zero and we find that $c_M = 0$. Deleting the Mth term from (15.2) and applying the induction hypothesis, we find that each of the remaining $n - 1$ coefficients c_k is zero.

THEOREM 15.5. *Let S be an independent set consisting of k elements in a linear space V and let $L(S)$ be the subspace spanned by S. Then every set of $k + 1$ elements in $L(S)$ is dependent.*

Proof. When $V = V_n$, Theorem 15.5 reduces to Theorem 12.8. If we examine the proof of Theorem 12.8, we find that it is based only on the fact that V_n is a linear space and not on any other special property of V_n. Therefore the proof given for Theorem 12.8 is valid for any linear space V.

15.8 Bases and dimension

DEFINITION. *A finite set S of elements in a linear space V is called a finite basis for V if S is independent and spans V. The space V is called finite dimensional if it has a finite basis, or if V consists of O alone. Otherwise V is called infinite dimensional.*

THEOREM 15.6. *Let V be a finite-dimensional linear space. Then every finite basis for V has the same number of elements.*

Proof. Let S and T be two finite bases for V. Suppose S consists of k elements and T consists of m elements. Since S is independent and spans V, Theorem 15.5 tells us that every set of $k + 1$ elements in V is dependent. Therefore, every set of more than k elements in V is dependent. Since T is an independent set, we must have $m \leq k$. The same argument with S and T interchanged shows that $k \leq m$. Therefore $k = m$.

DEFINITION. *If a linear space V has a basis of n elements, the integer n is called the dimension of V. We write $n = \dim V$. If $V = \{O\}$, we say V has dimension 0.*

EXAMPLE 1. The space V_n has dimension n. One basis is the set of n unit coordinate vectors.

EXAMPLE 2. The space of all polynomials $p(t)$ of degree $\leq n$ has dimension $n + 1$. One basis is the set of $n + 1$ polynomials $\{1, t, t^2, \ldots, t^n\}$. Every polynomial of degree $\leq n$ is a linear combination of these $n + 1$ polynomials.

EXAMPLE 3. The space of solutions of the differential equation $y'' - 2y' - 3y = 0$ has dimension 2. One basis consists of the two functions $u_1(x) = e^{-x}$, $u_2(x) = e^{3x}$. Every solution is a linear combination of these two.

EXAMPLE 4. The space of all polynomials $p(t)$ is infinite-dimensional. Although the infinite set $\{1, t, t^2, \ldots\}$ spans this space, no *finite* set of polynomials spans the space.

THEOREM 15.7. *Let V be a finite-dimensional linear space with $\dim V = n$. Then we have the following*:
   (a) *Any set of independent elements in V is a subset of some basis for V.*
   (b) *Any set of n independent elements is a basis for V.*

Proof. The proof of (a) is identical to that of part (b) of Theorem 12.10. The proof of (b) is identical to that of part (c) of Theorem 12.10.

Let V be a linear space of dimension n and consider a basis whose elements $e_1, \ldots, e_n$ are taken in a given order. We denote such an ordered basis as an n-tuple $(e_1, \ldots, e_n)$.

If $x \in V$, we can express x as a linear combination of these basis elements:

(15.4)
$$x = \sum_{i=1}^{n} c_i e_i .$$

The coefficients in this equation determine an n-tuple of numbers $(c_1, \ldots, c_n)$ that is uniquely determined by x. In fact, if we have another representation of x as a linear combination of $e_1, \ldots, e_n$, say $x = \sum_{i=1}^{n} d_i e_i$, then by subtraction from (15.4), we find that $\sum_{i=1}^{n} (c_i - d_i)e_i = O$. But since the basis elements are independent, this implies $c_i = d_i$ for each i, so we have $(c_1, \ldots, c_n) = (d_1, \ldots, d_n)$.

The components of the ordered n-tuple $(c_1, \ldots, c_n)$ determined by Equation (15.4) are called *the components of x relative to the ordered basis* $(e_1, \ldots, e_n)$.

15.9 Exercises

In each of Exercises 1 through 10, let S denote the set of all vectors (x, y, z) in V_3 whose components satisfy the condition given. Determine whether S is a subspace of V_3. If S is a subspace, compute dim S.

1. $x = 0$.
2. $x + y = 0$.
3. $x + y + z = 0$.
4. $x = y$.
5. $x = y = z$.

6. $x = y$ or $x = z$.
7. $x^2 - y^2 = 0$.
8. $x + y = 1$.
9. $y = 2x$ and $z = 3x$.
10. $x + y + z = 0$ and $x - y - z = 0$.

Let P_n denote the linear space of all real polynomials of degree $\leq n$, where n is fixed. In each of Exercises 11 through 20, let S denote the set of all polynomials f in P_n satisfying the condition given. Determine whether or not S is a subspace of P_n. If S is a subspace, compute dim S.

11. $f(0) = 0$.
12. $f'(0) = 0$.
13. $f''(0) = 0$.
14. $f(0) + f'(0) = 0$.
15. $f(0) = f(1)$.

16. $f(0) = f(2)$.
17. f is even.
18. f is odd.
19. f has degree $\leq k$, where $k < n$, or $f = 0$.
20. f has degree k, where $k < n$, or $f = 0$.

21. In the linear space of all real polynomials $p(t)$, describe the subspace spanned by each of the following subsets of polynomials and determine the dimension of this subspace.
    (a) $\{1, t^2, t^4\}$;   (b) $\{t, t^3, t^5\}$;   (c) $\{t, t^2\}$;   (d) $\{1 + t, (1 + t)^2\}$.

22. In this exercise, $L(S)$ denotes the subspace spanned by a subset S of a linear space V. Prove each of the statements (a) through (f).
    (a) $S \subseteq L(S)$.
    (b) If $S \subseteq T \subseteq V$ and if T is a subspace of V, then $L(S) \subseteq T$. This property is described by saying that $L(S)$ is the *smallest* subspace of V which contains S.
    (c) A subset S of V is a subspace of V if and only if $L(S) = S$.
    (d) If $S \subseteq T \subseteq V$, then $L(S) \subseteq L(T)$.
    (e) If S and T are subspaces of V, then so is $S \cap T$.
    (f) If S and T are subsets of V, then $L(S \cap T) \subseteq L(S) \cap L(T)$.
    (g) Give an example in which $L(S \cap T) \neq L(S) \cap L(T)$.

23. Let V be the linear space consisting of all real-valued functions defined on the real line. Determine whether each of the following subsets of V is dependent or independent. Compute the dimension of the subspace spanned by each set.
    (a) $\{1, e^{ax}, e^{bx}\}, a \neq b$.
    (b) $\{e^{ax}, xe^{ax}\}$.

    (c) $\{1, e^{ax}, xe^{ax}\}$.
    (d) $\{e^{ax}, xe^{ax}, x^2 e^{ax}\}$.

(e) $\{e^x, e^{-x}, \cosh x\}$.   (h) $\{1, \cos 2x, \sin^2 x\}$.
(f) $\{\cos x, \sin x\}$.   (i) $\{\sin x, \sin 2x\}$.
(g) $\{\cos^2 x, \sin^2 x\}$.   (j) $\{e^x \cos x, e^{-x} \sin x\}$.

24. Let V be a finite-dimensional linear space, and let S be a subspace of V. Prove each of the following statements.
   (a) S is finite dimensional and $\dim S \le \dim V$.
   (b) $\dim S = \dim V$ if and only if $S = V$.
   (c) Every basis for S is part of a basis for V.
   (d) A basis for V need not contain a basis for S.

15.10 Inner products, Euclidean spaces. Norms

In ordinary Euclidean geometry, those properties that rely on the possibility of measuring lengths of line segments and angles between lines are called *metric* properties. In our study of V_n, we defined lengths and angles in terms of the dot product. Now we wish to extend these ideas to more general linear spaces. We shall introduce first a generalization of the dot product, which we call an *inner product*, and then define length and angle in terms of the inner product.

The dot product $x \cdot y$ of two vectors $x = (x_1, \ldots, x_n)$ and $y = (y_1, \ldots, y_n)$ in V_n was defined in Chapter 12 by the formula

$$(15.5) \qquad x \cdot y = \sum_{i=1}^{n} x_i y_i \,.$$

In a general linear space, we write (x, y) instead of $x \cdot y$ for inner products, and we define the product axiomatically rather than by a specific formula. That is, we state a number of properties we wish inner products to satisfy and we regard these properties as *axioms*.

DEFINITION. *A real linear space V is said to have an inner product if for each pair of elements x and y in V there corresponds a unique real number (x, y) satisfying the following axioms for all choices of x, y, z in V and all real scalars c.*
   (1) $(x, y) = (y, x)$ *(commutativity, or symmetry)*.
   (2) $(x, y + z) = (x, y) + (x, z)$ *(distributivity, or linearity)*.
   (3) $c(x, y) = (cx, y)$ *(associativity, or homogeneity)*.
   (4) $(x, x) > 0$ *if* $x \ne O$ *(positivity)*.

A real linear space with an inner product is called a *real Euclidean space*.

   Note: Taking $c = 0$ in (3), we find that $(O, y) = 0$ for all y.

In a complex linear space, an inner product (x, y) is a complex number satisfying the same axioms as those for a real inner product, except that the symmetry axiom is replaced by the relation

$$(1') \qquad (x, y) = \overline{(y, x)} \,,$$

where $\overline{(y, x)}$ denotes the complex conjugate of (y, x). In the homogeneity axiom, the scalar multiplier c can be any complex number. From the homogeneity axiom and $(1')$, we get the companion relation

$$(x, cy) = \overline{(cy, x)} = \bar{c}\overline{(y, x)} = \bar{c}(x, y).$$

A complex linear space with an inner product is called a *complex Euclidean space.* (Sometimes the term *unitary space* is also used.) One example is complex vector space $V_n(\mathbf{C})$ discussed briefly in Section 12.16.

Although we are interested primarily in examples of real Euclidean spaces, the theorems of this chapter are valid for complex Euclidean spaces as well. When we use the term Euclidean space without further designation, it is to be understood that the space can be real or complex.

The reader should verify that each of the following satisfies all the axioms for an inner product.

EXAMPLE 1. In V_n let $(x, y) = x \cdot y$, the usual dot product of x and y.

EXAMPLE 2. If $x = (x_1, x_2)$ and $y = (y_1, y_2)$ are any two vectors in V_2, define (x, y) by the formula

$$(x, y) = 2x_1y_1 + x_1y_2 + x_2y_1 + x_2y_2.$$

This example shows that there may be more than one inner product in a given linear space.

EXAMPLE 3. Let $C(a, b)$ denote the linear space of all real-valued functions continuous on an interval $[a, b]$. Define an inner product of two functions f and g by the formula

$$(f, g) = \int_a^b f(t)g(t)\, dt.$$

This formula is analogous to Equation (15.5) which defines the dot product of two vectors in V_n. The function values $f(t)$ and $g(t)$ play the role of the components x_i and y_i, and integration takes the place of summation.

EXAMPLE 4. In the space $C(a, b)$, define

$$(f, g) = \int_a^b w(t)f(t)g(t)\, dt,$$

where w is a fixed positive function in $C(a, b)$. The function w is called a *weight function.* In Example 3 we have $w(t) = 1$ for all t.

EXAMPLE 5. In the linear space of all real polynomials, define

$$(f, g) = \int_0^\infty e^{-t}f(t)g(t)\, dt.$$

Because of the exponential factor, this improper integral converges for every choice of polynomials f and g.

THEOREM 15.8. *In a Euclidean space V, every inner product satisfies the Cauchy–Schwarz inequality:*

$$|(x, y)|^2 \leq (x, x)(y, y) \qquad \text{for all } x \text{ and } y \text{ in } V.$$

Moreover, the equality sign holds if and only if x and y are dependent.

Proof. When we proved the corresponding result for vectors in V_n (Theorem 12.3), we were careful to point out that the proof was a consequence of the properties of the dot product listed in Theorem 12.2 and did not depend on the particular definition used to deduce these properties. Therefore, the very same proof is valid in any real Euclidean space. When we apply this proof in a complex Euclidean space, we obtain the inequality $(x, y)(y, x) \leq (x, x)(y, y)$, which is the same as the Cauchy-Schwarz inequality since

$$(x, y)(y, x) = (x, y)\overline{(x, y)} = |(x, y)|^2 .$$

EXAMPLE. Applying Theorem 15.8 to the space $C(a, b)$ with the inner product $(f, g) = \int_a^b f(t)g(t)\, dt$, we find that the Cauchy-Schwarz inequality becomes

$$\left(\int_a^b f(t)g(t)\, dt \right)^2 \leq \left(\int_a^b f^2(t)\, dt \right)\left(\int_a^b g^2(t)\, dt \right).$$

The inner product can be used to introduce the metric concept of length in any Euclidean space.

DEFINITION. *In a Euclidean space V, the nonnegative number $\|x\|$ defined by the equation*

$$\|x\| = (x, x)^{1/2}$$

is called the norm of the element x.

When the Cauchy-Schwarz inequality is expressed in terms of norms, it becomes

$$|(x, y)| \leq \|x\|\ \|y\| .$$

Since it may be possible to define an inner product in many different ways, the norm of an element will depend on the choice of inner product. This lack of uniqueness is to be expected. It is analogous to the fact that we can assign different numbers to measure the length of a given line segment, depending on the choice of scale or unit of measurement. The next theorem gives fundamental properties of norms that do not depend on the choice of inner product.

THEOREM 15.9. *In a Euclidean space, every norm has the following properties for all elements x and y and all scalars c:*
   (a) $\|x\| = 0$ *if* $x = O$.
   (b) $\|x\| > 0$ *if* $x \neq O$ *(positivity).*
   (c) $\|cx\| = |c|\ \|x\|$ *(homogeneity).*
   (d) $\|x + y\| \leq \|x\| + \|y\|$ *(triangle inequality).*
   The equality sign holds in (d) *if* $x = O$, *if* $y = O$, *or if* $y = cx$ *for some* $c > 0$.

Proof. Properties (a), (b) and (c) follow at once from the axioms for an inner product. To prove (d), we note that

$$\|x + y\|^2 = (x + y, x + y) = (x, x) + (y, y) + (x, y) + (y, x)$$
$$= \|x\|^2 + \|y\|^2 + (x, y) + \overline{(x, y)} \,.$$

The sum $(x, y) + \overline{(x, y)}$ is real. The Cauchy-Schwarz inequality shows that $|(x, y)| \leq \|x\| \, \|y\|$ and $|\overline{(x, y)}| \leq \|x\| \, \|y\|$, so we have

$$\|x + y\|^2 \leq \|x\|^2 + \|y\|^2 + 2\|x\| \, \|y\| = (\|x\| + \|y\|)^2 \,.$$

This proves (d). When $y = cx$, where $c > 0$, we have

$$\|x + y\| = \|x + cx\| = (1 + c)\|x\| = \|x\| + \|cx\| = \|x\| + \|y\|.$$

DEFINITION. *In a real Euclidean space V, the angle between two nonzero elements x and y is defined to be that number θ in the interval $0 \leq \theta \leq \pi$ which satisfies the equation*

(15.6) $$\cos \theta = \frac{(x, \, y)}{\|x\| \, \|y\|} \,.$$

> *Note:* The Cauchy-Schwarz inequality shows that the quotient on the right of (15.6) lies in the interval $[-1, 1]$, so there is exactly one θ in $[0, \pi]$ whose cosine is equal to this quotient.

15.11   Orthogonality in a Euclidean space

DEFINITION. *In a Euclidean space V, two elements x and y are called orthogonal if their inner product is zero. A subset S of V is called an orthogonal set if $(x, y) = 0$ for every pair of distinct elements x and y in S. An orthogonal set is called orthonormal if each of its elements has norm 1.*

The zero element is orthogonal to every element of V; it is the only element orthogonal to itself. The next theorem shows a relation between orthogonality and dependence.

THEOREM 15.10. *In a Euclidean space V, every orthogonal set of nonzero elements is independent. In particular, in a finite-dimensional Euclidean space with* dim $V = n$, *every orthogonal set consisting of n nonzero elements is a basis for V.*

Proof. Let S be an orthogonal set of nonzero elements in V, and suppose some finite linear combination of elements of S is zero, say

$$\sum_{i=1}^{k} c_i x_i = O \,,$$

where each $x_i \in S$. Taking the dot product of each member with x_1 and using the fact that $(x_1, x_i) = 0$ if $i \neq 1$, we find that $c_1(x_1, x_1) = 0$. But $(x_1, x_1) \neq 0$ since $x_1 \neq O$ so $c_1 = 0$. Repeating the argument with x_1 replaced by x_j, we find that each $c_j = 0$. This proves that S is independent. If dim $V = n$ and if S consists of n elements, Theorem 15.7(b) shows that S is a basis for V.

EXAMPLE. In the real linear space $C(0, 2\pi)$ with the inner product $(f, g) = \int_0^{2\pi} f(x)g(x)\, dx$, let S be the set of trigonometric functions $\{u_0, u_1, u_2, \ldots\}$ given by

$$u_0(x) = 1, \qquad u_{2n-1}(x) = \cos nx, \qquad u_{2n}(x) = \sin nx, \qquad \text{for} \quad n = 1, 2, \ldots .$$

If $m \neq n$, we have the orthogonality relations

$$\int_0^{2\pi} u_n(x)u_m(x)\, dx = 0,$$

so S is an orthogonal set. Since no member of S is the zero element, S is independent. The norm of each element of S is easily calculated. We have $(u_0, u_0) = \int_0^{2\pi} dx = 2\pi$ and, for $n \geq 1$, we have

$$(u_{2n-1}, u_{2n-1}) = \int_0^{2\pi} \cos^2 nx\, dx = \pi, \qquad (u_{2n}, u_{2n}) = \int_0^{2\pi} \sin^2 nx\, dx = \pi .$$

Therefore, $\|u_0\| = \sqrt{2\pi}$ and $\|u_n\| = \sqrt{\pi}$ for $n \geq 1$. Dividing each u_n by its norm, we obtain an orthonormal set $\{\varphi_0, \varphi_1, \varphi_2, \ldots\}$ where $\varphi_n = u_n/\|u_n\|$. Thus, we have

$$\varphi_0(x) = \frac{1}{\sqrt{2\pi}}, \qquad \varphi_{2n-1}(x) = \frac{\cos nx}{\sqrt{\pi}}, \qquad \varphi_{2n}(x) = \frac{\sin nx}{\sqrt{\pi}}, \qquad \text{for} \quad n \geq 1 .$$

In Section 15.13 we shall prove that every finite-dimensional Euclidean space has an orthogonal basis. The next theorem shows how to compute the components of an element relative to such a basis.

THEOREM 15.11. *Let V be a finite-dimensional Euclidean space with dimension n, and assume that $S = \{e_1, \ldots, e_n\}$ is an orthogonal basis for V. If an element x is expressed as a linear combination of the basis elements, say*

$$(15.7) \qquad\qquad x = \sum_{i=1}^{n} c_i e_i,$$

then its components relative to the ordered basis $(e_1, \ldots, e_n)$ are given by the formulas

$$(15.8) \qquad\qquad c_j = \frac{(x, e_j)}{(e_j, e_j)} \qquad \text{for} \quad j = 1, 2, \ldots, n .$$

In particular, if S is an orthonormal basis, each c_j is given by

$$(15.9) \qquad\qquad c_j = (x, e_j) .$$

Proof. Taking the inner product of each member of (15.7) with e_j, we obtain

$$(x, e_j) = \sum_{i=1}^{n} c_i(e_i, e_j) = c_j(e_j, e_j)$$

since $(e_i, e_j) = 0$ if $i \neq j$. This implies (15.8), and when $(e_j, e_j) = 1$, we obtain (15.9).

If $\{e_1, \ldots, e_n\}$ is an orthonormal basis, Equation (15.7) can be written in the form

$$(15.10) \qquad\qquad x = \sum_{i=1}^{n} (x, e_i)e_i.$$

The next theorem shows that in a finite-dimensional Euclidean space with an ortho-normal basis the inner product of two elements can be computed in terms of their components.

THEOREM 15.12. *Let V be a finite-dimensional Euclidean space of dimension n, and assume that $\{e_1, \ldots, e_n\}$ is an orthonormal basis for V. Then for every pair of elements x and y in V, we have*

$$(15.11) \qquad\qquad (x, y) = \sum_{i=1}^{n} (x, e_i)(\overline{y, e_i}) \qquad (\text{Parseval's formula}).$$

In particular, when $x = y$, we have

$$(15.12) \qquad\qquad \|x\|^2 = \sum_{i=1}^{n} |(x, e_i)|^2.$$

Proof. Taking the inner product of both members of Equation (15.10) with y and using the linearity property of the inner product, we obtain (15.11). When $x = y$, Equation (15.11) reduces to (15.12).

Note: Equation (15.11) is named in honor of M. A. Parseval (circa 1776–1836), who obtained this type of formula in a special function space.

15.12 Exercises

1. Let $x = (x_1, \ldots, x_n)$ and $y = (y_1, \ldots, y_n)$ be arbitrary vectors in V_n. In each case, determine whether (x, y) is an inner product for V_n if (x, y) is defined by the formula given. In case (x, y) is not an inner product, tell which axioms are not satisfied.

(a) $(x, y) = \sum_{i=1}^{n} x_i |y_i|$.

(b) $(x, y) = \left| \sum_{i=1}^{n} x_i y_i \right|$.

(c) $(x, y) = \sum_{i=1}^{n} x_i \sum_{j=1}^{n} y_j$.

(d) $(x, y) = \left(\sum_{i=1}^{n} x_i^2 y_i^2 \right)^{1/2}$.

(e) $(x, y) = \sum_{i=1}^{n} (x_i + y_i)^2 - \sum_{i=1}^{n} x_i^2 - \sum_{i=1}^{n} y_i^2$.

2. Suppose we retain the first three axioms for a real inner product (symmetry, linearity, and

homogeneity) but replace the fourth axiom by a new axiom (4′): $(x, x) = 0$ if and only if $x = O$. Prove that either $(x, x) > 0$ for all $x \neq O$ or else $(x, x) < 0$ for all $x \neq O$.

[*Hint:* Assume $(x, x) > 0$ for some $x \neq O$ and $(y, y) < 0$ for some $y \neq O$. In the space spanned by $\{x, y\}$, find an element $z \neq O$ with $(z, z) = 0$.]

Prove that each of the statements in Exercises 3 through 7 is valid for all elements x and y in a real Euclidean space.

3. $(x, y) = 0$ if and only if $\|x + y\| = \|x - y\|$.
4. $(x, y) = 0$ if and only if $\|x + y\|^2 = \|x\|^2 + \|y\|^2$.
5. $(x, y) = 0$ if and only if $\|x + cy\| \geq \|x\|$ for all real c.
6. $(x + y, x - y) = 0$ if and only if $\|x\| = \|y\|$.
7. If x and y are nonzero elements making an angle θ with each other, then

$$\|x - y\|^2 = \|x\|^2 + \|y\|^2 - 2\,\|x\|\,\|y\|\cos\theta\,.$$

8. In the real linear space $C(1, e)$, define an inner product by the equation

$$(f, g) = \int_1^e (\log x) f(x) g(x)\, dx\,.$$

(a) If $f(x) = \sqrt{x}$, compute $\|f\|$.
(b) Find a linear polynomial $g(x) = a + bx$ that is orthogonal to the constant function $f(x) = 1$.

9. In the real linear space $C(-1, 1)$, let $(f, g) = \int_{-1}^{1} f(t)g(t)\, dt$. Consider the three functions u_1, u_2, u_3 given by

$$u_1(t) = 1\,, \qquad u_2(t) = t\,, \qquad u_3(t) = 1 + t\,.$$

Prove that two of them are orthogonal, two make an angle $\pi/3$ with each other, and two make an angle $\pi/6$ with each other.

10. In the linear space P_n of all real polynomials of degree $\leq n$, define

$$(f, g) = \sum_{k=0}^{n} f\left(\frac{k}{n}\right) g\left(\frac{k}{n}\right)\,.$$

(a) Prove that (f, g) is an inner product for P_n.
(b) Compute (f, g) when $f(t) = t$ and $g(t) = at + b$.
(c) If $f(t) = t$, find all linear polynomials g orthogonal to f.

11. In the linear space of all real polynomials, define $(f, g) = \int_0^\infty e^{-t} f(t) g(t)\, dt$.
(a) Prove that this improper integral converges absolutely for all polynomials f and g.
(b) If $x_n(t) = t^n$ for $n = 0, 1, 2, \ldots$, prove that $(x_n, x_m) = (m + n)!$.
(c) Compute (f, g) when $f(t) = (t + 1)^2$ and $g(t) = t^2 + 1$.
(d) Find all linear polynomials $g(t) = a + bt$ orthogonal to $f(t) = 1 + t$.

12. In the linear space of all real polynomials, determine whether or not (f, g) is an inner product if (f, g) is defined by the formula given. In case (f, g) is not an inner product, indicate which axioms are violated. In (c), f' and g' denote derivatives.

(a) $(f, g) = f(1)g(1)$.

(c) $(f, g) = \int_0^1 f'(t) g'(t)\, dt$.

(b) $(f, g) = \left| \int_0^1 f(t)g(t)\, dt \right|$.

(d) $(f, g) = \left(\int_0^1 f(t)\, dt \right) \left(\int_0^1 g(t)\, dt \right)$.

13. Let V consist of all infinite sequences $\{x_n\}$ of real numbers for which the series $\sum x_n^2$ converges. If $x = \{x_n\}$ and $y = \{y_n\}$ are two elements of V, define

$$(x, y) = \sum_{n=1}^{\infty} x_n y_n \, .$$

(a) Prove that this series converges absolutely.
[*Hint:* Use the Cauchy-Schwarz inequality to estimate the sum $\sum_{n=1}^{M} |x_n y_n|$.]
(b) Prove that V is a linear space with (x, y) as an inner product.
(c) Compute (x, y) if $x_n = 1/n$ and $y_n = 1/(n + 1)$ for $n \geq 1$.
(d) Compute (x, y) if $x_n = 2^n$ and $y_n = 1/n!$ for $n \geq 1$.
14. Let V be the set of all real functions f continuous on $[0, +\infty)$ and such that the integral $\int_0^\infty e^{-t} f^2(t) \, dt$ converges. Define $(f, g) = \int_0^\infty e^{-t} f(t) g(t) \, dt$.
(a) Prove that the integral for (f, g) converges absolutely for each pair of functions f and g in V.
[*Hint:* Use the Cauchy-Schwarz inequality to estimate the integral $\int_0^M e^{-t} |f(t) g(t)| \, dt$.]
(b) Prove that V is a linear space with (f, g) as an inner product.
(c) Compute (f, g) if $f(t) = e^{-t}$ and $g(t) = t^n$, where $n = 0, 1, 2, \ldots$.
15. In a complex Euclidean space, prove that the inner product has the following properties for all elements x, y and z, and all complex a and b.
(a) $(ax, by) = a\bar{b}(x, y)$.   (b) $(x, ay + bz) = \bar{a}(x, y) + \bar{b}(x, z)$.
16. Prove that the following identities are valid in every Euclidean space.
(a) $\|x + y\|^2 = \|x\|^2 + \|y\|^2 + (x, y) + (y, x)$.
(b) $\|x + y\|^2 - \|x - y\|^2 = 2(x, y) + 2(y, x)$.
(c) $\|x + y\|^2 + \|x - y\|^2 = 2 \|x\|^2 + 2 \|y\|^2$.
17. Prove that the space of all complex-valued functions continuous on an interval $[a, b]$ becomes a unitary space if we define an inner product by the formula

$$(f, g) = \int_a^b w(t) f(t) \overline{g(t)} \, dt \, ,$$

where w is a fixed positive function, continuous on $[a, b]$.

15.13   Construction of orthogonal sets.   The Gram-Schmidt process

Every finite-dimensional linear space has a finite basis. If the space is Euclidean, we can always construct an *orthogonal* basis. This result will be deduced as a consequence of a general theorem whose proof shows how to construct orthogonal sets in any Euclidean space, finite or infinite dimensional. The construction is called the *Gram-Schmidt orthogonalization process*, in honor of J. P. Gram (1850–1916) and E. Schmidt (1845–1921).

THEOREM 15.13.   ORTHOGONALIZATION THEOREM.   *Let* $x_1, x_2, \ldots$, *be a finite or infinite sequence of elements in a Euclidean space* V, *and let* $L(x_1, \ldots, x_k)$ *denote the subspace spanned by the first k of these elements. Then there is a corresponding sequence of elements* $y_1, y_2, \ldots$, *in V which has the following properties for each integer k:*
(a) *The element* y_k *is orthogonal to every element in the subspace* $L(y_1, \ldots, y_{k-1})$.
(b) *The subspace spanned by* $y_1, \ldots, y_k$ *is the same as that spanned by* $x_1, \ldots, x_k$:

$$L(y_1, \ldots, y_k) = L(x_1, \ldots, x_k) \, .$$

(c) *The sequence* y_1 , y_2 , . . . , *is unique, except for scalar factors. That is, if* y_1' , y_2' , . . . , *is another sequence of elements in V satisfying properties* (a) *and* (b), *then for each k there is a scalar* c_k *such that* $y_k' = c_k y_k$.

Proof. We construct the elements y_1 , y_2 , . . . , by induction. To start the process, we take $y_1 = x_1$. Now assume we have constructed y_1 , . . . , y_r so that (a) and (b) are satisfied when $k = r$. Then we define y_{r+1} by the equation

$$(15.13) \qquad\qquad y_{r+1} = x_{r+1} - \sum_{i=1}^{r} a_i y_i \, ,$$

where the scalars a_1 , . . . , a_r are to be determined. For $j \leq r$, the inner product of y_{r+1} with y_j is given by

$$(y_{r+1} , y_j) = (x_{r+1} , y_j) - \sum_{i=1}^{r} a_i (y_i , y_j) = (x_{r+1} , y_j) - a_j (y_j , y_j) \, ,$$

since $(y_i , y_j) = 0$ if $i \neq j$. If $y_j \neq O$, we can make y_{r+1} orthogonal to y_j by taking

$$(15.14) \qquad\qquad a_j = \frac{(x_{r+1} , y_j)}{(y_j , y_j)} \, .$$

If $y_j = O$, then y_{r+1} is orthogonal to y_j for any choice of a_j , and in this case we choose $a_j = 0$. Thus, the element y_{r+1} is well defined and is orthogonal to each of the earlier elements y_1 , . . . , y_r . Therefore, it is orthogonal to every element in the subspace

$$L(y_1 , \ldots , y_r) \, .$$

This proves (a) when $k = r + 1$.

To prove (b) when $k = r + 1$, we must show that $L(y_1 , \ldots , y_{r+1}) = L(x_1 , \ldots , x_{r+1})$, given that $L(y_1 , \ldots , y_r) = L(x_1 , \ldots , x_r)$. The first r elements y_1 , . . . , y_r are in

$$L(x_1 , \ldots , x_r)$$

and hence they are in the larger subspace $L(x_1 , \ldots , x_{r+1})$. The new element y_{r+1} given by (15.13) is a difference of two elements in $L(x_1 , \ldots , x_{r+1})$ so it, too, is in $L(x_1 , \ldots , x_{r+1})$. This proves that

$$L(y_1 , \ldots , y_{r+1}) \subseteq L(x_1 , \ldots , x_{r+1}) \, .$$

Equation (15.13) shows that x_{r+1} is the sum of two elements in $L(y_1 , \ldots , y_{r+1})$ so a similar argument gives the inclusion in the other direction:

$$L(x_1 , \ldots , x_{r+1}) \subseteq L(y_1 , \ldots , y_{r+1}) \, .$$

This proves (b) when $k = r + 1$. Therefore both (a) and (b) are proved by induction on k .

Finally we prove (c) by induction on k. The case $k = 1$ is trivial. Therefore, assume (c) is true for $k = r$ and consider the element y'_{r+1}. Because of (b), this element is in

$$L(y_1, \ldots, y_{r+1}),$$

so we can write

$$y'_{r+1} = \sum_{i=1}^{r+1} c_i y_i = z_r + c_{r+1} y_{r+1},$$

where $z_r \in L(y_1, \ldots, y_r)$. We wish to prove that $z_r = O$. By property (a), both y'_{r+1} and $c_{r+1} y_{r+1}$ are orthogonal to z_r. Therefore, their difference, z_r, is orthogonal to z_r. In other words, z_r is orthogonal to itself, so $z_r = O$. This completes the proof of the orthogonalization theorem.

In the foregoing construction, suppose we have $y_{r+1} = O$ for some r. Then (15.13) shows that x_{r+1} is a linear combination of $y_1, \ldots, y_r$, and hence of $x_1, \ldots, x_r$, so the elements $x_1, \ldots, x_{r+1}$ are dependent. In other words, if the first k elements $x_1, \ldots, x_k$ are independent, then the corresponding elements $y_1, \ldots, y_k$ are *nonzero*. In this case the coefficients a_i in (15.13) are given by (15.14), and the formulas defining $y_1, \ldots, y_k$ become

$$(15.15) \quad y_1 = x_1, \qquad y_{r+1} = x_{r+1} - \sum_{i=1}^{r} \frac{(x_{r+1}, y_i)}{(y_i, y_i)} y_i \qquad \text{for} \quad r = 1, 2, \ldots, k - 1.$$

These formulas describe the Gram-Schmidt process for constructing an orthogonal set of nonzero elements $y_1, \ldots, y_k$ which spans the same subspace as a given independent set $x_1, \ldots, x_k$. In particular, if $x_1, \ldots, x_k$ is a basis for a finite-dimensional Euclidean space, then $y_1, \ldots, y_k$ is an orthogonal basis for the same space. We can also convert this to an orthonormal basis by *normalizing* each element y_i, that is, by dividing it by its norm. Therefore, as a corollary of Theorem 15.13 we have the following.

THEOREM 15.14.   *Every finite-dimensional Euclidean space has an orthonormal basis.*

If x and y are elements in a Euclidean space, with $y \neq O$, the element

$$\frac{(x, y)}{(y, y)} y$$

is called the *projection of x along y*. In the Gram-Schmidt process (15.15), we construct the element y_{r+1} by subtracting from x_{r+1} the projection of x_{r+1} along each of the earlier elements $y_1, \ldots, y_r$. Figure 15.1 illustrates the construction geometrically in the vector space V_3.

EXAMPLE 1. In V_4, find an orthonormal basis for the subspace spanned by the three vectors $x_1 = (1, -1, 1, -1)$, $x_2 = (5, 1, 1, 1)$, and $x_3 = (-3, -3, 1, -3)$.

an approach to the general approximation problem and motivates the discussion that follows.

DEFINITION. *Let S be a subset of a Euclidean space V. An element in V is said to be orthogonal to S if it is orthogonal to every element of S. The set of all elements orthogonal to S is denoted by $S^\perp$ and is called "S perpendicular."*

It is a simple exercise to verify that $S^\perp$ is a subspace of V, whether or not S itself is one. In case S is a subspace, then $S^\perp$ is called the *orthogonal complement* of S.

EXAMPLE. If S is a plane through the origin, as shown in Figure 15.2, then $S^\perp$ is a line through the origin perpendicular to this plane. This example also gives a geometric interpretation for the next theorem.

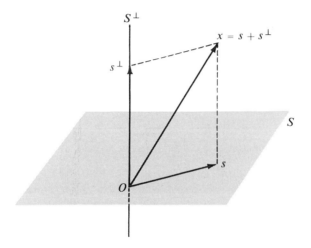

FIGURE 15.2   Geometric interpretation of the orthogonal decomposition theorem in V_3.

THEOREM 15.15. ORTHOGONAL DECOMPOSITION THEOREM. *Let V be a Euclidean space and let S be a finite-dimensional subspace of V. Then every element x in V can be represented uniquely as a sum of two elements, one in S and one in $S^\perp$. That is, we have*

(15.16) $$x = s + s^\perp, \qquad where \quad s \in S \quad and \quad s^\perp \in S^\perp.$$

Moreover, the norm of x is given by the Pythagorean formula

(15.17) $$\|x\|^2 = \|s\|^2 + \|s^\perp\|^2.$$

Proof. First we prove that an orthogonal decomposition (15.16) actually exists. Since S is finite-dimensional, it has a finite orthonormal basis, say $\{e_1, \ldots, e_n\}$. Given x, define the elements s and $s^\perp$ as follows:

(15.18) $$s = \sum_{i=1}^{n} (x, e_i)e_i, \qquad s^\perp = x - s.$$

Note that each term $(x, e_i)e_i$ is the projection of x along e_i. The element s is the sum of the projections of x along each basis element. Since s is a linear combination of the basis elements, s lies in S. The definition of $s^\perp$ shows that Equation (15.16) holds. To prove that $s^\perp$ lies in $S^\perp$, we consider the inner product of $s^\perp$ and any basis element e_j. We have

$$(s^\perp, e_j) = (x - s, e_j) = (x, e_j) - (s, e_j).$$

But from (15.18), we find that $(s, e_j) = (x, e_j)$, so $s^\perp$ is orthogonal to e_j. Therefore $s^\perp$ is orthogonal to every element in S, which means that $s^\perp \in S^\perp$.

Next we prove that the orthogonal decomposition (15.16) is unique. Suppose that x has two such representations, say

(15.19) $x = s + s^\perp$ and $x = t + t^\perp$,

where s and t are in S, and $s^\perp$ and $t^\perp$ are in $S^\perp$. We wish to prove that $s = t$ and $s^\perp = t^\perp$. From (15.19), we have $s - t = t^\perp - s^\perp$, so we need only prove that $s - t = O$. But $s - t \in S$ and $t^\perp - s^\perp \in S^\perp$ so $s - t$ is both orthogonal to $t^\perp - s^\perp$ and equal to $t^\perp - s^\perp$. Since the zero element is the only element orthogonal to itself, we must have $s - t = O$. This shows that the decomposition is unique.

Finally, we prove that the norm of x is given by the Pythagorean formula. We have

$$\|x\|^2 = (x, x) = (s + s^\perp, s + s^\perp) = (s, s) + (s^\perp, s^\perp),$$

the remaining terms being zero since s and $s^\perp$ are orthogonal. This proves (15.17).

DEFINITION. *Let S be a finite-dimensional subspace of a Euclidean space V, and let $\{e_1, \ldots, e_n\}$ be an orthonormal basis for S. If $x \in V$, the element s defined by the equation*

$$s = \sum_{i=1}^{n} (x, e_i)e_i$$

is called the projection of x on the subspace S.

We prove next that the projection of x on S is the solution to the approximation problem stated at the beginning of this section.

15.15 Best approximation of elements in a Euclidean space by elements in a finite-dimensional subspace

THEOREM 15.16. APPROXIMATION THEOREM. *Let S be a finite-dimensional subspace of a Euclidean space V, and let x be any element of V. Then the projection of x on S is nearer to x than any other element of S. That is, if s is the projection of x on S, we have*

$$\|x - s\| \le \|x - t\|$$

for all t in S; the equality sign holds if and only if $t = s$.

Proof. By Theorem 15.15 we can write $x = s + s^\perp$, where $s \in S$ and $s^\perp \in S^\perp$. Then, for any t in S, we have

$$x - t = (x - s) + (s - t).$$

Since $s - t \in S$ and $x - s = s^\perp \in S^\perp$, this is an orthogonal decomposition of $x - t$, so its norm is given by the Pythagorean formula

$$\|x - t\|^2 = \|x - s\|^2 + \|s - t\|^2.$$

But $\|s - t\|^2 \geq 0$, so we have $\|x - t\|^2 \geq \|x - s\|^2$, with equality holding if and only if $s = t$. This completes the proof.

EXAMPLE 1. *Approximation of continuous functions on* $[0, 2\pi]$ *by trigonometric polynomials.* Let $V = C(0, 2\pi)$, the linear space of all real functions continuous on the interval $[0, 2\pi]$, and define an inner product by the equation $(f, g) = \int_0^{2\pi} f(x)g(x)\, dx$. In Section 15.11 we exhibited an orthonormal set of trigonometric functions $\varphi_0, \varphi_1, \varphi_2, \ldots$, where

$$(15.20) \quad \varphi_0(x) = \frac{1}{\sqrt{2\pi}}, \qquad \varphi_{2k-1}(x) = \frac{\cos kx}{\sqrt{\pi}}, \qquad \varphi_{2k}(x) = \frac{\sin kx}{\sqrt{\pi}}, \qquad \text{for} \quad k \geq 1.$$

The $2n + 1$ elements $\varphi_0, \varphi_1, \ldots, \varphi_{2n}$ span a subspace S of dimension $2n + 1$. The elements of S are called *trigonometric polynomials.*

If $f \in C(0, 2\pi)$, let f_n denote the projection of f on the subspace S. Then we have

$$(15.21) \quad f_n = \sum_{k=0}^{2n} (f, \varphi_k)\varphi_k, \qquad \text{where} \quad (f, \varphi_k) = \int_0^{2\pi} f(x)\varphi_k(x)\, dx.$$

The numbers (f, φ_k) are called *Fourier coefficients* of f. Using the formulas in (15.20), we can rewrite (15.21) in the form

$$(15.22) \quad f_n(x) = \tfrac{1}{2}a_0 + \sum_{k=1}^{n} (a_k \cos kx + b_k \sin kx),$$

where

$$a_k = \frac{1}{\pi} \int_0^{2\pi} f(x) \cos kx\, dx, \qquad b_k = \frac{1}{\pi} \int_0^{2\pi} f(x) \sin kx\, dx$$

for $k = 0, 1, 2, \ldots, n$. The approximation theorem tells us that the trigonometric polynomial in (15.22) approximates f better than any other trigonometric polynomial in S, in the sense that the norm $\|f - f_n\|$ is as small as possible.

EXAMPLE 2. *Approximation of continuous functions on* $[-1, 1]$ *by polynomials of degree* $\leq n$. Let $V = C(-1, 1)$, the space of real continuous functions on $[-1, 1]$, and let $(f, g) = \int_{-1}^{1} f(x)g(x)\, dx$. The $n + 1$ normalized Legendre polynomials $\varphi_0, \varphi_1, \ldots, \varphi_n$,

introduced in Section 15.13, span a subspace S of dimension $n + 1$ consisting of all polynomials of degree $\leq n$. If $f \in C(-1, 1)$, let f_n denote the projection of f on S. Then we
have

$$f_n = \sum_{k=0}^{n} (f, \varphi_k)\varphi_k , \qquad \text{where} \quad (f, \varphi_k) = \int_{-1}^{1} f(t)\varphi_k(t) \, dt .$$

This is the polynomial of degree $\leq n$ for which the norm $\|f - f_n\|$ is smallest. For example,
when $f(x) = \sin \pi x$, the coefficients (f, φ_k) are given by

$$(f, \varphi_k) = \int_{-1}^{1} \sin \pi t \; \varphi_k(t) \, dt .$$

In particular, we have $(f, \varphi_0) = 0$ and

$$(f, \varphi_1) = \int_{-1}^{1} \sqrt{\frac{3}{2}} \, t \sin \pi t \, dt = \sqrt{\frac{3}{2}} \frac{2}{\pi} .$$

Therefore the linear polynomial $f_1(t)$ which is nearest to $\sin \pi t$ on $[-1, 1]$ is

$$f_1(t) = \sqrt{\frac{3}{2}} \frac{2}{\pi} \, \varphi_1(t) = \frac{3}{\pi} t .$$

Since $(f, \varphi_2) = 0$, this is also the nearest quadratic approximation.

15.16   Exercises

1. In each case, find an orthonormal basis for the subspace of V_3 spanned by the given vectors.
   (a) $x_1 = (1, 1, 1), \qquad x_2 = (1, 0, 1), \qquad x_3 = (3, 2, 3)$.
   (b) $x_1 = (1, 1, 1), \qquad x_2 = (-1, 1, -1), \qquad x_3 = (1, 0, 1)$.
2. In each case, find an orthonormal basis for the subspace of V_4 spanned by the given vectors.
   (a) $x_1 = (1 \; 1, 0, 0), \qquad x_2 = (0, 1, 1, 0), \qquad x_3 = (0, 0, 1, 1), \qquad x_4 = (1, 0, 0, 1)$.
   (b) $x_1 = (1, 1, 0, 1), \qquad x_2 = (1, 0, 2, 1), \qquad x_3 = (1, 2, -2, 1)$.
3. In the real linear space $C(0, \pi)$, with inner product $(x, y) = \int_0^\pi x(t)y(t) \, dt$, let $x_n(t) = \cos nt$
   for $n = 0, 1, 2, \dots$. Prove that the functions $y_0, y_1, y_2, \dots$, given by

$$y_0(t) = \frac{1}{\sqrt{\pi}} \qquad \text{and} \qquad y_n(t) = \sqrt{\frac{2}{\pi}} \cos nt \qquad \text{for} \quad n \geq 1 ,$$

   form an orthonormal set spanning the same subspace as $x_0, x_1, x_2, \dots$.
4. In the linear space of all real polynomials, with inner product $(x, y) = \int_0^1 x(t)y(t) \, dt$, let
   $x_n(t) = t^n$ for $n = 0, 1, 2, \dots$. Prove that the functions

$$y_0(t) = 1 , \qquad y_1(t) = \sqrt{3} \, (2t - 1) , \qquad y_2(t) = \sqrt{5} \, (6t^2 - 6t + 1)$$

   form an orthonormal set spanning the same subspace as $\{x_0, x_1, x_2\}$.

5. Let V be the linear space of all real functions f continuous on $[0, +\infty)$ and such that the integral $\int_0^\infty e^{-t}f^2(t)\,dt$ converges. Define $(f, g) = \int_0^\infty e^{-t}f(t)g(t)\,dt$, and let $y_0, y_1, y_2, \ldots$, be the set obtained by applying the Gram-Schmidt process to $x_0, x_1, x_2, \ldots$, where $x_n(t) = t^n$ for $n \geq 0$. Prove that $y_0(t) = 1, y_1(t) = t - 1, y_2(t) = t^2 - 4t + 2, y_3(t) = t^3 - 9t^2 + 18t - 6$.

6. In the real linear space $C(1, 3)$ with inner product $(f, g) = \int_1^3 f(x)g(x)\,dx$, let $f(x) = 1/x$ and show that the constant polynomial g nearest to f is $g = \frac{1}{2}\log 3$. Compute $\|g - f\|^2$ for this g.

7. In the real linear space $C(0, 2)$ with inner product $(f, g) = \int_0^2 f(x)g(x)\,dx$, let $f(x) = e^x$ and show that the constant polynomial g nearest to f is $g = \frac{1}{2}(e^2 - 1)$. Compute $\|g - f\|^2$ for this g.

8. In the real linear space $C(-1, 1)$ with inner product $(f, g) = \int_{-1}^1 f(x)g(x)\,dx$, let $f(x) = e^x$ and find the linear polynomial g nearest to f. Compute $\|g - f\|^2$ for this g.

9. In the real linear space $C(0, 2\pi)$ with inner product $(f, g) = \int_0^{2\pi} f(x)g(x)\,dx$, let $f(x) = x$. In the subspace spanned by $u_0(x) = 1$, $u_1(x) = \cos x$, $u_2(x) = \sin x$, find the trigonometric polynomial nearest to f.

10. In the linear space V of Exercise 5, let $f(x) = e^{-x}$ and find the linear polynomial that is nearest to f.

16

LINEAR TRANSFORMATIONS AND MATRICES

16.1 Linear transformations

One of the ultimate goals of analysis is a comprehensive study of functions whose domains and ranges are subsets of linear spaces. Such functions are called *transformations*, *mappings*, or *operators*. This chapter treats the simplest examples, called *linear* transformations, which occur in all branches of mathematics. Properties of more general transformations are often obtained by approximating them by linear transformations.

First we introduce some notation and terminology concerning arbitrary functions. Let V and W be two sets. The symbol

$$T : V \rightarrow W$$

will be used to indicate that T is a function whose domain is V and whose values are in W. For each x in V, the element $T(x)$ in W is called the *image of x under T*, and we say that T *maps x onto $T(x)$*. If A is any subset of V, the set of all images $T(x)$ for x in A is called the *image of A under T* and is denoted by $T(A)$. The image of the domain V, $T(V)$, is the range of T.

Now we assume that V and W are linear spaces having the same set of scalars, and we define a linear transformation as follows.

DEFINITION. *If V and W are linear spaces, a function $T: V \rightarrow W$ is called a linear transformation of V into W if it has the following two properties*:
  (a) $T(x + y) = T(x) + T(y)$ *for all x and y in V,*
  (b) $T(cx) = cT(x)$ *for all x in V and all scalars c.*

These properties are verbalized by saying that T preserves addition and multiplication by scalars. The two properties can be combined into one formula which states that

$$T(ax + by) = aT(x) + bT(y)$$

for all x, y in V and all scalars a and b. By induction, we also have the more general relation

$$T\left(\sum_{i=1}^{n} a_i x_i\right) = \sum_{i=1}^{n} a_i T(x_i)$$

for any n elements $x_1, \ldots, x_n$ in V and any n scalars $a_1, \ldots, a_n$.

578

The reader can easily verify that the following examples are linear transformations.

EXAMPLE 1. *The identity transformation.* The transformation $T: V \to V$, where $T(x) = x$ for each x in V, is called the identity transformation and is denoted by I or by I_V.

EXAMPLE 2. *The zero transformation.* The transformation $T: V \to V$ which maps each element of V onto O is called the zero transformation and is denoted by O.

EXAMPLE 3. *Multiplication by a fixed scalar c.* Here we have $T: V \to V$, where $T(x) = cx$ for all x in V. When $c = 1$, this is the identity transformation. When $c = 0$, it is the zero transformation.

EXAMPLE 4. *Linear equations.* Let $V = V_n$ and $W = V_m$. Given mn real numbers a_{ik}, where $i = 1, 2, \ldots, m$ and $k = 1, 2, \ldots, n$, define $T : V_n \to V_m$ as follows: T maps each vector $x = (x_1, \ldots, x_n)$ in V_n onto the vector $y = (y_1, \ldots, y_m)$ in V_m according to the equations

$$y_i = \sum_{k=1}^{n} a_{ik} x_k \quad \text{for} \quad i = 1, 2, \ldots, m .$$

EXAMPLE 5. *Inner product with a fixed element.* Let V be a real Euclidean space. For a fixed element z in V, define $T : V \to \mathbf{R}$ as follows: If $x \in V$, then $T(x) = (x, z)$, the inner product of x with z.

EXAMPLE 6. *Projection on a subspace.* Let V be a Euclidean space and let S be a finite-dimensional subspace of V. Define $T : V \to S$ as follows: If $x \in V$, then $T(x)$ is the projection of x on S.

EXAMPLE 7. *The differentiation operator.* Let V be the linear space of all real functions f differentiable on an open interval (a, b). The linear transformation which maps each function f in V onto its derivative f' is called the differentiation operator and is denoted by D. Thus, we have $D : V \to W$, where $D(f) = f'$ for each f in V. The space W consists of all derivatives f'.

EXAMPLE 8. *The integration operator.* Let V be the linear space of all real functions continuous on an interval $[a, b]$. If $f \in V$, define $g = T(f)$ to be that function in V given by

$$g(x) = \int_a^x f(t)\, dt \quad \text{if} \quad a \le x \le b .$$

This transformation T is called the integration operator.

16.2 Null space and range

In this section, T denotes a linear transformation of a linear space V into a linear space W.

THEOREM 16.1. *The set $T(V)$ (the range of T) is a subspace of W. Moreover, T maps the zero element of V onto the zero element of W.*

Proof. To prove that $T(V)$ is a subspace of W, we need only verify the closure axioms. Take any two elements of $T(V)$, say $T(x)$ and $T(y)$. Then $T(x) + T(y) = T(x + y)$, so $T(x) + T(y)$ is in $T(V)$. Also, for any scalar c we have $cT(x) = T(cx)$, so $cT(x)$ is in $T(V)$. Therefore, $T(V)$ is a subspace of W. Taking $c = 0$ in the relation $T(cx) = cT(x)$, we find that $T(O) = O$.

DEFINITION. *The set of all elements in V that T maps onto O is called the null space of T and is denoted by $N(T)$. Thus, we have*

$$N(T) = \{x \mid x \in V \ and \ T(x) = O\} .$$

The null space is sometimes called the kernel of T.

THEOREM 16.2.   *The null space of T is a subspace of V.*

Proof. If x and y are in $N(T)$, then so are $x + y$ and cx for all scalars c, since

$$T(x + y) = T(x) + T(y) = O \qquad and \qquad T(cx) = cT(x) = O.$$

The following examples describe the null spaces of the linear transformations given in Section 16.1.

EXAMPLE 1. *Identity transformation.* The null space is $\{O\}$, the subspace consisting of the zero element alone.

EXAMPLE 2. *Zero transformation.* Since every element of V is mapped onto zero, the null space is V itself.

EXAMPLE 3. *Multiplication by a fixed scalar c.* If $c \neq 0$, the null space contains only O. If $c = 0$, the null space is V.

EXAMPLE 4. *Linear equations.* The null space consists of all vectors $(x_1, \ldots, x_n)$ in V_n for which

$$\sum_{k=1}^{n} a_{ik}x_k = 0 \qquad for \quad i = 1, 2, \ldots, m .$$

EXAMPLE 5. *Inner product with a fixed element z.* The null space consists of all elements in V orthogonal to z.

EXAMPLE 6. *Projection on a subspace S.* If $x \in V$, we have the unique orthogonal decomposition $x = s + s^{\perp}$ (by Theorem 15.15). Since $T(x) = s$, we have $T(x) = O$ if and only if $x = s^{\perp}$. Therefore, the null space is $S^{\perp}$, the orthogonal complement of S.

EXAMPLE 7. *Differentiation operator.* The null space consists of all functions that are constant on the given interval.

EXAMPLE 8. *Integration operator.* The null space contains only the zero function.

16.3 Nullity and rank

Again in this section T denotes a linear transformation of a linear space V into a linear space W. We are interested in the relation between the dimensionality of V, of the null space $N(T)$, and of the range $T(V)$. If V is finite-dimensional, then the null space is also finite-dimensional since it is a subspace of V. The dimension of $N(T)$ is called the *nullity* of T. In the next theorem, we prove that the range is also finite-dimensional; its dimension is called the *rank* of T.

THEOREM 16.3. NULLITY PLUS RANK THEOREM. *If V is finite-dimensional, then $T(V)$ is also finite-dimensional, and we have*

$$\text{(16.1)} \qquad \dim N(T) + \dim T(V) = \dim V.$$

In other words, the nullity plus the rank of a linear transformation is equal to the dimension of its domain.

Proof. Let $n = \dim V$ and let $e_1, \ldots, e_k$ be a basis for $N(T)$, where $k = \dim N(T) \le n$. By Theorem 15.7, these elements are part of some basis for V, say the basis

$$\text{(16.2)} \qquad e_1, \ldots, e_k, e_{k+1}, \ldots, e_{k+r},$$

where $k + r = n$. We shall prove that the r elements

$$\text{(16.3)} \qquad T(e_{k+1}), \ldots, T(e_{k+r})$$

form a basis for $T(V)$, thus proving that $\dim T(V) = r$. Since $k + r = n$, this also proves (16.1).

First we show that the r elements in (16.3) span $T(V)$. If $y \in T(V)$, we have $y = T(x)$ for some x in V, and we can write $x = c_1 e_1 + \cdots + c_{k+r} e_{k+r}$. Hence, we have

$$y = T(x) = \sum_{i=1}^{k+r} c_i T(e_i) = \sum_{i=1}^{k} c_i T(e_i) + \sum_{i=k+1}^{k+r} c_i T(e_i) = \sum_{i=k+1}^{k+r} c_i T(e_i)$$

since $T(e_1) = \cdots = T(e_k) = O$. This shows that the elements in (16.3) span $T(V)$.

Now we show that these elements are independent. Suppose that there are scalars $c_{k+1}, \ldots, c_{k+r}$ such that

$$\sum_{i=k+1}^{k+r} c_i T(e_i) = O.$$

This implies that

$$T\left(\sum_{i=k+1}^{k+r} c_i e_i\right) = O$$

so the element $x = c_{k+1} e_{k+1} + \cdots + c_{k+r} e_{k+r}$ is in the null space $N(T)$. This means there are scalars $c_1, \ldots, c_k$ such that $x = c_1 e_1 + \cdots + c_k e_k$, so we have

$$x - x = \sum_{i=1}^{k} c_i e_i - \sum_{i=k+1}^{k+r} c_i e_i = O.$$

But since the elements in (16.2) are independent, this implies that all the scalars c_i are zero. Therefore, the elements in (16.3) are independent.

> *Note:* If V is infinite-dimensional, then at least one of $N(T)$ or $T(V)$ is infinite-dimensional. A proof of this fact is outlined in Exercise 30 of Section 16.4.

16.4 Exercises

In each of Exercises 1 through 10, a transformation $T: V_2 \to V_2$ is defined by the formula given for $T(x, y)$, where (x, y) is an arbitrary point in V_2. In each case determine whether T is linear. If T is linear, describe its null space and range, and compute its nullity and rank.

1. $T(x, y) = (y, x)$.
2. $T(x, y) = (x, -y)$.
3. $T(x, y) = (x, 0)$.
4. $T(x, y) = (x, x)$.
5. $T(x, y) = (x^2, y^2)$.
6. $T(x, y) = (e^x, e^y)$.
7. $T(x, y) = (x, 1)$.
8. $T(x, y) = (x + 1, y + 1)$.
9. $T(x, y) = (x - y, x + y)$.
10. $T(x, y) = (2x - y, x + y)$.

Do the same as above for each of Exercises 11 through 15 if the transformation $T: V_2 \to V_2$ is described as indicated.

11. T rotates every point through the same angle ϕ about the origin. That is, T maps a point with polar coordinates (r, θ) onto the point with polar coordinates $(r, \theta + \phi)$, where ϕ is fixed. Also, T maps O onto itself.
12. T maps each point onto its reflection with respect to a fixed line through the origin.
13. T maps every point onto the point $(1, 1)$.
14. T maps each point with polar coordinates (r, θ) onto the point with polar coordinates $(2r, \theta)$. Also, T maps O onto itself.
15. T maps each point with polar coordinates (r, θ) onto the point with polar coordinates $(r, 2\theta)$. Also, T maps O onto itself.

Do the same as above in each of Exercises 16 through 23 if a transformation $T: V_3 \to V_3$ is defined by the formula given for $T(x, y, z)$, where (x, y, z) is an arbitrary point of V_3.

16. $T(x, y, z) = (z, y, x)$.
17. $T(x, y, z) = (x, y, 0)$.
18. $T(x, y, z) = (x, 2y, 3z)$.
19. $T(x, y, z) = (x, y, 1)$.
20. $T(x, y, z) = (x + 1, y + 1, z - 1)$.
21. $T(x, y, z) = (x + 1, y + 2, z + 3)$.
22. $T(x, y, z) = (x, y^2, z^3)$.
23. $T(x, y, z) = (x + z, 0, x + y)$.

In each of Exercises 24 through 27, a transformation $T: V \to V$ is described as indicated. In each case, determine whether T is linear. If T is linear, describe its null space and range, and compute the nullity and rank when they are finite.

24. Let V be the linear space of all real polynomials $p(x)$ of degree $\leq n$. If $p \in V$, $q = T(p)$ means that $q(x) = p(x + 1)$ for all real x.
25. Let V be the linear space of all real functions differentiable on the open interval $(-1, 1)$. If $f \in V$, $g = T(f)$ means that $g(x) = xf'(x)$ for all x in $(-1, 1)$.
26. Let V be the linear space of all real functions continuous on $[a, b]$. If $f \in V$, $g = T(f)$ means that

$$g(x) = \int_a^b f(t) \sin(x - t) \, dt \qquad \text{for} \quad a \leq x \leq b.$$

27. Let V be the space of all real functions twice differentiable on an open interval (a, b). If $y \in V$, define $T(y) = y'' + Py' + Qy$, where P and Q are fixed constants.
28. Let V be the linear space of all real convergent sequences $\{x_n\}$. Define a transformation

$T: V \rightarrow V$ as follows: If $x = \{x_n\}$ is a convergent sequence with limit a, let $T(x) = \{y_n\}$, where $y_n = a - x_n$ for $n \geq 1$. Prove that T is linear and describe the null space and range of T.

29. Let V denote the linear space of all real functions continuous on the interval $[-\pi, \pi]$. Let S be that subset of V consisting of all f satisfying the three equations

$$\int_{-\pi}^{\pi} f(t)\, dt = 0\,, \qquad \int_{-\pi}^{\pi} f(t) \cos t\, dt = 0\,, \qquad \int_{-\pi}^{\pi} f(t) \sin t\, dt = 0\,.$$

(a) Prove that S is a subspace of V.
(b) Prove that S contains the functions $f(x) = \cos nx$ and $f(x) = \sin nx$ for each $n = 2, 3, \ldots$.
(c) Prove that S is infinite-dimensional.

Let $T: V \rightarrow V$ be the linear transformation defined as follows: If $f \in V$, $g = T(f)$ means that

$$g(x) = \int_{-\pi}^{\pi} \{1 + \cos(x - t)\} f(t)\, dt\,.$$

(d) Prove that $T(V)$, the range of T, is finite-dimensional and find a basis for $T(V)$.
(e) Determine the null space of T.
(f) Find all real $c \neq 0$ and all nonzero f in V such that $T(f) = cf$. (Note that such an f lies in the range of T.)

30. Let $T: V \rightarrow W$ be a linear transformation of a linear space V into a linear space W. If V is infinite-dimensional, prove that at least one of $T(V)$ or $N(T)$ is infinite-dimensional.

> [*Hint:* Assume $\dim N(T) = k$, $\dim T(V) = r$, let $e_1, \ldots, e_k$ be a basis for $N(T)$ and let $e_1, \ldots, e_k, e_{k+1}, \ldots, e_{k+n}$ be independent elements in V, where $n > r$. The elements $T(e_{k+1}), \ldots, T(e_{k+n})$ are dependent since $n > r$. Use this fact to obtain a contradiction.]

16.5 Algebraic operations on linear transformations

Functions whose values lie in a given linear space W can be added to each other and can be multiplied by the scalars in W according to the following definition.

DEFINITION. *Let $S: V \rightarrow W$ and $T: V \rightarrow W$ be two functions with a common domain V and with values in a linear space W. If c is any scalar in W, we define the sum $S + T$ and the product cT by the equations*

(16.4) $$(S + T)(x) = S(x) + T(x)\,, \qquad (cT)(x) = cT(x)$$

for all x in V.

We are especially interested in the case where V is also a linear space having the same scalars as W. In this case we denote by $\mathscr{L}(V, W)$ the set of all linear transformations of V into W.

If S and T are two linear transformations in $\mathscr{L}(V, W)$, it is an easy exercise to verify that $S + T$ and cT are also linear transformations in $\mathscr{L}(V, W)$. More than this is true. With the operations just defined, the set $\mathscr{L}(V, W)$ itself becomes a new linear space. The zero transformation serves as the zero element of this space, and the transformation $(-1)T$

is the negative of T. It is a straightforward matter to verify that all ten axioms for a linear space are satisfied. Therefore, we have the following.

THEOREM 16.4. *The set $\mathcal{L}(V, W)$ of all linear transformations of V into W is a linear space with the operations of addition and multiplication by scalars defined as in* (16.4).

A more interesting algebraic operation on linear transformations is *composition* or *multiplication* of transformations. This operation makes no use of the algebraic structure of a linear space and can be defined quite generally as follows.

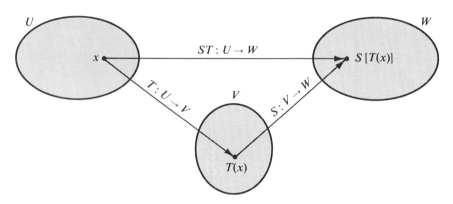

FIGURE 16.1   Illustrating the composition of two transformations.

DEFINITION. *Let U, V, W be sets. Let $T: U \to V$ be a function with domain U and values in V, and let $S : V \to W$ be another function with domain V and values in W. Then the composition ST is the function $ST : U \to W$ defined by the equation*

$$(ST)(x) = S[T(x)] \qquad \text{for every } x \text{ in } U .$$

Thus, to map x by the composition ST, we first map x by T and then map $T(x)$ by S. This is illustrated in Figure 16.1.

Composition of real-valued functions has been encountered repeatedly in our study of calculus, and we have seen that the operation is, in general, not commutative. However, as in the case of real-valued functions, composition does satisfy an associative law.

THEOREM 16.5. *If $T: U \to V$, $S: V \to W$, and $R: W \to X$ are three functions, then we have*

$$R(ST) = (RS)T .$$

Proof. Both functions $R(ST)$ and $(RS)T$ have domain U and values in X. For each x in U, we have

$$[R(ST)](x) = R[(ST)(x)] = R[S[T(x)]] \qquad \text{and} \qquad [(RS)T](x) = (RS)[T(x)] = R[S[T(x)]],$$

which proves that $R(ST) = (RS)T$.

DEFINITION. *Let* $T: V \to V$ *be a function which maps* V *into itself. We define integral powers of* T *inductively as follows*:

$$T^0 = I, \qquad T^n = TT^{n-1} \quad \text{for} \quad n \geq 1.$$

Here I is the identity transformation. The reader may verify that the associative law implies the law of exponents $T^m T^n = T^{m+n}$ for all nonnegative integers m and n.

The next theorem shows that the composition of *linear* transformations is again linear.

THEOREM 16.6. *If* U, V, W *are linear spaces with the same scalars, and if* $T: U \to V$ *and* $S: V \to W$ *are linear transformations, then the composition* $ST: U \to W$ *is linear.*

Proof. For all x, y in U and all scalars a and b, we have

$$(ST)(ax + by) = S[T(ax + by)] = S[aT(x) + bT(y)] = aST(x) + bST(y).$$

Composition can be combined with the algebraic operations of addition and multiplication of scalars in $\mathscr{L}(V, W)$ to give us the following.

THEOREM 16.7. *Let* U, V, W *be linear spaces with the same scalars, assume* S *and* T *are in* $\mathscr{L}(V, W)$, *and let* c *be any scalar.*
(a) *For any function* R *with values in* V, *we have*

$$(S + T)R = SR + TR \qquad \text{and} \qquad (cS)R = c(SR).$$

(b) *For any linear transformation* $R: W \to U$, *we have*

$$R(S + T) = RS + RT \qquad \text{and} \qquad R(cS) = c(RS).$$

The proof is a straightforward application of the definition of composition and is left as an exercise.

16.6 Inverses

In our study of real-valued functions we learned how to construct new functions by inversion of monotonic functions. Now we wish to extend the process of inversion to a more general class of functions.

Given a function T, our goal is to find, if possible, another function S whose composition with T is the identity transformation. Since composition is in general not commutative, we have to distinguish between ST and TS. Therefore we introduce two kinds of inverses which we call left and right inverses.

DEFINITION. *Given two sets* V *and* W *and a function* $T: V \to W$. *A function* $S: T(V) \to V$ *is called a left inverse of* T *if* $S[T(x)] = x$ *for all* x *in* V, *that is, if*

$$ST = I_V,$$

where I_V is the identity transformation on V. A function $R : T(V) \to V$ is called a right inverse of T if $T[R(y)] = y$ for all y in $T(V)$, that is, if

$$TR = I_{T(V)} ,$$

where $I_{T(V)}$ is the identity transformation on $T(V)$.

EXAMPLE. *A function with no left inverse but with two right inverses.* Let $V = \{1, 2\}$ and let $W = \{0\}$. Define $T : V \to W$ as follows: $T(1) = T(2) = 0$. This function has two right inverses $R : W \to V$ and $R' : W \to V$ given by

$$R(0) = 1 , \qquad R'(0) = 2 .$$

It cannot have a left inverse S since this would require

$$1 = S[T(1)] = S(0) \qquad \text{and} \qquad 2 = S[T(2)] = S(0) .$$

This simple example shows that left inverses need not exist and that right inverses need not be unique.

Every function $T : V \to W$ has at least one right inverse. In fact, each y in $T(V)$ has the form $y = T(x)$ for at least one x in V. If we select one such x and define $R(y) = x$, then $T[R(y)] = T(x) = y$ for each y in $T(V)$, so R is a right inverse. Nonuniqueness may occur because there may be more than one x in V which maps onto a given y in $T(V)$. We shall prove presently (in Theorem 16.9) that if each y in $T(V)$ is the image of *exactly one* x in V, then right inverses are unique.

First we prove that if a left inverse exists it is unique and, at the same time, is a right inverse.

THEOREM 16.8.   *A function $T: V \to W$ can have at most one left inverse. If T has a left inverse S, then S is also a right inverse.*

Proof. Assume T has two left inverses, $S: T(V) \to V$ and $S': T(V) \to V$. Choose any y in $T(V)$. We shall prove that $S(y) = S'(y)$. Now $y = T(x)$ for some x in V, so we have

$$S[T(x)] = x \qquad \text{and} \qquad S'[T(x)] = x ,$$

since both S and S' are left inverses. Therefore $S(y) = x$ and $S'(y) = x$, so $S(y) = S'(y)$ for all y in $T(V)$. Therefore $S = S'$ which proves that left inverses are unique.

Now we prove that every left inverse S is also a right inverse. Choose any element y in $T(V)$. We shall prove that $T[S(y)] = y$. Since $y \in T(V)$, we have $y = T(x)$ for some x in V. But S is a left inverse, so

$$x = S[T(x)] = S(y) .$$

Applying T, we get $T(x) = T[S(y)]$. But $y = T(x)$, so $y = T[S(y)]$, which completes the proof.

The next theorem characterizes all functions having left inverses.

THEOREM 16.9. *A function* $T: V \to W$ *has a left inverse if and only if* T *maps distinct elements of* V *onto distinct elements of* W; *that is, if and only if, for all* x *and* y *in* V,

(16.5) $$x \neq y \quad implies \quad T(x) \neq T(y).$$

Note: Condition (16.5) is equivalent to the statement

(16.6) $$T(x) = T(y) \quad implies \quad x = y.$$

A function T satisfying (16.5) or (16.6) for all x and y in V is said to be *one-to-one* on V.

Proof. Assume T has a left inverse S, and assume that $T(x) = T(y)$. We wish to prove that $x = y$. Applying S, we find $S[T(x)] = S[T(y)]$. Since $S[T(x)] = x$ and $S[T(y)] = y$, this implies $x = y$. This proves that a function with a left inverse is one-to-one on its domain.

Now we prove the converse. Assume T is one-to-one on V. We shall exhibit a function $S: T(V) \to V$ which is a left inverse of T. If $y \in T(V)$, then $y = T(x)$ for some x in V. By (16.6), there is *exactly one* x in V for which $y = T(x)$. Define $S(y)$ to be this x. That is, we define S on $T(V)$ as follows:

$$S(y) = x \quad means that \quad T(x) = y.$$

Then we have $S[T(x)] = x$ for each x in V, so $ST = I_V$. Therefore, the function S so defined is a left inverse of T.

DEFINITION. *Let* $T: V \to W$ *be one-to-one on* V. *The unique left inverse of* T (*which we know is also a right inverse*) *is denoted by* T^{-1}. *We say that* T *is invertible, and we call* T^{-1} *the inverse of* T.

The results of this section refer to arbitrary functions. Now we apply these ideas to linear transformations.

16.7 One-to-one linear transformations

In this section, V and W denote linear spaces with the same scalars, and $T: V \to W$ denotes a linear transformation in $\mathscr{L}(V, W)$. The linearity of T enables us to express the one-to-one property in several equivalent forms.

THEOREM 16.10. *Let* $T: V \to W$ *be a linear transformation in* $\mathscr{L}(V, W)$. *Then the following statements are equivalent.*
   (a) *T is one-to-one on V.*
   (b) *T is invertible and its inverse $T^{-1}: T(V) \to V$ is linear.*
   (c) *For all x in V, $T(x) = O$ implies $x = O$. That is, the null space $N(T)$ contains only the zero element of V.*

Proof. We shall prove that (a) implies (b), (b) implies (c), and (c) implies (a). First assume (a) holds. Then T has an inverse (by Theorem 16.9), and we must show that T^{-1} is linear. Take any two elements u and v in $T(V)$. Then $u = T(x)$ and $v = T(y)$ for some x and y in V. For any scalars a and b, we have

$$au + bv = aT(x) + bT(y) = T(ax + by),$$

since T is linear. Hence, applying T^{-1}, we have

$$T^{-1}(au + bv) = ax + by = aT^{-1}(u) + bT^{-1}(v),$$

so T^{-1} is linear. Therefore (a) implies (b).

Next assume that (b) holds. Take any x in V for which $T(x) = O$. Applying T^{-1}, we find that $x = T^{-1}(O) = O$, since T^{-1} is linear. Therefore, (b) implies (c).

Finally, assume (c) holds. Take any two elements u and v in V with $T(u) = T(v)$. By linearity, we have $T(u - v) = T(u) - T(v) = O$, so $u - v = O$. Therefore, T is one-to-one on V, and the proof of the theorem is complete.

When V is finite-dimensional, the one-to-one property can be formulated in terms of independence and dimensionality, as indicated by the next theorem.

THEOREM 16.11.   *Let $T: V \to W$ be a linear transformation in $\mathscr{L}(V, W)$ and assume that V is finite-dimensional, say* dim $V = n$. *Then the following statements are equivalent.*

(a) *T is one-to-one on V.*

(b) *If $e_1, \ldots, e_p$ are independent elements in V, then $T(e_1), \ldots, T(e_p)$ are independent elements in $T(V)$.*

(c) dim $T(V) = n$.

(d) *If $\{e_1, \ldots, e_n\}$ is a basis for V, then $\{T(e_1), \ldots, T(e_n)\}$ is a basis for $T(V)$.*

Proof. We shall prove that (a) implies (b), (b) implies (c), (c) implies (d), and (d) implies (a). Assume (a) holds. Let $e_1, \ldots, e_p$ be independent elements of V and consider the elements $T(e_1), \ldots, T(e_p)$ in $T(V)$. Suppose that

$$\sum_{i=1}^{p} c_i T(e_i) = O$$

for certain scalars $c_1, \ldots, c_p$. By linearity, we obtain

$$T\left(\sum_{i=1}^{p} c_i e_i\right) = O, \qquad \text{and hence} \qquad \sum_{i=1}^{p} c_i e_i = O$$

since T is one-to-one. But $e_1, \ldots, e_p$ are independent, so $c_1 = \cdots = c_p = 0$. Therefore (a) implies (b).

Now assume (b) holds. Let $\{e_1, \ldots, e_n\}$ be a basis for V. By (b), the n elements $T(e_1), \ldots, T(e_n)$ in $T(V)$ are independent. Therefore, dim $T(V) \geq n$. But, by Theorem 16.3, we have dim $T(V) \leq n$. Therefore dim $T(V) = n$, so (b) implies (c).

Next, assume (c) holds and let $\{e_1, \ldots, e_n\}$ be a basis for V. Take any element y in $T(V)$. Then $y = T(x)$ for some x in V, so we have

$$x = \sum_{i=1}^{n} c_i e_i, \quad \text{and hence} \quad y = T(x) = \sum_{i=1}^{n} c_i T(e_i).$$

Therefore $\{T(e_1), \ldots, T(e_n)\}$ spans $T(V)$. But we are assuming $\dim T(V) = n$, so $\{T(e_1), \ldots, T(e_n)\}$ is a basis for $T(V)$. Therefore (c) implies (d).

Finally, assume (d) holds. We will prove that $T(x) = O$ implies $x = O$. Let $\{e_1, \ldots, e_n\}$ be a basis for V. If $x \in V$, we may write

$$x = \sum_{i=1}^{n} c_i e_i, \quad \text{and hence} \quad T(x) = \sum_{i=1}^{n} c_i T(e_i).$$

If $T(x) = O$, then $c_1 = \cdots = c_n = 0$, since the elements $T(e_1), \ldots, T(e_n)$ are independent. Therefore $x = O$, so T is one-to-one on V. Thus, (d) implies (a) and the proof is complete.

16.8 Exercises

1. Let $V = \{0, 1\}$. Describe all functions $T: V \to V$. There are four altogether. Label them as T_1, T_2, T_3, T_4 and make a multiplication table showing the composition of each pair. Indicate which functions are one-to-one on V and give their inverses.

2. Let $V = \{0, 1, 2\}$. Describe all functions $T: V \to V$ for which $T(V) = V$. There are six altogether. Label them as $T_1, \ldots, T_6$ and make a multiplication table showing the composition of each pair. Indicate which functions are one-to-one on V, and give their inverses.

In each of Exercises 3 through 12, a function $T: V_2 \to V_2$ is defined by the formula given for $T(x, y)$, where (x, y) is an arbitrary point in V_2. In each case determine whether T is one-to-one on V_2. If it is, describe its range $T(V_2)$; for each point (u, v) in $T(V_2)$, let $(x, y) = T^{-1}(u, v)$ and give formulas for determining x and y in terms of u and v.

3. $T(x, y) = (y, x)$.
4. $T(x, y) = (x, -y)$.
5. $T(x, y) = (x, 0)$.
6. $T(x, y) = (x, x)$.
7. $T(x, y) = (x^2, y^2)$.

8. $T(x, y) = (e^x, e^y)$.
9. $T(x, y) = (x, 1)$.
10. $T(x, y) = (x + 1, y + 1)$.
11. $T(x, y) = (x - y, x + y)$.
12. $T(x, y) = (2x - y, x + y)$.

In each of Exercises 13 through 20, a function $T: V_3 \to V_3$ is defined by the formula given for $T(x, y, z)$, where (x, y, z) is an arbitrary point in V_3. In each case, determine whether T is one-to-one on V_3. If it is, describe its range $T(V_3)$; for each point (u, v, w) in $T(V_3)$, let $(x, y, z) = T^{-1}(u, v, w)$ and give formulas for determining x, y, and z in terms of u, v, and w.

13. $T(x, y, z) = (z, y, x)$.
14. $T(x, y, z) = (x, y, 0)$.
15. $T(x, y, z) = (x, 2y, 3z)$.
16. $T(x, y, z) = (x, y, x + y + z)$.

17. $T(x, y, z) = (x + 1, y + 1, z - 1)$.
18. $T(x, y, z) = (x + 1, y + 2, z + 3)$.
19. $T(x, y, z) = (x, x + y, x + y + z)$.
20. $T(x, y, z) = (x + y, y + z, x + z)$.

21. Let $T: V \to V$ be a function which maps V into itself. Powers are defined inductively by the formulas $T^0 = I$, $T^n = TT^{n-1}$ for $n \geq 1$. Prove that the associative law for composition implies the law of exponents: $T^m T^n = T^{m+n}$. If T is invertible, prove that T^n is also invertible and that $(T^n)^{-1} = (T^{-1})^n$.

In Exercises 22 through 25, S and T denote functions with domain V and values in V. In general, $ST \neq TS$. If $ST = TS$, we say that S and T *commute*.

22. If S and T commute, prove that $(ST)^n = S^n T^n$ for all integers $n \geq 0$.
23. If S and T are invertible, prove that ST is also invertible and that $(ST)^{-1} = T^{-1}S^{-1}$. In other words, the inverse of ST is the composition of inverses, taken in reverse order.
24. If S and T are invertible and commute, prove that their inverses also commute.
25. Let V be a linear space. If S and T commute, prove that

$$(S + T)^2 = S^2 + 2ST + T^2 \quad \text{and} \quad (S + T)^3 = S^3 + 3S^2T + 3ST^2 + T^3 .$$

Indicate how these formulas must be altered if $ST \neq TS$.
26. Let S and T be the linear transformations of V_3 into V_3 defined by the formulas $S(x, y, z) = (z, y, x)$ and $T(x, y, z) = (x, x + y, x + y + z)$, where (x, y, z) is an arbitrary point of V_3.
    (a) Determine the image of (x, y, z) under each of the following transformations: ST, TS, $ST - TS$, S^2, T^2, $(ST)^2$, $(TS)^2$, $(ST - TS)^2$.
    (b) Prove that S and T are one-to-one on V_3 and find the image of (u, v, w) under each of the following transformations: S^{-1}, T^{-1}, $(ST)^{-1}$, $(TS)^{-1}$.
    (c) Find the image of (x, y, z) under $(T - I)^n$ for each $n \geq 1$.
27. Let V be the linear space of all real polynomials $p(x)$. Let D denote the differentiation operator and let T denote the integration operator which maps each polynomial p onto the polynomial q given by $q(x) = \int_0^x p(t)\, dt$. Prove that $DT = I$ but that $TD \neq I$. Describe the null space and range of TD.
28. Let V be the linear space of all real polynomials $p(x)$. Let D denote the differentiation operator and let T be the linear transformation that maps $p(x)$ onto $xp'(x)$.
    (a) Let $p(x) = 2 + 3x - x^2 + 4x^3$ and determine the image of p under each of the following transformations: D, T, DT, TD, $DT - TD$, $T^2D^2 - D^2T^2$.
    (b) Determine those p in V for which $T(p) = p$.
    (c) Determine those p in V for which $(DT - 2D)(p) = O$.
    (d) Determine those p in V for which $(DT - TD)^n(p) = D^n(p)$.
29. Let V and D be as in Exercise 28 but let T be the linear transformation that maps $p(x)$ onto $xp(x)$. Prove that $DT - TD = I$ and that $DT^n - T^nD = nT^{n-1}$ for $n \geq 2$.
30. Let S and T be in $\mathcal{L}(V, V)$ and assume that $ST - TS = I$. Prove that $ST^n - T^nS = nT^{n-1}$ for all $n \geq 1$.
31. Let V be the linear space of all real polynomials $p(x)$. Let R, S, T be the functions which map an arbitrary polynomial $p(x) = c_0 + c_1 x + \cdots + c_n x^n$ in V onto the polynomials $r(x)$, $s(x)$, and $t(x)$, respectively, where

$$r(x) = p(0), \qquad s(x) = \sum_{k=1}^{n} c_k x^{k-1}, \qquad t(x) = \sum_{k=0}^{n} c_k x^{k+1} .$$

    (a) Let $p(x) = 2 + 3x - x^2 + x^3$ and determine the image of p under each of the following transformations: R, S, T, ST, TS, $(TS)^2$, T^2S^2, S^2T^2, TRS, RST.
    (b) Prove that R, S, and T are linear and determine the null space and range of each.
    (c) Prove that T is one-to-one on V and determine its inverse.
    (d) If $n \geq 1$, express $(TS)^n$ and S^nT^n in terms of I and R.
32. Refer to Exercise 28 of Section 16.4. Determine whether T is one-to-one on V. If it is, describe its inverse.

16.9 Linear transformations with prescribed values

If V is finite-dimensional, we can always construct a linear transformation $T: V \to W$ with prescribed values at the basis elements of V, as described in the next theorem.

THEOREM 16.12. *Let* $e_1, \ldots, e_n$ *be a basis for an n-dimensional linear space V. Let* $u_1, \ldots, u_n$ *be n arbitrary elements in a linear space W. Then there is one and only one linear transformation* $T: V \to W$ *such that*

(16.7)
$$T(e_k) = u_k \quad for \quad k = 1, 2, \ldots, n.$$

This T maps an arbitrary element x in V as follows:

(16.8)
$$If \quad x = \sum_{k=1}^{n} x_k e_k, \quad then \quad T(x) = \sum_{k=1}^{n} x_k u_k.$$

Proof. Every x in V can be expressed uniquely as a linear combination of $e_1, \ldots, e_n$, the multipliers $x_1, \ldots, x_n$ being the components of x relative to the ordered basis $(e_1, \ldots, e_n)$. If we define T by (16.8), it is a straightforward matter to verify that T is linear. If $x = e_k$ for some k, then all components of x are 0 except the kth, which is 1, so (16.8) gives $T(e_k) = u_k$, as required.

To prove that there is only one linear transformation satisfying (16.7), let T' be another and compute $T'(x)$. We find that

$$T'(x) = T'\left(\sum_{k=1}^{n} x_k e_k\right) = \sum_{k=1}^{n} x_k T'(e_k) = \sum_{k=1}^{n} x_k u_k = T(x).$$

Since $T'(x) = T(x)$ for all x in V, we have $T' = T$, which completes the proof.

EXAMPLE. Determine the linear transformation $T: V_2 \to V_2$ which maps the basis elements $i = (1, 0)$ and $j = (0, 1)$ as follows:

$$T(i) = i + j, \qquad T(j) = 2i - j.$$

Solution. If $x = x_1 i + x_2 j$ is an arbitrary element of V_2, then $T(x)$ is given by

$$T(x) = x_1 T(i) + x_2 T(j) = x_1(i + j) + x_2(2i - j) = (x_1 + 2x_2)i + (x_1 - x_2)j.$$

16.10 Matrix representations of linear transformations

Theorem 16.12 shows that a linear transformation $T: V \to W$ of a finite-dimensional linear space V is completely determined by its action on a given set of basis elements $e_1, \ldots, e_n$. Now, suppose the space W is also finite-dimensional, say dim $W = m$, and let $w_1, \ldots, w_m$ be a basis for W. (The dimensions n and m may or may not be equal.) Since T has values in W, each element $T(e_k)$ can be expressed uniquely as a linear combination of the basis elements $w_1, \ldots, w_m$, say

$$T(e_k) = \sum_{i=1}^{m} t_{ik} w_i,$$

where $t_{1k}, \ldots, t_{mk}$ are the components of $T(e_k)$ relative to the ordered basis $(w_1, \ldots, w_m)$.

We shall display the m-tuple $(t_{1k}, \ldots, t_{mk})$ vertically, as follows:

(16.9)
$$
\begin{bmatrix}
t_{1k} \\
t_{2k} \\
\cdot \\
\cdot \\
\cdot \\
t_{mk}
\end{bmatrix}.
$$

This array is called a *column vector* or a *column matrix*. We have such a column vector for each of the n elements $T(e_1), \ldots, T(e_n)$. We place them side by side and enclose them in one pair of brackets to obtain the following rectangular array:

$$
\begin{bmatrix}
t_{11} & t_{12} & \cdots & t_{1n} \\
t_{21} & t_{22} & \cdots & t_{2n} \\
\cdot & \cdot & & \cdot \\
\cdot & \cdot & & \cdot \\
\cdot & \cdot & & \cdot \\
t_{m1} & t_{m2} & \cdots & t_{mn}
\end{bmatrix}.
$$

This array is called a *matrix* consisting of *m rows* and *n columns*. We call it an *m by n* matrix, or an $m \times n$ matrix. The first row is the $1 \times n$ matrix $(t_{11}, t_{12}, \ldots, t_{1n})$. The $m \times 1$ matrix displayed in (16.9) is the kth column. The scalars t_{ik} are indexed so the first subscript i indicates the *row*, and the second subscript k indicates the *column* in which t_{ik} occurs. We call t_{ik} the *ik-entry* or the *ik-element* of the matrix. The more compact notation

$$
(t_{ik}), \qquad \text{or} \qquad (t_{ik})_{i,k=1}^{m,n},
$$

is also used to denote the matrix whose *ik*-entry is t_{ik}.

Thus, every linear transformation T of an n-dimensional space V into an m-dimensional space W gives rise to an $m \times n$ matrix (t_{ik}) whose columns consist of the components of $T(e_1), \ldots, T(e_n)$ relative to the basis $(w_1, \ldots, w_m)$. We call this the *matrix representation* of T relative to the given choice of ordered bases $(e_1, \ldots, e_n)$ for V and $(w_1, \ldots, w_m)$ for W. Once we know the matrix (t_{ik}), the components of any element $T(x)$ relative to the basis $(w_1, \ldots, w_m)$ can be determined as described in the next theorem.

THEOREM 16.13. *Let T be a linear transformation in $\mathscr{L}(V, W)$, where $\dim V = n$ and $\dim W = m$. Let $(e_1, \ldots, e_n)$ and $(w_1, \ldots, w_m)$ be ordered bases for V and W, respectively, and let (t_{ik}) be the $m \times n$ matrix whose entries are determined by the equations*

(16.10)
$$
T(e_k) = \sum_{i=1}^{m} t_{ik} w_i, \qquad for \quad k = 1, 2, \ldots, n.
$$

Then an arbitrary element

(16.11)
$$
x = \sum_{k=1}^{n} x_k e_k
$$

in V with components $(x_1, \ldots, x_n)$ *relative to* $(e_1, \ldots, e_n)$ *is mapped by T onto the element*

$$(16.12) \qquad T(x) = \sum_{i=1}^{m} y_i w_i$$

in W with components $(y_1, \ldots, y_m)$ *relative to* $(w_1, \ldots, w_m)$. *The* y_i *are related to the components of x by the linear equations*

$$(16.13) \qquad y_i = \sum_{k=1}^{n} t_{ik} x_k \qquad for \quad i = 1, 2, \ldots, m.$$

Proof. Applying T to each member of (16.11) and using (16.10), we obtain

$$T(x) = \sum_{k=1}^{n} x_k T(e_k) = \sum_{k=1}^{n} x_k \sum_{i=1}^{m} t_{ik} w_i = \sum_{i=1}^{m} \left(\sum_{k=1}^{n} t_{ik} x_k \right) w_i = \sum_{i=1}^{m} y_i w_i,$$

where each y_i is given by (16.13). This completes the proof.

Having chosen a pair of bases $(e_1, \ldots, e_n)$ and $(w_1, \ldots, w_m)$ for V and W, respectively, every linear transformation $T: V \to W$ has a matrix representation (t_{ik}). Conversely, if we start with any mn scalars arranged as a rectangular matrix (t_{ik}) and choose a pair of ordered bases for V and W, then it is easy to prove that there is exactly one linear transformation $T: V \to W$ having this matrix representation. We simply define T at the basis elements of V by the equations in (16.10). Then, by Theorem 16.12, there is one and only one linear transformation $T: V \to W$ with these prescribed values. The image $T(x)$ of an arbitrary point x in V is then given by Equations (16.12) and (16.13).

EXAMPLE 1. *Construction of a linear transformation from a given matrix.* Suppose we start with the 2×3 matrix

$$\begin{bmatrix} 3 & 1 & -2 \\ 1 & 0 & 4 \end{bmatrix}.$$

Choose the usual bases of unit coordinate vectors for V_3 and V_2. Then the given matrix represents a linear transformation $T: V_3 \to V_2$ which maps an arbitrary vector (x_1, x_2, x_3) in V_3 onto the vector (y_1, y_2) in V_2 according to the linear equations

$$y_1 = 3x_1 + x_2 - 2x_3$$

$$y_2 = x_1 + 0x_2 + 4x_3.$$

EXAMPLE 2. *Construction of a matrix representation of a given linear transformation.* Let V be the linear space of all real polynomials $p(x)$ of degree ≤ 3. This space has dimension 4, and we choose the basis $(1, x, x^2, x^3)$. Let D be the differentiation operator which maps each polynomial $p(x)$ in V onto its derivative $p'(x)$. We can regard D as a linear transformation of V into W, where W is the 3-dimensional space of all real polynomials of degree ≤ 2. In W we choose the basis $(1, x, x^2)$. To find the matrix representation of D

relative to this choice of bases, we transform (differentiate) each basis element of V and express it as a linear combination of the basis elements of W. Thus, we find that

$$D(1) = 0 = 0 + 0x + 0x^2, \qquad D(x) = 1 = 1 + 0x + 0x^2,$$

$$D(x^2) = 2x = 0 + 2x + 0x^2, \qquad D(x^3) = 3x^2 = 0 + 0x + 3x^2.$$

The coefficients of these polynomials determine the *columns* of the matrix representation of D. Therefore, the required representation is given by the following 3×4 matrix:

$$\begin{bmatrix} 0 & 1 & 0 & 0 \\ 0 & 0 & 2 & 0 \\ 0 & 0 & 0 & 3 \end{bmatrix}.$$

To emphasize that the matrix representation depends not only on the basis elements but also on their order, let us reverse the order of the basis elements in W and use, instead, the ordered basis $(x^2, x, 1)$. Then the basis elements of V are transformed into the same polynomials obtained above, but the components of these polynomials relative to the new basis $(x^2, x, 1)$ appear in reversed order. Therefore, the matrix representation of D now becomes

$$\begin{bmatrix} 0 & 0 & 0 & 3 \\ 0 & 0 & 2 & 0 \\ 0 & 1 & 0 & 0 \end{bmatrix}.$$

Let us compute a third matrix representation for D, using the basis $(1, 1 + x, 1 + x + x^2, 1 + x + x^2 + x^3)$ for V, and the basis $(1, x, x^2)$ for W. The basis elements of V are transformed as follows:

$$D(1) = 0, \qquad D(1 + x) = 1, \qquad D(1 + x + x^2) = 1 + 2x,$$

$$D(1 + x + x^2 + x^3) = 1 + 2x + 3x^2,$$

so the matrix representation in this case is

$$\begin{bmatrix} 0 & 1 & 1 & 1 \\ 0 & 0 & 2 & 2 \\ 0 & 0 & 0 & 3 \end{bmatrix}.$$

16.11 Construction of a matrix representation in diagonal form

Since it is possible to obtain different matrix representations of a given linear transformation by different choices of bases, it is natural to try to choose the bases so that the resulting matrix will have a particularly simple form. The next theorem shows that we can make all the entries 0 except possibly along the diagonal starting from the upper left-hand corner of the matrix. Along this diagonal there will be a string of ones followed by zeros, the number of ones being equal to the rank of the transformation. A matrix (t_{ik}) with all entries $t_{ik} = 0$ when $i \neq k$ is said to be a *diagonal matrix*.

THEOREM 16.14. *Let V and W be finite-dimensional linear spaces, with* $\dim V = n$ *and* $\dim W = m$. *Assume $T \in \mathcal{L}(V, W)$ and let $r = \dim T(V)$ denote the rank of T. Then there exists a basis $(e_1, \ldots, e_n)$ for V and a basis $(w_1, \ldots, w_m)$ for W such that*

(16.14)
$$T(e_i) = w_i \quad for \quad i = 1, 2, \ldots, r,$$

and

(16.15)
$$T(e_i) = O \quad for \quad i = r + 1, \ldots, n.$$

Therefore, the matrix (t_{ik}) of T relative to these bases has all entries zero except for the r diagonal entries

$$t_{11} = t_{22} = \cdots = t_{rr} = 1.$$

Proof. First we construct a basis for W. Since $T(V)$ is a subspace of W with $\dim T(V) = r$, the space $T(V)$ has a basis of r elements in W, say $w_1, \ldots, w_r$. By Theorem 15.7, these elements form a subset of some basis for W. Therefore we can adjoin elements $w_{r+1}, \ldots, w_m$ so that

(16.16)
$$(w_1, \ldots, w_r, w_{r+1}, \ldots, w_m)$$

is a basis for W.

Now we construct a basis for V. Each of the first r elements w_i in (16.16) is the image of at least one element in V. Choose one such element in V and call it e_i. Then $T(e_i) = w_i$ for $i = 1, 2, \ldots, r$ so (16.14) is satisfied. Now let k be the dimension of the null space $N(T)$. By Theorem 16.3 we have $n = k + r$. Since $\dim N(T) = k$, the space $N(T)$ has a basis consisting of k elements in V which we designate as $e_{r+1}, \ldots, e_{r+k}$. For each of these elements, Equation (16.15) is satisfied. Therefore, to complete the proof, we must show that the ordered set

(16.17)
$$(e_1, \ldots, e_r, e_{r+1}, \ldots, e_{r+k})$$

is a basis for V. Since $\dim V = n = r + k$, we need only show that these elements are independent. Suppose that some linear combination of them is zero, say

(16.18)
$$\sum_{i=1}^{r+k} c_i e_i = O.$$

Applying T and using Equations (16.14) and (16.15), we find that

$$\sum_{i=1}^{r+k} c_i T(e_i) = \sum_{i=1}^{r} c_i w_i = O.$$

But $w_1, \ldots, w_r$ are independent, and hence $c_1 = \cdots = c_r = 0$. Therefore, the first r terms in (16.18) are zero, so (16.18) reduces to

$$\sum_{i=r+1}^{r+k} c_i e_i = O.$$

But $e_{r+1}, \ldots, e_{r+k}$ are independent since they form a basis for $N(T)$, and hence $c_{r+1} = \cdots = c_{r+k} = 0$. Therefore, all the c_i in (16.18) are zero, so the elements in (16.17) form a basis for V. This completes the proof.

EXAMPLE. We refer to Example 2 of Section 16.10, where D is the differentiation operator which maps the space V of polynomials of degree ≤ 3 into the space W of polynomials of degree ≤ 2. In this example, the range $T(V) = W$, so T has rank 3. Applying the method used to prove Theorem 16.14, we choose any basis for W, for example the basis $(1, x, x^2)$. A set of polynomials in V which map onto these elements is given by $(x, \frac{1}{2}x^2, \frac{1}{3}x^3)$. We extend this set to get a basis for V by adjoining the constant polynomial 1, which is a basis for the null space of D. Therefore, if we use the basis $(x, \frac{1}{2}x^2, \frac{1}{3}x^3, 1)$ for V and the basis $(1, x, x^2)$ for W, the corresponding matrix representation for D has the diagonal form

$$\begin{bmatrix} 1 & 0 & 0 & 0 \\ 0 & 1 & 0 & 0 \\ 0 & 0 & 1 & 0 \end{bmatrix}.$$

16.12 Exercises

In all exercises involving the vector space V_n, the usual basis of unit coordinate vectors is to be chosen unless another basis is specifically mentioned. In exercises concerned with the matrix of a linear transformation $T: V \to W$ where $V = W$, we take the same basis in both V and W unless another choice is indicated.

1. Determine the matrix of each of the following linear transformations of V_n into V_n:
    (a) the identity transformation,
    (b) the zero transformation,
    (c) multiplication by a fixed scalar c.
2. Determine the matrix for each of the following projections.
    (a) $T: V_3 \to V_2$,   where $T(x_1, x_2, x_3) = (x_1, x_2)$.
    (b) $T: V_3 \to V_2$,   where $T(x_1, x_2, x_3) = (x_2, x_3)$.
    (c) $T: V_5 \to V_3$,   where $T(x_1, x_2, x_3, x_4, x_5) = (x_2, x_3, x_4)$.
3. A linear transformation $T: V_2 \to V_2$ maps the basis vectors i and j as follows:

$$T(i) = i + j, \qquad T(j) = 2i - j.$$

    (a) Compute $T(3i - 4j)$ and $T^2(3i - 4j)$ in terms of i and j.
    (b) Determine the matrix of T and of T^2.
    (c) Solve part (b) if the basis (i, j) is replaced by (e_1, e_2), where $e_1 = i - j$, $e_2 = 3i + j$.
4. A linear transformation $T: V_2 \to V_2$ is defined as follows: Each vector (x, y) is reflected in the y-axis and then doubled in length to yield $T(x, y)$. Determine the matrix of T and of T^2.
5. Let $T: V_3 \to V_3$ be a linear transformation such that

$$T(k) = 2i + 3j + 5k, \qquad T(j + k) = i, \qquad T(i + j + k) = j - k.$$

(a) Compute $T(i + 2j + 3k)$ and determine the nullity and rank of T.

(b) Determine the matrix of T.

6. For the linear transformation in Exercise 5, choose both bases to be (e_1, e_2, e_3), where $e_1 = (2, 3, 5)$, $e_2 = (1, 0, 0)$, $e_3 = (0, 1, -1)$, and determine the matrix of T relative to the new bases.

7. A linear transformation $T: V_3 \to V_2$ maps the basis vectors as follows: $T(i) = (0, 0)$, $T(j) = (1, 1)$, $T(k) = (1, -1)$.

(a) Compute $T(4i - j + k)$ and determine the nullity and rank of T.

(b) Determine the matrix of T.

(c) Use the basis (i, j, k) in V_3 and the basis (w_1, w_2) in V_2, where $w_1 = (1, 1)$, $w_2 = (1, 2)$. Determine the matrix of T relative to these bases.

(d) Find bases (e_1, e_2, e_3) for V_3 and (w_1, w_2) for V_2 relative to which the matrix of T will be in diagonal form.

8. A linear transformation $T: V_2 \to V_3$ maps the basis vectors as follows: $T(i) = (1, 0, 1)$, $T(j) = (-1, 0, 1)$.

(a) Compute $T(2i - 3j)$ and determine the nullity and rank of T.

(b) Determine the matrix of T.

(c) Find bases (e_1, e_2) for V_2 and (w_1, w_2, w_3) for V_3 relative to which the matrix of T will be in diagonal form.

9. Solve Exercise 8 if $T(i) = (1, 0, 1)$ and $T(j) = (1, 1, 1)$.

10. Let V and W be linear spaces, each with dimension 2 and each with basis (e_1, e_2). Let $T: V \to W$ be a linear transformation such that

$$T(e_1 + e_2) = 3e_1 + 9e_2, \qquad T(3e_1 + 2e_2) = 7e_1 + 23e_2.$$

(a) Compute $T(e_2 - e_1)$ and determine the nullity and rank of T.

(b) Determine the matrix of T relative to the given basis.

(c) Use the basis (e_1, e_2) for V and find a new basis of the form $(e_1 + ae_2, 2e_1 + be_2)$ for W, relative to which the matrix of T will be in diagonal form.

In the linear space of all real-valued functions, each of the following sets is independent and spans a finite-dimensional subspace V. Use the given set as a basis for V and let $D: V \to V$ be the differentiation operator. In each case, find the matrix of D and of D^2 relative to this choice of basis.

11. $(\sin x, \cos x)$.

12. $(1, x, e^x)$.

13. $(1, 1 + x, 1 + x + e^x)$.

14. (e^x, xe^x).

15. $(-\cos x, \sin x)$.

16. $(\sin x, \cos x, x \sin x, x \cos x)$.

17. $(e^x \sin x, e^x \cos x)$.

18. $(e^{2x} \sin 3x, e^{2x} \cos 3x)$.

19. Choose the basis $(1, x, x^2, x^3)$ in the linear space V of all real polynomials of degree ≤ 3. Let D denote the differentiation operator and let $T: V \to V$ be the linear transformation which maps $p(x)$ onto $xp'(x)$. Relative to the given basis, determine the matrix of each of the following transformations: (a) T; (b) DT; (c) TD; (d) $TD - DT$; (e) T^2; (f) $T^2D^2 - D^2T^2$.

20. Refer to Exercise 19. Let W be the image of V under TD. Find bases for V and for W relative to which the matrix of TD is in diagonal form.

16.13 Linear spaces of matrices

We have seen how matrices arise in a natural way as representations of linear transformations. Matrices can also be considered as objects existing in their own right, without necessarily being connected to linear transformations. As such, they form another class of mathematical objects on which algebraic operations can be defined. The connection with linear transformations serves as motivation for these definitions, but this connection will be ignored for the moment.

Let m and n be two positive integers, and let $I_{m,n}$ be the set of all pairs of integers (i, j) such that $1 \leq i \leq m$, $1 \leq j \leq n$. Any function A whose domain is $I_{m,n}$ is called an $m \times n$ *matrix*. The function value $A(i, j)$ is called the *ij-entry* or *ij-element* of the matrix and will be denoted also by a_{ij}. It is customary to display all the function values in a rectangular array consisting of m rows and n columns, as follows:

$$\begin{bmatrix} a_{11} & a_{12} & \cdots & a_{1n} \\ a_{21} & a_{22} & \cdots & a_{2n} \\ \cdot & \cdot & & \cdot \\ \cdot & \cdot & & \cdot \\ \cdot & \cdot & & \cdot \\ a_{m1} & a_{m2} & \cdots & a_{mn} \end{bmatrix}.$$

The elements a_{ij} may be arbitrary objects of any kind. Usually they will be real or complex numbers, but sometimes it is convenient to consider matrices whose elements are other objects, for example, functions. We also denote matrices by the more compact notation

$$A = (a_{ij})_{i,j=1}^{m,n} \qquad \text{or} \qquad A = (a_{ij}).$$

If $m = n$, the matrix is said to be a *square matrix*. A $1 \times n$ matrix is called a *row matrix*; an $m \times 1$ matrix is called a *column matrix*.

Two functions are equal if and only if they have the same domain and take the same function value at each element in the domain. Since matrices are functions, two matrices $A = (a_{ij})$ and $B = (b_{ij})$ are equal if and only if they have the same number of rows, the same number of columns, and equal entries $a_{ij} = b_{ij}$ for each pair (i, j).

Now we assume the entries are numbers (real or complex) and we define addition of matrices and multiplication by scalars by the same method used for any real- or complex-valued functions.

DEFINITION. *If $A = (a_{ij})$ and $B = (b_{ij})$ are two $m \times n$ matrices and if c is any scalar, we define matrices $A + B$ and cA as follows*:

$$A + B = (a_{ij} + b_{ij}), \qquad cA = (ca_{ij}).$$

The sum is defined only when A and B have the same size.

EXAMPLE. If

$$A = \begin{bmatrix} 1 & 2 & -3 \\ -1 & 0 & 4 \end{bmatrix} \qquad \text{and} \qquad B = \begin{bmatrix} 5 & 0 & 1 \\ 1 & -2 & 3 \end{bmatrix},$$

then we have

$$A + B = \begin{bmatrix} 6 & 2 & -2 \\ 0 & -2 & 7 \end{bmatrix}, \qquad 2A = \begin{bmatrix} 2 & 4 & -6 \\ -2 & 0 & 8 \end{bmatrix}, \qquad (-1)B = \begin{bmatrix} -5 & 0 & -1 \\ -1 & 2 & -3 \end{bmatrix}.$$

We define the zero matrix O to be the $m \times n$ matrix all of whose elements are 0. With these definitions, it is a straightforward exercise to verify that the collection of all $m \times n$ matrices is a linear space. We denote this linear space by $M_{m,n}$. If the entries are real numbers, the space $M_{m,n}$ is a real linear space. If the entries are complex, $M_{m,n}$ is a complex linear space. It is also easy to prove that this space has dimension mn. In fact, a basis for $M_{m,n}$ consists of the mn matrices having one entry equal to 1 and all others equal to 0. For example, the six matrices

$$\begin{bmatrix} 1 & 0 & 0 \\ 0 & 0 & 0 \end{bmatrix}, \begin{bmatrix} 0 & 1 & 0 \\ 0 & 0 & 0 \end{bmatrix}, \begin{bmatrix} 0 & 0 & 1 \\ 0 & 0 & 0 \end{bmatrix}, \begin{bmatrix} 0 & 0 & 0 \\ 1 & 0 & 0 \end{bmatrix}, \begin{bmatrix} 0 & 0 & 0 \\ 0 & 1 & 0 \end{bmatrix}, \begin{bmatrix} 0 & 0 & 0 \\ 0 & 0 & 1 \end{bmatrix},$$

form a basis for the set of all 2×3 matrices.

16.14 Isomorphism between linear transformations and matrices

We return now to the connection between matrices and linear transformations. Let V and W be finite-dimensional linear spaces with dim $V = n$ and dim $W = m$. Choose a basis $(e_1, \ldots, e_n)$ for V and a basis $(w_1, \ldots, w_m)$ for W. In this discussion, these bases are kept fixed. Let $\mathcal{L}(V, W)$ denote the linear space of all linear transformations of V into W. If $T \in \mathcal{L}(V, W)$, let $m(T)$ denote the matrix of T relative to the given bases. We recall that $m(T)$ is defined as follows.

The image of each basis element e_k is expressed as a linear combination of the basis elements in W:

(16.19) $$T(e_k) = \sum_{i=1}^{m} t_{ik} w_i \qquad \text{for} \quad k = 1, 2, \ldots, n.$$

The scalar multipliers t_{ik} are the ik-entries of $m(T)$. Thus, we have

(16.20) $$m(T) = (t_{ik})_{i,k=1}^{m,n}.$$

Equation (16.20) defines a new function m whose domain is $\mathcal{L}(V, W)$ and whose values are matrices in $M_{m,n}$. Since every $m \times n$ matrix is the matrix $m(T)$ for some T in $\mathcal{L}(V, W)$, the range of m is $M_{m,n}$. The next theorem shows that the transformation $m : \mathcal{L}(V, W) \to M_{m,n}$ is linear and one-to-one on $\mathcal{L}(V, W)$.

THEOREM 16.15. ISOMORPHISM THEOREM. *For all S and T in $\mathcal{L}(V, W)$ and all scalars c, we have*

$$m(S + T) = m(S) + m(T) \qquad and \qquad m(cT) = cm(T).$$

Moreover,

$$m(S) = m(T) \qquad implies \quad S = T,$$

so m is one-to-one on $\mathcal{L}(V, W)$.

Proof. The matrix $m(T)$ is formed from the multipliers t_{ik} in (16.19). Similarly, the matrix $m(S)$ is formed from the multipliers s_{ik} in the equations

(16.21) $$S(e_k) = \sum_{i=1}^{m} s_{ik} w_i \qquad \text{for} \quad k = 1, 2, \ldots, n \,.$$

Since we have

$$(S + T)(e_k) = \sum_{i=1}^{m} (s_{ik} + t_{ik})w_i \qquad \text{and} \qquad (cT)(e_k) = \sum_{i=1}^{m} (ct_{ik})w_i \,,$$

we obtain $m(S + T) = (s_{ik} + t_{ik}) = m(S) + m(T)$ and $m(cT) = (ct_{ik}) = cm(T)$. This proves that m is linear.

To prove that m is one-to-one, suppose that $m(S) = m(T)$, where $S = (s_{ik})$ and $T = (t_{ik})$. Equations (16.19) and (16.21) show that $S(e_k) = T(e_k)$ for each basis element e_k, so $S(x) = T(x)$ for all x in V, and hence $S = T$.

> *Note:* The function m is called an *isomorphism*. For a given choice of bases, m establishes a one-to-one correspondence between the set of linear transformations $\mathscr{L}(V, W)$ and the set of $m \times n$ matrices $M_{m,n}$. The operations of addition and multiplication by scalars are preserved under this correspondence. The linear spaces $\mathscr{L}(V, W)$ and $M_{m,n}$ are said to be *isomorphic*. Incidentally, Theorem 16.11 shows that the domain of a one-to-one linear transformation has the same dimension as its range. Therefore, $\dim \mathscr{L}(V, W) = \dim M_{m,n} = mn$.

If $V = W$ and if we choose the same basis in both V and W, then the matrix $m(I)$ which corresponds to the identity transformation $I: V \to V$ is an $n \times n$ diagonal matrix with each diagonal entry equal to 1 and all others equal to 0. This is called the *identity* or *unit matrix* and is denoted by I or by I_n.

16.15 Multiplication of matrices

Some linear transformations can be multiplied by means of composition. Now we shall define multiplication of matrices in such a way that the product of two matrices corresponds to the composition of the linear transformations they represent.

We recall that if $T: U \to V$ and $S: V \to W$ are linear transformations, their composition $ST: U \to W$ is a linear transformation given by

$$ST(x) = S[T(x)] \qquad \text{for all } x \text{ in } U \,.$$

Suppose that U, V, and W are finite-dimensional, say

$$\dim U = n, \qquad \dim V = p, \qquad \dim W = m \,.$$

Choose bases for U, V, and W. Relative to these bases, the matrix $m(S)$ is an $m \times p$ matrix, the matrix T is a $p \times n$ matrix, and the matrix of ST is an $m \times n$ matrix. The following definition of matrix multiplication will enable us to deduce the relation $m(ST) = m(S)m(T)$. This extends the isomorphism property to products.

DEFINITION. *Let A be any $m \times p$ matrix, and let B be any $p \times n$ matrix, say*

$$A = (a_{ij})_{i,j=1}^{m,p} \quad and \quad B = (b_{ij})_{i,j=1}^{p,n} .$$

Then the product AB is defined to be the $m \times n$ matrix $C = (c_{ij})$ whose ij-entry is given by

(16.22) $$c_{ij} = \sum_{k=1}^{p} a_{ik}b_{kj} .$$

Note: The product AB is not defined unless the number of columns of A is equal to the number of rows of B.

If we write A_i for the ith row of A, and B^j for the jth column of B, and think of these as p-dimensional vectors, then the sum in (16.22) is simply the dot product $A_i \cdot B^j$. In other words, the ij-entry of AB is the dot product of the ith row of A with the jth column of B:

$$AB = (A_i \cdot B^j)_{i,j=1}^{m,n} .$$

Thus, matrix multiplication can be regarded as a generalization of the dot product.

EXAMPLE 1. Let $A = \begin{bmatrix} 3 & 1 & 2 \\ -1 & 1 & 0 \end{bmatrix}$ and $B = \begin{bmatrix} 4 & 6 \\ 5 & -1 \\ 0 & 2 \end{bmatrix}$. Since A is 2×3 and B is 3×2,

the product AB is the 2×2 matrix

$$AB = \begin{bmatrix} A_1 \cdot B^1 & A_1 \cdot B^2 \\ A_2 \cdot B^1 & A_2 \cdot B^2 \end{bmatrix} = \begin{bmatrix} 17 & 21 \\ 1 & -7 \end{bmatrix} .$$

The entries of AB are computed as follows:

$A_1 \cdot B^1 = 3 \cdot 4 + 1 \cdot 5 + 2 \cdot 0 = 17,$ $\quad A_1 \cdot B^2 = 3 \cdot 6 + 1 \cdot (-1) + 2 \cdot 2 = 21,$

$A_2 \cdot B^1 = (-1) \cdot 4 + 1 \cdot 5 + 0 \cdot 0 = 1,$ $\quad A_2 \cdot B^2 = (-1) \cdot 6 + 1 \cdot (-1) + 0 \cdot 2 = -7.$

EXAMPLE 2. Let

$$A = \begin{bmatrix} 2 & 1 & -3 \\ 1 & 2 & 4 \end{bmatrix} \quad and \quad B = \begin{bmatrix} -2 \\ 1 \\ 2 \end{bmatrix}.$$

Here A is 2×3 and B is 3×1, so AB is the 2×1 matrix given by

$$AB = \begin{bmatrix} A_1 \cdot B^1 \\ A_2 \cdot B^1 \end{bmatrix} = \begin{bmatrix} -9 \\ 8 \end{bmatrix} ,$$

since $A_1 \cdot B^1 = 2 \cdot (-2) + 1 \cdot 1 + (-3) \cdot 2 = -9$ and $A_2 \cdot B^1 = 1 \cdot (-2) + 2 \cdot 1 + 4 \cdot 2 = 8$.

EXAMPLE 3. If A and B are both square matrices of the same size, then both AB and BA are defined. For example, if

$$A = \begin{bmatrix} 1 & 2 \\ -1 & 1 \end{bmatrix} \quad \text{and} \quad B = \begin{bmatrix} 3 & 4 \\ 5 & 2 \end{bmatrix},$$

we find that

$$AB = \begin{bmatrix} 13 & 8 \\ 2 & -2 \end{bmatrix}, \quad BA = \begin{bmatrix} -1 & 10 \\ 3 & 12 \end{bmatrix}.$$

This example shows that in general $AB \neq BA$. If $AB = BA$, we say A and B *commute*.

EXAMPLE 4. If I_p is the $p \times p$ identity matrix, then $I_p A = A$ for every $p \times n$ matrix A, and $BI_p = B$ for every $m \times p$ matrix B. For example,

$$\begin{bmatrix} 1 & 0 & 0 \\ 0 & 1 & 0 \\ 0 & 0 & 1 \end{bmatrix}\begin{bmatrix} 2 \\ 3 \\ 4 \end{bmatrix} = \begin{bmatrix} 2 \\ 3 \\ 4 \end{bmatrix}, \quad \begin{bmatrix} 1 & 2 & 3 \\ 4 & 5 & 6 \end{bmatrix}\begin{bmatrix} 1 & 0 & 0 \\ 0 & 1 & 0 \\ 0 & 0 & 1 \end{bmatrix} = \begin{bmatrix} 1 & 2 & 3 \\ 4 & 5 & 6 \end{bmatrix}.$$

Now we prove that the matrix of a composition ST is the product of the matrices $m(S)$ and $m(T)$.

THEOREM 16.16. *Let $T: U \to V$ and $S: V \to W$ be linear transformations, where U, V, W are finite-dimensional linear spaces. Then, for a fixed choice of bases, the matrices of S, T, and ST are related by the equation*

$$m(ST) = m(S)m(T).$$

Proof. Assume $\dim U = n$, $\dim V = p$, $\dim W = m$. Let $(u_1, \ldots, u_n)$ be a basis for U, $(v_1, \ldots, v_p)$ a basis for V, and $(w_1, \ldots, w_m)$ a basis for W. Relative to these bases, we have

$$m(S) = (s_{ij})_{i,j=1}^{m,p}, \quad \text{where} \quad S(v_k) = \sum_{i=1}^{m} s_{ik} w_i \quad \text{for} \quad k = 1, 2, \ldots, p,$$

and

$$m(T) = (t_{ij})_{i,j=1}^{p,n}, \quad \text{where} \quad T(u_j) = \sum_{k=1}^{p} t_{kj} v_k \quad \text{for} \quad j = 1, 2, \ldots, n.$$

Therefore, we have

$$ST(u_j) = S[T(u_j)] = \sum_{k=1}^{p} t_{kj} S(v_k) = \sum_{k=1}^{p} t_{kj} \sum_{i=1}^{m} s_{ik} w_i = \sum_{i=1}^{m} \left(\sum_{k=1}^{p} s_{ik} t_{kj} \right) w_i,$$

so we find that

$$m(ST) = \left(\sum_{k=1}^{p} s_{ik} t_{kj} \right)_{i,j=1}^{m,n} = m(S)m(T).$$

We have already noted that matrix multiplication does not always satisfy the commutative law. The next theorem shows that it does satisfy the associative and distributive laws.

THEOREM 16.17. ASSOCIATIVE AND DISTRIBUTIVE LAWS FOR MATRIX MULTIPLICATION. *Given matrices A, B, C.*

(a) *If the products A(BC) and (AB)C are meaningful, we have*

$$A(BC) = (AB)C \qquad (associative\ law)\ .$$

(b) *Assume A and B are of the same size. If AC and BC are meaningful, we have*

$$(A + B)C = AC + BC \qquad (right\ distributive\ law)\ ,$$

whereas if CA and CB are meaningful, we have

$$C(A + B) = CA + CB \qquad (left\ distributive\ law)\ .$$

Proof. These properties can be deduced directly from the definition of matrix multiplication, but we prefer the following type of argument. Introduce finite-dimensional linear spaces U, V, W, X and linear transformations $T: U \to V$, $S: V \to W$, $R: W \to X$ such that, for a fixed choice of bases, we have

$$A = m(R), \qquad B = m(S), \qquad C = m(T)\ .$$

By Theorem 16.16, we have $m(RS) = AB$ and $m(ST) = BC$. From the associative law for composition, we find that $R(ST) = (RS)T$. Applying Theorem 16.16 once more to this equation, we obtain $m(R)m(ST) = m(RS)m(T)$ or $A(BC) = (AB)C$, which proves (a). The proof of (b) can be given by a similar type of argument.

DEFINITION. *If A is a square matrix, we define integral powers of A inductively as follows:*

$$A^0 = I, \qquad A^n = AA^{n-1} \qquad for\ n \geq 1.$$

16.16 Exercises

1. If $A = \begin{bmatrix} 1 & -4 & 2 \\ -1 & 4 & -2 \end{bmatrix}$, $B = \begin{bmatrix} 1 & 2 \\ -1 & 3 \\ 5 & -2 \end{bmatrix}$, $C = \begin{bmatrix} 2 & 2 \\ 1 & -1 \\ 1 & -3 \end{bmatrix}$, compute $B + C$, AB,

BA, AC, CA, $A(2B - 3C)$.

2. Let $A = \begin{bmatrix} 0 & 1 \\ 0 & 2 \end{bmatrix}$. Find all 2×2 matrices B such that (a) $AB = O$; (b) $BA = O$.

3. In each case find a, b, c, d to satisfy the given equation.

(a) $\begin{bmatrix} 0 & 0 & 1 & 0 \\ 1 & 0 & 0 & 0 \\ 0 & 1 & 0 & 0 \\ 0 & 0 & 0 & 1 \end{bmatrix} \begin{bmatrix} a \\ b \\ c \\ d \end{bmatrix} = \begin{bmatrix} 1 \\ 9 \\ 6 \\ 5 \end{bmatrix}$; (b) $\begin{bmatrix} a & b & c & d \\ 1 & 4 & 9 & 2 \end{bmatrix} \begin{bmatrix} 1 & 0 & 2 & 0 \\ 0 & 0 & 1 & 1 \\ 0 & 1 & 0 & 0 \\ 0 & 0 & 1 & 0 \end{bmatrix} = \begin{bmatrix} 1 & 0 & 6 & 6 \\ 1 & 9 & 8 & 4 \end{bmatrix}$.

4. Calculate $AB - BA$ in each case.

(a) $A = \begin{bmatrix} 1 & 2 & 2 \\ 2 & 1 & 2 \\ 1 & 2 & 3 \end{bmatrix}$, $B = \begin{bmatrix} 4 & 1 & 1 \\ -4 & 2 & 0 \\ 1 & 2 & 1 \end{bmatrix}$;

(b) $A = \begin{bmatrix} 2 & 0 & 0 \\ 1 & 1 & 2 \\ -1 & 2 & 1 \end{bmatrix}$, $B = \begin{bmatrix} 3 & 1 & -2 \\ 3 & -2 & 4 \\ -3 & 5 & 11 \end{bmatrix}$.

5. If A is a square matrix, prove that $A^n A^m = A^{m+n}$ for all integers $m \geq 0, n \geq 0$.

6. Let $A = \begin{bmatrix} 1 & 1 \\ 0 & 1 \end{bmatrix}$. Verify that $A^2 = \begin{bmatrix} 1 & 2 \\ 0 & 1 \end{bmatrix}$ and compute A^n.

7. Let $A = \begin{bmatrix} \cos\theta & -\sin\theta \\ \sin\theta & \cos\theta \end{bmatrix}$. Verify that $A^2 = \begin{bmatrix} \cos 2\theta & -\sin 2\theta \\ \sin 2\theta & \cos 2\theta \end{bmatrix}$ and compute A^n.

8. Let $A = \begin{bmatrix} 1 & 1 & 1 \\ 0 & 1 & 1 \\ 0 & 0 & 1 \end{bmatrix}$. Verify that $A^2 = \begin{bmatrix} 1 & 2 & 3 \\ 0 & 1 & 2 \\ 0 & 0 & 1 \end{bmatrix}$. Compute A^3 and A^4. Guess a general

formula for A^n and prove it by induction.

9. Let $A = \begin{bmatrix} 1 & 0 \\ -1 & 1 \end{bmatrix}$. Prove that $A^2 = 2A - I$ and compute A^{100}.

10. Find all 2×2 matrices A such that $A^2 = O$.

11. (a) Prove that a 2×2 matrix A commutes with every 2×2 matrix if and only if A commutes with each of the four matrices

$$\begin{bmatrix} 1 & 0 \\ 0 & 0 \end{bmatrix}, \quad \begin{bmatrix} 0 & 1 \\ 0 & 0 \end{bmatrix}, \quad \begin{bmatrix} 0 & 0 \\ 1 & 0 \end{bmatrix}, \quad \begin{bmatrix} 0 & 0 \\ 0 & 1 \end{bmatrix}.$$

(b) Find all such matrices A.

12. The equation $A^2 = I$ is satisfied by each of the 2×2 matrices

$$\begin{bmatrix} 1 & 0 \\ 0 & 1 \end{bmatrix}, \quad \begin{bmatrix} 1 & 0 \\ c & -1 \end{bmatrix}, \quad \begin{bmatrix} 1 & b \\ 0 & -1 \end{bmatrix},$$

where b and c are arbitrary real numbers. Find all 2×2 matrices A such that $A^2 = I$.

13. If $A = \begin{bmatrix} 2 & -1 \\ -2 & 3 \end{bmatrix}$ and $B = \begin{bmatrix} 7 & 6 \\ 9 & 8 \end{bmatrix}$, find 2×2 matrices C and D such that $AC = B$

and $DA = B$.

14. (a) Verify that the algebraic identities

$$(A + B)^2 = A^2 + 2AB + B^2 \quad \text{and} \quad (A + B)(A - B) = A^2 - B^2$$

do not hold for the 2×2 matrices $A = \begin{bmatrix} 1 & -1 \\ 0 & 2 \end{bmatrix}$ and $B = \begin{bmatrix} 1 & 0 \\ 1 & 2 \end{bmatrix}$.

(b) Amend the right-hand members of these identities to obtain formulas valid for all square matrices A and B.

(c) For which matrices A and B are the identities valid as stated in (a)?

16.17 Systems of linear equations

Let $A = (a_{ij})$ be a given $m \times n$ matrix of numbers, and let $c_1, \ldots, c_m$ be m further numbers. A set of m equations of the form

(16.23)
$$\sum_{k=1}^{n} a_{ik}x_k = c_i \qquad \text{for} \quad i = 1, 2, \ldots, m,$$

is called a system of m linear equations in n unknowns. Here $x_1, \ldots, x_n$ are regarded as unknown. A *solution* of the system is any n-tuple of numbers $(x_1, \ldots, x_n)$ for which all the equations are satisfied. The matrix A is called the *coefficient-matrix* of the system.

Linear systems can be studied with the help of linear transformations. Choose the usual bases of unit coordinate vectors in V_n and in V_m. The coefficient-matrix A determines a linear transformation, $T: V_n \to V_m$, which maps an arbitrary vector $x = (x_1, \ldots, x_n)$ in V_n onto the vector $y = (y_1, \ldots, y_m)$ in V_m given by the m linear equations

$$y_i = \sum_{k=1}^{n} a_{ik}x_k \qquad \text{for} \quad i = 1, 2, \ldots, m.$$

Let $c = (c_1, \ldots, c_m)$ be the vector in V_m whose components are the numbers appearing in system (16.23). This system can be written more simply as

$$T(x) = c.$$

The system has a solution if and only if c is in the range of T. If exactly one x in V_n maps onto c, the system has exactly one solution. If more than one x maps onto c, the system has more than one solution.

EXAMPLE 1. *A system with no solution.* The system $x + y = 1$, $x + y = 2$ has no solution. The sum of two numbers cannot be both 1 and 2.

EXAMPLE 2. *A system with exactly one solution.* The system $x + y = 1$, $x - y = 0$ has exactly one solution: $(x, y) = (\frac{1}{2}, \frac{1}{2})$.

EXAMPLE 3. *A system with more than one solution.* The system $x + y = 1$, consisting of one equation in two unknowns, has more than one solution. Any two numbers whose sum is 1 gives a solution.

With each linear system (16.23), we can associate another system

$$\sum_{k=1}^{n} a_{ik}x_k = 0 \qquad \text{for} \quad i = 1, 2, \ldots, m,$$

obtained by replacing each c_i in (16.23) by 0. This is called the *homogeneous system* corresponding to (16.23). If $c \neq O$, system (16.23) is called a *nonhomogeneous system*. A vector x in V_n will satisfy the homogeneous system if and only if

$$T(x) = O,$$

where T is the linear transformation determined by the coefficient-matrix. The homogeneous system always has one solution, namely $x = O$, but it may have others. The set of solutions of the homogeneous system is the null space of T. The next theorem describes the relation between solutions of the homogeneous system and those of the nonhomogeneous system.

THEOREM 16.18.   *Assume the nonhomogeneous system* (16.23) *has a solution, say b.*
(a) *If a vector x is a solution of the nonhomogeneous system, then the vector $v = x - b$ is a solution of the corresponding homogeneous system.*
(b) *If a vector v is a solution of the homogeneous system, then the vector $x = v + b$ is a solution of the nonhomogeneous system.*

Proof.   Let $T: V_n \to V_m$ be the linear transformation determined by the coefficient-matrix, as described above. Since b is a solution of the nonhomogeneous system we have $T(b) = c$. Let x and v be two vectors in V_n such that $v = x - b$. Then we have

$$T(v) = T(x - b) = T(x) - T(b) = T(x) - c .$$

Therefore $T(x) = c$ if and only if $T(v) = O$. This proves both (a) and (b).

This theorem shows that the problem of finding all solutions of a nonhomogeneous system splits naturally into two parts: (1) Finding all solutions v of the homogeneous system, that is, determining the null space of T; and (2) finding one particular solution b of the nonhomogeneous system. By adding b to each vector v in the null space of T, we thereby obtain all solutions $x = v + b$ of the nonhomogeneous system.

Let k denote the dimension of $N(T)$ (the nullity of T). If we can find k *independent* solutions $v_1, \ldots, v_k$ of the homogeneous system, they will form a basis for $N(T)$, and we can obtain every v in $N(T)$ by forming all possible linear combinations

$$v = t_1 v_1 + \cdots + t_k v_k ,$$

where $t_1, \ldots, t_k$ are arbitrary scalars. This linear combination is called the *general solution of the homogeneous system.* If b is one particular solution of the nonhomogeneous system, then all solutions x are given by

$$x = b + t_1 v_1 + \cdots + t_k v_k .$$

This linear combination is called the *general solution of the nonhomogeneous system.* Theorem 16.18 can now be restated as follows.

THEOREM 16.19.   *Let $T: V_n \to V_m$ be the linear transformation such that $T(x) = y$, where $x = (x_1, \ldots, x_n), y = (y_1, \ldots, y_m)$ and*

$$y_i = \sum_{k=1}^{n} a_{ik} x_k \qquad for \quad i = 1, 2, \ldots, m .$$

Let k denote the nullity of T. If $v_1, \ldots, v_k$ are k independent solutions of the homogeneous system $T(x) = O$, and if b is one particular solution of the nonhomogeneous system $T(x) = c$, then the general solution of the nonhomogeneous system is

$$x = b + t_1 v_1 + \cdots + t_k v_k,$$

where $t_1, \ldots, t_k$ are arbitrary scalars.

This theorem does not tell us how to decide if a nonhomogeneous system has a particular solution b, nor does it tell us how to determine solutions $v_1, \ldots, v_k$ of the homogeneous system. It does tell us what to expect when the nonhomogeneous system has a solution. The following example, although very simple, illustrates the theorem.

EXAMPLE. The system $x + y = 2$ has for its associated homogeneous system the equation $x + y = 0$. Therefore, the null space consists of all vectors in V_2 of the form $(t, -t)$, where t is arbitrary. Since $(t, -t) = t(1, -1)$, this is a one-dimensional subspace of V_2 with basis $(1, -1)$. A particular solution of the nonhomogeneous system is $(0, 2)$. Therefore the general solution of the nonhomogeneous system is given by

$$(x, y) = (0, 2) + t(1, -1) \quad \text{or} \quad x = t, \quad y = 2 - t,$$

where t is arbitrary.

16.18   Computation techniques

We turn now to the problem of actually computing the solutions of a nonhomogeneous linear system. Although many methods have been developed for attacking this problem, all of them require considerable computation if the system is large. For example, to solve a system of ten equations in as many unknowns can require several hours of hand computation, even with the aid of a desk calculator.

We shall discuss a widely-used method, known as the Gauss-Jordan elimination method, which is relatively simple and can be easily programmed for high-speed electronic computing machines. The method consists of applying three basic types of operations on the equations of a linear system:

(1) *Interchanging two equations;*
(2) *Multiplying all the terms of an equation by a nonzero scalar;*
(3) *Adding to one equation a multiple of another.*

Each time we perform one of these operations on the system we obtain a new system having exactly the same solutions. Two such systems are called *equivalent*. By performing these operations over and over again in a systematic fashion we finally arrive at an equivalent system which can be solved by inspection.

We shall illustrate the method with some specific examples. It will then be clear how the method is to be applied in general.

EXAMPLE 1. *A system with a unique solution.* Consider the system

$$2x - 5y + 4z = -3$$
$$x - 2y + z = 5$$
$$x - 4y + 6z = 10.$$

This particular system has a unique solution, $x = 124$, $y = 75$, $z = 31$, which we shall obtain by the Gauss-Jordan elimination process. To save labor we do not bother to copy the letters x, y, z and the equals sign over and over again, but work instead with the *augmented matrix*

(16.24)
$$\begin{bmatrix} 2 & -5 & 4 & | & -3 \\ 1 & -2 & 1 & | & 5 \\ 1 & -4 & 6 & | & 10 \end{bmatrix}$$

obtained by adjoining the right-hand members of the system to the coefficient matrix. The three basic types of operations mentioned above are performed on the rows of the augmented matrix and are called *row operations*. At any stage of the process we can put the letters x, y, z back again and insert equals signs along the vertical line to obtain equations. Our ultimate goal is to arrive at the augmented matrix

(16.25)
$$\begin{bmatrix} 1 & 0 & 0 & | & 124 \\ 0 & 1 & 0 & | & 75 \\ 0 & 0 & 1 & | & 31 \end{bmatrix}$$

after a succession of row operations. The corresponding system of equations is $x = 124$, $y = 75$, $z = 31$, which gives the desired solution.

The first step is to obtain a 1 in the upper left-hand corner of the matrix. We can do this by interchanging the first row of the given matrix (16.24) with either the second or third row. Or, we can multiply the first row by $\frac{1}{2}$. Interchanging the first and second rows, we get

$$\begin{bmatrix} 1 & -2 & 1 & | & 5 \\ 2 & -5 & 4 & | & -3 \\ 1 & -4 & 6 & | & 10 \end{bmatrix}.$$

The next step is to make all the remaining entries in the first column equal to zero, leaving the first row intact. To do this we multiply the first row by -2 and add the result to the second row. Then we multiply the first row by -1 and add the result to the third row. After these two operations, we obtain

(16.26)
$$\begin{bmatrix} 1 & -2 & 1 & | & 5 \\ 0 & -1 & 2 & | & -13 \\ 0 & -2 & 5 & | & 5 \end{bmatrix}.$$

Now we repeat the process on the smaller matrix $\begin{bmatrix} -1 & 2 & | & -13 \\ -2 & 5 & | & 5 \end{bmatrix}$ which appears adjacent to the two zeros. We can obtain a 1 in *its* upper left-hand corner by multiplying the second row of (16.26) by -1. This gives us the matrix

$$\begin{bmatrix} 1 & -2 & 1 & | & 5 \\ 0 & 1 & -2 & | & 13 \\ 0 & -2 & 5 & | & 5 \end{bmatrix}.$$

Multiplying the second row by 2 and adding the result to the third, we get

(16.27)
$$\begin{bmatrix} 1 & -2 & 1 & | & 5 \\ 0 & 1 & -2 & | & 13 \\ 0 & 0 & 1 & | & 31 \end{bmatrix}.$$

At this stage, the corresponding system of equations is given by

$$\begin{aligned} x - 2y + z &= 5 \\ y - 2z &= 13 \\ z &= 31. \end{aligned}$$

These equations can be solved in succession, starting with the third one and working backwards, to give us

$$z = 31, \qquad y = 13 + 2z = 13 + 62 = 75, \qquad x = 5 + 2y - z = 5 + 150 - 31 = 124.$$

Or, we can continue the Gauss–Jordan process by making all the entries zero above the diagonal elements in the second and third columns. Multiplying the second row of (16.27) by 2 and adding the result to the first row, we obtain

$$\begin{bmatrix} 1 & 0 & -3 & | & 31 \\ 0 & 1 & -2 & | & 13 \\ 0 & 0 & 1 & | & 31 \end{bmatrix}.$$

Finally, we multiply the third row by 3 and add the result to the first row, and then multiply the third row by 2 and add the result to the second row to get the matrix in (16.25).

EXAMPLE 2. *A system with more than one solution.* Consider the following system of 3 equations in 5 unknowns:

(16.28)
$$\begin{aligned} 2x - 5y + 4z + u - v &= -3 \\ x - 2y + z - u + v &= 5 \\ x - 4y + 6z + 2u - v &= 10. \end{aligned}$$

The corresponding augmented matrix is

$$\begin{bmatrix} 2 & -5 & 4 & 1 & -1 & | & -3 \\ 1 & -2 & 1 & -1 & 1 & | & 5 \\ 1 & -4 & 6 & 2 & -1 & | & 10 \end{bmatrix}.$$

The coefficients of x, y, z and the right-hand members are the same as those in Example 1.

If we perform the same row operations used in Example 1, we finally arrive at the augmented matrix

$$\begin{bmatrix} 1 & 0 & 0 & -16 & 19 & | & 124 \\ 0 & 1 & 0 & -9 & 11 & | & 75 \\ 0 & 0 & 1 & -3 & 4 & | & 31 \end{bmatrix}.$$

The corresponding system of equations can be solved for x, y, and z in terms of u and v, giving us

$$x = 124 + 16u - 19v$$
$$y = 75 + 9u - 11v$$
$$z = 31 + 3u - 4v.$$

If we let $u = t_1$ and $v = t_2$, where t_1 and t_2 are arbitrary real numbers, and determine x, y, z by these equations, the vector (x, y, z, u, v) in V_5 given by

$$(x, y, z, u, v) = (124 + 16t_1 - 19t_2, 75 + 9t_1 - 11t_2, 31 + 3t_1 - 4t_2, t_1, t_2)$$

is a solution. By separating the parts involving t_1 and t_2, we can rewrite this as follows:

$$(x, y, z, u, v) = (124, 75, 31, 0, 0) + t_1(16, 9, 3, 1, 0) + t_2(-19, -11, -4, 0, 1).$$

This equation gives the general solution of the system. The vector $(124, 75, 31, 0, 0)$ is a particular solution of the nonhomogeneous system (16.28). The two vectors $(16, 9, 3, 1, 0)$ and $(-19, -11, -4, 0, 1)$ are solutions of the corresponding homogeneous system. Since they are independent, they form a basis for the space of all solutions of the homogeneous system.

EXAMPLE 3. *A system with no solution.* Consider the system

$$2x - 5y + 4z = -3$$
(16.29) $$x - 2y + z = 5$$
$$x - 4y + 5z = 10.$$

This system is almost identical to that of Example 1 except that the coefficient of z in the third equation has been changed from 6 to 5. The corresponding augmented matrix is

$$\begin{bmatrix} 2 & -5 & 4 & | & -3 \\ 1 & -2 & 1 & | & 5 \\ 1 & -4 & 5 & | & 10 \end{bmatrix}.$$

Applying the same row operations used in Example 1 to transform (16.24) into (16.27), we arrive at the augmented matrix

(16.30) $$\begin{bmatrix} 1 & -2 & 1 & | & 5 \\ 0 & 1 & -2 & | & 13 \\ 0 & 0 & 0 & | & 31 \end{bmatrix}.$$

When the bottom row is expressed as an equation, it states that $0 = 31$. Therefore the original system has no solution since the two systems (16.29) and (16.30) are equivalent.

In each of the foregoing examples, the number of equations did not exceed the number of unknowns. If there are more equations than unknowns, the Gauss–Jordan process is still applicable. For example, suppose we consider the system of Example 1, which has the solution $x = 124$, $y = 75$, $z = 31$. If we adjoin a new equation to this system which is also satisfied by the same triple, for example, the equation $2x - 3y + z = 54$, then the elimination process leads to the agumented matrix

$$\begin{bmatrix} 1 & 0 & 0 & | & 124 \\ 0 & 1 & 0 & | & 75 \\ 0 & 0 & 1 & | & 31 \\ 0 & 0 & 0 & | & 0 \end{bmatrix}$$

with a row of zeros along the bottom. But if we adjoin a new equation which is not satisfied by the triple (124, 75, 31), for example the equation $x + y + z = 1$, then the elimination process leads to an augmented matrix of the form

$$\begin{bmatrix} 1 & 0 & 0 & | & 124 \\ 0 & 1 & 0 & | & 75 \\ 0 & 0 & 1 & | & 31 \\ 0 & 0 & 0 & | & a \end{bmatrix},$$

where $a \neq 0$. The last row now gives a contradictory equation $0 = a$ which shows that the system has no solution.

16.19 Inverses of square matrices

Let $A = (a_{ij})$ be a square $n \times n$ matrix. If there is another $n \times n$ matrix B such that $BA = I$, where I is the $n \times n$ identity matrix, then A is called *nonsingular* and B is called a *left inverse* of A.

Choose the usual basis of unit coordinate vectors in V_n and let $T: V_n \to V_n$ be the linear transformation with matrix $m(T) = A$. Then we have the following.

THEOREM 16.20. *The matrix A is nonsingular if and only if T is invertible. If $BA = I$, then $B = m(T^{-1})$.*

Proof. Assume that A is nonsingular and that $BA = I$. We shall prove that $T(x) = O$ implies $x = O$. Given x such that $T(x) = O$, let X be the $n \times 1$ column matrix formed from the components of x. Since $T(x) = O$, the matrix product AX is an $n \times 1$ column matrix consisting of zeros, so $B(AX)$ is also a column matrix of zeros. But $B(AX) = (BA)X = IX = X$, so every component of x is 0. Therefore, T is invertible, and the equation $TT^{-1} = I$ implies that $m(T)m(T^{-1}) = I$ or $Am(T^{-1}) = I$. Multiplying on the left by B, we find $m(T^{-1}) = B$. Conversely, if T is invertible, then $T^{-1}T$ is the identity transformation so $m(T^{-1})m(T)$ is the identity matrix. Therefore A is nonsingular and $m(T^{-1})A = I$.

All the properties of invertible linear transformations have their counterparts for non-singular matrices. In particular, left inverses (if they exist) are unique, and every left inverse is also a right inverse. In other words, if A is nonsingular and $BA = I$, then $AB = I$. We call B the *inverse* of A and denote it by A^{-1}. The inverse A^{-1} is also nonsingular and *its* inverse is A.

Now we show that the problem of actually determining the entries of the inverse of a nonsingular matrix is equivalent to solving n separate nonhomogeneous linear systems.

Let $A = (a_{ij})$ be nonsingular and let $A^{-1} = (b_{ij})$ be its inverse. The entries of A and A^{-1} are related by the n^2 equations

$$(16.31) \qquad\qquad \sum_{k=1}^{n} a_{ik} b_{kj} = \delta_{ij},$$

where $\delta_{ij} = 1$ if $i = j$, and $\delta_{ij} = 0$ if $i \neq j$. For each fixed choice of j, we can regard this as a nonhomogeneous system of n linear equations in n unknowns $b_{1j}, b_{2j}, \ldots, b_{nj}$. Since A is nonsingular, each of these systems has a unique solution, the jth column of B. All these systems have the same coefficient-matrix A and differ only in their right members. For example, if A is a 3×3 matrix, there are 9 equations in (16.31) which can be expressed as 3 separate linear systems having the following augmented matrices:

$$\begin{bmatrix} a_{11} & a_{12} & a_{13} & 1 \\ a_{21} & a_{22} & a_{23} & 0 \\ a_{31} & a_{32} & a_{33} & 0 \end{bmatrix}, \quad \begin{bmatrix} a_{11} & a_{12} & a_{13} & 0 \\ a_{21} & a_{22} & a_{23} & 1 \\ a_{31} & a_{32} & a_{33} & 0 \end{bmatrix}, \quad \begin{bmatrix} a_{11} & a_{12} & a_{13} & 0 \\ a_{21} & a_{22} & a_{23} & 0 \\ a_{31} & a_{32} & a_{33} & 1 \end{bmatrix}.$$

If we apply the Gauss–Jordan process, we arrive at the respective augmented matrices

$$\begin{bmatrix} 1 & 0 & 0 & b_{11} \\ 0 & 1 & 0 & b_{21} \\ 0 & 0 & 1 & b_{31} \end{bmatrix}, \quad \begin{bmatrix} 1 & 0 & 0 & b_{12} \\ 0 & 1 & 0 & b_{22} \\ 0 & 0 & 1 & b_{32} \end{bmatrix}, \quad \begin{bmatrix} 1 & 0 & 0 & b_{13} \\ 0 & 1 & 0 & b_{23} \\ 0 & 0 & 1 & b_{33} \end{bmatrix}.$$

In actual practice we exploit the fact that all three systems have the same coefficient-matrix and solve all three systems at once by working with the enlarged matrix

$$\begin{bmatrix} a_{11} & a_{12} & a_{13} & 1 & 0 & 0 \\ a_{21} & a_{22} & a_{23} & 0 & 1 & 0 \\ a_{31} & a_{32} & a_{33} & 0 & 0 & 1 \end{bmatrix}.$$

The elimination process then leads to

$$\begin{bmatrix} 1 & 0 & 0 & b_{11} & b_{12} & b_{13} \\ 0 & 1 & 0 & b_{21} & b_{22} & b_{23} \\ 0 & 0 & 1 & b_{31} & b_{32} & b_{33} \end{bmatrix}.$$

The matrix on the right of the vertical line is the required inverse. The matrix on the left of the line is the 3×3 identity matrix.

It is not necessary to know in advance whether A is nonsingular. If A is *singular* (not nonsingular), we can still apply the Gauss–Jordan method, but somewhere in the process one of the diagonal elements will become zero, and it will not be possible to transform A to the identity matrix.

16.20 Exercises

Apply the Gauss–Jordan elimination process to each of the following systems. If a solution exists, determine the general solution.

1. $x + y + 3z = 5$
   $2x - y + 4z = 11$
   $-y + z = 3$.

2. $3x + 2y + z = 1$
   $5x + 3y + 3z = 2$
   $x + y - z = 1$.

3. $3x + 2y + z = 1$
   $5x + 3y + 3z = 2$
   $7x + 4y + 5z = 3$.

4. $3x + 2y + z = 1$
   $5x + 3y + 3z = 2$
   $7x + 4y + 5z = 3$
   $x + y - z = 0$.

5. $3x - 2y + 5z + u = 1$
   $x + y - 3z + 2u = 2$
   $6x + y - 4z + 3u = 7$.

6. $x + y - 3z + u = 5$
   $2x - y + z - 2u = 2$
   $7x + y - 7z + 3u = 3$.

7. $x + y + 2z + 3u + 4v = 0$
   $2x + 2y + 7z + 11u + 14v = 0$
   $3x + 3y + 6z + 10u + 15v = 0$.

8. $x - 2y + z + 2u = -2$
   $2x + 3y - z - 5u = 9$
   $4x - y + z - u = 5$
   $5x - 3y + 2z + u = 3$.

9. Prove that the system $x + y + 2z = 2$, $2x - y + 3z = 2$, $5x - y + az = 6$, has a unique solution if $a \neq 8$. Find all solutions when $a = 8$.

10. (a) Determine all solutions of the system

$$5x + 2y - 6z + 2u = -1$$
$$x - y + z - u = -2.$$

(b) Determine all solutions of the system

$$5x + 2y - 6z + 2u = -1$$
$$x - y + z - u = -2$$
$$x + y + z = 6.$$

11. This exercise tells how to determine all nonsingular 2×2 matrices. Prove that

$$\begin{bmatrix} a & b \\ c & d \end{bmatrix} \begin{bmatrix} d & -b \\ -c & a \end{bmatrix} = (ad - bc)I.$$

Deduce that $\begin{bmatrix} a & b \\ c & d \end{bmatrix}$ is nonsingular if and only if $ad - bc \neq 0$, in which case its inverse is

$$\frac{1}{ad - bc} \begin{bmatrix} d & -b \\ -c & a \end{bmatrix}.$$

Determine the inverse of each of the matrices in Exercises 12 through 16.

12. $\begin{bmatrix} 2 & 3 & 4 \\ 2 & 1 & 1 \\ -1 & 1 & 2 \end{bmatrix}$.

15. $\begin{bmatrix} 1 & 2 & 3 & 4 \\ 0 & 1 & 2 & 3 \\ 0 & 0 & 1 & 2 \\ 0 & 0 & 0 & 1 \end{bmatrix}$.

13. $\begin{bmatrix} 1 & 2 & 2 \\ 2 & -1 & 1 \\ 1 & 3 & 2 \end{bmatrix}$.

14. $\begin{bmatrix} 1 & -2 & 1 \\ -2 & 5 & -4 \\ 1 & -4 & 6 \end{bmatrix}$.

16. $\begin{bmatrix} 0 & 1 & 0 & 0 & 0 & 0 \\ 2 & 0 & 2 & 0 & 0 & 0 \\ 0 & 3 & 0 & 1 & 0 & 0 \\ 0 & 0 & 1 & 0 & 2 & 0 \\ 0 & 0 & 0 & 3 & 0 & 1 \\ 0 & 0 & 0 & 0 & 2 & 0 \end{bmatrix}$.

16.21 Miscellaneous exercises on matrices

1. If a square matrix has a row of zeros or a column of zeros, prove that it is singular.
2. For each of the following statements about $n \times n$ matrices, give a proof or exhibit a counter example.
   (a) If $AB + BA = O$, then $A^2B^3 = B^3A^2$.
   (b) If A and B are nonsingular, then $A + B$ is nonsingular.
   (c) If A and B are nonsingular, then AB is nonsingular.
   (d) If A, B, and $A + B$ are nonsingular, then $A - B$ is nonsingular.
   (e) If $A^3 = O$, then $A - I$ is nonsingular.
   (f) If the product of k matrices $A_1 \cdots A_k$ is nonsingular, then each matrix A_i is nonsingular.
3. If $A = \begin{bmatrix} 1 & 2 \\ 5 & 4 \end{bmatrix}$, find a nonsingular matrix P such that $P^{-1}AP = \begin{bmatrix} 6 & 0 \\ 0 & -1 \end{bmatrix}$.
4. The matrix $A = \begin{bmatrix} a & i \\ i & b \end{bmatrix}$, where $i^2 = -1$, $a = \frac{1}{2}(1 + \sqrt{5})$, and $b = \frac{1}{2}(1 - \sqrt{5})$, has the property that $A^2 = A$. Describe completely all 2×2 matrices A with complex entries such that $A^2 = A$.
5. If $A^2 = A$, prove that $(A + I)^k = I + (2^k - 1)A$.
6. The special theory of relativity makes use of a set of equations of the form $x' = a(x - vt)$, $y' = y$, $z' = z$, $t' = a(t - vx/c^2)$.) Here v represents the velocity of a moving object, c the speed of light, and $a = c/\sqrt{c^2 - v^2}$, where $|v| < c$. The linear transformation which maps the two-dimensional vector (x, t) onto (x', t') is called a *Lorentz transformation*. Its matrix relative to the usual bases is denoted by $L(v)$ and is given by

$$L(v) = a \begin{bmatrix} 1 & -v \\ -vc^{-2} & 1 \end{bmatrix}.$$

   Note that $L(v)$ is nonsingular and that $L(0) = I$. Prove that $L(v)L(u) = L(w)$, where $w = (u + v)c^2/(uv + c^2)$. In other words, the product of two Lorentz transformations is another Lorentz transformation.

7. If we interchange the rows and columns of a rectangular matrix A, the new matrix so obtained is called the *transpose* of A and is denoted by A^t. For example, if we have

$$A = \begin{bmatrix} 1 & 2 & 3 \\ 4 & 5 & 6 \end{bmatrix}, \quad \text{then} \quad A^t = \begin{bmatrix} 1 & 4 \\ 2 & 5 \\ 3 & 6 \end{bmatrix}.$$

Prove that transposes have the following properties:
(a) $(A^t)^t = A$.   (b) $(A + B)^t = A^t + B^t$.   (c) $(cA)^t = cA^t$.
(d) $(AB)^t = B^t A^t$.   (e) $(A^t)^{-1} = (A^{-1})^t$ if A is nonsingular.

8. A square matrix A is called an orthogonal matrix if $AA^t = I$. Verify that the 2×2 matrix $\begin{bmatrix} \cos\theta & -\sin\theta \\ \sin\theta & \cos\theta \end{bmatrix}$ is orthogonal for each real θ. If A is any $n \times n$ orthogonal matrix, prove that its rows, considered as vectors in V_n, form an orthonormal set.

9. For each of the following statements about $n \times n$ matrices, give a proof or else exhibit a counter example.
(a) If A and B are orthogonal, then $A + B$ is orthogonal.
(b) If A and B are orthogonal, then AB is orthogonal.
(c) If A and AB are orthogonal, then B is orthogonal.

10. *Hadamard matrices*, named for Jacques Hadamard (1865–1963), are those $n \times n$ matrices with the following properties:

  I. Each entry is 1 or -1.
 II. Each row, considered as a vector in V_n, has length $\sqrt{n}$.
III. The dot product of any two distinct rows is 0.

Hadamard matrices arise in certain problems in geometry and the theory of numbers, and they have been applied recently to the construction of optimum code words in space communication. In spite of their apparent simplicity, they present many unsolved problems. The main unsolved problem at this time is to determine all n for which an $n \times n$ Hadamard matrix exists. This exercise outlines a partial solution.
(a) Determine all 2×2 Hadamard matrices (there are exactly 8).
(b) This part of the exercise outlines a simple proof of the following theorem: *If A is an $n \times n$ Hadamard matrix, where $n > 2$, then n is a multiple of* 4. The proof is based on two very simple lemmas concerning vectors in n-space. Prove each of these lemmas and apply them to the rows of Hadamard matrix to prove the theorem.

LEMMA 1.   *If X, Y, Z are orthogonal vectors in V_n, then we have*

$$(X + Y) \cdot (X + Z) = \|X\|^2.$$

LEMMA 2.   *Write $X = (x_1, \ldots, x_n)$, $Y = (y_1, \ldots, y_n)$, $Z = (z_1, \ldots, z_n)$. If each component x_i, y_i, z_i is either 1 or -1, then the product $(x_i + y_i)(x_i + z_i)$ is either 0 or 4.*

ANSWERS TO EXERCISES

Introduction

⋆I 1.4   Exercises (page 8)

1. (a) $\frac{2}{3}b^3$ (b) b^3 (c) $\frac{1}{12}b^3$ (d) $\frac{2}{3}b^3 + b$ (e) $\frac{1}{3}ab^3 + bc$
2. (c) $\frac{1}{4}ab^4 + bc$
3. (b) $s_n < \dfrac{b^{k+1}}{k+1} < S_n$ (c) $\dfrac{ab^{k+1}}{k+1} + bc$

I 2.5   Exercises (page 15)

1. $A = \{1, -1\}, B = \{1\}, C = \{1\}, D = \{2\}, E = \{1, -17\},$
    $F = \{1, -17, -8 + \sqrt{47}, -8 - \sqrt{47}\}.$
2. $A \subseteq A, B \subseteq A, B \subseteq B, B \subseteq C, B \subseteq E, B \subseteq F, C \subseteq A, C \subseteq B, C \subseteq C, C \subseteq E, C \subseteq F,$
    $D \subseteq D, E \subseteq E, E \subseteq F, F \subseteq F.$ (Not counting "proper" inclusions.)
3. (a) True   (b) True   (c) False   (d) True   (e) False   (f) False
4. (a) True   (b) True   (c) True   (d) True   (e) False   (f) False
5. $\varnothing, \{1\}, \{2\}, \{3\}, \{4\}, \{1, 2\}, \{1, 3\}, \{1, 4\}, \{2, 3\}, \{2, 4\}, \{3, 4\}, \{1, 2, 3\}, \{1, 2, 4\}, \{1, 3, 4\},$
    $\{2, 3, 4\}, S$
6. (a) False   (b) False   (c) False   (d) True   (e) False   (f) False
    (g) True   (h) False   (i) True
17. (c) $A \subset C$ (d) Yes   (e) No

I 4.4   Exercises (page 35)

2. $1 - 4 + 9 - 16 + \cdots + (-1)^{n+1}n^2 = (-1)^{n+1}(1 + 2 + 3 + \cdots + n)$
3. $1 + \dfrac{1}{2} + \dfrac{1}{4} + \cdots + \dfrac{1}{2^n} = 2 - \dfrac{1}{2^n}$
4. $\left(1 - \dfrac{1}{2}\right)\left(1 - \dfrac{1}{3}\right) \cdots \left(1 - \dfrac{1}{n}\right) = \dfrac{1}{n}$
5. $\dfrac{n + 1}{2n}$
6. (b) $A(1)$ is false   (c) $1 + 2 + \cdots + n < \dfrac{(2n + 1)^2}{8}$
7. $n_1 = 3$

I 4.7   Exercises (page 39)

1. (a) 10   (b) 15   (c) 170   (d) 288   (e) 36   (f) $\frac{5}{6}$
8. (b) $n + 1$

9. Constant $= 2$

11. (a) True (b) False (c) False (d) False (e) False (f) False

12. $\dfrac{n}{n+1}$

I 4.9   Exercises (page 43)

2. $(a_1, b_2), (a_2, b_5), (a_3, b_7), (a_4, b_{10}), (a_5, b_3), (a_6, b_8), (a_7, b_9), (a_8, b_4), (a_9, b_6), (a_{10}, b_1)$

3. (a) False (b) True (c) True (d) False (e) False

★I 4.10   Miscellaneous exercises involving induction (page 44)

1. (a) 10 (b) 1 (c) 7 (d) 21 (e) 680 (f) 1

2. (b) 17 (c) 9 (d) No

5. $\displaystyle\prod_{k=1}^{0} a_k = 1; \quad \prod_{k=1}^{n+1} a_k = a_{n+1} \cdot \prod_{k=1}^{n} a_k$

8. 2^n

9. True if each $a_k \geq 0$

11. $n \geq 4$

Chapter 1

1.5   Exercises (page 56)

1. $f(2) = 3, f(-2) = -1, -f(2) = -3, f(\frac{1}{2}) = \frac{3}{2}, 1/f(2) = \frac{1}{3}, f(a+b) = a+b+1,$
   $f(a) + f(b) = a + b + 2, f(a)f(b) = ab + a + b + 1$

2. $f(2) + g(2) = 2, f(2) - g(2) = 4, f(2)g(2) = -3, f(2)/g(2) = -3, f[g(2)] = 0,$
   $g[f(2)] = -2, f(a) + g(-a) = 2 + 2a, f(t)g(-t) = (1+t)^2$

3. $\varphi(0) = 4, \varphi(1) = 2, \varphi(2) = 2, \varphi(3) = 2, \varphi(-1) = 6, \varphi(-2) = 8, t = 1.$

4. (a) All x (b) All x and y (c) All x and h (d) All y (e) All t
   (f) All a

5. (a) $|x| \leq 2$ (b) $|y| \leq 1$ (c) $|t| \geq \frac{1}{2}$ (d) $0 \leq a \leq 4$ (e) $|s| \leq 4$
   (f) $|x| \leq 2, \; x \neq 0$

6. (b) $\{x \mid 0 \leq x \leq 1\}$ (c) $\{x \mid 2 \leq x \leq 4\}$ (d) Domain is empty

7. Intersect when $x = 0, 1, -1$

8. Intersect when $x = -1, -3$

10. (a) $p(x) = 1$ (b) $p(x) = \frac{1}{2}x(x-1) + 1$ (c) $p(x) = ax(x-1) + 1$, a arbitrary
    (d) $p(x) = ax(x-1) + b$, a and b arbitrary

11. (a) $p(x) = ax(1-x) + b$, a and b arbitrary (b) $p(x) = c$, c arbitrary
    (c) $p(x) = ax$, a arbitrary (d) $p(x) = c$, c arbitrary

12. (a) $\displaystyle\sum_{k=0}^{2n} \binom{2n}{k} x^k$ (b) $\displaystyle\sum_{k=0}^{n} x^k$ (c) $\displaystyle\sum_{k=0}^{2^{n+1}-1} x^k$

1.11   Exercises (page 63)

5. $[nx] = \displaystyle\sum_{k=0}^{n-1} \left[x + \frac{k}{n}\right]$

1.15   Exercises (page 70)

1. (a) 2 (b) 4 (c) 6 (d) 4 (e) 6 (f) -6

2. One example: $s(x) = \frac{5}{2}$ if $0 \leq x < 2$, $s(x) = -1$ if $2 \leq x \leq 5$

5. (b) $2\sum_{k=1}^{8} k(\sqrt{k+1} - \sqrt{k}) = 2(21 - 3\sqrt{2} - \sqrt{3} - \sqrt{5} - \sqrt{6} - \sqrt{7})$
6. (c) $x = 1, x = \frac{5}{2}$
7. (a) 13
10. (a) $f(3) = 1, f(4) = -1, f[f(3)] = 0$ (b) $p = 14, p = 15$
11. (a), (d), (e)
12. (a), (b), (c)

1.26 Exercises (page 83)

1. 9	6. 2	11. $\frac{21}{8}$	16. $\frac{62}{27}$
2. 18	7. 0	12. 18	17. -78
3. 16	8. 0	13. $\frac{1}{3}$	18. $\frac{2592}{35}$
4. 0	9. 6	14. $-\frac{1}{3}$	19. $5^6/21$
5. 1	10. 11	15. 2	20. $-2^{11}/11$

21. (a) $0, \frac{3}{2}$ (b) 0
22. (a) $\frac{5}{6}$ (b) $c/2$
23. $p(x) = 6x - 6x^2$
24. $p(x) = 4x + 8x^2 + 3x^3$
27. $(1/A)\int_{Aa+B}^{Ab+B} f(x)\,dx$ if $A \neq 0$; $(b - a)f(B)$ if $A = 0$.

Chapter 2

2.4 Exercises (page 94)

1. $\frac{32}{3}$

2. $\frac{32}{3}$

3. $\frac{4}{3}$

4. $\frac{4}{3}$

5. $\frac{1}{12}$

6. $\dfrac{4\sqrt{2}}{3} - \dfrac{3\sqrt[3]{2}}{2} + \dfrac{1}{12}$

7. $\dfrac{4\sqrt{2}}{3} - \dfrac{3\sqrt[3]{2}}{2} + \dfrac{1}{6}$

8. $\frac{1}{3}(10 - 4\sqrt{2})$

9. $\frac{1}{4}(5\sqrt{5} - 3)$

10. $\frac{7}{4}$

11. $\frac{7}{3}$

12. $\frac{7}{3}$

13. $\dfrac{9\sqrt{3} - 1}{27}$

14. 5

15. $c = \frac{1}{2}$

16. $a = -2$

17. (a) $9\pi/2$ (b) $\pi/2$ (c) -6π

2.8 Exercises (page 104)

Note: In Exercises 1 through 13, n denotes an arbitrary integer.

1. (b) $\frac{1}{2}\pi + n\pi$
2. (a) $\frac{1}{2}\pi + 2n\pi$ (b) $2n\pi$ (c) $\frac{3}{2}\pi + 2n\pi$ (d) $(2n + 1)\pi$
6. $\tan(x + y) = \dfrac{\tan x + \tan y}{1 - \tan x \tan y}$; $\cot(x + y) = \dfrac{\cot x \cot y - 1}{\cot x + \cot y}$
7. $A = \frac{3}{2}, B = \frac{3}{2}\sqrt{3}$
8. $A = C\cos\alpha, B = C\sin\alpha$
9. $C = (A^2 + B^2)^{1/2}$. If $A^2 + B^2 \neq 0$, choose α so that $\cos\alpha = A/C$, $\sin\alpha = B/C$.
    If $A = B = 0$, choose any α.

10. $C = 2\sqrt{2}$, $\alpha = 5\pi/4$

11. $C = \sqrt{2}$, $\alpha = -\pi/4$

12. $\frac{1}{4}\pi + n\pi$

13. $\frac{1}{2}\pi + 2n\pi$; $\pi + 2n\pi$

17. (a) $1 - \frac{1}{2}\sqrt{3}$ (b) $1 - \frac{1}{2}\sqrt{2}$ (c) $\frac{1}{2}$ (d) 1 (e) 2 (f) 0 (g) 0
   (h) $\frac{1}{2}(\sqrt{3} - \sqrt{2})$

18. $\frac{1}{2}\pi^2 + 2$ 21. $2\sqrt{2} - 2$

19. $1 + \pi^3/24$ 22. $\frac{1}{2}\pi$

20. 0 23. $\sqrt{3} + \pi/6$

24. $\sqrt{3} + \frac{1}{2}x + \sin x + \pi/6$ if $0 \le x \le 2\pi/3$; $2\sqrt{3} - \frac{1}{2}x - \sin x + 5\pi/6$ if $2\pi/3 \le x \le \pi$

25. $(x^6 - x^3)/3 + \cos x - \cos(x^2)$

26. 1

27. 1

2.11   Exercises (page 110)

5. $4\pi^3/3$	9. 8π	13. 2
6. π	10. $\pi/8$	14. $3\pi/2$
7. 2π	11. $\pi/2$	15. $9\pi/2$
8. 4π	12. 2	

2.13   Exercises (page 114)

1. $\pi c^2 b^3/3$	5. $\pi^2/2$	9. $3\pi/10$	13. $(\frac{32}{3} - 4\sqrt{3})\pi r^3$
2. $\pi/2$	6. $\pi^2/4$	10. $\pi/2$	14. $a = \frac{4}{3}$
3. $2\pi/3$	7. π^2	11. $2\pi\sqrt{3}$	15. $16\sqrt{3}/3$
4. $33\pi/5$	8. $\pi/2$	12. $\frac{6}{5}$	16. $4a^5/5$

17. $\dfrac{h}{6}(B_1 + 4M + B_2)$

18. (a) $8\pi/5$ (b) 2π (c) $10\pi/3$ (d) $16\pi/15$

2.15   Exercises (page 116)

1. 60 ft-lb		5. 3750 ft-lb
2. 125 joules; 0.8 meter		6. 5000 ft-lb
3. (a) 441 joules (b) 425 joules		7. 20,000 ft-lb
4. $a = 3$, $b = -2$		8. 21,800 ft-lb

2.17   Exercises (page 119)

1. $(a^2 + ab + b^2)/3$	6. $2/\pi$
2. $\frac{7}{12}$	7. $2/\pi$
3. $\frac{4}{3}$	8. $1/\pi$
4. $\frac{45}{28}$	9. $\frac{1}{2}$
5. $2/\pi$	10. $\frac{1}{2}$

11. $c = a/\sqrt{3}$; $c = a/(n+1)^{1/n}$

12. (a) $w(x) = x$ (b) $w(x) = x^2$ (c) $w(x) = x^3$

14. All three

16. (a) $L/2$ (b) $L^3/3$ (c) $L/\sqrt{3}$

17. (a) $7L/12$ (b) $5L^3/8$ (c) $\sqrt{15}\,L/6$

18. (a) $2L/3$ (b) $L^4/4$ (c) $\sqrt{2}\,L/2$

19. (a) $11L/18$ (b) $31L^4/192$ (c) $\sqrt{62}\,L/12$

20. (a) $3L/4$ (b) $L^5/5$ (c) $\sqrt{15}\,L/5$
21. (a) $21L/32$ (b) $19L^5/240$ (c) $\sqrt{190}\,L/20$
22. $\rho(x) = x^2$ for $0 \le x \le L$ gives $\bar{x} = 3L/4$
23. (a) $6/\pi$ (b) $3\sqrt{2}/2$
24. $T = 2\pi$ sec; $80\sqrt{3}$

2.19 Exercises (page 124)

1. $x + x^2/2 + x^3/3$
2. $2y + 2y^2 + 8y^3/3$
3. $\frac{5}{6} + 2x + 2x^2 + 8x^3/3$
4. $-2x + 2x^2 - x^3$
5. $(3x^5 + 5x^3 + 136)/15$
6. $x^{10}/5 + 2x^6/3 - x^5/5 - 2x^3/3 + x^2 - x$
7. $x + \frac{2}{3}x^{3/2} - \frac{5}{3}$
8. $\frac{2}{3}(x^3 - x^{3/2}) + \frac{4}{5}(x^{5/2} - x^{5/4})$
9. $\sin x$
10. $\frac{1}{2}x^2 + \sin(x^2)$
11. $\frac{1}{2}x^2 - \frac{1}{2}x + \cos(x^2) - \cos x$
12. $\frac{1}{3}(x^3 - \cos 3x + 1)$
13. $\frac{1}{3}(x^6 - x^3 + \cos 3x - \cos(3x^2))$
14. $\frac{1}{2}y^2 + \frac{1}{2}y - \frac{1}{4}\sin 2y$
15. $2\sin\dfrac{x}{2} - \frac{1}{2}\cos 2x + \frac{1}{2}$
16. $\frac{3}{4}(x + \pi) + \sin x + \frac{1}{4}\sin 2x$
17. 0, $\pm\sqrt{2}$
18. (c) $P(x) = \frac{1}{2}(x - [x])^2 - \frac{1}{2}(x - [x])$ (d) $\frac{1}{12}$
20. (b) $g(2) = 2A, g(5) = 5A$ (c) $A = 0$

Chapter 3

3.6 Exercises (page 138)

1. $\frac{1}{4}$	5. $2t$	9. 0	13. 1
2. -1	6. -1	10. 0	14. -1
3. 4	7. 1	11. 1	
4. 1	8. 0	12. -1	

22. $a = (\sin c - b)/c$ if $c \neq 0$; if $c = 0$ there is no solution unless $b = 0$, in which case any a will do.
23. $a = (2\cos c - b)/c^2$ if $c \neq 0$; if $c = 0$ there is no solution unless $b = 2$, in which case any a will do.
24. The tangent is continuous everywhere except at $x = \frac{1}{2}\pi + n\pi$, where n is any integer; the cotangent is continuous everywhere except at $x = n\pi$, where n is any integer.
25. $f(x) \to 1$ as $x \to 0$. Define $f(0) = 1$ for continuity at 0.
28. No
29. No
30. $f(x) \to 0$ as $x \to 0$. Define $f(0) = 0$ for continuity at 0.
32. $f(x) \to 0$ as $x \to 0$. Define $f(0) = 0$ for continuity at 0.

3.8   Exercises (page 142)

1. $x^2 - 1$, all x
2. $(x - 1)^2$, all x
3. $|x|$, all x

4. 0, defined only at $x = 0$

5. x, $x \geq 0$

6. $-x$, $x \geq 0$
7. $\sin \sqrt{x}$, $x \geq 0$
8. $\sqrt{\sin x}$, $2k\pi \leq x \leq (2k + 1)\pi$, k an integer

9. $\sqrt{x + \sqrt{x}}$, $x > 0$

10. $\sqrt{x + \sqrt{x} + \sqrt{x + \sqrt{x}}}$, $x > 0$

11. -3 13. 1   15. 1   17. 0   19. 1
12. $\sqrt{3}$ 14. 1   16. 2   18. 2   20. $\frac{1}{2}$
21. x^2 if $x \geq 0$; 0 if $x < 0$
22. 1 if $1 \leq |x| \leq \sqrt{3}$; 0 otherwise
23. x^2 if $x \geq 0$; 0 if $x < 0$

3.15   Exercises (page 149)

1. $g(y) = y - 1$; all y
2. $g(y) = \frac{1}{2}(y - 5)$; all y
3. $g(y) = 1 - y$; all y
4. $g(y) = y^{1/3}$; all y
5. $g(y) = y$ if $y < 1$; $\sqrt{y}$ if $1 \leq y \leq 16$; $(y/8)^2$ if $y > 16$

3.20   Exercises (page 155)

3. $0.099\ 669$ rounded off in the sixth decimal place

Chapter 4

4.6   Exercises (page 167)

1. $f'(0) = 1, f'(\frac{1}{2}) = 0, f'(1) = -1, f'(-10) = -19$
2. (a) $1, -2$ (b) $0, -1$ (c) $3, -4$
3. $2x + 3$
4. $4x^3 + \cos x$
5. $4x^3 \sin x + x^4 \cos x$
6. $-1/(x + 1)^2$
7. $-2x/(x^2 + 1)^2 + 5x^4 \cos x - x^5 \sin x$
8. $-1/(x - 1)^2$
9. $\sin x/(2 + \cos x)^2$

10. $-\dfrac{2x^5 + 9x^4 + 8x^3 + 3x^2 + 2x - 3}{(x^4 + x^2 + 1)^2}$

11. $\dfrac{1 - 2(\sin x + \cos x)}{(2 - \cos x)^2}$

12. $\dfrac{\sin x + x \cos x}{1 + x^2} - \dfrac{2x^2 \sin x}{(1 + x^2)^2}$

13. (b) $v_0/32$ sec   (c) $-v_0$ ft/sec   (d) 16 ft/sec; 160 ft/sec; $16T$ ft/sec
    (f) $f(t) = v_0 t - 10t^2$ is one example
14. $3x^2$, where x is the length of an edge
16. $\frac{1}{2}x^{-1/2}$

17. $\dfrac{-1}{2\sqrt{x}(1 + \sqrt{x})^2}$

18. $\frac{3}{2}x^{1/2}$

19. $-\frac{3}{2}x^{-5/2}$

20. $\frac{1}{2}x^{-1/2} + \frac{1}{3}x^{-2/2} + \frac{1}{4}x^{-3/4}$

21. $-\frac{1}{2}x^{-3/2} - \frac{1}{3}x^{-4/3} - \frac{1}{4}x^{-5/4}$

22. $\dfrac{1 - x}{2\sqrt{x}(1 + x)^2}$

23. $\dfrac{2 + \sqrt{x}}{2(1 + \sqrt{x})^2}$

26. $\sec x(1 + 2\tan^2 x)$

27. $x \sec^2 x + \tan x$

28. $-(x^{-2} + 4x^{-3} + 9x^{-4})$

29. $\dfrac{2(1 + x^2)}{(1 - x^2)^2}$

30. $\dfrac{2(1 - 2x)}{(1 - x + x^2)^2}$

31. $\dfrac{x \cos x - \sin x}{x^2}$

32. $-\dfrac{1 + \cos x}{(x + \sin x)^2}$

33. $\dfrac{ad - bc}{(cx + d)^2}$

34. $-\dfrac{(2x^2 + 3)\sin x + 4x \cos x}{(2x^2 + 3)^2}$

35. $\dfrac{(2ax + b)(\sin x + \cos x) + (ax^2 + bx + c)(\sin x - \cos x)}{1 + \sin 2x}$

36. $a = d = 1; \ b = c = 0$

37. $a = c = e = 0; \ b = f = 2; \ d = -1$

38. (a) $\dfrac{nx^{n+1} - (n + 1)x^n + 1}{(x - 1)^2}$

   (b) $\dfrac{n^2 x^{n+3} - (2n^2 + 2n - 1)x^{n+2} + (n + 1)^2 x^{n+1} - x^2 - x}{(x - 1)^3}$

4.9 Exercises (page 173)

1. 1, 3

2. (a) $-1, \frac{1}{2}$ (b) $-\frac{1}{2}, 0$ (c) $-2, \frac{3}{2}$

3. $(2n + 1)\pi$, where n is any integer

4. $a = -2, b = 4$

5. $a = 1, b = 0, c = -1$

6. (a) $x_1 + x_2 + a$ (b) $\frac{1}{2}(x_1 + x_2)$

7. Tangent at $(3, -3)$; also intersect at $(0, 0)$

8. $m = -2, b = -2, a = \frac{1}{2}, c = \frac{3}{8}$

9. $a = 2c, b = -c^2$

10. $a = \dfrac{3}{2c}, b = -\dfrac{1}{2c^3}$

11. $a = \cos c, b = \sin c - c \cos c$

12. $-\dfrac{1}{\sqrt{x}(1 + \sqrt{x})^2}; \quad \dfrac{1 + 3\sqrt{x}}{2(x + \sqrt{x})^3}; \quad -\dfrac{3}{4}\dfrac{1 + 4\sqrt{x} + 5x}{\sqrt{x}(x + \sqrt{x})^4}$

13. $a = -4, \ b = 5, \ c = -1, \ d = -2$

14. (a) $\dfrac{15}{4}$ (b) 2   (c) $\frac{1}{2}$

15. (a) True   (b) True   (c) False if $f'(a) \neq 0$. Limit is $2f'(a)$
   (d) False if $f'(a) \neq 0$. Limit is $\frac{1}{2}f'(a)$

16. (a) $D*(f + g) = (1 + g/f)D*f + (1 + f/g)D*g$ when $f(x)$ and $g(x)$ are not 0;
         $D*(f \cdot g) = g^2 D*f + f^2 D*g$;
         $D*(f/g) = (g^2 D*f - f^2 D*g)/g^4$ when $g(x) \neq 0$
     (b) $D*f(x) = 2f(x) Df(x)$
     (c) $f(x) = c$ for all x

4.12 Exercises (page 179)

1. $-2 \cos x(1 + 2 \sin x)$
2. $x/\sqrt{1 + x^2}$
3. $(2x^3 - 4x) \sin x^2 - 2x \cos x^2 + 2 \sin x^3 + 6x^3 \cos x^3$
4. $-\sin 2x \cos (\cos 2x)$
5. $n \sin^{n-1} x \cos (n + 1)x$
6. $\cos x \cos (\sin x) \cos [\sin (\sin x)]$

7. $\dfrac{2 \sin x(\cos x \sin x^2 - x \sin x \cos x^2)}{\sin^2 x^2}$

8. $2/(\sin^2 x)$

9. $-\dfrac{16 \cos 2x}{\sin^3 2x}$

10. $\dfrac{1 + 2x^2}{\sqrt{1 + x^2}}$

11. $4(4 - x^2)^{-3/2}$

12. $\dfrac{2x^2}{1 - x^6}\left(\dfrac{1 + x^3}{1 - x^3}\right)^{1/3}$

13. $-(1 + x^2)^{-3/2}$

14. $\dfrac{1 + 2\sqrt{x} + 4\sqrt{x}\,g(x)}{8\sqrt{x}\,g(x)\sqrt{x + g(x)}}$, where $g(x) = \sqrt{x + \sqrt{x}}$

15. $\dfrac{6 + 3x + 8x^2 + 4x^3 + 2x^4 + 3x^5}{(2 + x^2)^{1/2}(3 + x^3)^{2/3}}$

16. $f'(x) = (x + 1)^{-2}$; $g'(x) = (2x + 1)^{-2}$

17.

x	$h(x)$	$h'(x)$	$k(x)$	$k'(x)$
0	0	-10	0	5
1	1	5	1	12
2	2	4	2	-10
3	3	12	3	4

18.

x	$g'(x)$	$g''(x)$
0	0	0
1	3	10
2	30	36

19. (a) $2xf'(x^2)$ (c) $f'[f(x)]f'(x)$
    (b) $[f'(\sin^2 x) - f'(\cos^2 x)]\sin 2x$ (d) $f'(x)f'[f(x)]f'\{f[f(x)]\}$
20. (a) $75 \text{ cm}^3/\text{sec}$ (b) $300 \text{ cm}^3/\text{sec}$ (c) $3x^2 \text{ cm}^3/\text{sec}$
21. 400 mph
22. (a) $20\sqrt{5} \text{ ft/sec}$ (b) $50\sqrt{2} \text{ ft/sec}$
23. 7.2 mi/hr
24. (a) and (b) $5/(4\pi) \text{ ft/min}$
25. $c = 1 + 36\pi$
26. $dV/dh = 75\pi \text{ ft}^3/\text{ft}$; $dr/dt = 1/(15\pi) \text{ ft/sec}$
27. $\dfrac{66}{7} \text{ cm}^2/\text{sec}$
28. $n = 33$
29. (a) $x = \frac{1}{2}$, $y = \frac{1}{4}$ (b) $\frac{1}{2}\sqrt{3}$

4.15   Exercises (page 186)

3. (b) $c = \frac{1}{2}$, $c = \sqrt{2}$
6. (a) $\theta = \frac{1}{2}$, $\theta \to \frac{1}{2}$

    (b) $\theta = \dfrac{x + \frac{1}{3}h}{x + \sqrt{x^2 + xh + \frac{1}{3}h^2}}$; $\theta \to \frac{1}{2}$ if $x > 0$

7. (b) f has at most $k + r$ zeros in $[a, b]$

4.19   Exercises (page 191)

1. (a) $\frac{3}{2}$ (b) f decreases if $x < \frac{3}{2}$; increases if $x > \frac{3}{2}$ (c) f' increases for all x
2. (a) $\pm\frac{2}{3}\sqrt{3}$ (b) f increases if $|x| > \frac{2}{3}\sqrt{3}$; decreases if $|x| < \frac{2}{3}\sqrt{3}$
    (c) f' increases if $x > 0$; decreases if $x < 0$
3. (a) ± 1 (b) f increases if $|x| > 1$; decreases if $|x| < 1$
    (c) f' increases if $x > 0$; decreases if $x < 0$
4. (a) $1, 3$ (b) f increases if $x < 1$ or if $x > 3$; decreases if $1 < x < 3$
    (c) f' increases if $x > 2$; decreases if $x < 2$
5. (a) 1 (b) f increases if $x > 1$; decreases if $x < 1$ (c) f' increases for all x
6. (a) none   (b) f increases if $x < 0$; decreases if $x > 0$
    (c) f' increases if $x < 0$, or if $x > 0$
7. (a) $2^{1/3}$ (b) f increases if $x < 0$, or if $x > 2^{1/3}$; decreases if $0 < x < 2^{1/3}$
    (c) f' increases if $x < 0$, or if $x > 0$
8. (a) 2 (b) f increases if $x < 1$, or if $1 < x < 2$; decreases if $2 < x < 3$, or if $x > 3$
    (c) f' increases if $x < 1$, or if $x > 3$; decreases if $1 < x < 3$
9. (a) ± 1 (b) f increases if $|x| < 1$; decreases if $|x| > 1$
    (c) f' increases if $-\sqrt{3} < x < 0$, or if $x > \sqrt{3}$; decreases if $x < -\sqrt{3}$, or if $0 < x < \sqrt{3}$
10. (a) 0 (b) f increases if $x < -3$ or if $-3 < x < 0$; decreases if $0 < x < 3$, or if $x > 3$
    (c) f' increases if $|x| > 3$; decreases if $|x| < 3$

Note. In Exercises 11, 12, and 13, n denotes an arbitrary integer.

11. (a) $\frac{1}{2}n\pi$ (b) f increases if $n\pi < x < (n + \frac{1}{2})\pi$; decreases if $(n - \frac{1}{2})\pi < x < n\pi$
    (c) f' increases if $(n - \frac{1}{4})\pi < x < (n + \frac{1}{4})\pi$; decreases if $(n + \frac{1}{4})\pi < x < (n + \frac{3}{4})\pi$
12. (a) $2n\pi$ (b) f increases for all x
    (c) f' increases if $2n\pi < x < (2n + 1)\pi$; decreases if $(2n - 1)\pi < x < 2n\pi$

13. (a) $(2n + \frac{1}{2})\pi$ (b) f increases for all x
    (c) f' increases if $(2n + \frac{1}{2})\pi < x < (2n + \frac{3}{2})\pi$; decreases if $(2n - \frac{1}{2})\pi < x < (2n + \frac{1}{2})\pi$
14. (a) 0   (b) f increases if $x > 0$; decreases if $x < 0$ (c) f' increases for all x

4.21 Exercises (page 194)

2. $\frac{1}{4}L$ ft wide, $\frac{1}{2}L$ ft long
3. Width $\frac{1}{2}\sqrt{2A}$, length $\sqrt{2A}$
7. $\sqrt{2}\,L$
10. $r = \frac{1}{2}h = R/\sqrt{2}$
12. $r = \frac{1}{2}R$, $h = \frac{1}{2}H$
13. $r = 2R/3$, $h = H/3$
14. $h = \frac{4}{3}R$, $r = \frac{2}{3}\sqrt{2}\,R$
15. A rectangle whose base is twice the altitude
16. Isosceles trapezoid, lower base the diameter, upper base equal to the radius
17. (a) $6\frac{2}{3}, 6\frac{2}{3}, \frac{5}{3}$
    (b) $8 + 2\sqrt{7}, 2 + 2\sqrt{7}, 5 - \sqrt{7}$
18. $\sqrt{5}$
19. (a) $20\sqrt{3}$ mi/hr; $10.39
    (b) $40\sqrt{2}$ mi/hr; $16.97
    (c) 60 mi/hr; $22.00
    (d) 60 mi/hr; $27.00
    (e) 60 mi/hr; $32.00
20. $\pi/4$
21. Crease $= \frac{9}{2}\sqrt{3}$ inches; angle $= \arctan \frac{1}{2}\sqrt{2}$
22. (a) max $= 3\sqrt{3}\,r$; min $= 4r$
    (b) $\frac{1}{4}L$
23. Rectangle has base $4P/(3\pi + 8)$, altitude $P(4 + \pi)/(6\pi + 16)$
24. $V = 48\pi$ for $0 \le h < 2$; $V = 4\pi(4 + h)^3/(9h)$ for $h \ge 2$
26. $A = 2(\frac{24}{7})^{7/2}$
27. $m(t) = 0$ if $t^2 \ge \frac{1}{3}$; $m(t) = t^2 - \frac{1}{3}$ if $t^2 \le \frac{1}{3}$

★4.23 Exercises (page 201)

1. $\dfrac{\partial f}{\partial x} = 4x^3 - 8xy^2$; $\dfrac{\partial f}{\partial y} = 4y^3 - 8x^2 y$; $\dfrac{\partial^2 f}{\partial x^2} = 12x^2 - 8y^2$; $\dfrac{\partial^2 f}{\partial y^2} = 12y^2 - 8x^2$;
   $\dfrac{\partial^2 f}{\partial x\,\partial y} = \dfrac{\partial^2 f}{\partial y\,\partial x} = -16xy$

2. $f_x = \sin(x + y) + x\cos(x + y)$; $f_y = x\cos(x + y)$; $f_{yy} = -x\sin(x + y)$;
   $f_{xx} = 2\cos(x + y) - x\sin(x + y)$; $f_{xy} = f_{yx} = \cos(x + y) - x\sin(x + y)$

3. $D_1 f = y + y^{-1}$; $D_2 f = x - xy^{-2}$; $D_{1,1}f = 0$; $D_{2,2}f = 2xy^{-3}$; $D_{1,2}f = D_{2,1}f = 1 - y^{-2}$

4. $f_x = x(x^2 + y^2)^{-1/2}$; $f_y = y(x^2 + y^2)^{-1/2}$; $f_{xx} = y^2(x^2 + y^2)^{-3/2}$;
   $f_{yy} = x^2(x^2 + y^2)^{-3/2}$; $f_{xy} = f_{yx} = -xy(x^2 + y^2)^{-3/2}$

5. $f_{yy} = 6x^2 y\cos(x^2 y^3) - 9x^4 y^4 \sin(x^2 y^3)$;
   $f_{xy} = f_{yx} = 6xy^2 \cos(x^2 y^3) - 6x^3 y^5 \sin(x^2 y^3)$

6. $f_{xy} = f_{yx} = 6\cos(2x - 3y)\cos[\cos(2x - 3y)] + 6\sin^2(2x - 3y)\sin[\cos(2x - 3y)]$

7. $\dfrac{\partial^2 f}{\partial x\,\partial y} = \dfrac{\partial^2 f}{\partial y\,\partial x} = -2(x + y)(x - y)^{-3}$; $\dfrac{\partial^2 f}{\partial x^2} = 4y(x - y)^{-3}$; $\dfrac{\partial^2 f}{\partial y^2} = 4x(x - y)^{-3}$

8. $f_{xx} = -3xy^2(x^2 + y^2)^{-5/2}$; $f_{yy} = -x(x^2 - 2y^2)(x^2 + y^2)^{-5/2}$;
   $f_{xy} = f_{yx} = y(2x^2 - y^2)(x^2 + y^2)^{-5/2}$

Chapter 5

5.5 Exercises (page 208)

1. $\frac{5}{4}(b^4 - a^4)$
2. $\frac{4}{5}(b^5 - a^5) + 6(a^2 - b^2)$
3. $\frac{1}{5}(b^5 - a^5) + \frac{1}{4}(b^4 - a^4) - (b^2 - a^2) - 2(b - a)$
4. $\dfrac{1}{2}(b^2 - a^2) - \left(\dfrac{1}{b} - \dfrac{1}{a}\right) + \dfrac{3}{2}\left(\dfrac{1}{b^2} - \dfrac{1}{a^2}\right)$
5. $(b - a) + \frac{4}{3}(b^{3/2} - a^{3/2}) + \frac{1}{2}(b^2 - a^2)$
6. $\sqrt{2}(b^{3/2} - a^{3/2})$
7. $\frac{2}{5}(b^{5/2} - a^{5/2}) - 2(b^{3/2} - a^{3/2}) + 7(b^{1/2} - a^{1/2})$
8. $\frac{3}{2}(b^{4/3} - a^{4/3} - b^{2/3} + a^{2/3})$
9. $\frac{1}{3}(b^6 - a^6) - 3(\cos b - \cos a)$
10. $\frac{3}{7}(b^{7/3} - a^{7/3}) - 5(\sin b - \sin a)$
14. $f(\frac{1}{4}\pi) = \frac{1}{2}\pi$; $f'(\frac{1}{4}\pi) = 2 - \pi$
15. $f(t) = -\sin t$; $c = \pi/3$
16. $f(t) = \sin t - 1$; $c = 0$
17. $f(x) = 2x^{15}$; $c = -\frac{1}{9}$
18. $p(x) = 3 + \frac{1}{2}x + \frac{1}{4}x^2$
19. $f''(1) = 2$; $f'''(1) = 5$
20. (a) $(1 + x^2)^{-3}$ (b) $2x(1 + x^4)^{-3}$ (c) $2x(1 + x^4)^{-3} - 3x^2(1 + x^6)^{-3}$
21. $\dfrac{2x^{13}}{1 + x^8} - \dfrac{3x^{20}}{1 + x^{12}}$
22. (a) 16 (b) $1 + \frac{3}{2}\sqrt{2}$ (c) $(36)^{1/3}$ (d) $\frac{1}{5}$
23. $f(a) = a(3 - \cos a)^{1/2}$
24. (a) $-\pi$ (b) $1 - \pi$ (c) 0 (d) $-\pi^2$ (e) $3\pi/2$
25. (a) $\pi - \frac{1}{2}$ (b) $\frac{1}{2}$ (c) $\frac{1}{2} + (\pi - \frac{1}{2})(t - 1)$ (d) $\frac{1}{2}(t - 1) + (\pi - \frac{1}{2})(t - 1)^2/2$
26. (a) None (b) One example is $f(x) = x + x^2$ (c) None
    (d) One example is $f(x) = 1 + x + x^2$ for $x \geq 0$, $f(x) = 1/(1 - x)$ for $x \leq 0$
28. (a) implies α and δ; (b) implies α; (c) implies α and γ; (d) implies α and δ;
    (e) implies α, δ, and ϵ.

5.8 Exercises (page 216)

1. $\frac{1}{3}(2x + 1)^{3/2} + C$
2. $(\frac{2}{45})(1 + 3x)^{5/2} - (\frac{2}{27})(1 + 3x)^{3/2} + C$
3. $\frac{2}{7}(x + 1)^{7/2} - \frac{4}{5}(x + 1)^{5/2} + \frac{2}{3}(x + 1)^{3/2} + C$
4. $-\frac{2}{27}$
5. $-\dfrac{1}{4(x^2 + 2x + 2)^2} + C$
6. $\frac{1}{3}\cos^3 x - \cos x + C$
7. $\frac{3}{7}(z - 1)^{7/3} + \frac{3}{4}(z - 1)^{4/3} + C$
8. $-\frac{1}{2}\csc^2 x + C$
9. $\frac{8}{3} - \sqrt{3}$
10. $\dfrac{1}{3 + \cos x} + C$
11. $\dfrac{2}{\sqrt{\cos x}} + C$
12. $2(\cos 2 - \cos 3)$
13. $-\dfrac{\cos x^n}{n} + C$
14. $-\frac{1}{3}\sqrt{1 - x^6} + C$
15. $\frac{4}{9}(1 + t)^{9/4} - \frac{4}{5}(1 + t)^{5/4} + C$
16. $x(x^2 + 1)^{-1/2} + C$
17. $\frac{1}{40}(8x^3 + 27)^{5/3} + C$
18. $\frac{3}{2}(\sin x - \cos x)^{2/3} + C$
19. $2\sqrt{1 + \sqrt{1 + x^2}} + C$
20. $-\frac{5}{2}(x - 1)^{2/5} + C$

5.10   Exercises (page 220)

1. $\sin x - x \cos x + C$
2. $2x \sin x + 2 \cos x - x^2 \cos x + C$
3. $x^3 \sin x + 3x^2 \cos x - 6x \sin x - 6 \cos x + C$
4. $-x^3 \cos x + 3x^2 \sin x + 6x \cos x - 6 \sin x + C$
5. $\frac{1}{2} \sin^2 x + C$
6. $\frac{1}{8} \sin 2x - \frac{1}{4} x \cos 2x + C$
15. (b) $(5\pi/32)a^6$
17. $\frac{2}{3}(3\sqrt{31} + \sqrt{3} - 11.35)$
18. $\tan x - x$; $\frac{1}{3} \tan^3 x - \tan x + x$
19. $-\cot x - x$; $-\frac{1}{3} \cot^3 x + \cot x + x$
20. (a) $n = 4$ (b) 2

★5.11   Miscellaneous review exercises (page 222)

1. $g^{(k)}(0) = 0$ if $0 \le k \le n - 1$; $g^{(n)}(0) = n!$
2. $6x^5 - 15x^4 + 10x^3 + 1$
6. 3
7. $\frac{67}{5}$
9. $y = 16x^2/9$
10. (b) $f'(0) = 0$
11. $-\frac{2}{5} \cos 5x + \frac{3}{25} \sin 5x - \frac{3}{5} x \cos 5x$
12. $\frac{1}{3}(1 + x^2)^{3/2}$
13. $-3^{10}/20$
14. $37/8281$
15. $\frac{1}{30}(1 + x^5)^6$
16. $1/265650$
17. $\cos \frac{1}{2} - \cos 1$
18. $[12(x - 1)^{1/2} - 24] \sin (x - 1)^{1/4} - 4[(x - 1)^{3/4} - 6(x - 1)^{1/4}] \cos (x - 1)^{1/4}$
19. $\frac{1}{4} \sin^2 x^2$
20. $-\frac{2}{9}(1 + 3 \cos^2 x)^{3/2}$
22. $a = 9$, $b = \frac{27}{2}$
23. $\frac{8}{15}$, $\frac{16}{35}$, $\frac{128}{315}$, $\frac{256}{693}$
24. $\frac{1}{13}x^{13} + \frac{1}{6}x^{12} + \frac{1}{11}x^{11}$
26. 3
27. $\frac{1}{2}\left(\frac{1}{2} + \frac{1}{\pi + 2} - A\right)$
34. (a) $p(x) = -x^2 + x - 1$
35. (a) $P_1(x) = x - \frac{1}{2}$; $P_2(x) = x^2 - x + \frac{1}{6}$; $P_3(x) = x^3 - \frac{3}{2}x^2 + \frac{1}{2}x$;
        $P_4(x) = x^4 - 2x^3 + x^2 - \frac{1}{30}$; $P_5(x) = x^5 - \frac{5}{2}x^4 + \frac{5}{3}x^3 - \frac{1}{6}x$

Chapter 6

6.9   Exercises (page 236)

1. (a) 1   (b) $(a + b)/(1 + ab)$

2. (a) 0   (b) $\dfrac{e - 1}{e + 1}$ (c) 4   (d) $\dfrac{(e^2 - 1)^2}{4e^2}$

3. Increasing if $0 < x < e$, decreasing if $x > e$;   convex if $x > e^{3/2}$, concave if $0 < x < e^{3/2}$

4. $(2x)/(1 + x^2)$

5. $x/(1 + x^2)$

6. $x/(x^2 - 4)$

7. $1/(x \log x)$

8. $(2/x) + 1/(x \log x)$

9. $x/(x^4 - 1)$

15. $-1/(x \log^2 x)$

16. $\frac{1}{3} \log |2 + 3x| + C$

17. $x \log^2 |x| - 2x \log |x| + 2x + C$

18. $\frac{1}{2} x^2 \log |x| - \frac{1}{4} x^2 + C$

19. $\frac{1}{2} x^2 \log^2 |x| - \frac{1}{2} x^2 \log |x| + \frac{1}{4} x^2 + C$

20. 3

21. $\log |\sin x| + C$

22. $\dfrac{x^{n+1}}{n + 1} \log |ax| - \dfrac{x^{n+1}}{(n + 1)^2} + C$ if $n \neq -1$; $\frac{1}{2} \log^2 |ax| + C$ if $n = -1$

23. $\dfrac{x^3}{3} (\log^2 |x| - \frac{2}{3} \log |x| + \frac{2}{9}) + C$

24. $\log |\log x| + C$

25. -2

26. $\frac{2}{3}(-2 + \log |x|)\sqrt{1 + \log |x|} + C$

27. $\dfrac{x^4}{4} \log^3 |x| - \frac{3}{16} x^4 \log^2 |x| + \frac{3}{32} x^4 \log |x| - \frac{3}{128} x^4 + C$

34. $4 \log x$

35. $3 + 3 \log x.$

36. $a \log a$

10. $\dfrac{n(x + \sqrt{1 + x^2})^n}{\sqrt{1 + x^2}}$

11. $1/[2(1 + \sqrt{x + 1})]$

12. $\log (x + \sqrt{x^2 + 1})$

13. $1/(a - bx^2)$

14. $2 \sin (\log x)$

6.17   Exercises (page 248)

1. $3e^{3x-1}$

2. $8xe^{4x^2}$

3. $-2xe^{-x^2}$

4. $\dfrac{e^{\sqrt{x}}}{2\sqrt{x}}$

5. $-\dfrac{e^{1/x}}{x^2}$

13. $e^x(x - 1) + C$

14. $-e^{-x}(x + 1) + C$

15. $e^x(x^2 - 2x + 2) + C$

16. $-\frac{1}{2} e^{-2x}(x^2 + x + \frac{1}{2}) + C$

17. $2(\sqrt{x} - 1)e^{\sqrt{x}} + C$

24. $a^a x^{a^a - 1} + ax^{a-1}a^{x^a} \log a + a^x a^{a^x}(\log a)^2$

25. $1/[x \log x \log (\log x)]$

26. $e^x(1 + e^{2x})^{-1/2}$

27. $x^x x^{x^x}\left[\dfrac{1}{x} + \log x + (\log x)^2\right]$

28. $(\log x)^x\left(\log \log x + \dfrac{1}{\log x}\right)$

6. $2^x \log 2$

7. $2^{1+x^2}x \log 2$

8. $(\cos x)e^{\sin x}$

9. $-(\sin 2x)e^{\cos^2 x}$

10. 1

11. $e^x e^{e^x}$

12. $e^x e^{e^x} e^{e^{e^x}}$

18. $-\frac{1}{2}(x^2 + 1)e^{-x^2} + C$

19. $b = e^a$, a arbitrary

21. $x^x(1 + \log x)$

22. $1 + (1 + 2x + 2x^2)e^{x^2}$

23. $4(e^x + e^{-x})^{-2}$

29. $2x^{-1+\log x} \log x$

30. $\dfrac{(\log x)^{x-1}}{x^{1+\log x}} [x - 2(\log x)^2 + x \log x \log (\log x)]$

31. $(\sin x)^{1+\cos x} [\cot^2 x - \log (\sin x)] - (\cos x)^{1+\sin x} [\tan^2 x - \log (\cos x)]$

32. $x^{-2+1/x}(1 - \log x)$

33. $\dfrac{54x - 36x^2 + 4x^3 + 2x^4}{3(1 - x)^2(3 - x)^{2/3}(3 + x)^{5/3}}$

34. $\displaystyle\prod_{i=1}^{n} (x - a_i)^{b_i} \sum_{k=1}^{n} \dfrac{b_k}{x - a_k}$

6.19 Exercises (page 251)

16. $\frac{5}{3}$

17. $\frac{3}{4}$

18. $\sinh x = \frac{5}{12}, \cosh x = \frac{13}{12}$

19. $\frac{37}{12}$

20. $\frac{24}{25}$

6.22 Exercises (page 256)

12. $\dfrac{1}{\sqrt{4 - x^2}}$ if $|x| < 2$

13. $\dfrac{1}{\sqrt{1 + 2x - x^2}}$ if $|x - 1| < \sqrt{2}$

14. $\dfrac{1}{|x| \sqrt{x^2 - 1}}$ if $|x| > 1$

15. $\dfrac{\cos x}{|\cos x|}$ if $x \neq (k + \frac{1}{2})\pi, k$ an integer

16. $\dfrac{\sqrt{x}}{2(1 + x)}$ if $x \geq 0$

17. $\dfrac{1 + x^4}{1 + x^6}$

18. $-\dfrac{2x}{|x|(1 + x^2)}$ if $x \neq 0$

19. $\dfrac{\sin 2x}{\sin^4 x + \cos^4 x}$ if $x \neq (k + \frac{1}{2})\pi$

20. $\dfrac{1}{2(1 + x^2)}$

21. $\dfrac{\cos x + \sin x}{\sqrt{\sin 2x}}$ if $k\pi < x < (k + \frac{1}{2})\pi$

22. $\dfrac{x}{|x| \sqrt{1 - x^2}}$ if $0 < |x| < 1$

23. $1/(1 + x^2)$ if $x \neq 1$

24. $\dfrac{4x}{\sqrt{1 - x^4}(\arccos x^2)^3}$ if $|x| < 1$

25. $\dfrac{1}{2x \sqrt{x - 1} \arccos (1/\sqrt{x})}$ if $x > 1$

27. $\dfrac{3x}{(1 - x^2)^2} + \dfrac{(1 + 2x^2) \arcsin x}{(1 - x^2)^{5/2}}$

29. $\arcsin \dfrac{x}{|a|} + C$

30. $\arcsin \dfrac{x + 1}{\sqrt{2}} + C$

31. $\dfrac{1}{a} \arctan \dfrac{x}{a} + C$

32. $\dfrac{1}{a}\sqrt{\dfrac{a}{b}} \arctan \left(\sqrt{\dfrac{b}{a}} x\right) + C$ if $ab > 0$;

$\dfrac{a}{2 |a|\sqrt{-ab}} \log \left| \dfrac{\sqrt{|a|} + x \sqrt{|b|}}{\sqrt{|a|} - x \sqrt{|b|}} \right| + C$ if $ab < 0$

33. $\dfrac{2}{\sqrt{7}} \arctan \dfrac{2x-1}{\sqrt{7}} + C$

34. $\frac{1}{2}[(1+x^2)\arctan x - x] + C$

35. $\dfrac{x^3}{3} \arccos x - \dfrac{2+x^2}{9} \sqrt{1-x^2} + C$

36. $\frac{1}{2}(1+x^2)(\arctan x)^2 - x \arctan x + \frac{1}{2}\log(1+x^2) + C$

37. $(1+x)\arctan \sqrt{x} - \sqrt{x} + C$

38. $(\arctan \sqrt{x})^2 + C$

39. $\frac{1}{2}(\arcsin x + x\sqrt{1-x^2}) + C$

40. $\dfrac{(x-1)e^{\arctan x}}{2\sqrt{1+x^2}} + C$

41. $\dfrac{(x+1)e^{\arctan x}}{2\sqrt{1+x^2}} + C$

42. $\dfrac{1}{2}\left(\arctan x - \dfrac{x}{1+x^2}\right) + C$

43. $\arctan e^x + C$

44. $\frac{1}{2}\log(1+e^{-2x}) - \dfrac{\operatorname{arccot} e^x}{e^x} + C$

45. $a \arcsin \dfrac{x}{a} - \sqrt{a^2-x^2} + C$

46. $\dfrac{2(b-a)}{|b-a|} \arcsin \sqrt{\dfrac{x-a}{b-a}} + C$

47. $\frac{1}{4}|b-a|\,(b-a)\arcsin \sqrt{\dfrac{x-a}{b-a}} + \frac{1}{4}\sqrt{(x-a)(b-x)}\,[2x-(a+b)] + C$

6.25   Exercises (page 267)

1. $\log|x-2| + \log|x+5| + C$

2. $\frac{1}{2}\log\left|\dfrac{(x+2)^4}{(x+1)(x+3)^3}\right| + C$

3. $-\dfrac{1}{3(x-1)} + \frac{2}{9}\log\left|\dfrac{x-1}{x+2}\right| + C$

4. $\frac{1}{2}x^2 - x + \log\left|\dfrac{x^3(x+2)}{x-1}\right| + C$

5. $\log|x+1| - \dfrac{3}{(2x+1)^2} + \dfrac{3}{2x+1} + C$

6. $2\log|x-1| + \log(x^2+x+1) + C$

7. $x + \frac{1}{3}\arctan x - \frac{8}{3}\arctan(x/2) + C$

8. $2\log|x| - \log|x+1| + C$

9. $\log|x| - \frac{1}{2}\log(x^2+1) + \dfrac{1}{2(x^2+1)} + C$

10. $\dfrac{9x^2+50x+68}{4(x+2)(x+3)^2} + \frac{1}{8}\log\left|\dfrac{(x+1)(x+2)^{16}}{(x+3)^{17}}\right| + C$

11. $\dfrac{1}{x+1} + \log|x+1| + C$

12. $\frac{1}{2}\log|x^2-1| - \log|x| + C$

13. $x + \frac{4}{5}\log|x-2| - \frac{9}{5}\log|x+3| + C$

14. $\log|x-2| - \dfrac{4}{x-2} + C$

15. $\dfrac{1}{2-x} - \arctan(x-2) + C$

16. $4 \log |x + 1| - \frac{3}{2} \log |x| - \frac{5}{2} \log |x + 2| + C$

17. $\frac{1}{4} \log \left| \dfrac{x + 1}{x - 1} \right| - \dfrac{x}{2(x^2 - 1)} + C$

18. $\frac{1}{3} \log \dfrac{(x - 1)^2}{x^2 + x + 1} + C$

19. $\log |x| + \dfrac{1}{x^2 + 1} + C$

20. $\dfrac{1}{4x} + \dfrac{1}{4x^2} + \dfrac{1}{8} \log \left| \dfrac{x - 2}{x} \right| + C$

21. $\log \dfrac{|x|}{\sqrt{1 + x^2}} - x + \arctan x + C$

22. $\frac{1}{4} \log |(x - 1)/(x + 1)| - \frac{1}{2} \arctan x + C$

23. $\dfrac{1}{4\sqrt{2}} \log \dfrac{x^2 + x\sqrt{2} + 1}{x^2 - x\sqrt{2} + 1} + \dfrac{1}{2\sqrt{2}} \arctan \dfrac{x\sqrt{2}}{1 - x^2} + C$

24. $(x^2 + 2x + 2)^{-1} + \arctan (x + 1) + C$

25. $-x/(x^5 + x + 1) + C$

26. $\dfrac{1}{\sqrt{5}} \arctan \dfrac{1 + 3 \tan (x/2)}{\sqrt{5}} + C$

27. $\dfrac{2}{\sqrt{1 - a^2}} \arctan \left(\sqrt{\dfrac{1 - a}{1 + a}} \tan \dfrac{x}{2} \right) + C$

28. $\dfrac{1}{\sqrt{a^2 - 1}} \log \left| \dfrac{a + \cos x + \sqrt{a^2 - 1} \sin x}{1 + a \cos x} \right| + C$

29. $x - \frac{1}{2}\sqrt{2} \arctan (\sqrt{2} \tan x) + C$

30. $\dfrac{1}{ab} \arctan \left(\dfrac{a}{b} \tan x \right) + C$

31. $-\dfrac{\cos x}{a(a \sin x + b \cos x)} + C$

32. $(\pi/4) - \frac{1}{2} \log 2$

33. $\frac{1}{2}x\sqrt{3 - x^2} + \frac{3}{2} \arcsin \left(\dfrac{x}{\sqrt{3}} \right) + C$

34. $-\sqrt{3 - x^2} + C$

35. $\sqrt{3 - x^2} - \sqrt{3} \log \left(\dfrac{\sqrt{3 - x^2} + \sqrt{3}}{x} \right) + C$

36. $\sqrt{x^2 + x} + \frac{1}{2} \log (2\sqrt{x^2 + x} + 2x + 1) + C$

37. $\frac{1}{2}x\sqrt{x^2 + 5} + \frac{5}{2} \log (x + \sqrt{x^2 + 5}) + C$

38. $\sqrt{x^2 + x + 1} - \frac{1}{2} \log (2x + 1 + 2\sqrt{x^2 + x + 1}) + C$

39. $\log (2x + 1 + 2\sqrt{x^2 + 1}) + C$

40. $-\dfrac{\sqrt{2 - x - x^2}}{x} + \dfrac{\sqrt{2}}{4} \log \left(\dfrac{\sqrt{2 - x - x^2}}{x} - \dfrac{\sqrt{2}}{4} \right) - \arcsin \left(\dfrac{2x + 1}{3} \right) + C$

6.26 **Miscellaneous review exercises (page 268)**

1. $f(x) + f(1/x) = \frac{1}{2}(\log x)^2$

2. $f(x) = \log \sqrt{3/(2 + \cos x)}$

4. 1

5. (a) $-\frac{7}{12}$ (b) $V = \int_1^4 \dfrac{\pi(4x + 2)}{x(x + 1)(x + 2)} dx$

6. (a) $x \geq 1$ (c) $F(ax) - F(a)$; $F(x) - \dfrac{e^x}{x} + e$; $xe^{1/x} - e - F\left(\dfrac{1}{x}\right)$

7. (a) No such function (b) $-2^x \log 2$ (c) $\frac{1}{2}x \pm 1$

9. (a) $g(3x) = 3e^{2x}g(x)$ (b) $g(nx) = ne^{(n-1)x}g(x)$ (c) 2 (d) $C = 2$

10. $f(x) = b^{x/a}g(x)$, where g is periodic with period a

12. (a) $-Ae^{-a}$ (b) $\frac{1}{2}A$ (c) $A + 1 - \frac{1}{2}e$ (d) $e \log 2 - A$

13. (b) $c_0 + nc_1 + n(n - 1)c_2 + n(n - 1)(n - 2)c_3$

(c) If $p(x) = \displaystyle\sum_{k=0}^{m} c_k x^k$, then $f^{(n)}(0) = \displaystyle\sum_{k=0}^{m} k!\binom{n}{k}c_k$

16. (a) $\frac{2}{3}x^2(x + |x|)$

(b) $x - \frac{1}{3}x^3$ if $|x| \leq 1$; $x - \frac{1}{2}x|x| + \dfrac{1}{6}\dfrac{|x|}{x}$ if $|x| > 1$

(c) $1 - e^{-x}$ if $x \geq 0$; $e^x - 1$ if $x < 0$

(d) x if $|x| \leq 1$; $\frac{1}{3}x^3 + \dfrac{2}{3}\dfrac{|x|}{x}$ if $|x| > 1$

17. $f(x) = \sqrt{(2x + 1)/\pi}$

18. (a) $\frac{1}{2}(1 - e^{-2t})$ (b) $\frac{1}{4}\pi(1 - e^{-4t})$ (c) $\frac{1}{2}\pi[1 - e^{-2t}(2t + 1)]$ (d) π

19. (a) $\log 3 - 2 \log 2$ (b) No real x exists

20. (a) True (b) False (c) True (d) False if $x < 0$

25. (d) $\displaystyle\int_0^x e^{-t}t^n \, dt = n!e^{-x}\left(e^x - \sum_{k=0}^{n} \dfrac{x^k}{k!}\right)$

27. (a) $f(t) = 2\sqrt{t} - 1$ if $t > 0$
(b) $f(t) = t - \frac{1}{2}t^2 + \frac{1}{2}$ if $0 \leq t \leq 1$
(c) $f(t) = t - \frac{1}{3}t^3 + \frac{1}{3}$ if $|t| \leq 1$
(d) $f(t) = t$ if $t \leq 0$; $f(t) = e^t - 1$ if $t > 0$

28. (b) $C_n = -2\displaystyle\sum_{k=1}^{n} \dfrac{(k - 1)!}{\log^k 2}$ (c) $b = \log 2$ (d) $e^2 \operatorname{Li}(e^{2x-2})$

29. $g(y) = -e^y$; all y

30. (b) constant $= \frac{3}{2}$

Chapter 7

7.8 **Exercises (page 284)**

8. (b) $\dfrac{55\sqrt{2}}{672} + R$, where $|R| \leq \dfrac{\sqrt{2}}{7680} < 2 \cdot 10^{-4}$

9. $0.9461 + R$, where $|R| < 2 \cdot 10^{-4}$

7.11   Exercises (page 290)

1. $1 + x \log 2 + \frac{1}{2}x^2 \log^2 2$
2. $\cos 1 + (\cos 1 - \sin 1)(x - 1) - \frac{1}{2}(2 \sin 1 + \cos 1)(x - 1)^2 + \frac{1}{6}(\sin 1 - 3 \cos 1)(x - 1)^3$
3. $x - x^2 - \dfrac{x^3}{6} + \dfrac{x^4}{2} - \dfrac{59x^5}{120} + \dfrac{x^6}{8}$
4. $a = 0, \quad b = 1, \quad c = -\frac{1}{2}$

5. $-\frac{2}{3}$ 10. 1 15. $\frac{1}{6}$ 20. -2 25. $-e/2$
6. a/b 11. 1 16. -1 21. $\frac{1}{6} \log a$ 26. $e^{-1/2}$
7. $\frac{2}{3}$ 12. $\log a/\log b$ 17. -1 22. $\frac{1}{6}$ 27. $e^{1/6}$
8. $-\frac{1}{6}$ 13. $\frac{1}{3}$ 18. $\frac{1}{6}$ 23. $1/e$ 28. $\frac{1}{2}$
9. $\frac{1}{2}$ 14. $\frac{1}{2}$ 19. 1 24. e^3 29. $\frac{1}{2}$
30. $a = 2; \quad \text{limit} = \frac{3}{2}$
33. $f(0) = 0; \quad f'(0) = 0; \quad f''(0) = 4; \quad \text{limit} = e^2$

7.13   Exercises (page 295)

1. $\frac{14}{3}$ 5. $(a/b)^2$ 9. 1
2. -2 6. $\frac{1}{6}$ 10. $-\frac{1}{3}$
3. $\frac{1}{3}$ 7. $1/\sqrt{2a}$ 11. $n(n + 1)/2$
4. $-\frac{1}{6}$ 8. -2 12. $\frac{1}{3}(a^2 - b^2)/(a^2 b^2)$
13. 6 as $x \to 0$; $4/\pi$ as $x \to \pi/2$
14. $a = -3; \quad b = \frac{9}{2}$
15. $a = 4; \quad b = 1$
16. (a) $T(x) = \tan \frac{1}{2}x - \frac{1}{2}\sin x$ (b) $S(x) = \frac{1}{2}x - \frac{1}{2}\sin x$ (c) $\frac{3}{2}$
17. tE/L
18. $-\dfrac{At \cos kt}{2k}$

7.17   Exercises (page 303)

1. 0 8. $e/2$ 15. 0 22. 1
2. 1 9. $+\infty$ 16. 1 23. e^e
3. $\frac{1}{3}$ 10. 1 17. -1 24. $e^{2/\pi}$
4. $1/\sqrt{b}$ 11. 0 18. 1 25. $-\frac{1}{2}$
5. $\frac{1}{24}$ 12. 0 19. e 26. $\log 2$
6. 1 13. $\frac{1}{2}$ 20. 1 27. $\frac{1}{2}$
7. 0 14. 0 21. $1/e$ 28. $c = \frac{1}{5}; \quad \text{limit} = \frac{7}{5}$
29. $\frac{1}{2}$
30. $c = 1; \quad \text{limit} = \frac{1}{2}\sqrt{3}$
32. (b) 11.55 years   (c) 11.67 years

Chapter 8

8.5   Exercises (page 311)

1. $y = e^{3x} - e^{2x}$
2. $y = \frac{2}{3}x^2 + \frac{1}{3}x^5$
3. $y = 4 \cos x - 2 \cos^2 x$
4. $y = x^2 - 2 + 2e^{-x^2/2}$
5. $x = \frac{1}{3}e^{2t} + \frac{2}{3}e^{-t}$
6. $y = (x + C)/\sin x$
7. $y = \dfrac{1}{2}\left(1 + \dfrac{1}{x}\right)(C - e^{-x^2})$
8. $y = \sin x + C/\sin x$
9. $y = \left(\dfrac{x - 2}{x - 3}\right)^2\left(x + \dfrac{1}{x - 2} + C\right)$
10. $y = xT(x) + Cx$
11. $f(x) = 1 + \log x$
12. Only the function given

14. $y = (\sqrt{2}e^{2x} + e^{2x} - e^x)^2$
15. $y = 1/(x^2 - x + 2 - e^{-x})$
16. $y = (x^3 - x)^2$
17. $y = 1/(x^2 + x - x^2 \log x)$

18. (a) $y = \left(\dfrac{e^x + e^{2-x}}{2x}\right)^{1/2}$ (b) $y = -\left(\dfrac{e^x + e^{2-x}}{2x}\right)^{1/2}$ (c) $y^2 = \dfrac{\sinh x}{x}$

20. (a) $y = \dfrac{Ce^{3x} + 2}{Ce^{3x} - 1}$ with $C = \dfrac{b + 2}{b - 1}$ (b) $y = \dfrac{e^{3x} + 2C}{e^{3x} - C}$ with $C = \dfrac{b - 1}{b + 2}$

8.7   Exercises (page 319)

1. $100(1 - 2^{-1/16}) = 4.2$ percent
2.   Four times the initial amount
3.   (a) $T = (\log n)/k$ (b) $w(t) = (b - t)/(b - a)$
4. $256(1 - e^{-t/8})$ if $0 \le t \le 10$; $16 + 166e^{20-2t}$ if $t \ge 10$
6. $v \to \sqrt{mg/k}$

7.   (c) 54.5 min   (d) $T = \dfrac{1}{10k} [1 + (600 - t)k + (1400k - 1)e^{-kt}]$

8. $55°$
9.   19.5 lb
10. 54.7 lb
13. For Equation (8.20), $x = x_0 e^{k(t-t_0)}$;   for Equation (8.22), $\alpha = Mk$

15. $x = M\left[1 + \exp\left(-M\int_{t_0}^{t} k(u)\, du\right)\right]^{-1}$

16. (a) 200 million   (b) 217 million
17. (a) 0.026 per year   (b) 0.011 per year;   260 million;   450 million
18. $dx/dt = kx(1 - at)$; $x = x_0 e^{k(t-at^2/2)}$;   curve (d)

8.14   Exercises (page 328)

1. $y = c_1 e^{2x} + c_2 e^{-2x}$
2. $y = c_1 \cos 2x + c_2 \sin 2x$
3. $y = c_1 + c_2 e^{4x}$
4. $y = c_1 + c_2 e^{-4x}$
5. $y = e^x(c_1 \cos \sqrt{2}x + c_2 \sin \sqrt{2}x)$
6. $y = c_1 e^x + c_2 e^{-3x}$
7. $y = e^x(c_1 \cos x + c_2 \sin x)$
8. $y = e^x(c_1 \cos 2x + c_2 \sin 2x)$
9. $y = e^{-x}(c_1 + c_2 x)$
10. $y = e^x(c_1 + c_2 x)$
11. $y = \frac{5}{3} - \frac{2}{3}e^{-3x/2}$
12. $y = -\cos(5x - 15)$

13. $y = \dfrac{a}{2} e^{b(x-1)} + \dfrac{b}{2} e^{a(x-1)}$,   where $a = 2 - \sqrt{5}, b = 2 + \sqrt{5}$

14. $y = 2e^{-2x}(\cos x + \sin x)$
15. $u(x) = \frac{1}{2}e^{2x-\pi} \sin 5x$; $v(x) = \frac{5}{6}e^{-2x-\pi} \sin 3x$
16. $u(x) = 6(e^{4x} - e^{-x})/5$; $v(x) = e^x - e^{-5x}$
17. $k = n^2\pi^2$; $f_k(x) = C \sin n\pi x$ $(n = 1, 2, 3, \ldots)$
19. (b) No   (c) If $k \ne 0$ the condition is $a_1 - a_2 \ne n\pi/k$
20. (a) $y'' - y = 0$
     (b) $y'' - 4y' + 4y = 0$
     (c) $y'' + y' + \frac{5}{4}y = 0$
     (d) $y'' + 4y = 0$
     (e) $y'' - y = 0$

8.17   Exercises (page 333)

1. $y = c_1 e^x + c_2 e^{-x} - x$
2. $y = c_1 e^x + c_2 - 2x - x^2 - \frac{1}{3}x^3$
3. $y = c_1 e^{-x} + c_2 + \frac{1}{3}x^3$
4. $y = e^x(c_1 \cos \sqrt{2}x + c_2 \sin \sqrt{2}x) - \frac{8}{27} + \frac{2}{9}x + \frac{2}{3}x^2 + \frac{1}{3}x^3$
5. $y = c_1 e^x + c_2 e^{4x} + \frac{9}{32} + \frac{1}{8}x + \frac{1}{4}x^2$
6. $y = c_1 e^{2x} + c_2 e^{-3x} - \frac{7}{12} + \frac{1}{2}x - x^2 - \frac{1}{3}x^3$
7. $y = (c_1 + \frac{1}{4}x)e^{2x} + c_2 e^{-2x}$
8. $y = c_1 \cos 2x + c_2 \sin 2x + \frac{1}{8}e^{-2x}$
9. $y = c_1 e^{-2x} + (c_2 + \frac{1}{3}x)e^x$
10. $y = c_1 e^{-2x} + c_2 e^x + \frac{1}{4}e^{2x}$
11. $y = c_1 e^{-2x} + (c_2 + \frac{1}{3}x)e^x + \frac{1}{4}e^{2x}$
12. $y = (c_1 + c_2 x + \frac{1}{3}x^3)e^x + x + 2$
13. $y = (c_1 + c_2 x - \log|x|)e^{-x}$
14. $y = c_1 \sin x + (c_1 + \log|\csc x + \cot x|)\cos x - 2$
15. $y = c_1 e^x + c_2 e^{-x} + (e^x - e^{-x})\log(1 + e^x) - xe^x - 1$
16. $y = (c_1 + \frac{1}{3}x)e^x + \frac{1}{3}e^{-x} + c_2 e^{-2x} - \frac{1}{6} - \frac{1}{3}(e^x + e^{-2x})\log(1 + e^x)$
17. $y = \begin{cases} (c_1 + c_2 x)e^{-3x} & \text{if } x < 1 \text{ or } x > 2, \\ (a + bx)e^{-3x} + \frac{1}{9} & \text{if } 1 \le x \le 2 \end{cases}$
18. $y = c_1 e^{3x} + c_2 e^{-3x} + \frac{1}{6}xe^{3x}$
19. $y = (c_1 - \frac{1}{6}x)\cos 3x + (c_2 - \frac{1}{18})\sin 3x$
20. $y = (c_1 - \frac{1}{2}x)\cos x + c_2 \sin x$
21. $y = c_1 \cos x + (c_2 + \frac{1}{2}x)\sin x$
22. $y = c_1 \cos 2x + c_2 \sin 2x + x \cos x + \frac{2}{3}\sin x$
23. $y = c_1 \cos 2x + c_2 \sin 2x + x \sin x - \frac{2}{3}\cos x$
24. $y = c_1 + c_2 e^{3x} - \frac{1}{5}e^{2x}(3 \sin x + \cos x)$
25. $y = c_1 \sin x + c_2 \cos x + \frac{1}{40}e^{2x}(3 \sin 3x - \cos 3x)$

8.19   Exercises (page 339)

1. $2\sqrt{2}$
2. $\pm 140\pi$
3. $A = C$, $m = k$, $\beta = \alpha - \frac{1}{2}\pi$
4. $y = 3 \cos 4\pi x$
5. $C = (y_0^2 + v_0^2)^{1/2}$
6. $y = \frac{1}{3}\sqrt{6}$, $y'' = -12y = -4\sqrt{6}$
7. $y = -A \sin \dfrac{\pi x}{3}$,   where A is positive
8. $I(t) = \begin{cases} \sin t + 1 - \cos t & \text{if } 0 \le t \le 2\pi, \\ \sin t & \text{if } t \ge 2\pi \end{cases}$
9. (a) $1/(2\pi\sqrt{2})$ (b) $R < \sqrt{2}$
10. $r(t) = \frac{1}{2}gt^2 - ct + c\left(t - \dfrac{w}{k}\right)\log\left(1 - \dfrac{kt}{w}\right)$
11. $r(t) = ct + c\left(\dfrac{w}{k} - t\right)\log\left(1 - \dfrac{kt}{w}\right)$
12. $r(t) = \dfrac{wv_0}{k}\log\dfrac{w}{w - kt}$

8.22   Exercises (page 344)

1. $y' + \frac{2}{3} = 0$
2. $y' + 2y = 0$
3. $yy' - x = 0$
4. $xy' + y = 0$
5. $2xy' - y = 0$
6. $(x^2 - y^2 - 1)y' - 2xy = 0$
7. $(x - 1)y' - xy = 0$
8. $(x^2 - 4)y' - y = 0$
9. $y' + y \tan x = 0$
10. $\sqrt{1 - x^2}\, y' + y^2 + 1 = 0$
11. $(x^2 - y^2 - 1)y' - 2xy = 0$
12. $(x^2 + 2xy - y^2 - 2)y' - y^2 - 2xy + x^2 + 2 = 0$
14. $x + y = -1$ is both an integral curve and an isocline
15. $y = Cx + C^2$;   envelope: $y = -\frac{1}{4}x^2$

8.24   Exercises (page 347)

1. $y^3 = \frac{3}{4}x^4 + C$
2. $\cos x = Ce^{1/\cos y}$
3. $y(C + \log|x + 1|) = 1$
4. $y - 2 = C(y - 1)e^x$
5. $y^2 + 2\sqrt{1 - x^2} = C$
6. $y = C(x - 1)e^x$
7. $\arctan y + \arcsin x = C$
8. $(1 + y^2)(1 + x^2) = Cx^2$
9. $y^4(x + 2) = C(x - 2)$
10. $1 + y^2 = Cx^2 e^{x^2}$
11. $(y + \frac{1}{2})e^{-2y} = e^x(\cos x - \sin x) + C$
12. $x^2 - 1 = C(y^2 + 1)$
13. $f(x) = 2e^{x-1}$
14. $f(x) = \sqrt{5x^2 + 1}$
15. $f(x) = -\log(1 + x^2)$
16. $f(x) = \pm 1$; $f(x) = \sin(x + C)$;   also, those continuous functions whose graphs may be obtained by piecing together portions of the curves $y = \sin(x + C)$ with portions of the lines $y = \pm 1$. One such example is $f(x) = -1$ for $x \le 0, f(x) = \sin(x - \frac{1}{2}\pi)$ for $0 \le x \le 3\pi$, $f(x) = 1$ for $x \ge 3\pi$
17. $f(x) = C$
18. $f(x) = Ae^{x/C}$
19. $f(x) = 0$
20. $f(x) = 0$

8.26   Exercises (page 350)

2. $x^2 + y^2 = C$
3. $y = x \log|Cx|$
4. $x^2 + y^2 = Cx^4$
5. $y^2 = C(x^2 + y^2)^3$
6. $x^2 + 2Cy = C^2$, $C > 0$
7. $y(Cx^2 - 1) = x$
8. $\arctan \frac{x}{y} + \log|y| = C$
9. $\frac{y}{x} - \frac{x}{y} + \log\frac{y^3}{x} = C$
10. $\tan\frac{y}{2x} = Ce^x$
11. $(x + y)^3 = Cx^4 y^4$

8.28   Miscellaneous review exercises (page 355)

1. $3x - 2y = C$
2. $x^2 - y^2 = C$
3. $x^2 + y^2 - Cx + 1 = 0$
4. $2x^2 + y^2 = C$
5. $2y^2 - x^2 = C$
6. $y^2 = x + C$
7. $xy = C$
8. $y^2 - \log(\sin^2 x) = C$
9. $(x - C)^2 + y^2 = C^2 - 1$
10. $x^2 + y^2 - C(x + y) + 2 = 0$
11. $y = -2x \log x$

12. $y = -\dfrac{1}{k} x \log x$

13. $f(x) = Cx^n, \ \ \text{or} \ f(x) = Cx^{1/n}$

14. $f(x) = Cx^{n/2}, \ \ \text{or} \ f(x) = Cx^{1/(2n)}$

15. $y = \dfrac{6}{\pi} \dfrac{x}{x^3 + 2}$

16. $y = \tfrac{3}{2}(1 - e^{x-1}); \ \ b = \dfrac{3}{2e} - 3$

17. $y = -6x^2 + 5x + 1$

18. 59.6 sec

20. $\dfrac{2\pi R^2 \sqrt{h}}{9A_0}$ sec, where R is the radius of the base and h is the height of the cone (in feet)

21. $y = e^x$

22. $y^3 = -\tfrac{1}{3}x + Cx^{-1/2} \ \ \text{for} \ x > 0, \ \text{or} \ y^3 = -\tfrac{1}{3}x \ \text{for all} \ x$

23. $m = -1; \ \ y^2 \log |y| = \tfrac{1}{2}e^{-2x} + Cy^2$

24. (a) $a = 0, b = \tfrac{1}{4}$ (b) $f(x) = 2x^{1/2}$

25. (b) $y = e^{4x} - e^{-x^3/3}$

26. (a) $1/(t + 1)$ grams in t years   (b) 1 gm^{-1}yr^{-1}

27. $[1 - \tfrac{1}{2}(2 - \sqrt{2})t]^2$ grams in t years; $\ 2 + \sqrt{2}$ years

28. (a) $365e^{-2.65t}$ citizens in t years   (b) $365(1 - e^{-2.65t})$ fatalities in t years

29. 6.96 mi/sec = 25,056 mi/hr

30. (a) Relative minimum at 0   (b) $a = \tfrac{2}{3}, b = \tfrac{20}{9}$ (d) $\tfrac{2}{3}$

31. (b) Minimum   (c) $\tfrac{1}{2}$

Chapter 9

9.6   Exercises (page 365)

1. (a) $2i$ (b) $-i$ (c) $\tfrac{1}{2} - \tfrac{1}{2}i$ (d) $18 + i$ (e) $-\tfrac{1}{5} + \tfrac{3}{5}i$ (f) $1 + i$
    (g) 0 (h) $1 + i$

2. (a) $\sqrt{2}$ (b) 5   (c) 1   (d) 1   (e) $\sqrt{2}$ (f) $\sqrt{65}$

3. (a) $r = 2, \theta = \tfrac{1}{2}\pi$ (b) $r = 3, \theta = -\tfrac{1}{2}\pi$ (c) $r = 1, \theta = \pi$ (d) $r = 1, \theta = 0$
    (e) $r = 2\sqrt{3}, \theta = 5\pi/6$ (f) $r = 1, \theta = \tfrac{1}{4}\pi$ (g) $r = 2\sqrt{2}, \theta = \tfrac{1}{4}\pi$
    (h) $r = 2\sqrt{2}, \theta = -\tfrac{1}{4}\pi$ (i) $r = \tfrac{1}{2}\sqrt{2}, \theta = -\tfrac{1}{4}\pi$ (j) $r = \tfrac{1}{2}, \theta = -\tfrac{1}{2}\pi$

4. (a) $y = 0, x$ arbitrary   (b) $x > 0, y = 0$ (c) All x and y (d) $x = 0,$
    y arbitrary; or $y = 0, x$ arbitrary   (e) $x = 1, y = 0$ (f) $x = 1, y = 0$

9.10   Exercises (page 371)

1. (a) i (b) $-2i$ (c) -3 (d) 1   (e) $1 + i$ (f) $(1 + i)/\sqrt{2}$
    (g) $\sqrt{2}\,i$ (h) $-i$

2. (a) $y = 0, x$ arbitrary   (b) $x = y = 0$ (c) $x = 0, y = (2n + 1)\pi$, where n is any
    integer   (d) $x = 1, y = \tfrac{1}{2}\pi + 2n\pi,$ and $x = -1, y = \tfrac{3}{2}\pi + 2n\pi$, where n is any integer.

3. (b) $z = 2n\pi i$, where n is any integer

6. $c_{-k} = \tfrac{1}{2}(a_{-k} + ib_{-k})$ for $k = 1, 2, \ldots, n$

10. (c) $\tfrac{1}{2}\sqrt{3} + \tfrac{1}{2}i, \ \ -\tfrac{1}{2}\sqrt{3} + \tfrac{1}{2}i, \ \ -i$
    (d) $a + bi, \ \ -a - bi, \ \ -b + ai, \ \ b - ai,$ where $a = \tfrac{1}{2}\sqrt{2 + \sqrt{2}}$ and $b = \tfrac{1}{2}\sqrt{2 - \sqrt{2}}$
    (e) $a - bi, \ \ -a + bi, \ \ b + ai, \ \ -b - ai,$ where a and b are as in (d)

11. (a) $1, e^{-\pi/2}, e^{-\pi}$ (c) $-\pi < \arg(z_1) + \arg(z_2) \le \pi$

13. $B = A/(b - \omega^2 + a\omega i)$

Chapter 10

10.4 Exercises (page 382)

1.	(a)	Converges	(b)	0	12.	(a)	Converges	(b) $\frac{1}{3}$
2.	(a)	Converges	(b)	-1	13.	(a)	Converges	(b) 0
3.	(a)	Diverges			14.	(a)	Converges	(b) 0
4.	(a)	Converges	(b)	$\frac{1}{5}$	15.	(a)	Converges	(b) 0
5.	(a)	Converges	(b)	0	16.	(a)	Converges	(b) 0
6.	(a)	Diverges			17.	(a)	Converges	(b) e^2
7.	(a)	Converges	(b)	0	18.	(a)	Diverges	
8.	(a)	Diverges			19.	(a)	Converges	(b) 0
9.	(a)	Converges	(b)	1	20.	(a)	Diverges	
10.	(a)	Diverges			21.	(a)	Converges	(b) 0
11.	(a)	Converges	(b)	0	22.	(a)	Diverges	

23. $N > 1/\epsilon$
24. $N > 1/\epsilon$
25. $N > 1/\epsilon$
26. $N > 1/\epsilon$
27. $N > \sqrt{2/\epsilon}$

28. $N > \dfrac{\log \epsilon}{\log (9/10)}$

34. (c) Let $s_n = \dfrac{b-a}{n} \displaystyle\sum_{k=0}^{n-1} f\left(a + k \dfrac{b-a}{n}\right)$, and define t_n similarly as a sum from 1 to n. Both

sequences $\{s_n\}$ and $\{t_n\}$ converge to the integral $\int_a^b f(x)\, dx$.

10.9 Exercises (page 391)

22. (a) 1   (b) $2e - 3$ (c) $e + 1$
23. (b) 5
24. (a) Identical   (b) Not identical   (c) Not identical   (d) Identical

★10.10 Exercises on decimal expansions (page 393)

1. $\frac{4}{9}$
2. $\frac{51}{99}$
3. $\frac{200}{99}$
4. $\frac{41}{333}$
5. $\frac{1}{7}$

10.14 Exercises (page 398)

1.	Divergent	8.	Convergent
2.	Convergent	9.	Divergent
3.	Convergent	10.	Convergent
4.	Convergent	11.	Divergent
5.	Convergent	12.	Convergent
6.	Convergent	13.	Divergent
7.	Convergent	14.	Convergent

15. Convergent for $s > 1$; divergent for $s \le 1$
16. Convergent
17. Convergent
18. Convergent

10.16   Exercises (page 402)

1. Convergent	7. Divergent
2. Convergent	8. Convergent
3. Convergent	9. Convergent
4. Divergent	10. Divergent
5. Divergent	11. Convergent
6. Divergent	12. Divergent

13. Convergent
14. Convergent if $0 < r < 1$, or when $x = k\pi$, k any integer

10.20   Exercises (page 409)

1. Conditionally convergent
2. Conditionally convergent
3. Divergent for $s \leq 0$; conditionally convergent for $0 < s \leq 1$; absolutely convergent for $s > 1$

4. Absolutely convergent	15. Divergent
5. Absolutely convergent	16. Absolutely convergent
6. Absolutely convergent	17. Absolutely convergent
7. Divergent	18. Absolutely convergent
8. Divergent	19. Conditionally convergent
9. Divergent	20. Conditionally convergent
10. Conditionally convergent	21. Divergent
11. Absolutely convergent	22. Conditionally convergent
12. Divergent	23. Divergent
13. Absolutely convergent	24. Conditionally convergent
14. Absolutely convergent	

25. Divergent for $s \leq 0$; conditionally convergent for $0 < s \leq 1$; absolutely convergent for $s > 1$

26. Absolutely convergent	38. All $z \neq 1$ satisfying $|z| \leq 1$
27. Absolutely convergent	39. $|z| < e^{-1/85}$
28. Divergent	40. All z
29. Absolutely convergent	41. All $z \neq 0$ satisfying $0 \leq |z - 1| \leq 1$
30. Absolutely convergent	42. All $z \neq -1$ satisfying $|2z + 3| \leq 1$
31. Absolutely convergent	43. All $z = x + iy$ with $x \geq 0$
32. Absolutely convergent	44. All z satisfying $|2 + 1/z| > 1$
33. $z = 0$	45. All z satisfying $|2 + 1/z| > 1$
34. All z	46. All $z \neq 0$
35. All z satisfying $|z| < 3$	47. $|x - k| \leq \pi/4$, k any integer
36. All z	48. $|x - k| \leq \pi/6$, k any integer
37. All z except negative integers	

10.22   Miscellaneous review exercises (page 414)

1. (a) 0
   (b) Converges if $c \leq 1$; limit is 0 if $c < 1$; limit is 1 if $c = 1$; diverges if $c > 1$
2. (a) 1   (b) The larger of a and b
3. $\frac{1}{3}a_1 + \frac{2}{3}a_2$
4. $\frac{1}{2}(1 + \sqrt{5})$
5. 0
7. Divergent
8. Convergent if $s < \frac{1}{2}$; divergent if $s \geq \frac{1}{2}$
9. Convergent

10. Divergent
11. Divergent
14. $c \leq 3$
15. $a \geq 3$

17. When $a \geq -1$, limit is $\dfrac{a+1}{a+2}$; when $a \leq -1$, limit is 0

10.24 Exercises (page 420)

1. Divergent
2. Convergent
3. Convergent
4. Convergent
5. Convergent

6. Convergent
7. Convergent
8. Convergent
9. Divergent
10. Convergent if $s > 1$; divergent if $s \leq 1$

11. $C = \frac{1}{2}$; integral has value $\frac{1}{4} \log \frac{5}{4}$
12. $C = \frac{1}{2}$; integral has value $\frac{1}{4} \log \frac{8}{3}$

13. $C = \frac{1}{2}\sqrt{2}$; integral has value $\dfrac{3}{\sqrt{2}} \log \sqrt{2}$

14. $a = b = 2e - 2$

15. $a = 1$; $b = 1 - \dfrac{\sqrt{3}}{\pi}$

16. (b) Both diverge
17. (c) Diverges

Chapter 11

11.7 Exercises (page 430)

1. $r = 2$; convergent for $|z| < 2$
2. $r = 2$; convergent for $|z| \leq 2, z \neq 2$
3. $r = 2$; convergent for $|z + 3| \leq 2, z \neq -1$
4. $r = \frac{1}{2}$; convergent for $|z| \leq \frac{1}{2}$
5. $r = \frac{1}{2}$; convergent for $|z| < \frac{1}{2}$
6. $r = e$; convergent for $|z| < e$
7. $r = 1$; convergent for $|z + 1| \leq 1$
8. $r = +\infty$
9. $r = 4$; convergent for $|z| < 4$
10. $r = 1$; convergent for $|z| < 1$
11. $r = 1$
12. $r = 1/e$
13. $r = +\infty$ if $a = k\pi$, k an integer; $r = 1$ if $a \neq k\pi$
14. $r = e^{-a}$
15. $r = \max(a, b)$
16. $r = \min(1/a, 1/b)$

11.13 Exercises (page 438)

1. $|x| < 1$; $1/(1 + x^2)$
2. $|x| < 3$; $1/(3 - x)$
3. $|x| < 1$; $x/(1 - x)^2$
4. $|x| < 1$; $-x/(1 + x)^2$

5. $|x| < \frac{1}{2}$; $\dfrac{1}{1 + 2x} + \dfrac{\log(1 + 2x)}{2x}$

6. $-\frac{1}{2} \le x < \frac{1}{2}$; $-\log(1 - 2x)$

7. $-2 \le x < 2$; $\dfrac{2}{x} \arctan \dfrac{x}{2}$

8. All x; e^{-x^3}

9. All x; $x^{-3}(e^x - 1 - x - \frac{1}{2}x^2)$ if $x \ne 0$, 0 if $x = 0$

10. All x; $\dfrac{e^{x-1} - x}{(x - 1)^2}$ if $x \ne 1$; $\frac{1}{2}$ if $x = 1$

22. $-\dfrac{\sqrt{2}\, 2^{97}}{98!}$

23. $a_0 = 4\sqrt{2}$, $a_1 = 0$, $a_2 = 5\sqrt{2}$, $a_3 = 0$, $a_4 = \frac{15}{8}\sqrt{2}$

11.16 Exercises (page 443)

1. $a_{n+2} = \dfrac{(n + 3)(n - 2)}{(n + 2)(n + 1)} a_n$ for $n \ge 0$; $f(x) = 1 - 3x^2$

2. $a_{n+2} = \dfrac{(n + 4)(n - 3)}{(n + 2)(n + 1)} a_n$ for $n \ge 0$; $f(x) = 2x - \dfrac{10}{3} x^3$

3. All x

4. All x

5. All x; $a = 1, b = 0$

6. All x; $f(x) = e^{x^2}$

7. All x; $f(x) = e^x - x - 1$

8. All x; $f(x) = \cos 2x$

9. All x; $f(x) = x + \sinh 3x$

12. $y = 1 + x + x^2 + \frac{4}{3}x^3 + \cdots$

13. $y = x + \frac{1}{4}x^4 + \frac{1}{14}x^7 + \frac{23}{1120}x^{10} + \cdots$

14. $y = \frac{1}{2}x^2 + \frac{1}{12}x^5 + \frac{1}{060}x^8 + \frac{7}{8800}x^{11} + \cdots$

15. $y = \displaystyle\sum_{n=0}^{\infty} \dfrac{\alpha^n x^n}{n!}$

16. $y = c_0\left(1 + \displaystyle\sum_{n=1}^{\infty} \dfrac{x^{3n}}{(2 \cdot 3)(5 \cdot 6) \cdots [(3n - 1) \cdot (3n)]}\right)$

$\qquad\qquad + c_1\left(x + \displaystyle\sum_{n=1}^{\infty} \dfrac{x^{3n+1}}{(3 \cdot 4)(6 \cdot 7) \cdots [(3n) \cdot (3n + 1)]}\right)$

17. $y = c_0\left(1 + \displaystyle\sum_{n=1}^{\infty} \dfrac{(-1)^n x^{2n}}{2 \cdot 4 \cdots (2n)}\right) + c_1 \displaystyle\sum_{n=1}^{\infty} \dfrac{(-1)^{n+1} x^{2n-1}}{1 \cdot 3 \cdots (2n - 1)}$

18. $a_1 = -1$, $a_2 = 0$, $a_3 = \frac{2}{3}$; $f(x) = (x + 1)e^{-2x}$

19. $a_5 = 0$, $a_6 = -\dfrac{7}{8!}$; $f(x) = \dfrac{\sin x}{x} + \dfrac{\cos x - 1}{x^2}$ if $x \ne 0$; $f(0) = \frac{1}{2}$; $f(\pi) = -2/\pi^2$

20. (c) $\sqrt{2} = 1.4142135623$

21. (b) $\sqrt{3} = 1.732050807568877$

Chapter 12

12.4 Exercises (page 450)

1. (a) $(5, 0, 9)$ (b) $(-3, 6, 3)$ (c) $(3, -1, 4)$ (d) $(-7, 24, 21)$ (e) $(0, 0, 0)$
5. $x = \frac{1}{5}(3c_1 - c_2)$, $y = \frac{1}{5}(2c_2 - c_1)$
6. (a) $(x + z, x + y + z, x + y)$ (c) $x = 2$, $y = 1$, $z = -1$
7. (a) $(x + 2z, x + y + z, x + y + z)$ (b) One example: $x = -2$, $y = z = 1$
8. (a) $(x + z, x + y + z, x + y, y)$ (c) $x = -1$, $y = 4$, $z = 2$
12. The diagonals of a parallelogram bisect each other

12.8 Exercises (page 456)

1. (a) -6 (b) 2 (c) 6 (d) 0 (e) 4
2. (a) $(A \cdot B)C = (21, 28, -35)$ (b) $A \cdot (B + C) = 64$ (c) $(A + B) \cdot C = 72$

   (d) $A(B \cdot C) = (30, 60, -105)$ (e) $A/(B \cdot C) = \left(\dfrac{2}{15}, \dfrac{4}{15}, \dfrac{-7}{15}\right)$

5. One example: $(1, -5, -3)$
6. One example: $x = -2$, $y = 1$
7. $C = \frac{4}{9}(-1, -2, 2)$, $D = \frac{1}{9}(22, -1, 10)$

8. $C = \frac{1}{11}(1, 2, 3, 4, 5)$, $D = \left(\dfrac{5}{11}, \dfrac{7}{44}, \dfrac{1}{33}, \dfrac{-5}{88}, \dfrac{-7}{55}\right)$

9. (a) $\sqrt{74}$ (b) $\sqrt{14}$ (c) $\sqrt{53}$ (d) 5
10. (a) $(1, -1)$ or $(-1, 1)$ (b) $(1, 1)$ or $(-1, -1)$ (c) $(3, 2)$ or $(-3, -2)$
    (d) $(b, -a)$ or $(-b, a)$

11. (a) $\dfrac{1}{\sqrt{42}}(4, -1, 5)$ (b) $\dfrac{1}{\sqrt{14}}(-2, -3, 1)$ (c) $\dfrac{1}{\sqrt{2}}(1, 0, 1)$

    (d) $\dfrac{1}{\sqrt{42}}(-5, -4, -1)$ (e) $\dfrac{1}{\sqrt{42}}(-1, -5, 4)$

12. A and B, C and D, C and E, D and E
13. (a) $(2, -1)$ and $(-2, 1)$ (b) $(2, 1)$ and $(-2, -1)$ (c) $(1, 2)$ and $(-1, -2)$
    (d) $(1, 2)$ and $(-1, -2)$
14. One example: $C = (8, 1, 1)$
15. One example: $C = (1, -5, -3)$
16. $P = \frac{11}{25}(3, 4)$, $Q = \frac{2}{25}(-4, 3)$
17. $P = \frac{5}{2}(1, 1, 1, 1)$, $Q = \frac{1}{2}(-3, -1, 1, 3)$

18. $\pm \dfrac{1}{\sqrt{2}}(0, 1, 1)$

20. The sum of the squares of the sides of any parallelogram is equal to the sum of the squares of the diagonals.
22. 4; $12\sqrt{2}$
23. $C = \frac{1}{11}(1, 2, 3, 4, 5)$, $D = \dfrac{1}{11}\left(10, \dfrac{7}{2}, \dfrac{2}{3}, \dfrac{-5}{4}, \dfrac{-14}{5}\right)$

24. $C = tA$, $D = B - tA$, where $t = (A \cdot B)/(A \cdot A)$

12.11 Exercises (page 460)

1. $\frac{11}{9}B$
2. $\frac{5}{2}B$

3. (a) $\dfrac{6}{7},\dfrac{3}{7},\dfrac{-2}{7}$ (b) $\left(\dfrac{6}{7},\dfrac{3}{7},\dfrac{-2}{7}\right)$ and $\left(\dfrac{-6}{7},\dfrac{-3}{7},\dfrac{2}{7}\right)$

5. $0,\ \sqrt{\tfrac{35}{41}},\ \sqrt{\tfrac{6}{41}}$

6. $7\pi/8$

8. $\pi/6$

9. 0

10. (b) Equation holds for all x and y if $\cos\theta = 1$; if $\cos\theta \neq 1$ the only solution is $x = y = 0$

14. All except (b).

17. (c) All except Theorem 12.4(a).

18. (a) All

12.15   Exercises (page 467)

1. (a) $x = y = \tfrac{1}{2}$ (b) $x = -\tfrac{1}{2},\ y = \tfrac{1}{2}$ (c) $x = 4,\ y = -1$
    (d) $x = 1,\ y = 6$

2. $x = \tfrac{1}{4},\ y = \tfrac{7}{8}$

3. $x = 3,\ y = -4$

7. All $t \neq 0$

9. (c) $7i - 4(i + j)$

10. (b) $j = B - A,\ \ k = \tfrac{1}{3}(C - B)$ (c) $\tfrac{1}{3}(15A - 14B + 5C)$

11. $\{A\}, \{B\}, \{C\}, \{D\}, \{A, B\}, \{A, C\}, \{A, D\}, \{B, C\}, \{C, D\}$

12. (a) Independent   (b) One example: $D = A$ (c) One example: $E = (0, 0, 0, 1)$
    (d) For the choice $E = (0, 0, 0, 1)$, we have $X = 2A + B - C + 3E$

13. (c) $t = 0, \sqrt{2}, -\sqrt{2}$

14. (a) $\{(1, 0, 1, 0), (0, 1, 0, 1), (2, 0, -1, 0)\}$ (b) The set given   (c) The set given

17. $\{(0, 1, 1), (1, 1, 1), (0, 1, 0)\},\ \ \{(0, 1, 1), (1, 1, 1), (0, 0, 1)\}$

18. $\{(1, 1, 1, 1), (0, 1, 1, 1), (0, 0, 1, 1), (0, 0, 0, 1)\},$
    $\{(1, 1, 1, 1), (0, 1, 1, 1), (0, 1, 0, 0), (0, 0, 1, 0)\}$

19. $L(U) \subseteq L(T) \subseteq L(S)$

20. One example: $A = \{E_1, \ldots, E_n\},\ \ B = \{E_1 + E_2, E_2 + E_n, \ldots, E_{n-1} + E_n, E_n + E_1\}$

12.17   Exercises (page 470)

1. (a) $-1 - i$ (b) $-1 + i$ (c) $1 - i$ (d) $-1 + i$ (e) $-1 - i$
    (f) $2 - i$ (g) $-i$ (h) $-1 + 2i$ (i) $-3 - 2i$ (j) $2i$

2. One example: $(1 + i, -5 - 3i, 1 - 3i)$

8. $\pi/3$

9. $3A - B + 2C$

Chapter 13

13.5   Exercises (page 477)

1. (b), (d), and (e)

2. (a) and (e)

3. (c), (d), and (e)

4. (b), (e), and (f)

5. (a) No   (b) No   (c) No

6. A, B, C, D, F are collinear

7. Intersect at $(5, 9, 13)$

8. (b) No

9. (a) $9t^2 + 8t + 9$ (b) $\tfrac{1}{3}\sqrt{65}$

13.8 Exercises (page 482)

1. (c) and (e)
2. (a), (b), and (c)
3. (a) $x = 1 + t$, $y = 2 + s + t$, $z = 1 + 4t$
   (b) $x = s + t$, $y = 1 + s$, $z = s + 4t$
4. (a) $(1, 2, 0)$ and $(2, -3, -3)$ (b) $M = \{(1, 2, 0) + s(1, 1, 2) + t(-2, 4, 1)\}$
6. (a), (b), and (c) $x - 2y + z = -3$
7. (a) $(0, -2, -1)$ and $(-1, -2, 2)$
   (b) $M = \{(0, -2, -1) + s(-1, 0, 3) + t(3, 3, 6)\}$
8. Two examples: $(-5, 2, 6)$ and $(-14, 3, 17)$
9. (a) Yes   (b) Two examples: $(1, 0, -1)$ and $(-1, 0, 1)$
10. $(-2, \frac{5}{2}, -\frac{7}{2})$
11. (a), (b) and (c)   No
13. $x - y = -1$

13.11 Exercises (page 487)

1. (a) $(-2, 3, -1)$ (b) $(4, -5, 3)$ (c) $(4, -4, 2)$ (d) $(8, 10, 4)$
   (e) $(8, 3, -7)$ (f) $(10, 11, 5)$ (g) $(-2, -8, -12)$ (h) $(2, -2, 0)$
   (i) $(-2, 0, 4)$
2. (a) $\pm \dfrac{1}{\sqrt{26}}(-4, 3, 1)$ (b) $\pm \dfrac{1}{\sqrt{2054}}(-41, -18, 7)$ (c) $\pm \dfrac{1}{\sqrt{6}}(1, 2, 1)$
3. (a) $\frac{15}{2}$ (b) $\frac{3}{2}\sqrt{35}$ (c) $\frac{1}{2}\sqrt{3}$
4. $8i + j - 2k$
6. (b) $\cos \theta$ is negative   (c) $\sqrt{5}$
9. (a) One solution is $B = -i - 3k$ (b) $i - j - k$ is the only solution
11. (a) Three possibilities; $D = B + C - A = (0, 0, 2)$, $D = A + C - B = (4, -2, 2)$,
    $D = A + B - C = (-2, 2, 0)$ (b) $\frac{1}{2}\sqrt{6}$
12. -4; $8\sqrt{3}$; $-\frac{1}{2}\sqrt{3}$

13.14 Exercises (page 491)

1. (a) 96   (b) 27   (c) -84
2. 0, $\sqrt{2}$, $-\sqrt{2}$
3. 2
6. (a) $(2b - 1)i + bj + ck$, where b and c are arbitrary   (b) $-\frac{1}{5}i + \frac{2}{5}j$
11. $-3i + 2j + 5k$
14. (b) 2
15. (b) $\sqrt{2005/41}$
17. $x = 1$, $y = -1$, $z = 2$
18. $x = 1$, $y = -1$, $z = 2$
19. $x = 1$, $y = 4$, $z = 1$

13.17 Exercises (page 496)

1. (a) $(-7, 2, -2)$ (b) $-7x + 2y - 2z = 0$ (c) $-7x + 2y - 2z = -9$
2. (a) $(\frac{1}{3}, \frac{2}{3}, -\frac{2}{3})$ (b) $-7, -\frac{7}{2}, \frac{7}{2}$ (c) $\frac{7}{3}$ (d) $(-\frac{7}{9}, -\frac{14}{9}, \frac{14}{9})$
3. $3x - y + 2z = -5$; $9/\sqrt{14}$
4. (b) $\frac{19}{18}\sqrt{6}$
5. (a) $(1, 2, -2)$ (b) $x + 2y - 2z = 5$ (c) $\frac{5}{3}$
6. $10x - 3y - 7z + 17 = 0$
7. Two angles: $\pi/3$ and $2\pi/3$

8. $x + 2y + 9z + 55 = 0$
9. $X(t) = (2, 1, -3) + t(4, -3, 1)$
10. (b) $N = (1, 3, -2)$ (c) $t = 1$ (d) $2x + 3y + 2z + 15 = 0$
     (e) $x + 3y - 2z + 19 = 0$
11. $x + \sqrt{2}\,y + z = 2 + \sqrt{2}$
12. 6
13. $\dfrac{1}{\sqrt{122}}\,(7, -8, -3)$
14. $x - y + z = 2$
15. $(\frac{3}{2}, 0, \frac{1}{2})$
17. $X(t) = (1, 2, 3) + t(1, -2, 1)$
19. (b) $P = -\frac{1}{25}(5, -14, 2)$

13.21   Exercises (page 503)

3. $r = ed/(1 - e \sin \theta);$ $r = -ed/(1 + e \sin \theta)$
4. $e = 1,$ $d = 2$
5. $e = \frac{1}{2},$ $d = 6$
6. $e = \frac{1}{3},$ $d = 6$
7. $e = 2,$ $d = 1$
8. $e = 2,$ $d = 2$
9. $e = 1,$ $d = 4$
10. $d = 5,$ $r = 25/(10 + 3 \cos \theta + 4 \sin \theta)$
11. $d = 5,$ $r = 25/(5 + 4 \cos \theta + 3 \sin \theta)$
12. $d = \frac{1}{2}\sqrt{2},$ $r = 1/(\cos \theta + \sin \theta + \frac{1}{2}\sqrt{2}),$ $r = 1/(\cos \theta + \sin \theta - \frac{1}{2}\sqrt{2})$
13. (a) $r = 1.5 \times 10^8/(1 + \cos \theta);$ 7.5×10^7 miles   (b) $r = 5 \times 10^7/(1 - \cos \theta);$
     2.5×10^7 miles

13.24   Exercises (page 508)

1.   Center at $(0, 0)$;   foci at $(\pm 8, 0)$;   vertices at $(\pm 10, 0)$; $e = \frac{4}{5}$
2.   Center at $(0, 0)$;   foci at $(0, \pm 8)$;   vertices at $(0, \pm 10)$; $e = \frac{4}{5}$
3.   Center at $(2, -3)$;   foci at $(2 \pm \sqrt{7}, -3)$;   vertices at $(6, -3), (-2, -3)$; $e = \sqrt{7}/4$
4.   Center at $(0, 0)$;   foci at $(\pm \frac{4}{3}, 0)$;   vertices at $(\pm \frac{5}{3}, 0)$; $e = \frac{4}{5}$
5.   Center at $(0, 0)$;   foci at $(\pm \sqrt{3}/6, 0)$;   vertices at $(\pm \sqrt{3}/3, 0)$; $e = \frac{1}{2}$
6.   Center at $(-1, -2)$;   foci at $(-1, 1), (-1, -5)$;   vertices at $(-1, 3), (-1, -7)$; $e = \frac{3}{5}$
7. $7x^2 + 16y^2 = 7$
8. $\dfrac{(x + 3)^2}{16} + \dfrac{(y - 4)^2}{9} = 1$
9. $\dfrac{(x + 3)^2}{9} + \dfrac{(y - 4)^2}{16} = 1$
10. $\dfrac{(x + 4)^2}{9} + (y - 2)^2 = 1$
11. $\dfrac{(x - 8)^2}{25} + \dfrac{(y + 2)^2}{9} = 1$
12. $\dfrac{(x - 2)^2}{16} + \dfrac{(y - 1)^2}{4} = 1$
13. Center at $(0, 0)$;   foci at $(\pm 2\sqrt{41}, 0)$;   vertices at $(\pm 10, 0)$; $e = \sqrt{41}/5$
14. Center at $(0, 0)$;   foci at $(0, \pm 2\sqrt{41})$;   vertices at $(0, \pm 10)$; $e = \sqrt{41}/5$
15. Center at $(-3, 3)$;   foci at $(-3 \pm \sqrt{5}, 3)$;   vertices at $(-1, 3), (-5, 3)$; $e = \sqrt{5}/2$

16. Center at $(0, 0)$; foci at $(\pm 5, 0)$; vertices at $(\pm 4, 0)$; $e = 5/4$
17. Center at $(0, 0)$; foci at $(0, \pm 3)$; vertices at $(0, \pm 2)$; $e = \frac{3}{2}$
18. Center at $(1, -2)$; foci at $(1 \pm \sqrt{13}, -2)$; vertices at $(3, -2), (-1, -2)$; $e = \frac{1}{2}\sqrt{13}$
19. $\dfrac{x^2}{4} - \dfrac{y^2}{12} = 1$
20. $y^2 - x^2 = 1$
21. $\dfrac{x^2}{4} - \dfrac{y^2}{16} = 1$
22. $(y - 4)^2 - \dfrac{(x + 1)^2}{3} = 1$
23. $\dfrac{8(y + 3)^2}{27} - \dfrac{5(x - 2)^2}{27} = 1$
24. $\pm\sqrt{\frac{23}{3}}$
25. $4x^2 - y^2 = 11$
26. Vertex at $(0, 0)$; directrix $x = 2$; axis $y = 0$
27. Vertex at $(0, 0)$; directrix $x = -\frac{3}{4}$; axis $y = 0$
28. Vertex at $(\frac{1}{2}, 1)$; directrix $x = -\frac{5}{2}$; axis $y = 1$
29. Vertex at $(0, 0)$; directrix $y = -\frac{3}{2}$; axis $x = 0$
30. Vertex at $(0, 0)$; directrix $y = 2$; axis $x = 0$
31. Vertex at $(-2, -\frac{9}{4})$; directrix $y = -\frac{13}{4}$; axis $x = -2$
32. $x^2 = -y$
33. $y^2 = 8x$
34. $(x + 4)^2 = -8(y - 3)$
35. $(y + 1)^2 = 5(x - \frac{7}{4})$
36. $(x - \frac{3}{2})^2 = 2(y + \frac{1}{8})$
37. $(y - 3)^2 = -8(x - 1)$
38. $x^2 - 4xy + 4y^2 + 40x + 20y - 100 = 0$

13.25 Miscellaneous exercises on conic sections (page 509)

3. $B > 0$, $A = \frac{1}{2}(1 + \sqrt{5})B$
4. $\frac{2}{3}bh$
5. 16π
6. (a) $\frac{8}{3}$ (b) 2π (c) $48\pi/5$
7. $x^2/12 + y^2/16 = 1$
8. $x^2 - 2xy + y^2 - 2x - 2y = 1$
9. $y^2 - 4x^2 - 4y + 4x = 0$
10. (a) $e = \sqrt{2/(p + 2)}$; foci at $(\sqrt{2}, 0)$ and $(-\sqrt{2}, 0)$ (b) $6x^2 - 3y^2 = 4$
15. (b) $y = Cx^2$, $C \neq 0$
16. $(4, 8)$
17. (a) $x = \frac{4}{3}a$ (b) $27pq^2 = 4a^3$
18. $(x - \frac{2}{5})^2 + (y - \frac{4}{5})^2 = \frac{4}{5}$

Chapter 14

14.4 Exercises (page 516)

1. $F'(t) = (1, 2t, 3t^2 + 4t^3)$; $F''(t) = (0, 2, 6t, 12t^2)$
2. $F'(t) = (-\sin t, \sin 2t, 2 \cos 2t, \sec^2 t)$; $F''(t) = (-\cos t, 2 \cos 2t, -4 \sin 2t, 2 \sec^2 t \tan t)$
3. $F'(t) = ((1 - t^2)^{-1/2}, -(1 - t^2)^{-1/2})$; $F''(t) = (t(1 + t^2)^{-3/2}, -t(1 + t^2)^{-3/2})$

4. $F'(t) = (2e^t, 3e^t);$ $F''(t) = (2e^t, 3e^t)$
5. $F'(t) = (\sinh t, 2\cosh 2t, -3e^{-3t});$ $F''(t) = (\cosh t, 4\sinh 2t, 9e^{-3t})$
6. $F'(t) = (2t/(1 + t^2), 1/(1 + t^2), -2t/(1 + t^2));$
   $F''(t) = ((2 - 2t^2)/(1 + t^2)^2, -2t/(1 + t^2)^2, (6t^2 - 2)/(1 + t^2)^3)$
8. $(\frac{1}{2}, \frac{2}{3}, e - 1)$
9. $(1 - \frac{1}{2}\sqrt{2}, \frac{1}{2}\sqrt{2}, \log\frac{1}{2}\sqrt{2})$
10. $\left(\log\dfrac{1 + e}{2}, 1 - \log\dfrac{1 + e}{2}\right)$
11. $(1, e - 2, 1 - 2/e)$
12. 0
15. $G'(t) = F(t) \times F''(t)$
20. $F(t) = \frac{1}{6}t^3 A + \frac{1}{2}t^2 B + tC + D$
22. $F''(1) = A,$ $F(3) = (6 + 3\log 3)A$
23. $F(x) = e^x(x + 1)A - eA$

14.7   Exercises (page 524)

1. $v(t) = (3 - 3t^2)i + 6tj + (3 + 3t^2)k;$ $a(t) = -6ti + 6j + 6tk;$ $v(t) = 3\sqrt{2}(1 + t^2)$
2. $v(t) = -\sin t\, i + \cos t\, j + e^t k;$ $a(t) = -\cos t\, i - \sin t\, j + e^t k;$ $v(t) = (1 + e^{2t})^{1/2}$
3. $v(t) = 3(\cos t - t\sin t)i + 3(\sin t + t\cos t)j + 4k;$ $a(t) = -3(2\sin t + t\cos t)i +$
   $3(2\cos t - t\sin t)j;$ $v(t) = (9t^2 + 25)^{1/2}$
4. $v(t) = (1 - \cos t)i + \sin t\, j + 2\cos\dfrac{t}{2}k;$ $a(t) = \sin t\, i + \cos t\, j - \sin\dfrac{t}{2}k;$ $v(t) = 2$
5. $v(t) = 6ti + 6t^2 j + 3k;$ $a(t) = 6i + 12tj;$ $v(t) = 6t^2 + 3$
6. $v(t) = i + \cos t\, j + \sin t\, k;$ $a(t) = -\sin t\, j + \cos t\, k;$ $v(t) = \sqrt{2}$
9. $A = ab\omega^3,$ $B = a^2\omega^3$
11. (b) $8e^{4t}/\cos^2\theta$
15. (a) $x(t) = 4\cos 2t,$ $y(t) = 3\sin 2t$ (b) $x^2/16 + y^2/9 = 1$
16. $3T/4$

14.9   Exercises (page 528)

1. (a) $T = \frac{1}{10}\sqrt{2}(-3i + 4j + 5k);$ $N = -\frac{4}{5}i - \frac{3}{5}j$ (b) $a = 12\sqrt{2}\,T + 6N$
2. (a) $T = -(1 + e^{2\pi})^{-1/2}j + e^\pi(1 + e^{2\pi})^{-1/2}k;$ $N = \dfrac{(1 + e^{2\pi})i + e^{2\pi}j + e^\pi k}{(1 + e^{2\pi})^{1/2}(1 + 2e^{2\pi})^{1/2}}$
   (b) $a = (1 + e^{2\pi})^{-1/2}[e^{2\pi}T + (1 + 2e^{2\pi})^{1/2}N]$
3. (a) $T = \frac{3}{5}i + \frac{4}{5}k;$ $N = j$ (b) $a = 6N$
4. (a) $T = i;$ $N = -\frac{1}{2}\sqrt{2}(j + k);$ (b) $a = \sqrt{2}\,N$
5. (a) $T = \frac{1}{3}(2i + 2j + k);$ $N = \frac{1}{3}(i + 2j - 2k)$ (b) $a = 12T + 6N$
6. (a) $T = \frac{1}{2}\sqrt{2}\,i + \frac{1}{2}j + \frac{1}{2}k;$ $N = -\frac{1}{2}\sqrt{2}\,j + \frac{1}{2}\sqrt{2}\,k$ (b) $a = N$
9. Counter example for (b) and (d):   motion on a helix
11. One example: $r(t) = 2\int e^{2t}\cos t\, dt\, i + 2\int e^{2t}\sin t\, dt\, j + e^{2t}k;$ $v(t)$ makes a constant angle
    with k, but $a(t)$ is never zero nor parallel to $v(t)$
12. (a) Counterclockwise   (b) 3   (c) $2\pi/\sqrt{3}$
13. $x^2/3 + y^2/4 = 1$
14. $y^2 = 4x;$ $y^2 = 8 - 4x$
15. (b) $\|A\|\,\|B\|\sin\theta$

14.13   Exercises (page 535)

1. $8a$
2. $\sqrt{2}(e^2 - 1)$

3. $2\pi^2 a$

4. $4(a^3 - b^3)/(ab)$

5. $2a\left(\cosh \dfrac{T}{2} \sqrt{\cosh T} - 1\right) - \sqrt{2}\, a \log \left(\dfrac{\sqrt{2} \cosh (T/2) + \sqrt{\cosh T}}{1 + \sqrt{2}}\right)$

6. $2\sqrt{2}\,\pi$

7. 50

8. $\sqrt{2} \log (1 + \sqrt{2})$

9. $|\omega| \sqrt{a^2 + b^2}\,(t_1 - t_0)$

10. $\int_c^d \sqrt{1 + [g'(y)]^2}\, dy$

11. $\dfrac{26\sqrt{13} - 16}{27}$

13. (a) $\displaystyle\int_0^1 \sqrt{1 + e^{2x}}\, dx$ (b) $\displaystyle\int_1^e \sqrt{2 + \dfrac{2}{t^2}}\, dt$

14. (c) $c \sinh \dfrac{2}{c}$

16. $f(x) = k \cosh \left(\dfrac{x}{k} + C\right)$,   or $f(x) = k$

19. $v(t) = 1 + 2t$;   3 units of time

14.15   Exercises (page 538)

1. (1) $\frac{1}{75}$ (2) $(1 + 2e^{2\pi})^{1/2}(1 + e^{2\pi})^{-3/2}$ (3) $\frac{6}{25}$ (4) $\frac{1}{4}\sqrt{2}$ (5) $\frac{2}{27}$ (6) $\frac{1}{2}$

3. $\dfrac{1}{\|B\| \sin \theta}$

4. (a) $x = z$

7. $\kappa = \|a\|/\|v\|^2$

9. $a = \frac{1}{4}$, $b = 2$;   intersect at $(0, 0)$

10. Vertex at $-\frac{1}{2} \cos \theta\, A + \frac{1}{4} \cos^2 \theta\, B$

11. (a) $\alpha(t) = \frac{1}{2}\pi - 5t^2$ (b) $v(t) = 5 \sin 5t^2\, i + 5 \cos 5t^2\, j$

12. $\sqrt{2}\, i + \sqrt{2}\, j$

14.19   Exercises (page 543)

1. $v(t) = u_r + t u_\theta$; $a(t) = -t u_r + 2 u_\theta$; $\kappa(t) = (2 + t^2)(1 + t^2)^{-3/2}$

2. (a) $v(t) = u_r + t u_\theta + k$; $a(t) = -t u_r + 2 u_\theta$; $\kappa(t) = (t^4 + 5t^2 + 8)^{1/2}(2 + t^2)^{-3/2}$
   (b) $\arccos \sqrt{2/(2 + t^2)}$

3. (b) $\frac{1}{2}\pi - t$

5. 32

6. (b) $L(c) = \dfrac{\sqrt{1 + c^2}}{c} (e^{2\pi c} - 1)$ if $c \neq 0$; $L(0) = 2\pi$. $a(c) = \dfrac{e^{4\pi c} - 1}{4c}$ if $c \neq 0$;
   $a(0) = \pi$

7. (a) $3\pi/16$ (b) $2 + \frac{1}{3}\sqrt{3} \log (2 + \sqrt{3})$

8. $\frac{1}{2}\pi(\pi^2 + 1)^{1/2} + \frac{1}{2} \log (\pi + \sqrt{\pi^2 + 1})$

9. $\sqrt{2}\, (e^\pi - 1)$

10. 4

11. 8

13. (a) $(\theta^2 + 1)^{3/2}/(\theta^2 + 2)$ (b) $\sqrt{2}\,e^\theta$ (c) $\frac{2}{3}\sqrt{2 + \sqrt{2}}$ (d) $\frac{2}{3}\sqrt{2}$

15. $r = r_0 e^{-\theta \cot \alpha}$; target at origin, missile starts at $r = r_0$, $\theta = 0$; α denotes the angle, $0 < \alpha < \pi$, determined by v and $-r$; for $0 < \alpha < \pi/2$ the path is a spiral for which $r \to 0$ as θ increases indefinitely; for $\alpha = \pi/2$ it is a circle about the origin; for $\pi/2 < \alpha < \pi$ it is a spiral for which r increases indefinitely as θ increases indefinitely.

16. Use as positive x-axis the line from position sighted four miles away to ground crew. Proceed three miles along this line (to allow for the possibility that the missile is returning to base) and then follow the spiral $r = e^{\theta/\sqrt{8}}$

17. $\log \sqrt{x^2 + y^2} + \arctan(y/x) = C$

14.21 Miscellaneous review exercises (page 549)

1. $\tan \alpha = \tan \theta/(2 + \tan^2 \theta)$

3. $(c/m^2, 2c/m)$

4. (a) $y - y_0 = m(x - x_0) + c/m$;   tangent at $(x_0 + c/m^2, y_0 + 2c/m)$
     (b) $y - y_0 = m(x - x_0) - cm^2$;   tangent at $(x_0 + 2cm, y_0 + cm^2)$

6. $(y_1 - y_0)(y - y_0) = 2c(x + x_1 - 2x_0)$; $x_1 y = 2y_1 x - x_1 y_1$;
     $(x_1 - x_0)(y - y_0) = 2(y_1 - y_0)(x - x_0) - (x_1 - x_0)(y_1 - y_0)$

7. (a) $(0, \frac{1}{2})$

     (b) Write $Q = (0, b(x))$. If $f''(0) \neq 0$ then $b(x) \to f(0) + \dfrac{1}{f''(0)}$ as $x \to 0$.

     Otherwise, $|b(x)| \to +\infty$ as $x \to 0$.

8. $r = \dfrac{1 + c}{2} \to \dfrac{1}{2}$ as $c \to 0$

13. $(2, 1), (-2, -1)$

14. $\frac{1}{2}\sqrt{2}$

15. $3x^2 - y^2 = 3a^2$; $\dfrac{A(r)}{r^3} \to \dfrac{1}{36a}$

21. (a) $f(\theta) = k \sin(\theta + C)$,   or $f(\theta) = k$
     (b) $f(\theta) = Ce^{\theta/\sqrt{k^2 - 1}}$,   where $k^2 > 1$
     (c) $f(\theta) = (2/k) \sec(\theta + C)$,   or $f(\theta) = 2/k$

Chapter 15

15.5 Exercises (page 555)

1. Yes	8. Yes	15. Yes	22. Yes
2. Yes	9. Yes	16. Yes	23. No
3. Yes	10. Yes	17. Yes	24. Yes
4. Yes	11. No	18. Yes	25. No
5. No	12. Yes	19. Yes	26. Yes
6. Yes	13. Yes	20. Yes	27. Yes
7. Yes	14. No	21. Yes	28. Yes

31. (a) No   (b) No   (c) No   (d) No

15.9 Exercises (page 560)

1. Yes; 2	5. Yes; 1	9. Yes; 1	13. Yes; n
2. Yes; 2	6. No	10. Yes; 1	14. Yes; n
3. Yes; 2	7. No	11. Yes; n	15. Yes; n
4. Yes; 2	8. No	12. Yes; n	16. Yes; n

17. Yes;   dim $= 1 + \frac{1}{2}n$ if n is even, $\frac{1}{2}(n + 1)$ if n is odd
18. Yes;   dim $= \frac{1}{2}n$ if n is even, $\frac{1}{2}(n + 1)$ if n is odd
19. Yes; $k + 1$
20. No
21. (a) dim $= 3$ (b) dim $= 3$ (c) dim $= 2$ (d) dim $= 2$
23. (a) If $a \neq 0$ and $b \neq 0$, set is independent, dim $= 3$; if one of a or b is zero, set is dependent, dim $= 2$ (b) Independent, dim $= 2$ (c) If $a \neq 0$, independent, dim $= 3$; if $a = 0$, dependent, dim $= 2$ (d) Independent; dim $= 3$ (e) Dependent; dim $= 2$ (f) Independent;   dim $= 2$ (g) Independent;   dim $= 2$ (h) Dependent;   dim $= 2$ (i) Independent; dim $= 2$ (j) Independent; dim $= 2$

15.12   Exercises (page 566)

1.   (a)   No   (b)   No   (c)   No   (d)   No   (e)   Yes

8.   (a) $\frac{1}{2}\sqrt{e^2 + 1}$ (b) $g(x) = b\left(x - \dfrac{e^2 + 1}{4}\right)$, b arbitrary

10.   (b) $\dfrac{(n + 1)(2n + 1)}{6n} a + \dfrac{n + 1}{2} b$ (c) $g(t) = a\left(t - \dfrac{2n + 1}{3n}\right)$, a arbitrary

11.   (c)   43   (d) $g(t) = a(1 - \frac{2}{3}t)$, a arbitrary
12.   (a)   No   (b)   No   (c)   No   (d)   No
13.   (c)   1   (d) $e^2 - 1$
14.   (c) $n!/2^{n+1}$

15.16   Exercises (page 576)

1.   (a) and (b) $\frac{1}{3}\sqrt{3}\,(1, 1, 1)$, $\frac{1}{6}\sqrt{6}\,(1, -2, 1)$
2.   (a) $\frac{1}{2}\sqrt{2}\,(1, 1, 0, 0)$, $\frac{1}{6}\sqrt{6}\,(-1, 1, 2, 0)$, $\frac{1}{6}\sqrt{3}\,(1, -1, 1, 3)$

     (b) $\frac{1}{3}\sqrt{3}\,(1, 1, 0, 1)$, $\dfrac{1}{\sqrt{42}}\,(1, -2, 6, 1)$

6. $\frac{2}{3} - \frac{1}{2}\log^2 3$
7. $e^2 - 1$
8. $\frac{1}{2}(e - e^{-1}) + \dfrac{3}{e}\,x;$ $1 - 7e^{-2}$
9. $\pi - 2 \sin x$
10. $\frac{3}{4} - \frac{1}{4}x$

Chapter 16

16.4   Exercises (page 582)

1.   Linear;   nullity 0, rank 2
2.   Linear;   nullity 0, rank 2
3.   Linear;   nullity 1, rank 1
4.   Linear;   nullity 1, rank 1
5.   Nonlinear
6.   Nonlinear
7.   Nonlinear
8.   Nonlinear
9.   Linear;   nullity 0, rank 2
10.   Linear;   nullity 0, rank 2
11.   Linear;   nullity 0, rank 2
12.   Linear;   nullity 0, rank 2

13.   Nonlinear
14.   Linear;   nullity 0, rank 2
15.   Nonlinear
16.   Linear;   nullity 0, rank 3
17.   Linear;   nullity 1, rank 2
18.   Linear;   nullity 0, rank 3
19.   Nonlinear
20.   Nonlinear
21.   Nonlinear
22.   Nonlinear
23.   Linear;   nullity 1, rank 2
24.   Linear;   nullity 0, rank $n + 1$

25. Linear;   nullity 1, rank infinite   26. Linear;   nullity infinite, rank 2
27. Linear;   nullity 2, rank infinite
28. $N(T)$ is the set of constant sequences; $T(V)$ is the set of sequences with limit 0
29. (d) $\{1, \cos x, \sin x\}$ is a basis for $T(V)$; dim $T(V) = 3$ (e) $N(T) = S$ (f) If $T(f) =$
     cf with $c \neq 0$, then $c \in T(V)$ so we have $f(x) = c_1 + c_2 \cos x + c_3 \sin x$; if $c_1 = 0$, then
     $c = \pi$ and $f(x) = c_1 \cos x + c_2 \sin x$, where c_1, c_2 are not both zero but otherwise arbitrary;
     if $c_1 \neq 0$, then $c = 2\pi$ and $f(x) = c_1$, where c_1 is nonzero but otherwise arbitrary.

16.8 Exercises (page 589)

 3. Yes; $x = v$, $y = u$
 4. Yes; $x = u$, $y = -v$
 5. No
 6. No
 7. No
 8. Yes; $x = \log u$, $y = \log v$
 9. No
10. Yes; $x = u - 1$, $y = v - 1$
11. Yes; $x = \frac{1}{2}(v + u)$, $y = \frac{1}{2}(v - u)$
12. Yes; $x = \frac{1}{3}(v + u)$, $y = \frac{1}{3}(2v - u)$
13. Yes; $x = w$, $y = v$, $z = u$
14. No
15. Yes; $x = u$, $y = \frac{1}{2}v$, $z = \frac{1}{3}w$
16. Yes; $x = u$, $y = v$, $z = w - u - v$
17. Yes; $x = u - 1$, $y = v - 1$, $z = w + 1$
18. Yes; $x = u - 1$, $y = v - 2$, $z = w - 3$
19. Yes; $x = u$, $y = v - u$, $z = w - v$
20. Yes; $x = \frac{1}{2}(u - v + w)$, $y = \frac{1}{2}(v - w + u)$; $z = \frac{1}{2}(w - u + v)$
25. $(S + T)^2 = S^2 + ST + TS + T^2$;
     $(S + T)^3 = S^3 + TS^2 + STS + S^2T + ST^2 + TST + T^2S + T^3$
26. (a) $(ST)(x, y, z) = (x + y + z, x + y, x)$; $(TS)(x, y, z) = (z, z + y, z + y + x)$;
     $(ST - TS)(x, y, z) = (x + y, x - z, -y - z)$; $S^2(x, y, z) = (x, y, z)$;
     $T^2(x, y, z) = (x, 2x + y, 3x + 2y + z)$;
     $(ST)^2(x, y, z) = (3x + 2y + z, 2x + 2y + z, x + y + z)$;
     $(TS)^2(x, y, z) = (x + y + z, x + 2y + 2z, x + 2y + 3z)$;
     $(ST - TS)^2 = (2x + y - z, x + 2y + z, -x + y + 2z)$;
     (b) $S^{-1}(u, v, w) = (w, v, u)$; $T^{-1}(u, v, w) = (u, v - u, w - v)$;
     $(ST)^{-1}(u, v, w) = (w, v - w, u - v)$; $(TS)^{-1}(u, v, w) = (w - v, v - u, u)$
     (c) $(T - I)(x, y, z) = (0, x, x + y)$; $(T - I)^2(x, y, z) = (0, 0, x)$;
     $(T - I)^n(x, y, z) = (0, 0, 0)$ if $n \geq 3$
28. (a) $Dp(x) = 3 - 2x + 12x^2$; $Tp(x) = 3x - 2x^2 + 12x^3$; $(DT)p(x) = 3 - 4x + 36x^2$;
     $(TD)p(x) = -2x + 24x^2$; $(DT - TD)p(x) = 3 - 2x + 12x^2$;
     $(T^2D^2 - D^2T^2)p(x) = 8 - 192x$ (b) $p(x) = ax$, a an arbitrary scalar
     (c) $p(x) = ax^2 + b$, a and b arbitrary scalars   (d) All p in V
31. (a) $Rp(x) = 2$; $Sp(x) = 3 - x + x^2$; $Tp(x) = 2x + 3x^2 - x^3 + x^4$;
     $(ST)p(x) = 2 + 3x - x^2 + x^3$; $(TS)p(x) = 3x - x^2 + x^3$; $(TS)^2p(x) = 3x - x^2 + x^3$;
     $(T^2S^2)p(x) = -x^2 + x^3$; $(S^2T^2)p(x) = 2 + 3x - x^2 + x^3$; $(TRS)p(x) = 3x$;
     $(RST)p(x) = 2$
     (b) $N(R) = \{p \mid p(0) = 0\}$; $R(V) = \{p \mid p$ is constant$\}$; $N(S) = \{p \mid p$ is constant$\}$;
     $S(V) = V$; $N(T) = \{O\}$; $T(V) = \{p \mid p(0) = 0\}$ (c) $T^{-1} = S$
     (d) $(TS)^n = I - R$; $S^nT^n = I$
32. T is not one-to-one on V because it maps all constant sequences onto the same sequence

16.12 Exercises (page 596)

1. (a) The identity matrix $I = (\delta_{jk})$, where $\delta_{jk} = 1$ if $j = k$, and $\delta_{jk} = 0$ if $j \neq k$
    (b) The zero matrix $O = (a_{jk})$ where each entry $a_{jk} = 0$
    (c) The matrix $(c\delta_{jk})$, where (δ_{jk}) is the identity matrix of part (a)

2. (a) $\begin{bmatrix} 1 & 0 & 0 \\ 0 & 1 & 0 \end{bmatrix}$ (b) $\begin{bmatrix} 0 & 1 & 0 \\ 0 & 0 & 1 \end{bmatrix}$ (c) $\begin{bmatrix} 0 & 1 & 0 & 0 & 0 \\ 0 & 0 & 1 & 0 & 0 \\ 0 & 0 & 0 & 1 & 0 \end{bmatrix}$

3. (a) $-5i + 7j, \quad 9i - 12j$
    (b) $\begin{bmatrix} 1 & 2 \\ 1 & -1 \end{bmatrix}, \begin{bmatrix} 3 & 0 \\ 0 & 3 \end{bmatrix}$ (c) $\begin{bmatrix} -\frac{7}{4} & -\frac{1}{4} \\ \frac{1}{4} & \frac{7}{4} \end{bmatrix}, \begin{bmatrix} 3 & 0 \\ 0 & 3 \end{bmatrix}$

4. $\begin{bmatrix} -2 & 0 \\ 0 & 2 \end{bmatrix}, \begin{bmatrix} 4 & 0 \\ 0 & 4 \end{bmatrix}$

5. (a) $3i + 4j + 4k$; nullity 0, rank 3   (b) $\begin{bmatrix} -1 & -1 & 2 \\ 1 & -3 & 3 \\ -1 & -5 & 5 \end{bmatrix}$

6. $\begin{bmatrix} 2 & 0 & -2 \\ 1 & -1 & 1 \\ 2 & 1 & 0 \end{bmatrix}$

7. (a) $T(4i - j + k) = (0, -2)$; nullity 1, rank 2   (b) $\begin{bmatrix} 0 & 1 & 1 \\ 0 & 1 & -1 \end{bmatrix}$
    (c) $\begin{bmatrix} 0 & 1 & 3 \\ 0 & 0 & -2 \end{bmatrix}$ (d) $e_1 = j, \quad e_2 = k, \quad e_3 = i, \quad w_1 = (1, 1), \quad w_2 = (1, -1)$

8. (a) $(5, 0, -1)$; nullity 0, rank 2   (b) $\begin{bmatrix} 1 & -1 \\ 0 & 0 \\ 1 & 1 \end{bmatrix}$
    (c) $e_1 = i, \quad e_2 = i + j, \quad w_1 = (1, 0, 1), \quad w_2 = (0, 0, 2), \quad w_3 = (0, 1, 0)$

9. (a) $(-1, -3, -1)$; nullity 0, rank 2   (b) $\begin{bmatrix} 1 & 1 \\ 0 & 1 \\ 1 & 1 \end{bmatrix}$
    (c) $e_1 = i, \quad e_2 = j - i, \quad w_1 = (1, 0, 1), \quad w_2 = (0, 1, 0), \quad w_3 = (0, 0, 1)$

10. (a) $e_1 - e_2$; nullity 0, rank 2   (b) $\begin{bmatrix} 1 & 2 \\ 5 & 4 \end{bmatrix}$ (c) $a = 5, \quad b = 4$

11. $\begin{bmatrix} 0 & -1 \\ 1 & 0 \end{bmatrix}, \begin{bmatrix} -1 & 0 \\ 0 & -1 \end{bmatrix}$

12. $\begin{bmatrix} 0 & 1 & 0 \\ 0 & 0 & 0 \\ 0 & 0 & 1 \end{bmatrix}, \begin{bmatrix} 0 & 0 & 0 \\ 0 & 0 & 0 \\ 0 & 0 & 1 \end{bmatrix}$

13. $\begin{bmatrix} 0 & 1 & 1 \\ 0 & 0 & -1 \\ 0 & 0 & 1 \end{bmatrix}, \begin{bmatrix} 0 & 0 & 0 \\ 0 & 0 & -1 \\ 0 & 0 & 1 \end{bmatrix}$

14. $\begin{bmatrix} 1 & 1 \\ 0 & 1 \end{bmatrix}, \begin{bmatrix} 1 & 2 \\ 0 & 1 \end{bmatrix}$

15. $\begin{bmatrix} 0 & -1 \\ 1 & 0 \end{bmatrix}, \begin{bmatrix} -1 & 0 \\ 0 & -1 \end{bmatrix}$

16. $\begin{bmatrix} 0 & -1 & 1 & 0 \\ 1 & 0 & 0 & 1 \\ 0 & 0 & 0 & -1 \\ 0 & 0 & 1 & 0 \end{bmatrix}, \begin{bmatrix} -1 & 0 & 0 & -2 \\ 0 & -1 & 2 & 0 \\ 0 & 0 & -1 & 0 \\ 0 & 0 & 0 & -1 \end{bmatrix}$

17. $\begin{bmatrix} 1 & -1 \\ 1 & 1 \end{bmatrix}, \begin{bmatrix} 0 & -2 \\ 2 & 0 \end{bmatrix}$

18. $\begin{bmatrix} 2 & -3 \\ 3 & 2 \end{bmatrix}, \begin{bmatrix} -5 & -12 \\ 12 & -5 \end{bmatrix}$

19. (a) $\begin{bmatrix} 0 & 0 & 0 & 0 \\ 0 & 1 & 0 & 0 \\ 0 & 0 & 2 & 0 \\ 0 & 0 & 0 & 3 \end{bmatrix}$ (b) $\begin{bmatrix} 0 & 1 & 0 & 0 \\ 0 & 0 & 4 & 0 \\ 0 & 0 & 0 & 9 \\ 0 & 0 & 0 & 0 \end{bmatrix}$ (c) $\begin{bmatrix} 0 & 0 & 0 & 0 \\ 0 & 0 & 2 & 0 \\ 0 & 0 & 0 & 6 \\ 0 & 0 & 0 & 0 \end{bmatrix}$

(d) $\begin{bmatrix} 0 & -1 & 0 & 0 \\ 0 & 0 & -2 & 0 \\ 0 & 0 & 0 & -3 \\ 0 & 0 & 0 & 0 \end{bmatrix}$ (e) $\begin{bmatrix} 0 & 0 & 0 & 0 \\ 0 & 1 & 0 & 0 \\ 0 & 0 & 4 & 0 \\ 0 & 0 & 0 & 9 \end{bmatrix}$ (f) $\begin{bmatrix} 0 & 0 & -8 & 0 \\ 0 & 0 & 0 & -48 \\ 0 & 0 & 0 & 0 \\ 0 & 0 & 0 & 0 \end{bmatrix}$

20. Choose $(x^3, x^2, x, 1)$ as a basis for V, and (x^2, x) as a basis for W. Then the matrix of TD is

$$\begin{bmatrix} 6 & 0 & 0 & 0 \\ 0 & 2 & 0 & 0 \end{bmatrix}$$

16.16 Exercises (page 603)

1. $B + C = \begin{bmatrix} 3 & 4 \\ 0 & 2 \\ 6 & -5 \end{bmatrix}$, $AB = \begin{bmatrix} 15 & -14 \\ -15 & 14 \end{bmatrix}$, $BA = \begin{bmatrix} -1 & 4 & -2 \\ -4 & 16 & -8 \\ 7 & -28 & 14 \end{bmatrix}$,

$AC = \begin{bmatrix} 0 & 0 \\ 0 & 0 \end{bmatrix}$, $CA = \begin{bmatrix} 0 & 0 & 0 \\ 2 & -8 & 4 \\ 4 & -16 & 8 \end{bmatrix}$, $A(2B - 3C) = \begin{bmatrix} 30 & -28 \\ -30 & 28 \end{bmatrix}$

2. (a) $\begin{bmatrix} a & b \\ 0 & 0 \end{bmatrix}$, a and b arbitrary (b) $\begin{bmatrix} -2a & a \\ -2b & b \end{bmatrix}$, a and b arbitrary

3. (a) $a = 9$, $b = 6$, $c = 1$, $d = 5$ (b) $a = 1$, $b = 6$, $c = 0$, $d = -2$

4. (a) $\begin{bmatrix} -9 & -2 & -10 \\ 6 & 14 & 8 \\ -7 & 5 & -5 \end{bmatrix}$ (b) $\begin{bmatrix} -3 & 5 & -4 \\ 0 & 3 & 24 \\ 12 & -27 & 0 \end{bmatrix}$

6. $A^n = \begin{bmatrix} 1 & n \\ 0 & 1 \end{bmatrix}$

7. $A^n = \begin{bmatrix} \cos n\theta & -\sin n\theta \\ \sin n\theta & \cos n\theta \end{bmatrix}$.

8. $A^n = \begin{bmatrix} 1 & n & \dfrac{n(n+1)}{2} \\ 0 & 1 & n \\ 0 & 0 & 1 \end{bmatrix}$

9. $\begin{bmatrix} 1 & 0 \\ -100 & 1 \end{bmatrix}$

10. $\begin{bmatrix} a & b \\ c & -a \end{bmatrix}$, where b and c are arbitrary, and a is any solution of the equation $a^2 = -bc$

11. (b) $\begin{bmatrix} a & 0 \\ 0 & a \end{bmatrix}$, where a is arbitrary

12. $\begin{bmatrix} 1 & 0 \\ 0 & 1 \end{bmatrix}$, $\begin{bmatrix} -1 & 0 \\ 0 & -1 \end{bmatrix}$, and $\begin{bmatrix} a & b \\ c & -a \end{bmatrix}$, where b and c are arbitrary and a is any solution of the equation $a^2 = 1 - bc$

13. $C = \begin{bmatrix} \frac{15}{2} & \frac{13}{2} \\ 8 & 7 \end{bmatrix}$, $D = \begin{bmatrix} \frac{33}{4} & \frac{19}{4} \\ \frac{43}{4} & \frac{25}{4} \end{bmatrix}$

14. (b) $(A + B)^2 = A^2 + AB + BA + B^2$; $(A + B)(A - B) = A^2 + BA - AB - B^2$
    (c) For those which commute

16.20 Exercises (page 613)

1. $(x, y, z) = (\frac{8}{5}, -\frac{7}{5}, \frac{8}{5})$
2. No solution
3. $(x, y, z) = (1, -1, 0) + t(-3, 4, 1)$
4. $(x, y, z) = (1, -1, 0) + t(-3, 4, 1)$
5. $(x, y, z, u) = (1, 1, 0, 0) + t(1, 14, 5, 0)$
6. $(x, y, z, u) = (1, 8, 0, -4) + t(2, 7, 3, 0)$
7. $(x, y, z, u, v) = t_1(-1, 1, 0, 0, 0) + t_2(-1, 0, 3, -3, 1)$
8. $(x, y, z, u) = (1, 1, 1, -1) + t_1(-1, 3, 7, 0) + t_2(4, 9, 0, 7)$
9. $(x, y, z) = (\frac{4}{3}, \frac{2}{3}, 0) + t(5, 1, -3)$
10. (a) $(x, y, z, u) = (1, 6, 3, 0) + t_1(4, 11, 7, 0) + t_2(0, 0, 0, 1)$
    (b) $(x, y, z, u) = (\frac{3}{11}, 4, \frac{19}{11}, 0) + t(4, -11, 7, 22)$

12. $\begin{bmatrix} -1 & 2 & 1 \\ 5 & -8 & -6 \\ -3 & 5 & 4 \end{bmatrix}$

14. $\begin{bmatrix} 14 & 8 & 3 \\ 8 & 5 & 2 \\ 3 & 2 & 1 \end{bmatrix}$

13. $\begin{bmatrix} -\frac{5}{3} & \frac{2}{3} & \frac{4}{3} \\ -1 & 0 & 1 \\ \frac{7}{3} & -\frac{1}{3} & -\frac{5}{3} \end{bmatrix}$

15. $\begin{bmatrix} 1 & -2 & 1 & 0 \\ 0 & 1 & -2 & 1 \\ 0 & 0 & 1 & -2 \\ 0 & 0 & 0 & 1 \end{bmatrix}$

16.
$$\begin{bmatrix} 0 & \frac{1}{2} & 0 & -1 & 0 & 1 \\ 1 & 0 & 0 & 0 & 0 & 0 \\ 0 & 0 & 0 & 1 & 0 & -1 \\ -3 & 0 & 1 & 0 & 0 & 0 \\ 0 & 0 & 0 & 0 & 0 & \frac{1}{2} \\ 9 & 0 & -3 & 0 & 1 & 0 \end{bmatrix}$$

16.21 Miscellaneous exercises on matrices (page 614)

3. $P = \begin{bmatrix} 2 & 1 \\ 5 & -1 \end{bmatrix}$

4. $\begin{bmatrix} 0 & 0 \\ 0 & 0 \end{bmatrix}$, $\begin{bmatrix} 1 & 0 \\ 0 & 1 \end{bmatrix}$, and $\begin{bmatrix} a & b \\ c & 1-a \end{bmatrix}$, where b and c are arbitrary and a is any solution of the quadratic equation $a^2 - a + bc = 0$

10. (a) $\begin{bmatrix} 1 & 1 \\ -1 & 1 \end{bmatrix}$, $\begin{bmatrix} 1 & 1 \\ 1 & -1 \end{bmatrix}$, $\begin{bmatrix} -1 & 1 \\ 1 & 1 \end{bmatrix}$, $\begin{bmatrix} 1 & -1 \\ 1 & 1 \end{bmatrix}$, $\begin{bmatrix} -1 & -1 \\ 1 & -1 \end{bmatrix}$, $\begin{bmatrix} -1 & -1 \\ -1 & 1 \end{bmatrix}$,

$\begin{bmatrix} 1 & -1 \\ -1 & -1 \end{bmatrix}$, $\begin{bmatrix} -1 & 1 \\ -1 & -1 \end{bmatrix}$

INDEX

California
MAP SHOWING LOCATION OF BANK OF AMERICA BRANCHES

LOS ANGELES AREA

TUJUNGA
MONTROSE
VAN NUYS
LA CANADA
BURBANK
PASADENA
NORTH HOLLYWOOD
GLENDALE
MONROVIA
TARZANA
SOUTH PASADENA
ARCADIA
SHERMAN OAKS
STUDIO CITY
SAN GABRIEL
GLENDORA
BEVERLY HILLS
ALHAMBRA
AZUSA
HOLLYWOOD
EL MONTE
COVINA
WEST LOS ANGELES
MONTEREY PARK
BALDWIN PARK
PUENTE
CULVER CITY
LOS ANGELES
6B Branches
MONTEBELLO
SANTA MONICA
VERNON
WHITTIER
OCEAN PARK
WASHINGTON CENTER
VENICE
HUNTINGTON PARK
LA HABRA
WESTCHESTER
FLORENCE
BELL
FULLERTON
INGLEWOOD
SOUTH GATE
HAWTHORNE
YORBA LINDA
MANHATTAN BEACH
DOWNEY
HERMOSA BEACH
LYNWOOD
NORWALK
PLACENTIA
GARDENA
COMPTON
ANAHEIM
REDONDO BEACH
PARAMOUNT
TORRANCE
ORANGE
LONG BEACH
SANTA ANA
WILMINGTON
NEWPORT BEACH
BALBOA
SAN PEDRO

BISHOP
LONE PINE
NEEDLES

ANGER
DEL REY
WOODLAKE
REEDLEY
DINUBA
EXETER
VISALIA
LINDSAY
TULARE
PORTERVILLE
TIPTON

BARSTOW
LAKE ARROWHEAD
VICTORVILLE
HIGHLAND
FONTANA
SAN BERNARDINO
WASCO
REDLANDS
SHAFTER
MOJAVE
CUCAMONGA
OILDALE
COLTON
RIVERSIDE
PALM SPRINGS
BAKERSFIELD
UPLAND
PALM DESERT
ARVIN
CLAREMONT
ONTARIO
INDIO
CALIPATRIA
LANCASTER
POMONA
CHINO
TAFT
PALMDALE
SAN DIMAS
CORONA
BRAWLEY
ADERO
EL CENTRO
NEWHALL
LUIS OBISPO
FILLMORE
SAN FERNANDO
CALEXICO
BAY
PIRU
SMO BEACH
OJAI
SANTA PAULA
FALLBROOK
ARROYO GRANDE
CAMARILLO
LAGUNA BEACH
ESCONDIDO
SANTA MARIA
SAN CLEMENTE
RAMONA
GOLETA
VENTURA
OXNARD
OCEANSIDE
LOMPOC
SANTA BARBARA
ENCINITAS
SOLANA BEACH
LA MESA
LA JOLLA
OCEAN BEACH
SAN DIEGO
CORONADO
NATIONAL CITY
CHULA VISTA

BIOGRAPHY OF A BANK

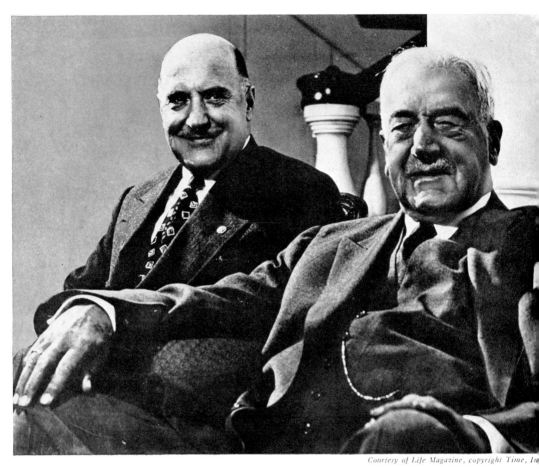

A. P. AND L. M. GIANNINI
Father and Son Photographed Early in 1949

BIOGRAPHY OF
A BANK

THE STORY OF
BANK OF AMERICA
N. T. & S. A.

by

MARQUIS JAMES

and

BESSIE ROWLAND JAMES

HARPER & BROTHERS
NEW YORK

Contents

Illustrations

BIOGRAPHY OF A BANK

A Bank for People
Who Had Never Used One Before

THE LARGEST bank in the world is not where most people would expect to find it. It is not in New York, which is the world's financial capital. It is not in London, which was the financial capital of the world for a hundred and fifty years, or until New York took the lead after the First World War. The largest bank is in San Francisco, the eleventh city in size in the United States.

This institution is the Bank of America National Trust and Savings Association. The Bank of America is a branch bank with 538 branches in 317 California cities and towns, and 9 branches overseas. It began the year 1953 with resources of $8,201,689,369.88, the largest aggregation of wealth ever assembled under one banking management in the history of mankind.* On the same date the deposits totaled $7,485,116,184.87, distributed among 5,136,285 separate accounts. No bank has ever been patronized by so large a proportion of our people in so large an area.

The average savings account balance is about $873; the average checking balance, $1,567. This last is a very small balance for a large bank. The average in some of the country's large banks is twenty times that much. These are banks doing business mainly with large corporations. Though the Bank of America has many well-heeled clients, corporate and individual, who carry impressive balances, it remains what its founder, the late A. P. Giannini, intended it to be—a bank for the person of moderate means, or, as Mr. Giannini put it, "the little fellow."

---

* We speak here of privately owned and managed banks, doing business with the public. The Federal Reserve Banks of New York and of Chicago exceed the Bank of America in assets. They are quasi government institutions.

Banks are safer institutions than they were in 1904, when A. P. Giannini entered the field, and they are immeasurably more useful to our economy. To this improvement the Bank of America (which until 1930 was called the Bank of Italy) has contributed more than any other privately owned banking institution, and Amadeo Peter Giannini more than any other banker.

A. P. Giannini was the greatest innovator in modern banking. The only other to approach his stature was J. P. Morgan, the elder. It is easier to contrast than to compare the services to society of these dissimilar men. Morgan was the banker for men of great wealth and for combinations of greater wealth. The locomotive fireman who worked on the railroad systems Morgan unified and the puddlers in the Morgan-financed steel mills never entered the great banker's consciousness; or his Wall Street banking house. Can you imagine J. P. Morgan carrying on a conversation with a track laborer? Giannini could talk to anybody.

As the Bank of America came up the House of Morgan declined. The times favored Giannini. The past half-century has witnessed a leveling process, as far as money goes: less for the Haves and more for the Have Nots. A. P. Giannini said this was a good thing. He helped it along. On the other hand Morgan probably turned over in his grave.

Somewhat by accident Mr. Giannini became a banker at the age of thirty-four. He did not go into banking for the reason that men customarily go into that or any business—to make money for himself. Giannini was then worth between $200,000 and $300,000. His young family was growing up in suburban San Mateo. Theirs was a roomy, comfortable home, called Seven Oaks, which Giannini had bought for $20,000. That was all the money and all the home Giannini intended that he or his family should ever have.

Seven Oaks was Giannini's home when he died in 1949, in his eightieth year, leaving an estate of $489,278. The depreciation of the dollar taken into account, that was less than he was worth when he opened the Bank of Italy. Giannini was never a heavy stockholder in the institution he created. He ruled the bank by force of character and not by force of money. The word of A. P. Giannini counted for more than all the money and the influence deriving from money that hostile forces could bring against it. On one occasion we shall see this strikingly demonstrated.

Giannini did not reach his eminence unopposed. He organized the Bank of Italy because he was indignant at the neglect of North Beach, San Francisco's Italian colony, by other banks. He served North Beach so notably that he was able to set up prospering branches of the Bank of Italy elsewhere in the city. It was not, however, until he began to spread branches through the agricultural valleys of California and to storm the citadel of Los Angeles that the real struggle began. Branch banking was then a controversial issue. Its advantages to the depositor, the borrower and the stockholder were hotly disputed. The upshot was a long series of tussles with the regulatory authorities, state and federal. Laws framed for the protection of old-style banking stood in the innovator's path. But Giannini found, by legal means, ways around obstructive regulations and statutes. He was simply ahead of the laws. Over the past thirty years much of the body of salutary banking legislation and regulation has followed the lead of Giannini.

The majority of the Bank of Italy's early patrons were immigrants who had never been inside a bank before. They had hidden their surplus cash under the mattress. When they borrowed they had usually borrowed from loan sharks at merciless rates. Giannini taught them the advantage of interest-bearing savings accounts. He would loan $25 at bank rates, often with no better security than the calluses on the borrower's hands. Very few San Francisco banks would loan as little as $100, in the belief that such small transactions were more trouble than they were worth.

After the earthquake and fire of 1906 the Bank of Italy was the first bank in San Francisco to resume operations. Its place of business was a plank laid across two barrels on the Washington Street wharf. Giannini's fortitude in that crisis and in the Panic of 1907, which came the following year, began to extend little Bank of Italy's reputation beyond the confines of North Beach.

Going into the agricultural regions, Giannini accepted farm mortgages at 7 per cent, against the going rate of 8 or more. But that was in character. The Bank of America has constantly labored to protect the small borrower against high rates of interest. It was the first bank to move on a large scale into various lending fields that had once been bonanzas for loan sharks. At bank rates it makes loans to purchasers of automobiles and nearly everything else that can be bought on installments. More and more large banks everywhere are now doing this. They advertise for borrowers, too, something they disdained to do for many years after Giannini started the practice.

Lawrence Mario Giannini was the person most responsible for the broad developments in installment-lending after he became president of the Bank of America in 1936. A. P. Giannini could not have been more fortunate in the son who entertained no other ambition than to get into the adventurous business his father daily discussed with so much enthusiasm at the family dinner table. When Mario became head of the bank, for more than three decades A. P. Giannini had been burgeoning through the long length of California buying banks, opening new ones, and turning banking upside down with his new ideas—all at a breathless pace. The studious Mario molded the Topsy-like growth into the compact, smoothly functioning statewide branch banking system that it is today. Yet under Mario the Bank of America grew faster than ever before, as also did the State of California.

Though Mario Giannini's contribution to the building of the largest bank in the world was a timely supplement, the Bank of America continues to such a degree a projection of the personality and the economic philosophy of Amadeo Peter Giannini that it seems proper to begin the detail of its history with a sketch of the early environment of that singular man.

2

He was born on May 6, 1870, in San Jose, in the Santa Clara Valley, fifty miles from San Francisco and near the southern end of San Francisco Bay. The birthplace was a twenty-room hotel that his father, Luigi Giannini, operated under a lease. This must have been something of an undertaking for a man of twenty-two who had come straight from Italy to learn the hotel business and the English language at the same time. When his son arrived Luigi had been married two years. The infant's mother, Virginia, was not quite sixteen. The young couple came from comfortably well-off farming stock near Genoa, their material circumstances attested by the fact that they had paid their passages to California and had enough left to take over the hotel. Few Italians arriving on the West Coast of the United States in that day were able to begin so far up the ladder. Some who were to rise to wealth and prominence, and will figure in this narrative, earned their passage as seamen, and, if they had wives, sent for them later.

San Jose is older than San Francisco or any other settlement in California, excepting missions and forts. The first Americans got there in 1845. The Santa Clara Valley was not gold country, nor was it in the pathway trod by the fortune hunters who in 1849 swarmed into California by sea and by land. But the Santa Clara Valley was rich farming land, especially suited to fruits and vegetables. San Francisco, which had shot up from almost nothing to a population of 25,000 in 1850, paid outlandish prices for foodstuffs, and paid in gold. San Francisco could afford the prices, being the richest city per capita in the world.

In this way during the early years of the Rush the average rancher gathered to himself as much yellow metal as the average miner. (Then as now in California "rancher" was the term for a rural landed proprietor, whether he owned ten acres or a hundred thousand and whether he raised cauliflower or cattle.) The completion of the transcontinental railroad in 1869, on which the Gianninis were pioneer passengers, brought a fresh boom to California in general and to the Santa Clara Valley in particular. Luigi Giannini did so well with the San Jose hotel that presently he was able to give up the place and move to forty acres he bought between the town and the bay.

After six years on the forty acres Luigi was killed by a workman in a dispute over a debt of one dollar. The widow—twenty-two at the time of her bereavement—was the mother of three boys of whom the oldest, Amadeo, was seven. After carrying on alone for a time she married Lorenzo Scatena, twenty-six, whose capital was a team and wagon in which he hauled ranchers' produce to the dock at Alviso on the bay or to the railroad in San Jose. Lorenzo had worked his way from Italy before the mast.

Amadeo Giannini was twelve when, in 1882, the family moved to San Francisco. Lorenzo Scatena had decided that more was to be made by marketing the produce of California's ranches than by growing it. This was proof of acumen; things went that way—and not in the field of agriculture alone. Some of the most profitable mining operations were conducted by those who mined the miners instead of the earth. From San Francisco's Italian colony of North Beach, Scatena could look at the bizarre mansions rising (or risen) on the summit of Nob Hill. He could board a cable car and have a closer view—as perhaps he did some Sundays, taking his wife and her three boys. Two Nob Hill nobs, Charles Crocker and Mark Hopkins, had started as dealers in miners' supplies in Sacramento, the jumping-off place for the gold region. James L. Flood had laid the foundation for his millions (as a little later he was to lay that of his palace built of brownstone from Vermont) by making available another requisite for miners. Mr. Flood had opened a saloon in San Francisco.

To break in, Lorenzo Scatena took a job with the commission house of A. Galli & Company. Before a year elapsed he had his own business. Three times in two years the firm of L. Scatena & Company moved to larger quarters in Washington Street, the main artery of San Francisco's throbbing, noisy, smelly commission district. Lorenzo was succeeding not only as a middleman in the fruit and vegetable business but as the head of a family. His three stepsons adored him. With the three children born of his marriage with the former Virginia Giannini they made a happy family. When L. Scatena & Company got on its feet the proprietor bought a home on Green Street, in the heart of North Beach. The house had a bay window. Even a casual observer of San Francisco architecture, old or new, Nob Hill or North Beach, knows what that means. To the end of his life A. P. Giannini remembered that bay window with pride.

Virginia Scatena wanted her children to get good educations. All six of them attended the Washington Grammar School. The student among them was the second boy, Attilio—destined to go on to college and study medicine. Though Amadeo got good marks, the mother would have been more pleased had her first-born not preferred the marts of Washington Street to the classrooms of the Washington Grammar School. After school Amadeo would head for the establishment of L. Scatena & Company. Late afternoon was a quiet time there, as it was for Washington Street in general. The real work of the day had been done. Quick turnover was indispensable to success in the wholesale fruit and vegetable business. Buildings were empty, or next to it, their worn and scarred floors swept clean. Little but odors remained. Horses were in their barns, men in their beds. The head of L. Scatena & Company would be asleep at his home on Green Street. But in the cluttered little office the bookkeeper, an elderly Irishman named Tim Delay, would be bending over his ledgers.

Amadeo made a friend of Tim and learned something of the mystery of books of account.

Like every schoolboy Amadeo looked forward to Saturday. On that day he was allowed to be a real part of the teeming enterprise of L. Scatena & Company. Washington Street's workday began as soon as the calendar day did, that is at midnight. In the dark, Lorenzo and Amadeo would climb into the firm's wagon and rattle over the cobblestones of Green Street on the way to the wharves to meet the fruit and vegetable boats from the Sacramento and San Joaquin rivers, from Alviso, and from the other little ports dotting the far shores of the bay.

At the waterfront Lorenzo would encounter his competitors from Washington Street. Many were Italians, like himself; also there were Chinese, Portuguese, Irish, Jews, Syrians as well as what we like to call representatives of the old American stock. Amid a babel of tongues, bidding and buying was keen. Several times Lorenzo Scatena would fill his wagon—with beans, potatoes, celery, corn, peas, turnips, cantaloupes, grapes, pears, cherries, plums—and cart the loads to Washington Street. There remained the job of pushing these wares out to the customers of L. Scatena & Company, who at this stage were mostly small retailers. By early afternoon the establishment would be empty again—that is, if it had been a good day. Otherwise spoilage might eat up the profits.

These Saturdays were such satisfying experiences that, when Amadeo Giannini finished the Washington Grammar School, he took a five months' course at Heald's Business College and became a permanent fixture at L. Scatena & Company. Of a sudden, apparently unsolicited consignments to the firm began to appear. Lorenzo Scatena learned that they were the results of letters Amadeo had sent to growers citing the excellence of his stepfather's house. At the age of fifteen "Young Scatena," as Amadeo came to be known in Washington Street circles, was a familiar figure at the postmidnight trading sessions on the waterfront. The boy was a shrewd judge of commodities and he had a "feel" for prices. Six feet tall when he was fifteen and weighing 170 pounds, he could hold his own in other ways. Waterfront barter was a rough-and-tumble game. In support of a zealously contested bid Young Scatena could use his fists as well as diplomacy.

At seventeen Amadeo was making buying trips for the firm. He toured the Santa Clara, the Napa and the Sacramento Valleys lining up commodities. The youth was a mixer and popular. He was liked by the ranchers, by the townspeople, by the rival buyers he met at nights in the country hotels. He worked longer hours than his colleagues. Soon the big San Francisco houses which for years had had standing arrangements with certain growers found L. Scatena & Company getting a share of the business.

Giannini tried to show ranchers how they, as well as L. Scatena, could make more money. Early peas commanded a good price in the San Francisco market, and the earlier they were the better the price. Amadeo urged men he had known as a child in the Santa Clara Valley to plant more peas and to pick them when they were small, sugary and tender. He was quick to observe successful growing methods and to pass the word along. If a rancher needed funds to improve his irrigation system, to buy a few trees, or to tide over a bad season, L. Scatena might make the advances. As his house expanded Scatena always had several thousand dollars out on such loans. Other commission houses did the same, though none appears to have depended on the recommendations of a seventeen- or eighteen-year-old boy.

Amadeo ventured farther and farther afield—into the great San Joaquin Valley and across the Tehachapi Range to Los Angeles. Two accounts he landed in the south were with orange growers who gave their addresses as Hollywood, a crossroads northwest of Los Angeles where the arrival of the stage to the San Fernando Valley was an event of the day. Lorenzo Scatena was so pleased that he made his stepson, at nineteen, a partner with a third-interest. Two years later this was increased to a half-interest.

By that time Amadeo Giannini was a young man of mark in San Francisco's Italian colony where he had a speaking acquaintance with almost everyone. In the near-by commission district he was regarded as "a live wire," and at times as "crazy with big ideas." An elderly lady of San Francisco remembers standing at her bay window on January 1, 1892. She saw Amadeo pass on his round of New Year's Day calls. He was six feet two. He wore a top hat, gloves and a Prince Albert. He carried a cane. The girl watcher, whose name was—and is—Eda Beronio, thought: there goes the handsomest man in North Beach.

A call that Amadeo made that day was at the Bay Street residence of Joseph Cuneo, one of the Beach's rich men. Italian-born Joseph

Cuneo had begun life in California as a miner but he found no gold. Opening a miners' supply store he had been ruined by an absconding employee. In San Francisco, however, his luck changed and he laid the foundations of a fortune in real estate. The object of the North Beach Brummell's visit to Bay Street was Joseph Cuneo's daughter, Clorinda Agnes. Before the year of 1892 was out she married him. Bride and groom were each twenty-two.

During the next nine years the prosperity of the house of L. Scatena & Company continued. Then, in 1901, the junior partner retired from the business. He had saved and invested in real estate enough to bring in $250 a month clear. On top of this was the half-interest in the commission house, which Giannini sold to four or five of the firm's employees for about $100,000. The proceeds from both sources provided enough income to support his family. At thirty-one A. P. Giannini had formulated the philosophy concerning the accumulation of personal wealth that he was to carry through life. "I don't want to be rich," he said. "No man actually owns a fortune; it owns him."

Just what a man of his energy and imagination calculated to do with his time is something Giannini did not make clear. He may have had some idea of continuing his political activities. Were this a biography of A. P. Giannini instead of a history of the bank he founded, those activities, brief as they were, would be worth a chapter. During the reform administration of Mayor (later United States Senator) Phelan, Giannini had taken a leading part in purging North Beach of the henchmen of Chris Buckley, the blind boss who was San Francisco's counterpart of Tweed.

It was the death of his father-in-law in 1902 that decided A. P. Giannini's future. Joseph Cuneo left a fortune of half a million dollars, largely in North Beach real estate. Also he left a widow and eleven children, but no will. Nevertheless, the family decided to keep the estate intact for administrative purposes, and to place its management in the hands of A. P. Giannini for a term of ten years. Considering that sons of the deceased were grown and in business this unusual arrangement was a tribute to a son-in-law. By common agreement legal niceties were waived in the distribution of the estate's income, needy children receiving more than others. For his services Giannini was to get 25 per cent of whatever increase there might be in the capital value of the estate during his stewardship.

Giannini's fee for ten years' work turned out to be $36,994. He had more than a hundred separate parcels of real estate to look after. There were also other holdings, among them shares in a little North Beach savings bank called the Columbus Savings & Loan Society. Joseph Cuneo had been a member of the board of that institution. Succeeding to his late father-in-law's place, A. P. Giannini began his banking career.[1]

3

In 1902, when Giannini took his seat at the directors' table of the Columbus Savings & Loan Society, that institution was controlled by its founder, John F. Fugazi, one of the most widely known Italian-Americans in the United States. After an unproductive go at mining, Fugazi had obtained the agency for the White Star Line in San Francisco. At this he was so successful that Agenzia Fugazi opened branches in other American cities and became a factor in the Italian immigration of the period. Italians brought their gold to Fugazi for remittance to families in the homeland, and, because Fugazi owned one of the few safes in North Beach, they asked to keep their savings in it. Thus John Fugazi became a banker, formalizing the matter in 1893 by opening the Columbus Savings & Loan, with Isaias W. Hellman, Senior, as godfather and adviser to the new institution. Hellman, president of the influential Nevada National Bank of San Francisco, had got into the banking business in 1859 the same way Fugazi did: his Los Angeles store was equipped with a big iron safe. The possession of safes, as well as facilities for transporting gold eastward, also had something to do with the entry of the Adams and the Wells Fargo express companies into the banking field in San Francisco.

As the first bank in North Beach the Columbus performed an unquestioned service to the community. It provided residents with a secure place to keep their money—hard money still being the rule on the West Coast—where it would earn interest. This was a big improvement over hiding coin about the house. The bank also provided credit for home builders and for merchants. Nevertheless, Mr. Fugazi and associates were in the banking business first of all to make money for themselves. Preferring large loans (large for North

[1] The notes will be found at the end of the book beginning on page 523.

Beach, that is) to small, they ran a conservative, tight little bank and thus made an opening for a more enlightened competitor, Andrea E. Sbarboro, who in 1899 started the Italian-American Bank. Sbarboro had come from Italy in 1852 and in the 1870's began laying up a fortune by lending to small home builders all over the San Francisco Bay district. About the same time he organized the Italian-Swiss wine colony at Asti, which brought him additional success financially. His new bank was a commercial (with checking accounts) as well as a savings institution. Catering to small borrowers as well as large, the Italian-American showed such vigor and enterprise that it gained rapidly on the Columbus.

As a Columbus director, the thirty-two-year-old Giannini did not fancy this state of affairs. After a quick look around the new director began to astonish, and then to irritate, the majority of his colleagues on the board with criticisms of their institution. Board meetings at the Columbus became lively affairs.

Giannini said the bank was not lending enough money—too much of the funds were "warehoused" and idle. It was not making enough loans on real estate. Giannini's handling of his late father-in-law's properties was giving him an insight into the real estate situation. He had taken a desk with the firm of Madison & Burke, one of the city's large operators, and was doing some trading on his own. Moreover, Giannini said the bank was not making enough small loans of any kind. North Beach was growing at the rate of two thousand inhabitants a year. Most of the newcomers were poor, as about every man around the Columbus board table had been in his young days. Judging by the past, most of these newcomers would get on and a certain number would be among the leaders of the next generation. Giannini saw these people as potential customers of the bank and now was the moment to win their friendship by offering small loans to help them get started. Go out and solicit their loans, advised the director who had no banking experience. In the long run the bank would prosper.

A. P. Giannini had touched a weak spot not only in the management of the Columbus Savings & Loan Society but in the financial machinery of San Francisco as well. Then as now the city by the Golden Gate was the money capital of the West Coast. It was a creditor community, providing funds for the development of the country around Los Angeles, four hundred miles away, for Seattle in Washington and Portland in Oregon. San Francisco money also went into the great agricultural valleys of California; it went East; it went to Europe. But in San Francisco itself it was hard for a man to borrow $100 from a bank, particularly if he was a foreigner.[2]

The big banks could not be bothered with such small potatoes. These banks fell into two categories, locally called "American" and "foreign." The "American" banks, like the Nevada and the Crocker-Woolworth, had been founded by native citizens. They represented the interests of the rough-hewn bonanza kings who had settled and given Nob Hill its name. "Foreign" banks were the outgrowth of branches established in San Francisco in the early days by such European houses as Rothschild, Lazard Frères and J. & W. Seligman & Company. The foreigner managers of these branches differed from pioneers of North Beach like Joseph Cuneo, who had never learned to write English or to speak it even passably. Cultivated men of the world, the European bankers and their descendants have left their impress upon San Francisco.

By 1902 Lazard Frères agency had become the London, Paris & American Bank, Ltd., and the Seligman branch the Anglo-Californian Bank, Ltd. Though then in the hands of American citizens (largely second generation), these institutions retained an Old World flavor and, indeed, were deeply involved with San Francisco's export and import trade. Whatever the contributions, cultural and financial, of the "foreign" banks and bankers to San Francisco, they meant little to the resident of North Beach who needed a small loan.[3]

Thus the little fellow was driven into the arms of loan sharks. If lucky, he might get a loan from a bank officer, acting in a private capacity. Such loans were above the going bank rates of 6 and 7 per cent, though below those of the sharks.

Another banking practice that A. P. Giannini did not like involved an established prerequisite of bank officers. When a borrower offered a building as security he was required to carry fire insurance. As agent for a fire insurance company a bank officer would issue the policy and pocket the commission. Giannini said such commissions belonged to the bank.

As if the critical young director had not proposed enough for the bank to take on in North Beach, Giannini said the Columbus should look beyond the Italian colony. He pointed to the record of the

Hibernia Savings & Loan Society. Founded and controlled by Irish-Americans, this institution appealed to all classes for patronage, and so had become the largest savings bank west of Chicago. Not far behind the Hibernia was the German Savings & Loan Society.

Only three Columbus directors saw any merit in Giannini's suggestions. One of these was Lorenzo Scatena, who was elected to the board shortly after his stepson. The others were Antonio Chichizola, an importer, and Joseph G. Cavagnaro, a lawyer. The weight of the board, including Fugazi and his two sons, held fast against changes. Giannini was regarded as an officious neophyte. When he proposed that his friend Charles F. Grondona fill the vacancy on the board created by the death of his father-in-law, Francesco Arata, the majority named its own man. Charley Grondona was an alert young real estate and insurance man with a lot of friends in North Beach. The rebuff did the popularity of the bank no good.

After a hot board session in the spring of 1904 Giannini appealed to Isaias Hellman, the bank's adviser. Obtaining no satisfaction in that quarter, Giannini resigned in a huff as a director of the Columbus Savings & Loan Society.[4]

His next call was on James J. Fagan, a jovial Irishman who was vice-president of the American National Bank where L. Scatena & Company had its account. Fagan and Giannini had long been friends and a good deal of horseplay went on between them. Giannini called Fagan "Giacomo" (Italian for James), and joked about his diminutive stature. The towering Giannini was in no jesting mood, however, when he burst into Fagan's office and announced defiantly: "Giacomo, I'm going to start a bank. Tell me how to do it."[5]

4

This was a rather large order, even in 1904 when to open a bank in California was a simpler process than it is in these days of exacting public regulation. Fagan was inclined to tease his friend about the tribulations that can perplex an amateur in the banking field, but clearly this was no time for joking. Giannini was in earnest and Fagan listened to what Amadeo had to say. Boiled down, his thesis was that North Beach needed and would support a bank determined to take a lively part in the material development of that community. As to capital, Giannini said he could raise it. His idea was to distribute the ownership widely, giving the greatest possible number of people a feeling that it was *their* bank.

Other meetings followed in Fagan's office and in the law office of Cavagnaro, one of the dissatisfied Columbus directors. To these gatherings Giannini brought such men of means as Chichizola, the importer; Giacomo Costa, a large investor in real estate; George G. Caglieri, part owner of the Agenzia Fugazi and a former Columbus director; Luigi DeMartini, head of a confectioners' supply house bearing his name. Also he brought young up-and-comers like Charley Grondona. All bore Italian names except Fagan, who listened to Giannini's glowing expositions and poked holes in some of them. Nevertheless, progress was swift. A new bank was agreed upon, and Fagan decided to go along. In July Grondona returned from Sacramento with the signature and seal of the secretary of state of California on a certificate of incorporation for the "Italian Bank of California."[6]

Courteously but firmly Sbarboro protested that the name was too much like that of his Italian-American Bank. Giannini took a long thoughtful walk. He foresaw the day when his dream child would break out of North Beach, as he had urged the Columbus to do. But first it must prove itself in the Italian colony. Returning to his backers Giannini proposed the name "Bank of Italy," which was adopted.[7]

The articles of incorporation called for a capital of $300,000. Half of this was to be paid in at once. The bank decided to accept both savings and commercial accounts. Thus at the outset the Bank of Italy would possess two potential advantages over the Columbus, with only one-third of its $300,000 capital paid and no checking accounts. The Bank of Italy's capital was divided into three thousand shares of $100 each. Giannini said he hoped that no one person would own more than one hundred shares. The first sales were to the bank's promoters—the men who had attended the preliminary meetings. Sitting as stockholders, this inside group chose from its number eleven directors. To start with the directors held one hundred shares apiece, for which they had paid $50 a share down.

The directors formed themselves into committees to further the work of organization. Though not a member of the committee charged with obtaining a home for the bank, Giannini himself performed this important work. The manner in which he did it seems to confirm his contention that the Columbus was anything but a wide-awake outfit.

The Columbus was located in the Drexler Building on Washington Street, at the intersection, or "gore," as San Franciscans call the apex of their triangular-shaped blocks, with two other thoroughfares, Montgomery Street and Montgomery Avenue. (Later Montgomery Avenue was helpfully renamed Columbus Avenue.) The Agenzia Fugazi was located around the corner on the Columbus Avenue side. These two tenants had made that intersection known to North Beachers as a place where banking could be done. This was an asset no one seeking a location for a new bank could have well overlooked. At the gore, wedged between the bank and the travel bureau, was the saloon of Anania Quilici. Giannini found that Quilici wished to retire and promptly bought his lease for $1,250. Next, Giannini leased from the Drexler estate the whole Drexler Building. The Columbus bank woke up to find itself a tenant of its ex-director who was starting a rival bank. Columbus was furious, naturally, and presently moved across the street. The Bank of Italy directors took the Quilici lease off Giannini's hands for what it had cost him.

Carpenters set to work turning the saloon into bank quarters, which was accomplished at a cost of $5,295. Office furniture cost $3,971 and a safe $750. These expenditures provided the projected bank with rather presentable quarters by North Beach standards of 1904.[8]

The sale of the bank's stock went apace. The 1,900 shares not taken by the directors failed to satisfy the demand. Consequently four of the eleven directors parted with a total of 195 shares to carry out Giannini's policy of wide distribution. That left the directors owning 905 of the 3,000 shares. Six additional stockholders had "large" holdings of 25 to 100 shares each. That put 1,620 shares in the hands of 143 small stockholders. The number of owners of 2, 3 and 4 shares was what delighted Giannini. By occupations these holders represented a cross section of North Beach: fish dealer, grocer, drayman, druggist, baker, accountant, restaurant proprietor, plumber, house painter, barber. Quilici, the retired saloonkeeper, bought five shares. The Beronio family, to whose support Eda contributed as a piano teacher, really plunged. Ten shares were taken in the name of Eda's widowed mother, Maria.[9]

The following officers were chosen by the board: Antonio Chichizola, president; A. P. Giannini, vice-president; Charles F. Grondona, secretary; George G. Caglieri, cashier. All were members of the board. Giannini was also made a member of the executive committee. Fagan was chairman of the auditing committee, and Lorenzo Scatena of the appraising committee. Officers were to serve without salary until the bank was able to pay them from earnings. Three salaried employees were engaged: Madeline Lagomarsino, stenographer; Victor A. Caglieri (a son of the cashier), teller; and Armando Pedrini, assistant cashier.

Armando Pedrini was a magnetic figure—as tall as Giannini and, in the judgment of the ladies of North Beach, almost as handsome. With considerable difficulty Giannini had hired him away from the Columbus bank. Having learned banking in Italy, Pedrini had gone to South America hoping to advance himself. This expectation disappointed, he had arrived in San Francisco as a seaman and worked as a longshoreman before obtaining a berth in the Columbus bank. With that behind him, Pedrini hesitated to leave an established bank for a new one.

For purposes of secrecy one of the conferences with Pedrini was held at Maria Beronio's house. Pedrini consented to change only when Giannini offered $150 a month, which was double his pay at Columbus, and a two-year contract. When Giannini took this proposition to the board for ratification he had more trouble. Why was Pedrini worth twice as much to the Bank of Italy as to Columbus? "Because he knows his business," Giannini replied, "and because he is polite and has a following. The women are crazy about him [he kissed their hands, Continental fashion], and he gives a man in overalls as much attention as a big depositor." Giannini intended to capitalize these assets in a manner the Columbus bank had never dreamed of. When the vice-president personally guaranteed Pedrini's pay in case earnings should not cover it, the board approved the deal.

At nine o'clock on Monday morning, October 17, 1904, all was ready. Giannini said to young Caglieri: "Vic, you may now open the front door."[10]

5

On the first day $8,780 was received in deposits. This represented twenty-eight accounts. Had the directors and other promoters wished to make an impressive opening-day showing they could have done so by transferring portions of their balances from other banks. The only director to make a deposit that day was Giacomo Costa who put in $800. Officers' and directors' families helped out, though. For example, A. P. Giannini's mother deposited $1,000 (the day's second largest deposit), and Rose Cuneo, a sister-in-law, $60. The wife, a daughter and a granddaughter of Cashier Caglieri were represented by three accounts totaling $165.

The bulk of the deposits came from small tradesmen and were in response to solicitation in which Grondona and Giannini played leading roles. Some of these men had never had bank accounts before. They did their business for cash and kept both working and surplus funds in gold about their houses or places of business. Many were unable to write English. Deposit slips, checks and savings withdrawal forms were filled out by the bank's personnel. One of Giannini's ambitions was to educate North Beachers in the use of a bank.

By the end of October, 1904, deposits were $41,610; by the end of November, $68,761; by the end of December, $109,413. Though this growth was sound, it was remarkable only in that so many of the Bank of Italy's patrons had never before been inside any bank. Still, at the rate of increase shown, the new bank would be a long while catching up with either the Columbus or the Italian-American banks, each of which had in the neighborhood of $2,000,000 in deposits.[11]

It does not appear, therefore, that the advent of the Bank of Italy caused any tidal wave of comment in North Beach. The fact is that it started off so modestly that A. P. Giannini made good his promise to pay Pedrini's salary, and kept it up for more than a year.

In Montgomery Street, which is San Francisco's Wall Street, the Bank of Italy went unnoticed altogether. The only newspaper to report the opening was *L'Italia* of North Beach. Though the bank's address was Montgomery Avenue and not Montgomery Street, it was only a step off Montgomery Street—but not in the section that invited comparison with Wall Street. That was some blocks south, near Market Street. Dr. Guido E. Caglieri, a successful young physician and son of the bank's cashier, presently succeeded his father as a director of the bank. Many years later Dr. Caglieri recalled the first time he heard the Bank of Italy spoken of in the famous end of Montgomery Street. It was referred to as "that little Dago bank in North Beach." Fagan affectionately referred to it as the "baby bank."[12]

From the start the "baby bank" was a free lender. At the end of the second month of its existence loans and overdrafts amounted to $92,950, as against deposits of $68,761. This meant that some of the capital was at work in the loan field. At the end of the third month —December 31, 1904—loans were $178,000 and deposits $134,000.

Obviously, had not the Bank of Italy's loans been good ones there would have been trouble ahead for the young institution.

Advances on real estate formed the bulk of the portfolio. These increased from $158,000 at the end of 1904 to $644,000 at the end of 1905. Many of the loans were not small, the bank's size considered, and many were secured by property not in North Beach. The first two borrowers had names alien to North Beach—R. P. Burns and George A. Webster. Their loans had been approved before the bank opened for business. Burns borrowed $5,000 on property valued by the bank's appraisal committee at $8,500 and Webster $8,500 on property appraised at $15,000. Webster was a prosperous Washington Street commission merchant and a friendly rival of Giannini.

In January, 1905, the bank made a useful lending connection with Jacob Heyman & Company, pioneer builders of small homes on the pay-as-rent plan. The following month Heyman borrowed $2,500 to develop a tract far from North Beach, in the neighborhood of Douglas and Twenty-Fourth Streets. The firm (now Heyman Brothers, Inc.) has been continuously a client of the bank to this day.

By and large, however, the North Beach money that came into the bank stayed in North Beach. Individual real estate loans in that district were as small as $375; personal and collateral loans, as little as $25. These tiny loans constituted one of the bank's reasons for being, and, for the first time in San Francisco, provided the small man in need of a small sum a place where he could borrow at bank rates. Records of such loans do not survive. Just how many were made, and what they amounted to in the aggregate, is impossible to say. The sum may not have been large—and whatever it was it is concealed in the totals for personal loans, collateral loans and overdrafts which, on December 31, 1905, stood at $239,318.[13]

6

Near the end of 1905 the bank was obliged to enlarge its quarters. Also, the remaining half of the capital was paid in, meaning that stockholders put up an additional $50 for each share they held. This had the effect of reducing the number of stockholders from 160 to 142, some of the large as well as small stockholders disposing of their shares rather than meet their assessments.

There were some personnel changes. Antonio Chichizola had accepted the presidency on a temporary basis. In May, 1905, he resigned and was succeeded by Lorenzo Scatena. Giannini could have had the post, but desired the election of Mr. Scatena because of the affection he bore his stepfather. Nevertheless, two directors unexpectedly cast their votes for A. P. Giannini. For this the vice-president did not thank them. The directors in question were also interested in the Columbus Savings & Loan Society. Feeling between the two banks was something keener than ordinary rivalry. The Bank of Italy had been acquiring stock in the Columbus with the hope of gaining control. Giannini took the action of the two directors as an attempt to divide the ranks of the Bank of Italy's supporters. The upshot was the resignation of the directors, whose shares Giannini took over. The following year the Bank of Italy disposed of its Columbus holdings, abandoning the effort to dominate the older institution.[14]

Clarence E. Musto was elected second vice-president. Musto was a member of one of the largest marble-importing firms on the West Coast.

James J. Fagan, who occupied about the same position with reference to the Bank of Italy that Isaias Hellman did to the Columbus, left the American National Bank to become cashier of the great Crocker-Woolworth National. As the Bank of Italy was not a member of the San Francisco Clearing House it had cleared through the American National. The Crocker-Woolworth now took over that service and, moreover, kept in its vaults the smaller bank's cash reserve. Every evening a buggy would make the trip along Montgomery Street with a pouch that contained principally gold. William H. Crocker, president of the Crocker-Woolworth and owner of the Nob Hill mansion his late father had built, thought enough of the "baby bank" to buy fifty shares of its stock.

In all, things went so well in 1905 that as a Christmas present Giannini raised the salaries of the bank's employees, the number now grown to six, and, without comment so far as the Minutes reveal, the board sanctioned this action. The board did more than that. It took over, on behalf of the bank, responsibility for Pedrini's salary which the Christmas raise brought to $175 a month. Everything Giannini had predicted in Pedrini's favor had been borne out.

Year-end figures for 1905 showed the bank's assets just over the million mark. Of the $700,000 in deposits, $387,000 represented savings accounts on which 3½ per cent interest was paid.

The Bank of Italy was getting somewhere. Sizable individual deposits had a good deal to do with this. These included personal and business accounts of the bank's directors and of well-to-do friends they lined up. In addition to his own account which might show a balance as high as $20,000 between investments, A. P. Giannini moved funds of the J. Cuneo Company to the Bank of Italy. This corporation owned the real estate holdings that Giannini managed for the Cuneo heirs.

These large accounts, however, were not the significant feature of the increase in deposits. The significant feature was the growing number of small accounts that came in principally as a result of personal solicitation by Giannini and Charley Grondona. From one end of North Beach to the other these busy men tramped explaining, in the Italian tongue and in simplest terms, the functions of a bank to men and women who had never used one. The result brought from hiding thousands upon thousands of dollars in gold and silver. Pedrini and Victor Caglieri displayed endless patience filling out deposit slips and checks and in general trying to make these new customers feel at home in the bank. Together with the small-loan policy this was the sort of thing that made the little Bank of Italy unique and, during the first year of its life, gave it an asset that the required periodical "statements of condition" took no account of.[15]

LOS ANGELES HEADQUARTERS, 1954

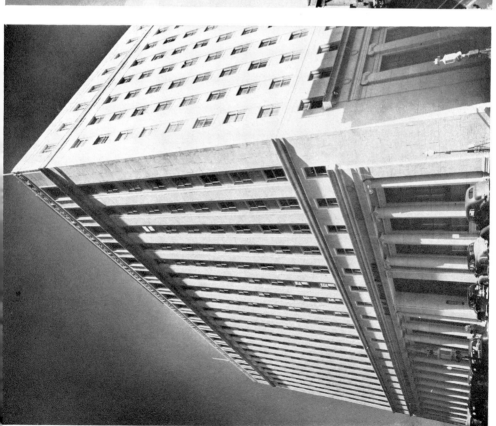

SAN FRANCISCO HEADQUARTERS, 1954

Opportunity Through Disaster

DURING the first quarter of 1906 the Bank of Italy grew faster than ever. Deposits went from $706,000 to $846,000. As the bank was located about a block from the city jail, some of the policemen attached to that institution opened accounts. In the opinion of Charley Grondona, this afforded the bank far better protection than the ten-dollar revolver bought in the opening week. The policeman on night duty made it his business to hang around No. 1 Montgomery Avenue. Bank employees always worked into the night to get caught up. With lights shining through the doors and windows, the uniformed depositor thought the former saloon might prove an attraction to holdup men.

Loans went from $883,000 to more than a million. Pursuing its unorthodox lending policy, all the bank's investments in bonds and stocks—which had never aggregated much more than $50,000— were disposed of so that, on March 31, 1906, the sole investments were loans, principally on real estate. The loan total exceeded deposits by $200,000.[1]

The first dividend to stockholders was voted—5 per cent on the paid-in capital as of July 1, 1905. The disbursement amounted to $5,250. Another evidence of prosperity was the board's recognition of the services of the bank's founder. Vice-President Giannini was voted a salary of $200 a month, beginning February 1, 1906. He was the only officer so rewarded, though directors—and all the officers were directors—received $5 apiece for each board meeting they attended. Giannini had spent more than $200 a month during the year and a half the bank was getting under way; and for some while to come these out-of-pocket expenditures continued to exceed his salary. In 1921 the bank reimbursed Mr. Giannini for these and subsequent outlays.

To provide additional funds for the bank's expanding operations it was decided to increase the capital by $200,000, bringing it up to half a million dollars. This action was taken on February 28. April 21 was the day fixed for the distribution, on a paid-up basis, of 2,000 additional shares at $105 each. A catastrophe prevented the completion of this transaction on time. On April 21, 1906, the richest part of San Francisco was in ruins from earthquake and fire.[2]

2

The first and severest of the shocks came at thirteen minutes past five o'clock on the morning of Wednesday, April 18. It lasted only twenty-eight seconds, a circumstance that residents of San Francisco later found difficult to believe. After the earth had ceased to rock, buildings still swayed and lurched. Unsubstantial ones tumbled to the ground. Plaster fell, dishes broke, furniture banged about, doors flew open with enough force to wrench them from the hinges, and brick chimneys toppled into the streets. Over a period of three days there were minor tremors. These were hardly noticed because by then San Franciscans were too busy trying to save themselves and their possessions from fire.

At the first shock people rushed from their houses in their night-clothes. They found that sidewalks and street pavements had buckled, particularly where they rested on filled land. Fissures had been opened in the streets. The twisting of tracks had stopped street-cars—the few that were running at that early hour. Telephones and electric lights were out of commission. Water and gas mains had burst. This was the situation in by all odds the greater part of the city which, standing on firm earth, suffered least from the earthquake proper. After the initial tremor residents in these districts thought the worst was over. They began to sweep up debris, and some even returned to bed. Three hours later thousands were making their way on foot to the business section to begin the day's work.

One could see from the hills that the business district was intact. Modern and well-built structures everywhere had sustained very minor damage. True, much of the domed, ornate City Hall had gone down. (It was a monument to graft and a masterpiece of jerry-building.) The roof of the Empire Theater had caved in. But things like this were exceptions. The Palace and the St. Francis hotels were unharmed; likewise the beautiful eighteen-story *Call* Building on the south side of Market, the Crocker Building (housing the Crocker-Woolworth Bank), and other important structures comprising the financial district on and near the "Wall Street" end of Montgomery Street.

In the district that lay between the south side of Market Street and the bay, it was a different story. For blocks back from the shoreline this was "made" land, created by filling tidal flats. Flimsy frame buildings prevailed in this area, some of them dating back to the Forty-Niners who rushed to California and rushed the construction of shelter. The first few seconds of the quake leveled these shacks which had already existed far beyond the time anticipated by their hurried architects. Some lives were lost beneath them, but worst of all the dry, shattered lumber fed the fires which suddenly broke out —from overturned stoves, from electric wires and severed gas pipes. Firemen found no water in the mains. Though hoses were rigged to draw water from the bay, the fires were soon out of control.

For that matter fire alarms had sounded almost immediately in all parts of the city, bringing out nearly all the city's fire-fighting equipment. In some sections there was water—at least for the time being —and blazes were quickly extinguished. The scattering of the fire department in the fight on little blazes was one of the contributing factors to the disaster in store for San Francisco. The fatal injury of the chief of the fire department by a falling wall in an early hour of the crisis, and the slowness of communication owing to the lack of telephones, also made difficult the launching of a co-ordinated, strategic attack on the flames before they got the upper hand.

Between eight and nine o'clock people employed in the financial district began to show up for work. A few blocks away Armando Pedrini, the assistant cashier, and Ettore Avenali, a clerk, were on hand at the Bank of Italy. These men roomed together in North Beach. When the city began to rock, they had hurried to the street. Though the buildings were not generally of first-class construction, this area rests on solid earth. The earthquake damage, therefore, had been relatively slight. There was plenty of excitement, naturally, and streets were filled with debris from thrown-down chimneys, signs and cornices. Pedrini found that the bank building had sustained no damage worth mentioning. He got Clarence Cuneo's horse and buggy and made the usual trip to the Crocker-Woolworth National for the Bank of Italy's cash, which may have amounted to about $80,000. At nine o'clock the bank opened amid scenes of commotion, but no panic.

Just what business the bank transacted that forenoon no surviving record discloses. Deposits and withdrawals seemingly balanced each other, for there was about $80,000 on hand when A. P. Giannini closed the bank in the early afternoon.

As the morning wore on tension mounted. Smoke from the burning districts drifted over North Beach. Yet the recollections of one of the bank's directors are testimony as to the generally unrealized nature of the danger. He was Dr. Guido Caglieri, who on the morning of April 18, 1906, arrived early at his office on Montgomery Avenue opposite the bank. A few squares away in Battery Street a fire was burning. It burned rapidly, for Battery Street, standing on made land like the neighboring section south of Market, had been torn up by the first tremor. Its buildings, also, were old and ramshackle. As Caglieri recalled, this fire did not give him a great deal of concern. Not until he heard that the lower end of the south side of Market Street was ablaze did he become alarmed. That news came about eleven o'clock.

At noon Giannini arrived. He had been more than five hours covering the seventeen miles from his home in San Mateo. As the trains were not running, he had started to walk to San Francisco. On the way he got a few lifts in wagons, but most of the traffic was headed the other way. Refugees he passed on the road shouted hysterical tales of calamity. Giannini did not have to be told about the fire on the south side of Market. As he circled the waterfront to reach the bank, he had seen it licking the walls of the Palace Hotel.

Market Street is one of the widest streets in the world. If the fire could be confined to the south side, the financial district and North Beach would presumably be safe. The Battery Street fire seemed under control. Nevertheless, Giannini decided not to take a chance. He closed the bank and watched the spread of the fires. When Pedrini came back from a trip to Market Street and reported that the famed Palace Hotel and the stately *Call* Building were torches, Giannini got two teams and wagons from L. Scatena & Company. The bank's cash, mostly gold, was carried to a wagon bed and hidden beneath crates of oranges. Then records were piled on top. No room remained for the new Burroughs adding machine which had cost $375, much too big an investment for the Bank of Italy, Giannini believed. Reluctantly he rolled it into the safe to which the bank's money had never been entrusted overnight.

A few blocks away, in the financial district, employees of the big banks were stowing records and cash in fireproof vaults. A strange scene took place at the Crocker. While distraught customers were arriving with valuables destined for the vault, the bank was moving out its records, securities and some gold. Pedrini heard the Crocker intended to put these belongings on a tugboat which would head for the middle of the bay.

The situation grew worse. Fantastic prices were offered for vehicles of any sort that could transport goods to Golden Gate Park, to the military reservation of the Presidio or to the fancied security of Telegraph, Russian and Nob Hills. Refugees by the thousand streamed by, with belongings on their backs, in pushcarts, wheelbarrows and baby carriages. The smallest child lugged something, if only a toy. Many a head of a family carried with him his savings in gold, perhaps congratulating himself for the moment that he had not been persuaded to deposit it in a bank.

Had it not been for the energetic behavior of officials chaos and panic would have been complete. Mayor Schmitz was acting resolutely—a bright spot on an otherwise corrupt public record. His right-hand man was an old political adversary, former Mayor Phelan who headed a citizens committee of safety. Brigadier General Funston, a hero of the Spanish-American War, marched the regulars from the Presidio into town during the first hour. The spread of the flames was checked at points by dynamiting buildings and by demolishing them with artillery. When looting began the order was passed to shoot on sight.

For reasons of security, Giannini decided to make the trip to San Mateo at night. With three others he took the wagons to Clarence Cuneo's flat at the far end of North Beach, where they had supper and at eight o'clock started for the country. So choked were the roads with refugees that the two wagons were all night making the trip. At Seven Oaks the bank's money was hidden in the ashes trap of the living room fireplace.[3]

3

Without sleeping, Giannini returned to the doomed city on the day following, Friday, April 20. It was a disheartening scene. The

Bank of Italy's building was in ruins and its safe unrecognizable in the embers. The financial district, the retail district, the Washington Street commission district, Nob Hill, Russian Hill, Telegraph Hill and Chinatown had been swept by the fire. On Saturday the northern end of the Beach continued to burn. That night a downpour of rain came to the aid of the exhausted men who were fighting the fires, mostly with dynamite. Nearly all the Bank of Italy's depositors had, like President Scatena, lost their places of business and their homes. From the refugee camps people wandered among the ashes, or crowded about the improvised morgues and hospitals.

The whole of 490 blocks and parts of 32 others had been laid waste. This comprised 2,593 acres, or about one-third of the built-up area of the city. That third took in virtually the whole business section. There had been about 500 deaths. Two hundred and fifty thousand persons were homeless. The property loss ran between $350,000,000 and $500,000,000.

With $80,000 in available cash to cover deposits of $846,000 and to meet requests for the loans that must be made if North Beach was to revive, A. P. Giannini saw in the calamity that had befallen San Francisco a great opportunity for the Bank of Italy to show its worth. That is confidence! Something of this confidence he transmitted to the bank's depositors in a circular letter that went out from San Mateo on Sunday, April 22. The letter said that the bank would open temporary quarters at the residence of A. P. Giannini's brother, Dr. Attilio H. Giannini, 2745 Van Ness Avenue, and on the Washington Street wharf. Checks would be cashed for limited amounts, deposits accepted, and loans made for rebuilding. The westward progress of the fire had been halted at Van Ness Avenue, a wide street. Hence Dr. Giannini's home, situated on the west side of the street, had been spared.[4]

On April 27, nine days after the earthquake and five days after the fire was extinguished, this newspaper advertisement appeared:

BANK OF ITALY

Temporarily Located at

2745 Van Ness Avenue

Corner Lombard St.

Address all communications above address

L. Scatena, President.[5]

The great banks were not able to act as quickly. Though most of their buildings, gutted by fire, were capable of being repaired, vaults were too hot to be opened for some time. To forestall runs Governor Pardee declared a bank holiday on the day following the earthquake.

The morning that the Bank of Italy's advertisement appeared the San Francisco *Examiner* reported: "The bankers repeat their statement that they will relieve the wants of their depositors at the earliest possible time, but have not yet reached any conclusion as to how or when they can do so." Next day the news appeared to be a little better. "Relief is coming from the banks. Within a few days they expect to make advances to their many depositors."[6]

The report was optimistic as to time. The holidays continued for more than a month and, by then, the bankers were a "thoroughly dispirited lot of men," according to James K. Lynch, vice-president of the First National Bank. "Our brains were in a fog." Mr. Lynch was not speaking for A. P. Giannini. His brain was in no fog.[7]

The Clearing House Association had taken charge of the financial situation, holding conferences daily at the home of Henry T. Scott, a director of the Crocker-Woolworth. A white banner bearing the Crocker name fluttered before the Scott mansion indicating the temporary location of the big national bank. Similar banners decorated neighboring houses which faced Lafayette Square where homeless victims of the fire had pitched their tents. To the line of mansions enclosing the square the campers gave the name "Bankers' Row."[8]

Though his bank was not a member of the Clearing House, Vice-President Giannini was invited to the meetings at the Scott home. He went to a couple of them, but decided he could better help the recovery of the stricken city by looking after depositors who flocked to the Washington Street wharf for relief. Because it was more convenient to North Beach, most of the Bank of Italy's business was transacted on the waterfront, rather than at "Doc" Giannini's home on Van Ness. The equipment of the wharf "branch" consisted of a plank counter and a bag of money from the hoard in the fireplace at Seven Oaks.

The popular assumption that the Bank of Italy was able to resume banking functions ahead of its colleagues because the small bank had got out its cash is only part of the story. The determining factors were the courage and foresight of A. P. Giannini and the faith he was able to impart to his bank's depositors. Unlike the big bankers who were hampered by the loss of records, A. P. did not need them. He knew every one of his distressed clients and, almost to the penny, their balances before disaster struck. Moreover, he knew how much they could stand in the way of loans. He made decisions quickly. It was unnecessary to turn to municipal assessment rolls, if any survived, for Giannini carried in his head the appraised values of all North Beach properties and of some other sections as well.

This all helped, but even more important was A. P.'s achievement in brightening the outlook of customers who had lost the heart to try again.

"We are going to rebuild San Francisco and it will be greater than ever," he would tell them in his deep, booming voice. Then he would confidently unfold his vision of the metropolis whose future could be realized only if every man, woman and child rolled up his sleeves. There are old-timers still living who recall how they were infected by his enthusiasm and their ambition returned.

When the listener said he was ready to do his part and start rebuilding in the ashes, Giannini praised his courage. "That's the spirit! We'll fix up a loan immediately." If the borrower asked for $3,000, the banker would offer him only $1,500 or even less. Holding up a sheaf of papers he'd say so all could hear: "Look at all these requests we have. If we give everybody all he wants there won't be enough money to go 'round. You raise half the money and we'll supply the other half."

In this way did Giannini spread the $80,000, making it do the work of a sum several times larger. His strategy also turned loose a small army of borrowers on the trail of the hoarded money of North Beachers. The result was that thousands of dollars in hidden gold which had been rescued from the flames became available at once for the rebuilding of San Francisco. Not all this money went for reconstruction. Much came to the bank in deposits—proof of the fact that confidence and optimism reproduce themselves. Italians who had distrusted banks all their lives felt that their money would be safer with Giannini than in the refugee camps or in the temporary shelters that were knocked together in a hurry. Six weeks after the earthquake the Bank of Italy's deposits were exceeding withdrawals.[9]

For more than three weeks the bank did business on the Washington Street wharf and on Van Ness Avenue. Then it crowded into Charley Grondona's real estate office on the ground floor of the Montgomery Block, on Montgomery Street, almost opposite the burned-out quarters on Montgomery Avenue. The Montgomery Block had survived because it stood near the appraiser's office and the post office which federal troops took extraordinary measures to save. On May 22 a newspaper advertisement announced:

BANK OF ITALY

632 Montgomery St.
(Montgomery Block)

NOW OPEN

FOR REGULAR BUSINESS

Absolutely no loss suffered by
reason of the recent disaster.[10]

The day following, May 23, marked the return to normal for the Clearing House banks, though most of them were still in temporary locations. The conferences at the Scott house had produced a Clearing House Bank which started up on May 1 in the United States Mint. Withdrawals were limited to $500 and a teller from each member bank was on hand at the Mint to look after the needs of the bank's depositors. Under this arrangement little hard money changed hands, the Clearing House settling daily balances of members through debits and credits.[11]

The Bank of Italy's temporary office in the Montgomery Block was like a beehive. In addition to real estate loans, the bank made personal loans to put little businesses on their feet again. There were loans to enable bay vessels to bring lumber and other building materials to North Beach. The city was still burning when the forehanded Giannini had tramped along the bay front hunting up captains he traveled with in his younger days. They did not *ask* for loans. A. P. shoved cash into their hands, saying: "Go up north and get lumber." In this way the Italian colony, despite inferior resources, got ahead of the rest of the city in the work of reconstruction. San Francisco's Italian-language daily, *L'Italia,* publishing in a makeshift plant across the bay in Oakland, singled out A. P. Giannini to thank for the "thousand different ways" his "energy and initiative" were helpful to North Beach in those trying days.[12]

To get things going, Bank of Italy accepted fire insurance policies as security for business loans. Most banks doubted the policies had much worth, considering how hard the insurance companies had been hit. Giannini believed that, if the borrower's character was good, no better security was needed than the heavy demand for goods to replace what had been destroyed. As it turned out, importer-borrowers usually had their shipments sold by the time they reached San Francisco. Loans would be repaid and Bank of Italy would make advances on the next boatloads. In this line, G. B. Schiaffino was probably the heaviest borrower. At one time he had $80,000 in goods on the way from Europe, all financed by one $10,000 policy. Another firm financed in this manner was A. Giurlani & Bro., olive oil dealers, still in business on Front Street.[13]

One could believe in an institution that showed such vitality and neighborliness; and believe in it North Beach did. Despite the unprecedented demands for money on every hand, the Bank of Italy within seventy days after the disaster had carried out its program to increase its capital to $500,000 by the sale of 2,000 additional shares of stock. This transaction was facilitated by the fact that A. P. Giannini and Mr. Scatena consented to accept 680 of the new shares at 105 in part payment for a site for a permanent home for the bank. The lot was at Clay and Montgomery Streets, two blocks nearer San Francisco's financial section and at the same time handy to North Beach. Scatena and Giannini offered this excellent site to the bank for $125,000 with the proviso that, at any time, they would take the property off the bank's hands at that figure, plus what the bank might expend in erecting a building, plus 5 per cent interest.[14]

The directors discussed details of the bank's new home. It was to be an impressive structure, ten stories high "if possible." Work did not begin until the following year, however, because the bank felt that the building needs of its patrons had first call on the bank's funds.

4

By autumn, 1906, the reconstruction of San Francisco was in full course. The city swarmed with workmen, hundreds of whom had come from long distances. Before the fire not more than twenty thousand persons in San Francisco were engaged in the building trades. Six months later forty thousand were at work there at wages averaging a third above the prevailing scale elsewhere. Sundays were almost as busy as other days. Insurance settlements, loans and accumulated capital provided the funds to meet the bills. Money became more plentiful than before the disaster. Temporary railroad tracks were laid through the ruins to speed the disposal of debris and the bringing in of building materials. In October the San Francisco *Examiner* remarked:

North Beach has been the first to resume its former aspect. . . . The former retail trade that flourished there has been reestablished to a great extent, and more dwellings, both flats and private houses, have been erected than in any portion of the city. Its residents put up 542 structures within four months.[15]

The part played in this by the Bank of Italy was recognized outside the Italian colony. James J. Fagan of the Crocker National ("Woolworth" was dropped from the title shortly after the fire) was proud of the achievements of his protege. Said the San Francisco *Call* in a review of the city's rebirth, published two years after the earthquake:

Some of the first loads of lumber that were hauled to North Beach were paid for out of money made available from the Bank of Italy. . . . The loyalty and confidence and judgment of the directors and of the bank and the good faith and energy of the homeless people were the elements that went into these first financial bargains after the calamity.[16]

North Beach stood by the bank that had stood by it. Before the disaster the growth of the Bank of Italy had been decidedly encouraging. After the disaster it was phenomenal.

By the end of the year the business of all San Francisco banks reflected the buoyant activities of rebuilding. Clearing House figures for the whole of 1906 were slightly above those for 1905 which had been a boom year. The Bank of Italy, however, had virtually doubled its business. As of December 31, 1906, assets stood at $1,899,947, against $1,021,290 on December 31, 1905. Deposits had gone from $706,000 to $1,355,000. Perhaps the most striking thing in figures was the number of new depositors. Savings accounts had more than doubled—from 1,023 to 2,644. Commercial accounts went from 280 to 451. Loans and discounts advanced from $883,000 to $1,471,000. The 5 per cent dividend to stockholders was continued.[17]

And once again the Bank of Italy closed a year in the possession of an incalculable new asset not shown on the books. This was the determination of A. P. Giannini to follow banking as a career. Years later Mr. Giannini said that the response he got from the people of North Beach in return for his labors after the earthquake and fire made him decide to become a banker for life.[18]

Learning from the Panic of 1907

THE OPENING of the year 1907 found the Bank of Italy in such prosperous condition and the rebuilding of San Francisco proceeding so satisfactorily that A. P. Giannini decided to take a trip East. In retrospect much that does not seem to have been in Giannini's mind when he set out has been read into the motives inspiring his journey. The controlling fact seems to have been that having had his nose to the grindstone for nearly three years, he wanted a vacation—and for that reason he planned to take Mrs. Giannini along. Also, he wanted to see the inside of some of the Eastern banks, with a view to getting pointers for the new home of the Bank of Italy that was beginning to rise on the southeast corner of Clay and Montgomery Streets. Moreover, having made up his mind to continue as a banker, Giannini wanted to meet and talk to other bankers. To meet people gave him ideas.[1]

So in January, 1907, the board of the Bank of Italy granted its first vice-president and general manager a leave of absence. The following month A. P.'s youngest brother, George J. Giannini, was made third vice-president. During the fire A. P. had drafted George away from L. Scatena & Company into the service of the bank.

When the A. P. Gianninis got away early in March, the prosperity of San Francisco was but a more intense version of the condition of the whole country. Nor was this situation peculiar to the United States. The whole world was flush—and, not satisfied with a healthy prosperity, had during the past two years gone in for speculation financed from London and the money centers of the Continent. There was, however, not enough money on earth to carry all the projects begun by promoters. With its reserves the lowest in years, the Bank of England, the world's most influential bank, tried to slow things down by jacking up its interest and discount rates, and by warning other European banks to curtail their lavish credits, in particular to New York. What happened to the Bank of England was also happening in a way to the Bank of Italy in its temporary quarters in Charley Grondona's real estate office. For the first time in its history deposits showed a slight drop. The same was true of nearly all San Francisco banks. The reason was not obscure: mounting prices and the demands for cash due to rebuilding. Yet, unlike the Bank of England, the Bank of Italy saw no reason to put the brakes on credit. In January, 1907, new real estate loans alone aggregated $92,421; in February, $119,823. The rate remained at 6 per cent.[2]

Warnings also were heard on this side of the Atlantic. The New York banking firm of Henry Clews & Company forecast the possibility of a credit stringency owing to increased prices and insufficient currency. Secretary of the Treasury Leslie M. Shaw said: "We who pray should ask God to save us from increased prosperity; we have all we can stand." Jacob H. Schiff told the New York Chamber of Commerce: "If the currency conditions of this country are not changed materially, I predict . . . a panic."[3]

The United States had the most confusing and inadequate monetary and banking system of any commercial nation. For money there were gold, silver, nickel and copper coins; and a variety of paper issued by the federal government and by national banks. Each kind had its peculiar legal-tender status. The banking system, stemming from an outmoded law of 1864, consisted of national and state banks, the latter in the majority. One glaring fault was the inelasticity of the currency, with no proper provision for expansion, contraction or free flow from one part of the country to another to meet the changing requirements of business. Another fault was the decentralization of deposit reserves. Small banks placed a share of these reserves at interest with city banks which in turn loaned a part on the call-money market. In times of uncertainty or of actual need the small banks demanded their money, call rates soared and security prices dropped.

As the Gianninis journeyed eastward this situation, together with the action of the Bank of England, brought a serious break on the New York Stock Exchange. Though the break was temporary Giannini found Eastern bankers "down in the mouth," as he later put it, and disturbed over the future. With plenty of good assets the banks

were short of money. In addition to local demands, some $200,000,-
000 had been siphoned off to San Francisco to meet fire insurance
settlements. Uneasy country banks continued to call for their reserves.

After visits in Chicago, Philadelphia and New York, Giannini
swung south and headed back west by way of New Orleans. There
a newspaper reporter described the traveling banker as an officer "of
one of the strongest institutions in California." In return Mr. Giannini paid New Orleans some pleasant compliments. Of what was
really on his mind he said nothing, though he had decided to see to
it that, for its size, the Bank of Italy should be all that the reporter
said it was. From what had been contemplated as a carefree junket,
Giannini arrived in San Francisco late in May to prepare his bank
to deal with troubled times.[4]

2

These preparations took three forms: curtailment of loans, increase of the bank's gold stock and a campaign to build up deposits.
Rates on real estate loans were raised from 6 to 7 per cent. Personal
loans remained at 6.

Giannini himself reviewed every loan on the books. With those
made before his departure he was already familiar; but he wanted
to know if anything untoward had happened to the borrower in the
meanwhile. As a result of the new policy real estate loans dropped
from $101,723 in May to $67,257 in June. They sank to $48,079 in
July and in August to $44,626. In August almost as much—$38,019
—was paid as was loaned. In September $17,399 in real estate loans
was paid whereas new loans amounted to only $10,488.[5]

To accumulate gold Giannini instructed his tellers to pay out
paper money unless the patron should request coin. Though San
Franciscans in general, and North Beachers in particular, preferred
gold such was the faith the Bank of Italy had instilled in its clientele
that a great deal more paper than normal was accepted without
question, and an equal amount of gold stashed away by the bank.
Curiously, the member of the Bank of Italy's board who had the
most banking experience thought this procedure unnecessary. Ordinarily it was the other way around between James J. Fagan and
Giannini, with Fagan curbing what he regarded as A. P.'s incautious

impulses. This time Fagan said San Francisco had plenty of gold and that there was no reason for Giannini to hoard it.

Fagan's indifference to gold gave Giannini another idea. Still not a member of the Clearing House, the Bank of Italy cleared through the Crocker National and every evening sent in Clarence Cuneo's buggy a bag of currency to take care of cleared checks. It had been customary to include a stated proportion of gold in this remittance. Since Fagan had said he did not need gold, Giannini ordered that the proportion of gold be cut down. The subtracted gold went into his own hoard which was kept in the Bank of Italy's safe deposit box at the Crocker bank. Giannini felt that the time would come when both he and Fagan might need that extra gold.[6]

The campaign to increase deposits was likewise successful. Giannini and Grondona resumed their persuasions among residents of North Beach who did their banking under a mattress. The disproportionate increase in commercial deposits also suggests that business acquaintances of directors were prevailed on to switch a portion of their accounts to the Bank of Italy. At any rate the decline in deposits was halted, and the money lost in that way more than regained by the end of September. This was quite an achievement because, taking San Francisco as a whole, bank deposits continued to decline.

A factor in the Bank of Italy's increase in deposits was the initial step toward A. P. Giannini's ambition to expand his bank beyond the confines of its birthplace in North Beach. On August 1, 1907, the bank opened its first branch at 3343 Mission Street. Before the fire this was a better-class non-Italian residential neighborhood with its own little shopping center, including a small bank—the Mission Bank, of which James Rolph was president. Good work during the fire had brought Rolph to the public's attention, starting him on a political career which was to include five terms as mayor of San Francisco and one as governor of California.

Untouched by the fire, the Mission district had boomed when a number of large burned-out stores and other concerns opened temporary quarters there. Two large banks, the California Safe Deposit and Trust and the Anglo-Californian, established branches. The Bank of Italy's was number three.

That this venture was the result of a fairly quick decision seems apparent from an entry in the board minutes, under date of August 13:

On motion of Mr. J. J. Fagan . . . Resolved that this Board of Directors of the Bank of Italy duly ratify the actions of the 1st Vice President Mr. A. P. Giannini in the opening of a Branch.

The neighborhood newspaper, *Mission Times,* cordially welcomed the branch and its manager, Victor Caglieri.

Under the Management of its vice-president, A. P. Giannini, the bank has become one of the most progressive and successful in the city. . . . Mr. Caglieri states that he intends to devote the resources of the Mission branch to the building up of the Mission district just the same as the main bank has been building up the North Beach district.[7]

3

The storm the little Bank of Italy made ready to meet was on the way. It had started in Egypt with a money panic, runs on banks and the failure of one of the largest banks in Alexandria. Japan was hit next, then Germany, then Chile. During the summer and early autumn of 1907, the credit situation tightened in the United States. Particularly was the pinch felt in the East as Western banks began to call reserve funds home. Country banks in California began to call on San Francisco. Like the rest of Montgomery Street, the Crocker National felt the drain.

Fagan reversed himself and told Giannini that he had been smart to conserve gold. By this time the Bank of Italy had a nest egg of about $100,000 above normal requirements. This was aside from the gold Giannini had withheld from the clearance remittances. Giannini told Fagan of that stratagem and said the gold, in the Bank of Italy's box in the Crocker National, was at Fagan's disposal. However touched by Giannini's thoughtfulness, the genial Crocker cashier must have smiled. Considering the great bank's liabilities of forty-odd million, the Bank of Italy's gold withholdings were hardly a drop in the bucket.[8]

After several distressing weeks marked by heavy industrial failures and two more market breaks, the panic struck New York in October when the National Bank of Commerce announced that it would not accept for collection checks of the Knickerbocker Trust Company. Through a loophole in the state banking regulations trust companies had entered the field of general banking, though they were not obliged to maintain any stated amount of reserves. Consequently some of them had reserves of less than 5 per cent of deposits as against 25 per cent required of national banks. The Knickerbocker withstood a run for a day and a half and then closed. By this time nearly every other trust company and many banks in the city were besieged. Six banks and four trust companies failed. One trust company performed the prodigious feat of weathering a run of fourteen days during which it paid out $34,000,000 of the $42,000,000 that had been on deposit. In the midst of this had come another stock market break of panic proportions.

The stampede was broken by the financial generalship of J. P. Morgan to whom such ardent foes as Harriman, Rockefeller and the trust-busting Theodore Roosevelt turned instinctively. The federal Treasury rushed $30,000,000 in cash to New York, Morgan raised $25,000,000 more, and handled the whole. It was the old banker's greatest hour.

Meanwhile the wave of fear and disaster was moving westward, though with diminished violence. Nothing anywhere equaled the wild scenes in New York. After the governors of Nevada, Washington and Oregon had proclaimed bank holidays, as a consequence of bank failures in their states, the crisis reached San Francisco on October 30, two weeks behind the Knickerbocker run in New York. The immediate occasion was the closing of the California Safe Deposit & Trust Company—one of the banks with a branch in the Mission district. The financial community had long known that this institution was poorly managed. Just how poorly came out only after investigation, however. More than three-quarters of its $11,000,000 in loans had been borrowed by directors and employees, or by companies in which they were interested.[9]

The day following the California Safe Deposit crash the governor of the state proclaimed a bank holiday. Successive proclamations kept up the holidays until December 21. Nevertheless, banks remained open, as they had during the greater part of the fire emergency the year before. The principal function of the holidays was to aid taxpayers. California law required that taxes be paid in gold and a payment fell due about the time the panic hit the West Coast. To relieve the commercial life of the city San Francisco banks adopted measures used in New York and elsewhere, issuing Clearing House scrip to make up for the scarcity of currency.

The Bank of Italy came through the crisis triumphantly. The gold Giannini had been accumulating since May was stacked high inside the cages for all to see. The spectacle created confidence. Moreover, the little bank paid gold on demand. At no time did it make use of Clearing House scrip; at no time did it place a limit on withdrawals by depositors; and at no time did it invoke the legal right to require advance notice on savings withdrawals. With very few exceptions the savings banks fell back on an old rule, long waived, and demanded from ten to ninety days notice for withdrawals of more than $100.

It would be difficult to cite a clearer example of the axiom that confidence breeds confidence than the performance of the Bank of Italy during the fifty-day crisis. Despite restrictions on withdrawals other banks lost deposits steadily. In instances these losses almost assumed the proportion of runs. One small bank failed. Yet the Giannini bank, with no restrictions and paying legal currency instead of Clearing House scrip (which San Franciscans distrusted far more than Easterners did), showed an excess of deposits over withdrawals for the tight-money period, taking it as a whole.[10]

Giannini derived immense satisfaction from being able to turn over some of the Bank of Italy's gold to the Crocker National. For a time the Crocker was quite short and paid $50,000 in premiums to obtain gold from Chicago and New York to stem runs on its country bank correspondents. The great bank more than returned Giannini's favor, however. When the panic broke the Bank of Italy held certificates of deposit from Crocker—constituting, in effect, a drawing account—in the amount of $150,000. After that was used up during the critical month of November, the Crocker honored Bank of Italy overdrafts running as high as $154,000. In December these overdrafts were converted into additional certificates of deposit.[11]

The bank finished the year with deposits of $1,660,000, an increase of more than $300,000 during the difficult twelve months. In the same period assets had gone from $1,899,900 to $2,221,000. The fact is that, in more than one respect, the Bank of Italy made a better record for the year than the Crocker, which lost nearly $4,000,000 in assets and $3,000,000 in deposits. It was also better than the records of the eight other national banks in San Francisco. Seven showed declines in assets, and all eight declines in deposits.

4

Though the aftereffects of 1907 were mild and of short duration, by comparison with what had followed in 1873, and 1893, they had people worried while they lasted. Industry, trade, railway receipts and so on continued to contract. Farm prices, in fact nearly all prices, went lower. Unemployment mounted—even the rebuilding of San Francisco slacked off—and dollars looked as big as stove lids. In January, 1908, the Bank of Italy lost $70,000 in deposits. February witnessed a further drop. That same month two small San Francisco banks that had survived the panic gave up the ghost. The outgo for the Bank of Italy's building continued high. By June 30, it amounted to $380,000. While the bank was protected against loss by its contract with Scatena and Giannini, the lean times brought criticisms of the wisdom of having embarked upon so ambitious an enterprise. Such a critic was Joseph F. Cavagnaro, the bank's attorney and one of its organizers. As a result Cavagnaro resigned as the bank's counsel, though Giannini persuaded him to remain as a director.

This was the atmosphere pervading California and the country in May of 1908 when A. P. Giannini went to Pasadena to attend the convention of the California Bankers Association. He kept his ears open but took no part in the deliberations. As with bankers everywhere, the main discussion was how to avoid a repetition of 1907. One of the speakers was Lyman J. Gage, then retired and living in California. Mr. Gage had been McKinley's Secretary of the Treasury. With an eminent banking career behind him, Gage had long believed that the salient defect in our system could be remedied by branch banking, somewhat as in Canada. He pointed to the "utter lack of unity and mutual cohesion among the units composing the ten thousand or more banks in the United States. Always in competition, at the moment of stress or strain, they fly apart . . . *each determined to save itself.*"

When it came to offering recommendations, the convention rather pointedly ignored Mr. Gage's suggestion. Nevertheless, the bankers advocated more stringent public scrutiny and regulation of certain aspects of their business. But they were timid and touchy about it, opposing, for example, the widely advocated and sensible proposal to separate the savings and commercial departments of banks. They named a committee to work with a committee of the state legislature which had under study the matter of banking reforms.[12]

Neither California nor any other state, whatever it might do, could cure the banking evils of the United States. The problem was national and so recognized. Within two weeks after the adjournment of the California convention Congress passed the Aldrich-Vreeland Act. This emergency measure aimed to give, on a temporary basis, additional elasticity to the currency through the national banks. Looking to an enduring solution it created a National Monetary Commission to investigate money and banking methods of other countries.

The American Bankers Association met that year in Denver. Here was a body capable of making recommendations national in scope. The principal speaker was Woodrow Wilson, president of Princeton University. His words were long remembered by those who heard them.

"The bank is the most jealously regarded and the least liked instrument of business in this country," said Mr. Wilson.

The banks of this country are remote from the people and the people regard them as not belonging to them but as belonging to some power hostile to them. . . .

If a system of branch banks very simply and inexpensively managed . . . could be established which would put the resources of the rich banks of the country at the disposal of whole countrysides to whose merchants and farmers only a restricted and local credit is now open, the attitude of plain men everywhere towards the banks and banking would be changed utterly within less than a generation. You know that you are looking out for investments; that even the colossal enterprises of our time do not supply you with safe investments enough for the money that comes in to you; and that banks here, there, and everywhere are tempted, as a consequence, to place money in speculative enterprises, and even themselves to promote questionable ventures in finance at a fearful and wholly unjustifiable risk in order to get the usury they wish from their resources. You sit only where these things are spoken of and big returns coveted. There would be plenty of investments if you carried your money to the people of the country at large and had agents in hundreds of villages who knew the men in their neighborhoods who could be trusted with loans and who would make profitable use of them. Your money, moreover, would quicken and fertilize the country. . . .

What have you done by your banking system? The local bank is built up by local resources. Only the local resources for the most part can be called upon for local advantages. Every community is as poor as its own resources. You cannot get the riches of the country in order to make it rich until it gets rich enough to establish a bank. It cannot get credit in the money centers until there accumulates enough capital to make it practically independent of that credit. You have set this country a task of developing in the most difficult and most improbable way. Do you suppose the country is not going to become aware of that? It is aware of it.[13]

Mr. Wilson's address was coldly received. Comparatively few of the bankers of the United States were abreast of this educator in seeing the possibilities of their business. The few who favored branch banking were nearly all large bankers, like James B. Forgan of Chicago's First National. Little bankers, who comprised most of the membership of A.B.A., saw in it only the extinction of their independence, their local prestige and their profits. Yet they had only to look across the border to Canada to see it in operation. With a branch banking system modeled after that in the British Isles, Canada had come through 1907 and 1908 with only two bank failures and slight distress.

A. P. Giannini was a little banker without the insularity and shortsightedness of his fellows; also without the fears. If branch banking was what Mr. Wilson said it was, and what the recent experience of Canada seemed to prove that it was, the fact that the speaker had recommended the branch idea only to banks with enormous resources did not scare Giannini. He foresaw no loss of independence. Should he decide to go into branch banking, and should that mean competition with the giants of the banking world—why, Giannini would compete, that was all. The prospect terrified him no more than had the San Francisco fire or the Panic of 1907.

As to prestige, that was something Giannini enjoyed as well as the next one. The local renown that had come as a result of the Bank of Italy's small but noteworthy triumphs was dear to him. He was ambitious to perpetuate and enhance that renown, though not by making money for himself. The more A. P. Giannini saw of rich men the less he wanted to be one. The more he saw of other banks the less he wanted his bank to be like them. Mr. Wilson was right when he said that the bigger banks grew the more remote seemed their contact with the ordinary concerns of ordinary people. Giannini did not want a bank of his to grow big in that way. He believed that, once a bank helpfully concerned itself with the fiscal aspect of the everyday problems of average men and women, there was no limit to that bank's growth in size or in usefulness. Giannini knew his California—its varied economy, the diverse ways men had of making a living. As to California's ultimate potentialities he was as little afflicted with the habit of understatement as most Native Sons. He came to feel that almost anywhere one might go in California there was room for a bank that would serve its community as the Bank of Italy was serving North Beach.

Possibly something along the line of the branch banking system of Canada would be the answer. Giannini was not unfamiliar with this system. As far back as he could remember, some of the great Canadian banks had maintained branches in San Francisco. The Bank of British Columbia had come there in 1864 and, at the time of its merger with the Canadian Bank of Commerce in 1901, was rated one of the three outstanding banks in California. To have a closer look Giannini took a trip through the western part of the Dominion. In frontier communities like Medicine Hat he saw branches of banks, whose home offices were in Montreal or Toronto, performing services that no bank depending on local capital and management possibly could have performed. These safe, well-conducted, economically operated institutions were at the other end of the pole from the speculative, loosely run banks of the American frontier, including San Francisco in its early days. Giannini had never been a great reader of history but that history he did know.[14]

5

By the fall of 1908 recovery from the brief postpanic depression was under way. The upswing for the Bank of Italy had come before that. On June 30, it showed for the half-year a gain in deposits of $110,000. Assets were up $121,000, loans down, surplus up.

August 17 was a proud day for A. P. Giannini when the Bank of Italy opened for business in its nine-story home at Clay and Montgomery. The officers and directors were on hand to welcome depositors and friends. A reporter for the *Coast Banker* was unmistakably impressed.

The building is noteworthy, because of its beauty and completeness and because it illustrates the enterprise of the management on account of the fact that it was one of the first big structures to be erected after the fire. . . . The structure is all of steel and is absolutely fireproof and class A in every particular. . . . Free rein has been given to artists and architects to carry out the general idea of the management to make the banking room ideally beautiful.

Earthquake-conscious Californians were assured that

the building is of most enduring construction . . . [with] concrete and cantilever foundations placed at a level of thirty-five feet below the curb. . . . The granite reaches to the third floor and the upper structure façades are laid up with Bedford, Indiana, limestone, the only example of this character of stone in San Francisco.

The basement space provides one of the most artistic, well-lighted and ventilated safe deposit departments in the city of San Francisco. . . . A great flight of marble steps from the main banking room leads directly to the safe deposit department. Here is a vault 20 feet wide by 30 feet in depth, containing 5,000 safety boxes, and provided with the highest type vault doors.

Clarence Cuneo's horse and buggy had made their last trip to the Crocker National with the Bank of Italy's cash.

The banking room occupies the entire first floor. . . . No banking room in this city will excel [it] in beauty. . . . Pavanazzo marble walls, desks, railings, partitions, counters and vault fronts, Italian marble flooring, bronze doors, window frames and candelabras and counter screens, to-gether with a most elaborate ceiling of complex lines heavily laid in gold and high color, and set off by richly wrought electroliers from wall surfaces and bronze stands, constitute the items of finish that go to make up a per-fect composition. . . .

The upper floors are entirely devoted to non-bank offices . . . for all of which at this date there is a great demand.[15]

A. P. Giannini had his desk in no private room, but in the open on the first floor where everyone entering the bank could see him and talk to him. "That's one trouble with bankers," he said. "They shut themselves off away from people and don't know what's going on. Why a banker should do that I can't imagine." To Giannini, people were the most interesting phenomena on earth. In the course of a day if fifty of the bank's customers didn't drop by his desk to say a word, A. P. might feel himself neglected.

The vitality of this friendly giant was one source of people's trust in him and in his bank. Giannini never seemed to tire. Recalling the days of the fire when the banker had been on his feet for twenty-four hours, people will assure you that he appeared neither weary nor worried; and that to be near him made others feel more secure. Fifty callers in a day had no discernible effect on the continuity or precision of his thought concerning the conduct of the bank. Giannini did not expect visitors to discuss money matters exclusively, or even mainly. He listened just as attentively to domestic news: of sickness or death; of an engagement, a wedding, a confirmation, a new baby. As Giannini looked at it, almost anything that concerned people also concerned the bank. If the father of a new baby was a poor man Giannini might fish a five-dollar gold piece from his pocket. "For the little fellow; and remember that a savings account in his name can be started with a dollar." In ninety-nine cases out of a hundred the parent would cross the marble floor to a savings window.[16]

In its new surroundings the bank continued to thrive. Early in 1909 Giannini's salary was doubled—to $400 a month. President Scatena was voted his first salary—$100 a month. Secretary Charley Grondona, who had worked more than four years for nothing, refused a salary of $25 a month. With the Bank of Italy over the hump, he resigned his office to give more time to his long-neglected real estate business, but remained on the board. Though George Giannini returned to his stepfather's commission business, the third vice-presidency stayed in the family. It was taken by "Doc"—A. H.—Giannini whose residence had provided the bank with shelter after the fire. Armando Pedrini became cashier in name as well as in fact. The bank's capital was increased to $750,000.

This last step, plus the accumulation of large cash reserves, was in preparation for expansion under the provisions of the new California banking bill that was shaping up in the legislature. This notable bill, destined to prove a milestone in state bank legislation in the United States, was the result of remarkable satisfactory teamwork between the lawmakers and the committee of bankers named at the Pasadena convention. The bankers' committee went much further in the right direction than the mandate of the convention as expressed by its mid-dle-of-the-road resolutions on the subject of reform.

Having passed the legislature, the Bank Act was signed by the governor on March 8, 1909, its provisions to become effective on July 1.

"It must be plain," said J. M. Henderson, Jr., of Sacramento, chairman of the committee that had assisted the legislators, "that the day is over when banks may be conducted exclusively as though they were in the line of ordinary business, without regard to the dependent interest of the public in their policies and management."[17]

The act provided for the most rigid supervision and regulation of state banks that had been imposed by any state government. Authority was centralized in one man, the state superintendent of banks, to be appointed by the governor. An important feature of the law separated the three types of banking that might be conducted by one institution: commercial, savings and trust. A bank engaged in more than one of these activities must keep the assets and accounts of each department distinct. The organization and operation of each department was minutely regulated as to capital, loans, overdrafts, investments, reserves and other matters. Examinations were to be more frequent and more revealing.

A section of the act, not much noticed until Giannini began to take advantage of it, had to do with branch banking. Because of the distances in California there had long been a certain amount of branch banking by a few large country banks. Nothing in the laws prior to 1909 authorized it or forbade it. The framers of the act of 1909 could hardly have foreseen branch banking as an important issue or they would not have treated it in the negative way they did. The act merely stated that no additional branches should be opened without the superintendent's approval, which should be given only after he had "ascertained to his satisfaction that the public convenience and advantage will be promoted by the opening of such branch office." An addition of $25,000 to the capital stock of the parent bank was required for each branch opened.[18]

It was a comparatively simple matter for the Bank of Italy to bring itself within the terms of the new law. There were, for instance, no loans to officers or employees, which the act prohibited. After the fire the total of loans had been reduced promptly to where they were covered by deposits without impinging upon the capital, another thing forbidden by the act. The old capital of $500,000 was assigned to the savings department and the new capital of $250,000 to the commercial.

On July 1, 1909, when the act went into force, the Bank of Italy had deposits of more than $2,000,000 and assets of more than $3,000,-000. Ready to enter the branch banking field, it lost little time in doing so.

The Start at Branch Banking

O N OCTOBER 12, 1909, a date of sentimental importance to Italian-Americans, the directors of the Bank of Italy, meeting in their handsome new room at Clay and Montgomery, named "a committee to call on the Superintendent of Banks and secure, if possible, permission to establish a branch at San Jose, California." This action foreshadowed something quite different from the bank's city branch opened on Mission Street two years before. A city branch answers a need arising from traffic problems rather than from economics and finance; it is simply another teller's window up the street.[1]

This would not be true of a branch in the Santa Clara Valley, fifty miles away. There the young Bank of Italy would find itself at grips with a whole set of problems for which the banking experience of the United States provided little to go by in the way of precedent.

Three weeks after the request was made, Superintendent of Banks Alden Anderson granted the Bank of Italy permission to open a branch in San Jose. His finding was that San Jose "needed" the banking facilities Giannini could supply. Behind an exchange of impersonal official communications lay a very human story which both Anderson and the Bank of Italy knew quite well, having talked it over.

The banks of the valley had been founded by the landowning gentry and were run for their benefit. In boom times these people were rich and the banks paid whopping dividends. In hard times the people borrowed more from the banks and increased the mortgages on their land. By and large those who made the land productive were hard-working immigrants who cultivated every corner of their small ranches. The banks made the task harder than it should have been.

The practice of favoring the owners of large tracts over those of small well-improved ones was not so much a matter of conscious class or race discrimination as it was of ignorance. Bankers simply hadn't awakened to where the real potentialities of the valley lay.

The third oldest bank in the valley and one of the oldest in California was the Commercial and Savings Bank of San Jose. Because of its land loans, this bank had been skating on thin ice for a number of years. A typical beneficiary was the fabulous Murphy clan one of whose properties—a ranch of fifty thousand acres—was in Santa Barbara County, two-thirds of the distance to Los Angeles. The bank's first president was a Murphy whose grandfather had come to California in 1845. Loans on Murphy land reflected the history of the family's ups and downs over a period of nearly thirty years. They were also accountable, to a considerable degree, for the fact that during this time the bank's capital had been pared from $500,000 to $150,000.

The Commercial and Savings had had a close call in the late nineties, after which worried depositors demanded the election of Lazard Lion to the presidency. A successful San Jose merchant, Lion struggled valiantly for a dozen years. He might have kept the bank rocking along for a while had it not been for California's new Bank Act, designed to clean up an unsound banking condition before disaster hit. Within sixty days after taking office Superintendent Anderson had been obliged to order the Commercial and Savings to dispose of its holdings in the Commercial Land Company. Under the Bank Act of 1909 they were not legal assets.

The Commercial Land Company was a device created by the bank to remove the many foreclosures of loans secured by land and carried for too long a time on the books. Officers of the land company held identical offices in the bank. Commercial Land was, in effect, a holding company, a new phase in banking development which appeared in the Northwest about 1900. To the holding company the Commercial Bank released the foreclosures and in return received shares of the land company.

In case of emergency these shares could hardly have been converted into liquid assets at the value they were carried on the books. Faced with the necessity of realizing on them in order to meet the stipulations of the Bank Act, Gus Lion, vice-president and son of the

president of the shaken institution, went to San Francisco to appeal
to A. P. Giannini. Such was the origin of the Bank of Italy's interest
in San Jose as a field for expansion.[2]

The opportunity fitted in fine with the plans of Giannini, who had
not lost touch with the neighborhood of his birthplace. Since Amadeo had played there as a child, and as a young commission merchant had climbed the slopes of the Coast Range to buy early peas,
many Italians and immigrants of other nationalities had settled in
the comely valley to take their livelihoods from its rich soil. Some of
his old friends and acquaintances had done well, some not so well.
But now as he looked upon the valley with the eyes of a daring and
unconventional banker it seemed to Giannini that few had done as
well as they could have, if the place had just one bank to do what
the Bank of Italy had done in five years' time for North Beach, learning as it went. The irony—or call it a sort of poetic justice—was that
not even the bankers had done well, as witness the straits of the Commercial and Savings. For all its backing by the grandee families of
the valley, here was aristocratic old Commercial asking the son of an
obscure immigrant to save it. A. P. Giannini would have been less
than human not to have felt a glow of pride.

2

When Superintendent Anderson consented to the aquisition of the
crippled bank the Bank of Italy moved rapidly. The simplest procedure would have been for it to buy enough Commercial and Savings
stock to exercise control. The Bank Act, however, forbade the purchase of one bank's stock by another bank. James A. Bacigalupi, the
brilliant young lawyer who had succeeded Cavagnaro as attorney for
the Bank of Italy, devised another way. It was roundabout, but legal.
Individuals, representing the Bank of Italy, would buy in their own
names a controlling number of shares. Then the Bank of Italy, as a
corporation, would buy the bulk of the *assets* (not the stock) of the
selling bank. Purchase of assets the law permitted. It also permitted
the consolidation of two banks. So the third step would be consolidation, in the course of which Commercial bank stock would be exchanged for Bank of Italy stock at ten shares for one.

At a special meeting of the Commercial's board in San Jose on
November 13, 1909, President Lion announced that control had been

purchased "by Mr. L. Scatena of San Francisco." Other new stock-holders were Dr. A. H. Giannini, J. A. Bacigalupi, George G. Ca-glieri and Nicholas A. Pellerano. Thereupon Lazard Lion resigned as president. His son, Gus, quit as vice-president and G. W. Rutherford as secretary. Lorenzo Scatena, A. H. Giannini and Armando Pedrini were elected in their places. Three directors also gave way to three Bank of Italy men. To get them off the bank's books, doubtful loans aggregating $32,000 were sold to a San Francisco speculator for fifty cents on the dollar.[3]

Dr. A. H. Giannini announced the change of management.

"The new institution," commented the San Jose *Mercury and Herald*,

is to pay special attention to the affairs of people who speak English with difficulty and will have employees who speak the French, Italian, Spanish and Portuguese languages. . . .

"The transformation of the local bank into a branch of the San Francisco institution," stated Dr. Giannini, "does not mean that San Jose coin will be taken away to San Francisco, but that San Francisco coin will be brought into San Jose. The officers are in no sense intruders in the local field as many of them are very well known in the community, having lived here."[4]

Four weeks later Jim Bacigalupi addressed the assembled stock-holders of the Commercial Bank. He told them that "new accounts had been gained daily in both the Savings and Commercial depart-ments, and prospects are most encouraging." To keep up the good work it would be necessary for the stockholders to ratify the proce-dure by which the Commercial Bank should become, by law, a branch of the Bank of Italy.

This would involve two steps: first, the sale of the Commercial's *assets,* over and above its paid-up capital, to the Bank of Italy in con-sideration of the assumption by the San Francisco bank of all indebt-edness of the San Jose institution; and, second, the exchange of stock, representing the capital, on the basis of ten shares for one.

Bacigalupi went on to explain that the unimpaired paid capital was not $150,000, but approximately $143,000, and this included only $16,000 in cash. The rest was land or land loans that could not be called quick assets. As the Bank of Italy had no excess stock, and pro-posed no new issue, A. P. Giannini would exchange from his personal holdings one share of B. of I. stock for ten of Commercial. The Commercial and Savings Bank corporation would then be dissolved. A. P. Giannini and Mr. Scatena, as trustees for the Bank of Italy, would liquidate the lands and land loans, representing the more-or-less frozen part of the capital of the dissolved corporation. Any profit on this deal would go to the bank.

The stockholders heartily approved the plan. The Bank of Italy stockholders concurring, on January 1, 1910, the Commercial and Savings Bank of San Jose became the San Jose branch of the Bank of Italy.[5]

Much as he found to admire in the conduct of Canadian branch banks, A. P. Giannini had spotted one defect which he did not intend to duplicate in his own branches. This was the absence of local, personal community ties. When a Montreal or a Vancouver bank opened an outlying branch the manager and his help would be sent from the home office. They held themselves a little aloof from the local residents and were, in consequence, regarded as aliens. Giannini wanted San Jose to feel that the San Jose branch belonged to the people of the Santa Clara Valley. That was why he had been anxious to have local stockholders. He went further. He retained as much of the local personnel as possible. On top of that he solicited the active participation of prominent valley citizens. To this end an advisory committee was created. Old families were represented. So were immigrant families, who for the first time had a voice in the management of a bank.[6]

3

When the Bank of Italy began its branch operations in the agricultural county seat of San Jose it knew that it was going to the type of region that produced the bulk of the wealth of California. Before the First World War California was almost purely a farming and stock-raising state. That conflict witnessed the beginnings of heavy industry in California.

In 1909, A. P. Giannini realized that, unless his branches could do more for the California ranchers than existing unit banks were doing, there would be little excuse for the branches. He was glad to start learning what they could do in the area of his state that he knew best. Though Giannini's experience was valuable from the first and a timesaver, thoroughness was not sacrificed for haste in getting the Bank of Italy ready to begin its real penetration of rural California. Not another country branch was acquired for more than six years—until February, 1916.

4

In 1910 the Bank of Italy purchased two banks in San Francisco, and in 1912 one in suburban San Mateo where A. P. Giannini had his home. James J. Fagan and other personages of the Crocker National were interested in these banks. They were in a position to see what the Bank of Italy could do to put an ailing bank on its feet and make it a force in the economic life of the community.

The first acquisition was the Bank of San Francisco, founded in 1905 as the Citizens National. Starting modestly as a neighborhood bank in Polk Street, remote from the financial center on Montgomery, the Citizens had "passed through a series of calamities seldom experienced in the history of financial institutions," as an officer recorded. To obtain greater latitude in making real estate loans, in 1907 the Citizens switched from a national to a state charter and became the Bank of San Francisco. It moved nearer downtown, to Market and Seventh, retaining the Polk Street office as a branch. There it staged something of a comeback and had resources of $1,234,000 and deposits of $987,000 when the Bank of Italy put in its bid.[7]

A week later the Bank of Italy took over the Mechanics Savings Bank, located near the Bank of San Francisco, in the Market, Turk and Mason Streets gore. Giannini was proud of that take-over. With a board adorned by some of the best financial names in San Francisco—James J. Fagan, Marshal Hale, Henry T. Scott, George F. Lyon, F. W. Dohrmann, Jr., J. U. Calkins, Ira Clerk, Charles C. Moore—the Mechanics had opened nine months ahead of the Bank of Italy in 1904. Starting out with almost $1,000,000 in resources, the Mechanics built a home costing $344,000. It never grew rich enough to afford that home, and, when purchased by the Bank of Italy, its deposits were under $600,000.

At the end of 1910, the Bank of Italy reported resources of $6,539,-000. They had almost doubled in twelve months. A little more than half of the increase consisted of assets purchased from the two banks just mentioned. The rest was natural growth. A majority of the bank's investments was still real estate loans. Yet the care with which borrowers were selected and watched seems evidenced by the fact that not until 1910 did the Bank of Italy foreclose a mortgage. The sum involved was $2,275.

Giannini cut down his overhead by consolidating the two purchased banks and the old Mission branch, opened in 1907, in the quarters of the former Mechanics Bank at Market, Turk and Mason. This was called the Market Street branch of the Bank of Italy. A little later the Polk Street branch, inherited from the Bank of San Francisco, was merged with the Market Street branch. This left the bank with one city branch, as it had had since 1907.

The advent into Market Street was no casual affair. Giannini, the former real estate operator, believed he detected a budding expansion of the retail district along that wide thoroughfare. One convincing indication was the crowd of shoppers flocking to Prager's, "the largest store west of Chicago." Like the Bank of Italy, Prager's had opened in 1904. If there was anything to the trend, then the Market Street branch was in the right location to make the most of it.

Not for a moment, however, did Giannini forget the birthplace of his bank. Like the rest of San Francisco, North Beach was growing in population and in wealth. Giannini took a step there that ran contrary to traditional notions of the dignity of a banker's calling. He hired a man to solicit accounts, just as a wholesale merchant would hire a city salesman. He was a tall, personable young fellow named Alfred A. Micheletti, whose work at the Swiss-American Bank Giannini had watched for some time. Micheletti took over the job that Giannini himself and Charley Grondona had performed in the bank's early days. He moved among people who had never had a bank account, explaining the advantages and showing them how to write deposit slips and checks. On top of that he showed small business men how to keep books, so they would know where they stood. To a man with push and energy he might suggest a bank loan to expand his business. Micheletti was a success from the word go. The trail he blazed has become a regular part of the Giannini institution's activities, and, in time it was adopted with profit by other banks.[8]

By 1911, the Bank of Italy was obliged to enlarge its home office at Clay and Montgomery. The following year the bank purchased the San Mateo Bank of which J. J. Fagan was the absentee president.

At this juncture Giannini was also spending some time and

The birthplace of the Bank of America, where A. P. Giannini opened the
Bank of Italy on October 17, 1904.

thought on a matter which, in view of later developments, is interesting. This was the establishment of an affiliated bank clear across the country in New York City. In December, 1911, Giannini and Fagan had attended the convention of the American Bankers Association in New Orleans. From there they proceeded to New York as a committee of the Bank of Italy's board with instructions "to make inquiries in the City of New York and to ascertain, if possible, the advisability of organizing a bank there to operate in connection with this bank and that if they should report the venture feasible and advantageous to this bank to invite the stockholders of the Bank of Italy to subscribe for stock in the proposed New York bank."

The Italian colony of New York numbered 800,000, making it about twice the size of the whole of San Francisco. Though there were private banks among them, the Italians in New York had no regularly chartered depository they could call their own. The San Franciscans had several meetings with officers of the Italian Chamber of Commerce of New York. No less a figure than James A. Stillman tried to interest Giannini in the Butchers & Drovers Bank which he controlled. Mr. Stillman had made his National City Bank of New York the largest bank in the United States. Giannini and Fagan listened to what everyone had to say. They returned home and reported that "circumstances . . . are at present unpropitious for undertaking such an important venture."

The verdict was a big disappointment to James F. Cavagnaro, an officer of the Savoy Trust Company of New York. Cavagnaro (no relation to the Bank of Italy's first attorney) had worked for several years to win Giannini's interest for New York. He knew what the banker had done for North Beach Italians. Cavagnaro wanted similar banking benefits for Manhattan's Lower East Side. Though the negotiations broke down, the trip gave A. P. Giannini an interest in the metropolis that never waned.

In the summer of 1912, Mr. and Mrs. Giannini spent four months in Europe. Back in Manhattan, the banker was again importuned to start a bank for Italians there. The Savoy Trust had merged with the East River National Bank and Cavagnaro was a vice-president of the latter institution. In his new affiliation, Cavagnaro got the East River interested in selling to Giannini. The matter went so far that early in 1913 Armando Pedrini was sent East in the hope of concluding the negotiations. But the New Yorkers wanted Giannini himself to move

East and run the new bank. Giannini declined to leave California, where he was preparing his boldest stroke yet. He offered, however, to send a younger man trained in the Bank of Italy's way of doing things. This did not satisfy the New York Italians.[9]

Thus, for the time being, New York faded from Giannini's consideration and he prepared to invade Los Angeles. Without a foothold in the south he could not hope to accomplish his object of demonstrating the worth of branch banking by covering California with offices of the Bank of Italy. On December 31, 1912, resources of the bank stood at $11,228,000 and deposits at $9,916,000. Capital had been increased to $1,000,000. In January, 1913, steps were taken to raise this by another quarter of a million. James and Samuel B. Fugazi, sons of the founder of the Columbus Savings & Loan Society, were added to the Bank of Italy's board. The younger bank had so far outstripped the older that they were no longer rivals.

In April of 1913, Giannini and Fagan went south to see how the land lay.

The Invasion of Los Angeles

THE EVENTS of the decade 1900–1910 foretold the shape of things to come in the struggle for economic ascendancy between northern and southern California. During those ten years the population of the region south of the Tehachapi Range increased 147 per cent compared with 60 per cent for the state as a whole. The population of Los Angeles trebled, from 102,000 to 319,000. In the same period San Francisco grew from 342,000 to 416,000. The wealth of California—the products of its agriculture, its industries, its mines, its fisheries, its forests and so on—multiplied even faster than the people. The south got the lion's share of that increase, too.

On the whole, San Francisco did not pay a great deal of heed to this. The graceful city by the Golden Gate had been the financial and commercial capital of the West too long to be disturbed by the bragging and tub-thumping of upstart Los Angeles. San Francisco had seen one boom send the price of town lots in Los Angeles to $1,000 a front foot; and then had seen those prices collapse to almost nothing. Moreover, much of Los Angeles' vaunted population growth had been due to the annexation of suburbs, a type of expansion to which San Francisco, confined to a narrow peninsula, was not adapted. San Francisco, with plenty of money, began to be chary of how it loaned in southern California; so, more and more, capital for southern expansion came from the Middle West—with the tourists, the winter residents and the permanent residents, who poured in from that region to enjoy the famous sunshine.

The lofty attitude of San Francisco did not retard the Los Angeles architects of empire. Behind boasts and exaggerations, the southern boosters planned for the future with awesome imagination. In 1900 it was easy to dismiss much of this as a delusion of grandeur. The city's water supply was altogether inadequate for a metropolis; much of the land surrounding Los Angeles was semiarid. Very well, southern California would irrigate; and Los Angeles would bring water, across mountains and desert, from the Owens River Valley up by the Nevada line two-hundred-odd miles away. Los Angeles was an inland city, and there was no natural harbor on the near-by coast. No matter, Los Angeles would extend its borders to the ocean, sixteen miles away, and repair an oversight of nature by creating a harbor, in time to reap a share of the benefits the imminent opening of the Panama Canal should bring to the West Coast. The town of San Pedro, looking upon an open roadstead, was absorbed and work begun to turn that anchorage into a first-class harbor. The federal government was conveniently drawn in to help foot the bill, but the driving power was all Los Angeles'.

By 1913 the harbor, far from complete, was handling nearly three million tons of ocean-borne commerce, and Owens River water coursed through Los Angeles mains. Building permits were ahead of San Francisco's. Bank deposits and loans had doubled in five years. The city's population had passed San Francisco's. One of the communities annexed was Hollywood, which had sprouted into a decorous residential suburb during A. P. Giannini's acquaintance with it. The first motion picture had been made in Hollywood two years before, in 1911. Since 1908, however, small movie outfits had been operating in southern California, and the boosters were saying this was another industry Los Angeles would take from Chicago and New York.

Giannini was a loyal San Franciscan; but he was also a loyal Californian, and the region south of the Tehachapi was, indeed, a part of California. When Giannini and Fagan had gone to New York the question was, *Shall* we break into this place? When they went south in April, 1913, that question had been settled, with reference to Los Angeles. The only issue was, *How* shall we do it?

2

The issue was soon resolved. Three weeks after its envoys had left San Francisco, the Bank of Italy had two branches in Los Angeles—through the purchase of the Park Bank of that city. Besides the downtown office the Park Bank had one neighborhood branch. The purchased institution was a small one, with resources of $1,908,000.

One reason for the speed of this acquisition was the fact that the

Park Bank was not in good shape. The superintendent of banks had directed it to improve the quality of some of its assets. A new man had replaced Alden Anderson in this office. He was William R. Williams, an appointee of California's reform governor, Hiram Johnson. Williams was an alert, conscientious public servant. Not only did he enforce the Bank Act of 1909 rigidly; over opposition from the banking fraternity he obtained amendments tightening that act. Though, at this time, Williams was inclined to question the soundness of some aspects of the Bank of Italy's rapid expansion, after conferences with Giannini and Jim Bacigalupi, the bank's attorney, he approved the purchase of the Park Bank.[1]

Before the transaction was completed the Bank of Italy was angling for two more Los Angeles banks. These deals fell through in a manner that suggests intervention by the larger banking interests of Los Angeles, who did not welcome a "foreigner" from San Francisco. One of the banks Giannini was after—the Traders—presently consolidated with a larger local bank. The other bank—the International Savings—the Bank of Italy eventually (1917) took over.[2]

In 1913 Giannini was successful, however, in acquiring the fourth bank he went after—the small City and County with assets of $740,100. Under the stewardship of a young vice-president, Irving S. Metzler, this institution had pulled out of one set of difficulties which had threatened its solvency only to meet trouble of another sort. Metzler's good work had prompted a Middle Western stockholder named F. H. Johnson to try to acquire control of the institution. When Metzler frustrated this, Johnson took his grievance to court. Moreover, a director of the bank who was also a director of an investment company was about to be sued for fraud by investment company stockholders. Metzler was afraid the suit might injure the bank, possibly to the point of starting a run.

The situation was made to order for Giannini, who could use in his own organization a man like Irving Metzler. A deal for the purchase of the City and County Bank was worked out. Moreover, the Bank of Italy promised to assume responsibility for the Johnson litigation. Giannini's activities in Los Angeles had brought Superintendent Williams to town. The San Franciscan told the superintendent what was going on and hurriedly returned to winding up arrangements for taking over the bank. Anticipating a public announcement of the fraud suit against the director, he and Metzler worked fast.

Directly they completed the transaction, the sign on the City and County Bank was changed to proclaim that institution a branch of the Bank of Italy.

When Williams learned of this he notified the Bank of Italy that it was operating the branch without authority; that permission to convert the City and County Bank into a branch had not been requested or granted in the manner specified by statute. Giannini said he thought the conversation with Williams in Los Angeles had taken care of that. The superintendent said no; and, under a brand-new amendment to the Bank Act, he fined the Bank of Italy $1,000. The penalty would have been heavier had Williams believed what certain rival Los Angeles bankers were saying about the invader. The superintendent thought that Giannini was impetuous and inclined to be careless of the *forms* of the law, but that "he was honest and he ran a clean bank." The fine, Williams made clear, was for an act of carelessness. In evidence of this fact, when the Bank of Italy submitted the proper request, a license was readily granted, effective September 1, 1913.

But the fine stood. Giannini protested. "DON'T YOU PAY A DOLLAR OF THAT FINE," he telegraphed Cashier Pedrini. "HE WILL HAVE A TOUGH TIME GETTING A CENT IF I HAVE ANYTHING TO SAY ABOUT IT."

Williams stuck to his guns and the bank paid the fine. Very sensibly the superintendent handled the whole matter without publicity. Though the capitulation rankled, before long Giannini was describing Williams as "the best superintendent of banks California ever had."[3]

With three Los Angeles branches in operation, the directors voted the general manager a bonus of $10,000 and raised his salary to $750 a month. Giannini took the raise but declined the bonus.

In accordance with the precedent of San Jose a strong advisory board was named in the south. The board of directors of the Bank of Italy was increased to twenty-one members. Several southern Californians were among those elected to the new chairs: Secondo Guasti, president of the Italian Vineyard Company; Giovanni Ferro, manager, Schiappi Pietra estate, Ventura County; John Lagomarsino, president of the California Lima Bean Growers Association; Peter J. Dreher, a citrus-fruit grower; J. Wiseman McDonald and Miles Pease, Los Angeles attorneys; W. C. Durgin, former president,

and James C. Kays, former cashier, of the Park Bank. The enlarged
board elected Mr. Guasti fourth vice-president of the bank.[4]

3

Though as badly in need of capital as it was of business enterprise
and population to further its ambitious schemes, Los Angeles did not
accord to the Bank of Italy the welcome usually vouchsafed to newcomers who could, by any stretch of imagination, be helpful in building up southern California. In six short words a newspaper headline
told one part of the story:

PARK BANK TAKEN OVER BY ITALIANS[5]

There was belittlement in that way of putting it, and more than a
hint of appeal to racial prejudice. The striving southern city was a
product of domestic immigration, largely from the insular Middle
West. In 1910 above 53 per cent of its population was native white of
native parentage, as compared with San Francisco's percentage of
less than 28. The number of foreign-born Italians in Los Angeles was
3,802; in San Francisco, 16,918. The racial group among which the
Bank of Italy had got its start in the north did not exist in the south
in sufficient numbers to support the role that Giannini had outlined
for his bank there.

Montgomery Street had never displayed hostility toward the Bank
of Italy. At first the Street had overlooked the new bank, but had not
consciously ignored or fought it. Of late the general sentiment of
Montgomery Street had been that, with his branch banking scheme,
Giannini had got off on the wrong foot; but that was something else.
From the first, as we have seen, the Bank of Italy had enjoyed the
support of one of the most important banking houses west of the
Mississippi. James J. Fagan, at that time executive vice-president of
the Crocker National, accepted a promotion to third vice-president of
the B. of I., and in that capacity continued as an active counselor
of Giannini in the branch banking campaign.

No such advantages as Giannini enjoyed in San Francisco awaited
him in the south. The real powers of Spring Street—the Montgomery Street of Los Angeles—may or may not have been involved in
the move that kept the Bank of Italy from taking over the Traders in

the spring of 1913, but thereafter they permitted the invader to keep the initiative in his own hands.

Southern California was fortunate in having a man like Joseph F. Sartori as its acknowledged leader in the field of banking. Giannini was fortunate in having so excellent a banker and so decent a citizen as an eventual competitor. In the matter of origin, Sartori was a fairly typical Angeleno. Born in Iowa, he was practicing law there when he went to southern California on his honeymoon and liked the place well enough to return for good. In 1889, when Los Angeles was in the trough between booms, Sartori helped to organize a bank with $20,000 borrowed from Isaias Hellman's Farmers and Merchants National of Los Angeles. In 1913, Mr. Sartori's bank, then called the Security Trust and Savings, had assets of $48,000,000, or double those of Los Angeles' second largest bank, the First National. These two banks, and eight others, did three-quarters of the city's banking business. The remainder was divided among twenty-eight smaller banks, counting the Bank of Italy's three branches as one bank.

Speculative banking and booms often go together. The alliance was not absent from the southern California picture, though Joseph F. Sartori had no part in this. Sartori was, in fact, something of an anomaly—an ardent boom-town booster with a sound, conservative bank. In one way or another the Security Trust and Savings was involved in many of the activities contributing to the beanstalk growth of southern California. Quite likely it was Mr. Sartori's influence that kept certain of those activities within the bounds of good banking risks.

There was one need, however, so clear in retrospect, that he did not see. This was branch banking. True, Sartori's bank had one branch, acquired some years earlier as a result of a merger. Another of the large banks, the Los Angeles Trust and Savings (resources, $20,600,000), had two branches. The Commercial Trust and Savings, also a large bank, had one branch. Aside from the Bank of Italy, three small banks had one branch apiece. One savings bank, the Home, alert to the trend though with resources of less than $8,000,-000, had seven branches. All these were city branches and not representative of the type of branch banking Giannini was introducing to California. Neither Sartori nor any other southern California banker saw any good reason for the innovation. Had they done so it is unlikely that they would have relished it at the hands of a "foreigner" from San Francisco's Italian colony.

4

At the time of the Bank of Italy's invasion, Joseph F. Sartori was disturbed by the interest-rate war flourishing among Los Angeles banks. Owing to the number of elderly people who go to southern California to live on fixed incomes, savings banks, then as now, attracted an abnormally large proportion of depositors. National banks were getting around the law prohibiting them from doing a savings business by paying interest on "time deposits." Moreover, they began making alliances with savings banks. The savings rate had been uniformly 4 per cent until the Hibernian Savings began paying 5. "Take the elevator to the second floor and make 1 per cent more."

Before approving a charter for a new bank or permitting an existing bank to open a branch, Superintendent Williams had adopted the practice of consulting other bankers of the community. On such an errand he had visited Sartori. In the belief that Giannini, with his aggressive methods, would bid for depositors by offering a risky rate, Mr. Sartori had urged Superintendent Williams not to admit the Bank of Italy to Los Angeles. Such a charge ignored the record of the bank in the north, where it had never been a leader in advancing interest rates on deposits; and it had led in lowering them on loans. "If the rates are too high," Williams told Sartori, "the Bank of Italy will not pay them. That would not be good business and Giannini is a good businessman."[6]

In those days banks rarely advertised except to publish periodical statements of conditions. Almost from the beginning, however, the Bank of Italy had bought newspaper space to set forth the advantages of savings accounts, its lending service to small homeowners, and so on. The first ads had appeared in *L'Italia,* of San Francisco. After the fire English-language newspapers also were used. In the north the campaign had been modest. Giannini knew that Los Angeles liked everything done in a larger way than it was done elsewhere. So more newspaper space was engaged. The first ad proudly listed the Bank of Italy's board of directors and its Los Angeles advisory board.[7]

Five days later Mr. Sartori's bank came out with a quarter-page announcement listing *its* directors, with the observation: "You will note that practically all have been residents of Los Angeles for over twenty years."[8]

When the Globe Savings Bank raised its rate to 5 per cent to meet the competition of Hibernian, Mr. Sartori forgot Giannini for a moment. The Security Trust's advertisement said: "THIS BANK PAYS THE HIGHEST RATE OF INTEREST CONSISTENT WITH SAFE CONSERVATIVE BANKING." The Hibernian had found its interest boost a magnet for deposits. Consequently Sartori must have been agreeably surprised when the Bank of Italy inserted an ad supporting his position: "SAFETY AND 4% AND NOTE THAT THE MATTER OF INTEREST COMES SECOND."[9]

When Giannini wrote that advertisement he was doing everything he could think of within the limits of safe banking to attract deposits to his new branches. For the first time in his experience he was failing in such an undertaking. Los Angeles banks normally lost deposits during the "dull months," the summer season, that is. Added to the seasonal dip a recession of business activity originating in the East had reached California. Instead of returning home as he had expected to when his southern branches were going concerns, Giannini spent a hot and anxious summer in Los Angeles. He sent for Armando Pedrini and other experts at the Bank of Italy's business-getting technique. And still deposits continued to fall.

Toward the end of July, A. P. tried a tack that had been successful in San Francisco. Splurging with a half-page advertisement, he announced: "BANK OF ITALY OFFERS MONEY TO SMALL MORTGAGE BORROWERS." Home builders needing $1,000 or less were invited to apply for loans. In a newspaper interview Giannini discussed details:

> It is our purpose to make a specialty of the interest of the small depositor and borrower. We aim to do all in our power to help in the building up of Los Angeles. . . . We have money to loan at all times to the man who wishes to build on property that he owns. We have no money for speculators. . . . We consider the wage-earner or small business man who deposits his savings regularly, no matter how small the amount may be, to be the most valuable client our bank can have.[10]

As an indication of where the small borrowers were to be found, some new lettering appeared overnight on the windows of the Bank of Italy's central branch, in the quarters of the old Park Bank, at Fifth and Hill Streets:

TOBOPN CE CPHCKN

GOVORI SE HRVATSKI

ON PARLE FRANÇAIS

SI PARLE ITALIANO

SE HABLA ESPAÑOL

MAN SPRECHT DEUTSCH

OME LAOYMAI EMHNIKA[11]

"WOULD MONEY HELP YOU?" was the headline over a succeeding advertisement. Another ad extolled "THE BANK FOR JUST PLAIN FOLKS." Next day the Security Trust called itself "THE FAMILY BANK OF LOS ANGELES." Mr. Sartori refrained from following the lead of the Bank of Italy in advertising for borrowers, however. With an eye to slackening business activity, the Security bank was preparing to curtail its lending. It was the Hibernian, of the 5 per cent interest rate, that accepted the challenge, announcing that it would make a hundred small loans to homebuilders who wished also to become depositors of the bank.[12]

Giannini himself took charge of the Bank of Italy's small-loans campaign. He virtually was that campaign. Days were spent tramping real estate developments in Los Angeles' baked, rainless, summer countryside, appraising the properties of applicants for money. Nights he sat up with Pedrini, discussing ways and means of getting more depositors. Both enterprises moved slowly, very slowly. Giannini was used to speedier conquests. It seemed clear to him—and to others—that the Bank of Italy was up against a definite movement to keep business away from it. Nevertheless, a few small loans were made. The drop in deposits was halted. A slow gain set in.[13]

In autumn, when cooler weather and rains refresh Los Angeles, business picks up. There was not much of a pickup in 1913, however. Yet the Bank of Italy's branches held their own, which was better than most Los Angeles banks did. The branches finished the year with deposits of $2,456,000, a gain of $731,000 over the combined deposits of the two banks that had been taken over. In the north the bank had finished the year with deposits of $11,682,000, a gain of $1,756,000. Despite this showing some northern directors had become skeptical of the southern move. Physically weary for the first time in his life, Giannini returned to San Francisco to talk to them.[14]

5

The discussions were in good humor. They could hardly have been otherwise with Giannini's friend Fagan, who had helped launch the southern venture, now enrolled among the doubters. No one thought of questioning the Bank of Italy's debt to A. P. Giannini. The issue was his unshakable confidence in the favorable outcome of the Los Angeles experiment, after an unpromising start. That branch banking, as Giannini saw it, was a new thing in this country, that a jump from San Francisco to Los Angeles, four hundred miles away and farther than that in terms of economic kinship between communities, were things no modern American banker had ever attempted—these rather measurable considerations deterred Giannini for not a second. He heard the dissenters but he did not budge. He said Los Angeles was over the hump; that what the situation called for was an aggressive business-getting policy and better locations for the downtown branches. He admitted that this would cost money.

To get business, Giannini dispatched Alfred Micheletti to Los Angeles. Then he said he wanted to move the main branch, which directed the activities of the two others, from Fifth and Hill to what was called the Abe Haas corner at Seventh and Broadway. This was in the thronged retail district, across the street from Bullock's department store. In a similar district in San Francisco the Market Street branch had proved a money-maker. What shocked some of the directors was the price Giannini was willing to pay for the Abe Haas corner—$60,000 a year for twenty-five years. The yearly rental at Fifth and Hill was $16,920.

Criticism persisted and the directors received another shock when they assembled for the meeting of January 13, 1914. A. P. Giannini served notice of his retirement from the bank. His letter, addressed to "My dear Colleagues," did not mention the disagreement over Los Angeles. It said merely that the branches there were on a "sound and good paying basis." As the directors knew, that statement smacked of optimism. Up to December 17, 1913, the Bank of Italy's "profit" on its $2,000,000 investment in the south was carried at $1,187—a figure that took no account of losses on doubtful southern assets or of Los Angeles taxes paid by the San Francisco office. Giannini was on firmer ground when he spoke of the state of the bank as a whole. It was "in a splendid and flourishing condition, second to no banking institution in the country in this regard." The burden of management, however, had become too great "for one in an exhausted physical state." Therefore, "I have deemed it but fair . . . to afford you timely notice that *under no condition* will I accept the position of director or officer of the bank at the next annual meeting of the stockholders." He would, however, serve his present term, which had a year to run. In that time a successor could be broken in.

"After some discussion," as the minutes have it, action on the letter was postponed until the next meeting of the board.

This took place on February 10. Efforts to talk Giannini out of quitting having come to naught, a prospective successor was found in J. H. Skinner, cashier of the First National Bank of San Francisco. A. P. Giannini moved Skinner's election as fifth vice-president at a salary of $15,000 a year for 1914 and $20,000 for 1915. Giannini's salary was $9,000. Giannini suggested that Mr. Skinner, "a person of distinction and exceptional executive ability . . . be welcomed amongst the officers of the Bank in some pleasant and satisfactory manner . . . [such as] at a banquet."

This done, the board voted to incorporate Giannini's letter of resignation in the minutes and gave its supposedly retiring first vice-president a three months' leave of absence to take a rest.[15]

While Giannini was vacationing in the West Indies and Skinner, the heir apparent, was familiarizing himself with his duties, A. P.'s allies at Clay and Montgomery were not idle. At a special meeting of the board in March, Dr. A. H. Giannini brought up the matter of the Abe Haas corner, moving that Skinner be given "authority to negotiate . . . a lease . . . on the lowest terms possible." James J. Fagan left the meeting before a vote was called for. When Director Prentis Cobb Hale saw that there were enough votes to carry the motion, he, too, left the room. This deprived the board of a quorum, and so defeated the motion.[16]

P. C. Hale had come to the directorate as a result of the bank's entry into San Jose in 1909. Member of a distinguished family of merchants with department stores in San Jose, San Francisco and other cities, Hale, rather than Skinner, was destined to become a power in the Bank of Italy.

On his return from his holiday A. P. Giannini spent a good deal of time in Los Angeles. The general picture was not rosy. A real slump was on, and every bank in town except the Hibernian losing deposits. The Bank of Italy shook up the personnel of its southern branches, now reduced to two. It collected inherited loans that had been regarded as doubtful. It made headway at building up a small-loan clientele. The result was that, despite diminished deposits, the branches made money. No sooner had this happened, however, than trouble developed in the San Mateo branch in the north. Doc Giannini went out and took charge. The Doc was getting a reputation as a trouble-shooter. Working part time, he had started off the San Jose and the Market Street branches. More and more the bank took the Doc away from his practice. Before long, it claimed all his time. This was a far cry from the isolation camps in the Spanish-American War where the young physician had ministered to smallpox victims.[17]

Skepticism concerning the southern venture did not subside. In November Giannini read to the directors a lengthy communication:

Inasmuch as there remain but two more meetings of this Board in which I shall participate . . . and because . . . it is my desire to retire fairly and honorably from participation in the management of the Bank, I deem it timely to now call the attention of this Board to several matters. . . . I . . . wish to leave you with the full satisfaction that no one connected with the institution shall have any occasion to regret any of the undertakings of the bank during my management, and shall have no reason to feel that I have abandoned the ship, leaving behind as a legacy to those who remain, anything other than sound and solvent holdings and assets.

The foregoing remarks have been prompted by certain criticism heretofore made by several local directors and officers of the Bank . . . to the effect that the establishment of a branch of the Bank of Italy in Los Angeles was now considered a mistake; that it was not paying, and that it was about to be closed down. . . . On January 1st 1914 the deposits of said branch amounted to $2,400,000.00 which deposits have since suffered a shrinkage of about $500,000.00. Said branch is at present, nevertheless, earning from $3500.00 to $4000.00 per month, net, of which about $1500.00 is to be attributed to profits on moneys furnished it by the head office, and about $2000.00 per month net is being realized by it on its present deposits. . . .

The criticisms and rumors to which I have hereinabove referred, have operated and will necessarily continue to operate as a serious detriment, and the situation should, without delay, be cleared up by either closing down or obtaining new quarters, which are absolutely essential for the bank's future growth.

Mr. Giannini then laid before the directors a lease he had negotiated for the Abe Haas corner for a period of twenty-five years at an average of $50,000 a year. This was $10,000 less than the figure discussed at the beginning of the year. Giannini submitted the lease "without recommendation," adding:

> In the event that this Board should decide to discontinue said branch . . . I hereby guarantee within 60 days to organize a syndicate, in which I shall have no interest whatever, to take over said branch and pay the Bank of Italy therefor every dollar it has paid out for the good will of both the Park Bank and the City and County Bank of Los Angeles together with a reasonable amount to be determined upon by the parties in interest, for any losses that may have been sustained on the loans taken over from the Park Bank.

He made a similar offer for the San Mateo branch.

Giannini followed up this proposal with a little lecture on fortitude:

> The Bank of Italy was launched and has had its remarkable record of growth on a policy of conservative yet energetic and enthusiastic optimism. The institution has never known and should never know the word "failure" in any matter, large or small; nor will "cold feet" ever bring it enduring or any sort of success. Our flourishing San Jose and Market Street branches are pertinent illustrations of what "boosting" and constant optimistic demeanor accomplished for us in the face of trying and at times disheartening odds.

Before sitting down Mr. Giannini thanked his colleagues on the board and in the bank, singling out James J. Fagan for especial mention.

> While we have had our differences in matters of policy, I know of no man who I more highly esteem and none more needed in such an institution [as this] to act as a safety valve. . . . I sincerely trust that he will find time and be disposed to continue his active services on behalf of our Bank.[18]

6

It is hardly surprising that the directors were impressed. Amadeo Peter Giannini was a figure to command more than a second glance in any company. At forty-four, his tall, muscular form, his tanned, firm, friendly face radiated strength and assurance. About him was an air of chieftainship which men are born with or born without; it cannot be acquired. There was no air of busy importance. The hardest-working banker in California, A. P. Giannini always seemed to have time for anyone. A mother with a couple of youngsters clinging to her skirts would come into a branch Giannini happened to be visiting. He would keep the children entertained while she transacted her business. Good policy? Certainly, and Giannini knew it; but also he liked children. Therefore they liked him. You can't fool a kid on that score.

To say that the employees of the bank liked their boss would be using too weak a verb. They would have done about anything for him. This was not because Giannini coddled them. He worked them harder than the hands in any other bank were worked. But he was a leader, not a driver. He paid his people well, and gave Christmas bonuses in a day when that practice was uncommon.

At this time Giannini was worth probably $500,000. He thought any man with more than that needed his head examined. He lived well, but simply. His one extravagance was travel. The most sociable being imaginable, he cared nothing for Society—with a capital S. Nor did "important" people in the business world—Big Names—impress A. P. Giannini. More than once he was to look through a Big Name as through a pane of glass, spot an underling who was doing the Big Name's work, and hire the underling.

In a practical as well as an emotional sense the directors whom Giannini faced on that November day in 1914 were not unmoved. Before them stood the creator of their bank, speaking what he said was his valedictory. In the same length of time, perhaps no other bank in the United States had grown so large and so strong from such minute beginnings. Giannini and no other had done this—a fact no person present, however greatly he might disagree with some of the general manager's ideas, could doubt for a moment. Nor could anyone doubt that plenty of other banks would welcome the services of the retiring first vice-president. What, then, would happen to the Bank of Italy?

It would be underestimating the perspicacity of Mr. Giannini, and his mastery over men, to doubt that he was aware of the impression his ostensible swan song would create.

In any event it carried all before it.

Before Giannini had settled in his chair a motion was put naming him and two others as a committee to negotiate for the Abe Haas corner in Los Angeles. The motion was carried and a month later a twenty-five-year lease was signed at an average annual rental of $49,996.

At the board meeting of January 12, 1915, Dr. G. E. Caglieri introduced a long resolution extolling the services of the first vice-president and declaring that "the said decision of Mr. A. P. Giannini [to retire] is not approved of or acquiesced in by this Board [and] that we believe that such a retirement would be most unjust to Mr. A. P. Giannini and detrimental to the Bank and its stockholders." The motion was carried unanimously, A. P. Giannini not voting.[19]

The directors experienced no difficulty in reversing themselves on the Los Angeles branch issue. Business had recovered with the demands on American industry and agriculture as a result of the war in Europe. The Los Angeles branches were prospering and a third one was opened there. Mr. Skinner was a good subordinate but no Giannini. The real article was available and past performance made him most desirable.

In April, 1915, the bank's southern headquarters moved into the Haas Building. The directors lent their presence to the housewarming and punch was served. The wine came from Vice-President Guasti's vineyard. The Bank of Italy was in Los Angeles to stay.

On September 22, 1915, on the eve of the Bank of Italy's eleventh anniversary, Lorenzo Scatena resigned as president and the office of chairman of the board was created for him. "Boss" Scatena was a modest, capable businessman, who never claimed to be much of a banker. The presidency of course went to A. P. Giannini. His salary was raised to $25,000.[20]

Birth of Statewide Branch Banking

THE BATTLE for a toehold in Los Angeles having been won, in 1916 the Bank of Italy turned to the agricultural valleys of California. Three years of whirlwind activity saw the bank's flag planted from Santa Rosa in the north to Ventura in the south, four hundred miles away. Between those geographical extremes ten other new rural branches were established. Moreover, the bank opened four branches in Oakland, across the bay from San Francisco, one in suburban Redwood City, and an additional branch in Los Angeles. By the end of 1918 only three banks in California topped the Bank of Italy in assets. The first statewide banking system in the United States was an accomplished fact.

The initial move was into the near-by Santa Clara Valley which the Bank of Italy had entered in 1909 to establish its first out-of-town branch at San Jose. In 1916, one bank was purchased in the town of Santa Clara and another in Gilroy. In neighboring Hollister two banks were bought. One was a commercial and the other a savings institution. The Hollister purchases were consolidated to form one branch of the Bank of Italy. Eight such mergers took place in the three years from 1916 to 1918.

While strengthening itself in the Santa Clara Valley, the Bank of Italy entered the largest and richest of California's agricultural domains, the great San Joaquin Valley. This vast cradle for crops stretches from the easternmost arm of San Francisco Bay to the Tehachapi Range, a span of three hundred miles. It averages more than forty miles wide. From Fresno, the "raisin capital," about midway, north and south of the valley, the bank marched northward, planting branches at Madera, Merced, Modesto and Stockton, head of tidewater on the San Joaquin River.

Moving north of San Francisco Bay for the first time, the bank established itself in Napa, the principal trading center of the rich little Napa Valley. Across a spur of mountains from Napa is the Sonoma Valley, where the Bank of Italy put a branch at Santa Rosa. The Napa and the Sonoma Valleys have no need for irrigation, as does so much of California's productive soil. Luther Burbank picked Santa Rosa as the place for his experiments in plant breeding that resulted in dozens of new fruits, vegetables, flowers, trees, grasses and nuts.

The branch at Ventura, on the coastal plain north of Los Angeles, tapped the lima bean region. This was the home of John Lagomarsino, head of the state association of lima bean growers, an original member of the Los Angeles advisory board and in 1918 a vice-president of the bank. Lagomarsino took the helm and the Ventura branch began an eventful history.

The acquisition of the International Savings and Exchange Bank in Los Angeles was interesting. Giannini had tried to get this bank in 1913, but its president and principal proprietor, John Lopizich, wouldn't sell. "Old John," as everyone called him, was quite a person. Born in Dalmatia, he had started a drugstore in Los Angeles in the nineties, and later got hold of the International bank—not because of an ambition to become a banker but because he wanted Los Angeles' small foreign colony to have a good bank. On a smaller scale he duplicated Giannini's success in North Beach. He declined to sell in 1913 because he hadn't made up his mind about Giannini. The San Franciscan kept after Old John, however, and in 1917 he let go of the International, which was in tiptop shape. Lopizich stayed on as branch manager. Trusted and beloved, he became a factor in the Bank of Italy's hold on the foreign colony of Los Angeles, which was growing like everything else in that part of California.

The four outposts in Oakland were acquired by taking over the Security Bank which had three branches.

The branches retained the flavor of local institutions. In each of the eighteen new localities were local stockholders of the Bank of Italy, a local advisory board and local employees. Giannini spent a busy three years rushing from place to place, often in his automobile. Everywhere he met and talked to people, high and low. Giannini enjoyed this; and a shrewder stroke in public relations could not have been devised.

During these three years the Bank of Italy had grown as no bank had ever grown in the history of California, or perhaps of any other state. On December 31, 1915, there were seven branches in four cities. Resources aggregated $22,321,861; deposits $20,474,873; capital, $1,250,000; surplus and undivided profits, $374,244. At the close of 1918 there were twenty-four branches in eighteen cities. Resources aggregated $93,546,162; deposits, $85,937,839; capital, $5,000,000; surplus and undivided profits, $2,000,000.[1]

This growth reveals some striking contrasts with the institutions of great California bankers who had come in contact with A. P. Giannini at various points in his career. To become California's fourth bank the Bank of Italy had nosed out Isaias Hellman's Wells Fargo Nevada National of San Francisco which had assets of about $80,000,000. Only by combining the resources of the Wells Fargo Nevada National with those of the Union Trust Company, its savings affiliate, did Mr. Hellman's two institutions loom larger than the Bank of Italy. Had Hellman in 1904 given a friendly ear to the reforms Giannini wished to institute in the Columbus Savings & Loan Society the Bank of Italy might never have existed.

In 1913, Joseph F. Sartori of Los Angeles had regarded branch banking with disdain and Giannini as an upstart. Now Mr. Sartori, whose Security Trust had $56,000,000 in assets to the Bank of Italy's $93,000,000, was, as we shall see, respectfully studying the methods of his San Francisco competitor. The Crocker National of San Francisco, in the early days the Bank of Italy's sponsor and invaluable friend, was less than half the size of its one-time protegé.

Of the $65,462,967 gained in deposits, the greater part, $39,560,000, came in with the purchased banks—the bulk of it in the years 1916 and 1917. In only two other years in the bank's history, 1927 and 1928, did purchased deposits exceed those acquired by natural growth.

The bank's stock remained widely distributed. At the close of 1918 the 50,000 shares outstanding were held by 2,522 persons or corporations, an average individual holding of just under 20 shares. Only 28 stockholders owned 215 shares or more. The 7 largest stockholders were: A. P. Giannini, 1,081 shares; Dr. G. E. Caglieri, 700; William A. Newsom, 700; Dr. L. D. Bacigalupi, a director, 580; John Lagomarsino, 500; Henry Cartan, 500; Lorenzo Scatena, 480. The price per share of the 20,000 new shares sold in 1918 was $147.50. In that year dividends of $7.00 a share were paid on bank stock and

$0.50 on stock of the Stockholders Auxiliary Corporation, to be mentioned presently.[2]

Dr. Caglieri had an interesting reminiscence of his stockholding during the period of the bank's early acquisitions of branches. He was not always the bona fide owner of all the shares credited to him in the stockbook. To insure a broader distribution of the shares, Giannini liked to have a number on hand to sell locally when the bank went into a new community. For that reason Giannini would buy shares in the names of a few trusted friends, with the understanding that they were to be available when needed. Dr. Caglieri was one of those trusted friends.[3]

2

Until the middle of 1917 the Bank of Italy acquired other banks by the indirect mode of purchase originated by Attorney James A. Bacigalupi in 1909. Though cumbersome, this formula served very well when only an occasional bank was bought. With four or five deals in the works at one time, however, it involved a burdensome amount of detail and it imposed enormous responsibilities upon A. P. Giannini and others who as *individuals* took the first step by acquiring control of the capital stock of the selling banks.

As the reader may recall, the 1909 formula was designed to meet the law that forbade one bank to buy the stock of another. One bank could, however, purchase the assets of another. No sensible stockholders would agree to a transfer of assets until some arrangement had been made about their shares. Consequently the stock would be purchased by individuals representing the Bank of Italy. B. of I., itself, would then acquire the assets and, in the course of liquidating the shell of the selling corporation, reimburse the individuals for what they had laid out for stock. That is a brief description of a complicated operation that involved obtaining consent of two-thirds of the stockholders of both the selling and the buying corporations. Moreover, it involved writing off all foreclosed real estate carried for more than five years. That was the law, irrespective of the value of the property; and in 1917 many of the foreclosures were perfectly good.

With the multiple acquisition of banks in the farming regions this write-off matter became serious. Serious also was the financial responsibility undertaken by A. P. Giannini, P. C. Hale, Lorenzo Scatena and others who acted in their private capacities as original purchasers of the stock of selling banks. In the acquisition of the Goodman Bank at Napa, Mr. Hale alone had obligated himself to the extent of $800,000. When four or five deals were under way at once the aggregate commitments of these gentlemen ran into millions. They borrowed the money from the Crocker National on their personal notes, repaying that bank when they were reimbursed in the final step of each deal. No brokerage or other fee was paid these friends of the bank for the use of their credit.[4]

The later recollection of A. P. Giannini was that the first person to suggest a simpler method of buying banks was that stern official, Superintendent of Banks William R. Williams. Mr. Williams himself says he may have done so. The written record begins with a hasty longhand letter from Giannini to Bacigalupi. It was written May 20, 1917, on hotel stationery in Santa Barbara. Two banks in Madera were being taken over and Giannini promised to be there to meet the selling directors whenever necessary. The letter continues:

> Would you mind, in your leisure moments if you have any, preparing a draft (in the rough) . . . concerning the organization of a syndicate to be participated in by all of the B of I stockholders—in proportion to their present holdings—which syndicate would be for the purpose of facilitating the purchase of banks.

In detail Giannini sketched the setup and powers of the corporation he wanted, concluding: "Go to it Jim. It's no dream I assure you."[5]

One month later to the day the Stockholders Auxiliary Corporation was born. Its composition and functions were almost exactly as Giannini had outlined in his letter. Though it was the bank's alter ego, the Auxiliary Corporation could do many things the bank could not do—for instance, buy stock of other banks and hold foreclosed real estate that was more than five years old. Starting off with $600,000 borrowed from the Crocker National, and presently repaid from profits, the Auxiliary assisted in buying its first bank in September, 1917. This was John Lopizich's bank in Los Angeles.

So came into being the earliest of the Bank of Italy's many corporate affiliates.

3

What did other bankers, especially in California, think of the Bank of Italy's achievement?

In January 1918, the *Coast Banker* tried to answer the question:

The rapidity with which he [Giannini] has brought these institutions together has unquestionably been a matter of amazement to the banking public, and it is not exaggerating to say there has been a doubt in the minds of some bankers . . . as to the ability of the Bank of Italy to assimilate these institutions, hold them together and develop them properly.[6]

That seems a fair statement of the case. The American Bankers Association, at the instance of the small bankers, in 1916 adopted a resolution against branch banking but the real fight over that issue had not started. Although the tendency of legislation to lag behind public sentiment should not be overlooked, something of the general American attitude toward branch banking is reflected in the fact that in 1916 only twelve states had laws permitting it. In twenty-seven states the statutes were silent on the subject. Nine states prohibited branch banking. Giannini's spectacular demonstration left California, in 1918, in a mood of astonishment and doubt. A popular thesis of the doubting bankers was that the local banker "is temperamentally in better tune with the small business man of his small town and with the farmer . . . than can possibly be the wealthy officers and directors of a rich and powerful bank with a head office in a city more or less distantly removed."[7]

Yet in California the educational effect of the Bank of Italy's work was beginning to come in evidence; and it was not unnoticed elsewhere. Exceptions to the general attitude of doubt began to appear. Several banks, particularly in Los Angeles, cautiously opened a few branches. Others added to the few branches already established. Almost without exception the additions were city branches. None tackled the diverse problems of branch banking as Giannini had.

But some of them were thinking about it. Four large banks engaged two Columbia University professors to study the subject. The interested banks were the Mercantile Trust Company and the American Bank of San Francisco, the First National and the Security Trust of Los Angeles. This represented quite a change on the part of Mr. Sartori of Security. Without waiting on the professors, Louis H.

Roseberry, vice-president and trust attorney of Mr. Sartori's bank, wrote a surprising letter to J. A. Bacigalupi who at that time held similar offices in the Bank of Italy:

I am going to take the liberty of imposing upon your good nature and professional experience in the matter of establishing branch banks, if you can consistently give me this information. We are considering the establishment of one or more branch banks in or about Los Angeles. We may do this either by opening branches in our own institution or by purchasing another bank and converting it into a branch of this bank. The experience that you have had . . . follows so closely our purposes that I felt you could give me some valuable ideas.[8]

Though the rivalry in Los Angeles was keen between Bank of Italy branches and the Sartori bank, which then had two branches, Bacigalupi answered this letter the day it was received:

We welcome indeed your inquiry as to the method employed by us in the acquisition of other banks and converting them into our own system. There is absolutely nothing secret or mysterious about branch banking or the method or procedure utilized in acquiring other banks. We are more convinced as time goes on of the absolute correctness and soundness of the branch banking system and, while we are indeed honestly proud of the fact that we have been pioneering on such an extensive scale in this direction, we more than welcome other banking institutions entering the field, for we feel that in competition not only the banks but the public will materially benefit.

Bacigalupi proceeded to narrate in detail the procedure of the Bank of Italy in taking over other institutions. He forwarded a duplicate file of the documents used in the recent purchase of the Security Bank of Oakland, and closed with an invitation to Mr. Roseberry to ask about anything he might wish to know. Roseberry asked several other questions and received cordial responses.[9]

Though this correspondence took place in 1919, not until after the Columbia professors had reported favorably on branch banking did Mr. Sartori, in 1921, enter the field.

4

William R. Williams, superintendent of banks, shares the credit of establishing the nation's first statewide banking system. Within his department Williams was a czar to whom Governor Hiram Johnson gave a free hand. Had not Williams become convinced—and it took convincing—that statewide banking was a good thing there would have been no statewide banking during his regime. Williams had the power to withhold the permits. Had not Williams become convinced —and this, also, took convincing—that the Bank of Italy was a competent instrument for the establishment of a statewide system there would have been no such system during the Williams tenure of office because no other bank was willing to try it.

Some of Williams' services were better appreciated in retrospect than at the time. Nor was Giannini alone in finding irksome the vigilance of the superintendent. He was generally disliked by California's bankers. Some of them thought the Bank of Italy the superintendent's "pet." Small-town bankers, among whom the opposition to branch banking was beginning to take form, feared the consequences of the branch policy. In defense of that policy Williams was outspoken. His report for 1916 contained a paragraph, inspired by the activities of the Bank of Italy, that some local bankers could scarcely call flattering to them:

Branch offices have been opened in places far removed from the principal place of business of the parent bank. These branch offices represent an endeavor of the banks to expand the field of their operations beyond the territory which in a strictly local sense is naturally or financially tributary to them. These branch offices offer to the communities in which they are greater assistance, larger loans and more extended credit than local institutions can afford. The justification of their existence rests in this fact and it is noteworthy that in every instance the parent bank entrusts very largely its loaning functions to the discretion of local advisory committees. . . . Still another cause has often influenced my course in granting the desired license. Occasionally it happens that the general banking tone of a community will measurably be improved by the licensing of a branch office of a well established, safely conducted institution. Involved in the wish of such a corporation to enter the field is its plan to absorb by purchase a stagnant bank and thus to strengthen the credit situation.[10]

Jim Bacigalupi and the superintendent were in almost constant controversy over the meaning of the words "public advantage and convenience," the statutory test for the establishment of a branch. Williams would study the banking and credit situation of a community. He continued the practice of interviewing local people, including officers of banks in competition with the one the Bank of Italy wished to buy. Bacigalupi thought that was carrying zeal too far.[11]

Minute books of the Bank of Italy and the files of its correspondence with the superintendent's office are studded with evidence of the surveillance under which the Bank of Italy and its branches lived. There were complaints about insufficient reserves; illegal loans in the savings department; improperly secured loans in the commercial department; interest accrued, but not collected, carried as profits; inadequate security posted for the deposit of public funds; "sloppy" bookkeeping.[12]

Williams regarded these deficiencies as growing pains. As he explained in later years: "A. P. moved so fast his accounting department could not keep up. My department had to call a halt every once in a while and give the Bank of Italy a chance to get acquainted with itself. When Giannini started his branch expansion nobody in California knew much about it. As the system grew the Bank Act had to be amended to cover new situations that arose."[13]

In 1917 Hiram Johnson went to the United States Senate and was succeeded by the lieutenant governor, William D. Stephens. In 1918, when Stephens retained the governorship by election, it was freely predicted that Williams' reign was near its end. After the election the superintendent expected Mr. Stephens to say whether he desired Williams to stay or to go. When he had heard nothing in three weeks Williams resigned, and presently accepted an appointment as cashier of the Bank of Italy.

Giannini had been warned that this might irritate Stephens. "What if it does?" remarked A. P. "Williams had the guts to clean up the banks of California, so I hired him to keep our bank clean."[14]

Rural Branches in Operation: 1916-1918

NOW FOR a closer look at the operation of the branches with which the Bank of Italy had dotted the San Joaquin, the Santa Clara, the Napa and the Sonoma Valleys.

By 1916, diversified farming had been carried to great lengths in California. The state exhibited all the types of agriculture found elsewhere in the country: the dairying of the Great Lakes, the grazing of the Rocky Mountains and Texas, the grain farming of the Midwest and the Northwest, the cotton growing of the South, the rice culture of Louisiana, the fresh-fruit and vegetable raising of Florida. In contrast to the dozen or fifteen crops typical of the corn or cotton belt, California farmers could boast of marketing over a hundred crops, some of which were being harvested every month in the year.

The regions into which Bank of Italy took its branches were among the most highly specialized in California. Prospective clients were business-minded farmers who regarded agriculture as a commercial pursuit rather than a means of subsistence. They had to be, for they worked lands requiring much capital. Deserts were changed into orchards and vineyards by expensive irrigation plants; wasteland and sloughs were converted into truck gardens by costly filling operations; large sums of operating cash were required to support great numbers of seasonal laborers. One farm authority estimated that a man who was going to farm in California in this period had to have capital and credit amounting to more than $20,000.[1]

The Bank of Italy went into the valleys when the business-minded farmer felt that he had struck a bonanza. Under the impetus of war, each year from 1916 to 1918 was a "banner year," both in production and in cash return. The canned fruit pack increased from 5,968,875 cases to 8,943,737; the dried fruit pack from 224,000 tons to 377,600. By 1918 the cash value of California's field crops, fruits, vegetables

and livestock totaled more than $684,000,000. Of this, orchards and
vineyards yielded $173,277,900; field crops, $287,663,774; poultry,
$54,426,056; and livestock, $113,052,045.[2]

Who would have been more aware of the impact of the banner-
year booms than a graduate of San Francisco's Washington Street?
In 1917, when the bank had been in the San Joaquin Valley over a
year, A. P. Giannini said to an interviewer in New York:

> Not until the spring of this year did the Coast awake to the evidences of
> a rapidly rising tide of war prosperity due to the unprecedented prices . . .
> for livestock and agricultural products. . . .
>
> No one could have foreseen the enormous increase in spring planting
> that followed the declaration of war. . . . The resulting crops that have
> been harvested this fall in the district tributary to San Francisco give sensa-
> tional evidence of what can be accomplished in the future. . . . The bean
> growers increased their 1916 output by over 75% leaping from 4,175,000
> bushels to 7,500,000. Barley advanced from 23,420,000 bushels to 35,206,000.
> These two crops were real thrillers. But the deciduous fruits reached new
> totals also; the peach crop exceeded last year's by nearly 1,400,000 bushels;
> the prune crops surpassed all existing records. The raisin output was the
> greatest in the history of the state. Even the sugar beet planters, although
> they suffered keenly from shortage of labor and from the high prices paid
> what labor was obtainable, made a new record of 1,660,000 tons.[3]

Rural prosperity had attained a stage where, as one observer remarked: "In California, a farmer raises poultry and has a Ford; he
raises grapes and keeps a Dodge; or he raises prunes and has an
Overland; oranges and a Cadillac; or lemons and a Franklin."[4]

For all that, the valley bank client was a borrowing farmer, borrowing for increased acreage, planting and irrigation. The borrowing habit had become so fixed that California's farm mortgage debt
trebled in eight years—rising from $107,415,000 in 1910 to $338,280,-
000 in 1918. To meet his dollar requirements, the farmer depended
more on his banker than on any other source. Although middlemen
played a significant role in short-term credit, local bankers held
more than 45 per cent of the farm mortgages; insurance companies
held little more than 8 per cent. Creameries, grain merchants, fruit
packers and so on, and individual lenders held the balance. Nearly
every county-seat capitalist had something "out on mortgage."[5]

These accommodations were costly to the farmer. "In most localities," complained the *Pacific Rural Press* early in 1916,

the farmer . . . must pay a high rate of interest and in many cases is compelled to pay [in addition] a bonus to a broker. . . . There are many banks which refuse to loan directly upon country property but will loan upon the same property to a broker who charges from two to five per cent for his services. Besides the brokerage, the farmer must pay an interest rate of eight per cent or more and from three to five times the actual cost of sending a man to appraise his property.[6]

The United States Department of Agriculture found the average interest rate in California on farm mortgages to be 7.4 per cent, plus an annual commission of 0.2 per cent, making a total of 7.6 per cent. More than 43 per cent of California's farmers paid 8 per cent plus commission. Some in isolated communities paid as high as 12 per cent. Moreover, these rates tended to be noncompetitive within each community.[7]

2

With the opening of the first branch in the San Joaquin Valley, at Merced on June 7, 1916, the Bank of Italy made its bid for patronage with an attack on high interest charges.

"There will be plenty of money available at 7 per cent," Director P. C. Hale, on hand at the opening, told a reporter for the Merced *Evening Star*.

That the Bank of Italy favored lower rates was no revelation to anyone who had followed its history. "You are putting the borrower out of business if you charge 10 or 12 per cent," argued Giannini. "The man who will fight hard to get cheaper interest rates is one that we want to loan money to, and if he is willing to pay any old price, look out."

L. G. Worden, former president of the Commercial and Savings Bank, one of the institutions purchased in Merced, became manager of the Bank of Italy branch. He gave out additional good news:

"Merced now has the largest and strongest bank in the San Joaquin Valley. . . . We want all the business we can get, whether large or small."[8]

Between these lines, the small rural borrower—and he would be the one with a $20,000 investment, at least—read a welcome message. It was not uncommon at this time for prominent merchants and farmers sitting on the board, or for a bank's officers, to safeguard their own financial needs by turning down the requests of others for loans. Nor was it uncommon for the officers of the local bank to have an interest in several community enterprises that required credit. Some were leading cattle buyers; others, grain merchants; still others, large ranch operators. Consequently, borrowers outside the magic circle, notably small farmers, sometimes found it difficult to obtain even small loans when the lending capacity of the local bank had been seriously reduced by the demands of a favored few.[9]

From the first, monopoly of loan resources, either by officers or by the advisory boards, was guarded against in the branches of the Bank of Italy. Equally important, perhaps, local lending is always subject to the scrutiny of a watchful home office. The policy of "no entangling or conflicting outside interests on the part of its officers or employees," as Bacigalupi expressed it, had gone a long way toward strengthening the Bank of Italy's position in the valleys. In 1917, the salary of the manager of the Madera branch was cut in half because the home office thought he was devoting too much of the bank's time to his grain business.[10]

It was the same story in Fresno. In the wake of the take-over, notices went to the signers of notes, inherited with the two banks purchased, informing them that the interest on their loans had been reduced to 7 per cent—a substantial reduction from rates that ran, in extreme cases, as high as 12 per cent. The reaction was immediate. The Farmers National Bank of Fresno, which was to give the branch stiff competition, announced that it had "several hundred thousand dollars" to put out at 7 per cent.

To a local newspaperman, Giannini enlarged on the new branch's loan policy. "We believe that in having a prosperous surrounding country, the city will prosper and we also think that high rates of interest are ruinous to the farmers. We are here to make good times and . . . 7 per cent will be our maximum rate of interest." The Bank of Italy was ready to loan at the lowered rate "$1,000,000 in the San Joaquin Valley and with resources of $32,000,000 . . . is in a position to negotiate a loan of any magnitude." The valley, Giannini affirmed, "is a great undeveloped field . . . and that is the reason we are here. Fresno is as much our home as San Francisco, and we are going to do all possible in financial aid for the businessman and farmer."[11]

A Fresno vineyardist told what this meant to those on his side of the fence: "It was a breather. For the first time we thought we could afford to borrow money."[12]

3

As a result of the bank's lower-interest policy, the Modesto branch landed one large account, opening up a new lending field where many small borrowers were helped, and practically no risk taken.

At that time Stanislaus County, of which Modesto is the seat, was one of the most diversified agricultural regions in the state. It yielded about everything from peaches to dairy products. The Borden Company was erecting a large condensed milk plant in Modesto. J. Lucas Williams, a vice-president of the Bank of Italy, wrote from the head office in San Francisco to the Borden home office in New York to solicit the Modesto plant's account. The Borden people turned the matter over to their Modesto superintendent who called on W. A. Harter, manager of the branch. Mr. Harter was well known in his community. He had been president of the Farmers and Merchants Bank, which the B. of I. had converted into its Modesto branch. To the San Francisco office Harter reported the upshot of his talk with the Borden superintendent:

"He was quite anxious to know if the patrons of the condensary would be well taken care of in case they desired loans, upon the proper security, and not be charged at an excessive rate of interest . . . I assured him . . . that we would make the rate of interest satisfactory to his company."

The superintendent came back a second time for enlightenment on another matter. "He wanted to know what terms we would make on loans to dairy farmers and what amount we would loan per cow. I informed him that we would make loans not exceeding $30.00 per cow at the rate of six per cent, interest payable monthly. He seemed pleased."

The Borden man had reason to be happy. California banks had never been eager to lend on livestock. "Never loan on anything that eats," was more than just a saying in the valley; it was banking policy. As president of the Farmers and Merchants Bank of Modesto, however, Mr. Harter had found a way of making such loans pay. "We . . . made dairy loans . . . for a number of years and never lost a cent," he informed the San Francisco office. The successful formula was an arrangement whereby creameries withheld for the benefit of the lending bank a portion of the dairyman's monthly checks. The loans amounted to "$25.00 or $30.00 per cow at the rate of 6 per cent." Nowadays Harter's solution is obvious, but, in 1918, it was not a common practice. The proposal pleased the Borden superintendent. It also satisfied the San Francisco office. These questions settled, the Modesto branch got the account of the Borden condensary.[13]

The fourth San Joaquin Valley branch went to Madera where interest rates were pegged at 9 per cent. James A. Bacigalupi, as spokesman for the Bank of Italy, was on the ground to give out the news:

Bank of Italy will . . . stand with and back all legitimate extensions of business enterprise. . . . It will be remembered that when the Bank of Italy began to operate a short time ago in Fresno, it reduced the interest rates on many loans to seven per cent. As there is no reason why Madera borrowers should not be under the same ruling and accorded the same treatment . . . notices will be sent out to all mortgagors to the effect that their rate of interest will be at seven per cent maximum on mortgage loans.[14]

The Madera *Daily Tribune* welcomed Bacigalupi's statement:

It means that the Bank of Italy brings to Madera all the experience, organization, and stability of a big city bank. The Bank of Italy's combined resources of over $45,000,000 are to be available for those who are and those who may become Bank of Italy depositors and clients. . . . Madera now will have a big benefactor in a business way, namely a bank that can handle as large a transaction here in Madera as it can in San Francisco. In truth, this brings big business to Madera and will make big business in Madera.[15]

Madera was the market for the beef cattle which grazed in the near-by foothills on the east side of the valley, and for the grapes grown by an Italian colony on the west. In a short time the branch was taking an active part in the campaign to secure gravity water for the west side by damming the San Joaquin River where it drops from the Sierras to the valley floor at Friant. Prime movers of the project were John B. High, Madera branch advisory board chairman, and Carl F. Wente, branch manager. Though destined for

These two accounts belonging to the Beronio family were among the twenty-eight opened on October 17, 1904.

The destroyed premises of the original bank, taken the day after the San Francisco fire of April 18, 1906.

defeat because of inadequate financial support, the plan was a forerunner of the great Central Valley Project, California's TVA sponsored by the federal government in the forties.[16]

The San Joaquin Valley National Bank, taken over in Stockton, was a lineal descendant of the Bours Bank, which dated from the magical year 1849. Port city of the valley, Stockton had a population in 1916 of more than forty thousand. At its river docks, ocean freighters loaded the harvests and livestock gathered from the valley's length for shipment to world markets. Smaller vessels hurried cargoes daily to San Francisco and other bay cities. Night and day three railway system switched their freight cars into long lines for the overland haul. The smoking chimneys of canning factories, flour mills and foundries contributed to give Stockton the appearance of one of the busiest towns in the West. The city was proud of its industries and wanted to grow. Like the Madera newspaper, the Stockton *Record* was enthusiastic about the advent of a Bank of Italy branch:

"The great resources of the Bank of Italy will be particularly helpful, in assisting the merchant, manufacturer, farmer and homebuilder in the building up of this city and county, working in harmony with the other financial interests of this community."[17]

An initial service of the branch was to join hands with the Sperry Flour Company's local mill in a campaign to induce "more and better" wheat from the San Joaquin Valley. The bank published and distributed a pamphlet to farmer customers, suggesting newer methods of planting and harvesting. The Sperry Company praised the pamphlet both as a "real service to the grain farmer" and a "war-winning work."[18]

Though big business was served, Giannini's little fellow was not overlooked in the region of Stockton where the small farmer made a good living out of comparatively small acreage. With the circumstances favoring them, the Stockton and all the valley branches were able to exploit the ample field of investment which the little farmer offered. In no time the farmer discovered that the Bank of Italy was more liberal than other banks in granting loans.

"We had a lot of little farmers who needed money," the manager at Merced later recalled. "The branch grew because A. P. insisted that we take care of the little farmer." In Madera, for example, after a year's operation, the Bank of Italy branch had acquired more than three-fourths of the accounts of the small orchardists and vineyardists.[19]

Moreover, circumstances tended to hold to a minimum the antagonism of independent bankers toward the newcomer in their midst. Nothing like the early inhospitality of Los Angeles was encountered by the Bank of Italy during those first years in the valleys, probably because everybody was too busy. In the main, valley banks had more business than they could handle. This condition lasted for several years after 1916.

4

Nevertheless, one type of financing, important to an agricultural economy, which local banks usually had to abandon to city banks, was the seasonal requirements of the local canner and packer. Advances to farmers, often as not, were more than sufficient to exhaust the resources of the local banks. Here, too, the Bank of Italy provided a financial prop. Santa Clara was an example singled out by Giannini, at a later day, to illustrate the services of branch banking in this respect.

When we bought the Santa Clara bank the lending limit was $10,000. There happens to be a large business there which has seasonal requirements running up to $200,000 or $250,000. . . . It was impossible for that business to satisfy its needs in the local field. . . . The moment we took . . . over we were able to handle that business locally, and to extend the same lending facilities there as obtained everywhere else throughout our system.[20]

Near-by San Jose had already reaped the same benefits through the coming of the Bank of Italy. A local banking competitor was quick to express his admiration of the branch's performance. Previously, said William Pabst, vice-president of the Growers Bank, when "the big canneries and packing companies . . . needed huge sums for short time loans . . . all the unit banks in San Jose put together could not advance them funds. . . . Now that the Bank of Italy is [here] big businesses . . . need not go outside for help."[21]

Such loans reached into the realm of big business. Valley farming is pretty big business. Many of the crops were perishable or semiperishable; their movement had to be rapid; their handling and packing, skillful; and their flow to the distant consumer, flexible and constantly under control. Moreover, the principal markets lay as far east as Chicago and New York. Much of the barley harvest was sold on the London market; valley orchardists had long supplied Europe with a good part of her prunes; delta rice was shipped to Japan; and Cuba and Puerto Rico were regular customers for California beans.

The valley farmer found it was no virtue to grow two blades of grass when only one could be marketed at a profit. Therefore he proceeded to organize large-scale co-operatives in the mold of large-scale private enterprises with a highly integrated system of production and marketing. By the time the Bank of Italy entered the valleys, selling activities had reached a higher stage of comprehensiveness, scale and complexity in California than elsewhere in the United States. In 1919, sales through co-operative marketing organizations totaled $127,990,981 in California, as compared with $82,760,459 for the next state, Minnesota. By 1920, California growers were operating approximately twenty-nine co-operative fruit-marketing agencies, twenty field-crop organizations, five poultry organizations, and ten dairying and livestock organizations.

The Bank of Italy did not hesitate to put its swelling resources behind this system which was already attracting Eastern banking interests. In March, 1918, on motion of A. P. Giannini, the executive committee of the bank granted to the newly organized California Prune and Apricot Growers Association a credit of $250,000, secured by warehouse receipts on a 60 per cent basis. In June, an additional credit of $300,000 was advanced for ninety days. In May, the California Growers Association (Los Angeles) got a credit of $100,000, also secured by warehouse receipts covering canned goods, at 75 per cent of the cost of the finished product.[22]

Before the end of 1918, events in the San Joaquin Valley also reflected the strong interest of the bank in the farmer's co-ops. In the Fresno area the California Associated Raisin Company, one of the pioneer California co-ops, enlisted the aid of the Fresno branch in its annual "sign-up" campaign to pool the harvest of seeded raisins. Representatives of the branch carried the campaign to growers in the outlying communities, and letters were sent to the Italian vineyardists. As a result, 125,000 bearing acres were contracted to the Associated, representing 85 per cent of the state's raisin crop. The bank's interest in this campaign stemmed from the fact that the co-op offered its borrowers a stable market for their crop, and thus protected the heavy investment in the raisin industry.[23]

The policy of meeting the valley's credit needs across the counter of the local branches was firmly established by 1918. With few changes, the details were the same as those described twelve years later by Bacigalupi at a House committee hearing on branch banking in Washington:

Loans are made direct by the branches, except in instances where the amount is unusually large or the branch manager wishes to secure the advice of the head office credit department. The customers of the branch deal with the local officers, and only in extraordinary circumstances are they brought into contact with the head office departments. Each branch has a general lending limit fixed by the bank's finance committee. Within this limit each branch may lend and report without previous consultation with the head office. These limits vary with the proven credit capacity of the various branch loaning officers. . . . All applications for unfixed lines of credit in excess of the lending limit of a given branch are promptly considered and acted upon by the proper central credit department and proper advice and instructions issued. The broad fundamental policies respecting credits are outlined by the general executive committee and application is then made by the credit department.[24]

"Proven credit capacity" was not left to conjecture, but was based on a careful study of the branch's loan paper and of local conditions. The lending limit at most branches did not exceed $5,000, although Fresno and Stockton, where loans averaged higher, were exceptions. During these years, whatever the limit, Giannini did not drop the reins on his managers. With Director Hale he made frequent forays into the valleys, burning the midnight oil as loan pouches were examined.

E. T. Cunningham, who became manager at Merced in 1919, recalled an example of how closely Giannini watched the activities of the branches. "The winter in 1918 had been a dry one. Feed was short; and local bankers and I agreed to raise the interest on cattle loans from 7 per cent to 8 per cent because of the poor risk. A. P. came in one day and asked for my loans. Just before he finished his examination, he ran across the cattle loans at 8 per cent. Without a word, he carefully crossed out the 8 and wrote in 7."[25]

At the manager's heels, of course, was a local watchdog, the advisory board, whose chief concern was loans. No mere list of impressive names, members of the advisory boards worked hard in their communities, or resigned. The head office in San Francisco formulated a uniform procedure for the monthly meetings of those boards. Concerning loans the instructions read:

Report of loans made since last meeting; also lists of overdrafts. Loans and overdrafts to be approved by motion.

List of past due loans to be read with statement from manager as to what the understanding is as to payment or extension. Discussion by members if they have any suggestions as to any of them.

List of loans maturing in next 30 days with suggestions from members as to action as to payment and extension.[26]

In 1917 the Bank of Italy created at the head office a country loan department to handle the increasing farm credits of the branches. L. G. Worden was transferred from Merced to be the farm loan manager. It was the duty of his department to examine loan applications, make appraisals and inspect soil. These functions were broadened when in 1918 the country loan department was absorbed by the newly created credit department which was directed by James E. Fickett.

5

As the war boom rolled on, farmland became a coveted possession, particularly in the valleys where "mud farming" had taken hold. A farm editor wrote that "everybody seems to be running around trying to buy something large enough to irrigate. . . . Our own people and our visitors seem to like the game of buying, ditching and cutting up." Land prices in California rose earlier and faster than those in any other part of the United States.[27]

The bonanza of a specialty crop usually shot land prices sky high. When raisins soared to $105 a ton in 1916, an increase of more than $39 over the 1914 bid, bearing vineyards in the Fresno area jumped from $250 to $1,000 per acre. In Ventura, where fortunes were piled up in a season's harvest of lima beans, land that once sold for $400 to $500 per acre could not be had for $1,000. Asparagus land in the Stockton delta hit a new high in 1918 with the asking price $350 to $400 per acre; hop land with bearing vines brought $1,000 to $1,500 per acre in the Sacramento Valley; and Santa Clara prune orchards touched $1,000 to $1,500 per acre.[28]

The impact of the boom—high prices for land, water, and labor
—could be seen everywhere in the rural economy. The runaway
prices took watching. The Bank of Italy was not led astray by the
inflated land quotations. Real estate loans approved by the Hollister
branch stand as one example:

	Amount of Loans	Appraised Value
January 24, 1917	$54,250	$116,500
June 20, 1917	25,704	66,450
January 16, 1918	19,035	79,200
June 19, 1918	39,215	98,937
January 15, 1919	38,500	63,000[29]

Appraisals were the bank's own, in most cases figured out by the
branch managers and the advisory boards.

That the branches established during the war years should have
made money is not surprising. Had they not done so it would have
been an indication of something seriously wrong with them. Ledgers tell a story of frequent losses during the first months after a
take-over, and then the beginnings of growth. The San Jose Safe
Deposit Bank, bought in November, 1917, lost almost $19,000 in
less than two months remaining in the year. After merger with the
old San Jose branch, profit of the consolidated branch in 1918 ran
to nearly $88,000. Fattened by Santa Clara Valley's food exports to
war-devastated Europe, in 1919 the gain was $159,000. The Santa
Rosa Bank, absorbed in December, 1917, lost $1,700 during the last
weeks of the year. In 1918, the branch had a profit of $11,000. By
the end of 1919 this had more than doubled.

In the last two months of 1918, when they were the property of
the Bank of Italy, the four Oakland branches lost $15,000. The fol-
lowing year three of them showed modest profits but the Melrose
branch was in the red to the extent of $650. Giannini promised
every employee of the branch a new hat if, by the end of 1919, deposits hit a half-million and the branch moved into the black. They
got the hats.

At the Fresno branch, profits had the biggest rise, from $9,449 in
1916 to $107,515 in 1917. In 1918, they dropped to $81,587 when expenses on the erection of a new bank building were charged off. In
1919, they were up again to $109,888. Another profitable branch was
Stockton: $22,982 in 1917; $131,778 in 1918, and $188,977 in 1919.[30]

The Education of a Superintendent of Banks

THE YEAR 1919 brought a change of atmosphere to the Bank of Italy. As we have seen, the period just preceding had been one of phenomenal growth. Those war-boom times were not a fair test, however. All banks did well. In the case of the Bank of Italy "natural" growth was supplemented by "purchased" growth. Indeed, about 60 per cent of the Bank of Italy's enormous increase in deposits during the war had come from banks bought in the course of the surge through the agricultural valleys. Some saw in this a case of the tail wagging the dog. The question was asked: How much growth would the bank have shown if it had not been allowed to buy it? Another question was: How will the bank fare when the war boom is over?

The bank fared well. In 1919, the first postwar year, it enjoyed the greatest growth in its history to then. Deposits went from $85,-938,000 to $127,258,000. This was all "natural" growth for, during 1919, not a single bank was purchased.

In 1920, deposits went to $140,993,000—an increase of $13,734,000. This, too, was "natural" growth exclusively. In 1921, deposits climbed to $177,867,000—an increase of $36,874,000. Of this $17,-490,000 was "purchased" growth.

By contrast with the boom times, these were years of deflation which put a bank on its mettle. As to economic conditions generally, California was more fortunate than the rest of the country. The collapse of commodity prices which hit the Midwest and the South in the middle of 1920, leaving war-inflated land prices up in the air, was slow reaching the Coast. The general industrial depression that followed the break in commodities, and lasted through 1921, was not so severe beyond the Rockies as it was elsewhere. Consequently, California banks were not subjected to the pressure that bore upon institutions in the Mississippi Valley where there was a wave of rural bank failures.

All the same, the Coast banks had their work cut out. There were hours of anxiety for all, the Bank of Italy included, and desperate hours for some.

Now to touch upon the salient events of the period as they concern the Bank of Italy.

2

Let us look first at the circumstances under which the bank affiliated with the Federal Reserve System in July, 1919.

Created in 1914 as a result of the impetus given to banking reform by the 1907 panic, the System was still regarded as an experiment despite its helpfulness with the abnormal currency, credit and other financial requirements of the war. There were twelve regional banks under the control of a Federal Reserve Board in Washington. National banks were required to join the System; state banks might join. Provision for the expansion and contraction of currency to meet changing business needs was made within the System. Member banks could obtain Federal Reserve notes by rediscounting with their regional Federal Reserve Bank the commercial paper of merchants, manufacturers, agricultural associations and others, to whom they had made loans. There was provision for the flow of credit from one part of the country to another. The Federal Reserve Bank of San Francisco might, for example, rediscount paper in Chicago.

At the outset comparatively few state banks joined the System. Together with the national banks, which were obliged to join, the affiliating banks numbered only about one in three of all the banks in the country. But they held much more than a third of the assets. This strength pulled the System through the war. The country would have been badly off without it.[1]

San Francisco was the seat of the Federal Reserve Bank for the Twelfth District, comprising the three coastal states, and also Idaho, Utah, Nevada and most of Arizona. The chairman of the bank's board was John Perrin, an Indianan who had entered investment banking in Los Angeles. Though Perrin worked to bring state banks into the system, only four of them in California joined. One obstacle was the state's banking law which did not recognize as legal reserves the reserves a bank must set up to unite with the Federal System. Thus a joining state bank had to double its reserve requirements. Another obstacle was a spirit of distrust. Some feared the Federal Reserve banks would compete with commercial banks for business. Others feared its branch banking features. When the Federal Reserve Board in Washington authorized national banks to establish branches within strict limits, the American Bankers Association in 1916 hurrahed through its convention a resolution opposing "branch banks in any form."[2]

The threat implicit in this action disturbed Giannini. In 1914 he had welcomed the Federal Reserve because it *is* a branch banking system. When Perrin pressed the Bank of Italy to join, Giannini replied that he would do so only if assured "that the Federal Reserve Board approves of the branch system as operated by us, and further that the necessary approval by the Board to our taking on additional branches will be based solely on the question of whether the new branch is in keeping with the general safety of the Bank." Adolph C. Miller of the F.R.B. in Washington visited Giannini. He was happy to find that the Bank of Italy, though not a member, was working closely with the federal bank in San Francisco. On his return to the capital Miller gave an affirmative answer to Giannini's question. "The Board," he wrote,

is not opposed to the principal of branch banking. . . . The sole concern . . . will be to satisfy itself that any proposed extension will not impair the . . . safety of your institution. . . . It would be a great pleasure personally to see your bank blazing the way in your state and setting a much needed example by taking membership in the Federal Reserve.

W. P. G. Harding, governor of the F.R.B., telegraphed that the Board "formally approved" Miller's statements and expressed the hope that "this will open the way to prompt application for membership."[3]

This interchange took place in the fall of 1917. Though the Bank of Italy won high praise from government officials for its co-operation with the Federal Reserve Bank of San Francisco in the matter of war financing, application for membership was delayed until 1919, when the State of California removed the disabilities concerning dual reserves. Then the Bank of Italy and ten other state banks qualified for membership on July 22, the day the law became effective. Joseph F. Sartori's Security Trust and Savings of Los Angeles did not join until the following December. Like Giannini, Mr. Sartori received assurances on the subject of branch banking.

It had been pleasant to be thus sought after by the banking arm of the United States government. Particularly was this true since California's new superintendent of banks, Charles F. Stern, had flatly rejected the first application submitted by the Bank of Italy for a branch since the retirement from office of W. R. Williams. Mr. Stern did not stop there. While the Federal Reserve Board prepared to welcome the bank into the System, the California superintendent was laboring over an extraordinary communication which expressed the strongest disapproval of certain aspects of the Bank of Italy's way of doing business.

3

The long letter in which Mr. Stern aired his doubts was dated June 23, 1919, seven months after he had taken office. "The Bank of Italy is unique in American banking," the superintendent wrote. "Your progress has been so rapid . . . the units added to your organization have been so numerous and so widely scattered, that the general situation . . . raises two distinct questions of paramount importance."

The first question implied that it was inadvisable for a bank to operate branches "in territory without close economic relationship to your home office." In other words, why should a San Francisco bank have branches in Los Angeles?

The second question concerned the administration of the rapidly thrown together institution. Instead of a well-knit, smoothly running, uniform organization Stern said it was a rather loose confederation. "Your branch offices are neither absorbed nor assimilated." This criticism contained some truth, as no one knew better than the Bank of Italy's cashier, W. R. Williams, whom Mr. Stern had succeeded as superintendent of banks. However, the alarming thing was the conclusion Stern drew from his premise. "We are not only disappointed, but we are very seriously concerned . . . from the standpoint of the safety and ultimate solvency of your institution."

Mr. Stern enumerated items to justify his strong language. Many dealt with nothing more serious than diverse bookkeeping methods.

One branch did a thing one way, another branch another. There were also bookkeeping omissions. Moreover, complaint was made that "several" branches carried unsecured loans that were past due. In the savings department, loans had been made in excess of 60 per cent of appraised value of the security. No figures were given to indicate the proportion of such loans to all loans.

Then came a serious accusation. "You indulge a practice vicious from every point of view, by paying dividends upon the basis of interest discount uncollected, thus misrepresenting the actual status of your affairs and invading your capital." Without supporting the statement with figures, the superintendent declared that the bank "inflated" its "gross earnings by approximately 25%."

Minor examples of negligence were cited. The bank had closed a Los Angeles branch without explanation to the department. In Fresno it had moved a branch to the next block without official permission. Still, the letter contained words of praise for the progress the bank had made to "eliminate the confusion in accounts." It closed with the statement that Mr. Stern did not believe the bank knowingly guilty of "unsound banking practice . . . or deliberate evasion of the law." It called, however, "for immediate and final reforms."[4]

The gist of what Mr. Stern had to say, W. R. Williams, when he was superintendent, had said many times, though in more temperate prose. Instead of writing, for the most part he had gone personally to Giannini or to Bacigalupi and advised the bank to slow down "and get acquainted with itself." Williams knew how to be firm without indulging in scare talk about insolvency or impairment of capital. On behalf of the Bank of Italy, Mr. Williams got the job of replying to Mr. Stern. He did so without raising his voice.

Admitting that "many of the things pointed out by you were . . . subject to criticism," Williams said that they had been or would be adjusted. In some cases the change might be slow because of local habit and custom. The public would have to be re-educated and branch personnel trained in new methods. In many instances the methods themselves would have to be devised. "These difficulties account for most of the lack of uniformity." Nevertheless, "we believe that we have solved the problem of co-relation, adjustment and digestion. . . . Each local management is held to a strict accountability for its conduct."

The issue raised by Stern concerning the "economic relationship" between the head office and remote branches Williams declared to be outside the scope of the law and consequently of the superintendent's authority. The boundaries of California imposed the only "limit upon the distance that a branch may be from the main office."

On the question of the bank's "ultimate solvency," Williams remarked that "we are somewhat astounded by this statement." Mr. Stern was asked to make a "careful personal investigation" of the sketchy evidence he had offered in support of it. Excepting only the depreciation of bond investments (the dip in the bond market had affected all banks), Williams said that "the sum total of all doubtful elements of our loans and investments criticized by you could be written off and there would be no possible encroachment upon our surplus."

As to encroachment upon capital, Williams said "the facts do not bear out this statement." Certain obscurities in bookkeeping, but no "primary error," were admitted. (Though he did not say so, one of Williams' jobs was to clarify the bank's system of accounting, which had not kept stride with the institution's complex growth.) Touching upon some of these matters, Williams assured the superintendent that

we do not pay dividends upon the basis of interest discount uncollected and we do not in this fashion nor in any other fashion invade our capital account. . . .

We do not claim to have reached perfection but we do claim that we are rendering a service that could not have been rendered by any individual bank whose business we have acquired nor could it have been rendered by all such banks collectively.[5]

When Superintendent Stern's reply ignored the solvency issue but continued the barrage of chicken-feed criticism, Williams asked for a conference. He said the vital issue of the bank's financial soundness must be cleared up. At this meeting Stern was satisfied on the score of solvency and wrote a letter obliquely admitting it.[6]

4

This by no means ended the differences between the superintendent and the bank.

While Williams was dealing calmly with the irresponsible reference to solvency, A. P. Giannini was anything but calm. He tried to keep quiet, but an indication of his feeling emerged in a piece he wrote for *Bankitaly Life,* the institution's house organ, on the occasion of the bank's fifteenth birthday. The structure the bank had erected was described in glowing terms. Admission to the Federal Reserve was heralded as an endorsement, despite the "open hostility to our further expansion" on the part of some banking competitors, and despite, also, that "certain official quarters . . . shared . . . these antagonistic views." Giannini closed by saying that the Bank of Italy would not be turned from its course. Though officials might deny additional branches, "nothing will deter it [the bank] from lawfully benefiting the residents of any and every part of California."[7]

From A. P. Giannini, the statement was news. That it did not reach a wider audience seems proof that financial writers were not in the habit of reading *Bankitaly Life.* Stern read it, however. He took Mr. Giannini's utterance as a challenge. The danger-to-solvency bogey having been dissipated, the superintendent moved the controversy to other ground. This was that branch banking, on the scale contemplated by Giannini, was against public policy. Notwithstanding "the unquestioned benefit your branch offices have brought to many specific localities," Stern wrote, "I cannot believe that the . . . public advantage . . . can be promoted by a theory of banking that, when its ultimate has been reached, four, or three or one Bank of Italy controls the finance of California."

On his part, the superintendent disclaimed any sentiment of "hostility." He said the case simply was that he and the Bank of Italy held "diametrically opposite points of view honestly arrived at. . . . You express the utmost confidence that your organization has wiped out time and distance and is operating your institution as a unit; I express the doubt whether, in view of the different economic problems . . . and the physical separation [of branches], you are so operating." As to who was right Mr. Stern was willing to "abide by the verdict of the future"; and he assumed that Giannini also would accept the verdict. The superintendent admitted that in a day to come he might possibly change his mind, but until that time the Bank of Italy would be subject to the following rule: "You may not go forward with further [branch] expansion, but you may rely upon the department for every support in your problems of correlation and digestion."[8]

This notice, privately served on the bank in November, 1919, completed the clarification of a hitherto cloudy situation. The bank knew where Stern stood, and vice versa. Ultimately one of them would have to give in. Not for an instant did A. P. Giannini think the eventual yielder would be the Bank of Italy. On his side, the superintendent, despite his profession of open-mindedness, seemed equally sure of himself. All the same, Mr. Stern gave evidence that he had learned something since beginning the controversy in June. The tone as well as the substance of later communications showed a growing respect for the institution whose branchwise spread over California, and particularly southern California, he had set out to curb. Moreover, the advice that the Bank of Italy digest its swift conquests was good advice, as Cashier Williams tacitly conceded. For that matter so did Giannini, but with this difference: A. P. wanted to digest existing branches and to take on more at the same time.

This development explains the fact that the Bank of Italy received only one license in 1919. It was to open a branch in North Beach, San Francisco. In 1920 it received one license—to move the North Beach branch across the street. Nor was Superintendent Stern open-handed with the Bank of Italy's branch banking competitors, such as they were. In 1919 only eighteen branch licenses were granted to other banks. In 1920 forty branch permits were granted. Actually, the pressure for branches was just beginning to make itself felt as certain other bankers, observing Giannini's success, continued to experiment with city branches and with country branches near home. This notwithstanding, no rival of Giannini's statewide system appeared.

Nevertheless, the Bank of Italy made good its promise to continue branch expansion. In 1919 the Stockholders Auxiliary Corporation, of which A. P. Giannini was president, bought six country banks in four towns. Four of the acquisitions were national banks. Two were state banks which Giannini immediately removed from Stern's jurisdiction by merging them with two of the newly purchased national banks. Then, in 1920, the Auxiliary bought four more national banks in four towns.

No effort was made to denationalize any of these eight banks and to convert them into branches of the B. of I. Giannini knew it use-less to ask Mr. Stern for the necessary licenses. Thanks to the broad powers with which Giannini's foresight had invested the Auxiliary in 1917, there was no limit to the time it could operate a bank. Con-sequently that useful corporation tranquilly retained ownership of all eight institutions. Though reorganized on Bank of Italy lines, they were operated as ostensibly independent entities under the au-thority of the United States government whose bank officials re-tained the friendly attitude evinced when the Bank of Italy was received into the Federal Reserve System. In this way Uncle Sam became Giannini's ally in a moderate circumvention of Mr. Stern's policy of no more branches for the Bank of Italy.[9]

Thus, with a foot in both camps, Giannini entered a period of wary and watchful waiting. There were moments when he seemed to look upon national banks with more favor than state banks as instruments for the attainment of his goal of a greater statewide banking system. From 1920 on, the possibility of eventually nation-alizing that system was never long absent from his mind.

5

Superintendent Stern also was watching and waiting, and doing what he could to shape events to defeat the ambitions Mr. Giannini held for the Bank of Italy. Stern felt that California was too big a place for any one bank to spread itself all over. Early in his regime the superintendent had opened a subsidiary office of his department in Los Angeles. He spent considerable time there. The plaints he heard—"southern California for southern California bankers"—strengthened his confidence in the belief that the Bank of Italy did not belong south of the Tehachapi.

A generation afterward, in conversation with one of the authors of this book, Mr. Stern freely recalled that feature of the situation as it stood in 1919.

"When I became superintendent I ran into a whispering cam-paign against Bank of Italy. Bankers beat a path to my office to complain about the monopolistic tendency of the bank. They com-plained about its aggressive methods, saying that it was getting so big it could do anything it desired to a competing bank. The Los Angeles bankers complained about a bank from San Francisco spreading itself over the south, and the more I thought about it, the clearer it became to me that the south should be left to southern bankers and northern banks should stay in their part of the state. Most of California's branch systems were already operating profitably and without contention in their particular zones of economic influence and, from the results obtained, that appeared to be the correct way. The Bank Act offered no solution to the problem, for it did not define the [territorial] limits of branch banking. All I had to go on was my judgment and the desires of the majority. Above all, I tried to keep in mind what was best for California."[10]

This illumination of the record corroborates what Giannini wrote for *Bankitaly Life* in 1919. Through life no small part of his success was due to a knack of knowing what his competitors were up to and keeping a jump ahead of them. In the period under review the jump materialized in the Auxiliary-held banks, which Giannini had every confidence of taking under the main tent in good time.

When 1919 came to an end the superintendent of banks received the annual statements of all California state banks. He was moved to write Mr. Giannini that the Bank of Italy's statement had been read "with a great deal of interest. . . . The showing there made entitles you to the warmest congratulations."[11]

That was not extravagant praise. The gain in assets was $44,-354,000—to $137,900,700. This was above any single bank in California. Only the assets of the Anglo & London Paris National Bank of San Francisco combined with those of its savings affiliate, the Anglo-California Trust Company, were larger by a narrow margin. It may be recalled that national banks, forbidden to accept savings accounts, frequently acquired control of savings institutions, rather than be cut out of that profitable business.

During the year the Bank of Italy had gained $41,320,000 in deposits—the largest increase of any bank in the country. It gained 27,885 deposit accounts, bringing the total to 189,511. This gave the Bank of Italy the largest body of depositors in the United States. Loans increased by $14,868,000—to $74,737,000. The ratio of loans to deposits stood at 58.7, a decrease from 68.7 for 1918. A million dollars had been added to capital, bringing it to $6,000,000. Earnings were $512,500, against $383,714 for 1918. The dividend rate was raised from 7½ to 10 per cent.

Mr. Stern had nothing to say this year about earnings being "inflated" or dividends being paid from capital.

6

What lay behind this performance of the Bank of Italy? The development of alert, aggressive outposts—branches—in every section of California? That much was obvious, but as an explanation of the bank's success it was far from complete. The bank was growing internally. For instance, a foreign business department was created, and John J. Arnold, formerly vice-president of the First National Bank of Chicago, was brought to San Francisco to head it. Bidding for international business, the department furnished information on market conditions, credit standing, transportation costs and routing, customs requirements and duties throughout the world. The Los Angeles branches made this service available to the business community there, which, through its man-made port, was entering overseas trade with little experience to guide it.[12]

A bond department was organized. The first year it handled $11,500,000 in securities, mostly municipals. Very early this activity attracted the notice of Superintendent Stern. The automobile, the truck and the bus were beginning in earnest their transformation of the American scene. Our business and industry, our personal lives, manners, morals and culture were in for remolding at the instance of the gasoline engine. Nowhere was this change so rapid or so profound as it was in California. This called for highways adapted to rubber tires. Where its material interests are concerned California rarely misses a trick. It had begun forehandedly to create a circulatory system for the automotive age.

With the bond market "off," a $3,000,000 road issue was "being kicked from pillar to post." In an effort to form a bankers' pool to take up these bonds and avoid an interruption of work so vital to California, Stern met with the directors of the Bank of Italy. They voted to take $221,000 in bonds and hold them off the market for six months. "My personal appreciation and heartfelt thanks," wrote the superintendent. "As a bank . . . you have done a very fine thing, which will be of tremendous value, not only to the state and the highway work, but to yourselves."[13]

The word "revolutionary" can be overworked in connection with the Bank of Italy. Some of the things it was doing had been done long before. B. of I. simply did them better. An example is savings by school children. The idea seems to have originated in Wisconsin in 1876. By 1907 banks in 113 cities in 22 states were collecting for deposit the pennies of pupils in 1,098 schools. Despite these statistics the activity was really minute and scarcely profitable to the participating banks. Children who learned habits of thrift were the main beneficiaries.

That was enough for Giannini who entered the field in 1911. Within two years $90,495 was on deposit. In 1916 the feature was added to the branches. A representative of the bank visited each affiliated school once a month. By 1918, 22,292 kids had over $400,-000 in the bank. Nearly 60 per cent of the accounts opened stayed on the books. By the end of 1920 deposits stood at $732,000. The Bank of Italy had done more with school savings than all the other banks had done in forty years. Nevertheless, administrative expense was so great that about the only profit was in making youthful friends for the bank. To Giannini that was worth the effort.

The bank continued to make friends of its employees. It made them feel a partnership in this institution, and savor the excitement of advancing the frontiers of their calling. This was all the work of Giannini, and of the other top men who caught his spirit. Christmas bonuses, instituted when the bank was small and poor, increased until in 1917 they were equal to a half-month's salary. In 1919 a pension system was introduced that was very liberal for its day. Employees could retire at sixty-five provided they had twenty years' service. Service in banks that were bought counted as far back as 1904. A widow of a pensioner, not more than ten years his junior, drew half-pension for life; but if fifteen years younger she drew only 40 per cent, and if twenty years younger 30 per cent. A widow thirty years younger than her late husband got nothing: Giannini thought her chances of remarriage too good.[14]

Bonuses were standardized in 1921 at 5 per cent of a year's pay for those employed one year. This went up to 10 per cent for those of five or more years' service, and was limited to workers getting less than $6,000. Group insurance and sickness benefits were instituted.

Hardworking but satisfied employees went a long way toward

infecting the bank's patrons with agreeable feelings. The air of aloofness that Woodrow Wilson had deprecated in banks and bankers was nowhere about a branch of the Bank of Italy. They were bustling, genial places with the friendliness of a country store on Saturdays. During their initial sojourn in California, one of the first—and one of the oldest—stories the authors of this book heard about the Bank of Italy concerned a stranger who gained the wrong impression from a quick look at the crowd passing in and out of one of the branches. He thought there was a run on the bank.

Wherever the Bank of Italy opened up, people who had never had a bank account before got the habit of going to the branch for advice of all kinds. Giannini encouraged this. Employees came to enjoy it; it helped to make life interesting. Some patrons had an idea the Bank of Italy could do almost anything. A Mexican woman with two men in tow entered the Ventura branch. With the air of one who had no time to waste, she inquired for the manager. She asked that official to divorce her from one of the men and marry her to the other.[15]

7

Charles F. Stern was too shrewd a man to overlook the significance of what he saw: the Bank of Italy entering into the stream of life, the multiplicity of concerns as varied as life itself, of the people of California. No other bank had so many points of contact with its patrons. In terms of banking, Giannini was expressing an insatiable curiosity about human nature.

As his second year in office—1920—wore on, Superintendent Stern's ideas began to shake down and crystallize. He paid less attention to the whispering campaign against the Bank of Italy and more attention to the bank itself. For its part, the statewide organization was tightening up. Inherited dissimilarities in procedure among branches, of which the superintendent had complained earlier, were disappearing. The accounting system caught up with territorial expansion. In a word, the process of digestion was going on at a rate quite satisfactory to Mr. Stern. All this was no little thing. It was necessary for the bank to originate methods, or adopt them from Canada, because modern American banking experience afforded no models to go by. Though Giannini had his own ideas about that, relations between the two men became pleasanter. "We will gladly abide by your rulings," the banker wrote on one occasion.[16]

Mr. Giannini could afford to be amenable, for things were coming his way. The annual statement of the Bank of Italy for 1920 was another thriller. Assets had climbed to $157,464,000. By $10,-994,000 they were ahead of the resources of the Anglo & London Paris National *and* of its savings affiliate. Not only was the Bank of Italy the largest bank west of Chicago; it was larger than any group of banks under common ownership. The statement drew a letter from the superintendent:

The State Banking Department desires to congratulate you, first, upon your conspicuous growth during the past year . . . and second, . . . upon a very material improvement of your internal condition, both as regards the mechanics of your institution and the character and condition of your loans. In both particulars your condition is now such that any extended discussion of individual loans, except as an occasional illustration of a point we desire to make, is superfluous. Your branches generally are in acceptable condition with perhaps the single exception of the Stockton branch. . . . We assume that your management, through your auditing and credit departments, is fully aware of the details of this situation.[17]

In one important respect, however, Mr. Stern clung to his position. This was, in effect, that the Tehachapi was California banking's Mason-Dixon line and Giannini had no business being south of it. Probably the superintendent's thinking was influenced by Henry M. Robinson, president of the First National Bank of Los Angeles, and of its affiliate, the Los Angeles Trust and Savings. Robinson was an advocate of territorial, or zonal, branch banking. Arguments based on the differing economy of northern and southern California could be adduced to support this thesis. On top of that, southern bankers would not have a Giannini to compete against. This is not to say that with the Bank of Italy permanently barred from further expansion in the south Mr. Robinson would be without branch banking rivals. Sartori gave every indication of starting new branches. G. A. Davidson had already pushed his Southern Trust and Commerce Bank of San Diego into the Imperial Valley. But in Los Angeles Robinson was the first to act when, in 1920, his savings bank merged with two institutions in Pasadena.

Very often a law means, in the short run at least, what a determined official wishes it to mean. In granting permits to Robinson and to Davidson, and in denying them to Giannini, Mr. Stern construed the "advantage and convenience" clause of the Bank Act to support the theory of zonal banking. At the same time he hoped for a change in the law. The complaints which unit bankers continuously poured into his ears led the superintendent, in fact, to expect that they would demand a change in the law and thus halt the spread of branch banking. In this, though, both Stern and the independent bankers were outdone by circumstances and by a bit of strategy within the California Bankers Association.

It was customary for the president of C.B.A. to appoint a committee to confer with the legislature on questions of amending the Bank Act. The president was Jesse B. McCargar of the Crocker National. He named a committee of seven, all friendly to the branch banking idea: John S. Drum of the Mercantile Trust of San Francisco, which eventually was to give Giannini his stiffest competition in the Bay area; W. R. Williams of the Bank of Italy; J. F. Sartori; G. A. Davidson of San Diego; W. R. Hervey of Robinson's Los Angeles Trust and Savings; J. M. Henderson, Jr., of the Sacramento–San Joaquin; and Russell Lowry of the American National of San Francisco which Drum was to take over in time. With opposition to *all* branch banking mounting among independent bankers, the committee tactfully let the subject of zonal banking alone and confined its recommendations to other problems.

Mr. Stern felt that he had been let down. "Giannini was pursuing me with reasonable arguments for branches," he recalled. "The opposition [to statewide banking] did not put in an argument."[18]

This development brings us into the year 1921 which witnessed events that neither Stern nor Giannini could have foreseen. Before going into the drama of 1921, however, it is necessary to catch up on other themes of the Bank of Italy's story.

8

Nowhere outside of California had the rise of the Bank of Italy been watched with more interest than by the leaders of the Italian colony in New York City. Since the lapse of negotiations in 1913 the Easterners had not ceased efforts to interest Giannini in a New

York bank. In 1918 the San Franciscan told the Italian Chamber of Commerce in New York that if it would get together $1,500,000 toward the acquisition of a bank he would manage the bank. James A. Bacigalupi and Dr. A. H. Giannini went east to help raise the money.

Half a dozen times a day Giannini scribbled instructions to his emissaries. One advised on the current New York shows they "should go to see." *Going Up* was especially commended. In the cast was a young actor, "a relative of a Santa Maria stockholder of ours who is a crackerjack." But A. P. gave his brother and Bacigalupi so much to do it seems debatable if they had leisure for Broadway.

The bank was to deal with all classes, "particularly the foreign elements—Italians, Greeks, Poles, Swiss, Slavonians, Spanish, etc., etc." The envoys were to see influential lawyers, doctors, priests, businessmen and financiers, including associates of J. P. Morgan & Company. For most of these gentlemen, "10 minutes talk should be enough," although the banker's experience had been that "a talk sitting down at small luncheons is more effective than standing up."

In no time Giannini's thoughts had leaped the Atlantic. "It may be well to bring out in your talks the possibility of . . . going to Italy to establish branches or [an] affiliated institution . . . [this] after it has made good in New York, *not before*. . . . Don't forget that war has brought Italy & America closer together. . . . When the war is over we will have plenty of fine trained young men available for the branches. . . . This is the best way to take care of our boys."[19]

Again: "There is one thing, Jim . . . and that is if we would have anything to do with . . . [a bank] in New York we would see to it that the managing officers, from the President down, were put out in front and in the open where they would come in contact with and greet the people as they would come in or go out of the bank. . . . That is one thing that is lacking in most of the New York banking institutions. . . . We certainly do not want our officers cooped up in an office."[20]

The money was raised and in 1919 the East River National Bank, deposits of $3,500,000, was bought. Dr. A. H. Giannini became president. James F. Cavagnaro, a Giannini booster for many years, remained as vice-president.

The purchase was made by a New York-chartered holding company Giannini devised for the purpose. Called the Bancitaly Corporation, it bore some resemblance to the Stockholders Auxiliary in California. We shall hear more of Bancitaly.

In nine months of the new management, the East River National added $9,000,000 in deposits. That fulfilled Giannini's requirement for making good, and the next step was taken. This was the purchase, by Bancitaly, of the Banca dell' Italia Meridionale, a branch banking system in Italy. Later the name was changed to Banca d'America e d'Italia.

Help for the Farmer

THOUGH they had no easy time, California farmers rode out the postwar deflation, beginning in 1919, with less discomfort than farmers elsewhere. For this there were several reasons. The principal one was the diversification of California's agriculture. When beans went to pieces in 1919 other commodities held up for the time being. Thus the descent was gradual by contrast with what happened in the one-crop Middle West and South. Another factor was an urban boom that started around Los Angeles and spread, providing additional consumers at home. Still another was the Bank of Italy which tapped for the West Coast farmer two new springs of credit.

The first of these was bankers' acceptances, which bankers to commerce and industry had been prompt to avail themselves of when the creation of the Federal Reserve System enlarged the discount market. A banker's acceptance is a draft or a bill carrying the guarantee of the signer's bank. Member banks could realize on this paper at the Federal Reserve Bank of their districts. No longer was it necessary for their funds to be tied up while goods moved to market.

Bankers who staked the farmers were slow to appreciate the virtue of acceptances, however, and particularly was this true on the West Coast. Giannini was the first to catch on. As in other innovations of the Bank of Italy, the immediate reaction of competitors was doubt; and later, imitation.

The California Prune and Apricot Association, hard hit because of a break in the prune market, was the first to benefit by the use of acceptances. While the harvests ripened in the summer of 1919, the Bank of Italy gave the association a $3,000,000 line of credit for parceling out to members in acceptance bills.[1]

The San Francisco *Bulletin* exuberantly commented on the new procedure:

California has been hitched to a star. That star is the Federal Reserve Board. The Bank of Italy did the hitching. . . . A new financial harness has been fitted for the first time on this Coast. . . . It will be the first time that fruit crops have been handled through bank acceptances. Heretofore, the crops have been moved with the assistance of straight bank loans.[2]

Actually, so liquid was the Giannini institution at this time that it found no need for the discount facilities of the Federal Reserve, but carried the load alone. Before the fruit moved from storage, the Prune and Apricot Association issued drafts, drawn on the Bank of Italy, for thirty, sixty or ninety days to growers in need of cash. The bank "accepted" the drafts, which were secured by warehouse receipts. Once the fruit was sold, the association started whittling down its indebtedness. Thus this initial transaction went off the same as the one the year before when the Bank of Italy loaned the newly formed co-op half a million dollars backed by warehouse receipts. The difference was that the facilities of the Federal Reserve gave the bank a hedge on the 1919 loan. Had times got bad, it *could* have discounted the growers' drafts with the Federal Reserve, replacing the paper with cash.

The experiment worked out so well that, two months after the fruit growers got their loan, the Bank of Italy utilized an acceptance credit to rescue the second postwar deflation casualty of West Coast agriculture, the bean growers and their co-ops.

2

From the Revolution down through World War I, the bean appears in the folklore of our land and sea forces. During the latter conflict California had responded so handsomely that the Armistice found it the first bean producer of the Union. More than that, it had on hand 5,500,000 bushels in a market that had collapsed to half the 1917 price. Once out of uniform, our boys had switched from a diet of beans.

Thus in 1919 distress hit the bean regions: in the north, the Sacramento–San Joaquin Delta, and, in the south, the coastal slopes around Ventura and Santa Barbara. To repay bank loans many growers had to sell at termendous losses; others, unable to obtain loans, faced bankruptcy. Independent banks in the bean country found a large part of their assets frozen. Superintendent Stern required several to increase their capitalization in order to liquify their condition.[3]

Grievous as were the losses that were taken, they would have been worse except for the financing made available by the Bank of Italy.

In the north the year-old co-operative California Bean Growers Association had in its warehouses beans worth between $3,000,000 and $4,000,000 at the panic prices prevailing. Members of the co-op needed money desperately, but to have shoved the beans, or any considerable portion of them, on the market would have driven prices still lower. The only hope lay in offering the crop piecemeal. In August, 1919, the Bank of Italy advanced the Association $100,000 to meet emergency needs. Two months later a credit of $1,500,000 was set up, "with the understanding that the security at all times be kept on a basis of two for one at the market value."[4]

Thus the crop began to move "smoothly as well as cheaply," according to the *Pacific Rural Press.* "The rate of 6 per cent per annum was exceedingly favorable. . . . The prevailing interest rates are 8 per cent in agricultural regions."[5]

In the same period, $520,000 was advanced on the lima bean crop in the south.

No small bank, or combination of small banks in the stricken areas, could have rendered this direly needed service to the bean raisers. No large city bank, remote from the scene and enmeshed in the correspondent system for transmitting funds, could have rendered it so quickly and cheaply. Only a system with a branch on the spot and backed by large resources was capable of it. Nor could a branch system readily give the same aid if all its offices were concentrated in one locality, in keeping with Mr. Stern's zonal idea. That was why Giannini clung to statewide banking, and why he fought to add to and expand his statewide system. He saw California as a whole, with all resources of all communities capable of being interchanged and utilized. He contended that regional branch banking meant barriers to the easy and economical flow of money and credit.[6]

The bean growers' loan furnished evidence in support of Giannini's conception of statewide branch banking. The two hardpressed areas were about four hundred miles apart. Under a regional banking system the Ventura growers would have gone most likely to a bank in Los Angeles, and the Stockton growers to Sacramento or to San Francisco. If to Sacramento, several banks there would have had to form a pool. As it was, with only one bank involved, red tape was out and a great deal of paper work eliminated. The bean growers got their money quicker and cheaper.

More than half of the $74,737,000 that the Bank of Italy loaned in 1919 in the ordinary course of business went to farmers, packers and canners. A sampling of some of the larger loans reveals the statewide and the industry-wide nature of these investments:

Amount	Security	Business	Locality
$35,000	eggs, butter	commission	San Francisco
$50,000	grain land	farmer	Loomis
$30,000	rice delta	farmer	Sacramento
$100,000	fruit land	farm company	Fresno
$500,000	canned goods	cannery	Los Angeles
$80,000	farm tools	supply house	Salinas
$60,000	dried fruit	packers	Fresno
$100,000	cattle	loan company	Los Angeles
$250,000	plant	farm-equip- ment manu- facturers	Stockton[7]

3

What has been said up to now comes under the head of credit that ran from a few weeks in the case of some bankers' acceptances to five years in the case of some mortgages. The farmer also needed longer-term credit for capital expenditures in the way of land, machinery, livestock, buildings and so on. A way to meet this need more adequately had been opened in 1916 by the government with its twelve regional Federal Land Banks, authorized to loan money on mortgage for periods of five to forty years at rates not above 6 per cent. Private lenders, united in the Farm Mortgage Bankers Association, had opposed this legislation. To appease them, the law made provision for the establishment of privately owned but federally controlled joint-stock land banks to deal in loans under about the same conditions as the federally owned land banks. Mortgages held by either institution did not mature, but were paid off in semiannual installments.

Giannini had favored the legislation because it gave the farmer a chance to obtain long-term credit more cheaply. It could also be a relief to banks, by leaving free for more immediate uses funds which otherwise might be tied up for a long time in mortgages.

While vacationing at Lake Tahoe in the spring of 1919, Mr. Giannini met Archer W. Hendrick, secretary of the Federal Land Bank of Berkeley which served the Pacific Coast. A former president of the University of Nevada, Hendrick had abandoned academic life to try to help the farmer. He was filled with zeal for the cause, and Giannini liked the way he talked. Hendrick had little trouble persuading Giannini to organize a joint-stock bank, although a fight was looming in Congress where the old farm-mortgage crowd had potent allies.[8]

Joint-stock banks accepted no deposits. They obtained funds by issuing tax-exempt bonds based on their farm mortgages. When Giannini applied for a charter he received it, with this semiofficial warning: "There is a movement on foot to repeal the legislation . . . [and eliminate] exemption from taxation both as to mortgages and bonds." It was the tax-exempt feature that made the bonds attractive to investors. Yet, in the face of this uncertainty the California Joint Stock Land Bank was chartered in the fall of 1919. Giannini was president. Such members of the Bank of Italy's inner circle as P. C. Hale, Scatena and Bacigalupi were on the board; also the sprinkling of newcomers Giannini was constantly testing out in his organization. Among these was his twenty-five-year-old son, Lawrence Mario Giannini, educated as a lawyer and now learning the branch banking business.

With the title of cashier, Hendrick got the job of running this latest Giannini creation. A portly man with a benevolent air, he bore the nickname of "Pop." His actions often belied the name. A crusader whom adversity did not dismay, Pop Hendrick could show little benevolence toward those who stood in his path. He was destined to go far in the Bank of Italy's long battle for the farmer.[9]

The California Joint Stock Land Bank was also entitled to do business in Oregon. Hendrick went to work briskly, explaining the operation of the institution to the public. The co-operation of country banks was solicited, Hendrick assuring them that the land bank was not a competitor, as it intended to make larger loans (up to $37,500) than the local banks could handle. Local banks would re-

ceive commissions on loans closed through them. Naturally, the
Bank of Italy branches were brought into the picture.

4

By mid-November, 1919, the California Joint Stock Land Bank
had received applications for $250,000 in loans. They continued to
pour in. By the end of December the machinery of the bank was in
full operation. One hundred thousand dollars in loans had been
made. The joint-stock bank got the cash by exchanging its 5 per
cent tax-free bonds for Liberties in the Bank of Italy's portfolio.
Hendrick's hopes ran high. During the first quarter of 1920, he expected to place between $3,000,000 and $4,000,000.[10]

These hopes received a jolt in Washington where a dozen bills
aimed at the dissolution of the joint-stock banks were in the congressional hopper. The constitutionality of the basic Farm Loan Act
was under attack in the United States Supreme Court. To fight for
survival, the threatened institutions, eighty-three in number, had
formed the American Association of Joint Stock Land Banks. The
Giannini land bank assumed a leading part in the activities of this
organization. Throughout the contest it played a conspicuous, and
perhaps the decisive, role.

E. C. Aldwell, secretary-treasurer of the California Joint Stock
Land Bank and assistant secretary of the Bank of Italy, hastened to
Washington. Johnson of California, McNary of Oregon, Pittman of
Nevada and other influential senators promised to stand by the
joint-stock banks. Every member of the California delegation in the
House got on their side. Before the Supreme Court the Farm Loan
Act was defended by such counsel as Charles E. Hughes, William G.
McAdoo and George W. Wickersham. In the opposing ranks was
Senator Reed Smoot of Utah, connected with private banking in-
terests in the farm-lending field. Senator Gronna of North Dakota
was the author of one of the hostile bills. Yet, on the whole, the
situation looked encouraging to the land bankers.[11]

Then came a blow. To try to save the rest of its organization, the
Farm Loan Board abandoned the joint-stock banks and threw its
support to the Gronna bill which called for the liquidation of those
banks. Hendrick snorted that this action lacked "even horse sense."

It was, nevertheless, very effective. With the general bond market weak, public interest in joint-stock bank bonds dropped to zero. Though practically all the other banks suspended action on new loans, the Giannini bank and Hendrick plowed on. Early in April, mortgages in the process of being closed touched $1,200,000. "You are very fortunate in your connection with the Bank of Italy," Commissioner Lobdell of the Farm Loan Board wrote Hendrick. "I am glad you have been able to move along steadily while most of us have been halting."

The Supreme Court put the Farm Loan Act case over until fall (1920) for reargument. The Bank of Italy could not be expected to absorb forever the unmarketable bonds of its farm-loan offspring. Though the worst features of the Gronna bill were knocked out, an escape hatch was provided for the stock banks through "voluntary liquidation" without loss. Few took advantage of it. Nevertheless, with $1,850,000 tied up in the bonds of its joint-stock land bank, the Bank of Italy withheld further advances. "Are you loaning any money?" a Watsonville, California, farmer wanted to know in January, 1921. "We wish we were, but God knows when we shall be," regretfully replied Hendrick. "It depends a little bit on the mind of the Supreme Court."[12]

On the last day of February the Court upheld the Farm Loan Act. The Bank of Italy promptly reopened the line of credit to its farm-loan associate, advancing another half-million dollars. With as many demands as banks had on their funds in February, 1921, not even an institution so well heeled as the Bank of Italy had $500,000 lying around loose and begging for investment. The credit required courage, and faith in the ability to win a hard fight, for the decision of the Court did not at once revive the market for joint-stock bank bonds. This was partly due to the state of the general securities market and partly to a renewed assault in Congress on the stock banks. The leader of this attack was Reed Smoot. Giannini started a backfire against the senator from Utah by fostering the organization of the Idaho-Utah Joint Stock Land Bank. He helped it financially and he sent a trusted lieutenant, James A. Migliavacca of Napa, a director of the B. of I., to take care of things in Washington. Smoot was beaten, and a friendly bill, increasing the rate on stock-bank bonds to 5½ per cent, was enacted.[13]

Some long breaths were drawn at Clay and Montgomery when

the market for the bonds of the joint-stock land bank revived. The Bank of Italy took another million of the bonds and disposed of others elsewhere. Pop Hendrick passed the money on to the farmers, by the end of 1921 closing loans in the aggregate of nearly $4,000,-000. For the first time agriculturists of California and Oregon were experiencing the boon of economical, long-term credit.[14]

What is more, the Bank of Italy's endeavors in that field had just fairly begun.

5

This relief had come when it was badly needed—by some commercial banks almost as much as by some farmers. The short-term credit problem was acute and commercial banks were fortunate in having the land bank to take care of a share of the long-term needs.

The 1920 break in wheat, corn, cotton and other "national" crops had affected California which grows considerable amounts of those commodities. The general agricultural situation was eased, however, by the specialty crops, mainly fruit, whose prices held up. Lands on which the specialty crops were grown continued to advance. As raisers of beans had done in 1919, growers of cotton, barley, wheat, rice and so on began to go in for fruit and vegetables.

In the late months of 1920 came the tidings that California's fruit pack was not moving as it should. Hard-hit Eastern wholesalers put in smaller orders. Shipments were delayed from October to December, from December to January, 1921. Cash was scarce in the East. California canners and packers were offered "trade acceptances, notes and other unheard-of financial arrangements"—in the words of the *Pacific Rural Press*. Next came outright cancellations. "Cancellitis" spread like the flu epidemic of 1918, one editor observed.[15]

In consequence of this, as 1921 wore on more country banks in California began to feel the pinch—a pinch that was closing banks right and left in the Midwest and South. Before the pinch was over Giannini was called upon to save entire communities from financial disaster by taking over tottering banks. The Bank of Italy had need to be big and to be strong to do that, too.

It entered this period of trial one of the strongest banks in California. At the end of the fateful year of 1921, Bacigalupi could write, with justifiable pride, to Chairman Perrin of the Federal Reserve Bank of San Francisco:

"We have gone through the war and the period of readjustment thus far without rediscounting a single note, and have not abused our secured borrowing privileges."[16]

This, however, is getting ahead of our story. The year 1921 opened with a run on a branch, a scant sixty miles north of the head office in San Francisco.

A Salvaging Operation

THE RUN on the Bank of Italy in Santa Rosa began on Friday, January 7, 1921, the moment the branch opened for business in the morning. For a while, frightened depositors blocked the street in front of the building. The run lasted all day and began again next morning when the branch opened at the usual hour of ten. However, most of those who showed up on the second morning, it turned out, were spectators merely. By the Saturday closing hour of noon the run had petered out.

What caused this sudden and short demonstration?

The bank tried hard to find out on its own. By the end of the first day private detectives from San Francisco were filtering through the crowd, hearing what they could hear. They remained on the ground for several days. The branch posted notice of a reward of one thousand dollars for "information leading to the arrest and conviction of the person or persons responsible for the false rumors circulated, which caused the recent confusion."

Superintendent of Banks Charles F. Stern tried to find out. He had a deputy on the scene before the run was over.

The district attorney of Sonoma County announced "an immediate investigation to fix responsibility."

The district attorney's efforts came to nothing. Though Mr. Stern's deputy submitted a report that contained items of interest, they were far from conclusive. The private detectives reported at length, but the root of the matter eluded them also. No one claimed the reward. For the most part the Santa Rosa run remains a puzzle in crowd behavior.

The plausible aspects of the affair pertain to the background of it. Repercussions of events in the East—and anything the other side of Denver is "the East" to Californians—had afflicted considerable areas of rural California with a moderate case of "nerves." Had Californians been aware of the difficulties some of their banks were experiencing, the affliction would have been more malignant than it was. All this is understandable, especially with the wisdom of hindsight.

What is not so understandable is that the first manifestation of anxiety should have occurred in Sonoma County. Almost at San Francisco's door, this lush region of specialty crops was at that time scarcely touched by the spreading disturbance in agriculture. Sonoma was not only one of the richest farming counties in California; it was one of the richest in the United States. Santa Rosa, the county seat, was an attractive town of ten thousand. Besides the Bank of Italy's branch, there were two unit banks—the Savings Bank of Santa Rosa and the Exchange. Both were in excellent condition. It would have been difficult to find a town of similar size and character where the banking facilities were more competent to deal with a run.

Not always, however, had Santa Rosa been so well endowed. Old timers recalled the failure in 1907 of the Santa Rosa branch of the California Safe Deposit & Trust Company of San Francisco which had ended Santa Rosa's first experience with branch banking. Ten years later, in 1917, the Santa Rosa Bank had been in trouble— "going to hell in a hand basket," as one citizen put it—when, at the request of stockholders, Giannini took it over as a branch. Despite the war boom, a third bank, the Santa Rosa National, had failed in 1918 as a result of bad management. So, when money got a little less plentiful in the Sonoma Valley, Santa Rosans began to think of their banks.[1]

Charles B. Wingate, Mr. Stern's representative on the ground, was a former resident of Santa Rosa. According to the record of his researches, rivalry between the Bank of Italy branch and the two unit banks was intense. One gathers that not the most cordial personal relations existed between Manager Murdock of the branch and his colleagues in the independent banks. An officer of the Savings Bank told Wingate that the branch had irritated people by its aggressive campaign for deposits and that, at times, it had declined local loans and sent local money to San Francisco to be loaned elsewhere. The whole history of the bank refutes his statement.

Nevertheless, these were factors that afforded a loquacious and gossipy laundry wagon driver the raw material for a field day. As he later admitted to a detective, two weeks before the run the driver had heard "them say" that one of the town's banks was in bad shape: which of the three banks was not at first specified, nor was the reason for its alleged condition given. Before long, however, the Savings Bank of Santa Rosa was identified as the weak one. When the driver added that particular to his narrative a woman customer, the wife of the local manager of the telephone company, corrected him. "No, it's the Bank of Italy," she said. The laundryman circulated the amendment over his route.

About the time this was going on, Santa Rosa's three banks were closed for an hour on the day of the funeral of the mayor of the town. Misreading the notices on the bank doors, a number of Italian women started rumors of their own. As a result there were a few withdrawals. Moreover, the story was told that, when a depositor sought to withdraw in cash his balance of $70,000 from the Bank of Italy branch, he was asked to wait until the money could be obtained in San Francisco. This could have been true: branches in towns the size of Santa Rosa often did not have that much currency on hand. Unit banks, with reserves less readily available, customarily kept more till cash on their premises than branches did. Also, in view of the talk that was going around, Santa Rosa's two independent banks had taken the precaution to accumulate cash above normal requirements. The B. of I. branch did not follow suit. Glenn E. Murdock was a self-reliant manager who preferred not to be troubling the home office all the time. On Thursday, January 6, when he closed up there was only $50,000 in currency in the branch. Deposits were around $3,000,000, two-thirds of which were in savings accounts.[2]

That evening L. B. McGuire, the proprietor of a lumber and building-materials yard, telephoned J. A. Lombardi, Murdock's assistant, to say that Italian employees of the yard were in a great state about the Bank of Italy. Without avail McGuire had tried to tell them that they were seeing things under the bed. Lombardi telephoned Giannini's old friend and the bank's watchdog north of the Golden Gate, J. A. Migliavacca of Napa. Migliavacca said he would come over next morning and to be on the safe side he would bring some currency from the Napa branch.

Early in the morning McGuire, the building-materials dealer, made a trip across the tracks to the Italian quarter. The place was in a ferment. Passbooks were being gotten out and wives were making ready to descend on the bank as soon as their husbands started to work. In some cases the husbands were taking the day off to make sure of rescuing their money. Children had declared a holiday to withdraw their school savings. At eight-thirty McGuire brought this news to Murdock at the bank. Still, the manager could not believe that he faced a run.[3]

2

A crowd began to collect outside. Migliavacca arrived with $20,-000. When the branch opened for business it was clear that a run was on. The word spread through the town and the crowd increased until the police closed to vehicles the street in front of the branch. Traffic within the building was regulated to minimize confusion. Depositors entered by the front door, formed lines in front of the windows, and left by the rear door. Many made straight for the unit banks and deposited the funds they had drawn from the branch. Yet not all the Bank of Italy's callers who pushed their way into the branch demanded their money. Several patrons, some of them stockholders or members of the advisory board, appeared with rolls of currency and ostentatiously made deposits. The effect was negligible.

At the pace things were going the money on hand would not last much longer. To invoke the advance-notice clause governing savings accounts would have scared everyone and made matters worse. Consequently the overconfident Murdock swallowed his pride and requested loans of currency from the two rival banks in Santa Rosa and from banks in Healdsburg and Petaluma. They responded immediately. In the course of the day $400,000 was received from those sources. Probably some of the identical money that had been withdrawn from the branch and deposited in one of the other Santa Rosa banks was brought back and paid out again. George H. Warfield, president of the Healdsburg National Bank, accompanied that institution's contribution. He moved among the crowd saying over and over that the Bank of Italy was sound.

There was no letup, however, and about noon Manager Murdock, taking counsel with Migliavacca and local leaders, conceded that the run was more than the branch could handle by itself. Reluctantly he telephoned San Francisco—and was later censured for having waited so long. A. P. Giannini being out of town, his stepfather, Boss Scatena, the chairman of the board, led the relief party which took with it a million and a half dollars, a third of it in gold. The party traveled in the Hudson automobile of Clarence Cuneo, whose horse and buggy had transported the bank's cash to and from the Crocker National in the days before the Bank of Italy possessed a dependable safe of its own.

The San Franciscans arrived around four o'clock, but the branch was still open and paying withdrawals. A show was made of carrying the money inside. Scatena edged through the throng telling everyone: "You can have your money, but don't worry. This bank is as safe as the Rock of Gibraltar." Later that evening A. P.'s son, Mario Giannini, brought in more money.[4]

Telegraph wires carried tidings of the run to all California. They also carried reassuring comments by Governor John U. Calkins of the Federal Reserve and by Superintendent Stern of the State Banking Department.

"The Bank of Italy," said Mr. Stern,

is in splendid shape. Its capital, surplus and undivided profits totaling over thirteen million dollars are unimpaired. It has seventeen million in cash on hand; over thirty-five million in bonds, mostly governmentals; and over ninety million in conservative loans, a large part of which are rediscountable with the Federal Reserve Bank. It has not speculated in foreign bonds, it has not overextended through borrowing, it has not become involved in any fashion. . . . The Santa Rosa situation is without any justification and should adjust itself promptly. The Bank of Italy has the full confidence and support of this department; it has the support of the Federal Reserve Bank and the larger banks in California; it is entitled to and will receive the people's support.[5]

These sentiments were echoed by Mr. Calkins.

The wires also carried a private message from Bacigalupi to every branch manager:

We have just been advised that a run has started on our branch at Santa Rosa. Just how general it is we have not yet learned but are taking every precaution against a possible spread throughout the system. By tomorrow morning you will receive an extra supply of currency. . . .

In the event that a flurry should start at your branch keep a stiff upper lip and let every man wear a big smile. Do business in the USUAL manner and honor all legitimate demands . . . without asking questions. . . .

Keep us advised by telephone . . . and you may count on it that we will back you at every turn.[6]

The publication of the Stern and Calkins statements, the assurances of Scatena, of Mario Giannini and of some of the town's leading citizens brought a measure of calm. Not only would depositors who desired it be paid promptly in full, the bankers said, but those who wished loans could obtain them on proper security.

Lights in the branch burned until two-thirty in the morning as the staff, reinforced from San Francisco, balanced the books of an eventful day and made ready for Saturday's opening. But the paramount convincers were the stacks of gold in each teller's cage that greeted the eyes of the crowd that morning. Nevertheless, doubtful depositors formed lines before the windows. Other depositors, who may have come to the branch with similar intentions, looked at the gold, stood about for a while, and then walked out again. By noon the run was over. In a day and a half, the branch had returned $500,000 of the $3,000,000 it had had on deposit. Although the moral effect of its presence had been enormous, about the only actual use for the imported San Francisco money was to reimburse the neighboring banks that had come to the aid of the Santa Rosa branch.[7]

For some weeks the head office at Clay and Montgomery maintained a close watch over its branches and kept a finger on the pulse of their communities. A few wisps of gossip were reported. In Fresno a nervous depositor drew out his $3,000 balance. This was the only withdrawal that could be traced to fear for the bank's condition, though anxiety was mounting in many localities where the state of agriculture grew progressively worse.

3

The manner in which the head office had handled the brief run on the Santa Rosa branch, and the fact that the remainder of the Bank of Italy system had withstood the flurry without a tremor, made a pleasing impression on Superintendent Stern. Giannini took advantage of this to request that eight national banks held by the Stockholders Auxiliary, or some of them at any rate, be admitted as branches. In so doing he was only asking equal treatment with other branch bankers to whom Stern had been generous in granting permits. After an exchange of letters and a few conferences, all more friendly in tone than previous discussions, Stern consented to the acquisition of one Auxiliary bank, the First National of Fresno. A formal application to convert the bank into a branch was duly submitted, but the license was not forthcoming—until four months later.

The reason for the delay was that the legislature was still in session and was expected, before adjourning, to settle the fate of statewide branch banking in California. If the law was amended to restrict branches to zones, which Stern favored, that would keep Giannini from getting any more branches in places as far from San Francisco as Fresno. Whatever the decision, Stern confided to intimates that he would accept it as the "will of the majority." As for his decision on the Auxiliary bank, having reconsidered, he informed Giannini that he would withhold the license until the legislators acted. If they failed to act, Stern promised not only to issue the permit enabling the Bank of Italy to acquire a second branch in Fresno, but to "entertain" applications to take over the seven other national banks.[8]

So Giannini was obliged to wait, in the meantime watching his Johnny-come-lately branch banking competitors acquire one branch after another. By June, 1921, A. M. Chaffey's California Bank of Los Angeles was operating seventeen branches—all within the city limits, however. Robinson's Los Angeles Trust and Savings had thirteen branches, seven in the city and six outside. Sartori's Security Trust had three branches, all in the city of Los Angeles. The Hellman Commercial Trust and Savings Bank, controlled by two nephews of Isaias Hellman of San Francisco, had six branches—four in Los Angeles and two outside. Davidson's Southern Trust of San Diego had five branches, all outside that city. In the north John S. Drum's Mercantile Trust of San Francisco had opened one city branch and had perfected plans to expand rapidly and heavily in the Bay area.

Thus Superintendent Stern, deliberately or not, had provided the Bank of Italy with plenty of competition in the branch field. Giannini did not mind that; in fact he preferred it. Over and over, he had said competition is a good thing in any line of business. However, Mr. Giannini had also said that it was unjust to hobble the Bank of Italy while giving a free rein to its rivals. He understood, of course, why Stern did this. Robinson, Sartori, Davidson, Drum and the others were creating regional systems, which conformed with the superintendent's theory of branch banking.

Actually it was only limited competition that Mr. Stern's policy built up for the Bank of Italy. Giannini would be opposed by Drum in the north, by Robinson and others in and around Los Angeles, by Davidson in the San Diego territory. He would not have to meet the same competitor in more than one field. He saw an advantage in this. Napoleon had summed it up when he said, "Give me allies to fight."

Privately and publicly Giannini clung to his intention of doing a statewide business, and of amplifying it many fold. In no other way could a bank minister so well to the needs of California. The very reasons Mr. Stern offered in support of his zonal banking theory—the great distances; the varied regional economies; crops maturing some place in all months of the year—Giannini offered in support of statewide banking. Regional banking limited a branch system's usefulness; it was only a step better than unit banking. Giannini never tired of repeating that, to give the best service, a bank should be *everywhere* in the state; and to do this it naturally would have to be big.[9]

4

Mr. Giannini wasted no time on recriminations when Mr. Stern changed his mind about licensing the new branch for Fresno. In the face of Montgomery Street gossip that Stern was about to resign as superintendent of banks and accept a high position with Robinson's Los Angeles Trust and Savings, it seemed best to keep quiet and await the coming of a new superintendent who might prove more understanding of the statewide system's need to expand. Giannini did not mark time for long. A chain of events unexpectedly developed consequences that more than fulfilled the Bank of Italy's immediate expectations in the branch line.

Though the Santa Rosa run had no effect on other branches of the Bank of Italy, various unit banks in the agricultural belts began to feel increasing pressure. The first casualty was the small First National of Gridley, a farming center of a thousand people in the Sacramento Valley. Frozen agricultural loans obliged it to close on January 29, 1921, three weeks after the Santa Rosa flurry.

At the same time trouble of a more serious nature was gathering in the lower San Joaquin Valley, at Visalia, forty miles southeast of Fresno. A town of seven thousand, Visalia is the seat of Tulare County. The difficulty was with the National Bank of Visalia and its affiliated Visalia Savings Bank and Trust Company. Controlled by the prominent Hyde family, these institutions for years had enjoyed a high reputation. With the deflation of the agricultural boom, that reputation was about all they had left.

Particularly was this true of the National Bank. Too much of its assets were tied up in farm mortgages on which the borrowers were defaulting interest, and the bank was suffering from a "slow run" as especially astute observers quietly drew out their balances. This had so depleted the institution's cash that, early in March, Richard E. Hyde and others of the bank's directors went to San Francisco to beg help of A. P. Giannini. W. H. Snyder, chief examiner of the Bank of Italy, was dispatched to Visalia.

Before the looming drama at Visalia had run its course, however, another soft spot in California's banking structure developed in the San Joaquin Valley at Modesto, where the Bank of Italy had maintained a prosperous branch since 1917. The institution affected was the California National Bank. A run began and, unable to discount its farm paper, the bank closed on April 13.

Now back to Visalia. Examiner Snyder reported the National Bank to be hopelessly insolvent. He recommended that the Bank of Italy keep its hands off.

For nearly a decade the National Bank of Visalia had poured too much of its resources into the Armenian colony of Yettem, ten miles to the north. With the bank's support the colonists had tied themselves recklessly to the boom, converting their land—thick black gumbo and "dry bog"—from pasture and wheat to vineyards. Ranches newly planted in Thompsons, Muscats and Emperors were plastered with mortgages touching $1,000 an acre. Loans at $600 an acre were common. Very favorable circumstances would have been necessary for the loans to pay out. Instead, the colonists ran into the worst luck imaginable. Late in 1920 heavy, dry frosts sapped the life of their new vines and that nightmare of vineyardists, phylloxera, began to rot the roots of the older plants.

Hyde and another director of the sinking bank made a second hurried trip to San Francisco. They were desperate. They offered to throw in the Visalia Savings Bank which, though overloaned, was fairly clean of frozen paper. Nevertheless, it would probably be pulled under by the failure of the National Bank. The visitors promised that the National's stockholders would shoulder any losses the Bank of Italy might encounter in a take-over. To Hyde it was more than a business deal; the reputation of his family, long respected in the community, was at stake.

The need for action was immediate. The slow run had brought the National Bank nearly to the end of its cash resources. Farmers would soon need money for spring planting; merchants had to be carried. The collapse of the Hyde banks might spread panic throughout the lower San Joaquin Valley.[10]

Giannini sent Marsden S. Blois of the inspection department to make a second examination. Blois found the savings bank in fair shape, but out of the National he tossed $900,000 in bad paper which National stockholders agreed to cover.

Accompanied by R. E. Hyde and Philip Baier of the Visalia banks, and by Bacigalupi and Blois of his own bank, Giannini took the Blois report to Superintendent Stern in his San Francisco office. After the two Visalians had confessed their plight, A. P. told Stern that he would intervene if Stern would give the Bank of Italy a branch license for Visalia.

Stern hesitated. For the same reasons holding up the Fresno permit, the superintendent objected to sanctioning the Bank of Italy's entry into Visalia. As another way out, he suggested an assessment of the National stockholders. Hyde and Baier said that the stockholders, in guaranteeing $900,000 in doubtful loans, had gone their limit. Stern then turned to Giannini. If he wanted the Hyde banks, let the Stockholders Auxiliary Corporation take them over and operate them. A. P. refused. "If I can't have them as a branch I don't want them." Then he left the meeting.

The confab carried on for several hours. Neither side gave ground, and the conference adjourned.

For two weeks the matter simmered, bringing the distressed banks to the very brink. With the truth of their condition known to so many persons, it seems a miracle that there was no open run as in Santa Rosa. A run would have closed the banks instantly. It was also an uncomfortable fortnight for Mr. Stern who, in happier days, had frequently hunted in the Visalia neighborhood. Old hunting companions pressed the superintendent to yield to Giannini's terms. Unknown to Stern, one such meeting was attended by Ralph S. Heaton, assistant manager of the Bank of Italy branch at near-by Fresno. Stern's nerves were on edge. After listening to the Visalians, the superintendent declared that Giannini was a "dangerous man . . . gobbling up everything in his way." He, Stern, was going to stop him.[11]

When, on April 13, a run closed the California National at Modesto, Hyde told one of his stockholders that he could hold out but little longer. "If this deal falls through I'm afraid we'll have to close on Monday." That would be April 18.[12]

On Friday the fifteenth, Hyde and Baier made their last plea to Giannini. He said the matter was in the hands of Mr. Stern. The Visalians visited the superintendent, who sent for Giannini and Bacigalupi. A national bank examiner was on hand to second the entreaties of the Visalians. Stern gave in, formally assenting to the acquisition on Monday of the Visalia banks as a branch of the Bank of Italy. A confidential memorandum accompanied the license:

> In reaching this conclusion I am deeply impressed with the necessity of preventing a disastrous conclusion to the affairs of National Bank of Visalia and the inevitable injury of Visalia Savings Bank and Trust Company. Such an event would work serious and dangerous harm to the community contributary to these two institutions, and after full consideration of the facts presented to me and an independent investigation of my own, I have determined that as a matter of necessity the public convenience and advantage will be promoted by the licensing of the branch office.[13]

Though the public announcement of the change was made on April 18, the Bank of Italy took *de facto* charge of the Visalia institutions on Saturday, April 16. At the close of business on that day the National Bank, with deposit obligations of about $1,500,000, had on hand just $112 in cash. On Sunday currency was brought from San Francisco in Chairman Scatena's limousine.

It seems an incredible stroke of good fortune that the prestige of the Hyde name should have kept the state of affairs from the general public. The *Coast Banker,* reporting the transfer, congratulated the Bank of Italy on acquiring "two of the strongest and best known banks in the San Joaquin Valley."[14]

The greatest beneficiaries of the Visalia affair were the people of

California. The failure of the Hyde banks would have entailed consequences unpleasant to contemplate. Superintendent Stern, also, was no inconsiderable gainer. The rumors of his prospective retirement to join the ambitious branch banking system of Henry M. Robinson were true. The last thing Mr. Stern wanted was to enter upon this important connection leaving a public record marred, at the very end, by disastrous bank failures.

5

On the heels of the salvaging operation at Visalia the legislature adjourned without touching the Bank Act. Forthwith A. P. Giannini reminded Stern of his promise, and applied for licenses for all eight Auxiliary-operated banks.[15]

Stern discussed the matter with the man who had been selected to succeed to the superintendency of banks, Jonathan S. Dodge, a Los Angeles lawyer and former banker. If Mr. Dodge preferred to grant the permits, Stern would willingly defer to the new appointee. Dodge said that he did not care to start off as superintendent by licensing at one swoop so many branches for the Bank of Italy; it would make him look like Giannini's man. Since Stern was resigning and had nothing to lose, he would rather that his predecessor issue the licenses.

Stern did so on June 18, 1921, two days before relinquishing office to become vice-president of the Los Angeles Trust and Savings Bank. Right away the story began to grow that Stern had made a "deal" with Giannini in connection with Visalia. Both men many times subsequently denied this. They denied it to one of the authors of this history. Examination of Mr. Giannini's private file relating to the take-over of the banks confirms that there was no "deal."[16]

The new branches were located in Fresno, Centerville, Hayward, King City, Los Banos, Paso Robles and Sunnyvale. They brought the total of the Bank of Italy system to thirty-four. In a covering letter Stern explained this reversal of the position he had taken with such assurance in 1919. In the first place, he said, the Bank of Italy had solved the problem of branch accounting and administration. In the second place, the legislature had declined to restrict territorially the branch systems. "It is fair to assume that California is now committed to this [statewide] type of banking."[17]

The establishment of the eight additional branches served as a curtain-raiser to the opening of the bank's new head office in San Francisco. The nine-story structure at Clay and Montgomery which Giannini and Scatena, with some misgivings on the part of associates, had erected as one little neighborhood bank's contribution to the rebirth of San Francisco after the fire, had been outgrown for the purposes of the bank. The structure was primarily an office building and most of its upper floors were under lease to outside tenants.

After a bout with sentiment over leaving the vicinity of North Beach, Giannini had consented to the erection of more suitable headquarters in the gore at the junction of Market, Powell and Eddy Streets. The seven-story California granite structure was the largest building devoted exclusively to banking in the United States, with the exception of the home of the nation's biggest bank, the National City of New York. One of its features, new to the Coast, was a women's department. Beginning with the employment of the chivalrous Pedrini in 1904, Giannini had gone out of his way to make women feel at home in the Bank of Italy. That was something entirely novel at the time.

The housewarming at No. 1 Powell, as the bank's new home came to be known, was an eye-filling affair. It began on June 27, 1921, and lasted three days. Sixty-three thousand nine hundred and forty-eight persons were guided through the premises, and the chances are that A. P. Giannini shook hands with every one of them. They came from all walks. The lately inaugurated superintendent of banks, Mr. Dodge, was there. He said that California was proud of the Bank of Italy. Engrossed by his new duties in Los Angeles, former Superintendent Stern sent his regrets. Bacigalupi replied that he was keenly disappointed. "Mr. Giannini joins me in wishing you all the success and contentment, so richly merited, in your new distinguished position."[18]

A Rift with the Federal Reserve Board

THE BANK OF ITALY got off to a good start with Jonathan S. Dodge. Two weeks after succeeding Mr. Stern as superintendent of banks in June, 1921, Dodge authorized the bank to open a branch in Sacramento, the capital of California.

For almost a year Giannini had been pounding at the city's gates. Stern had turned down two local petitions, one bearing 282 and the other 3,500 signatures. Mr. Stern explained his action by saying that Sacramento had too many banks already, a fact that Giannini did not dispute. Giannini's argument was that Sacramento was not getting the type of banking service it needed.

The Bank of Italy's president made a trip to the capital to show what his bank could do. He took over $1,200,000 in municipal bonds that had been issued to construct a filtration plant. The city saved a good deal of interest on the transaction. Then Giannini tried to buy a bank in the capital. He failed because, according to Bacigalupi, the bankers of Sacramento had agreed among themselves not to sell to Giannini. Oddly enough, the leader of the opposition was the president of the Capital National Bank, Alden Anderson, who as California's first superintendent of banks had helped to start the Bank of Italy on its branch banking course in 1909.[1]

When Dodge went into office Giannini began work in earnest. Vice-Presidents Leo V. Belden and J. Lucas Williams turned twenty-nine employees from the head office loose on the town. Granting a certain amount of aggressive solicitation, it does not appear that the results obtained would have been possible without a genuine desire for a branch of the Bank of Italy in Sacramento. Eight thousand of Sacramento's seventy thousand people signed petitions; in addition there were resolutions by the Chamber of Commerce and practically every other business organization. Dodge looked at the petitions, threw up his hands, and said to send in no more. Then, on the basis of "my own independent investigations," the superintendent found that "the public convenience and advantage" would be served by the establishment of a branch of the Bank of Italy in Sacramento.[2]

John S. Chambers resigned the office of state comptroller to manage the branch. A former editor of the Sacramento *Bee,* Chambers knew the financial pattern of wealthy, smug old Sacramento, and he knew the political currents always endemic to a state capital. He was not a man to shrink from the fight. One of his first tasks was to meet a whispering campaign by rival bankers which set forth that the branch's announced loan rate of 7 per cent was "camouflage" for an actual 8 or 9 per cent rate. At the Sutter Club, where the business autocracy of Sacramento had lunch, Alden Anderson offered to bet that the branch would not take a thousand dollars in deposits from the Capital National. A fellow banker, no ally of Giannini, said he thought that would be a foolish wager.

The second banker was correct. Within six months the branch had more than three thousand deposit accounts aggregating $3,000,-000 and was preparing to erect its own building. Manager Chambers' correspondence with the head office related how one account was obtained. A Veterans Welfare Board had been created to aid ex-servicemen of World War I. Alden Anderson was a member of this board. Chambers called at the Capital National Bank and solicited for deposit in the Bank of Italy branch a portion of the public funds under the board's control. Anderson said Chambers had "a crust"; that the Capital National would get the deposit. With considerable satisfaction Chambers explained that, because Anderson was a member of the Welfare Board, this would be against the law.[3]

Before the Sacramento opening, Superintendent Dodge gave the Bank of Italy three more branches—two in San Francisco and one in Tracy, where a bank recently acquired by the Stockholders Auxiliary Corporation was taken into the fold. This evidence of a new and generous policy pervading the State Banking Department encouraged Giannini. Accordingly, in August, 1921, the Bank of Italy's affiliate purchased the historic Rideout chain of six banks situated in five towns in the Sacramento River Valley. Giannini had known this rich farming region since his young days as a buyer for his stepfather's commission house. He had long wished to see the Bank of Italy represented there.

The Sacramento Valley was gold country when Norman D. Rideout had landed there from the State of Maine in 1851. He started a bank at Oroville and, in time, opened others in Marysville, Gridley, Live Oak and Wheatland. These banks were an example of what is known as chain banking, as distinguished from branch banking. In a branch system each branch has at its command the resources of the entire system. Likewise, the operations of each branch are influenced by the liabilities of the entire system. In a chain system, though there is common ownership of the different units, each is a separate corporation. For one thing, this places a narrow limit on the amounts of individual loans.

Aware of the weaknesses and disadvantages of chain banking Giannini preferred the branch system. He had, however, temporarily become a chain banker in a small way when Mr. Stern refused, until 1921, to admit to the Bank of Italy system the eight banks owned by the Auxiliary. In succeeding chapters we shall see this formula repeated on a much larger scale. With Giannini chain banking was only an interim arrangement essential to the development of branches for the Bank of Italy.

In Montgomery Street one heard that the acquisition of the Rideout chain was an example of Giannini luck. The facts hardly bear this out. Control of the chain was held by the founder's widow, a lady of advanced years. Management was in the hands of her late husband's nephew, Dunning Rideout. Though the banks were in good condition, they faced the nettling problems common to all farm belt banks in 1921. Old Mrs. Rideout decided to sell. John Drum of San Francisco's Mercantile Trust had the first chance to buy. At the moment, however, he was not ready to go so far afield with his branch operations. When a Sacramento bank had also declined them, the offer of sale was made to Giannini.[4]

After the Rideout purchases, Mr. Ginnini transferred his attention to the San Joaquin Valley where, in 1921, the Auxiliary bought banks in Bakersfield and East Bakersfield. The Bakersfield bank had three outlying branches. Later in the year, there were acquisitions in Oakland, Chico and Hanford; and in early 1922, in Woodland, and—moving south again—in Shafter and San Diego.

None of these banks, including the Rideout chain, became branches of the Bank of Italy until months after the Auxiliary had bought them. The time lag was due to the delay of the Federal Reserve Board and of the State Banking Department in approving their acquisition by the bank. In the board's case, this was a new cause for concern. Hitherto, Washington had assented promptly to all applications for branches submitted by the Bank of Italy. Superintendent Dodge's refusal to consider the applications until a later date marked his coming to grips, after three months in office, with the lively controversy that had engaged the attention of his predecessor. Inevitably Mr. Dodge's attention focused on Mr. Giannini's expanding branch system.

2

By September, the superintendent, conducting his first examination of the Bank of Italy's affairs, was uncovering a number of flaws. Most of his criticism had a familiar ring, such as the disorder in the accounting department where records were not up-to-date. "You are very slow to assimilate your branches." The branches of which Mr. Dodge complained were those licensed in June by Superintendent Stern. Dodge's gravest worry arose from his discovery that some branches, distant from No. 1 Powell, ran along for months without the head office getting around to an inspection of their activities. This was not "safe banking practice." Moreover, the state's examiners were handicapped in accurately determining the bank's "condition." The practice of "filing statements of your various branches" provided insufficient material. In the future, Superintendent Dodge recommended that the Bank of Italy "should maintain a complete record of daily statements of your institution as a whole."

For the lack of system in the bank, Dodge blamed the management. His examination disclosed that the directors "function in a perfunctory manner" and their "attendance is poor." As a result, "the management of your affairs is dominated by what may be termed your official family. This control is held so closely by President Giannini and his immediate associates that insofar as such a thing is possible in an institution of your size, your management may be likened to the well-known one-man bank."[5]

Until Mr. Giannini's bank was "more strictly regulated," Mr.

Dodge was not in favor of giving it additional branches. Accordingly he laid aside the applications to take over the Auxiliary's banks, saying he would not consider them "for some thirty or sixty days," the period deemed necessary for the Bank of Italy to put its house in order.

Superintendent Dodge sent the result of his examination to John Perrin, chairman of the Federal Reserve Bank of San Francisco. Perrin forwarded the report to Washington which had under consideration the same applications. It was then that the Federal Reserve Board decided to mark time with Dodge. Thus, the national and state banking authorities joined hands, for the first time, on California's branch banking controversy. Their action moved the issue into the national arena.[6]

Unfortunately Mr. Dodge could not mark time. In the thick of the debate, he was assailed from all sides by independent bankers demanding steps be taken to keep Mr. Giannini, or any other branch banker, from driving them out of business. To reassure them, Dodge imposed a regulation called the *de novo* rule which, several months later, provided the pattern for the Federal Reserve's restrictive measures.

The *de novo* rule distinguished between the acquisition of existing banks and the chartering of outright new branches. *De novo* branches would be permitted only in the home cities of the parent institutions. Elsewhere going banks must be acquired. "This rule," Mr. Dodge informed the Bank of Italy, "will be subject to exceptions such as I made in your behalf at Sacramento [before the rule's adoption], and I hope the exceptions will be few. . . . I will be unable to grant you a branch either in Santa Maria or San Pedro."[7]

In practice, the Bank of Italy had followed the substance of the *de novo* rule long before it was thought of. Giannini preferred to acquire going banks because California needed fewer banks, not more of them. With a going bank came local personnel and good-will. Sacramento, Santa Maria and San Pedro were special cases.

Giannini protested the *de novo* rule on several grounds. He said it favored certain branch bankers over others. That much was plain. Sartori in Los Angeles and Drum in San Francisco had acquiesced in the rule because their immediate plans did not call for expansion beyond their home cities. Especially did Giannini protest the denial of licenses in Santa Maria and San Pedro. In the instance of San

Pedro, embracing Los Angeles' harbor district, application had been made before the rule was promulgated, and the federal authorities had approved the application. Only after J. F. Sartori, who as a member of the California Bankers Association legislative committee had helped to frame the *de novo* rule, reminded Dodge that Giannini had a good case in San Pedro, did the superintendent relax his rule and grant the license.[8]

But there was no license for Santa Maria, a subject that will take up much of the next chapter of this book.

The Bank of Italy's biggest worry, the Federal Reserve's sudden coolness toward its branch expansion, was in no sense mitigated when Mr. Giannini, with almost equal suddenness, opened a new bank in San Francisco. John Perrin, agent for the Twelfth Federal Reserve District, took offense over the circumstances surrounding the establishment of the Liberty Bank which, though controlled by A. P. Giannini, was legally separate from the Bank of Italy. The highlights of that affair follow.

In event the California Banking Department yielded further to the importunities of the enemies of branch banking, Giannini had thought—this was before the Reserve Board started marking time— it would be a good idea to have a national bank. For several years the comptroller of the currency had been recommending that, in order to compete on better terms with state banks, national banks should be allowed to establish branches. Though Congress had failed to act, there was better than an even chance that, sooner or later, it would.

When the head office of the Bank of Italy moved to No. 1 Powell, the old Market Street branch, a block away, was closed. Giannini resolved to open his national bank in the vacated premises. Swiftly he went forward with plans, and no one could put a bank together more quickly than A. P. Giannini. The Stockholders Auxiliary Corporation would hold control. An application for a national charter was submitted. So confident was Giannini that he permitted the newspapers to announce the forthcoming opening of the Liberty National Bank. Even the names of the officers were given.

No public official likes to have his assent taken for granted, a fact the fast-moving Giannini at times had overlooked before. Mr. Perrin declined to recommend the charter to Washington. He was opposed to the Bank of Italy "owning a string of banks," through an affiliate.

The federal agent reminded Giannini that, in June, he and Super-intendent Stern had wiped the slate clean of the Auxiliary's banks when, upon his recommendation, the Federal Reserve Board approved their coming into the Bank of Italy system. Giannini then suggested the substitution of the Bancitaly, which was not an affiliate though it controlled the Giannini banks in New York and in Italy. Perrin said no to that. Actually, Perrin already had orders from Washington to go easy on encouraging the further growth of branches. The national banks were protesting against the competition.

A. P. Giannini could appear brusque without intending offense. His mind often worked too rapidly for explanations. Though at times displaying the "patience of an old ox," as a contemporary said, he was really not much good at waiting. On this occasion, without further parley he withdrew the application for a national charter and obtained from Superintendent Dodge a state charter, under which the Liberty Bank opened for business on August 8, 1921. The president was Marshal Hale, a brother of P. C. Hale, vice-president and one of the powers of the Bank of Italy. The new bank did not ask to join the Reserve System.

Perrin lost no time showing his displeasure over the Liberty Bank by-pass. Reverting to Dodge's description, in an interview with Giannini he called the Bank of Italy a "one-man" institution and asked what would happen if A. P. were "hit by an automobile." Giannini said nothing would happen to the bank. It was so organized and departmentalized, with a good man in charge of each department, that no one individual was indispensable. His reply made no impression. Returning to No. 1 Powell Street, Giannini said to Bacigalupi: "Something is up—Perrin is trying to discredit us at Washington."[9]

Sometime later Mr. Perrin served notice that henceforth it would be necessary to secure "approval of the Federal Reserve Board, at least tentatively, before proceeding to acquire any bank for the Bank of Italy, or any corporation affiliated with it." In other words the bank-purchasing activities of the Stockholders Auxiliary were placed under the jurisdiction of the Federal Reserve, a situation not contemplated by Giannini when the bank joined the Reserve System.[10]

W. P. G. Harding, governor of the Federal Reserve Board in Washington, backed up Mr. Perrin. He went further, for the time was near when Superintendent Dodge would reconsider the branch permits he had pigeonholed in September. Governor Harding notified Mr. Giannini that no action by his board could be expected on these acquisitions, until Washington had "definite advice from you as to the maximum number of branches it is contemplated that the Bank of Italy shall have." Mr. Harding, of course, meant "have" for all time.[11]

3

Giannini's reaction to this astonishing communication was to engage William Gibbs McAdoo as the bank's special counsel. McAdoo had helped in the joint-stock land-bank fight. He was especially well equipped to assist in the matter at hand. As Woodrow Wilson's Secretary of the Treasury, McAdoo had seen the Federal Reserve Board born, and had been, *ex officio,* one of its members. He knew the problems of the board and he knew the personages involved.

Mr. McAdoo saw the Reserve officials in San Francisco and in Washington. He went painstakingly into their questions and smoothed things over. In Washington there had been anxiety about whether the Bank of Italy had sufficient capital for so many branches. This was resolved by increasing the capital, which the bank had decided to do before the matter was mentioned by the federal people. Another point concerned the mode of examinations, and this was adjusted satisfactorily. As to the ultimate number of branches the bank might acquire, Mr. Giannini informed Mr. Harding that he frankly could not answer. The question seemed to become academic when, in January, 1922, Giannini entered into the following agreement with the Federal Reserve Board:

The Bank of Italy agrees that for the future it will not either directly or indirectly, through affiliated corporations or otherwise, acquire an interest in another bank in excess of 20 per cent or indirectly promote the establishment of any new bank for the purpose of acquiring such an interest in it, nor make any engagement to acquire such an interest, without first having received the approval of the Federal Reserve Board, following an application on a form approved by said Board.[12]

In this way the Reserve Board sought to control the Bank of Italy's branch growth, though the waiting Auxiliary banks received branch licenses. Moreover, Mr. Giannini sailed for Europe, to be gone nearly a year. One object of the sojourn was to show Mr. Perrin that the bank could get along without Giannini.

As we shall see in due course, the January, 1922, agreement did not halt the acquisition of banks earmarked to be branches of the Bank of Italy. Mr. Giannini found an entirely legal way to resume bank buying, the foregoing agreement notwithstanding.

In the meantime McAdoo continued his peace efforts. He understood the board's dilemma. National banks, the backbone of the Reserve System, had a grievance against the state of affairs that prevented their acquiring branches and thus competing with state banks. Small state banks, which had no branches, joined the fray. The leader of this movement was a country banker from Wisconsin named Andrew J. Frame who went about addressing state conventions of bankers. Frame's appeals were emotional and demagogic, but rather effective among the unthinking. Ignoring the established benefits of branch banking, he called it un-American, monopolistic and an enemy of free enterprise. Comptroller of the Currency Crissinger grew weary of waiting for Congress to give relief to the national banks. Despite Mr. Frame's fulminations, Crissinger took matters in his own hands and ruled that national banks could open extra tellers windows—banking offices or agencies, as some institutions called them—in their home cities. Though not full-fledged branches, the extra offices proved helpful in keeping the national banks in business.[13]

To prevent competition from getting more out of line, however, the Federal Reserve Board, on which the comptroller sat, opposed any further expansion by the Bank of Italy—at any rate for the time being. So did a new member of the board, John R. Mitchell of Minnesota. Nevertheless, Mitchell agreed to look at branch banking at the scene of its greatest development, California. Accompanied by a fellow member, Adolph Miller, long-time friend of branch banking and of the Bank of Italy, Mr. Mitchell arrived in Los Angeles early in April, 1922. By the time he reached San Francisco some of his preconceived notions had been altered. He said that, if he were going into the banking business in San Francisco or in Los Angeles, he would go into branch banking.

On April 13, the visiting officials began a series of conferences in San Francisco. John Perrin presided. Present were the top Federal

Reserve people on the Coast; California's principal branch bankers, both members and nonmembers of the Federal Reserve; Superintendent Dodge, and the superintendent of banks of Arizona. Bacigalupi, P. C. Hale and McAdoo represented the Bank of Italy.

Mr. Dodge led off with a rather full statement of what branch banks had done in California, particularly for agriculture. Giannini himself could hardly have improved on the superintendent's remarks. Although the Bank of Italy was not mentioned, nearly all the good work described had been inaugurated by that bank and most of it carried on by it exclusively, because the other branch systems were too small or too new. Scarcely had Mr. Dodge sat down when John S. Drum asked to be heard. After long and careful study of the subject of branch banking, and critical observation of its chief exponent in California, Mr. Drum had only lately become a convert. He surprised his competitors from No. 1 Powell with a eulogy of their institution:

Branch banking is not something that has gone forward with any promotion or hip-hurrah idea of current optimism. It has gone forward, on the contrary, under the greatest difficulties; and it has taken thirteen years for it to grow to this position. . . .

Obviously I am speaking of the growth and development of the Bank of Italy. No greater institution to my mind has ever been created in this country or has grown over a period of years practically through the strength and the courage and the vision of a very small group of men charged with responsibility than that bank. . . . During the entire period of growth, it has never been free from . . . constant criticism . . . constant fear and danger and suggestion made that this or that or the other thing is to be feared. . . . To my mind it has grown and developed because of the basic policy under which it was operating.

Most of the rest of the time was occupied with technical matters. Near the close of the first day's session, Superintendent Fairfield of Arizona said he was glad he had come. He said he looked to branch banking to strengthen the banking structure of Arizona. "We have in the last three years taken two weak banks and made them branches of strong banks."[14]

For the moment the San Francisco conferences stiffened the attitude of the Federal Reserve toward the swelling hostility to branch banking. They were a factor in obtaining the board's approval for turning the Auxiliary's banks into Bank of Italy branches.

4

The year proved a banner one—"a hummer," in the language of Jim Bacigalupi.

In 1922 the bank had added 20 branches, ending December with 61 of them in 42 communities. They reached from Chico in the Sacramento Valley to San Diego, which are farther apart than New York and Detroit. In twelve months resources had increased from $194,179,000 to $254,282,000; capital from $10,000,000 to $15,000,000; surplus from $2,500,000 to $500,000,000; loans from $116,911,000 to $152,989,000; deposits from $177,867,000 to $229,751,000; deposit accounts from 291,994 to 401,798. This indicated that there were 73.9 deposit accounts with the Bank of Italy for every thousand persons in California.

The fact that this had been achieved during the absence in Europe of A. P. Giannini was doubly gratifying to Bacigalupi, Hale and the others who carried the ball at No. 1 Powell. It was gratifying to Giannini who thought Mr. Dodge and Mr. Perrin had their answer about the B. of I. being a one-man show.

Some of the Bank of Italy's branch banking rivals also had done well. Two of them, Drum's Mercantile Trust and the Robinson-Stern Pacific-Southwest Trust and Savings (name changed from Los Angeles Trust and Savings), had acquired during the year more branches than had the Bank of Italy. This somewhat irritated Giannini, who attributed it to official favoritism. The following table shows the branch expansion of the Bank of Italy's principal rivals during the superintendency of Mr. Dodge.

	Number of Branches	
	June 20, 1921	January 31, 1923
Pacific-Southwest Trust and Savings (Robinson-Stern)	13 (7 in L.A. 6 outside)	61 (29 in L.A. 32 outside)
Mercantile Trust (Drum)	1 (in S.F.)	42 (26 in S.F. 16 outside)
California Bank (Chaffey)	17 (all in L.A.)	32 (29 in L.A. 3 outside)
Security Trust and Savings (Sartori)	3 (all in L.A.)	19 (10 in L.A. 9 outside)
Hellman Commercial Trust & Savings (Hellman brothers)	6 (4 in L.A. 2 outside)	16 (12 in L.A. 4 outside)
Citizens Trust & Savings (Dabney Day)	4 (all in L.A.)	13 (all in L.A.)

Still, the Bank of Italy remained the only statewide system. Of its competitors, the Pacific-Southwest had ventured the farthest afield, crossing the Tehachapi and establishing itself in the lower San Joaquin Valley.[15]

This agreeable state of affairs for the branch bankers of California was overhung by a cloud of uncertainty. Primarily, two things were responsible.

One was the impending retirement of Jonathan S. Dodge as superintendent of banks. A new governor of California, Friend W. Richardson, had been elected. Mr. Dodge would have liked to stay on as superintendent, and the branch bankers would have liked to have him, but Richardson wanted his own man.

The second factor was the rise of the California League of Independent Bankers. Spurred by the threat of the Crissinger ruling in Washington (allowing national banks extra city offices) and by the flowering of branch systems at home under Dodge, the League had come into being in the fall of 1922. The ambition of its president, Howard Whipple, head of the First National Bank of Turlock, was to stop branch banking in its tracks.

The Santa Maria Episode
and Its Consequences

WHEN it became apparent that Friend W. Richardson, elected governor of California in November, 1922, intended to make a change in the head of the Banking Department, both sides to the branch controversy were interested. Richardson heard both sides. When he asked W. W. Douglas, a vice-president of the Bank of Italy, and John S. Chambers, manager of the new Sacramento branch, for suggestions, they mentioned the name of J. Franklin Johnson, deputy state treasurer.

Johnson got the appointment, but not solely because of the Bank of Italy's or any other branch banker's endorsement. In a passive way Mr. Johnson was acceptable to everybody. He took office on February 1, 1923. One of his early utterances foreshadowed a middle-of-the-road course. "It is not the function of my office to be for or against branch banking."[1]

For all that, the selection pleased Chambers. "Mr. Johnson is a friend of the Bank of Italy," he wrote Bacigalupi, "and he happens to be a personal and a Masonic friend of my own."

At this juncture A. P. Giannini returned from abroad. A year's absence and many larger concerns touching the Bank of Italy had not effaced from his mind the town of Santa Maria, where the bank had received its one outright setback at the hands of the recent superintendent, Mr. Dodge. Dodge had refused the Bank of Italy a *de novo* branch in Santa Maria—the only license he had denied it during his nineteen months in office. Giannini asked Chambers to sound out Johnson on the subject of Santa Maria. After a talk with the superintendent Chambers was hopeful. "My impression is that you will be granted a permit in Santa Maria."[2]

2

Mr. Chambers was not the only person who had the ear of Superintendent Johnson. Howard Whipple, president of the California League of Independent Bankers, had it; and Mr. Whipple was moving with speed and determination. He had landed places for himself and two followers on the legislative committee of the California Bankers Association. The branch bankers still controlled the committee, however. This circumstance frustrated efforts to place the C.B.A. back of recommendations for antibranch amendments to the California Bank Act.

Nothing daunted, Whipple succeeded in getting friendly legislators to introduce a series of bills which, if enacted, would have played ducks and drakes with California's branch banking systems. One bill proposed to limit such systems to one office in any city other than the home city. The Bank of Italy had ten offices in Oakland and four in Los Angeles. Giannini made no secret of the fact that he intended to acquire many more in Los Angeles.

Another bill cast an undeserved aspersion upon former Superintendents William R. Williams and Charles F. Stern. It provided that a former superintendent of banks could not work for a bank in California until he had been out of office two years. Williams and Stern were honest public servants who had gone into office with prejudices against branch banking. The operations of the Bank of Italy, more than all other causes combined, had removed those prejudices and carried Williams and Stern into the branch banking field. Nor were they by any means the only converts to branch banking that A. P. Giannini had made to date, as witness his numerous competitors. He was to go on making converts, changing some of the bitterest and most vociferous of foes into practicing and preaching branch bankers.

After some sparring, Johnson brought together the executive committee of the California League of Independent Bankers and the legislative committee of the California Bankers Association and worked out a compromise. The Whipple bills were withdrawn in exchange for a restatement and tightening of the *de novo* rule. A loophole remained to the branch bankers, however. The superintendent could grant *de novo* permits if, in his judgment, "public convenience and advantage" required them. Giannini made use of the loophole almost immediately.

Under Chambers' management, the Sacramento branch had out-stripped every other branch in the Bank of Italy system, for the time it had been operating. After eighteen months the branch had 9,111 depositors and $7,096,000 in deposits. For the convenience of patrons, some of whom had to go long distances to transact their business, there was need for a second branch in the city. Chambers laid the case before Johnson and, almost before the ink was dry on the re-vised *de novo* rule, the superintendent approved a permit for another branch in Sacramento.[3]

This application, along with others not of the *de novo* character, was promptly disapproved by the Federal Reserve Board in Wash-ington. The rebuff was not aimed solely at the Bank of Italy. The Pacific-Southwest was denied permission to make branches of cer-tain Southern banks. The truce that McAdoo had worked out the year before with the F.R.B. seemed at an end.

This was a triumph for Andrew J. Frame whose pioneering agita-tion against branch banking had started prairie fires in widely sepa-rated parts of the country. The United States Association Opposed to Branch Banking had come into existence, and the little bankers, making their numbers count, had fought through the 1922 conven-tion of the American Bankers Association a resolution condemning all modes of branch banking. Yielding to this pressure, President Harding elevated Comptroller of the Currency Crissinger to the governorship of the Federal Reserve Board in the place of W. P. G. Harding, resigned. Henry M. Dawes, an antibranch man from Chi-cago, was named comptroller. Dawes announced that the time had come to settle the branch banking question. "If a desirable system it should be encouraged. . . . If it is not a desirable system, that fact should be developed and steps taken to eradicate it." To that end Comptroller Dawes inaugurated an investigation by the Federal Re-serve Board.[4]

When, in this situation, the Reserve Board disapproved the appli-cation for a second Sacramento branch, McAdoo advised Giannini to set up the office anyhow and, if challenged by the board, to go to court. The attorney did not think the board could legally "render nugatory the authority of the State Bank Superintendent." Giannini vetoed the suggestion, which might, temporarily at least, have cost the bank its Federal Reserve membership. He thought he had a bet-ter way.[5]

A story concerning the origin of the Liberty Bank, which Giannini started in San Francisco in 1921, has been repeated and published so often that it has the authority of tradition. The story is that Giannini concealed his connection with the institution until it was open for business. That isn't the way it happened. From the first, the federal and state officials concerned knew Liberty was a Giannini proposition because he had told them so; anyone who didn't know this could have easily found it out.

What the makers of this myth may have been trying to tell about was the formation of the Bank of Sacramento, which Giannini launched in the summer of 1923, in lieu of the second Bank of Italy branch which the Federal Reserve Board had denied him in the capital. Until the Bank of Sacramento was a going concern few people knew that Giannini was behind it. That was one reason why the stock was hard to dispose of, according to John S. Chambers who placed $80,000 worth of shares. The Stockholders Auxiliary took the remaining $20,000. "Congratulations!" Giannini wrote when the job was done. "You are certainly some stock salesman!" As soon as the bank had opened, under a state charter, the veil of secrecy was dropped, for the Giannini name meant droves of depositors. Because of the Auxiliary subscription, the state authorities of course knew of Giannini's connection before issuing the charter.

More than the magic of the Giannini name was responsible for the success of any banking institution that name was attached to. Back of the Bank of Italy's success was hard work. Giannini still inspired his corps of lieutenants and all those under them to put in more hours on the job than any other bank employees in the country. It was as Chambers wrote:

Long hours, Saturday afternoons and evenings and a business that grows every day, are the main causes of the condition existing here. One thing that has made this bank popular is the service it gives the public particularly through these longer hours. . . . The people look for it.[6]

"The people look for it." There was the key.

It was a proud but a sick and weary man who dictated that letter, the last one he was to write to the head office. Long a sufferer from diabetes, three days later John S. Chambers was dead.

3

While Giannini was gaining a second foothold in Sacramento, he was also reminding Johnson of the situation in Santa Maria, another place the San Franciscan conceived that he had a right to be. At length the superintendent found time to visit the town. After a look around he agreed that "the people of Santa Maria are entitled to additional banking facilities." Again invoking the convenience-and-advantage clause of the newly promulgated regulations, on July 13, 1923, Mr. Johnson granted a license for a branch.[7]

This having been done in the open, the California League of Independent Bankers was not caught napping as it had been over Sacramento. Carrying the fight to Washington, Mr. Whipple, by means we shall note presently, succeeded in keeping Giannini out of Santa Maria for three more years. In the meantime the Santa Maria case was a *cause célèbre*. Fanciful and hair-raising accounts of what Giannini and his minions had done there, or tried to do, were spread from one end of the country to the other. Santa Maria was held up as an unpleasant example of what might befall the nation were it not protected from the rapaciousness of the branch bankers.

Here it becomes necessary to pause and review the events in Santa Maria prior to the action of Superintendent Johnson in July, 1923.

4

Northwestern Santa Barbara County and southwestern San Luis Obispo County form a little economic principality which had long been firmly prosperous without ever having had a boom. The region lies between the Coast Range and the ocean, two-thirds of the way down from San Francisco to Los Angeles. The basis of its wealth, then as now, was oil, though the older occupations of dairying, grazing and sugar beet raising accounted for the livelihood of a majority of the inhabitants. The Union Sugar Company had a plant at Betteravia on Guadalupe Bay, less than ten miles west of Santa Maria. Affairs of the community were pretty much in the hands of descendants of thrifty Swiss-Italian immigrants who had gone there in the 1870's. The principal towns of this insular and conservative region were Santa Maria, in Santa Barbara County, and San Luis Obispo, the seat of San Luis Obispo County. The wide streets of Santa Maria were laid out by the Swiss-Italian pioneers so they could turn their eight-mule teams in them. In 1923, Santa Maria had a population of about 28,000, and San Luis Obispo about 20,000. The towns are thirty-three miles apart.

During the war Mr. Giannini decided that this locality presented a fertile field for a branch of the Bank of Italy. He made up his mind to try San Luis Obispo first. The town had two banks, the Union National and the Commercial. Both were long established and were controlled by old families. They operated along the traditional lines of well-dug-in country banks—high interest rates, favored borrowers—and, in Mr. Giannini's opinion, they neglected a world of opportunities. Nevertheless, the officers and boards of these institutions liked things as they were. Both banks were prosperous and Mr. Giannini was informed that neither was for sale.

In 1919, Giannini sent some of his confidential men down for a closer look. They reported a certain amount of dissatisfaction among clients of the banks, particularly borrowers not within the favored circle. Moreover, there was a restless element among the stockholders of the Union National. All this was an old story to A. P. Giannini, who began quietly to buy Union stock. With surprisingly little effort the Stockholders Auxiliary got hold of 45 per cent of the shares outstanding. Then the bank's officers woke up to what was happening. By an arrangement with the Commercial Bank, the Union National officers tied up the remaining Union shares. Giannini was brought to a standstill. Although the largest shareholder, the Auxiliary was refused representation on the board of the Union National Bank. Suggestions to liberalize the bank's practices were turned down.

All Giannini could do was wait. He knew from experience that the most closely held corporations are subject to intramural stresses, often due to family rivalries. That was what happened in San Luis Obispo a year after the act of exclusion against the Bank of Italy. Death took Ercole Biaggini, a wealthy dairy farmer who was a director of the Commercial and a considerable stockholder in the Union National. His widow was eager for her son Edward to succeed his father as a director. When Edward Biaggini was passed over, the disapproving mother sold her Union shares to the Stockholders Auxiliary. Thus, in November, 1920, Giannini acquired control.

But his troubles were far from ended. Officers, directors and staff of the Union National, with the exception of one girl stenographer and the janitor, quit in a body. William Sandercock, former president, and most of the former directors, organized the Citizens State Bank which began business eleven days later with the old Union

National crew. Left with an empty shell, Giannini hastened Edward C. Aldwell and Frank C. Mitchell to San Luis Obispo. Ed Aldwell was from the home office, where he had a reputation as a trouble-shooter. Mitchell, from the San Jose branch, was a native of San Luis Obispo, where his family was not without influence. These two men managed to keep the bank running, something of an undertaking, at the start, because the departing staff had left the files in a state of confusion. To add to the embarrassments of the new proprietors, the Sandercock crowd, before relinquishing authority, had leased half of the Union National's building to a wholesale grocery concern.

On top of this, Superintendent Stern refused the Bank of Italy a branch license for San Luis Obispo, thus depriving the Giannini acquisition of the pulling power of the Bank of Italy's name. Consequently the Union National Bank continued under its old name and under the nominal direction of the Stockholders Auxiliary Corporation.

In the face of these obstacles Mitchell and Aldwell did a good job. Temporary help from San Francisco was replaced by local people. Chief among these were Bert E. Jessee, formerly a bank cashier in near-by Santa Maria; William T. Rice, who had been Jessee's assistant there; and Lee Brown from near-by Guadalupe. Rice turned out to be particularly useful, for he was an energetic and piqued young man with important family connections. Mitchell rounded up a good advisory board, on which his own family was represented, and (this should surprise no one) the Biaggini family in the person of young Edward. A campaign to attract deposits was launched and a liberal loan policy inaugurated. The last was easy. A number of loans carried a 12 per cent interest rate. It was promptly reduced to 7. "The cut, more than anything else, brought the customers back," said Lee Brown.[8]

In a few months the surface manifestations of the conflict had begun to disappear. Giannini was thankful. Although ordinarily the last man to back away from a fight, he abhorred little civil wars of this kind. They damaged the bank's reputation for local popularity, which was one of its great assets. Giannini never held grudges against local bankers or businessmen who had opposed his efforts to take over an institution. He preferred to make friends of them and, if they had ability and were adaptable, to hire them. In 1921, twenty such men were performing important services within the Bank of Italy organization. Striking examples of this will be noted as time goes on.

At bottom, the trouble in San Luis Obispo was no new thing in the history of the Bank of Italy's progress. It was simply the most violent example of local resentment of an "intruder" that Giannini had encountered thus far, and he was glad to see it dying down as it had done elsewhere.

Thus matters stood in May and June, 1921, when the scene of action was unexpectedly enlarged to include the neighboring town of Santa Maria. This came about when Mitchell, in San Luis Obispo, informed San Francisco that the Bank of Santa Maria could be bought.

5

In Santa Maria were three banks—the Bank of Santa Maria; its affiliate the Valley Savings; and the First National. As in San Luis Obispo, they were controlled by a network of old settlers.

In January, 1921, when Giannini got hold of the Union National in San Luis Obispo, Bert E. Jessee, cashier of the Bank of Santa Maria, had resigned his position to join the Bank of Italy because he saw more of a future with the latter institution. Jessee advised his assistant, William Rice, to do the same, but young Rice thought the opportunities better at home. His father was a director of the Bank of Santa Maria and president of its offshoot, the Valley Savings. As the first step up the ladder Rice, Junior, expected to succeed Jessee as cashier of the Bank of Santa Maria. That ambition received a rude setback. The place went to a "dark horse," as Rice called him, a man who had married into one of the town's banking families.

The indignant Rice took a train to San Francisco and asked to see A. P. Giannini. He was surprised when he actually did see Mr. Giannini, and right away. So the story of the banker's accessibility was no fable. Giannini hired Rice and sent him to assist Mitchell in untangling affairs at San Luis Obispo.

Young Rice went to work with a will. Deposit accounts and loans began to follow him from Santa Maria to the Union National of San Luis Obispo. To help their son, Rice's father and mother opened savings accounts, totaling $12,000, in the Union.[9]

In May, 1921, Paul O. Teitzen, the elderly president of the Bank of Santa Maria, journeyed to Clay and Montgomery Streets to discuss the possible sale of his bank to the Bank of Italy. Mr. Teitzen had founded the bank thirty-one years before; his son had other interests; the old gentleman said he wished to retire. Terms were agreed to and C. B. Wingate, deputy of Superintendent Stern, was chosen to act as umpire in any differences among the contracting parties incident to the closing of the deal. Bacigalupi described the interview as "pleasant."[10]

The first hitch was a dismaying report from W. H. Snyder, the Bank of Italy's chief examiner who, as a routine matter, had been sent to Santa Maria. He found the Bank of Santa Maria in bad shape and said that its cashier had offered him a Cadillac car to soften his report. When Wingate was called upon to decide certain matters in connection with the bank's condition, Superintendent Stern refused to let his deputy serve. At that moment Mr. Stern was winding up his affairs in Sacramento preparatory to joining the Robinson bank in Los Angeles.

The negotiations foundered and the Robinson bank, of which Mr. Stern had become vice-president, went to the rescue of the Santa Maria institution. Eventually it became a branch of the Los Angeles bank. The Bank of Italy's negotiators felt that this explained Stern's behavior about Wingate. Nevertheless, Giannini was doing very well in Santa Maria, thanks largely to the efforts of William Rice and of Lee Brown. By the end of July the Union National in San Luis Obispo had $113,863 in deposits from Santa Maria and had loaned $335,752 in that territory.

With this amount of business in the town, in September, 1921, the Bank of Italy applied to Superintendent Dodge, who had succeeded Mr. Stern three months earlier, for a *de novo* permit to open a branch in Santa Maria. The application was accompanied by a petition signed by more than eight hundred residents, a resolution of the Chamber of Commerce, and a petition from workers in a near-by oil field. The workers pointed to the shortage of small homes, which they hoped the Bank of Italy would remedy.

Dodge denied the application and later Giannini learned one of the reasons. The Bank of Santa Maria's attorney, C. L. Preisker, and the superintendent had been classmates at school. Mr. Dodge accepted Preisker's advice that Santa Maria did not need a Bank of

Italy branch. He went further. All correspondence from the Bank of Italy relating to Santa Maria was turned over to Preisker. Thus not only the Bank of Santa Maria but the other two banks there were kept current with Giannini's moves to get a charter in Santa Maria.[11]

Dodge, however, did grant a permit to convert the Union National of San Luis Obispo into a Bank of Italy branch. The Federal Reserve Board held it up for some months but, during the McAdoo truce, the Union National was among the banks taken into the Bank of Italy system in 1922.

Therefore, one can understand Mr. Giannini's desire to push the Santa Maria case with J. Franklin Johnson when he became superintendent of banks in February, 1923; and his gratification when Johnson issued the *de novo* permit in July of that year.

It remained, however, for the bank to obtain federal permission to operate in Santa Maria. This was a long time coming.

6

Early in August, 1923, the Federal Reserve Board in Washington rejected three applications for branches by the Bank of Italy (including the one for Sacramento), and four by the Robinson-Stern Pacific-Southwest Trust and Savings. This additional evidence that the McAdoo truce had run out disturbed John Perrin, the Reserve agent for the San Francisco district, who knew what branch banks meant to California. For the moment Perrin forgot his tiff with Giannini over the Liberty affair and he suggested that Bacigalupi go with him to Washington to state the case for the branch banks. He extended a similar invitation to Charles F. Stern.

On his arrival in the capital, Bacigalupi, after a quick canvas, learned that the antibranch forces had a majority of the Federal Reserve Board: Dawes, Crissinger, James and Cunningham. All were new men, except Crissinger. On the other side were the veterans Platt, Miller and Hamlin. Mitchell, whom the branch bankers had won over in California the year before, had left the board. Bacigalupi also learned that, on being informed of the Perrin party's impending visit, the board had telegraphed invitations to the antibranch leaders to come to Washington. Howard Whipple and two executive committeemen of the California League of Independent Bankers were already in town. Also represented was the United

States Association Opposed to Branch Banking, which had introduced antibranch legislation in twenty states.[12]

With their opponents out in force, the branch people quickly
looked to their defenses. Though the Santa Maria case had produced
a certain coolness between Bacigalupi and Stern, in the presence of
the general threat they tacitly agreed to work together. The day before the hearing was to open Bacigalupi had a friendly talk with
Vice-Governor Platt of the board. "He gave me some tips," Bacigalupi wrote his boss in San Francisco. That night Perrin called at
Bacigalupi's hotel. The Federal agent predicted rough going for the
Bank of Italy spokesman. "He begged me to be patient and not lose
my head under any . . . provocation . . . [but] to placate the
Board and educate them. I promised to do my best."

The opening of the hearing, on September 12, 1923, bore out what
Perrin had had to say. The questions directed at Bacigalupi were
uniformly hostile. Crissinger plainly indicated that he thought
branch banking had gone far enough in California, particularly in
the case of the Bank of Italy.

After the midday recess Howard Whipple was called upon. He
took the familiar line that the branch banks represented the money
power that was out to crush independents, who were the people's
friends. One great branch bank in California, Mr. Whipple said, was
particularly adept in the use of strong-arm tactics to force independents to sell. Proof in affidavit form was hard to get, the speaker explained, because the victims were afraid to talk.

Bacigalupi asked Mr. Whipple to cite a specific instance.

He cited Santa Maria, and this is the story he told. The local bank
president was ill in a hospital in San Francisco when Giannini went,
or sent word, to him demanding the sale of the bank on terms arbitrarily fixed by the Bank of Italy. In event of refusal Giannini threatened to open a branch in Santa Maria and put the local institution
out of business. When the Santa Maria banker resisted the onslaught,
Giannini agents appeared in Santa Maria to buy up the passbooks of
depositors of the local bank. In desperation the Santa Maria man
sold out to the Pacific-Southwest, taking what satisfaction he could
in thwarting Giannini by that means.

Mr. Crissinger grimly asked Bacigalupi to explain the Bank of
Italy's actions at Santa Maria.

The San Franciscan kept his head. He replied that Whipple's story was news to him. At worst it was "a base and malicious fabrication"; at best, "an exaggeration." The results of the conference at Clay and Montgomery Streets, San Francisco, at which Giannini made and Teitzen accepted the offer of purchase of the Bank of Santa Maria, having been reduced to writing, Bacigalupi asked permission to submit this record to the board. He volunteered to produce data disproving the passbook-buying charge. In response to questions about the Santa Maria case, Bacigalupi was careful not to tread on the toes of Mr. Stern.

After that, representatives of the American Bankers Association (on record, at its latest convention, against branches) and of the United States Association Opposed to Branch Banking were allowed five minutes each. Bacigalupi later remarked that they spoke with the "zeal of Holy Rollers."

The following night the Bank of Italy's attorney wrote Giannini a long private letter. He believed he had acquitted himself fairly well, and, in the end, had taken the edge off Whipple's accusations. Perrin and Stern, he said, had behaved "decently." Not even for Whipple did the San Franciscan have a hard word. "He is essentially a fair fellow," misled by wrong information.[13]

But how far Bacigalupi had succeeded in educating the contrary-minded members of the Federal Reserve Board remained a question.

7

The answer came a couple of months later, in October when a San Francisco bank conference failed to make a dent in the attitude of Washington. The meeting was attended by Federal Reserve officials, Superintendent Johnson and advisers, and leading branch bankers. The hope had been to duplicate the results of the conferences in April, 1922. Giannini did not send representatives. He felt that Washington might be more kindly disposed if the Bank of Italy's competitors presented the entire case. The conferees came to an understanding on a number of technical matters which they hoped might mitigate the opposition in Washington, or at any rate open the way to further discussions. The gist of this was incorporated in a memorandum to the Federal Reserve Board by the participating bankers who expected it to bring a summons to Washington, but no summons came.[14]

In the meantime a phase of the question was before Congress. Comptroller Dawes testified at a committee hearing. What he said brought no comfort to the branch bankers. In a statement summarizing his testimony Mr. Dawes was even more explicit:

Branch banking, unless curbed, will mean the destruction of the national banks and thereby the destruction of the Federal Reserve System and the substitution of a privately controlled reserve system for a governmental system of co-ordination.[15]

Two weeks later, on November 7, 1923, the blow fell. Mr. Dawes had his way, and it meant a resounding victory for all shades of anti-branch opinion. By a vote of four to three the Federal Reserve Board adopted a resolution calculated to stop the spread of branch banking outside home cities and their immediate environs. The important provisions of the board's edict:

(a) That state banks entering the system must agree, as in the past, not to establish any branches without the consent of the board.

(b) That, as a general principle, state banks with branches outside the corporate limits of the city or town, or contiguous territory ought not to be admitted to the system unless they relinquish such branches.

(c) That, as a general principle, state banks which are members of the system ought not to be permitted to have branches outside the corporate limits of the city or territory contiguous thereto.[16]

Thus did the F.R.B. pass lightly over assurances given five years earlier when the Bank of Italy—and the Sartori bank—were urged to become members of the System.

In the first dissenting opinion of record in the history of the Federal Reserve Board, Vice-Governor Edmund Platt vigorously disagreed with his colleagues of the majority. The board's fundamental error, he said, was in trying to regulate competition between state banks, which were permitted branches, and national banks, which generally speaking, were not. "[The board] has no power to intervene in . . . [such a matter], and never was intended to have." The second error was in the manner of the intervention. Instead of curbing branch banking Mr. Platt said the board should encourage its extension.

"Branch banking," he continued,

has been recognized by the foremost authorities in banking in the United States as a natural method of extending banking facilities to small communities. . . . There is reason to believe that the agricultural sections of the United States would be far better served, and the deposits of farmers much more adequately safeguarded, under systems of branch banking whether limited to counties or statewide, than at present. California is trying the experiment, and no evidence has so far been presented to show that it is not serving the people of the state well. . . .

The two branch banking institutions which maintain the most outside branches have loaned in a dozen different agricultural communities more than the total deposits in each of these districts—in some of them more than double their deposits. No unit banking system can do that even if borrowing to the limit from the Federal Reserve System or from correspondent city banks. Furthermore it has been shown that in many cases they have lowered the rates of interest . . . and have done away with various exchange charges and commissions. . . .

The Comptroller wants to restrain the state banks in California from any further extension of this excellent service because national banks are not allowed to engage in it except to a limited degree and at a marked disadvantage. I disagree with him. Congress has had the same opportunity to enact progressive banking legislation that the California legislature has had and the Federal Reserve Act does not cure all the ills of unit banking. The California Banking Act of 1909 has so far at least proved itself better adapted to the needs of California than the national banking laws, and it is a significant fact that there have been fewer state bank failures in California . . . since 1909 than [failures] of national banks.[17]

8

Heartened by Platt's formidable dissent, California branch bankers strongly protested the Federal Reserve Board resolution. They found support in other quarters. W. P. G. Harding, former governor of the board, doubted the wisdom of the sweeping action. Perrin and Calkins of the Twelfth District doubted it very much. McAdoo wired that the board's action provided "justifiable ground" for the Bank of Italy's withdrawal from the Federal Reserve System. That was the last thing Twelfth District officials wished to see.

From Washington, John Perrin sent the Bank of Italy a long telegram containing the digest of a mollifying conversation with George R. James, a member of the board who had voted for the resolution. Mr. James said the board had attempted no final settlement of the branch banking question, but rather had tried to lay a basis for legislation by Congress clarifying the powers of the board. He added that, until February 1, 1924, when the restrictions became effective, the board would consider on merit applications for branches outside the applicant's home city as well as within it.

With the approval of Perrin, several applications were promptly submitted by the Bank of Italy. Except in the case of Santa Maria, they concerned banks held in the name of the Stockholders Auxiliary or of the Bancitaly Corporation. That Perrin should have recommended a *de novo* branch for Santa Maria suggests that his information concerning what had occurred there was more trustworthy than Mr. Whipple's. William H. Crocker of the Crocker National was in Washington in his capacity as Republican national committeeman. Giannini asked his old acquaintance to have "a word with the powers that be, especially Crissinger," urging favorable action on the applications. McAdoo also was very busy.

In December, 1923, the board approved applications for two branches in Long Beach and one in Watsonville. There was no action on Santa Maria or the others.[18]

Just before the February 1 deadline, eighty-seven additional applications were plumped before the board. Eighty-three asked for *de novo* permits—twenty-seven in San Francisco and "contiguous territory," fifty-six elsewhere in the state. Four concerned banks acquired by the Bancitaly Corporation. Bacigalupi telegraphed that these applications represented

our full program of desired expansion in order to completely balance our system by tapping the varied industries and resources of additional locations in California not as yet touched by our bank. . . . Our capital and organization as presently constituted are fully capable of adequately caring for this desired expansion and such expansion is necessary.

Privately the San Franciscan conceded that favorable action on the fifty-six outside applications would be doubtful; but he added that the time had come for the bank to place its ultimate aspirations "formally on record."[19]

The Winning of Southern California

THE FEDERAL RESERVE BOARD might propose, but economic conditions in California disposed. On February 25, 1924, twenty-five days after the branch restriction went into effect, the board had to break it by approving a deal that meant five additional branches for the Bank of Italy and two for the Pacific-Southwest in the lower San Joaquin Valley. In the Bank of Italy's case, four of the five towns involved appeared on the list of eighty-seven prospective branch locations it had just laid before the board.

Yet, for once, events outdistanced the fast-moving Giannini. Much as he desired to expand he did not want these particular branches on the terms on which he had to take them. Mr. Stern did not want the two that fell to the lot of the Pacific-Southwest. Nor did the Reserve Board want to sanction the acquisitions. All parties were powerless, however, in the face of the alternative that confronted them. This was a scandalous bank failure which, in the words of Superintendent of Banks Johnson, would have precipitated "the greatest financial collapse ever seen in the state of California."

For a matter of weeks the best banking brains of California had been desperately trying to devise *some* plan by which the Valley Bank of Fresno, with eight branches, could be kept afloat. Their failure brought an almost unanimous demand that A. P. Giannini take charge. Finally Giannini, who had worked as hard as any to find another way out, said he would do it if the Pacific-Southwest came in with him. Even the California League of Independent Bankers interrupted its antibranch crusade to join the pressure on the branch bankers to salvage the wreck of the Valley Bank.

"Little did I dream that I would ever be a partner of Mr. Giannini, but emergency makes strange bedfellows," observed Charles F. Stern.[1]

2

The case itself presented several object lessons. One was that branch banking per se will not solve all the banking problems of a community. Like other human creations, to be successful a branch banking system has to be built right and run right. Amadeo Peter Giannini went about his business with such apparent ease that sometimes to novices branch banking seemed deceptively simple.

That was the affliction of W. D. Mitchell of Fresno, who set out to imitate the founder of the Bank of Italy. Like Giannini, Mr. Mitchell had grown to maturity with no thought of becoming a banker. He had begun his business career as a butcher in the small outlying town of Sanger. By 1920 Mitchell had laid aside his apron and cleaver and was observing the apparently effortless prosperity the war boom had brought to the Bank of Italy's pioneer branches in the San Joaquin Valley. The possibility of deposits in those branches being drawn elsewhere pained Mr. Mitchell. Why not, he asked, start a local branch system and keep the money at home? That was small-town-banker talk of a very elementary sort. What it overlooked was the money the branches brought *in* when the community needed it. Nevertheless, with enthusiastic local backing Mitchell opened the Valley Bank of Fresno in January, 1921.

As long as the price of raisins held up it looked as if Mitchell had a bonanza. The Valley Bank's growth attracted attention all over that part of California. Branches blossomed in the vineyard towns of Sanger, Selma, Reedley, Kerman, Biola. A sixth was opened in West Fresno to attract foreign customers, mostly Japanese. Taking another leaf from Giannini's book Mitchell spread his risks, entering Coalinga (oil), and Monterey (fishing). By 1923 the Valley Bank had 33,000 depositors and $11,000,000 in deposits.[2]

Mr. Mitchell also did a number of things that were not in the book of A. P. Giannini or any other sensible branch banker. He paid extravagant prices for banks to convert into branches. He gave too little attention to doubtful paper that was in them. His operating overhead was excessive. He loaded his bank with speculative loans—including an abundance of unsecured loans to bank officers, which were in violation of the law.[3]

By the middle of 1923, raisins were in a slump and the Valley Bank was in trouble. A state examiner having found the bank's capital "seriously impaired," early in January, 1924, Superintendent Johnson read the riot act to Mitchell. Three frightened directors demanded the president's resignation and Mitchell made tracks for No. 1 Powell Street. Giannini said that with two branches in Fresno the Bank of Italy did not need another. Mitchell then asked for a loan of a million dollars. Giannini said that would depend on the condition of the Valley Bank. Reluctantly he consented to send his chief examiner, Snyder, to have a look.

Snyder reported the bank in horrible shape. The state examiner had estimated its bad paper at $275,000. Snyder's figure was $1,500,-000 which also proved to be too low. Pathetically Mitchell followed Snyder around. Would he recommend a loan of a million? No. Half a million? Half a million dollars, Snyder replied, would do no good. Would he recommend purchase on the basis of the bank's "appraised assets"? The weary examiner said that the bank had practically no assets. Actually, it had none at all.

The more Giannini heard of the bank's extremity the more anxious he was to help. Failure would have had calamitous effects on other small institutions, hard pressed but able to work out if there were no further shocks to public confidence. On the questions of loan or purchase the San Franciscan bowed to his examiner, however.[4]

By that time the word was getting about. After a "silent run" had taken $950,000 from the Valley Bank in five weeks, its largest creditor, the Crocker National of San Francisco, tried its hand at stabilizing the situation. Mitchell was forced out. James J. Fagan of the Crocker quietly sent J. E. Fickett, formerly of the Bank of Italy, to take charge in Fresno, hoping Fickett's knowledge of Giannini methods would pull the Valley Bank through. To carry the Valley's good accounts over the planting season, the Crocker advanced an additional half-million and persuaded the Bank of Italy and the Pacific-Southwest to set up similar credits. When about half of this money had been used, the Federal Reserve Bank of San Francisco, awakening rather tardily to the seriousness of affairs, refused to discount any more of the Valley Bank's paper. "It's your baby," Calkins told Superintendent Johnson, thus ending the Crocker National's effort in behalf of the Valley Bank.[5]

Johnson got on the telephone, and eight serious-looking men assembled at the Pacific-Southwest's Fresno office in the stillness of the afternoon of Sunday, February 24. They were the superintendent, Stern, Giannini and advisers. Fickett represented the sinking bank. One rescue scheme after another was brought up, talked over and dropped. The afternoon was drawing to a close when Johnson began an impassioned speech, appealing to Giannini and Stern to take over the bank jointly. "The time ought to have passed when a bank should fail in California," said the superintendent.

Giannini interrupted. "Stern, I'll give you $250,000 and I will step out."

"Mr. Giannini, that is very magnanimous of you," the Pacific-Southwest man blandly replied, "but I'll give you $250,000 and I will step out."

Johnson went on. "This does not mean only the Valley Bank going down. . . . You are the two largest banks in Fresno, and I appeal to you to protect the depositors and the banking situation in general."

The two bankers put their heads together, and presently Giannini looked up. "All right," he said, "we will stand in."

Then and there details were arranged. Giannini and Stern decided to close two branches and divide the others. Night had fallen when Johnson wired the Federal Reserve Board in Washington for the requisite branch permits. Action would have to be immediate. Otherwise, "Valley Bank . . . must close tomorrow," Mr. Johnson informed the board.

The permits were forthcoming. Johnson's attorney, James M. Oliver, got the unpleasant job of breaking the news to the bank's stockholders whose equities, had they only known it, long since had been wiped out. To convince them of the reality of their plight, as much as anything else, Oliver gave the stockholders ten days in which to get better terms. They bedeviled practically every large bank in California. None would touch the Valley Bank with a ten-foot pole. Giannini himself made a last try. To preserve appearances, a wealthy Fresno man named J. J. Graves had succeeded Mitchell with the nominal title of acting president. Vainly Giannini offered to loan Graves a million dollars to step into the shoes of the Bank of Italy and the Pacific-Southwest.[6]

The rescue cost the two banks about $500,000 apiece. From the viewpoint of the welfare of California—and that was what Giannini and Stern had in mind—it was certainly worth it. Incidentally, no harm was done the beleaguered cause of branch banking among Washington officials who were in the know. Tragedy descended most heavily upon Mitchell, who had thought branch banking as easy as Giannini made it look. He died in prison.[7]

3

Just as the Valley Bank affair was getting under way, A. P. Giannini told his board of directors that he wished to relinquish the presidency of the Bank of Italy. This was at the annual meeting in January, 1924. He said he would not accept re-election for the year ensuing. In response to urging, however, he consented to stay on, with the stipulation that he "be permitted to retire . . . on the date of the Bank's [twentieth] anniversary, October 17, 1924, in favor of some other executive officer whom he will, at that time, name." Note that Giannini and not the board was to name the successor; or so the minutes read.[8]

Then, as soon as the Valley Bank question was settled, Mr. Giannini went to Europe. Returning in June, he talked rather freely about the forthcoming change. "I am a young man," Giannini, who was fifty-three, told the editor of the *Coast Banker,* "but sooner or later I have got to give up the presidency, and I want to do it while I'm active, and can still be hanging around to help the boys. . . . My boys [the bank's staff] are coming along satisfactorily and I get a great satisfaction out of seeing their development."

Without being pontifical, the banker answered the stock journalistic inquiries concerning his "secret of success."

He said he had succeeded because he had stuck exclusively to his business, which was developing and managing a bank. "It's no trick to run any business if a man has the intelligence and industry to concentrate on the job. The great trouble with most men is that they scatter too much. A few men can go into many things and succeed, but they are very few."

Mr. Giannini said that his concentration on banking kept him from worrying, because people worried about what they hadn't mastered and this usually meant side issues. "We don't want on our staff anybody who worries." If a man had domestic trouble the bank got rid of him. "If a man gets into debt we don't want him either. He'll worry."

"I think," observed the editor of the *Coast Banker,*

the thing that Mr. Giannini is proudest of is the fact that he is a poor man. He has a salary, yes. It's a pretty good salary. But his tastes are simple and he spends very little of it on himself. . . . "When I die," said Mr. Giannini, "the world is going to be surprised at the little estate that I have left. It won't be a million. I have no sympathy for the man who just lives to make money. There may be pleasure in the game for some, but how futile!"[9]

Since 1920 Mr. Giannini's salary had been $50,000 a year, which was low for the head of an institution as large and as rich as the Bank of Italy. When he gave up the presidency, Giannini's bank salary was reduced to one dollar a year, the figure at which it remained until his death. He was quite comfortably remunerated, however, by the Bancitaly Corporation, and its successor, Transamerica, as will be told later.

Not for a moment did anyone dream that the power of A. P. Giannini in the Bank of Italy or the banking world would be less without the title of president. Giannini's power did not depend on titles or on money. His business power depended on Giannini himself. No inside group had stock control of the Bank of Italy, whose shares were owned by 13,692 persons. Only 28 individual holdings amounted to 350 shares or more. The aggregate of these large holdings was 23,364 shares. In 1924 Giannini was a large stockholder, with 1,010 shares of 175,000 outstanding. Thereafter his holdings formed a smaller and smaller proportion of the total stock issue. In 1927 the total comprised 1,500,000 shares and by 1948 it was up to more than 8,500,000. During this period, and indeed until his death in 1949, Mr. Giannini's holdings varied between 1,000 and 2,500 shares, including those he held in trust for others.

In September, 1924, the resignation of Mr. Giannini was accepted and James A. Bacigalupi was elected president of the Bank of Italy. Arnold J. Mount, lately cashier, was raised to Bacigalupi's old place of senior vice-president. William E. Blauer took the office of vice-president and cashier and Lawrence Mario Giannini that of vice-chairman of the board. The changes became effective on October 17.

The selection of Bacigalupi occasioned no surprise. He was forty-two, and had grown up with the bank. Excepting Giannini, no one had contributed so much to the unique position attained by the Bank of Italy.

Arnold Mount was a comparative newcomer, little known outside the head office. He was forty years old. In 1920 Mr. Giannini had hired him away from a bank in Oakland on the advice of James J. Fagan. His special talent was for administration. Seven months before his selection to be second-in-command under Bacigalupi, Mount had been made cashier succeeding W. R. Williams who became head of the trust department of the bank's southern division, with offices at Los Angeles.

Blauer was forty-seven and an old-timer in the service of the Bank of Italy. A son-in-law of Gus Lion, whose family had controlled the Commercial and Savings Bank of San Jose in 1909 when Giannini launched his branch banking career, Blauer had joined the bank at that time. He knew agriculture, especially the co-ops.

Under the eye of his father, Mario Giannini had been learning the ropes since his high school days working after hours and in summer vacations. Although a sufferer from hemophilia, whose recurrent attacks limited his activities, Mario had had a varied and all-round experience, both in the branches and the home office. In 1918, two years before he finished law school, A. P. Giannini yielded to his persistent young son and gave him a job as a junior clerk. Next came experience under Pop Hendrick in the land bank. In 1922 Mario was elected to the board. In 1923 he spent several months abroad with the Banca d'America e d'Italia. On his return he was given the title of assistant to the president.

No one put in longer hours at No. 1 Powell than Mario whose ambition, as far back as he remembered, was to be a banker like his father. "Relatives have to work harder than anyone around here to make good," warned Mr. Giannini when he put his son on the payroll. He need have had no misgivings on that score. Until his death in 1952, Mario Giannini averaged "fifteen or sixteen hours a day" working for the bank. As this history proceeds more will unfold of the story of A. P. Giannini's son who achieved much, though not one day of his life was passed without physical suffering.[10]

The board minutes undertook to state the reasons for promotion of Mario and of the other officers:

First, the advisability of convincing the general public that the Bank of Italy is not a so-called "One Man" Bank; Second, the prudence of not permitting one man to hold the office of President so long that the name of the bank and of said individual become synonymous in the public mind;

and Third, the desirability of holding out the incentive and encouragement to every officer and other employee of the bank of his eligibility to any office within the gift of the bank.[11]

After October 17 the only offices remaining to Mr. Giannini were those of director and chairman of the executive committee. Rather needlessly, however, he repeated that he was not "retiring."

"Far from it! I merely want to be free to concentrate on major policies."[12]

4

The policy that bulked largest in the mind of A. P. Giannini was branch expansion. Against this strong forces were operating, but Giannini was determined to circumvent them.

The recent dictum of the Federal Reserve Board, limiting branches to home cities and contiguous territory, had the effect of reviving Stern's old idea of regional banking. Exceptions were possible, of course, as in the Valley Bank affair, but Giannini did not wish to count on the imminence of catastrophe for federal assent to enlarge his bank. Other considerations aside, in the case of the Valley Bank the price had been too high.

Another restraining force with which the Bank of Italy had to contend was the State Banking Department of California. Both Superintendent Dodge and Superintendent Johnson had labored manfully to convince the Federal Reserve of the virtues of branch banking. For the Bank of Italy they had promptly approved permits that Washington held up for long periods and then sometimes rejected. But, with one or two exceptions, this applied only to permits for branches north of the Mason-Dixon banking line. South of the Tehachapi Range, Giannini was as effectively blocked by the state authorities as he was elsewhere (aside from San Francisco and environs) by the new ruling of the Federal Reserve Board.

This was the fruit of a deliberate campaign of the southern branch bankers. Nothing in the California law supported their position. Giannini's Los Angeles competitors were successful simply because they managed to persuade three superintendents in a row that branch banking in the south should be the exclusive prerogative of southern bankers.

Giannini's first step was to establish himself more firmly in southern California. The preliminaries had been taken before he announced his retirement from the presidency of the Bank of Italy. Early in 1923 he moved the Bancitaly Corporation, which owned the New York and the Italian banks, from New York to Los Angeles. Its new home was in the lately completed twelve-story Bank of Italy building at Seventh and Olive. At the same time Bancitaly's capital was increased from $10,000,000 to $20,000,000, and Californians were given a majority of the places on the board.

As a southern California institution Bancitaly wasted no time. In March, 1923, it bought the Commercial National Bank of Los Angeles, an institution with $11,000,000 in deposits and three city branches, acquired under the Crissinger ruling of 1922. Then, to show that Giannini was not looking to the south solely, Bancitaly bought eight small banks north of the Tehachapi. It also bought three south of the Ridge, as Californians call this landmark.

By these simple means Mr. Giannini evaded the agreement of January, 1922, with the Federal Reserve Board concerning the purchase of banks. The agreement provided that neither the Bank of Italy nor an affiliated corporation should buy a bank without the board's consent. This hamstrung the Stockholders Auxiliary, a corporate affiliate whose stockholders were identical with those of the Bank of Italy, and which, up to then, had been Giannini's only bank buyer in California. The agreement did not apply to Bancitaly, not by legal definition an affiliate of the Bank of Italy because the stockholders of the two corporations were not identical. Consequently, Giannini could do with Bancitaly what he could not do with the Auxiliary.

The advent of Bancitaly in southern California was a disconcerting surprise to Stern, Sartori and the other local branch bankers who had been having things pretty much their own way. More surprises were in store for them. In July, 1924, the merger of the Bancitaly-held Commercial National and the Bank of America of Los Angeles was announced. The combined resources of the two institutions amounted to $27,000,000. This gave Giannini eleven more offices in the southern city—three operated by the Bank of America of Los Angeles and eight by the Commercial National which had been reaching out with a will.

When Giannini took charge of it, the Bank of America of Los Angeles was an eighteen-months-old wonder. Its president, Orra E.

Monnette, had been a Los Angeles banker since 1907. As head of the Citizens Trust and Savings, he had joined the southern rush into branch banking in 1921. In 1922, however, he had a falling out with his directors over personal matters, and they removed him from office. A few months later Monnette launched the Bank of America of Los Angeles. The name was chosen with a view to competing with the Bank of Italy. When Monnette and Giannini came to terms, the new bank had resources of $11,000,000 and 16,000 depositors.

The merger was an unusual one. Each bank kept its old name and most of its old officers. The Commercial National was, of course, under federal jurisdiction. The Bank of America of Los Angeles, a state bank without a Federal Reserve membership, was under the sole regulatory authority of Superintendent Johnson. Their common owner was the newly-created Americommercial Corporation, Orra Monnette, president. Giannini did not even hold a directorship. He did not need to because Americommercial was a subsidiary of Bancitaly, of which Giannini was president.[13]

Bancitaly bowed out of the picture in southern California banking, leaving matters to its offspring. Americommercial's two branch systems, one national and one state, spread so rapidly that by the end of 1925 they had thirty-five offices between them. The Commercial National operated entirely within Los Angeles. In 1924 its name was elongated to the Commercial National Trust and Savings Bank following a merger with the sizable Continental National. The Bank of America of Los Angeles operated mostly outside the city, taking over the banks previously acquired by Bancitaly in the south and adding others until its activity extended from Santa Barbara to El Centro in the Imperial Valley near the Mexican border.

"Now what does it all mean?" asked the financial editor of the San Francisco *Chronicle*. Then he answered the question:

Giannini has at last invaded Los Angeles and has fortified himself very strongly with a banking combination of unquestioned strength.

What Los Angeles thinks of the whole transaction we know not and we venture the opinion that Giannini is not worried what anyone thinks. . . .

Well, it has been no secret that Giannini for many a day has been anxiously awaiting the opportunity of going to Los Angeles. He is there.[14]

Not the slightest difficulty had been experienced in obtaining the needed permits, though these same branches would have been flatly refused had Mr. Giannini asked for them in the name of the Bank of Italy. The manner in which he did ask for them made all the difference in the world. After six months in office, Comptroller Dawes, still opposed to branch banking, but wishing to aid the national banks, had fallen back on Crissinger's policy of approving extra tellers windows for them in their home cities. Los Angeles being its home city, the Commercial National Trust and Savings Bank got twenty banking agencies, as it chose to call its additional banking offices. Superintendent Johnson had in practice adopted the regional theory of branch banking, which excluded the Bank of Italy from further expansion in the south. But the Bank of America of Los Angeles was something else; it was a Los Angeles institution, eligible to have branches as far away as El Centro.

To one unfamiliar with the bureaucratic mind, or with corporate legerdemain, the foregoing may read like something from Gilbert and Sullivan. Given a free hand, it was not the method Mr. Giannini would have chosen to expand his banking operations in California. It was what he had to resort to, or abandon to competitors the southern field where, by state law, he had a perfect right to be.

5

A. P. Giannini was not satisfied with this side-door entrance to southern California. He felt the Bank of Italy entitled to more branches in its own name below the Ridge. His southern competitors were able to get plenty of them. From the time Superintendent J. Franklin Johnson took office on February 1, 1923, to March 1, 1925, fifty-four branch permits had dropped into the laps of the "big five" southern branch banks. Security Trust had obtained fifteen; Pacific-Southwest, eleven; Hellman Commercial, sixteen; Citizens Trust, seven; California Bank, five. Most of these branches were of the *de novo* character, Mr. Johnson having found ground for them under the convenience-and-advantage clause of the much discussed *de novo* rule. During the same fourteen months, only one *de novo* permit in the south had been granted the Bank of Italy. In Mr. Giannini's opinion the record amounted to an abuse of discretionary power.

So the Bank of Italy sought to do away with the *de novo* rule. It sponsored an amendment to the Banking Act obliging the superintendent to issue a permit to any branch bank in any community where 20 per cent of the registered voters petitioned for one. The amendment was defeated by united opposition of southern branch bankers and the California League of Independent Bankers.

Shortly thereafter Johnson refused a *de novo* permit to the Bank of Italy under circumstances that aroused Giannini. Los Angeles' monumental Civic Center was rising on the site of the bank's International branch. Still presided over by patriarchal "Old John" Lopizich, the International had been remarkably successful. Profits were $15,000 a month. By permission of Mr. Johnson the branch had made way for the Center by moving across the street from its former location. The erection of the Center was working a revolution in the character of the neighborhood, however. Much of the foreign element that constituted the branch's principal clientele had migrated north of Sunset Boulevard, several blocks away. The bank asked leave to follow with another branch, lest the International branch lose a big slice of its business to rivals already located on Sunset Boulevard. When Johnson invoked the *de novo* rule to refuse the license, Bacigalupi obtained Giannini's consent to go to law.[15]

In June, 1925, the Bank of Italy asked the Supreme Court of California for a writ of mandamus directing Superintendent Johnson to approve applications for branches on Sunset Boulevard and on the premises of the Women's Athletic Club of Los Angeles. (Just before turning down the bank in the International case, Mr. Johnson had refused a permit in the newly erected building of the Women's Athletic Club.) The bank's battery of lawyers was headed by Garret W. McEnerney, perhaps the most distinguished member of California's bar. The petition called Johnson's action "arbitrary and capricious" and part of a long history of favoritism to the Bank of Italy's competitors in southern California.[16]

The case of the Bank of Italy *versus* Johnson required a year and a half to run its course. The record is voluminous. Looking back, perhaps Mr. McEnerney tried to prove too much, namely that Johnson was a tool of the southern branch bankers in their fight to keep the Bank of Italy from expanding in the south. Giannini and Bacigalupi believed this to be true, as is clear from private correspondence, written with no eye to public effect. Belief is one thing and proof in court is another. This was pre-eminently a lawyers' battle

—in which the noteworthy counsel for the Bank of Italy received the surprise of their lives at the hands of a comparative unknown, James Oliver, counsel for the Banking Department. Oliver was their match at every turn, particularly in the matter of excluding evidence. In December, 1926, the decision of the court was that the bank had not proved its charge of "conspiracy"—the word was McEnerney's.

The court did not award the bank its two permits, and it did not set aside the *de novo* rule. Though the judges found the superintendent's original reasons for refusing the permits to be insufficient, they declined to substitute their discretion for that of Mr. Johnson.[17]

While this legal action created quite a stir at the time, it may be passed over summarily. By the time the court had handed down the decision, Superintendent Johnson had submitted his resignation and the *de novo* rule was on its way to limbo. All this was the result of a state election in California held the month before, in November, 1926. In that political free-for-all, A. P. Giannini had taken a belated and a reluctant part. Nonetheless, his intervention was decisive.

The Liberty Bank and the Election of 1926

THE KALEIDOSCOPIC history of the Bank of Italy is a chart of the mind of A. P. Giannini in action. This state of affairs kept the adversaries of California-wide banking on their toes. They had to meet moves from every direction.

The chronicler who would set down an account of these maneuvers is in pretty much the same fix. Rarely is it possible to travel for long in a straight narrative line. Too many things happened at once. You can carry forward a theme just so far. Then you have to drop it and pick up another. For example, before going into the election of 1926, which determined the future of branch banking in California, it is necessary to sketch the rise of Giannini's Liberty Bank system in northern California, and certain sequels to that event—all bearing on the election in question.

We have seen how Giannini set up the Bank of America of Los Angeles and the Commercial National systems to acquire branches forbidden to the Bank of Italy in the south. We have seen how the Federal Reserve ruling of November, 1923, prohibited the Bank of Italy from expanding in the north, except in San Francisco and environs. Consequently Giannini attempted to bring into the northern theater the Bank of America of Los Angeles, a state institution over which Washington had no jurisdiction. Early in 1925 that bank asked Superintendent Johnson for permission to take over a Chico bank as a branch. Johnson refused because the territory was "not tributary, financially, commercially, or otherwise, to Los Angeles" —a clear restatement of the zonal banking theory so dear to the hearts of Giannini's southern rivals.[1]

As witnessed in the south, the zonal theory was a knife that cut both ways. After the Chico turndown Giannini simply started a northern branch system, with the Liberty Bank in San Francisco as the home office. Unless the application was for a *de novo* branch, Superintendent Johnson could not consistently refuse branch permits to the Liberty; and he did not do so, though the birth of this new Giannini bank and the filing of the Bank of Italy's mandamus suit against the superintendent were almost simultaneous. During the summer of 1925, Liberty acquired twelve branches ranging from the lumbering country along the Oregon line to the lower San Joaquin Valley. In the fall it took over three banks in the Sacramento Valley. Two of these had belonged to Alden Anderson who had fought so hard to keep Giannini out of the city of Sacramento a few years before. Mr. Anderson became a member of the Liberty advisory board in the Sacramento Valley. Liberty was owned by the Bancitaly Corporation, whose subsidiary, Americommercial, owned Giannini's two branch systems in the south.[2]

2

The rapid strokes by which Giannini put together the Liberty system gave rise to various rumors on Montgomery Street. One was that Bank of Italy interests were buying into the Crocker National and the First National banks of San Francisco, with the object of obtaining control. "That is ridiculous," Giannini told the press; and with a touch of exaggeration he added: "Why, Mr. Crocker and his new associates could buy us out more easily than we could buy them out."

The truth behind the rumor was that Giannini smoothed the way for the merger of the Crocker and the First National banks because he had not forgotten the Crocker's friendliness in the Bank of Italy's earlier years. The merger was opposed by Rudolph Spreckels, who had resigned the First National's presidency after a disagreement with his directors. To interests known to be behind the merger Spreckels refused to sell his stock, which amounted to a sixth of the capitalization. He sold to Bancitaly, however, and shortly thereafter the merger went through. One newspaper headlined its account: "BREAD CAST UPON WATERS" BY CROCKER NATIONAL RETURNED BY BANK OF ITALY AFTER TWENTY YEARS.[3]

Another corollary of the Liberty success, coming as it did on top of statements revealing the striking prosperity of all the Giannini banks, was more serious. This was the soaring of Bank of Italy and of Bancitaly shares.

After four years in the doldrums of postwar adjustment, in 1924 the stock market had taken a brace, closing near the year's peak. Even conservative investors were gratified. In 1925 the market continued to go up and speculation became a little more general. Taken as a whole, the rise was justified by earnings. No one recognized, or could have done so on the evidence available, the beginning of a gambler's runaway market that was to sweep us into the Alice in Wonderland of "Coolidge Prosperity."

What disturbed Giannini was that his stocks had been among the leaders of the rise, and that they were becoming increasingly attractive to speculators. Giannini abhorred gambling. In that respect he insisted that his bank's officers and employees be like Caesar's wife. Mere presence in a public gambling house was cause for dismissal. He even disapproved in a mild way of his son Mario's occasional Saturday night poker games at home in San Mateo. Hitherto Giannini had prided himself that Bank of Italy stock had been a conservative investment conservatively priced and sought by savers, mostly of small means. The latest new issue—the result of an increase in capitalization in June, 1924—was priced at 225, certainly a justifiable increase over the 100 for which the original shares had sold in 1904 when the bank was founded. Dividends in 1924 were $13.75 a share.

In January, 1925, Bank of Italy shares were selling on the exchanges for 300. Bancitaly shares were quoted at 220, as against a low of 135 in 1924. Giannini took the almost unheard-of step of warning the public not to buy his own shares at the open-market figures.

"There is no ground for this wild trading in expectancy—for that is what it is," he said in a newspaper interview.

There will be no big melon cutting. It took me and my associates in the Bank of Italy 20 years to build up an institution whose shares now sell for $300. We started the Bancitaly Corporation six years ago. They must attribute miracle-working ability to me and those associated with me in the Bancitaly Corporation if they would justify such prices as are asked and paid for these shares.[4]

It is doubtful if corporate history in the United States exhibits a parallel to Giannini's effort to halt speculation in the Giannini stocks, and to get them out of the hands of speculators buying for a rise and into the hands of investors buying for income. In February, 1925, Bacigalupi warned officers of the Bank of Italy that the stock had risen "to a point beyond which we do not care to see it go." In March branch managers were directed to help "kill the speculative tendency." They were to accept "no orders whatever to purchase or to sell shares in open-market" operations.[5]

Nevertheless, the Giannini stocks continued to advance. When, in the latter part of August, Bank of Italy was quoted at 325 and Bancitaly at 226, Giannini directed that all his banking houses—the Bank of Italy, Liberty, Bank of America of Los Angeles and Commercial National—refuse loans on Giannini shares.

A good deal of our stock has been bought on money borrowed from other banks and from the brokers. This is not a healthy situation. We must get the stock in the hands of people who will pay for it and who are therefore in a position to hold it indefinitely. Those who buy it with borrowed money would, if a reaction came about, find it necessary to drop it on the market.[6]

In the case of Bancitaly, Giannini went to even greater lengths to keep the price of the stock down. He borrowed from friends 39,000 shares which he sold at $50 a share below the market—that is, for $1,950,000 less than the quoted price. The loss involved was easily double Giannini's personal fortune. At the end of the year, in his annual report to Bancitaly stockholders Mr. Giannini explained the transaction. To replace the borrowed certificates he asked permission to buy from the company 39,000 shares at 300. The stock was then selling for 350. In a further effort to hold the market in check he asked Bancitaly's shareholders to authorize the issue of 61,000 additional shares, to be sold (but not for less than 350) at the discretion of A. P. Giannini, president.[7]

Mr. Giannini had given Montgomery Street many surprises, but never, to that time, one like this. The reaction was well summed up by the financial editor of the *Chronicle:*

There are not many men in this cynical old world of ours who could come out with a statement to their stockholders saying that they have

borrowed . . . shares of stock from stockholders to maintain the price
of the securities at a sane level, then ask the holders to waive their rights
to a big block of new stock issued and get away with it.

Yet this is the very thing that A. P. Giannini has done. And this is the
very thing he will accomplish, for he has inspired the confidence of his
followers by his own personal honesty and by his unparalleled good judgment. He is almost an Aladdin personified, for it is his power to request
and the wish is granted.[8]

The *Chronicle* man's prediction was altogether accurate. Only
forty-three stockholders, out of ten thousand voting, refused to waive
their rights.[9]

These extraordinary efforts stabilized the Giannini stocks for the
next several months.

3

While this was going on Giannini began to move toward another
goal: the unification of his four branch systems. The subsidiary institutions, two south and one north of the Ridge, had been created
with no other eventual object in view, as nearly everyone knew.
Local patrons hailed the coming of a Liberty or a Bank of America
of Los Angeles branch as a forerunner of the Bank of Italy—a fact
that contributed materially to the branches' success. The ultimate
union of the subsidiary systems with the Bank of Italy would have
to await federal legislation, superseding the Federal Reserve Board
ruling of November, 1923. That question was already before Congress. But a merger of the two California state banks—Liberty and
Bank of America of Los Angeles—was possible beforehand, that
being a matter in which Superintendent Johnson had full and sole
authority.

Not only did Johnson have authority to merge these banks; it was
his duty to do so should the banks request it, and should they be
able to meet the technical requirements. That was the way the
Banking Act of California read. Giannini's lawyers gave the assurance that Mr. Johnson was without power to refuse to sanction
a merger. As a prelude, the Americommercial Corporation, which
owned the southern branches, took over from its parent corporation, Bancitaly, the control of Liberty in the north. Then, on November 30, 1925, formal application was made for the merger of the
Liberty and the Bank of America of Los Angeles.

Giannini seems to have had no thought of an adverse decision. Optimistic announcements appeared in the press. "The permit will be automatically granted," said a Los Angeles newspaper. San Francisco papers set the formal consolidation for January 2. Californians were brought up to date on the Giannini empire, and they rubbed their eyes at the sight of its proportions:

Liberty Bank, 15 branches in northern California; deposits, $17,000,000.

Commercial National Trust and Savings Bank, 20 branches in Los Angeles; deposits, $21,000,000.

Bank of America of Los Angeles, 24 branches in the south; deposits, $35,000,000.

Bank of Italy, 96 branches throughout the state but mostly in the north; deposits, $391,000,000.

This tallied up to 155 branches with $464,000,000 in deposits. The combined efforts of the Federal Reserve Board, Superintendent Johnson and the southern bankers to stop Giannini had been something short of effective.[10]

Weeks passed, and Mr. Johnson was silent on the merger application. The mandamus suit dragged on, and, in court, Johnson's lawyers and Giannini's lawyers continued to go at each other hammer and tongs. Yet the superintendent gave evidence that he could separate the suit from other considerations touching the Giannini banks. With the merger application pending, and the Giannini forces getting anxious, Mr. Johnson approved thirty-one applications for additional branches: eleven for Bank of America of Los Angeles; ten for Liberty; and one for the Bank of Italy.[11]

On March 5, 1926, the superintendent replied to the merger application in a letter of inquiry seventeen pages long. Until he received the bank's answer to the questions asked, Mr. Johnson said he could not rule on the application. The interrogations went into about every aspect of the Bank of Italy, the Stockholders Auxiliary, Bancitaly, Americommercial, Bank of America of Los Angeles, Liberty Bank, and Giannini bank holdings in the East and in Europe. What appalled Johnson was the size of it all.

"Is it not a fact," he asked,

that Bancitaly Corporation will, if and when its full purpose is accomplished, be in control of the largest, most scattered and diversified, and most difficult to control chain banking system so far devised?

We ask you . . . to inform us how it is possible for the State Banking Department of California to know what the condition of this chain is, and even if it were able to put its finger on a weak link in this chain, what control it would have over the situation, and what remedy it would be possible to apply? . . . What provision, if any, has been made to prevent a foreign disaster from endangering or even causing the collapse of the entire Bancitaly chain?

Is it the intention of your banks . . . to circumvent the law when it stands in the way of your expansion, by doing indirectly what cannot be done directly? . . .

Is it your intention, in co-operation with Bank of Italy, to thus attempt a monopoly of the banking business of the State of California? Do your intentions go further in this regard, and if so are they of national or international scope?

Kindly state, also, at what point, if any, short of the elimination of the independent banker, you propose to stop.[12]

The bank's first reaction to this letter was incredulity. Parts of it read more like a stump speech by Andrew J. Frame than an official communication from California's superintendent of banks. Eustace Cullinan wondered "whether to take the letter as a serious inquiry." Mr. Cullinan was the lawyer—and one of California's best—who had attended to the legal details of setting up the Liberty system. He was also assisting McEnerney in the mandamus suit.[13]

The decision was to take the letter seriously. Bacigalupi handled the matter, with all the help he could get from the bank's higher-ups and its lawyers. Drafts and redrafts of a reply were made. Giannini, who was in Europe, did not appear to be disturbed. At one point he cabled: "INSTITUTIONS WITH SOUND POLICIES AND EXCESSIVE [that is, more than ample] CAPITAL CANNOT BE SUCCESSFULLY ATTACKED." In July the bank's letter was ready. It ran fifty-eight pages.[14]

Your letter of March 5 [it began] puts to us a number of questions which . . . we regard as wholly irrelevant to our application; but inasmuch as the letter contains statements and suggestions by innuendo, which after full reflection we are not disposed to let remain unchallenged, . . . we here reply to them.

Nothing in the Banking Act, Mr. Johnson was informed, warranted "an exercise of power by the Superintendent of Banks of the type or kind implied by [his] letter." Therefore the superintendent's duty, in our opinion, is to approve the consolidation without further ado or delay. . . . It is plain that there can be no objection . . . based upon any inherent financial or structural weakness, or based upon the idea that we are not in a wholly sound condition . . . and no reason whatever exists upon which to challenge or question the right given us by statute to consolidate. . . .

If there were any substance to the chimeras of financial disaster which you vision, the danger certainly would not be less with one separate bank north of the Tehachapi Range and another separate bank south of that range . . . than it would be with a consolidated bank combining the strength of its two constituents, extending buttresses into every section of California, and enjoying . . . the advantages of stability and flexibility afforded by a highly diversified business covering a region whose wealth is as great and whose industries and crops are as various as those of this great state.

Johnson's letter was

an attack on the corporate form of ownership of bank stocks as distinct from personal or individual ownership. You assume that the duty of the state is to supervise and control the ownership of banks as well as the banks themselves, and you express fear that the police power of the state is inadequate for the task of supervision because of the magnitude and wide distribution of the constituent interests.

In troubled accents you ask how it is possible for the State Banking Department to know the condition of what you designate as the Bancitaly chain, since a large portion of the assets of Bancitaly Corporation is beyond the jurisdiction or control of any California or United States authority. Bancitaly owns about two per cent of the capital stock of Bank of Italy. Suppose that John D. Rockefeller owned two per cent of that stock. His interests . . . are spread across the globe. Would you object to his owning stock, or even controlling interest in a California bank, unless he agreed to bring all his property . . . under your supervision? . . .

It is not your duty to require any California bank to hold an annual roundup of its stockholders or their assets. Nor is it our task to uphold the entire financial structure of Christendom. The duty of every bank is to keep its own house in order; to be clean, and ready to meet its obligations. That we have done, and will continue to do so. . . .

This brings us to the chief object of the attack made in your letter, i.e., the Bank of Italy. . . . You know from your examinations . . . that the Bank of Italy compares most favorably with any bank in the State of California.

To Mr. Johnson's suggestion that Giannini had circumvented certain Banking Department regulations the bank pointed out that these regulations went beyond the law of California in denying the Bank of Italy branches in the south.[15]

No answer to this communication was ever received. Bacigalupi acted as if he expected none, or, at any rate, nothing favorable. On the ground that the forthcoming state election would settle the immediate future of branch banking in California, Bacigalupi urged his mentor to cut short his European sojourn and come home.

4

Disembarking in New York on one of the last days of July, 1926, A. P. Giannini was met by a long letter from Jim Bacigalupi setting forth the story of conflicting ambitions and interest underlying the approaching state campaign. Naturally, Bacigalupi's exposition was from the point of view of the Bank of Italy. As the Republican ticket was sure to win, his concern was with that party's primary, to be held August 31, only five weeks away. The leading contender for the governorship was the incumbent, Friend W. Richardson, who was seeking a second term. If he got it, Bacigalupi declared that the "stranglehold" of competing branch bankers on the office of superintendent of banks would be continued. This thesis was developed carefully, for Bacigalupi knew Giannini's aversion to political activity by officers of the Bank of Italy.

Bacigalupi sized up the four principal candidates for governor as follows:

Richardson had the support of the state organization and most of the local machines, by virtue of patronage. He had the support of big business, an element that had been pretty much under cover in California politics since Hiram Johnson had broken up the machine by which the Southern Pacific Railroad *et al.* had once ruled the state. Governor Richardson also enjoyed such strangely assorted support as the League of Independent Bankers, Charles F. Stern and Joseph F. Sartori.

Second choice of the conservatives was Judge Rex B. Goodcell of San Bernardino. The "Big Interests" were keeping him in the race to weaken Lieutenant-Governor Clement C. Young, the man they feared as greatly as they feared anyone, which was not very much.

It was also good strategy to have handy a substitute in case Richardson, a man of mediocre ability, should display some last-minute weakness as a vote getter. Giannini was a friend of Goodcell, and had contributed $5,000 to his campaign fund.

The organization's opposition was divided between two aspirants: C. C. Young and Will C. Wood, the state superintendent of schools. The schoolteachers were enthusiastic for Wood. Also for him was union labor. Of the two antiorganization men, Bacigalupi thought Young the stronger because of his greater political experience and his backing by the independent press. Senator Johnson was coming from Washington to mix in the senatorial fight. It was rumored that he might declare for Young. Bacigalupi was afraid this would harm Young more than it would help him, because the "Big Interests"— Bacigalupi's term—who got nervous chills every time they thought of Johnson, would then work harder to put Richardson over.

All these leading candidates except Wood had approached Bacigalupi. Goodcell had come in person, for funds. The "Big Money Bags" were not shelling out to their second-stringer. Goodcell said the fight was between him and Richardson, as "the Big Interests would not accept Young under any consideration." Bacigalupi said that the bank was not in politics, but that in their private capacities officers could contribute as they saw fit.

Friends of Young gave Bacigalupi the same line of talk in favor of their man. They got the same answer.

Richardson's approach was more cagey. His emissaries hinted about neutrality on the part of the bank and promised a fair shake from the Banking Department. Bacigalupi told them he would be satisfied with nothing short of permission to merge the Liberty and the Bank of America of Los Angeles. The Richardson men made friendly signs and went into a huddle. Bacigalupi told his superior that he was sure nothing would come of it. Nothing did.

Summing up, the writer said that he thought only Young had a chance of beating Richardson. Admitting the chance to be a rather slim one, Bacigalupi stated the alternative: under Richardson "we will continue to be the recipients of a rotten deal."

The letter closed with an ardent appeal.

It is deplorable that we should be forced into politics . . . but there are times when it is better to have fought and lost than not to have fought at all. . . . I think that you personally should, immediately upon returning home, come out openly for Young. This will technically not be the action of the bank and yet every one of our stockholders and friends . . . will catch the cue. . . . Our competitors have no compunctions in the matter, so why should we? . . . The time for stalling is past. Our actions have been clean and honorable and we should not fear. Let us take a stand and give them the best we have. . . . You are the *Big Chief,* and we anxiously await your orders, whatever they may be.[16]

<h1 style="text-align:center">5</h1>

The Big Chief was not swept off his feet by the argument and the rhetoric of his first lieutenant. Before leaving Europe he had cabled Bacigalupi his determination "to keep institution out politics if all possible." Instead of rushing to California Giannini tarried in New York and then went to Washington where there was much affecting the bank to engage his attention.[17]

It became apparent that, as Bacigalupi predicted, Young was the only man with a ghost of a show against Richardson. Wood saw the light, withdrew from the race, and started campaigning for the lieutenant-governor. Hiram Johnson came out for him. Thereupon Richardson's powerful backers, who had been counting on a walk-over, went to work. About the middle of August Giannini arrived in California. John Francis Neylan, a San Francisco attorney and Young supporter, believed Giannini the only man who could save Young. At first Giannini told Neylan he wasn't interested, but on a second try Neylan brought Young and the banker together briefly. This must have surprised Bacigalupi who had reported the lawyer out of humor toward the Bank of Italy because it had recently declined to loan a client of Neylan's a million dollars.[18]

Giannini entered the contest on August 24, seven days before California was to go to the polls in the primary. He issued no public statement, as Bacigalupi and others had urged him to do ostensibly in his capacity as a private citizen, though he did not rule out the possibility of an announcement later. Apparently he wanted to see how things went without it. Quietly word was sent to the branch managers of the four banking systems to beat the bushes for Young. The greatest effort was planned for the south, where Young was weakest and the opposition strongest. Mario Giannini and Vice-President Leo V. Belden of the B. of I. were in Los Angeles on August 24. Their news delighted Orra Monnette, president of

Americommercial, who right along had been working on Giannini to get him into the fight. After the southern branch managers had been alerted by telephone, Belden remained on the ground in general charge of that front.[19]

Next morning the Los Angeles *Times,* chief southern spokesman for the conservative Republicans and bellwether of the Richardson forces in that quarter, broke the story under this headline: "BANK OF ITALY GOES INTO POLITICS TO BACK YOUNG." The *Times* called this "a revolutionary departure from the customs and principles of modern banks." It said that Giannini "insisted on favors and privileges denied other institutions," and, to get them, was out to elect "a State administration amenable to his plans." It said that Young had promised to "name a superintendent of banks acceptable to Mr. Giannini."[20]

Taking California as a whole Young had the most newspaper support, however. Particularly was this true in rural districts that had profited by the ministrations of the Bank of Italy. The distress of the opposition press over a banker taking part in a political contest made curious reading. According to Bacigalupi "the *money,* the *influence,* the open and active support of every other bank in California was wholly with Richardson." That may have been an exaggeration. Nevertheless the issue of the *Times* that gave the first news of Giannini's decision carried an endorsement of Richardson by Robinson of the Pacific-Southwest.[21]

In one detail the *Times* was prophetic. From the Oregon to the Mexican borders Giannini let loose a swarm of campaigners for Young. The personnel of the branches, the advisory boards, stockholders, depositors, plunged into the fray. It was the first time Giannini had asked such a thing of his people, and they responded with pride. What they lacked in experience they made up in enthusiasm. In San Francisco Giannini received daily reports from all over. On August 27 he declined another suggestion that he make a public statement; and he never made one. Telegrams, such as this from Belden, indicated that none was needed: "COTANT, SANTA ANA, JUST GOT SOLID BLOCK OF FIFTEEN HUNDRED SWITCHED FROM OPPOSITION. . . . IT WOULD DO YOUR HEART GOOD TO SEE HOW OUR BOYS AND GIRLS ARE HITTING THE BALL DOWN HERE."[22]

Taken by surprise, the Republican organization struck back hard. "CALIFORNIA DOES NOT NEED A MUSSOLINI" was the title of one broadside. The result of the balloting was close. Young pulled through by twelve thousand votes. Giannini himself later said that had the campaign lasted two weeks longer the professional politicians would have had time to meet the impact of his amateurs, and that Richardson would have won.[23]

Giannini had enjoyed the battle. This man who had received so many proofs of devotion on the part of his "boys and girls" was touched by their latest response. "There was certainly never a more loyal bunch in the world than the Bank of Italy family!" He answered a flood of congratulatory messages. He also sent one to Young which, so far as Mr. Giannini's files reveal, was not acknowledged.[24]

Resting at his country home down the peninsula from San Francisco Jim Bacigalupi, who had pushed his boss into the campaign, meditated on the possible outcome for the Giannini banks. He put his thoughts on paper in an unstudied and revealing letter to the chief. Young had made no commitment. He had not been asked for one. He had promised "a square deal" and that was all. To Bacigalupi a square deal meant "the full enjoyment of our rights under the present California law"—in other words, approval of the merger. Now that the dust had settled and Young was the winner, Bacigalupi had to confess that he couldn't be certain whether that was what a square deal meant to the incoming governor. "I don't know Young very well, but if I have erred in my estimate of him then I shall lose my faith in human kind."[25]

The Great Victory

WHILE A. P. Giannini was waging his long battle against home-front opposition to statewide branches, he was also fighting for the same cause on the national front, in Washington. Had the views of officials such as Comptroller Dawes prevailed, the federal government would have frustrated the ambition Mr. Giannini held for his banks, no matter what the attitude of California.

Mr. Dawes's object was to strengthen the country's national banks. Hampered by outdated legislation and unrealistic restrictions, which among other things limited their branch banking operations, national banks in large numbers were surrendering their charters in order to enjoy the greater opportunities open to state banks. The Dawes remedy was, in the main, to curb branch banking. A minority of the Federal Reserve Board was just as anxious as the comptroller to help the national banks, but disagreed with him about the method. They preferred to strike the fetters from national institutions and permit them to open branches and thus meet competitors like the Bank of Italy on their own ground.

As we have seen, the Dawes people won the first round in November, 1923, when the board, by a vote of four to three, severely limited the further branch expansion of state banks that were members of the Reserve System. Comptroller Dawes moved quickly to embody the principle of this regulation in law. He had his deputy draft a bill which Representative Louis T. McFadden of Pennsylvania introduced in February, 1924. Charles W. Collins, Dawes's deputy, had been in California the previous year making a study of branch banking. For that reason the antibranch features of the new bill were a little less severe than those of the famous 1923 regulation.

Hearings on the bill began in April before the Banking and Cur-

rency Committee, of which Mr. McFadden was chairman. Having
been so conspicuous at the Federal Reserve conference of 1923,
which had preceded the imposition of the ruling of November of
that year, the Bank of Italy was not represented at the committee
sessions. Other California branch bankers were present, however.
They readily endorsed the bill with the exception of Section 9,
which contained the branch banking restrictions that would go
hardest with them. If this section stood, no state bank entering the
Federal Reserve after passage of the McFadden bill, could retain
its city branches; and furthermore, no state member bank could
establish extra city branches.

In the words of Edward Elliott of J. F. Sartori's Security Trust
and Savings Bank of Los Angeles, "Section 9 would oblige branch
bankers to decide whether membership in the Federal Reserve is
more desirable to them than future extension of their branch banking system." He reminded the committee that branch banks contributed to the Federal Reserve Bank of San Francisco 50 per cent
of the reserves it obtained in California.[1]

Speaking for the other side, Will F. Morrish, president of the
First National Bank of Berkeley, said that unless the restrictions
on branch banks were retained in the bill "within ten years . . .
independent banking will be a thing of the past . . . in California
outside of probably the cities of Los Angeles and San Francisco."[2]

John S. Drum of the Mercantile Trust of San Francisco was questioned about the forced-sale tactics alleged against branch banks in
their dealings with independents. Such talk was "hearsay," declared the banker. As a member of the committee that advised the
state legislature on banking bills, Mr. Drum had listened to a "long
catalogue of atrocities" which the California League of Independent
Bankers had been unable to substantiate.[3]

Superintendent of Banks J. Franklin Johnson corroborated this.

"Do you know of any banks which have been put out of business
or forced to sell by reason of competition with branch banks?" he
was asked.

"I do not," Mr. Johnson replied. "I have heard many rumors
and many assertions that has been done, but I have never been able
to run one down yet."[4]

Representatives of the League also appeared before the congressional committee. They stuck to their stories. Howard Whipple repeated his version of the Bank of Italy's activities in Santa Maria. Unabashed by the testimony of Mr. Johnson, he added: "I am quite sure that if we unit bankers had at our disposal the files of the superintendent of banks of California . . . possibly we might be able to get out other cases of coercion which he has knowledge of."[5]

It would appear that the antibranch spokesmen made the deeper impression. At any rate, the Committee on Banking and Currency reported the McFadden bill with Section 9 intact. Congress adjourned for the summer, however, before the bill could be taken up on the floor of the House.

2

Late in the summer of 1924, Representative McFadden made a trip to the Coast to see branch banks in action. The branch bankers were glad to have him there. They had won over visiting doubters before. Mr. McFadden was a personable man; and he was a banker, having risen from errand boy to president of the First National Bank of Canton, Pennsylvania, population two thousand. He found California's branch institutions "splendidly managed," and taking care of "the needs of the public in a thoroughly bankable way." He was not ready to say, however, that the California system would be good for the rest of the country. Nevertheless, after his departure the congressman and Mr. Giannini exchanged cordial letters.[6]

But Mr. McFadden's softened attitude had no effect on his colleagues who were bent on legislating branch banking out of existence. On reintroducing his bill at the opening of the short session in December, the representative yielded to pressure and accepted the so-called Hull amendments. Sponsored by Congressman Hull of Chicago, where chain banking flourished, the amendments expressed the wishes of the radical antibranch wing of the banking fraternity. On the surface, their acceptance by McFadden represented the antibranchers' second success within sixty days. The first had been scored at the convention in Chicago of the American Bankers Association by means that were something less than straightforward. In the closing hours of the convention the amendments were dexterously placed before the meeting in the form of a resolution that was adopted without debate and by unanimous vote. To say the least, there would have been no unanimity had all the delegates known what they were voting for.[7]

The object of the Hull proposals was to prevent the possible spread of branch banks into the twenty-eight states which in 1924 either had laws prohibiting, or had no laws permitting, branch banking within their borders. The Hull amendments endeavored to make it unlikely that permissive laws would ever be enacted. They did this by excluding from the benefits of such future laws all national banks and all state banks in the Reserve System. The only banks that could benefit would be state banks that were not Reserve members. It was reasoned that legislatures would be disinclined to pass laws favoring this one class of banks; that any attempt to do so would be swamped by opposition from all the other banks.[8]

Thus the amendments would not have affected California. They looked to other states—and to the future.

The fight for the amended McFadden bill was opened in the House by T. Alan Goldsborough of Maryland. Carried away by Howard Whipple's story of Santa Maria, which he repeated from the floor, Mr. Goldsborough predicted the end of branch banking, even in California. "The people there are seeing the effects of it, and in my judgment in a short time it will be broken up."[9]

Four days later the bill passed the House. In the Senate it came up against Carter Glass of Virginia. A former Secretary of the Treasury and one of the authors of the Federal Reserve Act, Senator Glass was a long-time friend of branch banking. The Senate Banking and Currency Committee threw out the Hull amendments and Section 9. At that stage the measure died on the calendar.

On the opening day of the Sixty-ninth Congress in December, 1925, Mr. McFadden reintroduced his bill—again with the Hull amendments and Section 9. The House passed it, and the fight started in the Banking and Currency Committee of the Senate. Again Carter Glass led the opposition, and he found allies on the Republican side of the table. Those were not the only allies the Virginia senator and the branch bankers were able to find. Early in the contest, it became apparent that in their zeal to make the McFadden bill an out-and-out antibranch measure the antibranch people had overreached themselves. Also changes in the membership of the Federal Reserve Board accomplished an important realignment of forces in that quarter. All this did not happen in a day. It was a development over a period of a year and a half.

3

First came the voluntary retirement of Mr. Dawes, to take the presidency of an oil company. The new comptroller of the currency, Joseph W. McIntosh, seems never to have believed that the salvation of the national banks lay in squelching the branch banks. Clearly, the relief promised by the McFadden bill was not checking the surrender of national bank charters. During Comptroller McIntosh's first year in office 166 of them, with resources of half a billion dollars, changed over into state institutions. Vice-Governor Platt of the board held to his belief that the best way to help the national banks would be to let them do more branch banking business, not less. The comptroller came to think enough of this theory to take a trip to California in the summer of 1925.

McIntosh and Giannini got along fine. The Californian brought up the blackest deed alleged against the Bank of Italy—the Santa Maria episode. He gave the bank's side of the case and asked Mr. McIntosh to investigate it. Two federal bank examiners, strangers to the Coast, were sent from Washington to Santa Maria. Their findings cleared the Bank of Italy. They recommended that Mr. Giannini be permitted to open a bank in Santa Maria. What Giannini wanted was a branch of the Bank of Italy, but he was quite happy to accept a compromise. As a result McIntosh issued a charter for the Commercial National Bank of Santa Maria, 60 per cent of whose shares were owned by the Stockholders Auxiliary and 40 per cent by local citizens. The Commercial opened for business in May, 1926. Thus did the comptroller dispose of the situation in the town that had provided the independent bankers with a war cry.[10]

When the visiting examiners had done with Santa Maria, Mr. Giannini invited them to look into all his banks, and they did. "From what I can learn," the banker wrote to one of his associates,

they are extremely pleased with the manner in which we conduct our business. Many of them were under the impression that we were running a rather sloppy institution, but they have come to the realization that there are very few institutions in the country that can compare with us as to . . . general A No. 1 condition.[11]

What the examiners learned was of interest to Comptroller McIntosh and to Chief Examiner John W. Pole, likewise a person of influence in the Federal Reserve organization. From that time on McIntosh was firm in the opinion that the best thing he could do for the national banking system on the Coast would be to get the biggest bank in California into it. Giannini said he would come in if he could merge his four branch systems and retain all the branches as a national bank. This last would, of course, depend on the ultimate form in which the McFadden bill was enacted.

But Mr. McIntosh was all for the merger, believing it "for the best interests of the banking community of California." One desirable result would be the elimination of the chain banking system that Giannini had found it necessary to resort to. The comptroller was no champion of chain banking. Moreover, by putting all Mr. Giannini's ramified banking "under one roof," the authorities would henceforth have less difficulty in controlling the San Franciscan. Then to climax the consolidation of this big bank with nationalization—naturally that would be for the best interests of the national system. Unlike Superintendent Johnson, the comptroller "felt he was justified in co-operating" with Giannini in rounding out his expansion program. Very candidly McIntosh, Deputy Collins and Chief Examiner Pole discussed questions of ways and means with the banker and his representatives in Washington.[12]

The Santa Maria procedure set the pattern under which Mr. Giannini was permitted to carry out his banking ambitions in northern California. With national charters he opened new banks in Oakland, Alameda and San Leandro. Unfortunately, the charters for five more potential candidates for the Bank of Italy's branch system—and incidentally for the national system—had to be held up because of the opposition of local unit bankers.

In southern California the Commercial National received eleven additional offices and the promise of ten more. If all the offices opened at once McIntosh was "afraid Sartori and his crowd would raise h——."[13]

At this juncture that was the last thing the comptroller desired. A new controversy might bring to light the Bank of Italy's consolidation plans and lose him the support of Giannini's southern competitors who were backing McIntosh's demands for revisions in the McFadden bill. Mr. McIntosh particularly wanted these revisions. They would be the means of bringing to the national banks the relief they so badly needed. Moreover, they provided inducements for the Bank of Italy to nationalize.

Comptroller McIntosh was fortunate to have the support also of Senator Carter Glass. At the start they agreed that the goal was a banking act which should make operations under the national system's regulations altogether as attractive as under state charter. It is more than likely that, as one public servant to another, McIntosh conferred with Glass before he started "co-operating" with Mr. Giannini. In any event, throughout the many debates over the McFadden bill, the senator from Virginia displayed an intimate and up-to-date knowledge of the benefits California had derived from branch banking. This is not to say that Glass's support was won by undue influence. During his lengthy public career, Carter Glass possessed a degree of independence hardly equaled in his generation. If he favored a measure it was because he believed it good for the country, regardless of whom it might incidentally help or hinder.

Senator Glass did not believe the Hull amendments would be good for the bankers. Accordingly he discarded them once again on the McFadden bill's third appearance in the Senate Banking and Currency Committee. More important to the comptroller, the senator succeeded in changing the bill's branch banking sections so as to permit national or state member banks to keep any branch or branches they had in operation on the date the bill became law. This revision also applied to state banks joining the Federal Reserve or the national system.

Senator George Wharton Pepper, Republican of Pennsylvania and committee chairman, took the revised bill to the floor. The most telling speech was made by Glass. In May, 1926, the bill was passed and, to iron out differences between it and the House measure, was sent to a conference committee of Senate and House members. Giannini wired his congratulations to Mr. McIntosh:

YOU HAVE WON YOUR FIGHT. YOU HAVE OUR HEARTFELT GRATITUDE AS I AM SURE YOU WILL IN TIME HAVE THE GRATITUDE OF ALL THE BROAD PROGRESSIVE BANKERS OF THE COUNTRY. . . . LET US HOPE THAT THE CONFERENCE COMMITTEE WILL ADOPT THE SENATE BILL, IN WHICH EVENT I PREDICT THE NATIONAL

SYSTEM WILL FIND ITS BANKING RESOURCES INCREASED BY AT LEAST COUPLE
OF BILLION DOLLARS, HALF OF WHICH I BELIEVE WILL COME FROM CALIFORNIA
STATE BANKS ENTERING THE SYSTEM. MORE POWER TO YOU.[14]

The conference could not agree, however, and the bill died at the
end of the session a little later.

Nevertheless, a change in the atmosphere surrounding our banking problems was discernible—not in Washington alone, but elsewhere in the country. The antibranch crusade had passed its zenith.
Figures on failures suggested that something was powerfully wrong
with the banking system of the richest nation on earth. During
1926, 967 banks had folded, and the number of failures since 1921
was 3,876. None of these institutions had been branch banks, though
technically 29 of them were so classified. These 29 banks had operated 54 branches altogether, or less than two apiece. That was not
branch banking as A. P. Giannini understood the term. As an indication of how things were going, at the American Bankers Association convention in October 1926 the McFadden bill was reconsidered. This time the delegates knew what was before them and
there was plenty of debate. The vote was 413 to 268 in favor of the
bill, minus the Hull amendments.

When Congress reassembled in December, 1926, Representative
McFadden once more introduced his bill—but without the Hull
amendments and with other alterations favored by Senator Glass.
On January 24 the congressman himself telegraphed Mr. Giannini
that his bill "PASSED HOUSE JUST NOW EXACTLY AS I WANTED IT. BILL
NOW GOES SENATE FOR FINAL ACTION."[15]

4

By the time California's Governor-elect Young took office in
January, 1927, the doubts Mr. Bacigalupi held about the incoming
administration's attitude toward the Giannini banking program had
deepened considerably. In the period between his election and inauguration, Mr. Young had kept disturbingly silent on the subject.
Particularly, there was no intimation of his choice of a successor to
Superintendent Johnson. From the activity at No. 1 Powell, it was
generally assumed that the governor's attitude would be friendly
and financial circles buzzed with rumors. Although Mr. Giannini
discreetly declined to comment, newspapers asserted that his ambi-

tion was to bring all his California banks under the main tent—
the Bank of Italy. Better kept, however, was the secret that Giannini
would have Comptroller McIntosh's approval of this arrangement,
and that the greater Bank of Italy would emerge as a national
bank.[16]

With the way prepared for the series of consolidations required
to bring this about, Giannini launched a whirlwind bank-buying
campaign in order to have more to consolidate. Before the month
of January was half over, he bought, through Bancitaly, twenty-
eight institutions with resources of $81,000,000. One was a branch
system—G. A. Davidson's Southern Trust and Commerce of San
Diego, with nine offices extending from La Jolla on the Coast to
the Imperial Valley. Other old and well-known institutions that
changed hands were the French-American and the Italian-American banks of San Francisco.

Governor Young had been in office nearly three weeks when he
announced the appointment of Will C. Wood to be superintendent
of banks. The popular and progressive educator having resigned as
head of California's school system, the governor believed Wood's
reputation for "honesty" and "rigidity of backbone" could be useful in restoring calm to the Banking Department. Also in the
appointee's favor, said the executive, was the fact that he "is
not a banker" and so not allied with "any faction in the banking
world."[17]

Before accepting the post, Wood received assurance that he would
be allowed to run the superintendent's office in a "free and un-
trammeled manner." Because everyone expected the Bank of Italy
to be rewarded for helping Young win the election, Wood asked
the governor point-blank if he intended to "recognize his assumed
obligation" to Giannini. The governor replied that he "considered
himself under obligations to no one." Furthermore, he doubted
"whether the support of the Bank of Italy had helped him more
than it had harmed him."

"It cut both ways," said Young.

The new superintendent hurried to San Francisco to begin his
duties. On his second day, among the earliest callers were President
Bacigalupi and Vice-President W. R. Williams bearing an application for the merger of the Bank of America of Los Angeles with
the Liberty Bank and "about sixty sales and purchase agreements."

The bankers gave notice that, if the merger went through, additional permits would be submitted.

"I was thunderstruck!" Wood later recalled.

The superintendent said he would refer the merger to his legal division for an opinion before making his decision. He suggested that the Bank of Italy use the time meanwhile to get together applications for permits for all the branches to be requested. Though the conference was "a cordial one," Wood thought the applicants appeared disappointed that the merger was not approved then and there.

Nevertheless, the bankers promptly carried out the superintendent's instructions. Next morning Williams returned with applications for thirty-eight *de novo* branches in Los Angeles. Nor was this all. Additional applications, covering other cities and towns, would be filed as soon as they could be prepared. It was evident, the superintendent noted, "that the Bank of Italy [*sic*] would not be modest in its requests."

On succeeding days representatives of the bank appeared urging haste because of the imminent passage of the McFadden bill. If the new branches were not operating before the bill became law, then they would not be eligible as branches in the ultimate consolidation with the B. of I. On the fourth day Vice-President Williams arrived "visibly agitated." The word from Washington was that the voting would start at any moment. Not until the sixth day, however, did Wood's counsel advise that the decision was entirely up to the superintendent's "discretion." Reviewing the record the superintendent could find no precedent for refusal. "Since 1909 when the Bank Act was enacted, every application for merger has been granted." Wood had a talk with his chief bank examiner, John McNaub. If the merger application was denied, McNaub said, Americommercial could run all the banks involved as independent units. In other words—chain banking. The superintendent regarded chain banking as "dangerous and unsatisfactory."[18]

Accordingly, on January 26, after a week in office, Superintendent Wood formally approved the merger of all four "outside" Giannini banking systems—Liberty of San Francisco, Bank of America of Los Angeles, Commercial National of Los Angeles and the newly purchased Southern Trust of San Diego. The name taken by the consolidated institution was Liberty Bank of America. Also brought in as branches were 61 "independent" banks owned by the Bancitaly or the Americommercial corporations. In all, the new Liberty Bank of America began its short life with 136 branches scattered through the state. Resources were above $200,000,000.

In his announcement to the newspapers, Superintendent Wood declared that the merger would serve the "public convenience and advantage." Moreover, he pointed out that such mergers were in keeping with the policy of his predecessor; that within the preceding eleven months seven similar mergers had been approved in California; and that the only application not acted on favorably had been Giannini's. One of the mergers referred to was that of Drum's Mercantile Trust and the American National Bank of San Francisco. Under the title of the American Trust Company this institution, with Drum at the helm, remained Giannini's chief competitor in the north.[19]

Two weeks after the four-way Giannini merger Superintendent Wood abrogated the *de novo* rule as "unsound and discriminating," and awarded the Liberty Bank of America 19 *de novo* branches. (Vice-President Williams had applied for 115 *de novo* permits; Wood's were only for Los Angeles and Alameda where investigation showed that "Giannini had been discriminated against.")[20]

The Bank of Italy meantime was quietly making ready to absorb the Liberty. Superintendent Wood had given his "verbal" sanction to the move. It was planned to withhold public announcement until the Federal Reserve Board had acted on the matter. The board did not care to act until the McFadden bill was safely through the Senate. Until then, the Bank of Italy–Liberty merger was to remain a secret, lest the news alienate some of the bill's supporters.[21]

Largely through Comptroller McIntosh's exertions, the McFadden bill, notwithstanding its greatly modified antibranch sections, was now enjoying the support of the California League of Independent Bankers. Of particular appeal to its membership were the sections broadening the powers of national banks. The bill would permit them to make real estate loans for a period of five years instead of only one year; they might exceed their legal lending limit on individual agricultural loans; they could add savings departments and the lucrative safe deposit business; and they would have perpetual charters instead of ninety-nine-year charters which hampered their administration of long-term trusts.

These provisions are the core of the McFadden Act. As a state-chartered institution, the Bank of Italy had reaped a rich harvest from the same privileges. Take away one of them and the bank would have been handicapped to continue in business. Therefore, these sections also had a particular appeal for Mr. Giannini, if he put the Bank of Italy into the national system. A further revision, with probably more appeal for the San Francisco banker than for the run of unit bankers, made it no longer imperative for a national bank to occupy new premises directly after purchase. To have continued this requirement would have worked an expensive hardship on a branch banker who bought and held property for future branches.

With the situation touch and go in the Senate, on February 15 Mr. Wood let the cat out of the bag in a newspaper interview. He said he approved the Bank of Italy–Liberty merger because the two banks "are now owned by the same people and are all but technically under the same management. Bankers are generally agreed that it is neither good banking policy nor good public policy to keep banks separate in operation when the ownership is practically identical."[22]

Bacigalupi wired Vice-President Leo Belden in Washington that Wood had spoken "without our knowledge or consent and I deplore it greatly."[23]

For two weeks the McFadden bill had been having rough sledding. Much of the debate centered upon the Bank of Italy. Opponents dragged in the old mare's nest of Santa Maria and gave accounts of the bank's part in the 1926 election that would have been outrageous if true. Carter Glass and one of the bill's adversaries, Senator Wheeler of Montana, had a fist fight. The immediate issue was a parliamentary one. The bill's supporters had a decisive majority; the problem was to bring about a roll call. The bill's foes threatened a filibuster, by which small minorities have from time to time blocked legislation in the Senate. California's independent bankers stood staunchly behind the bill's supporters. They had not been responsible for the resurrection of the Santa Maria fable. Egging on the Senate foes were the state's branch bankers south of the Ridge who suddenly woke up to the advantages the Bank of Italy would have after the bill's passage. Mr. Giannini *had* his branches all lined up and ready to be added to his statewide system—precisely under the provisions stipulated in the McFadden bill. Enactment would automatically stop the southerners' expansion excepting in their home cities, if they remained in the Federal Reserve. Their only hope then was to filibuster the legislation to death.

This frantic move was defeated by the imposition of a cloture on debate—the first time that had ever been done on a domestic issue. February 16 was the date set for a vote. News of Wood's announcement reached Washington the night before. It made little difference. The bill was enacted, seventy-one to seventeen.

Though the premature Wood announcement had had no effect on the Senate situation, it upset Comptroller McIntosh, who had spent a nerve-racking winter. According to Belden, the comptroller felt that "A. P. has not been playing the game with him and has been using him to pull his chestnuts out of the fire"—in other words that Giannini was trying to force McIntosh's hand. Now, this was not true. Far from inspiring Wood's announcement, Giannini had been greatly disturbed by it. All along Giannini had appreciated McIntosh's difficult position, and on one occasion had reminded Bacigalupi of it in these words: "McIntosh has simply been between the devil and the deep sea." With the climax of his whole operation at hand, Giannini would hardly have picked this moment to ruffle the temper of the most influential member of the Federal Reserve Board.[24]

So it was that the Wood announcement gave everyone an anxious time on February 17, the day following the passage of the McFadden bill. McIntosh demanded a promise that the Bancitaly Corporation should not own over 25 per cent of the capital stock of the Bank of Italy, or of any independent bank in California, during the next five years, except for periods of thirty days or less. The demand was in keeping with the comptroller's desire to discourage chain banking. After some hours of hesitation, Giannini agreed. On the day following, February 18, 1927, the Federal Reserve approved the consolidation of the Bank of Italy and the Liberty Bank of America. That was Friday. Over the week end signs on the buildings were changed and on Monday morning, February 21, the 175 Liberty branches opened as components of the Bank of Italy. On February 25 President Coolidge signed the McFadden Act.[25]

5

In this way the Bank of Italy became the third largest bank in the United States. Only the National City Bank and the Chase National, both of New York, surpassed it in resources, which stood at $675,-000,000. Deposits were $616,000,000, and the number of depositors over a million.

With 276 branches in 199 localities, Giannini had outstripped once and for all his California competitors. The Pacific-Southwest of Los Angeles was second with 99 branches and the American Trust of San Francisco third, with 95. Then came the three other Los Angeles systems: the Security Trust with 50 branches; the California Bank with 46; and the Citizens with 25.

"SOME BANK!" Bacigalupi jubilantly telegraphed Leo Belden in Washington.[26]

The final step in the grand program, the nationalization of the Bank of Italy, came as an anticlimax that attracted little more than passing notice. Arrangements were completed with the comptroller and the Federal Reserve Board on the day President Coolidge signed the McFadden Act. The change became effective March 1, when the institution at No. 1 Powell Street took the name of the Bank of Italy National Trust and Savings Association.

A feature of the situation that Giannini did not like was the rise in the prices of Bank of Italy and Bancitaly stock, despite all that he and his circle could do to prevent it. The "Great Bull Market," destined to end so abruptly in the fall of 1929, was under way. The gambling craze spread like a fire. People who had never before bought or sold a share of stock were enticed by the tales that they heard of quick and handsome profits. With almost every stock going up regardless of worth or prospects, it was asking too much of a public that had tasted the sweets of easy money to ignore the achievements of A. P. Giannini.

In the case of Bancitaly, the measures indicated earlier served to hold the stock steady during all but the closing days of 1926. Quoted at 340 in January of that year, it sold at 85 on the first of December. As there had been a four-for-one split, the 85 for the new shares just equaled the 340 for the old. Then the rise started, and on March 1 Bancitaly shares sold for 112. The climb of the Bank of Italy shares was steeper. Opening at 449 it had risen during 1926 to 530. On the day of nationalization, March 1, 1927, it sold for 672.

The merger of two village banks involves changes of personnel, procedure, records and so on. Man being a creature of habit, it takes a little while for the consolidated institution to shake down and run smoothly. By this time A. P. Giannini had had more experience starting and merging banks than anyone else in the history of the business. The multiple consolidations that had resulted in the Bank of Italy National Trust and Savings Association represented the most gigantic undertaking of that kind America has ever seen, before or since. Consequently a few weeks were needed to get everything going as it should. This meant day and night work. When it was far enough along Mr. Giannini sailed for Europe.

As soon as they could be spared from their duties, President Bacigalupi invited more than nine hundred officers and employees of the bank to San Francisco for a victory dinner in the Palm Court of the Palace Hotel. The speakers' table presented an array of the old and the new; pioneers of the great adventure in branch banking like Boss Scatena, Jim Bacigalupi, W. E. Blauer and the Hale brothers; younger veterans like A. J. Mount, L. M. MacDonald, H. C. Capwell and Mario Giannini; and the newcomers such as Orra E. Monnette, G. A. Davidson and H. C. Carr.

Bacigalupi had a word for the new people in the branches. It was up to them, he said, to carry A. P. Giannini's concepts of banking to their home towns: "To be human, to be democratic, to be cosmopolitan, to be progressive, to be helpful, and to be different."

"The Bank of Italy," he continued,

is essentially a bank of the people; operated only as a bank, for the exclusive benefit of all of its stockholders—about 15,000 Californians, representative of every race, religious creed, and political belief, and scattered over the entire state. Nor is this scattered and widespread ownership, a fortuitous coincidence or a mere sham, for the overwhelming control is designedly possessed by those stockholders who form no part of the official family of the institution and who tomorrow—should they become convinced that this great and powerful instrumentality is being perverted to the selfish purposes of one, a few, or even of many, within its administration—are fully capable of rectifying the situation by ousting the old and installing a new regime. . . .

Sound human progress comes in general and sweeping waves of public sentiment. At first the wave is almost indiscernible save to those of keener perception and of stouter heart, but once it gathers volume and momentum, the frenzied cries and feeble efforts of the stand-patters are as chaff in the hurricane, before its irresistible advance. This is the age in our country of quality, economy and service. People want the best, as cheaply and as easily as possible. It is the day of quantity production, of rapid turnovers, of concentration and economy in overhead. It is the hour of specialization and of big capitalization. This spells but two things in business—mergers and branches. Let us have fewer but stronger and more helpful banks, and the nation will fare immeasurably better than has been its doleful banking experience in many of its sections . . . during the past few years.[27]

Mr. Bacigalupi could have said more than that. He could have pointed out, as had John S. Drum on an earlier occasion, that everything Giannini had accomplished was done in the face of steadfast and skillful opposition. Since 1920, at every turn he had had to fight to keep alive his idea of banking. His victory had been more than a victory for the Bank of Italy. A. P. Giannini and his allies had changed the course of banking in the United States, and changed it for the better.

It may be helpful to indicate again just who Mr. Giannini's allies were.

Any bank with $616,000,000 on deposit should have a number of persons well disposed toward it. The strength of the Bank of Italy was not so much in its dollar assets as in the attitude of the million people who had put those dollars there, and who borrowed and did other business with the bank every day. These people were not experts on banking; but they were for Giannini because of what his bank had done for them. Skeptic after skeptic had found that out. Everywhere in California they had found the same brand of personal loyalty that was evident in North Beach when the Bank of Italy was a little neighborhood institution in the days of the San Francisco fire. Without that loyalty it is difficult to see how Giannini, for all his talent, could have triumphed in the seven-year fight for branch banking.

Nor was this the only indispensable support that Mr. Giannini enjoyed. He had the help of Senator Carter Glass of Virginia, Senator George Wharton Pepper of Pennsylvania, Comptroller of the Currency Joseph W. McIntosh, Deputy Comptroller Charles W. Collins,

Chief Examiner (in 1928 to become comptroller) John W. Pole, Representative Louis T. McFadden and a majority of the Federal Reserve Board. These men *were* banking experts. They beat down the barrier of antibranch sentiment sufficiently to kill the Hull amendments and Section 9. That helped the Bank of Italy, but it also helped all national banks. McIntosh and his colleagues maneuvered with Superintendent Wood—another essential supporter—to give Giannini his branches before the McFadden Act became operative by presidential approval. For this they were roundly criticized in antibranch quarters. Only the unassailable probity of the officials themselves and the nature of their motives saved them from less partisan censure.

A Glance at the Inside of No. 1 Powell

THE BANK OF ITALY National Trust and Savings Association had come a long way since the days of its infancy in San Francisco's North Beach. The year-end statement for 1927 showed deposits of $645,002,139 distributed among 1,083,303 accounts. Of these, 347,504 were checking and 745,799 were savings accounts. The average balance in the checking accounts was $586.90; in savings accounts, $596.53. The first year-end statement of the Bank of Italy, submitted for 1904 after two and a half months of operation, showed $109,413 on deposit in about three hundred accounts, mostly savings because the "baby bank" had to educate depositors in the mysteries of check writing.

In 1927 the average depositor, besides having more in his balance than his predecessor of 1904, lived in a better home, wore better clothes, farmed better, marketed his crops more profitably, and his children remained longer in school. With this progress the Giannini method of banking had something to do. In 1927 one of every five Californians of all ages was a depositor in the Bank of Italy N. T. & S. A. No other banking institution in the United States had even remotely approached this density of patronage—a record to be surpassed only by the Bank of Italy itself, and by its successor the Bank of America N. T. & S. A. The well-being of the State of California and of the Bank of Italy had become synonymous.

The dark prophecies made by the foes of branch banking in the long struggle just closed were not confirmed by the experience of clients of the Bank of Italy. If the depositors or borrowers considered themselves writhing in the tentacles of an octopus they gave no evidence of it. One could hear stories, of course. Faint echoes of the Santa Maria "atrocity" were floating about in 1947, when the present writers began work on this history. At that late date one could still hear that A. P. Giannini's indifference to personal wealth was a fake; that he highjacked unit bankers into selling their institutions and ground down competitors who held out against him.

In 1927 the average patron of the Bank of Italy did business with a branch whose architecture, inside and out, is repeated in many California towns, resulting in a simple square or oblong building with few embellishments. Business in the branches grew so rapidly that usually the banking quarters acquired by purchase had to be replaced or enlarged within a few years. The interior pattern of the branches seldom varies—tellers' cages strung along the length of one wall and almost the length of the wall opposite. Where cages leave off begins the open space occupied by the desks of the branch manager, other executives and secretaries. Invariably this space is at the entrance to the branch. Anyone can lean over the low railing separating the officers from the lobby—always as wide as possible—and say what he has come to say without the formality of first telling a secretary the purpose of his visit. Usually the only private rooms are for advisory board meetings and vaults.

It was Giannini's idea that the "marble palace" type of bank made people timid about entering. Heavy bronze grills over tellers' windows were unfriendly. He aimed at keeping his banking premises simple and cordial. But he varied them with the neighborhood. Montgomery Street, for instance, in the heart of great wealth, received a more elaborate and expensive building than the branch in a strictly working class neighborhood.[1]

At the end of 1927 the average of deposits in a Bank of Italy branch was $2,231,844. In the larger cities deposits might amount to several times that sum, and in the remote small towns a tenth of it. So, what the average depositor saw was in many ways a little bank. Familiar faces were behind the tellers' windows and at the manager's desk. Nearly everyone knew a neighbor who owned a few shares of Bank of Italy stock. Men of local prominence served on the advisory boards. The average patron's loyalty was to the branch he did business with. Beyond that his conception of the Bank of Italy might be rather hazy. Branch personnel shared this local pride—to such an extent that, on occasions, the head office in San Francisco had to intervene to stop overzealous competition among branches themselves.

All this was an extension of the personality of A. P. Giannini, who who was first of all an approachable man, interested in people low and high. He surrounded himself with none of the trappings of a great and powerful financier. At No. 1 Powell or at Seventh and Olive in Los Angeles he had no private office, nor, at that time, a private secretary, though some of the bank officers whose secretaries he was always borrowing probably wished he had.

By and large, what Giannini had created was a decentralized country bank—a neighborhood bank, as it would be called in a city. In most ways the Bank of Italy differed from the National City and the Chase National of New York, the only banks that were larger, as day from night.

At the end of 1927 the bank was capitalized at $37,500,000. Undivided profits and surplus brought the total of capital funds to $63,-000,000. In 1920 the capital was $9,000,000. Something was added nearly every year thereafter. The increases were necessary to care for branch expansion, mainly. All new issues of shares, not subscribed for by old stockholders, were disposed of through the facilities of the bank, without the payment of brokerage fees or commissions. In 1922 an issue of $10,000,000 was floated, half of which went to capital and the rest to surplus and to the Stockholders Auxiliary. Giannini was in Europe, to show John Perrin that the bank was no one-man institution. The postwar slump was not over and money was tight. Bacigalupi managed to sell the 50,000 new shares at 200. It was quite a feat. Subsequent issues went easily. In order to distribute the bank's ownership more widely, in 1927 individual shares were split four for one, making 1,500,000 outstanding as against 90,-000 at the close of 1920.

2

It is hard to get used to the fact that A. P. Giannini's title was simply that of director. Besides him, Chairman Scatena and Vice-President Armando Pedrini were the sole remaining members of the inner circle who had seen the Bank of Italy open its doors in 1904. Among other things Pedrini had charge of the Italian department—of which more later.

James J. Fagan had relinquished his office as vice-president, and, though rarely present at meetings, he remained on the board at Giannini's insistence until the early part of 1928. The little Irishman's health was failing, and the affairs of the Crocker bank were

about all he had strength for. Yet sometimes when Giannini was in
a quandary he would seek out "Giacoma," who had probably disagreed with A. P. more often than had any other associate in his
banking career. Other veteran directors were Dr. G. E. Caglieri,
Charley Grondona, Dr. L. D. Bacigalupi (no kin of the bank's president) and James and Samuel B. Fugazi. When A. H. (Doc) Giannini left the board to run the East River National Bank in New
York his place was taken by the youngest of the three brothers,
George Giannini, who was president of L. Scatena & Company.

Until the advisory committee was established in 1926 the ranking
committees of the board were the executive and the finance committees. The only director serving on both of them was Prentis Cobb
Hale, with whom Giannini came in contact when he bought the first
out-of-town bank in San Jose. His family being in the branch department store business, Hale saw at once the virtues of branch banking. In the early days of the Bank of Italy's expansion Hale and
Giannini made a matchless bank-buying team. The white-haired and
distinguished-looking merchant was a Yankee trader from away
back. He had the additional advantages of being a Protestant, a Mason and the possessor of an Anglo-Saxon name. In the early days,
and later, Hale won over groups among whom Giannini's name and
religion were handicaps.

While the "outside" systems were being united into the Liberty
Bank of America and preparations were being made for the absorption of that institution by the Bank of Italy, the membership of the
board was increased to thirty-six and then to fifty. Among the new
directors were Orra E. Monette of the Bank of America of Los Angeles; W. A. Bonynge, president of the Commercial Trust of Los
Angeles (after his death to be succeeded by his son of the same
name); G. A. Davidson of the Southern Trust of San Diego; Marshal Hale, president of the Liberty Bank of San Francisco; Charles C.
Chapman of Los Angeles, sometimes called the orange king; Eustace Cullinan, the attorney; Mrs. Giannini's brother, Clarence Cuneo;
M. E. Fontana, of the Fontana Products Company; Robert D. Rossi,
of Italian Swiss Colony wine; A. E. Sbarboro, son of the founder of
the Italian-American Bank of North Beach in San Francisco, which
Bancitaly acquired in 1927; Myer Siegel, Los Angeles department
store executive.

These men made a large and representative board. To shape the general policy of the bank between board meetings, the advisory committee was created. Giannini resigned as chairman of the executive committee to head the advisory committee. The other members were Lorenzo Scatena, P. C. and Marshal Hale, R. E. Miller, president of the Owl Drug Company of San Francisco, and Charles C. Chapman.

In an earlier chapter we spoke of the controversy between Superintendent Stern and the Bank of Italy over the supervision of branches, with particular reference to the accounting and auditing system by which the head office in San Francisco kept track of what was going on. As the bank grew, that problem became more complicated. It was a subject of much discussion between the bank and the succeeding superintendents, Dodge and Johnson. Though W. R. Williams, on whom the burden of the problem fell as cashier, was inclined at times to think the superintendents captious in their criticism, on the whole it served a good end.

Under Williams was a young auditor named George O. Bordwell, who had helped to set up the auditing and accounting system of the Federal Reserve Bank of San Francisco. Bordwell and E. C. Aldwell, an assistant secretary of the bank, took a trip to Canada to study branch accounting methods. They brought back a lot of useful data. As a result the Bank of Italy instituted a more effective check on daily branch balances and also on loans. Bordwell had found the Canadians' daily statements "a marvel of simplicity." However, because of legal reserve requirements, which entered a more complex phase when the bank joined the Federal Reserve in 1919, the Bank of Italy's statements had to carry more detail.

Another thing Bordwell found in Canada was a rulebook for the guidance of branch managers. He started to compile one. "It takes years to make a rulebook," said Bordwell. It is, in fact, a work that is never finished. Mario Giannini, who was always interested in administrative improvements, later revised the rulebook and titled it the *Standard Practice Manual*. Today the *Manual* is nearly a foot thick, but fortunately it has a good index.

Rather early in its branch banking career Canadians began to find employment with the Bank of Italy. During the twenties there was a fairly heavy immigration from the Dominion. "The Canadian Bank of Italy," they called themselves. At first the newcomers were a little shocked by the air of breezy informality that characterized

Mr. Giannini's bank. But they soon caught on. Canadian bankers, for all they had to teach the Bank of Italy, had not learned the knack of making *local institutions* of their branches.[2]

3

The trust department was the first of the Bank of Italy's fifteen (in 1927) departments to divide itself for administrative purposes into northern and southern jurisdictions. This was in 1924. Williams, by then a vice-president, went to Los Angeles to manage the southern division. Inaugurated by Bacigalupi in 1917 and further developed by Louis Ferrari, who became trust attorney in 1918, the department gained importance under W. J. Kieferdorf.

A former schoolteacher, Kieferdorf introduced an educational program for branch employees and patrons alike. Employees were instructed in the problems, legal and practical, that arise in the making of wills, the investment of legacy funds, the service as trustee or escrow agent and so on. After bank employees had been urged to make their wills, patrons were solicited to take advantage of the bank's facilities in that particular. A contest was started among the branches, which were rated on the basis of "ratio of wills to number of depositors." Thus was popularized the familiar line of services long offered by trust companies, but never before carried to the mass of the people.

From the beginning Giannini had belived that his bank should solicit patronage, as other business concerns did. In the early days, and later when there was a hard nut to crack like the small-home-loan campaign in Los Angeles in 1913, Mr. Giannini himself took to the pavements as a solicitor. Out of this activity grew the business extension department, headed by Vice-President W. W. Douglas who had survived an error of judgment in his young days with the bank. As manager of the Market Street branch Douglas had loaned $10,000 to an automobile firm in which he was interested. The company went into receivership, and, though Douglas made good its indebtedness to the bank, his resignation was requested. The Giannini rule—"no entangling alliances outside the bank"—had been violated. A year later Mr. Giannini took Douglas back at a quarter his previous salary, and he worked up from there.

Douglas spread his people all over California. His department took over the work among the foreign colonies, Italians excepted. That remained the pride of Armando Pedrini. An industrial-savings program was started. As with school savings, the services of the bank were taken to the depositors. On "bank days" field workers made collections in factories, mining camps, lumber camps, and among the migratory workers who move through the agricultural valleys the year round. Industrial savings were introduced among seamen by solicitors who boarded the ships. The results modify a tradition of centuries about the improvidence of mariners. Their accounts proved among the most stable on the bank's books.[3]

The business extension department made a specialty of helping people to go into business. If a man wanted to start a hair net factory the bank would look into the hair net situation thoroughly. Before the borrower started to manufacture, the bank would have a pretty good idea of the pitfalls he should avoid, and would know, often within a few hundred dollars, the return he could expect on his investment in the first year.

In 1927, following the consolidation, the administrative machinery of the entire bank was reorganized. Northern and southern divisions were created, the latter with headquarters at Los Angeles. While the board of directors functioned for the bank as a whole, the two divisions were placed under boards of management made up of all senior officers and heads of departments within the respective divisions. The state was further divided into twenty-one districts, each under an officer, usually a vice-president, residing in that district. In addition, three regional boards were established—in Los Angeles, in the East Bay Area with headquarters at Oakland, and in San Diego. Members were chosen from the advisory boards of the branches of those areas.

Mario Giannini became chairman of the board of management of the northern division, and Lloyd M. MacDonald head of the southern division. In and out of the Bank of Italy, MacDonald's career had been an active one. Resigning as a branch manager in Canada, he went to Livermore, California, for his health and became president of a bank that in 1917 was bought by Giannini. Four years later he was a vice-president of the Bank of Italy. When Americommercial bought the Commercial National of Los Angeles, MacDonald went there as executive vice-president. His next post was chair-

man of the Bank of America of Los Angeles. After the grand consolidation he was back with the B. of I.

Advisory boards which formed a part of every branch in the system excepting city branches in San Francisco continued to play an
important role. The total membership of these boards was seventeen
hundred. One of the duties of each of the twenty-one district officers
was to attend every advisory board meeting in his territory. For a
time boards in the northern division came under the head-office supervision of Vice-President Harry C. Carr, a newcomer to No. 1
Powell Street. A former president of the California Bankers Association and once a leading light in the League of Independent Bankers,
Carr had joined the Bank of Italy when Giannini purchased the
bank in Porterville which Carr had built up.

Carr's work at No. 1 Powell was essentially that of a supervisor
of country branches. He set out early in his career there to eliminate
the antagonism that had grown up between the branch managers
and the bank's traveling inspectors. The visits of the inspectors were
unannounced. They went into all things a federal bank examiner
would go into and more, for it was their duty to see that the regulations of the Bank of Italy as well as those of the government were
observed. Mr. Carr called an inspector's lot "trying at best." He
taught them to approach branch managers in a spirit of helpfulness
rather than of faultfinding. It was a delicate achievement in personal
relations.[4]

Even this quick sketch of the interior of the bank would be incomplete without mention of Frank Risso who, in 1927, had the title
of assistant vice-president, but was presently to become the V.P. in
charge of personnel. Frank Risso never worked for anyone except
the Bank of Italy and its successor the Bank of America. He began
as a messenger and in the early days of motorcars he was Mr. Giannini's chauffeur. In that era a chauffeur had to be a specialist in road-
side repairs. Frank has some classic stories about breakdowns in the
middle of the night and of nowhere. Since Giannini used to do a
good deal of his thinking at night, a breakdown might not incon-
venience him too much.

At times when Frank had a chance to sleep in a bed, his boss
would rout him out and take him on a long country walk while
wrestling with a bank problem. Frank was doing some thinking of

his own about this time and suggested that the bank issue its own travelers' checks. Giannini adopted the idea and rewarded Frank with a bonus of one dollar. A. P. treated Risso about as he treated his sons, which included making sure that the young men did not have any money to throw away. The travel check idea has proved one of the bank's profitable sidelines.[5]

4

The Bank of Italy's staff of three salaried employees in 1904 had increased to 4,300 in 1927. Eighteen hundred of those came in with the Liberty merger. As far back as 1923, however, Mr. Giannini was turning over in his mind an idea for liberalizing the extracompensation plan for the bank's working force. "It is my wish to leave the control of the bank in the hands of its employees," he told the *Coast Banker*. The following year the new plan was announced. All the features of the old program, such as life insurance and pensions, were retained. In addition provision was made for the acquisition of bank stock. These benefits were open to all employees and to all officers, with the exception of A. P. Giannini.

Under the new arrangement the bank annually set aside 40 per cent of its net earnings as a gift to its workers. How much an individual received depended on his own thrift. What he saved from his salary toward the purchasing of stock the bank matched with a like amount, plus additional contributions computed on the basis of length of service, the employee's pay, and whether he was single or married.

The object was to reward officers and employees for "refraining from all outside interests," and attending "solely to the business of banking." Moreover, the directors held the plan to be a "sound economic move."

"The Plan," read the minutes of their meeting,

is put forward not as profit-sharing but rather as a plan of employee compensation—over and above normal salaries—to be used by employees in acquiring an ever-increasing share in the ownership and control of the Bank. Employees are thus put in a position to capitalize their efforts in behalf of the Bank and build themselves up to a position it would otherwise be impossible for them to attain. That in working out this plan stockholders would be benefited has been frankly admitted. That is only fair.

And, that the stock they acquire shall have an increasing value is as important to the employee stockholder as to any other.

Funds contributed by the bank and by employees were turned over to the Bancitaly Corporation as trustee to be used for the purchase of the bank's stock which, in 1924, carried with it certain beneficial interests in the Stockholders Auxiliary Corporation. Voting power remained with the trustee for ten years, after which the employee was to receive a trust certificate. At the end of twenty years, the stock was to be delivered.[6]

By the close of 1925, the first year of the plan's operation, the employees' share of the profits of the bank and of the Auxiliary amounted to $891,723. After deductions of a little over $50,000 for the pension fund and insurance premiums, this was used, along with employees' contributions in the amount of $271,590, to purchase 3,083 shares of bank stock for 2,300 employees. At the end of 1927, after the consolidation, the bank paid in $900,258 and employees $256,797. By that time the trustee held for the employees and officers 39,617 shares, valued at $10,300,420. In July, 1928, when the plan was three and a half years old, the bank's personnel owned 44,682 shares or 2.23 per cent of the 2,000,000 outstanding.

5

The story of California has always been the story of newcomers. In 1921 immigrant foreigners and their children owned 35,000 of the state's 100,000 farms. At the doorsteps of the Swiss and Portuguese, one might place dairying; artichokes, lettuce and wine grapes at the Italians'; berries and rice at the Japanese'; apples, at the Slavonians'; and sheep, at the Basques'. Through the twenties, the Bank of Italy's history is inextricably woven around these rural North Beaches, whether on the land or in the small town.

In many instances these colonies had been ignored or overlooked by the local banker. The most obvious reason was the language barrier. Another was the ignorance, and timidity perhaps, of the settler about banks, and his fondness for the stocking, tin box and mattress. Then there was banking, itself. The needs of the foreign born, whether a citizen or not, were often dissimilar to those of the American. Not only his heart but his purse strings were open to the fatherland. Prosperous in his new home, he sent a flood of dollars to the old—money to bring the less fortunate over, to feed and clothe those who remained, or to liven up their holidays. Bank accounts on the "other side" were not uncommon among the immigrants. Such remittances, particularly after World War I, amounted to millions and millions in foreign exchange. Add to this, the periodic "going home," the travelers' checks, letters of credit, old-country currency, steamer tickets, etc., and there were many things a rural banker might not understand.

Cosmopolitan San Francisco thrived on it. Steamship lines, travel agencies, speculators in exchange including not a few unscrupulous operatives, drained off handsome profits from the country cousins. San Francisco also had its "foreign" banks that took care of their own: the San Francisco Bank, formerly German Savings and Loan Society; the Italian-American for the Swiss; the Bank of Canton for the Chinese; the Sumitomo Bank, Ltd., for the Japanese; the French-American Bank; the Portuguese-American; and so forth. Giannini competed with these banks on their own ground in San Francisco—in 1927 taking over the Italian-American and the French-American—and he did not stop there. To remote country districts he extended the type of banking facility needed by the foreign born, and, by organized solicitation, he made them aware of it.

At No. 1 Powell this multilingual activity was bunched together in what was called the country foreign department, which presently was split into separate departments—or divisions as they were later known—the Italian, Greek, Russian, Chinese, Slavonian, Portuguese, Spanish and Latin-American. All except the Italian department, with Armando Pedrini still in charge, eventually came under the wing of the business extension department.[7]

It was inevitable that the Italian department should dominate the scene. At first the crusade for new business was largely a Bay Area affair. Solicitors under Pedrini's disciple, Assistant Vice-President Robert Paganini, pounded the pavements and the highways. Paganini himself in a fifteen-months campaign among the "little fellows" —barbers, bakers, butchers, peddlers, janitors, marble cutters, scavengers—brought in more than eight hundred new accounts, ranging up to $20,000 and in all aggregating nearly $500,000. The news of a record catch by the Alaskan salmon fleet sent Solicitor F. P. Tommasini to the docks to meet the returning Italian fishermen. In ten days he got the Montgomery Street branch new deposits well over $65,000.[8]

By this time Pedrini was scattering his emissaries farther afield. Two years before the Bank of Italy had a branch in Monterey, Solicitor A. Ponzio was down there drumming up interest among the eight-hundred-odd Sicilians who fished for sardines out of that port. Banking was a fearful thing to the salt-bitten veterans. Ponzio got a promise here and there, a deposit or two, and little else. But he paved the way for the branch. Less than ten months after taking over the Valley Bank's Monterey office, the Bank of Italy enjoyed the patronage of most of the fishing folk and the tradesmen they dealt with.[9]

An advance guard also invaded the timberlands, the fir- and pine-fringed Mount Shasta region, dotted with the camps of Italian lumberjacks, loggers, mill hands and box makers. This was during the lively times of national prohibition. "Every family sells wine," one solicitor discovered, "and every cabin has its vat. The result is that an American laborer is always without money, and the Italian is always increasing his savings account." After a trip to the north, Solicitor Louis Perna reported: "Everyone was very glad to shake hands with some one from 'our big bank' and to have '*un banchista*' among them." The handshaking came easy but a branch was a different matter. Mill towns were company owned. Outside enterprises were frowned upon; and employees hesitated to cross the company by banking with an intruder. Gradually, however, a few deposits trickled in to the neighboring "free towns," such as Redding and Yreka, where Giannini had branches.[10]

6

In the San Joaquin Valley the story differs only in detail.

Take Kern County, for instance. Though Kern is not California's largest county, you could lose the State of Massachusetts in it. There the Bank of Italy had the luck to gain a large share of the Italian business by inheritance, through the purchase of the Ardizzi-Olcese Bank in Bakersfield in 1922. The president, L. V. Olcese, was one of the few country bankers who understood the banking needs of the immigrant. Italians swore by him and he had made headway among the Basques whose bands of sheep in Kern County aggregated

200,000 head. As manager of the East Bakersfield branch of the Bank of Italy, Mr. Olcese continued his work.

The Italian who lived in town worked on the railroad (Bakersfield is a division point for the Southern Pacific and the Santa Fe), or in the oil fields. But it was the soil that attracted most of them. Cheap land, abundant water and the Los Angeles market just over the Ridge led the biggest single group of Kern County Italians to dairying on the outskirts of town. Something over a hundred families—and bear in mind the usual size of Italian families—were familiar with the cow barn and the alfalfa field. Sixty-odd of these families became patrons of the East Bakersfield branch. They were good customers, prompt to pay interest and eager to build up their savings. Money going to the old country passed through the Bank of Italy. A few even had passbooks on the Banca d'America e d'Italia. Forty-three of the families were represented among the Bank of Italy's stockholders.[11]

The grain farmers were located in the foothills of the Ridge, thirty miles to the south. Of Tuscan stock, these immigrants—about sixty families—had caught the grain fever in World War I. Each had rented three or four sections from California's land empires, Miller & Lux, Inc., and the Kern County Land Company. (The latter was the largest landholder in the county, with nearly 400,000 acres, and a payroll, in 1925, of 400 hands.) After 1921 and the bust, the renters continued to gamble and were willing to pay dearly for credit. At an independent bank in Tehachapi they paid 10 to 12 per cent. For the few who pulled in their horns and had good security, the East Bakersfield branch made loans at 7 per cent.[12]

Moving northward in the San Joaquin Valley, the field men of Armando Pedrini had their ups and downs. With ease, nearly 85 per cent of the Italian population was converted at Hanford. Vineyardists and dairymen, whose wives and children spent their summers in the fruit packing sheds, each family had savings of around $1,000 and owned a share or two of stock. At near-by Visalia, new business came in much more slowly. For one reason, the Hyde institutions, taken over in 1921, had never catered to Italians, whereas a competitor, the First National Bank of Visalia, had a very useful citizen on its staff named Joe Barboni. Mr. Barboni later became Visalia's mayor. The First National also held 80 per cent of the Italian col-

REPORT
OF
Bank of Italy

(Incorporated *August 10* , *1904*)

Showing its Financial Condition at close of business *JAN 5 1905* , 190

The

Ant. Chichizola President.

Geo. G. Caglieri Cashier.

BALANCE SHEET.

RESOURCES	DOLLARS	CTS.	LIABILITIES	DOLLARS	CTS.
Bank Premises,			Capital Paid in Coin,	150 000	—
Real Estate taken for Debt,			Reserve Fund, $		
United States Bonds, $			Profit and Loss, and Contingent Fund, $		
Miscellaneous Bonds and Stocks, $	34446	25	Deposits—Individual, Subject to Check, $ 41318.08	41 318 08	
County Warrants, $			Deposits—Demand Certificates, $ 29122.50	29 122 50	
Loans on Real Estate,	160 450	—	Deposits—Time Certificates, $ 84208.80	84208 80	
Loans on Stocks, Bonds and Warrants,			Due Banks and Bankers,		
Loans on other Securities (Grain, etc.),	4000	—	Dividends Unpaid, $	10237 0	
Loans on Personal Security, 1570 4·35	15700		Bills Payable, $		
Overdrafts,		4 35	Other Liabilities, $		
Money on hand, $ 3730.49	3730 49		Commission $ 40		
Exchanges for Clearing House, $ 467.55			Certif. exs $ 3140	3180	
Checks and other Cash Items, $ Foreign Currency	467 55				
Due from Banks and Bankers,	77295 77		Interest receive since Jan 1st	203 50	
Furniture and Fixtures, $ 10 683.07	1068307		Special Deposit	100 2 60	
Expenses, Rent 120 Sundries 13.50	133 50				
Taxes, $					
Interest Paid, $					
Other Assets, $					
TOTAL RESOURCES, $	306 910 98		TOTAL LIABILITIES, $	306 910 98	

DETAILS

The amount of Capital Stock is $ *300.000* — ; amount subscribed is $ *300.000* ; amount paid in coin is $ *150.000*

The total number of Shares of Stock issued is *3.000* shares ; the amount paid on each share of stock is $ *50* —

The names of the Directors, and number of shares of stock held by each, are as follows :

Antonio Chichizola	60	Shares	*Louis Demartini*	100 Shares
A. P. Giannini	100	"	*G. B. Levaggi*	100 "
Geo. G. Caglieri	25	"	*L. Scatena*	100 "
Chas F. Grondona	80	"	*G. Jaccheri*	100 "
Jos F Cavagnaro	20	"	*G. Costa*	100 "
James F. Fagan	100			

Total number of shares held by the Directors is *885* Shares.

REAL ESTATE OWNED BY THE BANK AND TAKEN FOR DEBT. (EXCLUSIVE OF BANK PREMISES.)

COUNTY SITUATED IN	COST ON BOOKS	MARKET VALUE	COUNTY SITUATED IN	COST ON BOOKS	MARKET VALUE
		none			
TOTALS, $			GRAND TOTALS, $		

N. B.—Please state "Market Value" in each case as required.

The first formal report of the Bank of Italy to the Board of Bank Commissioners of California was made on January 5, 1905, two and a half months after the founding of the bank.

ony's mortgages. After the Pacific-Southwest took over the First National, a drift toward the Bank of Italy set in; but it was slow.[13]

While manager at Madera, Carl Wente had been a good salesman for the Bank of Italy. Ninety per cent of the three hundred Italians settled there, on twenty- to forty-acre vineyards, were depositors. Merced, thirty miles away, was another story. Over half of the Italians, about a hundred in number, were customers, but the remainder were bitterly antagonistic in the early twenties. The antagonism grew out of a three-cornered fight within the local tomato co-op, in which the Bank of Italy intervened, making it a four-cornered scrap. To protect itself against a $15,000 loan, the branch slapped a banker's lien on the co-op's deposits. Unity came quickly—with nearly all the growers against the Bank of Italy. Though the co-op collapsed, it took years for the rancor to wear off and accounts to come back to the branch.[14]

Lying north another thirty miles on the Tuolumne River is Modesto, seat of rich, farming Stanislaus County. The branch had a difficult time both bringing in and holding the Italian vineyardists and dairymen. As in Visalia, the predecessor bank had taken little interest in foreigners. This frame of mind the branch inherited, temporarily bringing about a state of affairs that was far from the ideal Mr. Giannini held for his branches. Farmers complained that "little trust or cordiality" was shown by the management. "We know no one in your bank," a farmer told Solicitor Louis Valperga. It was not difficult to determine why nearly two-thirds of the farmers' mortgages were held by a banking competitor. Big Carl Wente came along and, as he had done at Madera, his management improved the situation. "The staff worked with a snap and vim and were on their toes eager to develop new business," noted a bank official after a visit to Modesto.[15]

Stockton, at the northern end of the valley, presented an odd problem. When the Bank of Italy bought the San Joaquin Valley National Bank in 1917, scarcely a dent had been made in the large and growing Italian colony of the area. Pedrini's men constantly roved the countryside for business in the early twenties. Up to 1927 accounts flowed in steadily. Then the Bank of Italy acquired the Commercial & Savings Bank, and a fierce rivalry developed between the old and the new branches. Each preyed upon the other's customers. Seizing the opportunity, the old and well-handled Stockton Savings and Loan Bank, which had a loyal following in the rural districts, put on a campaign for new accounts. Pedrini sent Paganini to the scene. Heads rolled in the Bank of Italy branches after he made his report. Ten months later Paganini returned to find "everyone well satisfied with the service rendered" in Stockton.[16]

Far and wide Pedrini's crusaders spread the Giannini gospel that years before had converted North Beach to the checkbook. One example was Chico, in the upper Sacramento Valley. In 1922, shortly after the Butte County National Bank had been taken over, Solicitor Louis Perna paid a call and found the old management clinging to "old ideas about banking." "They do not think it is very dignified to go out and shake hands with the farmer and groceryman," Perna reported. The personnel of the branch was almost totally ignorant of the foreigners in their midst. An assistant cashier knew *two* Italians —one of whom did business with the competitor. Perna suggested that the assistant cashier and his colleagues "shake hands with people who handle good American money although they sometimes did not speak good English." A tour of Italian homes brought the Bank of Italy several "good boosters and stockholders." An Italian-speaking teller was put behind a window, something that frequently followed a visit by a representative of the Italian department.[17]

South of the Tehachapi lived nearly thirty thousand Italians. Competition for their business in urban Los Angeles was keen among the banks. The Bank of Italy's International branch pulled in a fair share, but that was all. The Plaza branch of the competing Citizens National Trust & Savings had all the business of the immigrants from the Italian province of Abruzzi, about five hundred accounts, because of a manager of Abruzzi stock. The Pacific-Southwest enjoyed the bulk of the Italian trade in the San Fernando Valley, then undergoing a boom in small acreages devoted to figs and poultry. Other warmly contested spots were Santa Barbara, Santa Monica, Cucamonga and San Bernardino.

San Bernardino County was a favorite stalking ground for the Italian department. Forays had begun early in the twenties among the grape growers of Wineville, Cucamonga, Etiwanda and Guasti. The Secondo Guasti domain naturally was a pushover. The thirty-odd families there, all Italian Vineyard Company employees, were depositors at Ontario, the closest branch, a six-mile walk for most of them since few owned an automobile. So, in 1925, a teller started coming to the colony twice a month. He cashed checks, accepted deposits and dealt in foreign exchange. The same service was soon extended to neighboring communities. These customers also invested in a share or two of Giannini stock.[18]

In Ventura, San Pedro, Venice, Escondido, Burbank, San Diego and Imperial, the Italian department had little to fear from competitors. At San Diego, for example, some two thousand Ligurian fishermen, dairymen, bean growers, barbers, grocers, etc., banked at the several branches. As further service Louis Perna became a notary, the only notary in the county speaking several languages.[19]

In 1928 Paganini estimated that 20 per cent of the Bank of Italy's deposits came from Italians; and that 40 per cent of the stockholders were of Italian extraction. They did not own 40 per cent of the outstanding shares, however. In 1926 the Italian department obtained 5,291 accounts for the bank, representing $3,354,000. It sold stock in the amount of $1,232,000, foreign exchange in the amount of $290,000, and forwarded deposits of 2,622,000 lire to the Banca d'America e d'Italia.[20]

7

The other foreign divisions were smaller but no less interesting. Largely a one- or two-man operation, their services differed according to the needs of their colonies.

The Chinese division was housed at the Montgomery Street branch under Nelson N. Yue, who kept close tab on Chinese business in Los Angeles, Sacramento, Stockton and Oakland. Foreign exchange, amounting to $1,500,000 yearly, was Mr. Yue's big item, and he saw to it that the proper branches had Chinese tellers. From their efforts, the Bank of Italy gained, in 1926, 1,755 new accounts totaling $1,806,362; in 1927, 2,002 accounts, for $1,514,637; and in 1930, 1,323 accounts, for $795,996.[21]

At the start, the Greek division went to work spreading good will in the Greek colony of the Bay Area, numbering upwards of 5,000. Under Assistant Cashier B. Metropoulos, by 1926 the division had 4,155 Greek clients with deposits of nearly $5,000,000.

In April 1927, Metropoulos, ever alert, received a report that took him post haste to Tracy. A customer had heard a rumor that caused him to withdraw his $5,800 balance. It was the type of rumor that on other occasions had run through foreign colonies in California. The disturbed depositor was a machinist in a car-repair gang in the Southern Pacific shops. He told Metropoulos that a fellow worker had read in a newspaper that the president of an Italian bank somewhere in the East, or perhaps in Italy, had died. Whereupon, the bank had been taken over by the government which surrounded the building with soldiers. Depositors would get forty or fifty cents on the dollar. The supposedly deceased banker was guessed to be A. P. Giannini, and he had killed himself. When Metropoulos convinced the depositor that the report was untrue, the branch not only got the $5,800 account back, but an additional $5,000 which the machinist transferred from another bank.

By 1930 Greek accounts had climbed to more than ten thousand in number. The International branch at Los Angeles had a good deal to do with this growth.[22]

Central California was the principal scene of operations of the Portuguese division under J. L. Viery. He started out in territory which was once a part of the cattle kingdom of Miller & Lux, Inc. Practically all the land on the west side of the San Joaquin River, from Tracy to Firebaugh, at one time belonged to Henry Miller and Charles Lux whose partnership began in 1851. At their deaths they left over a million acres in California, Oregon, Nevada and Arizona. A start was made at breaking up the California holdings in 1906 with the laying out of the town of Gustine.

A branch of the Liberty Bank opened in Gustine twenty years later. Most of the town's 2,500 population was Portuguese. Their income came from alfalfa and dairying. Though farms averaged only forty acres milk checks were well over $3,000,000 annually. Viery saw to it that a good part of this found its way to the branch. He was helped by two Portuguese merchants on the advisory board and two dairymen's daughters, one the branch's assistant cashier and the other the bookkeeper.[23]

Before the breakup of the Miller & Lux holdings reached the Firebaugh district in Fresno County, some sixty miles south of Gustine, a Liberty Bank branch was opened there also. It was a headache for the home office and a nightmare for the branch manager. A shack town of one thousand, Firebaugh was at the center of the Miller & Lux ranches. You could travel twenty-five miles in almost any direction without getting off company property. Of the town's business establishments, Miller & Lux owned the general store, the meat market and the lumber yard. The rest were mostly blind tigers that bootlegged to five hundred ranch hands. The nearest movie was sixteen miles away. Gambling was the favorite pastime. Vice-President W. H. McGinnis, Jr., said Firebaugh was "without semblance of law and order." This was a branch where the bank *was* close with credit. The first year's loans were $18,000 and $3,000 of this required considerable nursing. Three years later loans had only increased to $30,000, though deposits climbed meanwhile from $199,376 to $268,000.[24]

California had a population of about fifty thousand Serbs, Croats and Slavonians when the Slavonian division was organized under Assistant Cashier A. Pilcovich. Eight thousand potential customers lived in the Bay Area, and the rest were scattered up and down the state. In the south, "Old John" Lopizich of the International branch had the trade under his thumb, no small part coming through the branch at San Pedro where the Slavonians were strongly entrenched in the sardine and tuna fishing industry. Their foreign exchange business at San Pedro alone touched $200,000 annually.[25]

Up the coast, a hundred miles south of San Francisco, was Watsonville, the agricultural hub of Pajaro Valley, famed as the berries and apples center. Its twenty thousand acres of Bellflowers, Newtowns and Pippins gave California a place among the first ten apple-producing states in the nation. Many of the Slavonians who had pioneered the valley's apple culture were rich. When the Bank of Italy entered the valley in December, 1923, through the purchase of two old-timers, the Bank of Watsonville and the Watsonville Savings Bank, these orchardists owned most of the land and the storage and packing sheds. They controlled a competing bank, the Fruit Growers National.

Getting business for the Bank of Italy branch was difficult because the predecessor banks had turned away the accounts of many new orchardists. Pilcovich sent a Slavonian-speaking teller from the Montgomery Street branch and began an aggressive campaign. Deposits went from $1,734,658 in 1925 to $2,619,000 in 1930. A factor in this increase was the acquisition of the Fruit Growers National Bank, via the Liberty Bank, in 1927. But larger loans also helped. Where the unit bank had been limited to $20,000 loans, the branch had on the books in 1929 seventeen loans, ranging from $21,000 to $248,000.

The Slavonian division handled nearly 4,000 remittances to Yugoslavia in 1928. The same year Manager Pilcovich sold 5,741 shares of Bancitaly stock to his countrymen. At the end of the decade, its work had brought in a grand total of 13,543 accounts with initial deposits aggregating $6,642,952.[26]

The Spanish and Latin-American division made little headway in northern California when it first started. Most of the prospects were migratory workers in the agricultural valleys—too poor and too few in numbers to make an impression on the bank's ledgers. The head of the division, Emilio L. Dominquez, had better luck with well-to-do travelers arriving from south of the border by steamer. He met the ships, recommended hotels and performed other appreciated services. For the visitors' children he suggested American schools and, in some instances, acted as their guardian.

Southern California was more likely territory, although the excellent Spanish departments of the California Bank and the Security Trust made strong bids for the business of Los Angeles' large Mexican colony. To offset this, Dominquez had twenty-five Mexican tellers placed in strategic branches. Three years of his work up to 1930 showed a total of 1,886 new accounts with initial deposits of $1,410,694.[27]

Small as it was, the Russian division probably filled the role of financial adviser and friend more completely than any of the Bank of Italy's foreign units. Events abroad were largely responsible. The Red Revolution, followed by a long unrecognized Soviet regime, left Russian colonists the world over without consular or diplomatic ties. San Francisco's colony numbered eighteen thousand when the bank's Russian division began in 1921 under C. Shanowsky who had long represented the czar's government on the Pacific Coast.

The Bank of Italy, at the time, had about six hundred Russian customers. Using the technique of Pedrini's crew—the door-to-door hunt for new patrons—Shanowsky, in a short while, doubled the bank's Russian business with 585 new accounts, for $451,488.

In 1922, when the major powers abandoned their economic blockade against the Red regime, Shanowsky arranged for the newly opened State Bank of the U.S.S.R. to handle his customers' dollar remittances to their families at home. The next six years saw 25,810 remittances cross his desk. This worked out well for the Bank of

Italy. The dollars collected from the customer were credited to the Soviet government's account in the Bank of Italy and an order forwarded to Moscow for payment to the customer's relative. The Soviets then drew upon the dollars deposited with the Bank of Italy for the purchase of American machinery. At the time, this was probably the largest dollar account of a foreign government with the Bank of Italy. More important in Shanowsky's eyes, some 2,303 remitters became the bank's clients.

Other friends were won through the division's efforts to aid the Russian immigrants fleeing the Red regime. About 1924, the United States had let down the bars for refugees with relatives on this side willing to fill out an affidavit of support. To do this, the relative either had to be a citizen or have his first papers. Nearly a thousand such papers were prepared by the division. In eight years' time the bank had 8,119 Russian customers.

Among them was a small community of Dukhobors—Tolstoyans, as they liked to be called—who had come down from Canada and settled just outside of Manteca about 1922. By 1928 the crops had all but paid for the small farms, which amounted to from seven to eighteen acres per family. When the Bank of Italy levied a monthly service charge of fifty cents on small but active checking accounts, a number of the Dukhobors took their business to another bank. They did not know that all banks had initiated a charge for these accounts which were carried at a loss. Shanowsky went to Manteca where the Dukhobors obligingly assembled to hear the Bank of Italy's Russian representative. What happened is best told in Shanowsky's words:

I found a houseful of people—more than fifty—and as is the custom of Dukhobors, they opened the meeting with prayers and songs. Then I talked to them for over an hour, explaining all about the Bank of Italy, and also about the stocks as most of them are stockholders of our bank. For a while after, I was busy answering questions. Finally we came to an agreement that, inasmuch as all the banks will soon make a 50¢ service charge, it would be best for all the Dukhobors to remain clients of the Bank of Italy. . . . I also told them that our Branch Manager advises everyone not to expand this year but to save their money for next year in case the crops fail; or if the crops are as good next year, they would have the advantage of going ahead—building new homes—and also have money in the bank. They seemed to like this idea. After the business meeting was over, they entertained me with their folk songs and we parted in the best of friendship.[28]

Giannini Does It Again

IN 1927 when he merged his various banking interests into the gigantic Bank of Italy National Trust and Savings Association, A. P. Giannini was not content to rest on his oars. For one thing he considered the statewide system incomplete. He would not be satisfied until his branches reached into every California community that needed them.

Aside from that, Giannini looked ahead to bigger things for the branch banking principle. He conceived of the day when a branch banking system could cross state lines and become national in scope, like the Federal Reserve System or the commercial banks of Canada. Until this happened he believed the nation's banks could not do a thorough job for their patrons. Such interstate banking would require amendment of the McFadden Act which restricted to one state the operations of any one bank. Giannini's activities in preparation for this change in the law (to the present day unrealized) will be told later. This chapter will deal with his further expansion of branch operations in California of the Bank of Italy N. T. & S. A. —under the McFadden Act.

The McFadden Act permitted a national bank to add branches in its home city, if the comptroller of the currency approved. Accordingly, from time to time the Bank of Italy opened new branches in San Francisco to the limit to which they could be operated profitably. It was also possible to strengthen branches elsewhere without, however, adding to their number. This was done by buying an independent bank and consolidating it with an existing branch.

The trouble was that these methods of expansion opened no new territory. Giannini thought he saw a way to pick a path through the McFadden Act that would lead to new territory. To make sure he asked for the opinion of Charles W. Collins. If anyone knew, it seemed that Collins would. As deputy comptroller of the currency he had written much of the McFadden Act, and had followed every twist and turn of its long course through Congress. He was familiar with every word of the act and with the legal possibilities behind every word. Lately Mr. Collins had left the government service to be the legal representative in Washington of various large banks including the Bank of Italy.

The section of the McFadden Act that interested Giannini provided that a national bank could absorb another bank, if both parties to the transaction had head offices in the same city. Branches thus acquired could be retained wherever they might be, provided they were in operation on February 25, 1927, when the McFadden Act became law. Giannini wanted to make certain he understood this portion of the act correctly. Suppose, he said to Collins, he bought a number of small and medium-sized California banks—some of them with a few branches—and united them in a state system apart from the Bank of Italy, after the pattern of the old Liberty Bank and the Bank of America of Los Angeles. Could he merge the younger system with the Bank of Italy, if the state branches had been in existence under other ownership prior to February 25, 1927?

Collins replied that what Giannini proposed could be done. "Emphasis [in the law] is upon the previous existence of the branches as branches, and they may be retained . . . no matter how many different banks originally established them."[1]

Such was the origin and such the ultimate destiny of the branch banking system Mr. Giannini began to put together in 1927 and which, after a series of mutations, became known as the Bank of America of California.

2

Actually, the first step had been taken before the McFadden Act was through the Senate. The French-American Bank of San Francisco, acquired in December, 1925, by Bancitaly, was omitted from the consolidations that resulted in the Bank of Italy National Trust and Savings Association. The omission was deliberate. A high-class institution of $24,000,000 in resources, the French-American was a descendant of French banks dating from the Gold Rush. The head of it was Leon Bocqueraz, a native Californian who had been edu-

cated in Paris. As his father before him had been, Bocqueraz was a
leader of San Francisco's French colony. A state bank without Federal Reserve membership, the French-American did not come under
the McFadden Act. It was responsible to the California authorities
solely.

Giannini's next move was to acquire from Rudolph Spreckels the
United Bank and Trust Company of California, a $49,000,000 institution, and to merge the Bocqueraz bank with it. This took place at
the end of April, 1927, sixty days after the nationalization of the
Bank of Italy. The Spreckels deal gave Giannini eight more San
Joaquin Valley branches ranging from Sacramento to Fresno.

As the former Spreckels bank was a member of the Federal Reserve, Giannini could not use it in his expansion drive unless the
Reserve membership was surrendered. Instead of doing that, he
formed an auxiliary called the French-American Corporation which,
during the summer of 1927, picked up fifteen independent banks extending from the Oregon to the Mexican borders. A few of these
small banks had a branch or two each. Some of the branches were
eligible, under the circumstances mentioned, to become branches of
the Bank of Italy. Others were ineligible, but that did not stop Giannini from buying them. In the fullness of time he expected to find a
way to link them up with No. 1 Powell Street.

In September, 1927, the French-American Corporation formed the
Security Bank and Trust Company, with headquarters at Bakersfield. The components were three banks, two in San Jose and one in
Bakersfield, each of which had the word "Security" in its title. Giannini kept this institution out of the Federal Reserve. Being free of
the McFadden Act, Security of Bakersfield began to blossom as a
branch system by taking over the scattered banks the French-American Corporation had lately acquired.

All went well until application was made to absorb a bank at La
Habra, in Orange County. This was Los Angeles territory, and J. F.
Sartori strenuously objected to Giannini's use of the word "Security"
in a branch banking system south of the Tehachapi. Protesting to
Superintendent Wood, the Los Angeles banker called it unfair competition, alleging that Giannini's Security Bank and Trust Company
of Bakersfield might be confused with Sartori's Security Trust and
Savings of Los Angeles. Though it was tentatively ruled that Giannini could not use the word "Security" in a branch system below the

Ridge, A. P. was not convinced he did not have the right to do so. In a letter to Leo Belden he wrote:

Who has given Sartori exclusive right to the word security? . . . Security Savings Bank of San Jose is a 39 year old institution and in the Security Bank and Trust Company there are merged about four or five other Security banks. . . . I see no reason why anyone should pick on us for the use of a name that we have purchased. There are First National Banks all over the State and in other parts of the country and nobody seems to object to it. Robinson's Bank the Los Angeles First National Bank is in many other towns where there are other First National Banks and nobody seems to pay any attention to same.[2]

In spite of Sartori, the drive for banks went on. In six months' time a collection, aggregating $100,000,000 in assets, had been swept up and they were Giannini banks regardless of the name on the window. Not even in the heyday of the Liberty Bank and the Bank of America of Los Angeles had Giannini bought banks faster. The time was ripe and he made the most of his opportunities. In the first place the money was available from the phenomenal profits of Bancitaly Corporation. The rise of Bancitaly shares in the booming stock market made selling bankers eager to exchange them for the shares of their own institutions, despite Giannini's periodical reminders that Bancitaly stock was selling for more than it was worth. Another factor was the presence of Will C. Wood in the office of superintendent of banks. Unlike his immediate predecessors, Wood did not reject applications for branches simply because they came from the Giannini organization, but made a conscientious effort to give "them the same sort of treatment that is given others." Over the purchase of banks the superintendent had no control. Undoubtedly, in this period, Wood more than once experienced a sense of relief when Giannini took over rural banks that agricultural troubles had reduced to a position where they had to sell or close. Not knowing how long this dispensation of affairs would last Giannini determined to make hay while the sun was shining.[3]

He pushed into the remote high country of California—the timberlands, the cattle domains, the fishing and hunting areas, the mining centers. He went into Dunsmuir at the base of Mount Shasta; into Alturas in the far northeast, so isolated that hitherto it had always looked to Reno; into Grass Valley, one of the richest of the gold camps of the fifties and home of those darlings of the diggings, Lotta Crabtree and Lola Montez. In 1927 Grass Valley was a quieter place, though it was then California's largest gold-producing center, with more than a hundred mines working.

In the northern Sierras, a region of timber and waterpower, Giannini went into Susanville, Bieber and Fall River Mills. Entry into these towns was by means of the purchase of the Lassen Industrial Bank of Susanville, with two eligible branches. Here was an institution that Superintendent Wood must have been relieved to see fall into capable hands. For close to two decades, the Lassen banks had served the rugged, frontier area, lending perhaps too generously on timber and dairying. Then suddenly California's dread, hidden enemy—alkali—rose up through the soil and laid waste grain lands and pastures. Matters for the bank reached a climax after a $100,000 defalcation. The whole region was boiling with uneasiness when the French-American Corporation took over. The advent of strangers into the faraway community was unusual enough to start up fresh rumors that threatened serious consequences. From a correspondent bank in Reno—that was quicker than from over the mountain in San Francisco—$100,000 in currency was hurried to Susanville. The gleaming stacks of money displayed in the tellers' cages dissipated the tension, as they had done at other crucial times for the Bank of Italy.[4]

Giannini then went into Owens Valley which had been left without banking facilities by the closing of the Watterson brothers' three banks, a calamity that seemed the last straw for that troubled community.

Owens Valley lies in the lofty Sierras near the Nevada line, some two hundred miles from Los Angeles. It is about a hundred miles long, and fifteen miles wide on the average. Dwellers in this mountain cradle grew most of what they ate, and raised cattle and sheep for the market. They were not wealthy, but they got along; and they liked their independence and isolation. In her far-ranging search for water Los Angeles had sent engineers to the Owens Valley. The engineers said the Owens River was the answer to their problem, and projected the aqueduct across the desert. The valley people understood that only the "surplus flow" of the river was to be siphoned off, and to this they had no objection. The surplus flow did not satisfy booming Los Angeles, thirsty for population, wealth and power as well as for water. Nearly all the Owens River water was taken. Many of the valley's irrigation ditches went dry, and farms reverted to desert.

Valley residents exploded dynamite against the aqueduct and opened spillway gates to divert water to their parched fields. This was the state of affairs when the Watterson banks went under, catching about every solvent person in the area. Five weeks later Giannini opened at Independence, the principal settlement in the valley, a branch of one of his French-American Corporation banks. He would have been there sooner, except for the hold of the Watterson brothers on the valley people. "They have been terrorized to a point where they are slow to assert themselves, even in a crisis like this," Superintendent Wood wrote Governor Young. Though the Wattersons had "confessed the embezzlement of vast sums of money," the brothers managed to leave the impression that once more "they are suffering a great wrong at the hands of Los Angeles." This was all that was needed to rally their depositors and backers who loyally canceled out what the bankers owed them.

"The Wattersons are clever," said Wood, whom the bankers tried to make the victim of their artful innuendoes. Those with faith in the brothers complained to the governor that his superintendent of banks had taken "advantage of the 'temporary' difficulties of the Owens Valley banks to put in a new bank to please the Bank of Italy." "Ridiculous," said Wood. The "only application" to replace the Watterson banks had come from Giannini. Since the valley was entitled to banking facilities and Wood's job was to provide them, the permit went to the French-American Corporation.

Once Giannini banking methods got to work, the much-betrayed residents of Inyo County were quick to foreswear Watterson allegiance. A second branch was opened at Bishop and another at Lone Pine. By then, the *Inyo Independent* was hailing Mr. Giannini as a deliverer. This was somewhat true for, during the first year, the branches loaned in the stricken valley far more money than they received in deposits. When Los Angeles bank robbers held up the Lone Pine office and drove away in a car with $2,100, mountain men showed their appreciation of favors extended. They turned out in pursuit, taking a short cut by stationing guards at all waterholes. The city-bred hoodlums got lost in the hills and were captured without much trouble.[5]

The Giannini banks helped the valley during its darkest days. In the thirties conditions improved. In the forties the economy underwent a complete change. Agriculture, with the exception of some cattle grazing, began to disappear as tourists, mountain resorts, fishing, hunting and skiing became the principal sources of the valley's income.

3

Continuing its bank-buying, in 1928 the French-American Corporation took over, among others, two banks in Turlock and two in Berkeley. All four institutions were in flourishing condition and the Giannini organization got two able banking officers with them. They were Howard Whipple of Turlock, who had been the principal organizer of the California League of Independent Bankers, and Will F. Morrish of Berkeley, one of the League's most effective members. These latest converts to branch banking began their new careers as vice-presidents of the United Bank and Trust Company of San Francisco (the consolidated Spreckels and Bocqueraz institutions). Mr. Whipple's talents as an advocate soon reasserted themselves. From the platform and in print he extolled the virtues of branch banking as ably as once he had extolled those of the unit system.

Giannini next merged his United Bank and Trust Company into his Security Bank and Trust. Thus the Federal Reserve lost a member and all elements of the fast-growing new California branch system came under the authority of Superintendent Will C. Wood. With a strong nonmember state system competing alongside his Federal Reserve member bank, Giannini's position now was pretty much like the one in which he had brought about the consolidation of the Liberty Bank. He moved a step nearer his goal of an ultimate merger with the Bank of Italy by transferring Security's headquarters from Bakersfield to San Francisco.

The next development was the merger with Security of the gilt-edge $30,000,000 Humboldt Bank, one of the oldest banks in San Francisco. In the Humboldt deal Giannini again gave evidence of his appreciation of favors received from the Crocker bank. Control of the Humboldt was for sale because its president, A. D. Keyes, was old and in failing health. W. H. Crocker would have liked to have had the bank. Eager as Giannini was to expand his new branch system, he stood aside until Crocker failed to come to terms with Keyes.

In the course of the Humboldt transaction Mr. Giannini altered the name of his new branch system to the United Security Bank and Trust Company, hoping this would placate Mr. Sartori. But it did not. Sartori still objected to the word "Security" and obtained a court injunction to prevent its use in the south by Giannini. This move kept out of the United Security system nearly fifty French-American Corporation banks.[6]

Nevertheless, the purchase of the Humboldt gave United Security a system with 53 branches, perhaps half of which were eligible to become Bank of Italy branches whenever Giannini was ready to say the word. As yet he was not ready because he wanted still more branches. United Security had deposits of $146,882,000. In northern California only the American Trust, with 98 branches and $257,-403,000 in deposits, was larger—excepting of course the Bank of Italy, with 286 branches and $668,944,000 in deposits. If the individual banks operated by the French-American Corporation are added, the assets of the "outside" Giannini institutions topped $200,000,000. These figures are as of June 30, 1928, only sixteen months after the start of the campaign to round out the statewide system.[7]

September of 1928 rolled around, and the courts still denied Giannini use of the name "Security" south of the Ridge. To Giannini this seemed a miscarriage of justice. As a consumer of valuable time, the controversy was proving irksome and so Bacigalupi broached a possible solution to Louis Ferrari, whose friendly counsel Giannini valued. It was to abandon the name fight and bring United Security and the French-American banks together under the new title of Bank of America, to which Mr. Sartori could take no exception. Forehandedly, the charter of Orra Monnette's Bank of America of Los Angeles had not been surrendered, but transferred for safekeeping to a little institution that Bancitaly owned in the San Pedro district. As Bacigalupi telegraphed Ferrari, the stumbling block was that the "Chief dislikes giving in [to Sartori] and [is] apprehensive . . . [that such a course] would be construed by public as weakness." There seemed a graceful way out, however. "He has some idea," continued Bacigalupi, "the Merchants or some other deal will materialize and . . . offer plausible excuse change name."[8]

4

The "Merchants deal" had to do with the Merchants National Trust and Savings Bank of Los Angeles. Marco and Irving Hellman, nephews of Isaias Hellman of San Francisco, had inherited from their father interest in several Los Angeles banks. With that to start on, the brothers had built up the Hellman Commercial Trust and Savings Bank of that city. It was a branch bank with twenty-six offices in or near Los Angeles. In 1926 it was supposed to be overextended in Los Angeles boom real estate when a merger was arranged with the Merchants National Bank of Los Angeles. Merchants National was an excellent institution which, until his death, had been controlled by Herman Hellman, the father of Marco and Irving. The merger infused needed liquid assets into the Hellman Commercial. The consolidated institution took the name Merchants National Trust and Savings Bank. The Hellman brothers were vice-presidents and Edward J. Nolan, their attorney, was president. In 1928, the bank's resources were then stated to be $100,000,000.

When Bacigalupi telegraphed Louis Ferrari in September of that year, a proposal to absorb the Merchants National was nearing the contract stage after eight months of negotiation. Ordinarily when Giannini wanted a bank that was for sale he came to terms quickly or not at all. The long-drawn-out affair with the Hellmans was due to an unusual combination of causes. What made Giannini hesitate was the high price asked and the doubtful attitude toward the offer of his trusted examiner, W. H. Snyder. On the other hand the Hellman bank had assets Giannini ardently desired. There were by this time thirty-odd branches—quite a prize to bag at one swoop. Also, the Merchants National had an extensive commercial business, perhaps exceeded in Los Angeles only by that of the banks of Sartori and Robinson. For all its success, the Bank of Italy remained essentially a savings institution, and more so in Los Angeles than in San Francisco.

The Hellman proposal had been brought to Giannini in New York by a San Francisco broker named J. E. Byrnes. The turnover in banks had reached such dimensions in California that a handful of brokers had added selling banks to their regular line of business. Byrnes was about the cleverest of the lot. It was he who had brought A. P. and Orra Monnette together. Giannini called him "Gumshoe" Byrnes and claimed he could read people's minds. Giannini said that more than once he had picked a bank he wished to buy and by the time he got around to making an offer there would be Byrnes ahead of him, representing the local banker.[9]

The Los Angeles people wanted a guarantee of $40,000,000 for 100,000 of the Merchants National's 160,000 outstanding shares, plus berths in the Giannini hierarchy for Nolan, the Hellmans and some of their associates. Notwithstanding the advantages, Giannini thought the price steep. As to giving the Merchants National people jobs, Giannini was always on the lookout for talent. Though they had made mistakes, the Hellman "boys" had good reputations in Los Angeles as bankers. The forty-one-year-old Nolan had a rather dazzling reputation. Aviator, soldier, sportsman, lawyer and financier, Nolan would be somewhat of a novelty in the Giannini organization. A. P. turned to Snyder who had been shifted to the New York office of Bancitaly. The veteran examiner, who had passed on so many banks that Giannini had had under consideration, said that he did not like the Hellman proposal. Giannini was due to sail for Europe. He sailed, leaving the Merchants affair in the hands of subordinates.

From New York Snyder wrote to Mario Giannini. It seems to have been the intangibles of the situation that disturbed the examiner. "The sellers," he wrote, "are not converted to our [style of] organization the way they should be converted before completing a transaction." The impatience of the sellers also bothered Snyder. "Mr. Byrnes has been urging the completion of a written contract and the more I have thought these conditions over the more I have considered that we should take ample time . . . [and proceed] in a most careful manner."

With Snyder out of it, Byrnes and others spent the summer (of 1928) pestering Bacigalupi and Louis Ferrari with sales talk and an engaging collection of figures on the excellence of the Merchants National Bank.[10]

This was the situation when A. P. Giannini returned from abroad. He wanted the branches and he wanted the commercial business of the Merchants National; and he was ready to close out the profitless name controversy with Sartori. Though aware that the Merchants was still overextended in boom real estate, Giannini deemed himself something of an expert at straightening out the affairs of ailing banks.

On November 1 a contract was signed. The selling stockholders were to get $40,000,000 in this way: $20,000,000 in securities was placed in escrow, to be exchanged within four years for $40,000,000. Jobs were promised the principal Merchants men. The sellers consented to remove objectionable paper that might be found by an examining committee made up of one Giannini man, one Merchants man and an arbitrator from the State Banking Department.[11]

The examining committee set aside paper in the amount of $3,500,000 which the selling stockholders assumed responsibility for. They protested, however, that the committee was unduly strict because this same paper had lately been passed by the local national bank examiner and by the Los Angeles clearing house. Giannini demanded a second inspection of the bank. When the Merchants people objected A. P. wired Louis Ferrari: "Unless they are willing to do business in this way . . . pack your grip and come home and of course see to it that all securities [in escrow] come with you. Evidently those fellows down there are trying to put something over on us." Giannini got his second inspection, and, as a result, $400,000 in additional paper was thrown out. The selling stockholders reluctantly took it up.[12]

The deal was closed. All that remained was the completion of corporate formalities. On December 8, 1928, the newly constituted Bank of America of California took over the Merchants National. Previously it had absorbed the United Security and fifty-five French-American Corporation independents. Giannini had done it again. With 138 branches and $357,974,000 in deposits, his latest creation started off as the second largest state bank in the country, the first being the Guaranty Trust Company of New York. Lumped together, Giannini's California banks and their associated corporations entered the select circle of American business enterprises whose resources exceeded the billion-dollar mark.

The chief officer of the Bank of America of California was Leon Bocqueraz, chairman of the board. He had survived all the winnowing of top personnel that had attended this typical Giannini operation since its inception early in 1927 with the purchase of the Boc-queraz bank in San Francisco. Among the vice-presidents were Will F. Morrish and Howard Whipple. The Bank of Italy's contribution was G. M. McClerkin, a former national bank examiner from Arkansas who had become Giannini's star bank buyer. As provided in the selling contract, there were places for the old Merchants crowd. Edward J. Nolan became president and his man Friday, Canadian-born Charles R. Bell, senior vice-president. There were vice-presidencies for Marco and Irving Hellman and two others.

It was the dashing Nolan who attracted the most attention.

"You ask me about my success, as you call it," he told a newspaper reporter. "Better call it 'my luck,' for I am an opportunist, pure and simple."[13]

We shall meet Mr. Nolan again, when his luck was running out.

5

The Bank of America of California grew, Giannini fashion. There was a repetition of scenes that had characterized all the Giannini expansions.

In the San Joaquin Valley, Livingston, a trading center for grape growers, sweet potato raisers and dairymen, had been without a bank since the failure of the local institution two and a half years before. When the Bank of America of California opened its branch the whole town turned out—merchants, farmers, city fathers and the high school band. The editor of the Livingston *Chronicle* wrote: "[We] expect the Bank of America to take its place as a community leader, as a community builder, as a community counselor. We do not expect it to be a Santa Claus to us, but constructive and helpful, stern and wise."[14]

Giannini achieved an ambition of five years' standing when the Bank of America of California obtained a *de novo* permit to open in Calexico, a free-spending town that is literally on the Mexican border. With a population of six thousand, Calexico was the trading point for a section of the hot and fertile Imperial Valley, then undergoing rapid development. It was there that farm hands repaired for their lively Saturday nights along the international street, the north side of which is in Calexico, California, and the south side in Mexicali, Mexico. In those days saloons, dance halls and other recreational retreats of Mexicali constituted quite an attraction to Norte Americanos who were weary of the Eighteenth Amendment. Mexicali was also the capital of the Mexican state of Lower California, and the gateway to that region with its heavy population of industrious Chinese, Japanese and Hindus.[15]

Among the banks that were absorbed was San Francisco's oldest private banking house, the Donohoe, Kelly Banking Company, which dated from 1861. Formed on the model of Drexel, Morgan & Co. (a predecessor of J. P. Morgan & Co.), Donohoe, Kelly's history was identical with much of the early financial history of San Francisco. Millions upon millions in bullion passed over its counters. The times had outrun the Donohoe, Kelly Banking Company and, though its prestige was high, deposits were down to $2,000,000 when the Bank of America of California purchased it in 1929.

There was also a typical rescue wherein the B. of A. of C. joined the Bank of Italy in saving the Pacific National Bank of Los Angeles, a small ($15,000,000) and tottering branch system. For some time this institution, with assets frozen in speculative land and oil ventures, had been under the scrutiny of the comptroller of the currency. After an effort to raise fresh capital had failed, Giannini took over in July, 1929. Five branches went to the Bank of America of California and three were merged with existing branches of the Bank of Italy.[16]

By the summer of 1930 the Bank of America of California possessed 163 branches. Of this number 106 were eligible for transfer to the Bank of Italy. Before we go on with this thread of the story, however, a number of other themes in our crowded chronicle must be taken account of.

California's Own "Boom Twenties"

THE "BOOM TWENTIES" have earned their place in American history as a fool's paradise. The boom that most people recall or have read about was the stock market boom—a gambling craze that was the most widespread of its kind the country has ever seen. On top of it Florida and California had booms of their own.

The Florida frenzy started first (in 1920), and ended first (in 1926). It was a land boom entirely; and a winter-resort land boom at that, for the industrial resources of Florida are small and the agricultural resources, though special and considerable, bear no comparison with those of California. The reckoning was tragic, indeed, for the bust closed nearly one in four of Florida's three hundred banks.

The California boom started in 1921, and, though subdued and tapering off, there was no collapse until after the stock market debacle had upset the general economy in 1929. For all the delusion, flimflam and downright dishonesty, this boom had a much sounder foundation than the Florida one had. It was a plural affair: real estate, oil and the movies. Back of these were the other diverse resources of the state. Most of the people who went to California went to stay—and did stay, even after the dream of getting rich without working was a thing of the past. You can find them there now, contemplating a bit wistfully the memories of vanished paper fortunes in oil; in subdivisions, with their "beneficial shares"; or the easy-come, easy-go movie money they thought would last forever. They all make a living, and some have got rich after all. In either case, not many would trade California for any other place.

The California boom started where most California booms have started once the Gold Rush was over—in the south. It crossed the Ridge and crept up the San Joaquin Valley and the seacoast to Oakland, across the bay from San Francisco. But the hub and heart of the commotion remained in Los Angeles which, having become California's largest city, announced as a matter of manifest destiny the intention of becoming the largest city in the world. The Angelenos did not go about this in a timid way. During the boom's seven best years, 3,233 subdivisions, embracing 49,608 acres, were cut up into 246,612 building lots. Most of these lots were sold more than once, at prices that doubled and squared. With all outdoors to operate in, subdividers clustered about Los Angeles as if drawn by a magnet. Zigzagging roads up hillsides, they sliced the precipitous slopes into pocket-handkerchief "parcels," as if land were California's scarcest commodity. Judging from the prices they paid, a good many people must have thought it was.

Not all these lots were occupied, however, and have not been occupied to this writing. In the case of some of the mountainsides, east and north of town, they are not apt to be occupied until something is done about the law of gravity. One subdivision was disposed of with the understanding that a resident could reach downtown Los Angeles by subway in fourteen minutes—a thing that still remains to be seen.

Add oil and the movies and you had a three-ring circus. There were also sideshows: cults, creeds, fads and fancies, each pointing to novel and easier ways to fame, social position, wealth, health, wisdom, education, contentment, spiritual salvation and other items calculated to make life more endurable here and hereafter—or, modestly summed up, the millennium. Lest the remainder of the United States be tempted to stick its nose in the air at these manifestations (which did not begin or end with the boom), it would be well to listen to what certain California writers have said with considerable truth and objectivity.

Their thesis is that southern California doesn't really originate these things; it just makes larger than life what other Americans have started elsewhere. "Let anything happen in the rest of the country," writes Idwal Jones, "in Arkansas or Maine, and there is instant repercussion inside the borders of Southern California." Farnsworth Crowder adds: "Here American institutions sharpen into focus so startling as to give the effect, sometimes, of caricature." Mr. Crowder ventures an opinion of the cause: "National currents of thought, passion, aspirations and protest, elsewhere kept decently in subterranean channels, have a way of boiling up in the Pacific sun to mix in a chemistry of . . . unexpected crystallizations." That is, it's the climate.[1]

Amid these distractions the banks of California conducted themselves much better than the banks of Florida. Still, there were failures on the West Coast; and there would have been more had not the Giannini and other branch systems taken over some of the wayward ones. Charles F. Stern and the Pacific-Southwest were unpleasantly involved, with the result that both Mr. Stern and the bank disappeared from the scene—the latter taken over by J. F. Sartori, who became, in size, Giannini's principal rival in the south. In importance he had always been that.

With all its follies, the decade left substantial achievements in California: an expanded oil industry; a motion picture industry; a two-million increase in population, making California the Union's sixth most populous state. No state has grown so fast for so long. When the Bank of Italy opened its doors in 1904 California was the twenty-first state.

Those two million newcomers had to find places to live and to work. Mostly "little fellows," they were the people Giannini concentrated on. The grandiose aspects of the boom he tried to bypass. "Mr. Giannini's slogan all through his career has been 'safety before profit,'" P. J. Dreher, who had been with Giannini in the south since 1913, told a meeting of the Los Angeles regional board of the Bank of Italy when it was considering a dubious investment.[2]

With this philosophy as a guide the Bank of Italy made remarkably few unfortunate boom loans. Most of its later troubles were the result of investments inherited from purchased banks, especially the Merchants National of Los Angeles.

2

The career of Edward Garner Lewis will serve to illustrate the mode of operation of a large-scale California real estate promoter. Leaving an unsuccessful venture in St. Louis behind him, in 1913 Lewis bought a 23,000-acre ranch midway between San Francisco and Los Angeles, making a down payment of $500 which he is said to have borrowed. This was the beginning of the town of Atascadero, conceived as a co-operative undertaking in which the good things of life would flourish. Ownership of the domain was vested in a holding company set up as a fifty-year trust. Lewis sold "beneficial shares" in the trust, thus inaugurating a new wrinkle in land-boom financing that was to have a long history in California before the boom of the twenties played out. Mr. Lewis also sold town lots and outlying acreage. He was a wonderful salesman. He was a showman whom the impresarios of Hollywood should have envied. Every state in the Union was represented among the buyers. From time to time the beneficial shares paid dividends.

People who knew him said Lewis "could talk you out of anything." He tried to talk A. P. Giannini out of a loan, but the San Franciscan kept his hands in his pockets. Mr. Lewis was more successful with another distinguished banker, Frank A. Vanderlip, who had retired from the presidency of the world's largest bank, the National City of New York. This was in 1921, at the opening of the boom. Mr. Vanderlip himself had recently purchased a California ranch called Palos Verdes, comprising 16,000 rugged acres (almost the area of Manhattan Island) along the seacoast southwest of Los Angeles. Lewis bought 3,200 acres of Vanderlip—it was said for $5,000,000, a million down.

The promoter duplicated the Atascadero formula on a grander scale. "THE NEW CITY WITH MILLIONS BEHIND IT—PALOS VERDES," he advertised. "AMPLY FINANCED BY 4229 UNDERWRITERS—REPRESENTS AN ASSET OF $17,500,000."[3]

With typical Lewis fanfare, the New City was introduced to prospects rounded up by the "bird dogs" who roved the Los Angeles area for game. An eyewitness wrote:

> [There were] free programs of music, Spanish dancing, stunt flying, athletic contests, aquaplaning and yacht racing. . . . There was a Kiddies' Tent . . . with playground teachers, physicians and free toys . . . [Adults] were led into a tent for a snappy lecture, to clinch the travelogue and the good food. Afterward they were taken out to the long rows of salesmen's "closing" offices, tiny frame huts looking like confessionals. Here, one to a hut, they were destined to sign on the dotted line.[4]

Money rolled in, and it also rolled out. Roads were carved around cliffs; eight hundred acres of park were landscaped; thirty acres laid out for a hotel; work started on apartment buildings, homes and a $100,000 swimming pool. Things were looking rosy in Palos Verdes when, in 1923, Lewis' earlier paradise at Atascadero blew up with

"11,000 creditors claiming they faced a 98 per cent loss on their $12,000,000 investments." One San Francisco bank was in for a million.[5]

The fall of Atascadero finished the promoter at Palos Verdes. As a part of the salvage work Mr. Vanderlip organized a new trust, which for purposes of administration was turned over to Orra Monnette's Bank of America of Los Angeles. When Giannini absorbed the Monnette bank the Palos Verdes trust came under the wing of the trust department of the Bank of Italy. Times grew hard, and the bank advanced the trust money for taxes. When over a period of years this account had mounted to $250,000, the bank refused to make further advances and took a number of Palos Verdes lots in settlement of the debt. The lots were eventually traded off. The Bank of Italy closed its books on Palos Verdes, out about $175,000.[6]

Of all the Los Angeles banks the most deeply involved in subdivisions was the Merchants National. A year after Giannini's Bank of America of California absorbed the Merchants, A. J. Mount of the Bank of Italy foresaw trouble ahead. "I am inclined to believe that we have quite a serious situation in these subdivision loans, and it is going to take a lot of skillful, careful handling to work the bank out without material loss."[7]

An example of what Mount had in mind was the Carthay Circle Theater, a feature of the Carthay Circle development, launched by Charles R. Bell, a vice-president of Merchants National (and subsequently of the Bank of America of California), whose exploits as a subdivider had given him the local name of "Wonderboy." The Carthay Circle development comprised 136 acres far out (for the times) on Wilshire Boulevard. It was in the van of subdivisions that included shopping centers, rendering them almost independent of downtown Los Angeles. The lots sold fast, picture-book houses went up on them, and the development was successful but for the Carthay Circle Theater.

This costly structure was designed to fill the niche, though on a grander scale, in Hollywood life that is occupied by Sid Graumann's Chinese Theater, as the scene of those fantastic movie openings—or premieres, as they say in moviedom. Having missed its destiny, the Carthay Theater became a white elephant. Giannini was left to hold the bag to the tune of several hundred thousand dollars.

It took the Bank of America National Trust and Savings Association (successor in 1930 to the Bank of America of California *and* the Bank of Italy: see Chapter Twenty-two for details of merger and change of name) twelve years, or until 1942, to work off the Carthay Theater debt without loss of principal or interest. It settled down to a comfortable and profitable existence as a neighborhood playhouse.

It took even longer to get out of the red on another Merchants National inheritance called Casa del Mar, a beach club on the Santa Monica shore. Casa del Mar was the last word in showy luxury, and it went flat as a flounder with the ending of the easy-money illusion. Its salvage was the masterpiece of Ralph C. Groner, the Bank of America's specialist in bizarre real estate loans. It was Groner who pulled out the Carthay Theater and other Merchants National legacies. Eight times he was in and out of the management of Casa del Mar. For years, the harder he worked the less he seemed to accomplish. The Casa's debt grew from $240,000 in 1928 to $667,000 in 1941.

Groner's job was to transform this monument to parvenu tastes into something people could afford to patronize. He made it into a come-and-bring-the-family proposition. "I had to pack 5,000 people a week into the restaurant and ballroom to give us the profit we needed." Groner finally managed it. In 1947 the Bank of America kissed Casa del Mar good-by, with the debt squared.

Other Merchants National inheritances also were worked out. Some, like San Clemente, almost a whole town, are still being carried. But prospects are good for the "dream city" started by Ole Hanson, Seattle's former mayor. In two recent years San Clemente's population has more than doubled. Near-by Camp Pendleton, the nation's largest permanent Marine base, has livened up things for business which fared poorly under Hanson's aspiration merely to create a "fine place to live and enjoy life."[8]

The northern limit of the real estate boom was Oakland. When Giannini took over the Oakland Bank in December, 1929, he accepted nearly $4,000,000 in loans on twelve subdivisions. Over the years all were worked out except one called Piedmont Pines, which the bank wrote off for a loss of $700,000. This land had ended up in the red with the previous owner. F. M. Smith, who dug a fortune in borax from Death Valley (remember the twenty-mule team?), had retired up north and invested $5,000,000 in forty miles of hilltops overlooking San Francisco Bay. The Smith Reserve bankrupted its namesake and might have done as badly by the Oakland Bank under the name of Piedmont Pines had not Giannini decided to take his loss and get out. He was to remember in the forties that he got out too soon. That was not altogether his fault. Banking regulations limit the time a bank can hold onto foreclosures.[9]

3

Inherited paper that brought losses or slow recoveries stands in conspicuous contrast to the Bank of Italy's own urban real estate lending during the boom period. It made no loans to subdividers. It sold no trust certificates, which were the common feature of subdivision developments. Joe Toplitzky, a big Los Angeles operator, several times tried to interest Giannini. Once he wired: "WILLIAM RANDOLPH HEARST, JOSEPH SCHENCK, IRVING HELLMAN AND MYSELF ARE BUYING MORTGAGE BEING FORECLOSED ON LARGE RANCH ADJACENT TO LOS ANGELES CONSERVATIVE VALUATION TWO MILLION CAN WE OBTAIN LOAN FROM YOU FIVE HUNDRED SEVENTY FIVE THOUSAND." He received this answer: "WE ARE NOT INTERESTED IN MAKING LOANS ON LARGE RANCHES." Toplitzky again telegraphed: "YOU MISUNDERSTOOD MY WIRE. . . . THE LOAN ASKED FOR IS ON THE NAMES OF THE PRINCIPALS SOLELY." Those were good names in California. Mr. Giannini replied: "HAVE TO SAY AGAIN WE ARE NOT INTERESTED."[10]

Loans were made to erect hotels or apartment buildings only in exceptional cases, where the need for such structures antedated the boom, or an old client wanted accommodation. Loans on "unimproved" land also were rare.

Generally speaking, the bank steered fairly clear of the boom area. When the reckoning set in, it held almost twice as many real estate loans in San Francisco, where there was no boom, as it did in Los Angeles. Figures for the two cities were 15,070 loans for $84,300,000, and 7,739 for $46,208,000.[11]

Giannini was fortunate in the man he found to execute, and, indeed, to assist in formulating the bank's mortgage policy during these difficult years. He was A. W. Hendrick—none other than Pop Hendrick who had entered the Giannini organization in 1919 via the California Joint Stock Land Bank. In 1923, when the value of Bank of Italy's mortgage portfolio, taking urban and rural loans together, passed $100,000,000, the central real estate loan department was created at No. 1 Powell and Hendrick was placed at the head of it. No mortgage over $10,000 could be taken without the department's approval. It served as the eyes and ears of the executive and the finance committees of the board. In 1927, when things were tightening up, the finance committee, under W. E. Blauer, passed on all real estate loans of more than $2,500. At that time the bank's mortgage investments amounted to $215,000,000. About 75 per cent of this was on urban and 25 per cent on farm property. The distribution coincided pretty closely with that of California's population between town and country.

With three booms going on at once—real estate, oil and movies—in addition to the general stock market boom, the Bank of Italy's real estate loan policy sought out the small borrowers who had little part in the grand schemes for easy money. This is not to say that the little people were not affected by these multiple booms. Everyone was affected by them somewhat. But the people who came to California and worked for wages or started small businesses and saved for a rainy day were affected least of all. They made up the bulk of the bank's borrowers, and the loans were on small homes, small stores and the like, where the liquidation of the debt did not depend on income from the property. Moreover, appraisals were made with studied disregard of unrealistic boom values.

To keep his branch managers alert, and also to find out what was going on, Giannini himself would appear at a branch and ask for a list of rejected applications for loans. He would go over them with the manager and find out why this man and that man had not been accommodated. And woe betide the manager who had failed to find the way to make a loan, if there was the possibility of showing the applicant how to finance it. Yet all the time there was a tightening of the reins. Renewals of loans that had not been materially reduced since the original advance required the approval of Hendrick. Provision was made for monthly payments of interest. In 1930 city real estate loans were written for one year only.

The bank received complaints about its closeness with credit. In Hanford a man said that a more liberal policy would "increase values and better conditions." "I went to some lengths to explain," reported the branch manager, "the fallacy of endeavoring to boost real estate values by banks making excessive loans on real estate." But it was pretty hard to convince some people of this, particularly real estate men. One such dealer said to Will Rice in San Luis Obispo: "I think branch banks are a curse to the country. . . . Branch banks will not make loans unless they are gilt-edge . . . and this prevents progress."[12]

A member of the advisory board in Placentia, just southeast of Los Angeles, said that occasionally "thoroughly deserving" applicants were turned down, and, in other instances, "considerable time was consumed" while the bank looked up the record of a prospective borrower. "This was never the case in the old independent banks."[13]

That was one way the Bank of Italy kept liquid. In 1921 real estate loans, urban and rural, constituted 30 per cent of its assets. In 1923, at the peak of the land boom, they touched 38 per cent. Thereafter the proportion steadily declined to 26 per cent at the end of 1928. This was lower by 7 per cent than the average for all banks in California. The Bank of Italy's ratio of *all loans* to resources also was lower in 1928. It stood at 49 per cent, whereas the average for the state was 61 per cent. The Bank of Italy's holding of United States government securities aggregated 11 per cent of its assets in 1921 and 25 per cent in 1928. The average investment of a California bank in "governments" in 1928 was 7.55 per cent of its resources.[14]

4

The checkered history of the oil boom can be passed over briefly because the Bank of Italy had so little to do with it. On its own the bank had no original dealings whatever with boom companies or their promoters. There was, however, a cleanup job with the Richfield Oil Company, of California, another loan inherited from the Merchants National Bank and Trust Company of Los Angeles.

But Giannini's name was momentarily linked with that of C. C. Julian, perhaps the most colorful of the flush-time promoters, when both men supported Young for governor in 1926.

"DO YOU WANT BANKER GIANNINI AND PROMOTER JULIAN TO RUN THE BANKING DEPARTMENT AND THE CORPORATION COMMISSION OF CALIFORNIA?" the Richardson organization asked in a political advertisement.[15]

That was before the Julian oil scandal broke—with which Mr. Julian, incidentally, had nothing to do. He had sold his interest in the Julian Petroleum Corporation in 1925 when the organization was highly solvent. The purchasers were S. C. Lewis, from Texas, and Jacob Berman, also known as Jack Bennett, a bucket-shop operator of Los Angeles. This pair bankrupted "Julian Pete" and rearranged the banking map of southern California in the process.

Soon after making their purchase Lewis and Berman became deeply involved with a number of bankers. In the course of a refinancing operation they paid a fee of $100,000. It had long been reported that certain bankers were exacting "bonuses" of promoters in exchange for financial assistance. A grand jury put that construction on the $100,000 fee, and returned indictments against Charles F. Stern, president of the Pacific-Southwest, and J. E. Barber, vice-president of the allied First National Bank of Los Angeles. Henry M. Robinson, who dominated both banks in question, defended the acceptance of the $100,000 which he said was for proper services. The indictments were dismissed. Later, Lewis and Berman were convicted of misuse of the mails.

In the course of these proceedings the Pacific-Southwest received some very unfavorable public notice. Subsequently, Robinson merged the Pacific-Southwest with his First National, thereby doing away with the name that appeared over more branch banks in the United States than any other name except the Bank of Italy. Eighteen months later, early in 1929, Joseph F. Sartori took over the consolidated institution, and joined it to his own bank under the name of Security–First National Bank of Los Angeles. Thus Mr. Sartori emerged from the situation with the second largest bank on the Coast.[16]

Another stock gambled in heavily was that of the Richfield Oil Company of California. Richfield had large assets, and it was the third largest marketer of gasoline in California. The collapse of the stock market in 1929 was followed by a drop in the price of oil. Production had been stepped up without regard for consumption and there was an enormous surplus. In 1930 Richfield owed California banks $6,500,000, the largest creditor being Sartori's Security–First National which held the company's paper in the amount of $1,750,-000. Giannini's Bank of America of California, having absorbed the Merchants National, was in for $1,250,000. Richfield asked the bankers to increase their loans. Generally they complied, though A. J. Mount who handled the matter for Giannini did not like the look of it. "We are just doing business with a group that we cannot be happy with, and sooner or later somebody is going to have trouble."[17]

Everybody had trouble. Early in 1931 Richfield went into receivership, owing the Bank of America N. T. & S. A. (successor to the Bank of America of California and the Bank of Italy) $2,110,924. Three top officers of Richfield went to prison. The company was reorganized, and in 1937 the Bank of America N. T. & S. A. accepted $999,685 in settlement of the debt.

5

And now the movies.

If land, one of the oldest investments known to man, and oil, which had been a part of American finance since 1859, could produce the blue-sky operations that have been touched on, what of this brand-new industry which started without precedents and promptly became famous for prodigality with money and with language? The vocabulary that sufficed Shakespeare, Strindberg and Shaw was inadequate to the needs of the cinema. So Hollywood coined its own words, such as supercolossal. An early example of the Hollywood imagination at work was furnished by Carl Laemmle. He announced that in honor of the opening of Universal City the Pacific fleet would steam up the Los Angeles River and fire a salute—a compliment difficult of realization because the Los Angeles River wouldn't float a canoe.

Therefore the authors of this book were somewhat surprised to discover that as a field of investment for bankers the motion picture industry proved to be a paradox. The Bank of Italy, one of the pioneer lenders to the pioneers of the industry, does not appear to have lost a dollar on a movie loan during the boom period. The experience of the few other bankers who were early in the field also seems to have been highly satisfactory. For any new industry that is not only a creditable record; it is a remarkable one.

It was Dr. A. H. Giannini who took the Bank of Italy into the movie field. In 1909 he was responsible for a loan of $500 to Sol L. Lesser, a partner in a "nickelodeon" on Fillmore Street in San Francisco. Seven years later Lesser was the head of All Features Distributors, which had a regular line of credit with the bank. In 1918 the bank loaned $50,000 to the Famous Players–Lasky Company. That seems to have been its first large advance to a producer.

In 1919 Doc Giannini went to New York, in charge of the East
River National Bank located on Broadway a few blocks south of
Fourteenth Street, which had been the proving ground for the city's
earliest movie houses. The Schenck brothers got their start there and
then built a studio across the Hudson on top of the Palisades. Others
whose names one day were to become prominent in Hollywood
were beginning their careers on the same street in 1919. They
worked in the penny arcades and flea circuses, as ushers in picture
theaters, as waiters, as pants pressers, and in the sweat shops.

Doc Giannini took pains to know them, their relatives and their
friends and to get their accounts. As a result the East River National
took the lead with the individual loans to the motion picture industry. By that time twenty-five distributing organizations were circulating films to sixteen thousand picture theaters in the country. What
the Doc had learned about distribution in San Francisco from Sol
Lesser was one key to his lending. Proven stars was another. After a
flow of small loans—$500 to $2,000—to producers like Biograph,
General Films, Mack Sennett, Vitagraph and Lubin, Doc Giannini
made history with a $250,000 advance to First National Distributors.
The security was Charlie Chaplin's *The Kid*. The loan was repaid in
six weeks. Up to then, such movie capital had come from miscellaneous sources, and rates of interest up to 20 per cent had been paid.

"If a film is offered me starring Doug [Fairbanks], Charlie
[Chaplin], Harold [Lloyd], or any of a half dozen leading actors it
is as good as cash," A. H. Giannini said in 1926. "Where I am in
doubt I call up any of a half-a-dozen theater managers and get an
immediate rating."[18]

The activities of the East River National Bank were duly noted in
California, and not by the Bank of Italy alone. In Los Angeles the
Robinson banks made a special study of the motion picture industry
as a source of bankable loans. "Motion picture loans, when properly
guarded, offer good security and liquidity," the study concluded and
Robinson entered the field.[19]

Although he remained in New York, Doc Giannini had a good
deal to do with the Bank of Italy's movie lendings in California.
When some of the B. of I. directors expressed doubts, Doc cited the
East River's experience with *The Kid*. He said the movie had been
a better investment than government bonds would have been, pointing out the dip that governments had taken during the period in

San Jose was the site of the bank's first out-of-town branch; it was opened in 1909.

1921, when the East River's money was out on the Chaplin film.[20]

By 1923 pictures had attained the supercolossal stage of their development. Joseph M. Schenck, who had gone to California, and Cecil B. DeMille, were named to the advisory board of one of the Los Angeles branches of the Bank of Italy. As time went on and the number of southern branches increased, Conrad Nagel, Will Rogers, Sol Lesser and others were on the boards of branches. DeMille served as president of the Commercial and Savings Bank of Culver City when that institution was owned by the Americommercial Corporation. One of President DeMille's first acts was to reduce the interest on loans from 8 to 7 per cent. Subsequently the Culver City depository became a branch of the Bank of America of Los Angeles and, in 1927, of the Bank of Italy.[21]

In 1926 Schenck asked for a loan of $300,000 on top of one of $600,000 that he already owed the Bank of Italy. A. P. Giannini turned him down. "You must admit, Joe, that a $600,000 loan unsecured is pretty heavy. I have always told the boys in the bank that I would not loan Messrs. Rockefeller, Senior or Junior, nor Mr. Henry Ford or even J. P. Morgan himself . . . $600,000 without security."[22]

So much for Giannini's caution.

Financing Agriculture in the Twenties

DURING the twenties the Bank of Italy moved into first place as a backer of agriculture in California. At the end of the decade its investment in farm mortgages alone amounted to $71,-296,899. This was just under 9 per cent of the state's farm-mortgage debt. The bank held mortgages on 12,147 farms, which was one out of eleven of all the farms in California. Not included in the foregoing are several items, each running into millions of dollars: mortgages held by the bank's affiliate, the California Joint Stock Land Bank; loans made by a new affiliate, popularly called "Giannini's cow bank"; loans to co-operative marketing organizations; seasonal loans to farmers, sometimes secured by crops, sometimes unsecured.

As noted earlier, the California farmer came through the postwar readjustment better than farmers elsewhere. He continued to do better throughout the twenties, although in the country at large agriculture continued to go to the "damnation bowwows," as Pop Hendrick put it. During the ten years ending in 1930, California increased its vineyard acreage 94 per cent. (National prohibition proved a help in that particular.) Citrus fruits, which had had a big spurt a decade earlier, expanded their acreage by something over 25 per cent; subtropical fruits and nuts, by 82 per cent; temperate-zone fruits, by 61 per cent. This is not to say that California did not have its agricultural headaches in the twenties. The vineyard acreage increase, for example, was too great. The disaster that befell raisins will be noted further on.

Still there was growth and prosperity in rural California. Within ten years the over-all value of California's farm lands and buildings climbed nearly $337,000,000. Annual farm income hovered around $500,000,000 until 1925. After that it went up to $690,000,000. A factor in this was the expanding market California enjoyed at home. Those two million people added to the state's population had to eat.

All this created a demand for new capital. California's farm-mortgage debt rose from $404,000,000 to $615,000,000.

When Hendrick set up the central real estate department to take charge of the bank's mortgage investments, urban and rural, he stressed the need for accurate appraisals—"the very life of a loaning institution." While many rural banks, and not a few in the cities, permitted themselves to be influenced by rising sales values, Pop Hendrick was able to say: "We are not interested in the sales value of land until a loan goes bad. We know of plenty of districts in this state where land is selling at $5,000 per acre that we would not appraise for $800."[1]

Equally conservative were the loans themselves. Seldom did a branch manager receive approval from the central real estate department to make a loan on 50 per cent of the appraised value. Even in the citrus districts, where groves were up to $5,000 an acre, the bank's average loan per acre was $347.67. For agriculture as a whole, the average loan was $41.39 as against a general average valuation of $112.32 per acre. Average loan per farm roughly valued at $25,000, was $5,869.50.[2]

2

The refusal of loans brought protests, naturally. Some disappointed borrowers concluded that branch banking was "predatory," as one critic expressed it. "Branch banks are a curse to the state; they send all of their money to the big cities."[3]

The facts dispute this claim. In 1930 one hundred branches loaned over 70 per cent of local deposits in the local communities. Not a few rural branches absorbed in loans all their deposits and more besides. In Gilroy the figure was 110 per cent of deposits; in Napa, 119 per cent; Shafter, 121; Arcadia, 150; Wasco, 148; Ukiah, 123; Manteca, 148; Yuba City, 169; King City, 174. Towns of less than 50,000 were the heaviest borrowers, with loans averaging 67 per cent of deposits. Towns above 50,000 registered loans of 63 per cent. Actually it was city money that went to the country.[4]

Another way of looking at the credit picture is to compare the Bank of Italy's loans with those of country competitors. Below are given the June, 1929, figures for six representative agricultural centers scattered through the state. In one the loan ratio of an independent bank exceeded that of the Bank of Italy.

City	Bank	Ratio of Loans to Deposits (Per Cent)
San Jose	Bank of Italy, Main branch	97
	San Jose National	91
	First National Bank	61
Salinas	Bank of Italy	105
	Monterey Co. Tr. & Sav.	53
Marysville	Bank of Italy	105
	Decker-Jewett Bank	89
	No. California Sav.	40
	First National Bank	34
Stockton	Stockton Sav. & Loan	86
	Bank of Italy, Commercial & Savings branch	81
	Bank of Italy, main branch	73
	Union Safe Deposit	51
	First National Bank	49
Madera	Bank of Italy	75
	First National Bank	55
Ontario	Bank of Italy	126
	First National Bank	52
	Citizens National	49

How well California's agricultural interests were served during the twenties can be told through one community's experience. In June, 1921, with the acquisition of the First National Bank of King City, the Bank of Italy entered a small marketing center (1,500 townsfolk, 3,500 farmers) of the southern Salinas Valley to which Giannini promised to bring the facilities of a big city bank. The following table, contrasting the First National's and the branch's loans, shows that he made good his promise:

	Year	Deposits	Loans
First National	Jan. 1918	$209,000	$ 216,000
	" 1919	340,000	344,000
	" 1920	558,000	535,000
	" 1921	688,000	608,000

Bank of Italy	Dec. 1921	491,000	1,069,000
	" 1922	485,000	1,213,000
	" 1923	577,000	1,302,000
	" 1924	563,000	1,047,000
	" 1925	535,000	891,000
	" 1926	400,000	913,000
	" 1927	432,000	845,000
	" 1928	462,000	852,000
	" 1929	601,000	1,325,000
	" 1930	783,000	1,362,000[5]

The First National's legal limit on a single loan had been $12,229. In 1929, of the forty-five largest borrowers from the Bank of Italy's branch, thirty-five were ranchers. A sheep man got $338,107; a dairyman, $38,200; a bean grower, $42,000; an orchardist, $37,000; a cattleman, $120,000.[6]

Large loans, such as the above, helped to pull King City through the disastrous short seasons that hit California ranges off and on in the early twenties. Lack of rain, high prices for feed and low prices for cattle had the area on the ropes. Loans to retrieve the situation went far beyond the sum customarily allocated to the King City branch.

"We did not like to see the cattle go off the ranges," said Hendrick.

We realized if the cattle went off the land, our real estate loans were of little value. We were in a position . . . to finance both ends of the game. We had the real estate loans, and we put the stock on them. We would have put it on there anyway if we had taken the land over. We reasoned that the man who was running it could run it better than we could and the best thing we could do was to give him the chance rather than to take the farm and try to do it ourselves.

To Hendrick, "No real estate loan [was] really secure unless you [were] in a position to take care of the current, everyday need of the farmer as well."[7]

Thus it was that about this period the Bank of Italy began putting the borrowing farmer on a budget, a radical departure in that day. The budget ran the whole gamut of farming costs: capital expenditures, such as a team or tractor; materials and supplies, from gasoline to twine; operating costs for crop-plowing, cultivating, irrigating, pruning, harvesting and hauling; an estimate of monthly advances; and crop forecasts. Behind every budget was a watchful Bank of Italy man—branch manager, field man or appraiser—to see that the borrower lived up to his contract which incidentally carried with it object lessons in efficiency and farm management.

Carl Wente recalls one such vigil, lasting from 1921 until the mid-thirties, over a $200,000 mortgage on a four-thousand-acre grain ranch located in the fertile, silt-laden Tulare Lake region. Year by year Wente revised the rancher's budget, made advances, sold the crop and trimmed something off the principal of the loan. In the end, the farmer owned his ranch mortgage free.[8]

Most farmers are set in their ways and not always are they good managers. The budgets were not a popular innovation, though some saw the light. A Yuba County peach farmer wrote the head office:

> I have never said this publicly, for I would have been run out of town, but I believe the system . . . of making farmers keep records, submit budgets when borrowing and questioning their methods of operation has, during this period of low prices and crop losses, forced them to be better business men. Because they are better business men, when there are good prices or good crops they will be able to make more money than ever before.[9]

The 12,147 farms on which the bank held mortgages in 1930 covered the whole range of California agriculture:

Security	Acres	No. Loans	Amount	Percentage of Farm Loans
Citrus groves	11,603	616	$ 4,034,361	5.7
Vineyards	55,838	1,289	6,354,787	8.9
Diversified farms	241,370	1,470	9,028,214	12.7
Deciduous orchards	105,175	3,032	18,611,856	26.1
Cereal, field crops, alfalfa and pasture	1,267,591	5,740	33,267,679	46.6

Geographically they were distributed as follows:

District	No. Loans	Amount
Los Angeles	138	$ 2,277,442
San Diego–Imperial	537	2,249,773
Santa Barbara	382	2,741,386
Riverside–San Bernardino	750	4,307,205
Santa Clara–Salinas Valleys	1,456	14,520,691

San Joaquin	2,565	14,635,951
Sacramento	1,738	11,071,159
Long Beach	18	139,445
San Francisco	201	4,106,185
North Coast Area	1,767	9,188,890
East Bay	2,076	3,415,226
Bakersfield	519	2,551,540[10]

3

Additional aid to the farmer was afforded by the Bank of Italy's affiliate, the California Joint Stock Land Bank, which achieved a brilliant record through the twenties. It was a profitable venture all round. Farmers benefited from long-term credit at 6 per cent. By the end of the decade the Land Bank, which had begun business late in 1919, had loaned nearly $21,000,000. The Bank of Italy benefited by having a profitable affiliate whose earnings ran from $100,-000 to $175,000 a year. The Land Bank also helped to keep the parent bank in a liquid condition.

"When we get a mortgage loan in one of our branches that we are quite certain will not be paid off in two or three or four or five years, we put it in the Joint Stock Land Bank," Hendrick explained in 1922. "Putting it in the Joint Stock Land Bank . . . leaves them [the branches] with money to loan to the farmer for his seasonal needs."[11]

The California Joint Stock Land Bank's record shines the more brightly because of the unfortunate history of joint-stock land banks during the period. Due to overlending and mismanagement many of the country's eighty-three joint-stock land banks failed and others were obliged to take drastic measures to keep from doing so. All this tended to give the joint-stock banks a poor name, from which the Giannini institution was happily exempt, as the ready sale of its bonds indicated.

The secret of the California Joint Stock Land Bank's success is not hard to find: sound loans. While land banks generally, and particularly those in the Middle West, increased their loans from year to year between 1922 and 1926, the Giannini institution was pulling in its horns—this notwithstanding that California farmers were in better shape than their colleagues east of the Rockies. The new-loans record of the Giannini land bank:

1922	$4,345,000
1923	3,445,000
1924	1,504,000
1925	1,565,000
1926	1,586,000

In 1923, on the 327,000 acres mortgaged, the average loan per acre was around $30 or about 37 per cent of the bank's appraisal of the value of the land. Three years later, the average was 56 cents higher on 391,000 acres. Loans were made on the basis of less than 36 per cent of the bank's appraisals, and were far below the values borrowing farmers placed on their property.[12]

As a result, few ragged mortgages troubled the California Joint Stock Land Bank. In fact, Hendrick often found loans paying out faster than they were being made. Midway in the twenties less than a half-dozen borrowers were delinquent. Six years later, in 1930, installments delinquent ninety days or over totaled only $3,345. At that time, the Land Bank held $16,341,150 in mortgages.[13]

In May, 1927, the joint-stock land bank in Kansas City, one of the largest in the system, failed. The Milwaukee bank went under in July, and a third, the Ohio, in September. For a moment Hendrick was fearful lest "we be punished because of other people's wrong doings." His anxiety was needless. Presently he was able to say:

"The California Joint Stock Land Bank . . . is about the only land bank in the United States that is not in trouble and there is plenty of money on hand to continue making loans . . . for two years without selling any further bonds."[14]

The banks that were having a hard time clamped down sharply on new loans whereas Hendrick went ahead in his careful way. In 1929 the California Land Bank loaned $769,000, the most money loaned in that year by any joint-stock land bank in the United States. The loans of the nearest contender amounted to $417,000.

4

We turn now to a less agreeable subject—raisins.

The story opens on a scene of boom, in 1920. The bean and the citrus people—in fact California farmers as a class—had weathered their postwar crises, had learned their lessons, and were working out. Not so with the raisin growers. They were getting $296 a ton for their product, as against $100 five years before. They behaved as if the price would never go lower. Raisin land sold for as much as $2,000 an acre. Lawyers, doctors and other speculators, who knew little more about growing grapes than they did about growing rubber, rushed in to buy.

In 1922 the boom came to an abrupt end when the price of raisins dropped to $73. With the foreign market vanishing in the face of European recovery, more raisins were on hand than could be sold. Thereupon began a struggle to curtail production, increase consumption and raise the price. During the ensuing eight years to 1930, one expedient after another was tried without success. In this discouraging undertaking the Bank of Italy played an important role, sticking by the sick and suffering industry when there seemed no good reason to hope.

The first year of bad news had the raisin producers' co-operative, the California Associated Raisin Company, up against it. Like the growers, the co-op had overreached itself, in plants, equipment and debt. By 1922, it owed $8,500,000 to banks, the largest creditor being the Bank of Italy, in for $890,000. Giannini took counsel with officers of the Mercantile Trust and the First National of Los Angeles. Collapse of the co-op would ruin every vineyardist in the San Joaquin Valley and carry with it a number of local banks. The three large banks agreed to advance additional funds to make over the industry's marketing machinery for a fresh start.

The co-op was reorganized under the name Sun-Maid Raisin Growers. With creditors taking heavy losses, debts contracted by the old outfit were scaled down to $3,000,000. To bolster the general economy the Bank of Italy and the Pacific-Southwest took over (very unwillingly, as related in an earlier chapter) the Valley Bank of Fresno, which was wrecked when the raisin collapse added its burden to that of foolish management.[15]

Sun-Maid was managed by Ralph Merritt, who set out to do what California's citrus co-op had done in its "Sunkist" campaigns to make Americans eat more oranges. In 1924 Sun-Maid scraped together a considerable sum to advertise raisins nationally. One slogan was "Wednesday is Raisin Bread Day." On distant Long Island a bakery built up a monthly demand for eight thousand loaves. Little red packages of Sun-Maid raisins appeared on counters along with candy bars. People bought them and liked them. The consumption of raisins went from two and a half pounds per capita to nearly four.[16]

This was a notable achievement; but it was not enough. The more raisins Merritt sold, the more California produced. A few farm papers jeered at Merritt and took incidental swipes at the banks. Hard-pressed and impatient growers began to desert the Sun-Maid organization and to dispose of their crops wherever a buyer could be found. By the end of 1926, 45 per cent of the original membership was gone, and the price of raisins had slipped to $62. The disillusioned Merritt resigned.

The Bank of Italy's direct credits to Sun-Maid had risen to $3,750,-000. This was in addition to other loans in the Fresno area amounting to $9,655,000, most of which went to farmers. One morning in 1927 the president of the Reedley National Bank of Reedley crossed the street and entered the Bank of Italy branch. He said that he was at the end of his road. The independent bank had $700,000 in deposits and $600,000 in loans, mostly frozen because of raisins. Giannini consented to take the bank over.[17]

With Sun-Maid on the verge of foundering, the Bank of Italy and other large creditors tied the growers into the California Vineyard Association, which had been organized the year before (1926) as a service organization for the fresh-grape industry. C. V. A. attempted to tackle the stubborn evil of overproduction. Its proposal for "orderly marketing" contemplated leaving as much as half the harvest on the vines. The banking group behind Sun-Maid agreed to hold off the market another 75,000 tons over which they had control.

The scheme might have accomplished a good deal had all the raisin growers come in. Only 60 per cent of them signed up, however. On top of that, 1928 brought a bumper crop. The desperate nonsigners dumped their product on the market. The year 1930 promised another bumper yield which would boost the unsalable surplus of raisins to 300,000 tons. The situation was critical. It would have been chaotic except that help from Uncle Sam was at hand.[18]

The aim of the Agricultural Marketing Act of 1929 was to get rid of farm surpluses and to raise prices. The administrative agency created by the act was the Federal Farm Board. Though wheat and cotton represented the board's most pressing problems, early in 1930 it came out with a plan for California's grape industry, including raisins. With this aid in prospect the Bank of Italy, the Anglo-California Bank of San Francisco, and the Security–First National of Los Angeles advanced $5,500,000 to keep Sun-Maid afloat until the government could get its program going. This scheme called for a sort of super-co-operative for the whole grape industry. The Federal Farm Board offered to contribute $6,667,000, provided the faithful bankers would put in $4,500,000.[19]

The bankers were willing to do their part once more, if 85 per cent of the raisin growers would join up. The Bank of Italy took the lead in a campaign to bring them in. The badly mauled vineyardists, whose hopes had been frustrated so often, responded slowly. But they did respond, and in the early summer of 1930 the program got under way. With the government as well as the bankers behind them, the raisin people took heart and looked forward to better times.[20]

5

The raisin troubles brought sobering thoughts to the California farmer, particularly when the prices of other crops tended to wobble.

Pop Hendrick preached more crop diversity and improved marketing. As early as 1920, he wrote to the Canadian minister of agriculture:

The cold storage plant, the elevator, the creamery, distributing stations, all provide the speculator with a means of postponing the sale of produce until such time as it suits him, and by so doing, force an artificial price. This we shall never be able to circumvent unless some agency provides the machinery by which products of the soil can be sent into the market through the year.[21]

The subject of agriculture, the country's one unprosperous industry during the booming twenties, occupied many minds. Mr. Giannini's mail was full of it. A popular suggestion was that the bank establish within its organization a sort of department of agriculture to plot the course of the farmer and his co-op. A student of European agriculture wrote:

Your great network of banks lends itself admirably to leadership in this matter. . . . Why is not the State entitled to the use of your organizing ability in the field of agriculture, which definitely is the backbone of our State's prosperity. You know of the great success attained in this field in certain European countries. In every instance, some man assumed leadership. . . . Why not—in California Giannini?[22]

The wife of a turkey raiser in the barren Lost Hills west of Wasco began thinking along the same lines when the price of dressed turkeys fell from forty-two to twenty-six cents a pound.

As you very well know, every branch of industry is now consolidating under one central head, and then having branches [she wrote]. My idea is this—let one corporation own *all* the land, giving the farmers and workers on the farm a share or stock in the corporation. Have men at the head of this corporation who are trained men and who know the selling game. . . . You mark my words—under such a plan foodstuff would be lowered to the consumer and every farmer and farm worker would certainly have a great deal more than they do now—and no worry. . . . I do wish you would tackle this job.[23]

Vice-President Harry C. Carr told the lady in the Lost Hills that, if she had attended old-time revival meetings, she would recall that

the evangelists always insisted upon an orderly program of bringing people into the church, and it was first necessary that they should be convinced of their sins and then converted to the new idea of life. The question at the present is not what we can do for the farmer but what the farmer is willing to let us do for him.[24]

At the moment, Mr. Carr was deep in plans to turn the farmer's attention to dairy cattle, something California did not have enough of. Each year 25,000,000 pounds of butter, 20,000,000 of cheese and 20,000,000 pounds of condensed milk were shipped in. The time appeared ripe to lift dairy production by enlarging and by bettering the herds. "The best way we can do this," Carr wrote the California Dairy Council, "is to develop cows of high productive power that are free from disease, and locate them on lands of high feed production that can be operated at low cost so far as irrigation and cultivation are concerned." He plugged for cow-testing associations to weed out poor producers, the "boarders" in the herds. "No manufacturer in the world who is successful will continue to use a piece of machinery . . . that does not render a fair return for the money expended."[25]

There were drawbacks to the realization of Carr's idea. On the hoof, a good milker was bringing between $100 and $125 a head. Few dairymen had enough cash to buy them. Sources for borrowing were limited, most banks being willing to risk a maximum of $30 a head on livestock loans. Finance companies and commission houses, particularly in Los Angeles, were willing to lay out more, and thus had gained "a stranglehold" on California's cow barns. "These institutions," a Los Angeles livestock inspector declared, "have simply broken the old cow's back with charges." "Extras" imposed in connection with loans ran interest rates to 25 per cent.[26]

The irony was that a good many of the loan sharks made their exorbitant profits on money obtained from the Federal Intermediate Credit Bank at less than 6 per cent. Set up by Congress in 1923 to ease credit between harvests, the Federal Intermediate Credit Bank rediscounted farmers' paper held by commercial banks, cattle-loan companies, livestock commission houses and the newly devised agricultural credit corporations. After nearly five years, the business of the Intermediate Credit Bank was far below expectations. For one thing, commercial institutions that did not soak their patrons with usurious "extras" found that the $1\frac{1}{2}$ per cent they were permitted to charge above the government bank's discount rate afforded too narrow a margin of profit. Particularly was this true in the case of small banks. Yet, raising the charge to $2\frac{1}{2}$ per cent did not prove any more inviting. Actually, much of the paper of these institutions was too badly frozen to be eligible for rediscount.[27]

These difficulties did not affect the Giannini organization, which could handle business in such volume that the small margin would mean a worth-while profit. Consequently on March 1, 1928, there came into being the Bankitaly Agricultural Credit Corporation, colloquially known as "Giannini's cow bank." The entire capital of $1,000,000 was owned by the National Bankitaly Company, which had succeeded the Stockholders Auxiliary in 1927. A. W. Hendrick was named president of the cow bank and H. C. Carr, vice-president and general manager. Before a year was out Carr was obliged to devote all his time to the Bank of Italy. His successor in the cow bank was Fred L. Washburn, a livestock commission man well known among Western cattle raisers and packers.

At first loans were confined to California, with patrons of the Bank of Italy getting first attention. As security, preference was given to "tuberculin tested herds, located in the districts where milk testing associations function and where dairymen appreciate high grade cattle"; and to range cattle and sheep "where the stockmen own their own ranges, produce sufficient feed for the herd, and appreciate the value of better grades of cattle and sheep."[28]

To the stockman prepared to meet these conditions the cow bank offered loans ranging from $1,000 to $250,000, payable in monthly installments up to eighteen or twenty months. No commissions were charged. Appraisal and inspection fees were nominal—ten cents a head for feeder cattle; five cents for sheep; twenty cents for dairy cows. The corporation announced it would have no part in buying, selling or "leasing" livestock to borrowers, favorite nooses of the finance companies. Other good news was that money was to be had at 6½ per cent.

The rate was lower by one-half of one per cent than the limit specified by the government. Moreover, it was lower by one-half of one per cent than the cow-loan rate charged by the Bank of Italy. This caused a stir at No. 1 Powell. Even Carr objected at first but changed his mind because, as he said, "we are really doing something constructive." He meant in the long-range view. It was believed that the 6½ per cent rate would make dairymen of some of the National Bankitaly Company's leaseholders who were farming foreclosures for the Bank of Italy. As an added incentive, the cow bank stood ready to advance a herd's full purchase price, one more step toward getting farmers away from overcrowded crops.[29]

The start was slow. At the end of July (1928), cow-bank loans were only $212,000; in August, $236,000; September, $240,000. When Washburn, the cattleman, succeeded Carr, the cow bank's major interest became range cattle, with sheep running a close second. By the end of 1929, loans had leaped in one year from $1,000,000 to $4,800,000. Most were fairly large, the number for the year being 93. A few loans were extended to Arizona and Nevada stockmen on range cattle. Sheep and dairy loans were then neck and neck. Overproduction, plus a dry year, put a crimp in the wool growers. Thereafter the cow bank went light on sheep loans, the San Francisco office informing the Arcata branch which had a prospective customer in tow: "It would be a wise move to discourage any new people going into the sheep business."[30]

The wisdom of this policy was clearer a year later when a district supervisor talked to a sheep and wool buyer from Willows. The buyer said that sheepmen who had turned elsewhere for advances "are now finding themselves worrying about the present low price [of wool]. A number of sheep men have told me that the Bank of Italy in refusing them a loan did them a big favor."[31]

At the end of eighteen months, the cow bank's loans aggregated over $15,000,000. The money went into thirty-two of California's fifty-eight counties.

6

During the twenties the cotton-raising industry was reorganized in California and put on a permanent basis. This provided another means by which the farmer in the Imperial and the lower San Joaquin Valleys could diversify his production.

Hitherto cotton had been a more or less experimental crop, despite the boom brought on by World War I. Some cotton had been grown in the Imperial Valley since the beginning of the century. With the coming of the war and higher prices, cotton fields spread northward into the San Joaquin. By 1920 they yielded 67,000 bales.

The cotton planter in California as elsewhere seemed to be sitting on the top of the world when the war ended. In 1919 his crop brought thirty-seven cents a pound. But a year later the price crashed to fourteen.

This meant trouble for banks in the California cotton belt. Even as shrewd a banker as George A. Davidson of the Southern Trust and Commerce of San Diego was caught for a loss of $300,000.

A notable exception in Imperial Valley was the First National Bank of El Centro. The institution's policy stemmed from the founder, Leroy Holt, who arrived in 1900 when the valley was opened for settlement. The pioneer banker guided the First National through the aftermaths of disastrous floods of the untamed Colorado River in the early days, through the wartime cotton boom, and was in the van of the bankers' rush to alfalfa and livestock investments when the Stockholders Auxiliary bought his bank in 1923. He remained with the Bank of Italy, directing the branches in the Imperial.

The Bank of Italy had made no cotton loans, though it watched somewhat anxiously the gradual recovery of California's cotton raisers. The price collapse of 1920 had brought acreage away down.

When recovery set in, the crop continued moving into the San Joaquin Valley where climate and soil were found to be better for cotton than in Imperial. In 1926 California produced 131,000 bales on 162,000 acres and the product was superior. Of the medium-long-staple variety, it was well suited to the manufacture of automobile tires and was responsible for the opening of tire factories in southern California.

Although a campaigner for diversification, the Bank of Italy did not get into the cotton-loan field until late 1924. The practice of lending directly to planters was then being abandoned in favor of credit to ginners and brokers who, with a better understanding of the risks involved, loaned to the growers. Adopting this practice, the Bank of Italy plunged into cotton loans in a big way. In 1926 it made one loan of more than $1,000,000. By 1929 the bank's cotton loans, aggregating more than $10,000,000, financed half of California's crop.[32]

The achievement was another milestone in Giannini's ambitions for his native state. "California enjoys," he said, "the distinction of being the only cotton-growing state able to finance its crop through its own banks. . . . All other states in which this staple is grown must seek outside help . . . the major portion coming from New York."[33]

In 1929, 260,000 bales of cotton grown in California brought in the market $9,000,000, more than was realized from raisins. Hendrick hired away from the United States Department of Agriculture W. B. Camp, who had fathered and developed the federal experimental cotton farm at Shafter where the state's famed Acala strains originated. An outspoken South Carolinian, Camp assumed the missionary role of preaching the merits of a cash crop, like cotton or alfalfa, over the vineyard or orchard.

"The bank wants to keep the people on the farms," wrote a country editor of Camp's appointment, "and desires to show them how to make it worthwhile to stay there."[34]

While the Bank of Italy and other progressive lenders were opening new possibilities to the farmer, 31 California banks failed between 1921 and 1930. This was 4.3 per cent of the state's banks doing business at the start of the decade. The showing is creditable by comparison with failures in other agricultural areas. Illinois lost 138 banks or 8.6 per cent of its total number; Kansas, 223 (17.9 per cent); Missouri, 296 (17.9 per cent); Texas, 299 (18.9 per cent); Minnesota, 411 (27 per cent); Nebraska, 339 (29.3 per cent); and Iowa, 528 (29.9 per cent). The national toll was 5,640 or 18.8 per cent.

The part that the branch systems played in keeping California's record low cannot be overlooked. Mostly large institutions, the branch banks were able to make heavy commitments to agriculture by using a very small fraction of their investable funds. During the decade the Bank of Italy's resources increased eightfold, from $157,-000,000 to $1,162,000,000. Many more than thirty-one banks would have closed had it not been for the large branch banking systems. In the Bank of Italy's case the rescue of the Hyde banks in Visalia and of the Valley Bank of Fresno were not isolated examples. During the twenties the Giannini organization saved rural banks in the following places: Reedley, Calexico, Ventura, Hanford, Tulare, Fowler, Clovis, Pittsburg, Antioch, Paso Robles, Sonora, Sebastopol, Santa Cruz, Healdsburg, Susanville, Fall River, New Bieber, Quincy, Yuba City and Alturas. And this list is incomplete.[35]

Considering the amount of doubtful loans inevitably assumed from other banks, the Bank of Italy's foreclosure record through the twenties is not high. Figures available are for urban and farm real estate combined, farms comprising perhaps roughly one-fourth of the totals. Through 1925, when there were 18,000 real estate loans on the books, the score was:

Year	Foreclosures	Book Value
1921	15	$ 101,029
1922	26	326,225
1923	52	447,186
1924	89	993,611
1925	102	1,028,964

In the last half of the decade the total of foreclosures went up faster:

Year	Foreclosures	Book Value
1926	132	$1,087,165
1927	169	1,458,626
1928	228	1,907,735
1929	380	3,694,072
1930	412	4,591,091[36]

During these five years the average per branch was slightly over one foreclosure each year.

Answering the inquiry of a member of the Federal Farm Labor Board in 1924, Hendrick stated the policy from which the bank was not to deviate in the worst years of the depression: "We hesitate to commence any foreclosure proceedings where the farmer can make a payment out of the proceeds of a coming crop and where a delinquency is no real fault of his but rather due to the present condition of agriculture." Hendrick instructed the men sent into the field that, as long as "a delinquent borrower would match his labor against the bank's capital," foreclosure should not be considered. That this policy prevailed is evident from the record in Fresno County, center of the raisin crisis, where in 1926 only eighteen farms were taken over, an average of three per branch in the county.[37]

No matter how necessary, foreclosures are always criticized in some quarters. An item in a weekly newspaper published in Siskiyou County in 1930 furnishes an extreme example:

> The Bank of Italy has acquired through various ways much of the choice farming land of California and is still gathering it in. The great octopus is near to us in Yreka and ready for all and sundry of the unwary. They, you know, are exploiting the country the same as all other foreigners do. . . . As sure as they get their talons into you, you'll lose. Their policy was spawned by the devil and their chain of banks is, each one, a little hell.[38]

The facts are that less than one-fifth of the farms foreclosed in the twenties was mortgaged originally to the Bank of Italy. Vice-President Carl F. Wente, who sweated out many a foreclosure, put it in more earthy terms. "The bank got a black eye skinning the other fellows' skunks."[39]

7

An axiom of the mortgage business is that a foreclosed farm is never a bargain. The farmer about to lose his place neglects the perpetual work of maintenance that is necessary to keep fences and buildings in repair and the land productive. To help the bank keep liquid, foreclosed properties had long been transferred to the Stockholders Auxiliary (and after 1927 to its successor the National Bankitaly Company). The administration of the properties remained with Hendrick's central real estate department of the Bank of Italy. The detail work, however, fell upon the branch managers. Carl F. Wente, then at Modesto, was the first branch manager to rehabilitate a foreclosure of the bank. This was in 1921. With a mortgage of $83,000 hanging over 400 acres of neglected orchards, Hendrick decided the place could never be sold as it was. Wente hired a farmer and bought half a dozen mules. In two years he spent $8,000 on the ranch, after which it was sold for $120,000.[40]

At his next post, Visalia, Wente found the branch burdened by troubles old and new. There was still a load of slow paper from the Hyde regime, and, on top of that, the results of the raisin collapse. Unpicked grapes rotted on the vines. The branch had eighty-five foreclosures in the mill, all old mortgages. The situation was getting bad elsewhere—at Tulare, Hanford, Fresno and Madera. Mario Giannini, chairman of the bank's executive committee, went to Visalia and spent many a night hour with Hendrick and Wente trying to find a way out. The result was the formation of the valley farms committee "to supervise and direct all farming activities in connection with properties owned by the Bank or the Auxiliary Corporation."

At the start in 1925 the valley farms committee was responsible for 161 scattered farms of some 12,000 acres. The first step was to budget each farm to the bone. Field Superintendent A. Colussi and his assistant T. F. Malesani had charge of operations on the ground. They were crackerjacks. Both had years of experience as superintendents for the Italian Swiss Colony wineries. When prohibition came in Colussi had turned to ranching for himself. For seven years his yields had been double those of other ranchers in his community.[41]

Colussi and Malesani gave their attention first to Tulare County, and the Yettem district in particular, where the old Visalia bank had ruined itself on vineyards. Foreclosures represented 50-odd farms, ranging from 20 to 320 acres. A base of operations called central camp was set up, and Malesani began collecting horses, mules and implements from the run-down farms. It was a meager collection: 8 double plows, 5 single plows, 5 spring tooth harrows, 4 discs, 4 horse hoes, 2 vineyard trucks, 20 head of horses, 50 tons of hay and washtubs for water troughs. Old-timers were amazed at the work that followed. Row upon row of phylloxera-ridden and worn-out vines were pulled up. Old orchards got the same treatment. Levels were run across the land by surveyors; teamsters with Fresno scrapers graded it; subsoilers took care of bad spots; wells were drilled for needed irrigation. Much of the land was converted to cotton, alfalfa, gyp corn and grain. Where the soil warranted vines, not Thompsons but the more profitable "juice grapes" were planted. As operations progressed, carpenter and paint gangs were brought on the scene.[42]

Weekly the valley farms committee examined the operation of each ranch, its work, expenses, budget, crop prospects, harvest, etc. Though Hendrick watched costs like a hawk they climbed to $10,-000 a month. By 1927 expenses had far outdistanced income, $225,-000 to $57,000. Of 127 farms operated in 1927, only 9 made more than expenses.[43]

The operations of the valley farms committee continued to run behind as fresh foreclosures added to expenses. When the board started criticizing the rehabilitation program as a losing proposition, Hendrick vigorously defended it. "The farms which the Bank of Italy owns in the San Joaquin Valley," he said,

were mostly acquired through banks purchased during the last year or two. . . . We are not offering lands for sale at a sacrifice. . . . It wouldn't be fair, because we had a small amount invested in a piece of property, to sell it for the amount of our investment if that amount were one-half of what a neighbor considered his property worth. . . . Because of our faith in California and our faith in its agriculture, we believe our investment in land will ultimately be profitable. . . . We would not do anything which would cause the farmers of this State to feel that this bank did not have confidence in the one great industry of the State which, year after year, pours into the coffers of our citizens more created wealth than any other industry.[44]

The second Giannini branch banking system, the United Security Bank and Trust Company (presently to become the Bank of America of California), was having the same sort of problem with foreclosed farms. Here the French-American Corporation took title to the properties, as did Bankitaly in the case of the Bank of Italy. In 1928 it was decided to consolidate the administration of the foreclosures of the two banks under a joint committee, representing both institutions.

Within fifteen months the job had outgrown the joint committee, which was superseded by California Lands, Inc. California Lands began business in March, 1929. Its directing heads were the men who, in each bank, had been wrestling with the problem all along. Howard Whipple, of the Bank of America of California, was president; Carl Wente and W. F. Morrish, vice-presidents. Among the directors were Hendrick, W. E. Blauer, A. J. Mount and Charles R. Bell.

By the end of 1929, California Lands was administering 1,125 properties with a total of 216,596 acres, and more coming in all the time. The "take-over" value (meaning principal plus interest, court costs, etc.) was $14,498,375. Sixty-three per cent of this lay in the San Joaquin Valley, with the Visalia district heading the list with $3,532,000. Not far behind were Fresno with $2,910,000 and Modesto, $2,677,000.[45]

California Lands was to have a long work to do.

The Dream of Nationwide Banking

WITH the victory for statewide banking won in 1927, A. P. Giannini regarded as only half done the task of improving the country's banking system. The other half was to permit branch banks to cross state lines. That would mean a type of banking not practiced in this country since 1836, when Andrew Jackson won his fight to prevent the recharter of Nicholas Biddle's Bank of the United States. Jackson expressed no opposition to nationwide branch banking per se, but to the fact that Biddle enjoyed a monopoly that was susceptible of abuse. Events sustained the President when, during the recharter contest, Biddle corruptly abused his power. Though Giannini meant to be first in the field, as he had been with statewide banking, he desired no monopoly. His idea called for transcontinental or regional banks that would transact most of the banking in the United States. Giannini foresaw benefits to the country as positive as those that branch banking had brought to California.

This, of course, would require amendment of the McFadden Act. Characteristically, Giannini did not wait for a change in the law. He simply went ahead and began his arrangements for nationwide banking, expecting lawmakers to catch up with him. That is what had happened before.

A. P. Giannini's attempt to reform the banking system comprises a significant, though perhaps no longer prophetic, chapter in the history of American banking. The theme is difficult to follow because of its ramifications and complexities. At times it is interrupted by distractions such as the crisis precipitated by gambling in Giannini stocks, and the arch attempt of J. P. Morgan & Co. to bring within its sway the financial empire of the trail-blazing Californian. Such episodes all but obscure the ultimate intention of Giannini's titanic operations: the creation of a transcontinental bank.

In the end he did not succeed. This was partly because of mistakes of Mr. Giannini's own making. In an endeavor to pick younger associates who would probably survive him, he picked too many of the wrong men. Then he stepped aside and gave them a free hand to deal with responsibilities that proved not only beyond their capacities but foreign to their natures. For the most part they were Wall Street men who never caught the possibilities of a great bank, a greater bank than Morgan ever dreamed of, run in the interest of average people. Following the economic tidal wave set in motion by the panic of 1929 these men lost their heads, like many another. The sea of troubles assailing all business and all finance overwhelmed them; it overwhelmed the transcontinental banking plan; and it gave the Bank of America N. T. & S. A. several anxious years. Mr. Giannini was not invited back to restore his beloved and threatened bank. The new men had plans of their own. A. P. Giannini had to fight his way back—and he saved his bank.

It will take four chapters to tell all this.

2

It is not known how early Giannini began to think about nationwide branch banking. James F. Cavagnaro says A. P. mentioned it in 1912 when the two men first met in New York, where Giannini had gone to talk to New York Italians who wanted a Giannini bank. Though nothing came of those talks, in 1919 Giannini established the East River National. For a Californian with the idea of a transcontinental bank in mind, a foothold in New York was a logical move. The East River National was a small bank, however. In 1919 the Bank of Italy was also too small for a transcontinental undertaking. So, Giannini devoted himself to strengthening and solidifying the Bank of Italy's position in California—an operation that helped to bring into notice the Bancitaly Corporation.[1]

With $1,500,000 in cash Bancitaly had been formed in 1919 to hold the majority of the stock of the East River National of New York. Presently it acquired a bank with branches in Italy, renaming it Banca d'America e d'Italia. In 1921 Bancitaly opened the Liberty Bank in San Francisco. These enterprises prospered and in 1922 the profits of the holding company were $414,000. In 1923 a new task fell to Bancitaly. The State Banking Department of California and the Federal Reserve having blocked the way to further expansion of the Bank of Italy via the Stockholders Auxiliary Corporation, Giannini brought Bancitaly to the scene as a substitute bank buyer. The result was the merger of the three major branch systems with the Bank of Italy in February, 1927.

Meanwhile Bancitaly was becoming more like an investment trust than a holding company. It purchased stock in banks, railroads and industrial corporations in this country, and stock in some of the leading banks of Europe. It invested heavily in the Bank of Italy. From 13,000 shares in 1919, its holding was increased to 212,700 shares (of 1,200,000 outstanding) early in 1927. Even stronger was the Bank of Italy's hold on Bancitaly; 90 per cent of Bancitaly's stock was owned by Bank of Italy stockholders. Giannini had deliberately brought about this close relation. He recommended Bancitaly shares to Bank of Italy stockholders and to others, being particularly anxious to spread the shares 2 and 5 and 10 at a time among investors of small means.

In California, where Aladdin-like qualities were attributed to Giannini, this was not difficult. The earnings of Bancitaly were a recommendation in themselves. Profits went from $1,216,000 in 1924 to $4,556,000 in 1925, and to $11,000,000 in 1926. By that time assets were well over the $100,000,000 mark. While anxious for bona fide investors to have Bancitaly stock, Giannini wanted to keep it out of the hands of speculators. In view of Bancitaly's record and with the bull market hitting its stride, this was a hard thing to do. The price of Bancitaly shares bounded upward despite the measures that Giannini took to hold it down.

The grand consolidation of February, 1927, made the Bank of Italy N. T. & S. A. big enough to take part in the development of transcontinental banking. By this time it was also apparent that Giannini meant to use Bancitaly on the national scene, somewhat as he had used the Stockholders Auxiliary in the Bank of Italy's early days.

3

Though there had been newspaper allusions connecting the Californian's name with the subject before that, Giannini's first public mention of nationwide banking came in a newspaper interview in

1924. He merely touched on the general topic, saying nothing of his own plans:

Under nationwide branch banking, an enterprise located in either the big city or the small village would have equal potential reservoirs of credit —perhaps running into hundreds of millions. Big business could do business anywhere. More: this borrowing power would be absolutely independent of local conditions.

The explanation, of course, is found in the word *diversification. . . .* Why has California been an ideal proving ground for branch banking? Because its productive resources are remarkably diversified. But we do not, of course, represent California as being so fully diversified as the entire United States. Hence, a nationwide system has far more assurance of success from the very outset than had our statewide system. Under a nationwide system a section distressed through crop failures, floods, unemployment, or for any other reason, would experience no diminution in its local financial support for any legitimate purpose. A new factory, for instance, would be financed as well in a distressed section as in a prosperous one. The amount of distress would be lessened and recovery greatly speeded up.

Giannini's plans were in process of execution, however. In 1925 he improved his foothold in New York. Bancitaly purchased the Bowery National Bank, merging it with the East River National under the title of Bowery and East River National Bank. This made a $70,000,000 institution. Dr. A. H. Giannini, its president, proceeded to establish twelve city branches.

In 1926, Armando Pedrini and Robert Paganini were sent on a sort of national good-will tour. Their mission was to make friends among influential Italians and incidentally to sell small blocks of Bancitaly stock. In five and a half months they visited fifty-six cities and sold nine thousand shares to eight hundred individuals. From Memphis the missionaries telegraphed their chief: "ENTHUSIASM GROWING AS WE PROCEED. . . . YOU WILL HAVE WONDERFUL ARMY FUTURE EXPANSION." At the same time Bancitaly was buying bank stocks heavily. Early in 1927, it owned shares valued at $43,383,000 in eighty-one banks in twenty-three of the country's large cities. In addition it held stock worth $9,197,000 in lesser domestic banks, and stock worth $11,067,000 in foreign banks.[2]

In his annual report released early in January, 1928, President Bacigalupi formally committed the Bank of Italy to the policy of nationwide banking.

We do not [he wrote] hold the opinion that our unusual success has been due to any superior knowledge or ability on our part . . . but we are convinced that the key to our success is to be found . . . in the economic, social and political soundness of branch banking itself. . . .

It is indeed difficult to understand why banks and their customers should be denied the efficiencies of large scale "production" of nation-wide scope. . . . It is equally difficult to comprehend why, under our existing laws and practices, branches of American banks . . . are permitted to be established and operated in foreign countries, but denied the right of establishment in other American states. . . .

In our humble opinion this nation-wide development should be patterned after the structure of the Federal Reserve, rather than the English or Canadian systems. . . . The establishment of nation-wide banks— owned and controlled by the people of the country—dividing their responsibilities and operations into twelve regional districts, each presided over by a Regional Board, and dependent only upon a grand Central Head Office for general major policies and sanction as to major investments, does not seem unworkable or improbable, and we make bold to hope that the day may soon arrive when such banks will be given legal approbation.[3]

When the shareholders received this sanguine announcement A. P. Giannini was on an eastbound train, prepared to take the first major step toward the realization of his dream. This was the establishment of the New York bastion of his proposed nationwide banking system. The resources of the Bowery and East River National had grown to $106,000,000. In addition Bancitaly owned the Commercial Exchange Bank, with $45,000,000 more in assets. This was not enough. Giannini needed a larger bank, one with prestige and the right connections.

He had sent Leo Belden to New York the autumn before to look around. In the Bank of America at 44 Wall Street, Belden discovered what his boss wanted. Founded in 1812, it was one of New York's oldest banks. Though comparatively small (deposits $167,000,000), it had a fine reputation and an excellent trust business. Moreover, the Bank of America had exactly the right name for Giannini's purposes. As for connections, the proud old bank was within the sphere of influence of J. P. Morgan & Co.

Morgan, the elder, was dead, and no other man in American finance has since wielded his power. Nevertheless, in 1928, under the second J. P. Morgan the firm at the corner of Wall and Broad Streets was still the most potent single force in finance in the country. If a purchaser of the Bank of America was to enjoy the friendship of Morgan, the transaction would have to have the approval of "the Corner," which was Wall Street idiom for the House of Morgan. Naturally, Mr. Giannini did not want to alienate Morgan. Belden had made the acquaintance of some of the partners. Francis D. Bartow mentioned criticisms of Giannini that had sifted eastward from some of the Bank of Italy's West Coast rivals. Mr. Belden felt that he was able to disabuse Mr. Bartow of most of the things he had heard.[4]

The circumstance that gave Giannini a chance to buy the Bank of America was a contest for control between Ralph Jonas and Edward C. Delafield, the bank's president. Jonas had worked up from the sidewalks of Brooklyn to direct (with his brother) the livest bank in the town, the Manufacturers Trust Company, which had a string of thriving branches in the borough and was beginning to branch out in New York City. Edward Delafield was a Long Island aristocrat of pre-Revolutionary lineage. Morgan favored Delafield. Though Jonas held a majority of the bank's stock, a legal action prevented his voting part of it. Matters were at a stalemate when Giannini appeared on the scene.

After meeting all the interested parties—Jonas, Delafield and the Morgan people—Giannini persuaded Jonas to sell him his stock. He also tried to buy the Manufacturers Trust. Giannini liked Ralph Jonas' attitude toward banking and wanted to offer him the chairmanship of the board of the new bank. He sounded out some of the leading figures in the New York Clearing House and the Federal Reserve Bank of New York. They were thumbs down on Jonas and it was no secret that Morgan was behind this opposition. Accordingly, Giannini decided he would have to get along with Delafield, a Morgan man. Though the Westerner and Jonas closed their deal with a handshake and no signed agreement binding them until papers were drawn, Mr. Delafield could not act with such informality. He consented to Giannini's purchase of the Jonas stock, provided that it was satisfactory to the Corner. At Frank Bartow's home Mr. Giannini went over proposed arrangements with Mr. Morgan himself. "A. P. was informed," wrote one who was there, "that his acquiring control of the Bank of America would . . . have the blessing of J. P. Morgan & Company."[5]

Why was the blessing bestowed? Mario Giannini had it figured out. "Morgan chose us in preference to Jonas because he felt he could dictate."[6]

On February 25, 1928, the deal was consummated. The Bancitaly Corporation paid $16,959,540 for the Jonas shares, which numbered 33,254 of the Bank of America's 65,000. Quickly outlining the next steps, Mr. Giannini departed for San Francisco. The steps were: merger of the Bowery and East River National and the Commercial Exchange with the Bank of America; nationalization of that institution under the title of the Bank of America N. T. & S. A.

4

The prompt departure was in character. A. P. Giannini was accustomed to trusting his associates; and he expected much of them in the way of detail.

It was the Morgan men who were surprised that he should have left, with so much on the fire. Mr. Delafield and his first vice-president, John E. Rovensky, discussed the eventful six weeks that had passed. In one way Giannini had not come up to their expectations. They had braced themselves to deal with a half-man-half-alligator type of Westerner, whose revolutionary notions of banking would turn everything upside down overnight. To their surprise they had found a man they genuinely liked. The only instruction he had given concerning the management of the bank was that he expected it to make money. Still they knew that if Giannini had his way the staid old bank would not remain the same. Rovensky wondered when the changes would start and how far they would go.

"Morgan won't let him get far," said Delafield. "He'll button him up."[7]

While changing trains at Chicago, Mr. Giannini received a telegram from Leo Belden. The news was good. "MORGAN AND OTHERS APPROVE NATIONALIZATION." When the Californian had left New York, approval of nationalization had not been specifically among the Morgan blessings.

The next word of the Corner's attitude was not so good. It exposed a fundamental difference between the Wall Street and the Giannini conceptions of banking. "AM ASSUMING," A. P. had telegraphed, "THAT NATIONALIZATION PLAN PROVIDES FOR N. T. AND S. A. BEING ADDED TO TITLE. . . . IT WOULD SERVE TO ADVERTISE TO THE PEOPLE OF NEW

YORK THAT STRONG INSTITUTIONS ARE NOW DOING A SAVINGS BUSINESS." It was a point important to Giannini, considering the share that savings accounts had had in his success in the West. On the other hand the great commercial banks of New York regarded savings accounts with disdain. Belden replied that the letters "N. A.," indicating a national bank, were the only additions to the title contemplated. In Belden's opinion, to raise the savings-account question "at this time" would "scatter antagonisms." Giannini grumbled a little, but he acquiesced. Straightway came another wire from Belden saying that it "WOULD BE MOST HELPFUL IF WE COULD INCREASE OUR BALANCE WITH MORGAN AT LEAST MILLION DOLLARS. . . . THIS IDEA NOT MY SUGGESTION BUT CAME FROM CORNER."

The million was transferred. Morgan made other objections on small matters, and Giannini gave way. But when the Corner opposed reducing the par of the Bank of America's capital stock to $25 because of the New York tradition that the par of bank shares should not be less than $100, A. P. spoke his mind. "See no reason why the fellows downtown should have a say as to the price we are putting out our holdings. This appears to be exclusively our own affair." This time it was Morgan who gave way. The consolidation of the three banks was agreed upon under an arrangement whereby Bancitaly would own 504,066 shares of the greater Bank of America, or a majority of those outstanding.[8]

Officers and a directorate were selected. Delafield remained as president. Clare W. Banta, whom Giannini had induced to leave the Wells Fargo Bank in San Francisco, went East to become executive vice-president. Dr. A. H. Giannini was chairman of the board and Rovensky vice-chairman. The board of thirty-six included some distinguished New York names. There were also Italian-American names, but not enough of them to please the chairman. Men who had been with Giannini from the beginning in New York were relegated to the advisory board. Friction developed at the first meeting of the directors, when Delafield tried "to deny me the right of presiding," as the Doc complained to his brother. A. P. Giannini recommended patience. Let Delafield and the rest "start out on their own. . . . Later on if we find that things are not progressing as they should we could step in and take charge."[9]

Since a majority of the stock was to be owned by Bancitaly, A. P. Giannini, president, taking charge should not be too difficult an affair. As yet, however, Giannini wanted no internal dissension, for the reorganizers of the Bank of America had one more river to cross: nationalization, with trust powers. This was a matter for the Federal Reserve Board to grant. Having sensed the influence of Morgan with the Federal Reserve Bank of New York, Giannini invited no slip between the cup and the lip.

Yet that is what almost happened, and it came in a peculiar way.

The bank had filed the requisite applications for conversion into a national bank with authority to do a trust business. Examined by the national bank examiners and by the New York Clearing House, its condition had been found satisfactory. The rest seemed a matter of form. Anticipating no difficulty, a meeting of shareholders had been scheduled for Monday, March 26, 1928, at 10 A.M., to act upon a formal resolution to convert into a national banking association.

On Friday, March 23, a notice was served by telephone on the Bancitaly Corporation at its New York offices by Gates W. McGarrah, Federal Reserve agent for the Second District. Mr. McGarrah used the phone to save time. The notice was that, unless Bancitaly agreed in writing to transfer to individual ownership its stock interest within six months, the Federal Reserve Bank of New York would not recommend to the Federal Reserve Board in Washington that trust powers be given the Bank of America. This would not affect nationalization, only the inclusion of trust powers.

No reason was assigned for this demand. So far as is known the Reserve Board had never denied trust powers to a converted national bank whose condition was sound. In the Second Federal Reserve District were other banks owned by holding companies. No steps had been taken to oblige these companies to divest themselves of their stock. Again, Mr. McGarrah's notice had been served not on the bank but on Bancitaly, a stockholder.[10]

By chance or design it was a squeeze play. No time was allowed in which to contest the issue without postponing the stockholders' meeting. This would have caused confusion. To have accepted nationalization without trust authority—or even a brief lapse of that authority during the transition from a state to a national bank— would have been ruinous to the bank's trust business. There was nothing to do but to comply with McGarrah's demand—and in a matter of hours. Accordingly, on the next day, Saturday, March 24, 1928, the Reserve Board approved the application making possible

THE ROUND-UP

—*Howard Stivers in the Wall Street News*

the Bank of America N. A., with trust powers and forty-five city branches.

And so A. P. Giannini acquired the Eastern bastion of his proposed transcontinental banking system. The New York press made much of the Westerner's invasion, with friendly personal references to the engaging Californian. Nevertheless, the acquisition of the Bank of America differed from Mr. Giannini's clean-cut West Coast triumphs. On the strange and hostile ground of Wall Street he had not acted with his old independence. His emissary, Belden, was in awe of Morgan. Giannini himself had compromised more than he had compromised ever before. He endured internal tension within the bank; he believed that the removal of Bancitaly as a stockholder was an attempt to weaken him in the East; and he maneuvered for time.

Bancitaly began to transfer its shares to individual ownership, stockholders of the Bank of Italy and other Giannini corporations being given preference. Despite a bear raid on Giannini stocks, in six months all the Bancitaly shares had been distributed except 173,882. These were held to meet options.[11]

What had inspired the demand transmitted by McGarrah?

Even at this late date it is hard to say. Morgan's "buttoning-up" process is an obvious surmise. Curiously, some of the evidence also points in the direction of J. F. Sartori. The controversy over Giannini's use of the word "Security" in southern California was going on. Sartori sent to the country's 28,000 bank presidents a 1,200-word letter, aiming at something like a national stop-Giannini movement. The letter made such an impression on the Federal Reserve Board that one of its members went to California to investigate. He returned to Washington "very much worked up." The next thing was McGarrah's telephone call.[12]

5

The pursuit of A. P. Giannini's transcontinental banking idea is a little like the pursuit of a white rabbit through the snow. At times the quarry is hard to see. We are going to lose sight of it now, because of a necessary digression.

In the furtherance of Mr. Giannini's plans no factor was more important than the profits of the Bancitaly Corporation. That is why

Giannini had devoted so much thought and energy to Bancitaly. Also he had devoted considerable sums of his own money. That had been a way of his since 1904 when he paid half the salary of Assistant Cashier Armando Pedrini. In 1924 Mr. Giannini resigned the presidency and went off the payroll of the Bank of Italy. The presidency of Bancitaly, which Giannini had held since 1919, carried no salary or other form of remuneration. In 1925 and 1926 the directors of Bancitaly allowed the president to draw "expenses"—business and personal. Mr. Giannini's drawings for the two years amounted to $167,727.

In 1927 his remuneration was put on a different footing. It was to be 5 per cent of the net profits. That form of "incentive pay" to corporation executives—usually supplementing a generous salary—was a custom of the times. It was soon apparent that the profits of Bancitaly in 1927 would be very large. They turned out to be treble the amount in 1926—to be exact, $35,295,103. Five per cent of that was $1,764,755. One day at lunch in Charlie's Fashion Restaurant near No. 1 Powell Street in San Francisco, Giannini remarked that he was going to take no such money as that. P. C. Hale, Bacigalupi, Ferrari, Blauer and others remonstrated. Another noon hour, when the bank's agricultural problems were under discussion, Giannini said he was going to ask Bancitaly to divert some of his commissions to help California's farmers. That was the origin of a $1,500,000 gift with which the University of California established the Giannini Foundation of Agricultural Economics.

Nevertheless, in 1927, Mr. Giannini drew on his own account just under $246,000. In 1928 he drew $680,993 of the $2,000,000 to which he was entitled after Bancitaly had turned over $1,500,000 to the University of California. These drawings made A. P. Giannini one of the country's highly paid corporation executives. The notable thing is that, in view of his previous attitude toward personal wealth, Giannini accepted as much as he did. The subject will enter these pages again. Suffice to say now that Mr. Giannini spent much of this money for the benefit of his companies, and when the commission arrangement came to an end he was no millionaire.[13]

Mr. Giannini's increased compensation was one of the minor consequences of the leaping profits of Bancitaly. Much more important was the fact that Bancitaly's earnings made possible Giannini's dream of transcontinental banking, and the step to that end represented by the creation of the Bank of America N. A. That on one hand; on the other, Bancitaly's profit record (itself due largely to stock trading in a runaway market) posed its problems. Foremost of these was the rise of Giannini shares. In April, 1927, a four-for-one split had brought Bank of Italy stock down to 172. On the first business day in January, 1928, it was back to 263. During the same period Bancitaly had gone from 112 to 142, despite Giannini's efforts to discourage speculation.

Giannini anticipated that the consummation of the Bank of America transaction would be an additional spur to the speculators. While negotiations were under way he issued another of his numerous warnings:

> All of our stockholders have fared very well in the matter of profits, and I would like to see them "clean up" their loans and place themselves in the strongest possible market position. It might be necessary for some of them to sell a portion of their holdings—at a profit—in order to do this. . . . We want them to own their stock out-right. We do not want it held as security for loans. . . . We want our stockholders so firmly entrenched that they cannot be forced to sell at some unfavorable time.[14]

The last sentence will be worth remembering.

On top of this, and while still in New York, Mr. Giannini asked Eastern correspondents of the Giannini banks to withhold credit from "persons who are attempting to promote speculation in our securities." This drew praise from a source not hitherto alarmed by the spread of speculation. "The California banker's attitude," said the *Wall Street Journal,* "has gone a long way to recommend his entrance into New York banking circles. . . . It is the first time anything like that has been done by the head of a banking institution."[15]

The New York press dealt conservatively with what it was able to learn of the successive steps by which Giannini brought about the purchase of the Bank of America. Not so the press of California, where Giannini's name was magic. One San Francisco paper suggested that the ticker abbreviation of Bancitaly—BIC—"be changed to BIG—Believers in Giannini." Another called the New York transaction a step toward "the most colossal financial plan ever projected," namely the establishment "throughout the United States [of] a banking system patterned after the Federal Reserve System which has 12 regional bases. Giannini's three bases now are San

Francisco, New York and Los Angeles. Entrance of Chicago is anticipated within four months." Nor was that all. A contemplated invasion of "London, Paris and Berlin appears to set the stage for entrance of A. P. Giannini as the new colossus of world finance."[16]

In the six weeks before the old shares in the three component banks could be exchanged for shares in the new Bank of America N. A., they doubled or trebled in price. To carry out the McGarrah order Bancitaly offered Bank of America N. A. stock at 225 to shareholders in other Giannini enterprises. On April 25, the day this issue was admitted to trading in San Francisco, it closed at 287. Bancitaly itself was crowding 200 and Bank of Italy 300—against 142 and 263 at the first of the year. San Francisco was in the midst of a "speculative orgy" revolving about Giannini stocks. According to one newspaper, "Not even the wild days of the Comstock and the old mining exchange witnessed such 'plunging,' such a fierce rush to 'get aboard' the latest favorite."[17]

B. C. Forbes, editor of the financial magazine bearing his name, went to the West Coast to report the delirious events.

Stepping off the train [he wrote], I entered a barber's and, as usual, asked "How's business?" The reply astounded me: "Poor, very poor. Nobody here's spending any money. Everybody's saving every cent and buying Bank of Italy stock. . . . Giannini is the big hero of California these days. . . ."

That was only the start. Almost everywhere I turned the talk was of fortunes made in Giannini's stocks; of the pinching and saving on the part of thousands to buy the shares; of the effect this has been having on business; of the prospects for making additional fortunes; of the danger of overdoing the rise; of Giannini's daring, ability, foresight, unselfishness; of what the final outcome is likely to be. . . .

Such has been the eagerness of all classes—particularly the poorer classes —to get hold of Giannini shares that millions of dollars of Eastern money has been brought West and lent at 11 to 15 per cent on Giannini stocks as collateral. Neither the banks nor brokers in California nor in New York have encouraged speculation in these stocks by lending money freely on them. Both Mr. Giannini and James A. Bacigalupi . . . have urged stockholders to limit their purchases to what they can own outright. But such conservative advice appears to be widely ignored. Usurious lenders continue to advertise in the newspapers and the daily transactions run into large figures.

Whenever every Tom, Dick and Harry becomes wild over any stock or over real estate or anything else and speculates blindly in it, I, for one, cannot but feel apprehensive. . . . I would earnestly urge that Giannini's advice . . . be solemnly heeded.[18]

6

It was not heeded, and A. P. Giannini was a frankly worried man. More than once, after a sharper than usual rise in the market, he would walk through the floors at No. 1 Powell saying to employees: "Our shares are too high. Don't gamble in them. Pay off your debts and sit tight. If you own your stock you have nothing to fear."

At the bank's "suggestion," clubs organized by employees (and often including outsiders) for the installment purchase of stock were disbanded and the shares sold.[19]

This was a drop in the bucket. The torrent of speculation was still fed by Eastern money for the newly sprung-up "finance companies," of which Mr. Forbes had written. Montgomery Street had no call-money market and did not carry margin accounts in the New York fashion. Nevertheless, to accommodate the greenhorns who had gone crazy over Giannini stocks, a system had come into being whereby a man could "buy" more than he had money to pay for. This is the way it worked, as described at the time by a financial writer:

A speculator, owning 200 shares of Bancitaly outright, for example, desired to use them as collateral for additional purchases of the same stock. Banks and brokers [with a few exceptions] refused to lend a penny on the stock, not because it was worthless, but because they were cooperating with Giannini to curb speculation. The speculator, therefore, visits one of the newly organized "finance companies." Assuming a 75% loan when the stock was at $200 a share, and he owned 200 shares, he could borrow $30,000 on stock valued at $40,000. The 200 shares would then be deposited in the escrow department of a bank, under an agreement giving the lender full authority to sell the stock at any time in order to protect this loan. The banks . . . frowned upon the procedure, but permitted it. . . .

With $30,000 of new money, our speculator proceeds to buy 150 shares of Bancitaly at 200. He then repeats the borrowing operation on perhaps a 66⅔ basis, and received $20,000 of new money. He then buys 100 shares, and repeats the operation.[20]

At the end of that long limb the amateur California speculator was in a hopeless position should the market take much of a dip. The banks would sell him out. Stock thus dumped would inevitably drive the price lower. The piling up of escrow agreements created what market operators call a "weak technical position" for Bancitaly, notwithstanding its daily advances. The situation was getting ready-made for a bear raid. Both in Wall Street and in Montgomery Street professional "shorts" watched Bancitaly like so many hawks.

For the first time in his life Giannini admitted that he was tired. In April he announced that he was going to Europe with his wife and daughter Claire for a rest. One bright spot, however, climaxed the grueling winter. Mario Giannini had entered St. Francis Hospital in San Francisco for orthopedic treatment. For a year or more, the young man had suffered agonizing pain in his legs, as a result of the tensing of muscles and ligaments affected by the dual maladies that were his cross through life. After a few weeks word from the hospital was that Mario's torment was abating, though several months of traction and thermal packs still lay ahead of him.

A. P. Giannini hoped that this vacation from business would have a sobering effect on the market. The reverse proved to be true. A between-trains lunch in Chicago with an officer of the Union Trust Company revived rumors of the San Franciscan's entry into that city. A flood of buying orders sent Union Trust stock up 120 points on the local board. In Paris the Banque de Paris et de Pays Bas gained 300 points for no discoverable reason except that Giannini was in town. His arrival in Italy was heralded by a spree on the Milan exchange in the shares of Banca d'America e d'Italia and a new subsidiary called Ameritalia. Many of the orders came from San Francisco. Giannini cabled Bacigalupi: "STOCK SELLING TOO HIGH. DISCOURAGE PURCHASE."[21]

7

Possibly this latest—and last—warning from A. P. Giannini had something to do with what happened in May, 1928, though the action of the Federal Reserve Board seems a likelier guess. Long apprehensive of the speculative jamboree, the board sought to curb brokers' loans by raising the discount rate from 3½ to 4 per cent. Quotations on the New York Stock Exchange leveled off from their steep climb in April. The Giannini stocks, however, took their cue from Montgomery Street rather than Wall Street. Though San Francisco's buying was less avid than it had been, it was sufficient to lift Bancitaly to a new high of 218 on May 14, and Bank of America N. A. to a new high of 317. On the other hand United Security (presently to become the Bank of America of California) sold at 280, off 12 for the fortnight. Bank of Italy sold at 305, off 3.

During the last half of May the whole list sagged. Every lively market performer moved in an aura of rumor. The story of the adverse technical position of Bancitaly, and to less extent of Bank of Italy, was getting about; and it was true. The Federal Reserve turned the screws again, lifting the rate from 4 to 4½. A dispatch from Rome announced the illness of A. P. Giannini. The four Giannini issues dropped more than usual that day, and a determinedly optimistic San Francisco financial writer questioned the story of A. P.'s illness. He was mistaken. The banker was suffering from pleurisy and neuritis, and more ill than he had ever been in his lifetime.

During the first days of June, with the list still falling, the Giannini stocks became definite targets. Over brokers' private wires from New York crackled the "inside dope." According to P. C. Hale it set Montgomery Street buzzing with

wild rumors . . . that there was going to be a raid on the [Bancitaly] Corp. stock the following Saturday and Monday and Tuesday, and that they were going to drive the price down to 75. Several brokerage houses advised their clients to sell . . . and not only their clients that came to see them, but they telephoned . . . others to sell.[22]

In the nervous state of the market no stock would have been impervious to such tactics. From his bed in the St. Francis Hospital, Mario Giannini telephoned his father, in bed in a Rome hotel. The plight of Bancitaly's gambling shareholders was their own doing. Had they heeded A. P. Giannini's advice three and a half years before, there would have been no cause for anxiety. As it was, they were sitting ducks and it seemed that the Gianninis would have to rescue them from their predicament. Though the prices were too high, the most important thing at the moment was to try to keep them high, or, at the very least, to prevent their dropping to a point that would bring wholesale dumping of the shares of sold-out novices. A sharp break might deal a disastrous blow to the prestige of the Bancitaly Corporation, so closely tied in with realization of nationwide banking.

Father and son decided to support their stocks. Rumor set the start of the raid for Saturday, June 9. Orders were secretly placed with dealers in San Francisco and New York. The actual purchaser would be Bancitaly itself.

The inside buying began on June 8, with plenty of stock offered. On Saturday, June 9, the selling pressure made itself felt, but prompt buying held the losses down. Bancitaly closed at 195, off 8; Bank of Italy at 284, off 3. On Sunday the Giannini leaders conferred at Mario's bedside. Bacigalupi opposed a continuance of the supporting tactics and appears to have swayed P. C. Hale to some extent. Mario Giannini was for keeping on. Each side put its case before the Chief in Rome. He cabled to continue support.

Monday, June 11—"Blue Monday"—was a wild day on the San Francisco Stock Exchange. Bancitaly opened at 175, off 20. That was enough to make the bankers with stock under escrow agreements look in the direction of their vaults. Though it took heavy buying to hold that figure, it was held for an hour, the price even inching up to 177. But there was no holding it any longer against the flood of selling. It dropped to 170, and the dumping began. "Brokerage office scenes were described as pitiful," reported one chronicler. "Old men cried, women fainted, brokers were frantic, the exchange [clogged with selling orders] temporarily suspended operations." Under the impact of distress offerings the price fell like a rock, losing 3, 5 and even 10 points at a time. Around eleven o'clock it stood at 109. The next sale was for 110. The next, 130. Stimulated by inside buying, the rally brought the stock to 160, and it closed at 153.

Bank of Italy ran the same course as Bancitaly. Opening at 250, off 34, it gained a little and then fell, that fall gathering momentum until dumped shares were absorbed. The price was then 125. Recovery took it to 212 at the close of the day.

The two Giannini stocks traded on the San Francisco Curb—Bank of America N. A. and United Security—received the same rough treatment.

For six more days the bears continued to hammer away, but never with the violence of the initial assault on Blue Monday. Speculators in California and elsewhere were pretty well shaken loose from their mortgaged holdings, with losses running into millions. On the last day of the drive, June 19, Bancitaly closed at 114, off 89 points since June 8, which meant a deflation of 43.8 per cent. Bank of Italy closed at 183, off 104, or 36.2 per cent; Bank of America N. A., 188, off 88, or 30.3 per cent; United Security, 160, off 96, or 37.5 per cent.

The Giannini stocks were the major casualties of the June break. Of other California bank stocks, next in rate of decline were the American Trust Company of San Francisco, 16.7 per cent, and the First National of Los Angeles, 15.7 per cent. In New York the Chase National lost 21.8 per cent and the National City just under 9. Some industrial issues, exclusive of low-priced ones, lost 30 per cent.

About $60,000,000 of Bancitaly's money went into the fight against the bear raiders. To show for this, the corporation had thousands of shares of Giannini stocks that were not worth $60,000,000 on June 19. What the loss was seems unascertainable. Twenty million dollars is a guess. Both Hale and Bacigalupi confessed that they lacked sufficient experience to cross swords with professional market operators in Wall Street, whence the moves of the bears were directed. They said the same of Leo Belden, who handled the latter part of the New York end of the campaign.[23]

8

On August 2, 1928, when the break was over and the dust had settled, P. C. Hale reported to his chief, who had sufficiently improved in health to journey to London:

We have had a real shock, but I have never known such loyalty in all of my life. The stockholders have behaved magnificently. . . . It is too bad that you could not have been here, as Jim and I had had no experience of this kind in the stock market, and Mario was in the hospital. He has a good level head and was very heroic. I know you could have done better, and I know we could do it better if we had it to do all over again.[24]

Orra Monnette addressed the Los Angeles regional board of the Bank of Italy in the same vein:

Not a single account or a piece of business has been lost traceable in any particular to a lack of faith in or loss of friendship for the institution during the period. The normal deposits of the bank have gained very materially and at a season of the year in which we expect heavy fluctuations.[25]

Many stockholders and patrons cabled or wrote to Mr. Giannini. This wire was from Robson Brothers, real estate dealers of San Francisco:

Contributions to welfare of California and elsewhere made by you and your great institutions cannot be offset by stock market fluctuations. Being amongst your oldest clients and friends we are for you. The money you have helped us make is loyally at your service. Cordial wishes for your good health.[26]

Mr. Hale was correct about the loyalty of the stockholders. It was remarkable. Hundreds had been sold out and among them were many who had lost about everything they had. In San Francisco Italians who had moved into fine houses in the Marina, the filled-in land where the World's Fair of 1915 had been, were ruefully moving back to the slopes of Telegraph Hill. At such times it matters not if the foolhardy have been warned and warned again. When flush-times winnings go, and not only winnings but the hard-earned stake they started with, people are apt to blame almost anyone except themselves. Men suddenly poorer are not usually suddenly wiser. Even the relatively conservative investor, who owns his shares outright and on a break loses paper profits only, finds nothing cheerful in the fall of his stock from 200 to 100. It's only human to wish that he had sold at 200. At this late date it is not surprising that one should find Californians who recall 1928 with a shake of the head. "If we'd only listened to A. P.!" The singular thing is that so many felt that way at the time.

Many, but not all. There were shareholders who felt, and with justification, that they had been pushed into buying by enthusiastic officers and employees of the bank. As we know, Armando Pedrini's Italian department had been especially active in selling both Bancitaly and Bank of Italy shares. He sold them outright, but when the shares zoomed in price there was a strong temptation for an owner to take on a few more on margin. Until the last weeks of the upsurge, bank employees had been active in installment-buying clubs. During a trip through the San Joaquin Valley in August, Vice-President Harry Carr touched on the consequences of this state of affairs:

Tony Sala [assistant cashier at Fresno] tells me that the greater part of the loss of accounts, including some very substantial balances that left us the first weeks in July, was because of a dissatisfaction on the part of our clients, occasioned by a feeling they had against some of our officers and employees who advised them to buy bank stock and [Bancitaly] Corp. stock, during the first months of this year. In fact, Sala frankly states that he, himself, urged the purchase of the stocks. . . . He had been instructed to do it by someone over him, and had even a list presented to him of his own countrymen that he might solicit.[27]

Louis Ferrari, general counsel for the bank, consulted Charles W. Collins in Washington about requesting the Department of Justice to investigate the bear raid. After talking to Comptroller McIntosh and Federal Reserve officials, Collins advised against it. "There is nothing more difficult to prove than conspiracy," he pointed out. Moreover, an inquiry would afford the chance to launch the rumor "that the Department of Justice was investigating the Bank of Italy and its affiliates, and thus a new crop of irresponsible gossip might get started."[28]

Appearing on the heels of the break, the semiannual statements of the Bank of Italy and of the Bancitaly Corporation were scrutinized as never before. With the bank's statement Bacigalupi enclosed a prideful letter to the stockholders:

You will undoubtedly be pleased to know that throughout the organized drive of the past few weeks to depreciate the market value of our stock . . . fully ninety-five per cent of our stockholders "stood pat."

The statement of the condition of our Bank, as of the close of business June 29, 1928, is our best answer to our antagonists and to the rumors which they have placed in circulation.[29]

Mr. Bacigalupi was right about that. A condensation of the statement, with corresponding figures for six months earlier, tells its own story:

	December 31, 1927	June 29, 1928
Loans and Discounts	$403,864,138	$410,543,481
Securities Owned	238,856,707	233,154,274
Cash and Due from Banks	83,913,310	103,287,932
Banking Premises, etc.	22,073,854	25,945,668
Other Resources	16,480,967	31,744,169
TOTAL RESOURCES	$765,188,976	$804,675,524

Deposits, Savings	$437,713,376	$445,140,320
Deposits, Commercial	207,288,761	221,803,874
Capital Paid In	37,500,000	50,000,000
Surplus and Undivided Profits	25,540,829	54,759,004
Other Liabilities	57,146,010	32,972,326
Number of Depositors	1,290,315	1,347,357
Combined Capital Investment (Bank and Affiliate)	104,900,000	206,000,000
Net Profit to Stockholders	20,125,371 (for the year)	11,127,676 (for six months)

The Bancitaly statement was likewise exceptional. A condensation, with corresponding figures for six months earlier:

ASSETS	January 20, 1928	July 19, 1928
Cash in Banks and Call Loans	$ 8,593,317*	$ 20,485,752
Bills and Accounts Receivable	21,603,396	12,293,695
Securities	252,430,801	254,972,867
Business Properties	6,412,439	7,007,332
Subsidiaries	176,041	184,304
	$289,215,994	$294,943,950
LIABILITIES		
Capital Stock	$130,000,000	$130,000,000
Surplus and Undivided Profits	120,561,776	149,971,328
Capital Investment	$250,561,776	$279,971,328
Bills Payable	$ 32,656,868	
Reserves for Taxes, Etc.	4,497,350	13,497,622
Foundation of Agricultural Economics, University of California	1,500,000	1,475,000
	$289,215,994	$294,943,950

* This figure represents cash in banks only.

The Bancitaly report was submitted by L. M. Giannini, executive vice-president. In a statement to the press Mario remarked that the chief item of Bancitaly's assets—securities—was valued "below the cost or market, whichever is lower." That certain recent additions to the securities portfolio were a result of tactics employed to stem the June raid was not mentioned. Bancitaly's support of the market was still a secret. As further evidence of the corporation's flourishing condition, Mario noted the payment of all outstanding bills, which in January had amounted to $32,000,000; the accumulation of reserves of $13,000,000; $20,000,000 in cash in banks or loaned on call.

These items, he said, contributed to place Bancitaly in "a stronger position than at any previous period in its history."

The Corporation's six-months' profits (slightly more than Bancitaly had made in the entire year of 1927), the younger Giannini said "far exceeded expectations." He noted that profits arising from the exchange of securities in connection with the consolidation of the three New York banks were not included in this sum. Moreover, he drew attention to a word of caution the Bancitaly management had uttered a year before when it "asked our stockholders not to expect that records [of earnings] established during boom times could be sustained permanently."[30]

9

On September 4 Mr. Giannini and his family walked down the gangplank of the *Île de France* in New York. The banker showed the effect of his illness. His tall form was thinner, his eyes darkly circled and his step slower. To the press he gave a brief prepared statement. The "midsummer stock market slump" had not surprised him. Stockholders who had heeded his warnings and not bought on margin had not been hurt. The Giannini companies were more prosperous than ever. He had in mind "definite recommendations for the benefit of our stockholders," but could not discuss them until he had talked to his directors in San Francisco.[31]

Giannini had more on his mind than that. He was disappointed, to put it mildly, in his New York contact man, Leo Belden, who, he thought, had become little more than an errand boy for Morgan. The banker had hoped to proceed straight home. While he was at sea, however, a radiogram from Belden said the Corner wished to see him. Giannini went down, and Francis Bartow started to talk turkey. He said there could be no more supporting the market. Giannini replied that he would be in the East again before long and they could go into that then. Bartow added that he would like to see in advance any public statement Giannini intended to make on his arrival in San Francisco. Giannini said he refused "point-blank."

The main thing the banker had planned to say in San Francisco was that Bancitaly would increase its dividend from $2.24 to $4 a share. Bacigalupi, who had met his chief in New York, rode with him to San Francisco. He begged that Bartow be given notice of the announcement. Very reluctantly Giannini consented and telegrams were exchanged from the train. The thought of having got the Corner's approval of such a matter galled Giannini for years afterward.[32]

Back at Powell Street, Giannini was greeted by his son Mario, walking in comfort with the assistance of a cane, and the traces of pain gone from his countenance. He appeared in wonderful health. There could have been no more heartening sight for the father who had had a close call.

Giannini took hold of his business problems with his old-time zest. He consulted directors about the "definite recommendations." The object was a scheme to put his bank shares out of the reach of market speculators. The germ of the measure proposed had originated in the mind of Mario during the June break. The plan was to form a vast new holding company that would assume control of the Bank of Italy, the Bank of America N. A., and the United (soon to be the Bank of America of California). There would then be no bank stocks to trade in. The holding company's stock would be the only Giannini issue on the exchanges. As Bacigalupi had written Giannini in Europe: "Any reaction in this stock could not react upon our banks, and our various banking organizations would be freed of concern regarding market fluctuations and more efficient in attending strictly to their banking business."[33]

An enlarged Bancitaly Corporation might have filled the bill, except for the agreement Giannini had made with the comptroller of the currency in February, 1927, that Bancitaly would not own more than a fourth interest in any national bank in California. Therefore, it would be necessary to form a new corporation to swallow Bancitaly and, with the Bancitaly assets as a start, set about taking over the banks through an exchange of stock. Louis Ferrari drafted articles of incorporation, and everything was ready except a name for the new company. All agreed that "America" should be in the title. A. P. and others offered names, but none seemed right. It was Mr. Ferrari's secretary, Rose Walter, who hit the nail on the head. She suggested "Transamerica." The imposing word described what A. P. Giannini intended his new giant to be—the repository for the stocks of Giannini banks that he hoped would dot the continent from one ocean to the other.

With an authorized capital of $250,000,000 represented by 10,000,-000 shares of $25 par, Transamerica Corporation was chartered in Delaware. At the end of October, 1928, A. P. Giannini introduced it in a circular letter to the stockholders of the Bank of Italy and the Bancitaly Corporation. Transamerica was to continue the new $4 dividend rate of Bancitaly.[34]

The buffeted shareholders' confidence in Giannini was as strong as ever. In a little over a month's time 90 per cent of the Bank of Italy's and of Bancitaly's stock had been turned in for exchange. Attorneys got busy with the corporate details. Bancitaly would quietly pass out of existence in January, 1929. The Bank of Italy, naturally, remained exactly as before, except that the stockholders' certificates read "Transamerica" instead of "Bank of Italy." With control of the Bank of Italy went control of all its affiliates: National Bankitaly Company, California Joint Stock Land Bank, Bankitaly Agricultural Credit Corporation (the "cow bank"), Bankitaly Mortgage Company, Americommercial Corporation and the Pacific National Fire Insurance Company.

The fire insurance company, a small ($1,000,000) institution, had been acquired earlier in the year. It was owned by George W. Peltier who was also president of the Farmers & Mechanics Bank of Sacramento. The risks of the company were all in Sacramento, where one big fire could have dealt it a body blow. Giannini had long wanted to buy the Peltier bank. Watching the rise of Giannini stocks, Peltier at length agreed to sell, provided A. P. would also take over the fire insurance company. This Giannini did and, with the assistance of his banks, began to spread its risks throughout the state.

The absorption of Bancitaly and the Bank of Italy and affiliates gave Transamerica control of corporations with assets of $1,294,000,-000 with $816,000,000 more on the way. Four hundred million of this would come from the Bank of America of California, formed in December, 1928, by the amalgamation of the United Security branch system and the lately purchased Hellman bank, the Merchants National of Los Angeles. The remainder ($416,000,000) represented the resources of the Bank of America N. A. in New York.

On January 1, 1929, officers and directors of Transamerica were announced. Giannini was president, Mario and W. H. Snyder executive vice-presidents. The board of nineteen was made up of the chief men in the two Banks of America and the Bank of Italy. Thus Californians—old Giannini men for the most part—took charge of the new titan.

New Hands at the Wheel

THE TRANSAMERICA CORPORATION was designed to do more than prevent gambling in bank shares. It was designed to give A. P. Giannini the direct control of the Bank of America N. A., that the Federal Reserve Bank of New York had impaired by forcing Bancitaly to relinquish its 51 per cent stock interest. At the start of his contest for control, Giannini would be at a disadvantage, the June, 1928, market raid having weakened his prestige in the East as it had not done in the West.

The Bank of America N. A. reflected this. It was a house divided. After eight months of ostensible Giannini operation it presented a sorry contrast with other Giannini banks. Missing from the institution at 44 Wall Street was the originality, the purpose, the verve, the savvy, the good-natured but earnest drive to win friends and get business, no matter how small or large, that were the hallmarks of Giannini banks in California—and under Dr. Giannini had been hallmarks of the Bowery and East River National in New York. Edward C. Delafield and his colleagues did not understand branch banking, and they distrusted it. About the source of Giannini's success in the West and the foundation of his place in history, they knew not a thing, nor did they care to know. The idea of strengthening an economy with the protected savings of workers, small tradesmen and small farmers was not a part of the Morgan conception of banking. Mr. Delafield and his people disdained it. Moreover, since the June break they had been notably cockier, as if certain that the crude Westerner who imagined himself a banker had finally got his comeuppance.

This and more is discernible in the long and anguished communications Dr. A. H. Giannini poured upon San Francisco. He said he was fighting singlehanded to sustain Giannini traditions. He asked his brother for help. Delafield was set to "raid the treasury" for salary raises unjustified by the bank's earnings or the officers' services; and the raises were going to Morgan men, not the faithful from the Bowery and East River. There were expense accounts on which officers put their golf-club dues—"all new to us and more or less shocking." Of graver import was the Doctor's recital of Mr. Delafield's appearance "before the Executive Committee, composed of big business men. . . . [He] tells them we are losing a $200,000 deposit and a half-million-dollar trust account because of the bad influence of the Gianninis."

"Ingratiating methods will never do with these fellows," stormed the Doctor. "For many years they have been impossible and must be told where to head in. . . . The gang downtown never cared for our kind and never will. It is true we need them now, but is not necessary to have them ride over us."

Though Amadeo sympathized with his brother's position, he could be irritated by the Doc's impatience. All would come right in time, he repeated; the Bank of America N. A. would be a Giannini bank in fact as well as name.[1]

A. P. Giannini fully intended to tell the Easterners where to head in. But he did not intend to begin with the small fry. He meant to begin with J. P. Morgan and the Federal Reserve Bank of New York which was playing the Morgan game. After that, Delafield and his golfing vice-presidents should prove no particular problem. But first of all Mr. Giannini must get Transamerica in a position to back up his words.

2

Giannini had determined to resist any attempt of the Federal Reserve Bank of New York to try to oblige Transamerica to live up to the Bancitaly agreement not to hold stock in the Bank of America N. A. He had no choice. Unless Transamerica could own B. of A. N. A. and other bank shares, nationwide branch banking would be up Salt Creek.

A recent move of the Jonas brothers encouraged Giannini. Their Manufacturers Trust Company had absorbed the State Bank and Trust Company. A majority of the stock in the consolidated institution, which did a trust business, was in the hands of a holding company. "Apparently these fellows had no trouble in getting the Federal Reserve's consent to the merger," Giannini pointed out to Leo Belden. "It seems to me we ought to go right ahead openly soliciting exchange of stock [between Transamerica and the Bank of America N. A.]." Belden was fearful of "friction" with the Reserve Bank. "Any break with Federal will lose us Corner and other support."[2]

Giannini was not keeping the Corner abreast of Transamerica's moves or plans. When he transferred Bancitaly's deposit with J. P. Morgan & Co. to the Bank of Italy's account, he explained that it was merely part of the winding up of Bancitaly's affairs. Next, he transferred the deposit to the account of the Bank of America N. A. Then he stepped up the process of exchanging Bank of America for Transamerica shares. When the Corner saw what Giannini was up to, a disturbed telegram came from Belden. It was partly in code: "MONTGOMERY [Morgan] MUCH EXERCISED. . . . PLEASE TELL ME WHAT TO SAY TO MONTGOMERY."[3]

Giannini went East to do his own talking, arriving February 6, 1929. He took with him Prentis Cobb Hale.

"I would like to know how you are getting along with the Federal Reserve," said Frank Bartow, the Morgan partner, "in regard to holding stock of the Bank of America by Transamerica."

Mr. Giannini said he was getting along very well; that Transamerica stock seemed to be in demand among the New York bank's stockholders, with the result that by exchange Transamerica possessed to date about 59,000 bank shares. Concerning the Federal Reserve, Mr. Giannini said that this exchange of shares was none of its affair.

Mr. Bartow disagreed. He said that Giannini's course was a violation of the spirit of the agreement in the Bancitaly case.

A. P. flared up. "I will fight this issue to the last ditch. We are absolutely right. The Federal Reserve . . . have treated us badly and you and J. Pierpont Morgan ought to uphold us."

Mr. Bartow replied with an ultimatum. "Right or wrong we are for the Federal Reserve Bank." Giannini could either do what the Federal people asked or "take your account away from J. P. Morgan & Company."

The calm, silvery-haired Hale smoothed things over by saying that Mr. Giannini and he were going to Washington and would let Mr. Bartow know their plans within a few days.

From this significant interview the visitors went to lunch with

Jackson Reynolds, president of the First National Bank of New York. A transplanted Midwesterner, Reynolds had had his schooling in New York banking. After A. P. had stated his case, the amiable Reynolds observed:

"You may be within your legal rights, and you may be within your moral rights. . . . You may have received the worst kind of treatment, but knowing the situation as I do, even if you were shanghaied, knocked down and jumped on, I would advise you to . . . divest Transamerica of all the stock it holds of Bank of America."[4]

The Californian was not likely to surrender before the battle. His Washington attorney, Collins, attested the legality of Transamerica's position. Collins said the action in the Bancitaly case had been high-handed. Giannini decided to break with Morgan and see what happened. It was either that or give up nationwide banking.

He wrote to McGarrah, the Federal Reserve agent in New York. As yet the Second District of the Federal Reserve had taken no formal notice of Transamerica. Nevertheless, Mr. Giannini stated that, from informal talks with Reserve officials in New York, he had "gained the impression" that the Reserve Bank there disapproved of the stock relationship between the holding company and the Bank of America N. A. Giannini made his position clear by affirming that Transamerica was "not bound legally or morally" by the Bancitaly agreement. It could own all the Bank of America N. A. stock it wanted to.

In a second letter, of one sentence, Mr. Giannini withdrew from J. P. Morgan & Co. the accounts of the Bank of Italy N. T. & S. A. and the Bank of America N. A.[5]

So ended an episode; and it ended tamely considering the dramatic nature of the threats that had been made. Giannini's letter to McGarrah was never acknowledged. Nor did the Federal Reserve accept its challenge. Without hindrance Transamerica went on to acquire 63 per cent of the outstanding shares of the Bank of America N. A.

3

The breach with Morgan left Giannini looking for talent that knew the ways of Wall Street, had the proper entree there and a sympathetic understanding of nationwide banking, including holding-company ownership (which was the only way it could be done under the law). For some time he had had his eye on the old, blue-ribbon private banking and investment house of Blair & Company. From what he knew of their work, A. P. admired Elisha Walker, the president of Blair, and some of Walker's energetic young executives, like Jean Monnet, a French industrial expert in charge of foreign operations.

Giannini and Hale made it a point to get better acquainted with the Blair outfit. Walker was forty-nine, a native New Yorker and a graduate of Yale and of the Massachusetts Institute of Technology. The Californians saw in him "none of that cold aloofness which we are accustomed to associate with men of Wall Street." In a banking way Walker seemed to be positively enthusiastic about the things that Giannini wanted to do. In the spring of 1929 a bargain was struck whereby Blair & Company was merged with the Bank of America N. A. Mr. Walker became president of the securities affiliate of the bank, Bancamerica-Blair Corporation, and chairman of the executive committee of the bank. This was intended as a step in the internal reorganization of the bank to meet the voluble criticisms of Dr. Giannini.

So glowing were the accounts A. P. sent to the Coast that a Bank of Italy house organ compared Elisha Walker to Giannini himself. "Both men are known above all for their human qualities." Most of the Bank of Italy men later to work with Walker were unable to agree with this estimate. They found him "cold as a fish."[6]

Thinking he had in Walker the man he wanted, Giannini prepared Transamerica for great undertakings. Subsidiaries were formed to handle detail, and a 150 per cent stock dividend was announced for distribution in September, 1929. W. H. Snyder began to travel about looking for banks that might be taken over.

The stock market zoomed upward; Mr. Hoover entered the White House; the preponderant majority of financiers, industrialists, bankers, businessmen and statesmen acted as if prosperity was going to last indefinitely. Doubters were brushed aside. In February, 1929, the Federal Reserve Board issued sharp warnings about the speculative mania. Paul M. Warburg, international banker and one of the architects of the Reserve System, said the current "orgy" could lead only to disaster. F. H. Ecker, president of Metropolitan Life, led a successful fight to prevent common stocks from being declared eligible investments for life insurance companies in New York. These warnings brought a serious break in the market. Charles E. Mitchell, president of the National City Bank, led the fight against the disciples of sanity and he defeated them. The market recovered, speculation resumed its mad course. Professional bulls began to take their profits and quit, professional bears to watch their chance.

The only Giannini stock traded on the exchanges, Transamerica, performed conservatively. Mr. Giannini still tried to prevent margin buying. He urged outright ownership; and the break of 1928 carried its lesson. It also dampened the enthusiasm in the East for Transamerica as a speculative bonanza. So in the spring of 1929 Trans, though in healthy demand, sold in the 130's, a modest increase over the price of Bancitaly when that stock had disappeared from the boards in December, 1928.

Traveling through the country east of the Mississippi as he once had traveled through California, W. H. Snyder carried on a steady correspondence with his chief. It concerned banks that were anxious to sell, and banks that were hard to get but which Giannini would have liked to have. Some were group banking systems, a phase in banking that had begun to manifest itself in the Middle West and the South about 1925. In a group system a holding company controls various banks that have separate charters and boards of directors.

Armando Pedrini also was on the road again, selling small blocks of Transamerica to influential Italians. Almost every place he visited he reported eager for a Giannini bank. In Tampa, Florida, where a large bank had failed disastrously, there was a fervent hope, which Pedrini seemed to share, that Giannini would resuscitate the institution.[7]

Giannini scanned the reports of his envoys and pushed the work of improving Transamerica's structure; but he bought no banks outside of California.

Other banks and bankers took the headlines from Giannini. The securities affiliates of the Chase and the National City bought bank stocks all over the country, as Bancitaly had done years before. The Guaranty Trust absorbed the National Bank of Commerce to form the first $2,000,000,000 bank in the country. A few months later National City topped Guaranty in assets by acquiring the Farmers Loan and Trust. In Chicago two big banks came together. In St. Paul a series of mergers left that city with only one large bank. So it went.

4

Although Giannini bought no more banks in furtherance of his transcontinental system, he did make a new sales contract with the Hellman brothers *et al.* which rectified to some extent the mistake made the year before (1928) when, on the reports of three sets of examiners, A. P. committed himself to pay $40,000,000 for control of the Merchants National Trust and Savings Bank of Los Angeles. The opportunity to make this correction came about through the Hellmans' immediate need for cash and their belief that Transamerica stock was going up in value.

Every afterlight on the Merchants transaction indicated that Giannini had agreed to pay too much for the bank. The boom real estate and oil involvements have been mentioned. Other supposed assets were turning out to be worthless, or even mythical. At the time of purchase the Merchants' books indicated $16,000,000 of the bank's funds out on call—a very profitable investment. It developed, however, that this investment belonged to a depositor of the bank and not to the bank itself.

Reporting this matter, Leon Bocqueraz and Will F. Morrish told Bacigalupi they had lost "confidence in . . . the Southern bunch." Moreover, Nolan and other former Merchants men were accused of freezing out old Giannini hands, as if to protect secrets. Conveying this to Giannini, Bacigalupi said that it might be a good idea to get rid of Nolan, who was president of the Bank of America of California and whose contract had four years to run.[8]

The sales contract of 1928, calling for the payment in 1932 of $40,000,000 for 100,000 shares of Merchants stock, had been made on the basis of examinations of the bank by the Los Angeles Clearing House and the national bank examiners over a period of years; and by the Bank of Italy's examiner, R. E. Trengove. Giannini marveled how all of them could have overlooked so much, and was disposed to criticize Trengove, who had thrown out $3,900,000 of doubtful paper—which obviously was not enough. Yet Trengove had merely accepted, as accurate, data on loans furnished by officers of the bank whom A. P. himself trusted sufficiently to employ.[9]

This was the situation when the chance came to rewrite the 1928 agreement. The six sellers were willing to accept $350 apiece for their 100,000 shares if forthcoming at once, instead of $400 in 1932.

they were willing to accept in payment Transamerica 63, which was the approximate market rate after the 150 stock dividend of September, 1929. As ultimately drawn, ntract brought about an elimination of nearly $6,000,000 in tful paper, against $3,900,000 by the original contract. The reed instrument became effective on October 9, 1929.

The revision represented the improvement of a bad situation; and at that Mario Giannini, who engineered the transaction, was lucky in his timing. Before the month was out the Great Bull Market had gone over the precipice. Transamerica would never again (to the date of this writing) sell at 63.

The week following the new Merchants' agreement the Bank of Italy celebrated its twenty-fifth anniversary, on October 17. At a huge party at San Francisco's Fairmont Hotel, A. P. cut the birthday cake. At another party in the former Flood mansion, then quarters of the Pacific Union Club, the directors gave a testimonial dinner to James A. Bacigalupi who was retiring from the bank's presidency. Mr. Bacigalupi's successor was Arnold J. Mount, a quiet and hardworking man soon to be elected head of the California Bankers Association. Five years before, Giannini had raised him to senior vice-president, with the idea that one day he should step into Bacigalupi's shoes. During those five years the Bank of Italy had grown from 86 branches in 58 towns to 292 branches in 166 towns. Resources had almost tripled, to $851,705,000.

Giannini, for one, believed that the bank's growth in size and in usefulness had only started. That was the tenor of the whole celebration. Mr. Bacigalupi was moving to a larger field of endeavor with the Transamerica Corporation.

5

Decisive events in history are not always so recognized at the time, even by those closest to them and most roughly handled by them. This was signally true of the end of the Great Bull Market in October, 1929, in the most catastrophic financial crash in American history. It ended not only the most spectacular of runaway markets, but also an economic era. Yet, to this day there are people in Montgomery Street who recall more vividly the "June break" of 1928, directed, as it was, primarily against Giannini stocks. The 1929 crash overwhelmed all stocks, in fact all securities. Before the dismal aftermath had reached its nadir in 1932 the soundest investment in the world, long-term United States government bonds, were selling at 82.

In September, 1929, the market reached its dizzy pinnacle. Adams Express, an investment trust that had been acquired in April by the Chase National Bank of New York, sold at 660; Du Pont at 231; General Electric, 396; General Motors, 79; U.S. Steel, 262; Transamerica, 67. It was a nervous market, however, and these highs were not sustained except in very rare cases. On the last day of the month Adams sold at a low of 550, off 110 from the month's high. Du Pont was off 53; GE, off 30; GM, off 13; Steel, off 41. Transamerica was one of the rare exceptions. It closed at 67, the equal of its high. Nolan and the Hellmans were not alone in feeling that Trans was a desirable investment at 63.[10]

October came in with increased uncertainty—rumors of bear activity, European selling and so on. A bad flurry blew up on Saturday the nineteenth, two days after the anniversary celebration of the Bank of Italy. All the leaders sold off sharply. Transamerica stood firm at 63 and 64, but this was largely due to market support from the corporation itself. A. P. Giannini had given the order to support the stock. The next week was critical. The entire list broke, and would have broken worse but for a bankers' pool, in New York managed by Morgan who bought Steel and other pivotal stocks, and for Giannini's support of Transamerica in San Francisco. Monday, October 28, witnessed the last of the supporting operations, East and West. On the next day the market collapsed and panic took the New York Stock Exchange for the first time since 1907.

Overnight there had accumulated a tremendous volume of selling orders, and this was especially true of Transamerica. The New York exchanges opened two hours and a half before those in San Francisco, because of the difference between Eastern and Pacific time. The first sale of Transamerica in New York was at 20, after which it rallied so encouragingly that the San Francisco opening was at 30. The rally continued, the stock closing in New York at 39 and in San Francisco, two and a half hours later, at 41.

During the rest of the year the market worked up and down within a narrow range; but the trend was mostly down. Transamerica closed the year at 42. From the September high, that represented a loss of just over 37 per cent, which was about the average for listed stocks generally.

Giannini was undismayed. He reckoned the book value of Trans-

). At the close of the day of pandemonium,
nt this wire to a subordinate in New York:
THE RECENT [*sic*] MARKET SLUMP CHANGE OUR
.EAD WITH THE WORK AS IF NOTHING HAD HAP-

6

30 opened big with projects. Giannini's eyes were on
.ve work of establishing a transcontinental bank, rather
stock ticker. To that end, he did what he had long had
He relinquished the presidency of Transamerica and
.e corporation over to younger men.

Elisha Walker became executive head of Transamerica, with
.le of chairman of the board and a salary of $100,000. Jean
.net, salary $50,000, was made vice-chairman. The officer next to
.ker was Lawrence Mario Giannini, president. His salary was
.o $50,000. A. P. Giannini became chairman of the advisory com-
.iittee of the board, with P. C. Hale and Bacigalupi vice-chairmen.
There were some changes in the board. Leo Belden had resigned in
September. Actually he had been dismissed. A. P. suspected that for
his personal account Belden had sold Giannini stocks short during
the Blue Monday episode. In A. P.'s book, there could have been no
greater sin. W. H. Snyder resigned because, after the October crash,
he doubted the wisdom of going ahead with Transamerica's mam-
moth program. He and the chief talked the matter over, and the
parting was friendly.

The new officers were named on February 8. Giannini was in
Palm Beach, Florida. Mario sent his father this telegram:

WILL ENDEAVOR TO SO CONDUCT MYSELF AS TO BE WORTHY OF THE LOVING
TRUST AND CONFIDENCE WHICH YOU HAVE REPOSED IN ME. AM UNDERTAKING
THE TASK IN ALL HUMILITY AND IN RELIANCE UPON YOUR CLOSE GUIDANCE AND
CONSTANT ADVICE. MY ONE GREAT HOPE IS THAT I SHALL PROVE WORTHY.[12]

Elisha Walker telegraphed:

AM DELIGHTED AT HAPPY CLOSING OUR AGREEMENT AND OUR THOROUGH
UNDERSTANDING. I AM ENTERING MY NEW RESPONSIBILITIES WITH DETERMINED
SPIRIT HIGH HOPES OF REAL ACCOMPLISHMENT AND COUNT ON YOUR HEARTY
COOPERATION. I HOPE YOU WILL TAKE A WELL EARNED REST AND MONNET
JOINS ME IN SENDING YOU OUR WARMEST REGARDS.[13]

The thorough understanding to which Mr. Walker alluded had been reduced to writing. The first item on the Transamerica program called for the development of nationwide branch banking.[14]

On his initial visit to San Francisco in his new capacity, Walker made a brief speech before the California leaders of Transamerica. It left a good impression.

I can promise that we will do our best to try to follow in the footsteps of Mr. Giannini. We want Transamerica to be a California institution as well as a national and international one. . . . We need the help of all you men who have been in Transamerica's service up and down and through California. . . . As to the future of Transamerica—within the last short period we leaped the boundaries of California and brought over to New York Transamerica with its excellent bank, the Bank of America. It seems to me it is little to what we can hope for in the future.[15]

In a newspaper interview Mr. Walker said:

Transamerica is really only starting. Recently it was only a local institution. Now it has the world at its feet. It has no serious competition in its field. . . . The American people must adopt branch banking. . . . The Giannini institutions . . . are operated for the benefit of stockholders and depositors. Mr. Giannini never thought of holding a large amount of stock himself. I will conduct the organization in the same unselfish way he did. I am not in this for individual gain but for the good of the company.[16]

The year-end reports of Transamerica's principal holdings, the two California branch banking systems and the New York bank, had been excellent. The effect of the market crash seemed negligible. When a bond issue to complete the San Francisco–Hetch Hetchy water system went begging, the Bank of Italy had taken the first block of $4,000,000. Later Giannini arranged for his banks and others to move the balance of the issue amounting to $37,000,000.

In March, 1930, Transamerica bought the Occidental Life Insurance Company of Los Angeles, a small concern as life insurance companies go, with insurance in force amounting to $150,000,000. An aggressive program of expansion was launched. Two years earlier, it will be recalled, Giannini had acquired the Pacific National Fire Insurance Company.

In April, 1930, Transamerica announced the purchase of a million shares, carrying control, of the General Foods Corporation.

Though the Giannini banks continued to show gains in deposits, this was contrary to the experience of the country. The great depression was inexorably descending. The long decline of prices and wages had set in. Unemployment began to loom as a national problem. Transamerica got its first taste of this when it launched a truly ambitious campaign to increase its body of stockholders from 175,000 to 500,000. The aim was to interest investors who could purchase twenty-five shares or less. The Giannini organization was expert at such drives. The remarkable thing is that, considering the deepening of the depression and the spread of anxiety, it was able to bring the list up to 217,000 by the end of the year.

On his sixtieth birthday—May 6, 1930—A. P. Giannini was en route to Washington to testify before the House Committee on Banking and Currency. The committee was examining means of strengthening the banking structure against the advance of hard times. Bacigalupi spent two days before it. His testimony fills a volume forming perhaps the most valuable exposition extant of the practice of branch banking.

Mr. Giannini's examination required a couple of hours. The committee's attitude was friendly, almost deferential. In a mellow frame of mind, the Californian described himself as "retired," with the affairs of his banks and of Transamerica in other hands. He urged legislation permitting a bank to do business in more than one state, like railroads and telephone companies. This would eliminate the necessity of holding companies such as Transamerica, and make possible true nationwide branch banking instead of group banking. The use of holding companies, he said, "is not an ideal way of doing business"; but it was superior to unit banking. After the inadequacies of the existing system had been discussed, Mr. Giannini was asked: "What remedy do you suggest to this committee?"

"Branch banking, nationwide and worldwide," replied the Californian.[17]

The Walker Regime

WITH less than a year's experience in the Giannini organization, Elisha Walker began his regime as head of Transamerica at a difficult time in the national economy.

In 1930, the country's income slipped from $81,000,000,000 to $68,000,000,000. All lines of business were off, excepting such lines as secondhand clothing. Installment sellers were repossessing automobiles, household furniture, electric refrigerators, jewelry and fur coats. The wage cut, the lay off, the blue slip were everyday things. For the last nine months of the year unemployment mounted by an average of 750,000 a month. In January, 1931, 6,000,000 were out of work. The soup kitchen, the bread line, the street-corner apple seller began to appear. (The last-named was an inspiration of the International Apple Shippers Association which sold the fruit on credit to the unemployed as a means of disposing of its surplus.) The number of new dwelling units constructed dropped from 509,000 in 1929 to 330,000. Those who could no longer pay rent for the old units doubled up with relatives. Those having none to double up with built shack towns on the edges of cities, and in the fullness of time these settlements took the name of Hoovervilles.

Mr. Hoover's policy was that the relief of individuals was not a government matter, but one for private agencies supported by voluntary contributions. His policy concerning the relief of business was similar, with the exception that he had signed the bill creating the Farm Board. He recommended to states and cities the inauguration of public works to tide over the unemployed.

There was insistence that the country's troubles were temporary and that "prosperity is just around the corner." Someone suggested "coroner" as an apter word. Stress was laid on a return of confidence. Lions Clubs sponsored a Business Confidence Week. Confidence is important, but the trouble lay deeper than that. What *was* wrong, then, in a country where people went hungry while surpluses rotted on farms or were stored in granaries; where people went without decent clothing when there was cotton and wool to spare, and idle mills to work it up?

There was a failure of leadership—in public office and in the councils of industry and finance. With isolated exceptions, the captains of business had done nothing to indicate the perils of Mr. Harding's Normalcy or Mr. Coolidge's Prosperity. Glance for a moment at New York City in 1930: bread lines on the Bowery, apple sellers on Fifth Avenue. One of Mayor Jimmy Walker's remedial suggestions was that the movie industry release only cheerful pictures. On the other hand, the Hawley-Smoot Tariff Act, which Mr. Hoover signed, was not written by Broadway playboys. It was written by congressmen whose economic thought was that of the 1890's. To its credit, the American Bankers Association protested the enactment of this high-tariff measure, which brought immediate retaliation abroad, assisted in the rapid ruin of our foreign trade and spread distress over the globe.

Prior to 1933, it had never taken more than a touch of hard times to demonstrate the weakness of our banking system. In 1930 bank failures numbered 1,345, only 8 of which were in California. Though farming sections of the Middle West suffered most heavily, there were also failures in cities, the most conspicuous being the Bank of United States in New York. Because of the similarity in name, this caused flurries in some of the outlying branches of Transamerica's Bank of America N. A. in New York. One jerry-built example of group banking, the Caldwell group with headquarters in Nashville, Tennessee, went under.[1]

2

Amid these untoward circumstances Mr. Walker ran into trouble. One factor was the decline of Transamerica stock. On June 2 it sold for 45; on August 8, 20. Though other stocks were down also, Trans was a particular target. The many who followed its fortunes were confused by a conflicting array of figures on the value of the corporation's assets. Moreover, in July Mr. Walker gave notice that the October quarterly dividend would be cut from forty to twenty-five cents. At the same time Mr. Walker informed stockholders that the Transamerica shares had been revalued on the records of the corporation. Though the "book value" of $49.82 was not discarded, the figure of $28.75, called "knock-down" value, was declared to be more realistic. The knock-down value was practically market value, exclusive of good-will. Shortly after, in an application for admission of Transamerica to the New York Stock Exchange (it had previously been traded on the Curb), a "net asset value" of $14.50 a share was stated. On that basis Transamerica was worth only $335,000,000. Had it been for sale, the Bank of Italy alone would have brought more than that—one San Francisco broker said twice that much.[2]

Another thing that plagued Mr. Walker was a disagreement with the Gianninis, father and son. Walker and the two Californians were separated by a difference in training, outlook, ideas—in short, by the differing worlds they had grown up in. In normal times these differences might possibly have been reconciled, could the men involved have had a chance to work together long enough. Witness the useful service of Howard Whipple in the Giannini organization. But these were not normal times. An economic world was falling apart.

The following were some of the causes of the initial rift between Walker and the Gianninis.

Mario objected to the reduction of the dividend in such panicky times.

Cabling from London, A. P. wanted to go roughshod after the bears who were driving down Transamerica. Among them was Leo Belden who had set up as a broker in San Francisco. A. P. asked Mario to "start hitting . . . that discharged traitor and tool" and "drive him out of state." Walker firmly demurred. Bear operations were within the law. It would be a mistake to dignify them with attention. "Believe he [Belden] will fall by his own weight and eventually pay the penalty."[3]

There was also the matter of Transamerica's earnings for 1929. In January, 1930, Giannini had announced the gross figure, subject to deductions, of $96,000,000. Walker's July letter to stockholders gave the net as $67,316,309. The principal items making up the difference were undistributed earnings of subsidiaries, credits to surplus and taxes. This was not explained, however. The result was various speculations in the press. Reading some of these in the London *Daily Mail* and feeling that silence reflected on his management, Giannini was for putting the *Mail* straight. Walker opposed "any public discussion of this question." Nevertheless, A. P. gave his own explanation to the London paper. It was, of course, cabled to New York. Walker mailed Giannini the accountants' version of the $67,000,000 figure which differed in unimportant respects from Giannini's. The New Yorker suggested that if A. P. was going to talk to the papers he should have his figures right.[4]

Giannini wired his son:

DON'T YOU FOLKS THINK TIME HAS ARRIVED FOR CALLING A SPADE A SPADE BY TELLING ELISHA [AND] JEAN [MONNET] TAKE BACK THEIR ORIGINAL STOCK AND TO GO AHEAD OUT OF THE ORGANIZATION. . . . IT'S MY DUTY TO BE BACK ON THE FIRING LINE REGARDLESS OF MY PHYSICAL WELFARE. . . . WE WILL ALL GET TOGETHER AND PUT THE THING OVER WITH A WHOOP.[5]

A few days later he was on the ocean, but it was not the affairs of Transamerica primarily that had called him. His adored stepfather, Lorenzo Scatena, chairman of the board of the Bank of Italy, was critically ill. To try to get "there in time to see grandpa [as A. P.'s children called the old man] alive," Giannini dashed from New York to the Coast by rail and plane. He lost the race by a matter of hours.

After the burial of Mr. Scatena, Giannini turned to business. Elisha Walker and Jean Monnet had come on from the East. Now was the time to get them quietly out of the organization—if in the considered judgment of A. P. and his associates the situation called for their departure. Before leaving England, Giannini had wired Mario to go over the question with Bacigalupi and P. C. Hale. These old lieutenants were not for it. They did not share their chief's misgivings about the new men. Again, considering the times, another reorganization might be bad for the bank. Yet Giannini's presence in California was most helpful. Bacigalupi remarked that it "put heart into old stockholders whose morale was quite low." To them, Transamerica and the bank were still Giannini. In view of his "retirement," this put A. P. in a peculiar position. Wherever he sat was the head of the table, regardless of who had the titles.[6]

3

So Walker stayed.

At a series of meetings, several changes were made in the Trans-america setup, the most important of which was the decision to merge the Bank of Italy and the Bank of America of California under title of the Bank of America National Trust and Savings Association. The news was given first to some seven hundred executives, directors, branch managers and advisory board members assembled in San Francisco on September 3, 1930.

"This marks the culmination," Bacigalupi told them,

of a plan conceived by A. P. Giannini when the Bank of America of California was formed two years ago. The consolidation includes the Bank of Italy with resources of approximately $1,000,000,000 and the Bank of America with resources of $350,000,000, and through control by Trans-america Corporation of both the newly consolidated institutions in California and the Bank of America in New York, with its $500,000,000 resources, in effect inaugurates the establishment of a nationwide banking organization.[7]

Many who were present—Giannini among them—felt a pang at the passing of the old name, Bank of Italy. During its lifetime of twenty-six years no other privately owned bank had stood for so much in the hard struggle to improve the banking structure of the United States.

A. P. Giannini was chairman of the committee to work out the details of the consolidation. How Californians seized upon that fact! As one country editor expressed it: "The old financial war horse, has taken up the reins again . . . and it seems that whatever plan is evolved will protect . . . Healdsburg."[8]

A tour about the state was made, ostensibly to discuss the announcement with stockholders but actually to introduce them to Elisha Walker. Though it was A. P. Giannini who brought the crowds, he let Walker and Bacigalupi do the talking. Concerning the recent market decline, Mr. Walker said that he was the largest individual owner of Transamerica stock; that he had not sold a share, "and I have never been less disposed to sell than now." With a Bank of America on each coast, he said that Transamerica would "enter the branch banking field in every state and in foreign countries." One bank, the First National of Portland, Oregon, resources $50,000,000, had already been purchased.[9]

When Walker and Monnet departed for the East, there was a ripple of optimism through the Giannini empire. Transamerica shares climbed to 25. There was a rumor of a consolidation with Goldman Sachs Trading Corporation, an Eastern holding company which had obtained control of the American Trust Company of San Francisco, long the Bank of Italy's closest rival in northern California. Goldman Sachs had fared worse than Trans since the debacle of October, 1929, tumbling from 121 to 32.

As the depression deepened and bank failures increased there were rumors about banks everywhere. Robert Paganini reported to A. J. Mount that the story was going about that the consolidation in California was due to the fact that the Bank of Italy was "losing business and on the edge of bankruptcy." Some such story reached the ears of the party-line telephone operator at Lone Pine, in the Owens River Valley. She lost no time informing her subscribers. The next morning there was a run on the Lone Pine branch of the Bank of America of California. It spread to the Bishop branch, sixty miles away. Prompt reinforcements of currency ended these demonstrations.[10]

The multitude of details incident to the amalgamation of the two banking systems proceeded. To satisfy the McFadden Act, which provided for the merger of banks only when their head offices were in the same city, the board of the Bank of America of California removed the home office to San Francisco. Of the 163 branches of the state bank 106 were eligible, under the law, for merger. Twenty-six of the eligibles were marked for consolidation with existing Bank of Italy branches; 80 would be continued. The 57 ineligible branches, plus 7 individual California banks owned by Transamerica, would be united in a new state bank called the Bank of America. (To distinguish this Bank of America from the two other Giannini banks of similar name it will be referred to in these pages as "the Bank of America (state).")

The Bank of America N. T. and S. A. and the Bank of America (state) came formally into being on Monday, November 3, 1930. Never were two legally separate banks more closely bound together. With the same officers and directors, and virtually the same name, about the only distinction was that the national bank operated under federal authority and the state bank under state authority. Their

THE BANK OF ITALY has been, from its inception and is now, ready and anxious to make loans to people owning, or intending to build, their own homes — to the smaller mortgage borrowers who need $1000 or less. ¶ The BANK OF ITALY has built up, its present reputation, its present enormous resources, largely through catering to the small depositor—the wage earner, the producer, the small business man, the man who owns a small home or a piece of improved property, the man who is the bone and sinew of Southern California's progress. ¶ This bank has never catered to speculators. ¶ To men of the home-owning type particularly, we hold out now the opportunity to effect a loan, the opportunity to borrow money on their small holdings. ¶ And in this bank there is no need for the payment of brokers' fees or commissions, no need for working through a third party, no expenses in connection with the drawing of mortgage papers. ¶ No cost of any kind.

Advertising such as this heralded the entry of the Bank of Italy into Southern California in 1913.

combined worth was nearly a billion and a quarter dollars, distributed as follows:

RESOURCES	Bank of America N.T.&S.A.	Bank of America (state)	Combined
First Mortgage Loans on Real Estate	$ 306,609,659	$15,771,823	$ 322,381,482
Other Loans and Discounts	377,977,871	14,587,968	392,565,839
U.S. Bonds and Certificates of Indebtedness	178,914,770	3,178,776	182,093,546
State, County & Municipal Bonds	78,844,287	7,186,826	86,031,113
Other Bonds & Securities	18,893,571	4,987,630	23,881,201
Stock in Federal Reserve Bank	2,850,000		2,850,000
Due from Federal Reserve Bank	31,120,938		31,120,938
Cash & Due from Other Banks	62,016,948	11,816,550	73,833,498
Banking Premises, Furniture, Fixtures & Safe Deposit Vaults	46,879,806	2,281,786	49,161,592
Customers' Liability Under Letters of Credit & Acceptances	44,707,147	8,700	44,715,847
Customers' Liability on Bills Purchased & Sold	12,109,949		12,109,949
Interest Earned on Bonds and Loans	8,475,089	655,643	9,130,732
Other Resources	2,025,751	355,912	2,381,663
TOTAL RESOURCES	$1,171,425,786	$60,831,614	$1,232,257,400

LIABILITIES			
Deposits: Savings	$ 664,636,113	$36,263,426	$ 700,899,539
Commercial	314,143,299	17,443,709	331,587,008
Letters of Credit and Acceptances	44,707,147	8,700	44,715,847
Bills Sold without Endorsement	12,109,949		12,109,949
Circulation	10,000,000		10,000,000
Bills Payable & Other Liabilities	4,551,822	50,222	4,602,044
Items in Transit between Head Office & Branches	4,130,199		4,130,199
Capital	50,000,000	4,000,000	54,000,000
Surplus and Profits	56,155,638	2,685,088	58,840,726
Reserves for Interest, Taxes, etc.	10,991,619	380,469	11,372,088
TOTAL LIABILITIES	$1,171,425,786	$60,831,614	$1,232,257,400

4

The acquiescence of the Gianninis to the retention of Elisha Walker brought no tranquillity to the councils of Transamerica. On

December 3, 1930, a month after the Bank of Italy had changed its name, Mario Giannini submitted his resignation as president of the holding company. At Mr. Walker's request he consented to remain until the annual meeting in March.

Mario Giannini and Elisha Walker differed about a hundred things. As bankers they simply were poles apart. The actual break centered about a new market sinking spell which carried Transamerica to 13 despite the operations of a supporting pool. Mario criticized the operation of the pool, and his father, who was ill in Florida, again suggested a public campaign against those he believed to be the leaders of a bear movement against Trans. He startled Mr. Walker by making a public statement in which he accused "a certain California competitor" of being "a most active participant."

The competitor was Herbert Fleishhacker, president of the Anglo California Bank. In a Christmas message to Armando Pedrini, A. P. said: "Oh, how I do wish, Ped, I could have my old health back . . . and properly show up the Herbert Fleishhackers et al."[11]

Mr. Walker was still opposed to making an issue of bear operations. According to a story Mario Giannini passed on to his father, Walker, while on a trip to San Francisco, called at Mr. Fleishhacker's office, and meditated issuing a statement that he knew of no bear operations, but was dissuaded by Bacigalupi.[12]

The latter part of January, 1931, Elisha Walker was again in San Francisco. He asked Mario to a conference, but kept him waiting outside his office while others went in. Then Mr. Walker went to dinner without seeing the second officer of his company. That was too much for Mario Giannini. He resigned again and returned his January paycheck. The intervention of Hale and Bacigalupi kept the matter quiet until March 26, when it was soft-pedaled in a brief announcement. A week later Mario withdrew from his committee assignments in the bank, but retained his directorship.[13]

In a tone of obituary the magazine *Time* noted the passing of the younger Giannini from the office his father had held:

"Master of the [Transamerica] temple for one year now has been Chairman Elisha Walker, a quiet, diplomatic, keen-eyed New Yorker. . . . The great shouts of big, jovial Amadeo Peter Giannini have faded further and further into the distance, are gradually becoming echoes."[14]

Walker was on his own.

5

The general outlook was darker than when Elisha Walker had joined Trans a year before, as the annual statement for 1930 vividly reflected. Profits were $18,537,000, against $67,316,000 for 1929. This news had its effect on the price of shares which slipped from 14 in January, 1931, to 9 in May.

The annual reports of the Bank of America N. T. & S. A. and of the Bank of America (state) made better reading though they, too, left something to be desired. For instance, during the first six months of the year the banks had gained deposits, a trend that was reversed in the last six months during which the figure went from $1,139,000,000 to $1,054,000,000, a drop of 7.5 per cent. (To give a realistic picture it is necessary to use the combined figures of the two banks. To compare the Bank of Italy deposits for June 30 with the Bank of America N. T. & S. A. deposits for December 31 would be misleading because of the intervening merger.) This loss was slightly larger than the 7.2 per cent decline sustained during the same period by the American Trust of San Francisco. The state's second largest branch system, Sartori's Security-First National of Los Angeles, showed a gain of 4.2 per cent.

On February 28, 1931, the federal bank examiners completed an examination of the Bank of America N. T. & S. A. Their report, confidential of course, showed a decline in eight months in the total of loans from $628,000,000 to $507,000,000. But slow loans had increased from $56,000,000 to $92,000,000, doubtful loans from $3,000,000 to almost $11,000,000, loan losses from $3,000,000 to $12,000,000. Los Angeles showed up particularly badly—largely the old story of weak assets inherited from the Merchants National. There slow loans amounted to $22,000,000, doubtful loans to $6,600,000, and losses to $6,000,000. Los Angeles was responsible for more than half of the doubtful loans and losses of the bank. By contrast, slow loans in San Francisco were $4,965,000, doubtful loans $455,000, and losses $1,000,000.[15]

Bear in mind that this was the bank examiners' characterization of these loans. With the banking situation of the country going from bad to worse, examiners were under orders from the comptroller's department to be drastic. A. P. Giannini would not have agreed with their classification of the Bank of America loans. At a later date we shall see that he vigorously opposed Washington's pessimistic policy. We shall see also that loans they regarded as hopeless eventually paid out.

Nevertheless, at the time, one feature of the situation seemed to justify the examiners. The life blood of the bank, deposits, continued to ebb. During the first six months of 1931, those of the Bank of America N. T. & S. A. fell from $998,000,000 to $909,951,000, a loss of 8.8 per cent. The state bank went from $56,695,000 to $53,-472,000, a loss of 5.7 per cent. Most banks throughout the country were losing deposits, but Transamerica's California banks were losing them faster than their principal rivals. For the same period the loss for the American Trust of San Francisco was 1.5 per cent and for the Security–First National 2.8 per cent. A thing like that had never happened before.

Though the bank still made a profit, it was greatly reduced and even then was maintained only by cutting expenses deeply. The bank's staff was reduced by 10 per cent, which meant layoffs for 850 persons. In the last half of 1930, earnings were $11,450 a month below the average for the previous six months. During the first half of 1931 they were $186,000 below. Expenses, however, had been cut $202,000 a month.[16]

As bread lines lengthened and Hoovervilles spread, every factory, plant, shop, bank, office, store and corner filling station in the land was a center for hard-times rumors. Orra Monnette in Los Angeles reported to Mr. Mount "ugly and depressing gossip" about the bank, which he traced to sources that could not have been in collusion: brokerage houses and "the Reds." The manager at Stockton reported a woman's story: "The men in Wall Street were tired of the Italians running the banking business . . . and that the Bank of America was in bad shape and if they had any money in it they had better take it out." A near-by farmer told a depositor that Transamerica and the bank were going broke and that he had better sell his stock.[17]

Similar stories were going the rounds in New York. Several B. of A. N. A. branches experienced minor runs. The gossip leaped the Atlantic. Bancamerica-Blair's French representative cabled: "BROKERS REPORT RELUCTANCE ENTRUST DEPOSITS TO BANK OF AMERICA N. T. AND S. A." A. P. Giannini, who was abroad, wired his son that in

London and Paris "propagandists had been working overtime" to undermine the bank.[18]

In New York, Doc Giannini put his finger on a vital aspect of the deteriorating situation. "I do not mind the price of the stock," he wrote Armando Pedrini,

if we had a happy organization where everybody was pulling together— but to be working with people who do not possess the same motives we do, makes it doubly hard. . . . Walker assures me that everything will work out satisfactorily, but he moves too slowly to suit me. I will stand it just a wee bit longer and, if there is nothing doing, I will do as Mario did.[19]

Morale among the workers in his California banks was something Giannini had maintained in superlative degree. At the time of Mario's departure this morale was going to pot; and it was not the only thing in the realm of confidence and good feeling that was going to pot, according to Will F. Morrish who wrote thus revealingly to Elisha Walker:

"Our first and greatest problem is to reestablish ourselves in the good graces of the public, our stockholders, and our employees."[20]

Then came a further blow to morale and to public confidence. The source of it was that old sore spot, the Merchants National of Los Angeles. Since the national bank examiners' critical report on the Los Angeles situation, P. C. Read, chief inspector of the Bank of America N. T. & S. A., had been quietly at work down there. His report was submitted in June, 1931. The authors of this book have not been able to find it. In 1933, however, Mr. Read undertook to give A. P. Giannini a summary of it, in which he wrote:

Four officers of the [Merchants National] Bank over a period of years . . . wilfully misapplied funds of the Bank through the device generally of causing notes to be signed by third persons upon the understanding and agreement that such persons would not be liable thereon and applying the funds to the personal use of the officers. These same officers, after the funds had been obtained, continued to conceal from National and State Bank Examiners and superior officers of the Bank the true condition of these loans by giving false information when questioned concerning them, accepting renewal notes when the Loan Committee directed notes to be collected, and by placing false financial statesments in credit files of such accommodation borrowers, with the result that the misapplication of funds in excess of five and one-half million dollars was concealed from officers of the Bank and National and State Bank Examiners and the Comptroller of the Currency.[21]

Comptroller John W. Pole was sufficiently exercised over the examiners' report to request a change in the management at the Los Angeles office. With the Read findings in his hands, Walker was altogether ready to comply. As a result Edward J. Nolan, Irving H. and Marco Hellman, Charles R. Bell and two others submitted their resignations. Beset with troubles, Mr. Walker's object was to pass the ugly incident off as smoothly as possible. When a branch manager asked questions, Mr. Mount replied: "The less said about that particular subject the better."[22]

Some of the resulting speculation did the harassed bank no good. Three advisory board members were approached by people "who were under the impression that the bank is in a bad way and that the officers in question had resigned because they did not approve of our policies and were getting out before anything happened."[23]

6

With matters getting worse for Transamerica as well as for everyone else in the country, Chairman Walker summoned the executive committee of Trans to assemble in New York early in June, 1931. "SENTIMENT VERY BLUE," Bacigalupi telegraphed the Coast on arriving. Mr. Bacigalupi understated the case. Walker was frightened, and he was by no means the only financier in or out of Trans in that state. He was not paralyzed by his fears, however. He had formulated a program and he intended to act.[24]

The program was Draconian. It contemplated the abandonment of the transcontinental banking project to which Mr. Walker had so ardently committed himself. That was the least of it. It contemplated the dismemberment of the financial empire A. P. Giannini had created, much of it as an instrument for the realization of that project. The banks were to be divorced from their principal affiliates and perhaps sold. Definitely marked for the block was the New York institution, Bank of America N. A. Certain affiliates were to be sold. Dividends were to be cut. Transamerica's other security holdings were to be marked down further and large blocks of them dumped.[25]

Walker was pressed on every side. Transamerica owed $51,800,000. Comptroller of the Currency Pole came forward with a demand for $15,000,000 to cover bank loans that the national examiners had marked off as "losses." Moreover, Pole indicated that Trans might be called on for another $20,000,000 to cover loans from the big California bank that his examiners had labeled "slow" or "doubtful." All, or virtually all, the loans involved were inheritances from the Hellman bank. What the examiners, public and private, had missed when they went over that bank's books before Giannini bought it in 1928 seems, in the light of subsequent events, incredible.[26]

As Walker and his associates saw it, the general situation called for contraction and for liquidation. But whether it called for unconditional surrender, the pulling down of the whole Giannini edifice and the distress sale of many of its parts, left room for a dissenting opinion.

The dissent that counted in the end came from A. P. Giannini. What the shrewd Bacigalupi thought at first is hard to say. He seems to have gone quite a way with Walker's thinking, which both men believed to be simply realism in a crumbling world. Nevertheless, for a time, he entertained the idea of Giannini's return to the helm. P. C. Hale was, for once in his life, simply bewildered. The news Bacigalupi had brought from New York was too much for the old merchant. He took a steamer to Hawaii for rest and reflection.

Nor was A. P. Giannini himself when the news of the New York meeting reached him at the health resort of Badgastein, Germany. He was convalescing from a desperate illness in which for months polyneuritis had threatened to cripple him for life—if he lived. He had been in the hands of doctors in various parts of the United States and in Europe. He was still in pain and under medical supervision which included an injunction to avoid excitement, an injunction Mrs. Giannini and his daughter Claire attempted to enforce. The first tidings from New York were received by transatlantic telephone.[27]

The sick man was outraged. All he had built in a lifetime to be torn down and scattered to the winds! In a torrent of cablegrams to Walker, to Bacigalupi, to Mario, A. P. Giannini curled the wires with denunciation of the scheme which he branded a "plot" and a "conspiracy" to rob the stockholders. He laid about him in every direction. "Most extraordinary [and] boldest of bold steals," he stormed. "Whoever heard of writing down everything [to] knocked down value and then after this value has been publicly established go out and sell." By such tactics insiders could clean up, and Giannini said that was according to the Wall Street school of finance. "Ours was an institution with soul and working solely interests stockholders [of moderate means]." He saw Morgan as an immediate beneficiary. "Whole scheme is get me permanently out way by casting lasting reflection. Corner never liked our substantial interest in leading companies, nor our going into Europe for business, and issuing travelers checks which Bankers Trust [a Morgan Bank] strongly objected [to]."[28]

Giannini meant to fight. His cables breathed indignation and defiance, but no hint of despair. In them was the spirit that had carried him and his bank through the San Francisco fire. The veteran was unafraid. That was an important thing, considering the role that fear was taking in the unhappy drama of American life. But for all that, he labored under a heavy handicap. In the old days, the last thing A. P. Giannini had to consider was his health. Now the doctors, actually, were in control of the destinies of Transamerica. "What I'm really trying to do over here," he assured his son, "is to get myself in sufficiently good shape to be able to give . . . [Walker] a real stiff battle."

Giannini sparred for time. The Walker program was to be laid before the board of Transamerica in San Francisco on June 17. A. P. suggested that a committee, independent of the management, be named to study the proposal and report in sixty days, and, further, that the bylaws be amended to require submission to the stockholders of proposals to sell or merge companies. A. P. asked Mario, who had resolved not to attend the meeting, to communicate his suggestions to friendly members. Bacigalupi especially was urged to support them.[29]

Instead, Bacigalupi supported the Walker program and used the powers of persuasion for which he was famous to swing other members into line. The Giannini proposals never got before the meeting. It was a complete victory for Walker. This is the more notable because only twelve members attended besides Chairman Walker who came from New York to preside. Nearly all were old friends of Giannini: Bacigalupi, Blauer, Bocqueraz, Ferrari, W. W. Garthwaite, C. N. Hawkins, Morrish, Mount, Pedrini, A. E. Sbarboro and George A. Webster.

The chairman painted a black picture of Transamerica's present and future. He read a "comprehensive memorandum" (which did not get into the minutes) explaining the proposals recommended at the New York meeting of a fortnight before. In addition to the proposed or possible sale of banks and companies he recommended the reduction of Transamerica shares from $25 par to no par value. He recommended a dividend cut from twenty-five cents to ten cents a quarter. He admitted that A. P. Giannini disapproved of this and read cables exchanged with him.

Bacigalupi spoke in favor of the plan, and, as the minutes read, after "full discussion" the board approved it "in principle." Then Bacigalupi called for a unanimous vote of confidence in the management and got it.

Next, Chairman Walker moved to eliminate the last means remaining by which Giannini could control Transamerica without an appeal to the stockholders. Since Bancitaly days Giannini had headed the proxy committee, which controlled a majority of the voting shares. The committee consisted of A. P., Mario, Dr. Giannini, P. C. Hale and J. F. Cavagnaro. It held the voting rights (revocable at will by the stockholders) of fifteen million shares. Asked to approve a new committee, the board did so. It consisted of Walker, Monnet, H. P. Preston, Bacigalupi and Cavagnaro.[30]

Mario was furious over the result of the meeting, for which he blamed Bacigalupi. "Thus you have, unwittingly I hope, accomplished for your Wall Street superiors that which they so ardently desired." Mario was easier on the other directors, "most of whom are beholden to the proponents of the [Walker] plan for their positions."[31]

Certainly men like Louis Ferrari, Bill Blauer, Will Morrish and Armando Pedrini did not believe they were abetting a "conspiracy" or consorting with "crooks" when they voted to sustain Mr. Walker. Nor were they. Some of the language that Giannini used to describe Mr. Walker and his program cannot be taken literally. That certain directors were, as Mario indicated, moved by fear, fear of loss of their earnings, is easy to believe. At least two of them were deeply in debt. Very few persons escaped such fears in those days. Mr. Walker's program of ruthless and desperate liquidation, which would fall hardest on those who had least, was motivated by some such fear. Yet it was a program whose general principle—drastic liquidation—had endorsement in high quarters, from the White

House and the Federal Reserve Board down. Defeatism was rife. No one had yet appeared in public life or in business life with sufficient stature, creative optimism and gift of leadership to make headway against it.

7

A. P. Giannini took his reverse at the hands of the board more easily than Mario did. He sent Bacigalupi his resignation from the directorates of Transamerica and its affiliates, and said that he would make his fight simply as a stockholder. He also began to talk about coming home and starting the fight very soon. This alarmed Bacigalupi. He suggested that, if A. P. came, he should do one of two things: resume full command of Transamerica, or co-operate with Walker in working out a solution. What he should not do was start a fight. Both men spoke as if there were no question of A. P.'s ability to resume command if he would take it. What Walker might think of the idea was mentioned by neither of them.[32]

In response, Giannini cabled Bacigalupi what he had already cabled Mario, namely, that he was getting himself in physical condition to lock horns with Walker. He could not co-operate with the New Yorker because he had lost faith in him. When he came home he would fight. He intimated that he might appear at the stockholders meeting in Wilmington, Delaware, on July 21. The meeting was to pass on the recent board actions. Bacigalupi submitted that Transamerica's condition would not stand a civil war. He begged not to be obliged to present Giannini's resignations. Above all he begged A. P. to make no "fuss or sideshow" at Wilmington.[33]

"Where do you get that sideshow stuff, Jim?" Giannini retorted.

Have I no right to tell people my reasons for disassociating myself from New York bunch and to frankly confess my error for bringing them into organization?. . . Plan sell asset value Diocese [Bank of America N. T. and S. A.] to stockholders will turn out deliberate steal for as you know very few our stockholders have ready cash to exercise rights and to think that you folks can't see through this scheme is beyond me.[34]

"Calling names does no good," replied Bacigalupi, again urging Giannini to keep quiet.

"Yes, calling names, Jim, may be bad," Giannini admitted, "but haven't I always called a spade a spade?"[35]

On the same day he cabled Mario:

REMEMBER IT'S RIGHT OR PRINCIPLE WE ARE BATTLING FOR . . . AND THERE'S
NO COMPROMISING WITH RIGHT OR PRINCIPLE REGARDLESS CONSEQUENCES. NO,
SIR, NEVER MY BOY.

DAD[36]

In California the bank, through its branches, solicited proxies for the new committee. The omission of Giannini's name brought a flood of inquiries. One branch manager wrote A. J. Mount that stockholders "did not have the same confidence in the present set up as formerly." A stockholder in Monterey sent Mr. Walker his proxy form, with this written on the back: "I haven't as much confidence . . . as I had when A. P. Giannini was boss."[37]

At length Bacigalupi dissuaded his old chief from making a personal appearance at Wilmington and got him to refer the matter of his resignations to P. C. Hale. Hale proved difficult to reach in Hawaii, and the Wilmington meeting was held before he was heard from. The Walker program went through. Hale declared that for Giannini to resign now would be to court disaster. He defended Bacigalupi as doing his honest best in an almost impossible situation. Hale said he himself remained on the board "only [for] two reasons: . . . one, you; other, Lenient [Bacigalupi]."[38]

Giannini shook his head over his old friend's advice, but he followed it.

Mario began to hear unfriendly stories about his father. A. P. told his son not to worry. He attributed the rumors to the "propaganda factory," as he dubbed the high-priced public relations staff Mr. Walker had attached to Transamerica. One story suggested that Giannini's private fortune and income were by no means as small as people supposed. A. P. informed Mario that he would gladly make the facts public. "Present net worth is under half million exclusive special [undrawn commissions balance in Bancitaly account] which had intended drawing over period years." At the end of 1931, this balance was $791,816.[39]

A surprising development of the two months past had been the improvement in Giannini's health. It was as if the June news from New York, which would have crushed many a man, had been a tonic. The thought of a battle to save his banks and their dependencies seemed to invigorate their creator.

"LET'S CALL THEIR BLUFF," he wired Mario on August 17. The message was filed in Lucerne, Switzerland. Giannini was on his way home.[40]

Traveling alone, he booked passage for Quebec under the name of S. A. Williams. On September 4, father and son met secretly in Vancouver. Meantime the division in the Transamerica family had reached the newspapers. It centered about the sale, believed imminent, of the New York bank. "Walker, it is understood, is anxious to put through the program of distributing the Bank of America N. A. stock, while Giannini is believed to be opposed to such a step," cautiously ventured the San Francisco *News*. "The two groups, however, are expected to reach an eventual unanimous agreement." Mr. Giannini was assumed to be in Europe.[41]

Father and son dropped down to the Tahoe Tavern, a well-patronized mountain resort on the shore of Lake Tahoe through which runs the California-Nevada line. Certainly Giannini knew that his incognito could not long be preserved there. On September 11, he stepped from a barber chair and found himself face to face with, of all people, Herbert Fleishhacker. In no time the news of A. P. Giannini's return was flying the length of Montgomery Street, the North Beach end as well as the "Wall Street" end.[42]

Giannini Regains Control

FOR ONE purpose and one only had A. P. Giannini returned from Europe to the West Coast. That was to wrench control of Transamerica from Elisha Walker and so defeat the Walker program of dismemberment and liquidation. For the sake of the corporation, Giannini hoped there would be no open fight. But, with the work of a lifetime at stake, he did not shrink from the prospect.

Open fight or not, Giannini could use allies among his old lieutenants who had helped to build up Transamerica and the banks. Chief among these was James A. Bacigalupi, who had succeeded Mario Giannini as president of Trans. Where did Bacigalupi stand? Mario believed that he subscribed to the panicky thinking of Walker, and, in the struggle impending, had already gone over to the Walker camp. On the other hand, P. C. Hale believed Bacigalupi to be doing his best; and not many weeks earlier Bacigalupi himself had suggested that A. P. return and take charge. Accordingly, on September 13, 1931, before leaving Lake Tahoe for San Francisco, Giannini sent Bacigalupi a long telegram which the addressee was asked to communicate to

MY OTHER B. OF I. AND B. OF A. COWORKERS AND [to the] RESIDENT CALIFORNIA DIRECTORS OF TRANSAMERICA. . . . MY PRESENCE IN CALIFORNIA [read the telegram] DOESN'T CHANGE MY ATTITUDE IN THE LEAST AND I SHALL EXPECT JIM TO PROCEED WITH THE PRESENTATION OF MY RESIGNATION [as a director] FROM TRANSAMERICA AND AFFILIATES. . . . I HAVE NOT CHANGED MY OPINION ONE IOTA WITH REGARD TO THE CHARGES I HAVE MADE.

Giannini requested that his communications from Europe on the Walker plan be made a part of the Transamerica records. He reiterated that he did not intend to submit

AT THE POINT OF A GUN . . . [to] WALL STREET. . . . [My] ACTIONS ARE
PROMPTED ONLY THROUGH MY INTENSE INTEREST IN THE WELFARE AND FUTURE
SUCCESS OF THE INSTITUTIONS TO WHICH WE HAVE ALL GIVEN SO MUCH.[1]

After showing the wire to two "old co-workers," whom he did not
name, Bacigalupi suggested that A. P. "be brought up to date," after
which he was invited to "point out a better course." Replying from
his home in San Mateo, Giannini said that to discuss the "old plan"
would be a waste of breath. To Giannini, the Walker plan represented a "conspiracy" to "steal" Transamerica bit by bit from the
stockholders, tearing it asunder and knocking down its parts at
distress prices. This involved the sale of the insurance companies,
the cow bank, the country banks and securities, domestic and foreign. Nor was that all. It involved the sale of the Bank of America
N. A. in New York (already on the block), and the securities affiliate Bancamerica-Blair; the Italian branch banking system, and
in time the Bank of America N. T. & S. A. in California. In effect, these sales would be advertised in advance, thus further beating
down prices when all prices were on the toboggan. Already, said
Giannini, adverse rumors about the Transamerica companies were
being "deliberately circulated" to further the ends "of the conspiracy
which I have charged."

No, Giannini would not discuss such a plan. But if Bacigalupi
had a new plan, "widely different in conception . . . I will be glad
to see it and give you and my old associates . . . my comments."[2]

There was no new plan and consequently no discussion. Bacigalupi was, indeed, in the Walker camp, where he used his influence
to bring in other old Giannini men. Walker seemed confident. He
acted as if he had won his fight in June when, with Bacigalupi's
aid, the confused Western contingent of the Trans board had
knuckled under and endorsed "in principle" the Walker plan. Jean
Monnet, vice-chairman of Transamerica, was in San Francisco when
Giannini arrived. His mission was to push matters swiftly to conclusions. In this, Jim Bacigalupi became Elisha Walker's chief lieutenant among the Californians, as, for so long, he had been A. P.
Giannini's.

2

Giannini bided his time. On September 14, the morning after
his arrival, he appeared in the little office of the A. P. Giannini

Company in a building at California and Montgomery Streets. The A. P. Giannini Company dated back to when the banker was in the real estate business and was administrator of the estate of his father-in-law. It took care of the considerable investments of Mrs. Giannini stemming from her inheritance, of the more modest investments of the Giannini children and other members of the Cuneo and Giannini families, and some of their friends.

The place was filled with flowers and a crowd of Transamerica stockholders was on hand. Newspapermen were there. "This is not the time," Giannini told them, "for me to express an opinion concerning Transamerica's affairs." Anyone should know, he added, that he would offer no opposition to plans that "are equitable and, in my opinion, in the interest of Transamerica's stockholders."[3]

Old friends were shocked by Giannini's appearance. "He looked like a man who did not have long to live," one of them has said. Many wondered whether a man brought so low by illness could bear the burden of Transamerica.[4]

On September 22, the first public announcement of the Walker plan was made, after separate meetings of the boards of Transamerica and of the Bank of America N. T. & S. A. At the Trans meeting Mr. Monnet presided, and eleven others attended: Bacigalupi, Blauer, Bocqueraz, Ferrari, Garthwaite, Hawkins, Morrish, Mount, Pedrini, Sbarboro and Webster. All were Californians except Monnet and all except him had attended the June meeting. Before the meeting got down to business A. P. Giannini entered the room. His stay was brief. According to the minutes, he "made a verbal protest against the action of approval he believed this board was about to take. . . . Immediately following his protest Mr. Giannini withdrew."[5]

Thereupon Bacigalupi presented A. P. Giannini's long-delayed resignation as a director which was accepted "with regret." Later, at the bank meeting, Bacigalupi offered A. P.'s resignation from the bank board. Dreher of Los Angeles asked that action be postponed until a committee could ask Giannini to reconsider. Bacigalupi said A. P. wanted the resignation accepted; and it was, "with regret."

As Giannini had predicted, the Transamerica board promptly approved certain details of the Walker plan. A letter to stockholders, prepared in advance, was passed around the table. With some circumlocution it announced the abandonment of the nationwide banking project, "in the light of important changes which have taken place in business conditions" and because a change in the law permitting nationwide banking seemed unlikely.

Transamerica would "dispose of the majority interest in each of the banks which the Corporation now controls": this to be done "when conditions are favorable . . . [and] in a manner which will be advantageous to both . . . Transamerica stockholders and the banks themselves." Banks would be separated from affiliates "not directly concerned with banking."

The net assets of Transamerica were marked down to $172,000,000 or $7 a share, though with the assurance that the "intrinsic value" was "materially greater."

The October dividend was to be passed.

Lynn P. Talley, head of the Federal Reserve Bank of Dallas, Texas, would succeed Nolan as chairman of the board of the Bank of America N. T. & S. A. He had been recommended by Comptroller of the Currency Pole. This was significant. It assured a banking policy in harmony with that of the comptroller's office and of the Federal Reserve. This was a policy of write-offs and liquidation at current depression prices. It was the policy Elisha Walker subscribed to, but Giannini strenuously opposed.

News that the Gianninis were out was conveyed in a negative way. Transamerica stockholders were informed that "the Board of Directors is being reconstituted with a view to strengthening the position of the corporation." The membership of the new board of sixteen was given, with the statement that others might be added. There were ten Easterners, two Midwesterners, two Europeans and two Californians—Bacigalupi and Pedrini. The Californians who had been dropped—Blauer, Bocqueraz, Ferrari, Garthwaite, Hawkins, Morrish, Mount and Sbarboro—remained on the bank board, however. Stockholders also were proudly informed of an alliance Walker had forged between Transamerica and the Boston house of Lee, Higginson & Company. Four of the new directors were associated with that famous old firm. Among the new directors were men of high position, such as Charles W. Nash, president, Nash Motors and Fred W. Sargeant, president, Chicago and North Western Railway.[6]

The Lee, Higginson connection was interesting because the firm was the American banker for Ivar Kreuger, the Swedish "match king" with reputation for making millions faster than he could count them. Lee, Higginson partners sat on boards of more than one dazzling Kreuger enterprise. Two of the new Trans directors, Frederic W. Allen, a senior partner, and H. O. Havenmeyer of New York, were directors of Kreuger's International Match Company. Elisha Walker and Jean Monnet were directors of the Diamond Match Company of the United States which Kreuger was trying to get hold of to round out his global monopoly.

The election of Walker and Monnet to the Diamond board came about under circumstances that led *Barron's,* the financial weekly, to believe that Transamerica itself had become a heavy investor in Kreuger. During a recent recapitalization, Diamond had sold 350,-000 shares of new common stock to bankers for a client. A very unusual feature of the transaction was the price—$37 a share, or $20 above the market. The bankers would not identify their client, whom *Barron's* took to be Transamerica, pointing out that Walker and Monnet had just joined the Diamond board. *Barron's* was mistaken. The actual purchaser was Kreuger himself who at once pledged the stock for a $4,000,000 loan.[7]

Though the tie between Kreuger and Transamerica was not what *Barron's* thought, there nevertheless was a tie—and Kreuger sought to realize upon it. Unknown to the public, but not to his bankers, Ivar Kreuger's fantastic mosaic of 12 holding and 140 operating companies was in dire financial distress. Two months after Walker brought Lee, Higginson into Transamerica, the Swede arrived in New York in desperate search of money. One of the first places he went was to the Bank of America N. A.

The feature of the meeting that Walker played down in his announcement of September 22 to the stockholders was the one that the newspapers played up from coast to coast. The New York *Times* headline was typical:

GIANNINIS LOSE RULE OF HUGE BANK CHAIN

Next in order of interest was the advent of Lee, Higginson & Company.

"Transamerica," observed *Business Week,* "is now to . . . [be] guided by the Lee, Higginson firm, recently rejuvenated, and reputed to work closely with Morgan." The San Francisco *Daily*

News forecast the pattern: "Transamerica's activities will be some-what . . . along the line of Kreuger & Toll, the great investment company headed by Ivar Kreuger."[8]

The *American Banker* of New York was not sorrowful about what it thought had happened to Giannini:

A meteor in the banking firmament disintegrates with **A. P. Giannini's** loss of control of Transamerica Corp. and its far-flung affiliates. Viewing the results, the majority of bankwise and financially minded observers abroad as well as at home, will be likely to breathe easier. . . . Giannini overshot the mark. The shortening of his shadow in the banking world will be good for banking in a future that should look askance at too large financial egg-baskets.[9]

Transamerica stockholders breathed no easier, however. The Walker announcement touched off a wave of selling that drove the shares down to 4. A feature that aroused Giannini was that most of the sellers were Californians and most of the buyers Easterners. He had repeatedly predicted that this was the way the Walker plan would work out—that Wall Street insiders, who had contributed nothing to the upbuilding of Transamerica and its banks, would reap where they had not sown and make fortunes in depressed Giannini stock. In a public statement he begged stockholders not to sell, pointing out the ridiculous undervaluation of the Transamerica Corporation with its stock at 4. He said that the Bank of America N. T. & S. A. alone was worth "very much" more than that. Mr. Giannini could have put it stronger and been within the facts.[10]

3

Now that Walker had shown his hand and Giannini had something tangible to go on, he began to move in earnest. His first commentary was temperately worded:

The present plan offered by Mr. Walker is primarily objectionable in that it proposes to take out of the corporation the control of its principal and most valuable institutions and does not give the stockholders an opportunity to express themselves regarding the terms and time of sale, merger, or other disposal.

No assurance is given that they will remain in control of these institutions, as would be the case in the event of a free distribution, or that allowance will be made for normal time value, earning capacity, good will, and control value.[11]

Two days after Mr. Giannini had made this statement, the prime and inevitable result of Mr. Walker's announcement of September 22 disclosed itself. This was a spontaneous movement toward A. P. Giannini. A committee of stockholders, headed by Charles W. Fay, a former postmaster of San Francisco and director of the Bank of America N. T. & S. A., called on the banker. They said they represented the holders of 2,000,000 of Transamerica's 24,800,000 outstanding shares. Mr. Giannini told his visitors that they would have his "aid and counsel," but not his leadership until a majority of the stockholders had signified they wanted him.

Mr. Fay gave the newspapers a statement about the committee's call. "This committee," he said, "was absolutely opposed to the disposition of any stock of the Bank of America of California, Bank of America National Trust and Savings Association, Bank of America of New York and their major affiliations without due notice and approval of the stockholders [of Transamerica]."[12]

The effect of the announcement was electric. Though reasons of health obliged Giannini to husband his strength, putting a premium on his leadership was excellent tactics. Fay was flooded with applications to join his movement which, twenty-four hours after it became known to the public, took the name of Associated Transamerica Stockholders.

The fight was in the open, and the first tentative moves of the Giannini forces led by Fay threw the Walker camp on the defensive. Already President Mount was working overtime at the difficult task of "selling" the Walker plan to the rank and file of the bank organization. In an effort to halt the slump in morale, pep talks streamed from his office to the branch managers and advisory board members.

The day following publication of the Fay statement, Mount took notice of the sudden uprising: "The difference of opinion between holders of substantial blocks of Transamerica stock, as given publicity in the metropolitan press, is, in our opinion, a healthful condition, as it will assure that the return of the Bank's ownership will be on the soundest basis."[13]

Bacigalupi was smoked out. In a long and labored production he deplored the fact that "some of our stockholders have misconstrued . . . the letter of September 22. . . . There is no design of taking the Bank of America N. T. and S. A. away from the stockholders by selling it to outside interests. One of the underlying principles of the new plan is to return the banks now controlled to local ownership."

The reception of this statement was not all its author could have desired. A Fresno editor believed in Bacigalupi's honesty but wondered "if the situation permits him to be frank." An advisory board member in Whittier asked: "If Mr. Walker and his eastern crowd have a plan for a distribution of Bank of America that is fair . . . why don't [they] tell us what it is?" A sixty-six-year-old widow who earned her living selling Bibles and counted on dividends from her 467 shares of Transamerica to pay her rent, declared a lack of faith in the management and said that things had been different under Mr. Giannini.[14]

Charles W. Fay at once put his finger on the weak spot in the Bacigalupi statement. "The president of Transamerica omitted any assurance relating to the Bank of America in New York." He could have given no such assurance. Walker had been hawking the bank about New York for months, and, when Bacigalupi wrote his statement, negotiations for its sale to the National City Bank were in the final stages.

A week later, on October 1, 1931, this transaction, called a merger, was announced. It was contingent upon the deposit of 85 per cent of the B. of A. stock, a certainty because Transamerica owned 63 per cent of it. One of the apologies for the sale was the "greatly reduced" deposits of the B. of A. The loss for the quarter ending October 1 had been 14.4 per cent, against 14.1 for the First National, 13.3 for Chemical, 11.9 for Chase, and 5.3 for National City. The selling bank nevertheless was making money and was in excellent condition, with liquid assets to the extent of 83.7 per cent of demand deposits—a remarkable showing.

In the subsequent exchange of stock, Transamerica received 552,-014 shares of National City for 826,736 of B. of A. On the basis of National City's $4 dividend in the place of B. of A.'s $2 dividend, Transamerica was $370,000 a year ahead on current income. The merger made Transamerica the largest single stockholder in the National City Bank, owning 8.7 per cent of the total issue. This condition, however, was declared to be temporary. In the papers constituting the merger agreement, it was declared that Transamerica would reduce its National City holdings "in a constructive and gradual manner," and that it would not "seek to influence the policies and management of the National City Bank." To make sure of this, National City declined to admit a representative of Transamerica to its board.

Whatever the heartburnings of A. P. Giannini over the disappearance of his New York bastion on which he had counted so much, he kept them to himself. His only public comment at the time was that he would try to see that the stockholders of Transamerica had something to say about the disposition of the corporation's holdings in the National City Bank.[15]

So was realized the first step in the plan to tear down Transamerica. It was the only step ever realized. True, a few of Transamerica's minority bank holdings were dumped during the month of October—1,305 shares in the Farmers & Merchants Bank of Los Angeles; 2,011 shares in the Crocker First National of San Francisco; 1,100 shares in the Security–First National of Los Angeles—but this was nothing like the "liquidation" Walker was intent upon. What stopped him? Simply the watchful form of A. P. Giannini, with an army of stockholders flocking to his standard. The New Yorker was obliged to turn from his program of dismemberment and fight to try to retain his hold on Transamerica.[16]

4

The sale of the New York bank marked the point at which the initiative in the contest passed to Giannini. On behalf of Associated Transamerica Stockholders, Fay requested of Bacigalupi a list of Transamerica's 200,000 stockholders. After bringing lawyers upon the scene he got it, though not for more than a month because of Bacigalupi's delaying tactics.

Fay made good use of that month, however, laying the ground work for a statewide organization to solicit stockholders' proxies with the object of unseating Walker at the annual meeting of Transamerica at Wilmington, Delaware (Trans being a Delaware corporation), on February 15, 1932. Contrary to medical instructions, Giannini himself appeared at a gathering of Fay lieutenants in San Francisco. Though not a public meeting, 150 were present. Giannini told the assemblage that there was a plan to sell a huge block of the National City stock to "friends of the management." That must be blocked, he added; and moreover the Bank of America N. T. & S. A. must be returned to the shareholders "as a gift." He closed by saying that, if "five to seven" million shares were signed up he would publicly lead the crusade.[17]

Similar organization meetings were held in every part of the state. Four hundred attended at Fresno. Pledge cards rolled into Associated's San Francisco headquarters.

The volume of the response troubled the Walker group. Peter Michelson, the bank's advertising manager, reported after a tour of the Sacramento and San Joaquin valleys: "[There is] a surprising sentiment favoring Mr. Giannini. The public, pretty generally, seem to blame Mr. Walker for the ills of Transamerica." Thereupon President Mount dispatched drastic instructions to the bank's district managers:

> See to it that every branch manager in your territory is advised that employees must not take part in the activities of the socalled "Associated Transamerica Stockholders"—either in the organization of groups, the attendance of meetings, or the soliciting or gathering of proxies—and that anyone violating this order will be immediately dismissed from the service of the bank.[18]

As can be imagined, this did nothing to lift the morale of the bank's personnel, who missed the hard-working comradeship Giannini had always inspired. Morale had been slipping since early in the year when Mario Giannini left Transamerica. The workers knew then that something was wrong. Subsequent events furthered that feeling: the departure of the Hellmans and Nolan, amid lugubrious hints touching the reputation of the bank and not of the dismissed officers; federal examiners shaking their heads over farm loans and dropping remarks no bank examiner should make except in a confidential report, whatever the occasion; wholesale layoffs as the bank's business declined; a summer of rumor culminating in the open break between Walker and Giannini; and, lastly, the edict forbidding a display of loyalty toward their old boss.

Moreover, the advent of Lynn P. Talley as chairman of the board quickly made itself felt. Talley ordered a severe tightening on loans. President Mount prefaced his instructions with the statement that "we are running a bank and not a charitable institution." No real estate loans were to be made except after approval by district vice-presidents, and then only in "unusual circumstances." Many other loans were called alienating some old-time customers of the bank. At least one of them was fifteen years coming back. Five million dollars worth of mortgages were sold to the Metropolitan Life Insurance Company. They were good mortgages, or Metropolitan, as astute as any real estate lender in the country, would not have bought them. Like Giannini, Metropolitan was prepared to wait out slow loans. This was not, however, in line with the instructions of the bank examiners who shut their eyes to the depressed times and proceeded, according to custom, listing as "doubtful" or "losses" millions of dollars' worth of mortgages that eventually paid off.[19]

Because of the delay in receiving a list of the shareholders, it was not until November 7, 1931, that Mr. Fay was able to address them in behalf of Associated Transamerica Stockholders. He made a dignified presentation of the issues. Personalities were avoided. Mr. Walker was mentioned in only one sentence, which read: "We do not favor the re-election of Elisha Walker as a director or as an executive." A proxy form was enclosed in favor of A. P. Giannini, L. M. Giannini and Charles W. Fay. Stockholders were assured that proxies would be kept confidential, "in the custody of A. P. Giannini." Not unless the dissenters were sure of victory would any of them be voted. This would protect employees or borrowers against possible recriminations.

To this letter Giannini added a postscript: "If a sufficient and prompt response, through proxies, indicates that it is desired that I take the leadership of the Association I stand ready to do so."[20]

Judging from the comment passed among members of Transamerica's public relations staff, the mildness of the Fay-Giannini circular disappointed the Walker people. They had anticipated a "stronger document," meaning, no doubt, one spiced with the explosive language A. P. was apt to use when aroused. Ralph Hayes, head public relations man in New York, wired Fred Kerman, his opposite number in San Francisco, that the letter was "puerile, unpersuasive, and ineffective." Mr. Kerman did not act as if that were the case, however. He made the rounds of the principal newspapers and local offices of the news services to urge them to play down the looming struggle. Kerman reported to Hayes that the "Coast situation as far as papers are concerned is pretty well corked except possibly for United Press. Your fine touch on this outfit would help."[21]

Though city newspapers in California soft-pedaled news of the Giannini revolt, and none took sides editorially, a majority of rural papers came out for Giannini. "There is not much question as to how the California stockholders will line up, if the thing comes to a showdown," observed the Santa Rosa *Press Democrat*. "They will get behind Giannini. So long as he was in control the stockholders were well taken care of and made money."[22]

The bank management took measures to counter the effect of the Fay-Giannini appeal. Branch managers were requested to approach large stockholders, and they did approach some five thousand of them. The result was dismaying to the Walkerites. "We may as well face the facts," Orra Monnette told President Mount. "Some stockholders . . . who have followed Giannini leadership so long . . . are not willing to turn their backs on it." G. A. Davidson of San Diego asked if something could not be done "to bring all the interests together in some sort of compromise." Mount replied that it "would be absolutely useless for you to endeavor to effect any compromise with 'A. P.' "[23]

One of the many difficulties in which the Walker people found themselves was the attitude of the bank's personnel and, indeed, of most of its officers. Despite the fact that their jobs depended upon a show of loyalty to the management, it was plain that in their hearts they were for Giannini. Bacigalupi addressed himself to the impossible task of winning them for Walker. In a long letter Mr. Bacigalupi called the controversy with "our old Chief and Friend . . . the most bitter and distressing experience" of his life. But, "in the light of an intimate knowledge of the facts," he was obliged to place "duty" ahead of "an old allegiance." Then he made the rather curious observation that, if Mr. Giannini was determined to get rid of Walker, he should have done so earlier, when he was head of the proxy committee. Bacigalupi blamed the passing of the dividend on Giannini's management. He said that no Eastern interests were trying to get control of the California banks.[24]

Giannini proxies continued to roll in, and at the end of November Mr. Fay claimed that Associated Stockholders had received 150,000 proxies. This represented more than half of the stockholders. Nothing was said, however, about the proportion of shares held by them. In any event, it was enough to bring Giannini to the forefront of the campaign.

5

A barnstorming tour of the state was under way within three days. A. P. Giannini went along, and his presence brought out the people in numbers that surpassed the most sanguine expectations. Although he sat on the platform during the meetings, he had not intended to address the audiences because he disliked public speaking. After the regular speakers had had their turn, however, a period was given over to questions from the audience. Many of the inquiries were addressed to Mr. Giannini. He would rise and give his answers, sometimes launching into an informal talk.

Before and after the meetings A. P. would enjoy himself by walking through the throngs, shaking hands and displaying his encyclopedic memory for names. Wherever he went he visited the local branches. He greeted customers, their wives and children and tried to allay rumors that were afloat as a result of the increasingly hard times and the decline of confidence in the Walker management. He said the bank was sound and that depositors should leave their money in it.

There had been misgivings on the part of family, friends and physicians about A. P.'s undertaking the tour. Some predicted that his health would not be up to the rigors of the road. They were mistaken. The tour did him more good than the doctors had. A. P. Giannini had never been a side-line fighter. In the thick of the fray once more, battling for things he believed in as truly as he believed in the immortality of his soul, he was borne above the ills of the flesh. Within a month he looked better than he had looked in two years.

The spontaneity of the Giannini meetings made them more effective than all the expert planning in the world. Local people, ordinary folks as well as community leaders, got a chance to talk, while A. P. sat on the platform and nodded and waved to acquaintances. Mr. Fay and Mario Giannini usually said a few words. Mario was no orator either, and his remarks were usually brief and business-like. But the visitors had brought along an orator in the person of A. J. Scampini, a young San Francisco lawyer who had been in the Bank of Italy's trust department. "Scamp" burned with zeal for the cause. He dramatized the issue like any campaign spellbinder.

Four thousand stockholders gathered in the Civic Memorial Auditorium at Stockton for the first meeting. The mayor and most of the city officials were among them. Scampini called it a contest between Wall Street and California.

Do these two or three Wall Street bankers imagine we are a bunch of fools—200,000 California investors who will sit still in the face of a financial "clean out" carrying the economic and political control of California to two or three persons in New York? Do they think they can get away with Russian methods in giving orders to their employees that if they do not dissuade stockholders from joining our organization they will be fired?

Thirty clerks collected proxies. At the close of the evening's work 90 per cent of Stockton's shareholders were in the Giannini camp.[25]

In Sacramento three thousand filled the Native Sons Hall to overflowing. Mario Giannini handed out some level-headed advice. "Give your business to the banks of Transamerica," he said,

to the insurance companies and other subsidiaries for the success of your corporation. You should not indulge in reprisals because of the foolish acts of some of its officers. . . . If you all cooperate and pull together there will be no doubt about the outcome and we will have much happier days in the near future.

The fireworks were provided by a local speaker and by Mr. Scampini. The local speaker wanted to know whether "we are to be dictated to by the golfers of Long Island or the cocktail sippers around some mahogany bar in the Bronx [sic]?" Scamp gave the salaries enjoyed by the top officers of Transamerica and the bank: Walker, $100,000; Mount, $75,000; Talley, $75,000; and so on.[26]

After the meeting a representative of the advertising firm that handled the Bank of America account asked the San Francisco *News* man to omit reference to the salaries. The *News* man refused to do so. A few days later Walker and Bacigalupi addressed to the stockholders and gave to the papers a letter stating that A. P. Giannini had been awarded by the Bancitaly Corporation bonuses aggregating $3,700,000. Of this amount all but $792,000 had been drawn by Mr. Giannini. The statement added that Mr. Giannini had asked for this balance and that payment had been refused. Giannini was also criticized for supporting Transamerica shares in the market. By innuendo he was accused of deserting Transamerica in the face of trouble. "In the Fall of 1929, [when] the Corporation faced a difficult future . . . Mr. Giannini retired."

A. P. called the attack "mudslinging." Mario outlined the terms of the 5 per cent arrangement, which his father had not taken full advantage of. Mario added that his father had not demanded the $792,000 balance to which he was entitled, and that much of the $2,908,000 drawn over five years had been spent in behalf of the corporation.[27]

The principal effect of this facet of the controversy seems to have been to arouse sentiment for Giannini. Mr. Bacigalupi received many critical letters of which this is a sample:

It is unjust on your part to attack Mr. Giannini's compensation. He is the man, and not you, that deserves the credit and esteem of founding one of the biggest banks and corporations in the world. . . . The public is amazed to think that you are biting the hand of the man who is responsible for your past success. . . . People gave credit to Giannini for the support of the market and today they are not blaming him for that.[28]

There were harsher letters and even harsher word-of-mouth gossip in North Beach. Plain-clothes men guarded the Transamerica headquarters at 460 Montgomery Street.

The Walker forces intensified efforts to bring in proxies. Trust officers of the bank were instructed to execute Walker proxies for the 600,000 shares in their custody. Pressure was put on borrowers who had 1,600,000 shares pledged as security. A million and a half shares were held by officers and employees of the bank, who received a stern warning to fill out Walker proxies within five days.

A more ill-advised move would be difficult to imagine. Resentful employees came to Giannini with renewed pledges of loyalty. These employees were in a ticklish position, however. What if the bank fired them for refusing to fill out Walker proxies? A. P. said there was a way around that. "Fill out the Walker proxy if you have to," he told one inquirer. "Then later you may change your mind and want to fill out one for me. You don't have to take the bank into your confidence. It's the proxy you execute *last* that counts, remember."[29]

Giannini was not willing to let it go at that. A temporary court injunction was obtained restraining the bank from the coercion of its employees in the matter of proxies.

6

This stress and strain, coupled with the increasing pressure of hard times, was reflected in the year-end statement of the bank for 1931.

Within six months deposits had gone from $908,000,000 to $750,000,-000. Cash in vaults and in the Federal Reserve and other banks had dropped from $116,000,000 on June 30 to $74,000,000 on December 31. Further evidence of measures taken to meet the drain on deposits was shown in the holdings of U.S. bonds: June 30, $161,000,-000; December 31, $148,000,000.

The bank was borrowing heavily and the end of this was not in sight. In the last half of 1931 borrowings averaged $40,000,000, against an average of $5,642,000 for the first half. The money came from four lines of credit aggregating $80,000,000, which the bank had established by pledging bonds, stocks and mortgages. For the most part the credit was supplied by New York banks and by the National Credit Corporation, a voluntary pool formed by a group of New York banks. Mr. Walker was proud of his ability to obtain this Wall Street support, though the rate, including commissions, was above 7 per cent.[30]

Economy measures had lopped another $2,000,000 off the bank's overhead during the past six months. Nearly half of this had fallen on the personnel in the way of layoffs. During the fourteen months since the consolidation of November, 1930, the staff of the Bank of America N. T. & S. A. had been reduced from 7,679 to 6,168.[31]

The board of directors passed the dividend, payable December 31 —the first dividend to be omitted in the bank's history.

Although all banks were losing deposits, the Transamerica institutions were losing them to other banks as well as to the demands of the depression. Apparently no banks were losing to the Transamerica banks. On June 30, 1930, the Trans banks contained 31.17 per cent of the deposits in California. By June, 1931, they had shrunk to 27.7 per cent and on December 31 to 25.5 per cent. On June 30, 1930, the unit banks of California had held 26.5 per cent of the state's deposits, and on December 31, 1931, 30 per cent. Rival branch banks had held 41.8 per cent on June 30, 1930, and 44.5 per cent on December 31, 1931.[32]

Adverse as they were, these figures did not alarm A. P. Giannini. He reiterated that the bank was sound, and, given proper management, was perfectly capable of weathering the rigors of the times. Moreover, by the end of the year Giannini was fairly confident that victory would be his, with Walker beaten and his management repudiated by the stockholders.

Consequently, Giannini set his face against efforts to compromise the differences between Walker and himself. Inside the bank and out this had been mentioned for some time. The San Francisco *News,* a staunch admirer of Giannini, had made an urgent appeal. Another friend, John Francis Neylan, whose law firm represented W. R. Hearst, prevailed on all the San Francisco papers to relegate news of the proxy fight to their inside pages.[33]

Despite the friendly source of some of the peace efforts, Giannini regarded them as playing into Walker's hands. The mounting evidence of Giannini's hold on the mass of stockholders, patrons and employees of the bank seems, strangely enough, to have come as a surprise to Walker. In an attempt to offset it and to influence large Eastern stockholders, Mr. Walker was holding a series of private luncheons in New York. According to a report Giannini received of such a meeting on January 7, 1932, Mr. Walker declared that Giannini could not command the "support" of Wall Street; that his victory would mean the loss of deposits brought in by Lee, Higginson; and that "none of present directors" would serve under Giannini. Nevertheless, A. P.'s informant got the idea that Walker was angling for a compromise. He advised Giannini to be on watch for "a scheme to put pressure on [you] for patching up."[34]

Giannini's New York observer called the turn. On the next day, January 8, John U. Calkins, governor of the Federal Reserve Bank of San Francisco, on orders from the Reserve Board in Washington summoned to his office representatives of Transamerica, the Bank of America N. T. & S. A. and Associated Stockholders. With the exception of A. P. Giannini, all appeared with their attorneys on January 9. Monnet and Bacigalupi represented Transamerica; Talley, the bank; Mario Giannini and Charles W. Fay, Associated Stockholders. A. P. Giannini left off campaigning in Los Angeles only to wire his son: "PLEASE MAKE CLEAR TO CALKINS THAT THERE CAN BE ABSOLUTELY NO COMPROMISE THAT WILL INCLUDE ELISHA WALKER IN THE PICTURE. . . . HE HAS NO PLACE IN A BUSINESS THAT WHOLLY DEPENDS ON PUBLIC CONFIDENCE FOR ITS SUCCESS."[35]

If Giannini declined to go along with conciliatory efforts initiated by friends, he could hardly be expected to rejoice in the intervention of John U. Calkins. In the first place, Giannini opposed the Federal Reserve's general policy of drastic write-offs and liquidation, as carried out through the comptroller's examinations. It was too much like the Walker policy. In the second place, he distrusted Calkins on personal grounds. The coolness between these men went back a long way. Calkins had been cashier of the Mechanics Savings Bank of San Francisco which was saved from the embarrassments of poor management in 1910 when the Bank of Italy took it over. Calkins announced that he was quitting rather than work for a "Dago bank." Also in the Mechanics Bank at the time had been William A. Day, now the next ranking officer to Calkins in the Twelfth Federal Reserve District.[36]

Mr. Calkins opened the first meeting of the conferees on Saturday, January 9, 1932, with a reference to the dire consequences that would follow "the failure of this bank." Then he asked Chairman Talley to give some figures on the bank's condition. Talley stressed the decline in deposits and the bank's borrowings. He made the alarming announcement that $20,000,000 in deposits had left the bank in the first week of January. At that rate Eastern credit would be exhausted in thirty days. In part, he blamed the state of affairs on the proxy "agitation." Calkins then called "the condition of the bank . . . definitely precarious." He asked each side to the controversy to submit, on the next day, or the day after, "minimum conditions that will make it possible to compose this fight and, if possible, save the bank."

Mario Giannini regarded Calkin's statement as an outrageous misrepresentation of the bank's condition. So certain of this was the younger Giannini that he did not reply to Mr. Calkins' charges.

The following day, Sunday, representatives of the two sides met privately, without Mr. Calkins. The Walker people beat a swift retreat. They proposed that there should be no sale of the bank without a vote of the stockholders (though other Transamerica properties might be sold without such a vote); a bank board of Californians entirely, none of whom should be officers or directors of Trans; an independent California committee of three should name additional members of the Transamerica board.

This did not, however, go far enough to suit Associated Transamerica Stockholders, whose representatives presented their "minimum requirements." The chief provisions were that Associated should name a majority of the Transamerica board, and that Elisha Walker should be neither an officer nor a director of the corporation. Telegrams were exchanged and telephone conversations were held with A. P. in an effort to get him to consent to let Walker stay on the board. The elder Giannini refused; even refused to come to San Francisco to discuss the matter. His prescription for the bank's ills was to get rid of Walker, and nothing could budge him.

Having reached this impasse, the two groups again appeared before Mr. Calkins on Monday, January 11. Attorney Garret W. McEnerney, representing the bank, announced that Elisha Walker "has offered to sacrifice himself" by retiring, "but those of us who are concerned with the welfare of the bank" would not permit him to do so. If Walker went, "the support and strength we have enjoyed for the last few months in New York . . . particularly from the Lee, Higginson group" also would go.

When Mr. McEnerney sat down Governor Calkins burst out:

"It is perfectly preposterous. In effect, Mr. Fay and Mr. Mario Giannini are sitting at this table and insisting upon tearing down two great banks of which they are directors. . . . They are also insisting upon a result that will destroy absolutely any value that remains in the stock of Transamerica. . . . Close those banks, and the stock of the Transamerica Corporation . . . won't be worth a cent."

Mario Giannini was a quietly spoken man. Those who knew him well say he never raised his voice. He replied as follows to Mr. Calkin's eruption:

"We believe the things that we have said of Mr. Walker and his administration. . . . It seems to me that the history of the trend of deposits in these banks, over which we are all so concerned, would indicate that there is something fundamentally wrong . . . with the present administration. . . . In the first six months of last year, 1931, [deposits declined in the amount of] $93,000,000; in the third quarter, you had a decrease of $118,000,000; and in the fourth quarter, [the quarter of the proxy 'agitation'] . . . the loss has been but $43,000,-000. We attribute the reduced loss to the fact that the stockholders and depositors have felt encouragement over the fact that Mr. A. P. Giannini was going to represent their interests and try to correct the situation which has existed in the management."[37]

Mario's figures on deposits were correct, and the conclusion he drew from them is borne out by later events. At the same time, however, Mr. Talley's report on the trend of deposits also was correct: $20,000,000 lost in a week, against $43,000,000 for the entire previous quarter. Why? One reason, of course, was normal year-end withdrawals. The adverse year-end statement also may have been a factor. Another factor was the pressure on clients, borrowers and personnel of the bank for Walker proxies. Another was Giannini's campaign; though it heartened most Californians, it frightened Eastern corporations into withdrawing or easing their balances.

Yet A. P. Giannini remained steadfast in his demand for the dismissal of Walker. "RESTORATION OF PUBLIC CONFIDENCE," he repeated by telegraph, "IS A CONDITION PREREQUISITE TO SUCCESS AND FUTURE PROSPERITY OF INSTITUTIONS. THIS IS IMPOSSIBLE WITH WALKER ON BOARD." On that issue the Calkins conferences ended on January 11.

Nevertheless, peace efforts went on. The Secretary of the Treasury, the Federal Reserve Board and the newly created Reconstruction Finance Corporation pushed them until the eve of the stockholders meeting at Wilmington on February 15. As an indication of the seriousness with which the government regarded the situation, Comptroller of the Currency Pole visited San Francisco. His appearance (wearing a morning coat and striped pants, in themselves enough to alarm Californians) started the rumor that he had come to take over the bank. Actually, he merely proposed another compromise, to which A. P. Giannini said no.[38]

7

Though the conciliation efforts were not a matter of general knowledge, a good deal was known of them by way of the grapevine. They showed the plight of Walker. Four months before, the New Yorker had been implacable in his drive to get rid of the Gianninis. Indeed the nation's press had accepted that as an accomplished fact. Now Mr. Walker was ready to settle for a place on the board. This admission of defeat was not the only source of encouragement to the old fighter battling to regain control of his buffeted financial empire. The mounting size and enthusiasm of the Giannini meetings were proof that the preponderant majority of stockholders were with him. As he told Senator Hiram Johnson: "California people are up in arms against Wall Street control."[39]

Giannini kept his cohorts fighting, for a majority of stockholders was not the same as the holders of a majority of the stock. Seven thousand persons, each owning 500 shares or more, accounted for an aggregate of 13,300,000 shares, or a clear majority of the 24,847,484 shares outstanding. On the other hand, 207,055 stockholders own-

SHIRTSLEEVE BANKING

A view of a banking day in one of the larger branches in the Central Valley. This photograph was taken in 1945.

ing less than 100 shares apiece accounted for only 6,247,000 shares. Giannini needed twice that number to win. A great many of the large Eastern stockholders were Walkerites.

Originally Mr. Walker had announced there would be no Walker meetings, no "undignified" scramble for "blue" proxies. The Walker ballots were on blue paper, Giannini's on white. In the last month of the fight the effect of Giannini's campaign altered this strategy. Jim Bacigalupi, Louis Ferrari and Orra Monnette took the stump for Walker. The comparatively slender turnouts at their meetings were significant. In Los Angeles Giannini asked Monnette for an invitation to one of his meetings. The astonished Monnette complied. A former lawyer, Mr. Monnette was a pleader of considerable talent. When he had been heard, A. P. Giannini asked to say a few words. He kept his promise to speak briefly; but he went away with a pocketful of white proxies.

A. J. Scampini, the Patrick Henry of the Giannini forces, had trained a number of understudies. Their theme, Wall Street versus California, was a popular one. They raised the multitudes to concert pitch. "Throw Walker out!" "Save the bank from the Wall Street racketeers!" Ten thousand persons jammed Dreamland Auditorium in San Francisco for Scampini's farewell performance on the Coast. Then Scamp took off for New York to encourage the rank and file of eastern stockholders.

Before the campaign ended, the Walker front in California all but fell apart. Will C. Wood, the former superintendent of banks, resigned a vice-presidency of the Bank of America N. T. & S. A. to work for Giannini. The workers in the banks were overwhelmingly for their old boss. A story is told of the girls in the mail room at the San Francisco headquarters of Transamerica. One of their duties was to open Walker proxies. It seems that some of those proxies never reached Wilmington because the girls had "mislaid" them.[40]

On February 15, 1932, the count of the proxies in Wilmington gave Giannini a landslide victory. The owners of 15,371,578 shares called for his return. The record does not give the Walker vote. Had every share been voted and had every vote not for Giannini been for Walker, Mr. Walker would have had a total of 9,475,906. It has been estimated that perhaps a million shares were not voted. Giannini telegraphed a Fresno stockholder that "victory is ours by 7,000,000 votes."[41]

The victor was on hand in Delaware to take charge. The entire Walker directorate was dropped. A. P. Giannini was elected chairman, to serve without compensation. Bacigalupi, salary $60,000, was superseded as president by John M. Grant, salary $20,000. Mr. Grant had been head of the international department of the Bank of Italy and chief of the London office of the Bank of America N. T. & S. A. He was born in Scotland and economy was his middle name.

When word of the count reached San Francisco, the board of the two banks assembled at No. 1 Powell. The resignations of Lynn P. Talley, chairman, A. J. Mount, president, and George A. Webster, director, were accepted. By acclamation A. P. Giannini was elected chairman and president. He announced that he would serve without compensation.

Giannini took his victory soberly and modestly. "This is not the time to crow," he said. "The big work is ahead of us. Only the best and most capable men in banking circles of California will be on the permanent board. There will be no attempt at reprisals or discriminations. The personnel from both sides will be represented so as to gain the greatest harmony."

When he heard of plans to meet him with a brass band in California he telegraphed to "call off the fireworks."[42]

The comment of the nation's press amounted to a spontaneous and heartening tribute. Here was a man not cowed into inaction or retreat by the menacing aspect of the times. He was *doing something*. Editors picked up a phrase of B. C. Forbes, who dubbed Giannini "the Lochinvar who came out of the West" and bested Wall Street. His victory was called greater than those Henry Ford and Will C. Durant had, in their time, won over Wall Street. As might be expected, California about burst with pride. Sample headlines:

A. P. GIANNINI OUSTS WALKER
GIANNINI HA VINTO!

While Eastern comment was more restrained, what the country's most influential newspaper, the *New York Times,* had to say was representative:

Although Wall Street has failed to see eye-to-eye with Mr. Giannini . . . there was general admiration in the Street for the fashion in which, at the age of sixty-two he had returned from retirement to wrest control of the huge holding corporation which he originally created from the men to whom he relinquished the management two years ago.[43]

Not only was Giannini hailed for his victory but for the means by which he had achieved it. Perhaps the most significant about face was that of the *American Banker* of New York. In October, 1931, this journal had, with satisfaction, published Giannini's obituary as a banker. In February, 1932, it called his return to power a triumph of "confidence" over "fear."

Even in times like these . . . [Californians] could not see the value of the defeatist policy that was being advocated [by Walker]. . . . Bankers may do well to . . . take their courage in their hands to do the things that they know must and can be done, regardless of who may try to say to them "Nay."[44]

Notwithstanding the injunction against a public reception, a crowd of five hundred was on hand when Giannini stepped from the train at Los Angeles. On February 23, he was back at No. 1 Powell in San Francisco. Flowers filled the place. A. P. had telegraphed ahead to rip out the partitions installed during the Walker regime and bring the officers' desks into the open where the customers of the bank could get at them. "You can't run a bank from Wall Street or a private office." Giannini's old desk had been brought out, but it was the only one in the room without a name. Nobody could find his old nameplate. A secretary appeared with an armload of mail and memoranda. The veteran sat down and, oblivious to the bustle about him, went to work as he had done in happier times.[45]

His goal was to restore something of those times. Should he succeed he would be the first banker to do so.

On the Way Back

IN FEBRUARY, 1932, when Giannini took back control of Trans-america, the times were much more difficult than when he had handed it over to Elisha Walker two years before. The affairs of Transamerica reflected both the nature of these times and the nature of Walker's management, with particular reference to his obsession about liquidation, which the *American Banker,* a former Walker supporter, discovered to have been "born in fear." Particularly was this true of Transamerica's greatest asset, the Bank of America N. T. & S. A.[1]

There was no end of fear abroad in 1932, which made Giannini's work of rehabilitation so much harder than otherwise it would have been. The national income for the year was $41,000,000,000, a shade more than half what it had been in 1929. From thirteen to fifteen million wage earners were unemployed. Those who had jobs worked shorter hours for less pay. There were bread riots and "hunger marches." A "bonus army" of war veterans encamped on the outskirts of Washington to agitate for the prepayment of their "adjusted compensation" certificates, due some years hence. In a classic example of the wrong way to do something the needy vets were dispersed by troops with tear gas and bayonets. Probably no single incident incensed the country more than this.

Farmers banded together to prevent the foreclosure of mortgages. In Oklahoma a representative of the farm-mortgage department of a life insurance company was invited to leave town, and after a mild demonstration he took the hint. In Iowa a county judge who had refused to promise not to sign farm foreclosures was escorted from his home at night. A rope was placed around his neck and his trousers were removed. Then the escort departed. In Wisconsin three thousand farmers surrounded a courthouse and blocked foreclosure sales. Illinois started the "penny sales," at which a team of horses would be bid in by the owner's friends for ten cents.

Protests concerning the majesty of the law seemed strangely out of place in such cases. Daniel Willard, president of the Baltimore & Ohio Railroad, who had begun life as a track laborer, told an audience: "I would steal before I would starve."

Still, there was no national leadership in public life to give people much hope for salvation. There was little such leadership in business until A. P. Giannini aroused even the reluctant admiration of Wall Street. Mr. Hoover had, however, done this: he had accepted the Reconstruction Finance Corporation which was a departure from the principle of no government aid to the victims of hard times, excepting farmers. The R.F.C. was called "a bread line for business." Its operations cut bank failures from 2,228 in 1931 to 1,456 in 1932.

The deficiency of leadership made easy sailing for the false prophets—the Huey Longs, the Father Coughlins, the Gerald Smiths. Communists, Fascists and Nazis had their missionaries among us. There was no lack of home-grown utopians—share-the-wealthers, Technocrats, Ku-Kluxers and so on. Some were knaves, but more were simply bewildered by adversity.[2]

2

When A. P. Giannini sat down at his old desk at No. 1 Powell this is a sample of the mail he read:

> I am in desperate need of money, not having received any dividends for nearly two years. . . . I voted for you, Mr. Giannini, with confidence that you would soon be able to work out a plan . . . [for] people like me. . . . I am 82 years old, having pioneered in Modoc County, beginning October 1872, raised ten children and four grandchildren. I sold my ranch and invested every available cent in Transamerica stock.[3]

To spread a little cheer, Giannini's first official statement held out the promise that dividends might be restored by Christmas. This was a big order, but A. P. was encouraged by the spontaneous reaction to his return. Overnight the flight of deposits from the bank had diminished, perhaps by half, and big and little accounts began to return. This was a mark of confidence, in contrast to the "lack of confidence," to use the words of the *American Banker,* that depositors had expressed in the Walker regime. The change had come simply on the strength of A. P. Giannini's name, and before Giannini had time to turn a hand to the immense task of reconstruction.

Two days after the news had flashed from Wilmington, the Pacific Telephone & Telegraph Company instructed its outlying offices to resume depositing with the branches of the Bank of America. I. Magnin & Co., the Los Angeles and San Francisco apparel store, reopened its account. The Dow-Jones Company and the Nestle's Milk Company returned. An important restoration was that of the F. W. Woolworth Company which, during the last stages of the proxy battle, began making daily withdrawals to reduce its balance. What was equally gratifying to Giannini was the return of small depositors. "Needless to say," added one journalist a week after the proxy victory, "Italian-Americans were and are proud of A. P. Giannini for what he had done. . . . In addition, thousands of Californians of non-Italian birth . . . have come back to re-deposit their money."[4]

After eight days in office Mr. Giannini resigned the presidency of the bank, which he had taken merely as a morale booster. He retained the chairmanship of the board, however. Will F. Morrish became president and Lawrence Mario Giannini senior vice-president. The elder Giannini and Leon Bocqueraz succeeded Bacigalupi and Pedrini on the executive committee. Dr. A. H. Giannini and Bill Blauer were chairmen of the executive and of the finance committees. These six men ran the bank. Among the replacements on the board were three heroes of the proxy fight—A. J. Scampini, Harry A. Mazzera and Dr. Celestine Sullivan.

Drastic economies were introduced. As an alternative to laying off fifteen hundred employees the pay of all who earned more than $100 a month was cut 5 per cent, and up to 20 per cent for officers in the higher brackets. A month's furlough on half-pay was required of every one. In all, overhead expense was cut $4,131,000 over the year previous. At Transamerica, John M. Grant went through the place like a cyclone, reducing yearly costs $9,200,000.

The staff took the reductions "in a splendid spirit," Giannini reported. "Out of six thousand-odd officers and employees I have learned of one complaint and that from a manager of one of the smaller branches." In fact, morale continued to go up. In addition to cutting their pay, Giannini piled work on his people. The main and immediate goal of this work? Simply to stop the loss of deposits. He asked managers "to set a fair quota of deposit increases which you believe can be secured by your branch between . . . now and July 15." Turn deposit loss into deposit gain and the Bank of America would help more than itself, he said. "[It] will redound . . . to the welfare of our State and Nation, and will go far in turning toward prosperity the tide of depression which has enveloped the world."[5]

As of old, the bank's "boys and girls" pitched in, working night and day. Giannini himself took to the streets to solicit deposits. So did his old friend Charley Grondona, who had performed the same service for the Bank of Italy twenty-five years before. So did Will Morrish, Leon Bocqueraz, Carl Wente, Mario Giannini and the rest of the bank's high officers. Nearly all the officers, and employees when needed, cheerfully reported for duty during their half-pay holidays. They felt they were working for themselves as well as for their bank and for their country; and indeed this was true, for nearly all were stockholders in Transamerica. In the evenings, with Mario and Morrish, Giannini would visit outlying branches in the Bay area. Employees from miles about would gather to meet him. After shaking hands all around he would thank them for their good work and tell them to keep it up. Get those deposits back was his theme. Lick this depression!

"You never saw anything like it," recalled an old-timer. "We believed A. P. was the only man who could rebuild the bank and Transamerica, and that, with them on their feet, the depression would be licked. Pretty soon all California was believing it."[6]

The only protests of record are that the boss was working himself too hard. Grant squandered money on a long telegram that he would have rebuked a subordinate for not sending by mail. He had learned that A. P. reached his desk at six-thirty in the morning and left it at ten at night. In impassioned phrases he begged Giannini to stop this.

You in good health are a better asset than our present holdings in [National] City Bank. Won't you for the sake of your stockholders, for the sake of your family, and for the sake of your associates who love you, conserve your health? . . . Please move into a private room, have a secretary to answer your phone and see people, and get down at 10 and go home at 4.

An old friend in Los Angeles, who had heard that Giannini was abroad among the vegetable dealers at five in the morning, made a

similar plea. A. P. protested that he was not there until "a little before seven." And he had a fine time tramping Washington Street.
"These are all sincere friends of mine whom I have known many,
many years and it was a great pleasure . . . to shake hands and talk
with them once more."[7]

After hearing from the branch managers, Giannini set the goal for
increased deposits at $50,000,000 by July 15, five months after his re-
turn to control. More than that, he began the organization of a
"Back to Good Times" campaign designed to make California shake
off its depression fears. The benefits would accrue to all banks, to all
California.

It may be well to pause for an instant to consider the nature of this
undertaking. Here was a bank upon which the welfare of the Pacific
Coast depended as it depended upon no other bank. Because of bad
management and because of the general psychology of fear that
gripped the country, this bank was losing deposits at a rate of
$3,000,000 a day when Giannini took charge. Every other bank, save
one, in California was losing deposits—a proportion that probably
obtained throughout the United States. Before there could be any
gain whatever, the Bank of America must stop these losses.[8]

This Giannini accomplished in forty-one days after taking charge
on February 15, 1932. On March 26 deposits in the Bank of America
N. T. & S. A. stood at $617,177,000, which was lower than at any
time since the Liberty consolidation in 1927. The next day they
showed a gain. It would be difficult to pay a greater tribute to A. P.
Giannini as a banker than is inherent in that fact.

Before taking a closer look at deposit-building campaigns it is necessary to dispose of another matter.

3

Two days before he had reversed the flow of deposits, A. P. Giannini received notice of the continuing unfriendliness of John U.
Calkins, governor of the Twelfth Federal Reserve Bank, who had
done everything he could to save Elisha Walker's skin. The notice
came in the form of a letter that began:

Now that you have had time to familiarize yourself with the situation
of the Bank of America National Trust & Savings Association . . . it will

be greatly appreciated if you will write outlining . . . your plans for bringing about a decrease in, and ultimate extinguishment of, its indebtedness for borrowed money.

The pertinent items, to secure which collateral is pledged, appear to be approximately—

Due Federal Reserve Bank	$72,900,000
Due Reconstruction Finance Corporation	40,000,000
Due National Credit Corporation	7,500,000
Due Group of New York Banks	19,000,000
War Loan Account	13,200,000
Public Funds	71,800,000
Postal Funds	19,500,000[9]

The communication made Giannini see red.

Your letter [he replied to Calkins] . . . convinces me that you do not understand or sympathize with our problem. It appears to me that the bank is being harassed by those who should normally be . . . cooperating with us in the inherited task of reconstruction. . . . The feeling that I have had that there has been a conspiracy to bring about the ultimate liquidation of our institution . . . has been strengthened . . . through knowledge of the destructive policies pursued by the former management with the apparent acquiescence of the Federal Reserve Bank.

Having thus delivered himself, Mr. Giannini took up what Calkins called the bank's indebtedness, totaling $243,000,000. The last three items should not be there, he said. War loan quotas were parceled out to banks, with no choice but to accept them. Public funds and postal funds were likewise parceled out, and banks put up collateral to protect these deposits. That cut the Calkins figure on the bank's debts to $139,300,000, which Mr. Calkins admitted to be an estimate. Giannini's figure was $135,000,000. In the six weeks since he had taken over from Walker and before he had reversed the flow of deposits, $7,000,000 had been repaid.

Mr. Giannini charged Calkins with flagrant discrimination against the Bank of America. The West Coast committees of the Reconstruction Finance Corporation and the National Credit Corporation were made up of representatives of rival banks. Of all the Coast banks of any consequence only the Bank of America had been kept off them. "The exclusion," said the banker, "cannot have occurred without design and appears to be a part of a studied plan to shake public confidence and destroy our institution."

Even so, despite the lack of "constructive co-operation" from the Twelfth Federal Reserve Bank, Giannini said he was "thoroughly convinced that today our bank is in a more sound and clean condition than any other bank of equal size and importance in the United States." This being the case, he was at a loss to understand Mr. Calkins' attitude.

Why do you find it necessary, in your conversations with us and your fellow-officers, to continuously suggest the failure of our institution, and why should there be this very evident hesitancy on the part of the Federal Reserve Bank to endorse and recommend our institution? A word of encouragement . . . would greatly hasten the recovery in which we are all so deeply interested.[10]

Giannini had an essentially simple plan for getting the Bank of America out of debt. First, he meant to borrow (at 5½ per cent) from the R.F.C. to retire advances from the New York banks and from the National Credit Corporation, which cost 6½ and 7 per cent. Then he intended that Transamerica should borrow from the R.F.C. —up to $65,000,000 if possible. This would enable Trans to repay $48,000,000 it owed the bank. With the money thus received, and from increased deposits, the bank would repay R.F.C. The end Giannini had in view was this: Transamerica to owe the government and not the bank—and the bank to owe no one. "With a clean bank," wrote Morrish, "we can go before the public without fear of our standing being questioned. This will aid us in building up our deposit line."[11]

Perhaps the nature of the Transamerica indebtedness of $48,000,-000 to the bank should be briefly noted. It did not arise from a loan. It arose from the proceeding by which assets that examiners called unbankable were removed from the bank and held by affiliates of Transamerica until such time as they could be realized on without sacrifice at depression prices. Thirty-five million in such assets had been taken over, with the approval of Comptroller Pole, by the Corporation of America, a Trans affiliate, which agreed to reimburse the bank. Much of the Corporation of America holding comprised slow paper inherited from the Merchants National Bank of Los Angeles. The remaining $13,000,000 comprised purchases of foreclosed real estate from the bank by California Lands, Inc., and the Capital Company.

To resume. When the R.F.C. began operations on February 2,

1932, the bank, under Walker, had already filed some heavy requests. In response, the first loan ($15,000,000), incidentally the government agency's first bank loan, came through on February 15, the day Giannini was voted in at Wilmington. On the way home A. P. paused at Washington to see General Charles G. Dawes, former Vice-President of the United States and then head of the R.F.C. Although a brother of Henry Dawes, the former comptroller of the currency who was an opponent of branch banking, the general was an admirer of Giannini. To Dawes and to Eugene Meyer, chairman of the Federal Reserve Board, the Californian told how he intended to restore the bank. The officials were favorably impressed. Dawes offered to lend "up to $100,000,000, if required."[12]

The second R.F.C. loan ($25,000,000) in response to an application made by the Walker management was received on March 16. Meanwhile Giannini himself had made three applications for money, the last one, for $10,000,000, being submitted on March 24, the day Mr. Calkins was writing his letter. Though Giannini fretted over the delay—pointing out that Talley, Mount, Howard Preston, Walker's son and other refugees from the Walker regime had landed jobs with R.F.C. or other government credit agencies—the requests all came through. This brought the bank's borrowings from the R.F.C. to $61,416,000.

Meantime General Dawes was having his troubles. Deposits were leaving his Chicago bank, the Central Republic, with the speed they had left the Bank of America before Giannini took hold. Dawes was obliged to give up the presidency of R.F.C. in favor of Eugene Meyer and hurry home. R.F.C. advanced the Dawes bank $90,000,000 and Chicago's banking panic got no worse.[13]

In June, Will F. Morrish went to Washington, armed with lists of assets of Transamerica Corporation and its affiliates on which he hoped to borrow $65,000,000. The Administration connections of Mr. Morrish were of the best. He was a friend of President Hoover, and, in an effort to accomplish his mission, he buttonholed about everyone of influence he knew except Mr. Hoover. "His performance was excellent," Comptroller Pole informed the Coast. Morrish ended up by borrowing $30,000,000 on the credit of the Bankitaly Mortgage Company. The security was real estate mortgages aggregating $65,000,000, which the Bank of America had sold to the Transamerica affiliate.

Fifteen years later, in a conversation with one of the authors of this book, Eugene Meyer readily recalled the loan and the collateral. Though his career has been in the East, Mr. Meyer comes from an early California banking family, and he is no disciple of Giannini. "But," he said, "as I looked over that collateral I was deeply impressed by the service Mr. Giannini was rendering the people of California. There it was—$65,000,000 in real estate mortgages, and the majority of them under $2,500."[14]

Before leaving Washington in July, Morrish was about to tackle Meyer again when Giannini said to never mind. Things were going so well that further government loans might not be needed. As it turned out, they were not needed. Indeed, the bank was already paying back Uncle Sam. By June 30, it had returned nearly $40,000,000, bringing its R.F.C. debt down to $22,050,000. So much for five months of Giannini at No. 1 Powell. Thirty of the forty million repaid had, of course, come from the Bankitaly Mortgage Company which had obtained the money from R.F.C.[15]

As the California picture brightened, Giannini saw one further memento of Transamerica's late administration disintegrate in the gaunt financial atmosphere. Though never quite able to put his finger on the connection, A. P. always believed that the bank had had a close call at the hands of Ivar Kreuger, the Swedish "match king" who had come to America to mend his finances. Giannini's suspicions had been strengthened when Kreuger prolonged his stay less than two weeks after the proxies were counted in Wilmington on February 15. Sailing for France, the mysterious foreigner left in the hands of Lee, Higginson partners, $8,000,000 in securities that turned out to be worthless. At the National City Bank he had renewed a $4,000,000 loan, protected by good securities. This help was not enough. Two days after his arrival in Paris, Kreuger killed himself. The outlines of the debacle were soon known. Ivar Kreuger was no depression-made breaker of the law. He had been a swindler from the start. One novel detail was the counterfeiting of Italian government bonds in the amount of $150,000,000. What if the assets of the Bank of America had been drained to bolster this man's so-called "empire"?

An afterlight on Kreuger concerns Jean Monnet, who had been vice-chairman of Transamerica under Walker. The acquaintance of Kreuger and Monnet went back to the days when the Frenchman was an officer of Blair & Company, before Giannini took it over.

Keep your dollars *moving!*

PROSPERITY STRAIGHT AHEAD →

Prominent Speakers · Fine Music
Saturdays ... 7:15 P.M.
KFI — KGO
"BACK TO GOOD TIMES"

SIGNS OF BETTER TIMES*

A savings deposit increase of $26,000,000—for the four weeks ending May 4—has been reported by the member banks of the Federal Reserve System in the seven western states.
—*Wall Street Journal*

During May, $2,600,000 worth of highway and bridge construction was started in California. This will create new employment in 14 counties from Siskiyou to San Diego. —*California Department of Public Works*

*Latest available data at the time this information was compiled.

HELP MAKE PROSPERITY BY SUPPORTING CALIFORNIA FARM PRODUCTS DAY

The nation's dollars are rapidly getting back to work. Confidence and common sense are with us again. This is especially true throughout California ... The *moving dollar* is the stabilizer of prosperity, the life of industry, the power behind the payroll. It is the infallible remedy for unemployment ... The goal of "Good Times" can be reached *only* by dollars that *move!* .. Move your money by banking, sensibly spending or investing it. Banked dollars create credit—credit finances business—business creates *prosperity* ... California courage and initiative are *leading* the nation back to good times!

Open a California "Back-to-Good-Times" Account in this bank — or any bank

BANK of AMERICA
NATIONAL TRUST & SAVINGS ASSOCIATION

Bank of America National Trust & Savings Association, *a National Bank* and ... Bank of America, *a California State Bank* ... are identical in ownership and management ... 410 offices in 243 California communities

ADVT.—BACK-TO-GOOD-TIMES, 1932.

After the death of Kreuger, Monnet went to Europe to liquidate the "match king's" business affairs. He found such an appalling mess, with so few real assets, that he threw in the sponge.[16]

4

While Giannini was getting the bank's indebtedness under control, he launched a "Back to Good Times" campaign. The full recovery of the bank, he knew, depended on the recovery of the money-making power of California's industry and agriculture. Psychology plays a large part in the breaking up of any depression. Confidence must take the place of fear. The recovery of the United States had to start somewhere. Why not in California? reasoned Giannini.

At a time when he was watching every penny of expense, Giannini set aside $200,000 for the "Good Times" campaign. It was launched by Governor James Rolph, Jr., at a luncheon in the Gold Ballroom of the Palace Hotel. The governor's words of confident optimism were carried by radio to similar gatherings throughout the state. The campaign was kept rolling by the press, billboards, by direct mail and, above all, by the two Banks of America, national and state. With 410 offices in 243 localities, with 6,000-odd employees under the spell of a leader they believed could do anything, with 200,000 stockholders who had demonstrated their fighting quality, with 1,800 advisory board members, and with an army of depositors that was attracting recruits at the rate of a thousand a day, in the whole country there were no other institutions better qualified to spearhead such a crusade.

Not since the patriotic "drives" of wartime had California thrown itself into anything of the kind with such fervor. Everywhere one looked slogans met the eye: "Keep Your Dollars Moving," "California Can Remove the Nation's Blue Glasses," "Speed up the Wheels of California's Industry." A. P. Giannini broke rules of a lifetime concerning personal publicity. He posed for newsreel cameramen and, when the bank inaugurated a weekly radio program, he broadcast a few remarks:

I can say with *real* conviction that I believe that the hysterical stage of the depression is past. I have confidence in the courage and resourcefulness of the American people. And I have unbounded faith in the people and resources of California. A movement, such as ours, can give the momentum so necessary to the complete restoration of public confidence and normal business conditions.

Giannini toured the branches, checking every loan on the books, talking to the staffs, and telling the townfolks over and over again: "Depressions are the products of fear."

The campaign caught on. Fear began to wane. Hale Bros. commenced remodeling their San Francisco store at once, instead of waiting for better times. In Hollywood, United Artists reopened its studio and started a production program that called for the expenditure of nearly $2,000,000. The secretary of the Los Angeles Chamber of Commerce gave "Back to Good Times" credit for another million dollars' worth of business expenditures in that area. The bank bought numerous local bond issues that made work for Californians: $180,000 for a high school in Vallejo; $118,000 for a highway near Bakersfield; $690,000 for a breakwater at Santa Monica; $4,554,000 for relief and general improvements in San Francisco; $6,000,000, the first delivery of a $35,000,000 issue, to begin the Golden Gate Bridge. "GIANNINI SCORES OVER DEFLATION," read a headline in the Pacific Coast edition of the *Wall Street Journal*.

In retrospect one marvels at the Giannini "Good Times" campaign. In essentials, indeed in most of its details, it differed little from many similar attempts whose achievements were meager. It was simply old-fashioned American boosting. The only unique ingredients were the personality of A. P. Giannini and California's unswerving belief in him. He was still the miracle man, the idol of the "little guy."

Within the bank itself the main effort was directed toward winning back depositors. To this end employees worked around the clock. During the month of July they made 114,000 individual solicitations. This feature marked the rise of Renolds Barbieri, who began as a messenger for the Bank of Italy. From the success of the personal solicitations evolved Barbieri's idea for the employee-salesman plan which has played an effective part since in deposit-building campaigns by the Bank of America. In "Good Times" the plan was credited with bringing in as much as $1,000,000 in a single day. Early in June the $50,000,000 goal set for July 15 was passed. The semiannual statement of the thirtieth of that month showed deposits of $710,903,000, or $91,826,000 above the low point of March 26.

More than half of what was lost between January 1 and March 26 had been recovered.[17]

This feat enabled the bank to retain its standing as the fourth largest in the country. Compared with the other leading institutions of the United States and of California:

	Amount of Deposits			Percentage
	12–31–31	6–30–32	Loss	of Loss
Chase National (N.Y.)	$1,459,114,886	$1,302,456,351	$156,658,535	10.74
National City (N.Y.)	1,418,702,860	1,214,266,592	204,436,268	14.41
Guaranty Trust (N.Y.)	1,070,021,916	928,343,300	141,678,616	13.24
Bank of America (S.F.)	799,220,729	710,903,867	88,316,862	11.05
Continental Illinois (Chgo.)	773,437,525	599,008,621	174,428,904	22.55
Security–First National (L.A.)	479,012,860	444,754,020	34,258,840	7.15
First National (Chgo.)	476,150,224	407,546,554	68,603,670	14.41
American Trust (S.F.)	220,205,170	205,445,530	14,759,640	6.70

In the closing weeks of 1932 "Good Times" ran into difficulties. A wave of fear swept westward from the Mississippi Valley, beginning the banking crisis that reached its climax early in 1933. Still, during the last half of 1932 the Bank of America gained $39,000,000 in deposits, closing the year with $749,658,000. This involved the acquisition since March of 217,500 accounts, mostly of former patrons who had left during the Walker stampede.

Though the Bank of America was making money, dividends were not resumed by Christmas, as Giannini had momentarily hoped. Instead, he had cleaned up the bank in spectacular fashion. R.F.C. loans in the amount of $54,541,000 had been repaid, leaving a balance of only $6,875,839 at the end of the year. Bills payable had been reduced from $147,000,000 to $11,000,000. The $30,000,000 R.F.C. loan to the Bankitaly Mortgage Company had been whittled to $21,997,000.

5

Although he managed to make no formal public declaration in the matter, A. P. Giannini was drawn into the presidential campaign of 1932 because he could not avoid it and do his duty to the bank and to California. While he did not openly declare for Franklin D.

Roosevelt, all Giannini's friends knew he intended to vote for him. Mr. Hoover's friends knew it, too.

As a young man A. P. Giannini had been an independent Democrat. His first presidential vote was for Grover Cleveland. Later, in the rough-and-tumble of ward politics in San Francisco, he was responsible for some local triumphs of good government. When good banking became his dominating interest Giannini dropped politics except when the issues directly touched banking. Such a situation had arisen in 1926 when statewide banking was at stake in the state election. Then, as we have seen, Giannini publicly backed a candidate.

In 1932 the depression and how to end it was the only real issue. What A. P. Giannini had done for the bank and for California in a few months' time in 1932 had raised his popularity to a peak not enjoyed since the twenties. Naturally, therefore, the political field marshals of both Mr. Hoover and Mr. Roosevelt were anxious to know where Giannini stood. At first Giannini himself did not know. Nevertheless, he thought that Mr. Hoover had done badly. He had let the morale of the country sink lower and lower. He had not taken hold as a leader and inspired the people. Another thing Giannini held against the Administration was the seeding of the R.F.C. and other government credit agencies with Walker men, and the retention of John U. Calkins in the Federal Reserve.

The Californian's temper came out in August in a bristling telegram to the President. Congress had enacted a harmful provision requiring that henceforth the names of R.F.C. borrowers be made public. The first published list included the Bank of America, for $3,800,000. This loan had not been made. The Bank had asked for it but, as deposits rolled in, had canceled the request. Giannini wired Mr. Hoover that the publication "APPEARS TO US AS EVIDENCE OF MALICIOUS INTENT TO DISCREDIT THIS BANK ON THE PART OF DISGRUNTLED AND CONSPIRING FORMER EMPLOYEES . . . WHO ARE APPARENTLY DIRECTING THE AFFAIRS OF THE RECONSTRUCTION FINANCE CORPORATION."[18]

Although the president of the bank, Will Morrish, was out-and-out for Hoover, September saw Giannini leaning toward Roosevelt. McAdoo was the Democratic candidate for senator, and A. J. Scampini was campaigning for him. Scamp told A. P. that Roosevelt would make branch banking's old friend Carter Glass Secretary of the Treasury. Between Glass and McAdoo, John U. Calkins might get his walking papers. Scamp asked Giannini to give the California Democrats a personal contribution of $10,000. The proxy fight had been a heavy drain on Giannini's funds, but he let the Democrats have $2,500. As no one in California seemed to know much about Roosevelt, Giannini got in touch with Joseph P. Kennedy, who had handled some of Transamerica's security business in New York and was one of the few members of the Wall Street community working for Roosevelt. Obviously pleased by the inquiry, Kennedy wired that he was coming West with the candidate and invited Giannini to meet him. The banker said he would be glad to.[19]

All the same Giannini continued to push the "Good Times" campaign, knowing that it helped Hoover as well as California and the bank. Indeed, the exchange of wires with Kennedy took place while Giannini was touring the northern branches. He came to San Francisco, however, to meet Franklin D. Roosevelt. The banker had a chat with the candidate, Kennedy and James A. Farley. When he emerged from the interview, newspapermen asked Giannini if he would support Roosevelt. "Can't say," the banker replied. "Haven't decided to support anybody yet."[20]

Naturally, the Republicans were alarmed, and A. P.'s Republican friends went to work on him. These included W. H. Crocker in addition to several men who were high in the Giannini bank. They got little satisfaction. The Democrats also continued to importune. They knew that he liked Roosevelt and the higher-ups knew that he intended to vote for him, but what they wanted was an open declaration. Giannini refused. He said it "might do considerable harm to our institution." Besides, he deemed it unnecessary. From the talk around the branches, Giannini felt that Roosevelt would win. Finally, the Republicans applied the ultimate pressure, a personal appeal from Mr. Hoover himself.[21]

The President's long-distance telephone call reached Mr. Giannini at the bank's branch in the little town of Gustine. With him were Carl Wente, accompanying the banker on his tour, the branch manager and a local newspaper editor. Though this was not the item the editor had come to get, he recognized a piece of news when he came across it and filed a dispatch to the San Francisco office of a news service for which he was correspondent. The telephone call was described in these words:

"You're wanted on the phone," said an attendant.

"Who is it?" demanded the banker.

"It's President Hoover."

"Quit your joshing," laughed Giannini, casually taking up the receiver. But it was in reality the President.

"I'd like to have you come in for me," said Hoover, after an exchange of greetings.

"Why should I?" asked Giannini. "Every man I've dropped out of my organization you've appointed to some post of honor. Why only last week I kicked out so-and-so and you appointed him on the—"

"But," insisted Hoover, "I'd like to have your support. You're a man of tremendous influence in California and . . ."

"Well, I'm sorry, Mr. President, but I'm not in politics at all," replied Giannini.

"The President hung up."[22]

Giannini had moved on to Pacific Grove before he learned what the editor had done. Though he could not deny the story, he did

very much deprecate the publicity given to a private conversation between the President and myself. Naturally I have my opinion on political affairs, but it is only a personal one which I hold as a private citizen. Any implication that I or any of the institutions with which I am associated have taken a political stand is wholly unauthorized.[23]

When Carter Glass tore into the President's financial policies, Giannini wired J. F. Cavagnaro at the New York office of Transamerica:

PLEASE PHONE JOE KENNEDY MY CONGRATULATIONS ON SPLENDID WAY HE AND FARLEY ARE HANDLING CAMPAIGN ALSO SAY IF HE WILL KEEP CARTER GLASS ON RADIO BETWEEN NOW AND ELECTION HE WILL ROLL UP SEVERAL MORE MILLION VOTES FOR HIS CANDIDATE. I THINK GLASS' SPEECH MOST EFFECTIVE OF CAMPAIGN AND SHOULD LIKE HAVE JOE CONVEY TO HIM MY CONGRATULATIONS. . . . THIS IS CONFIDENTIAL WIRE. PLEASE DESTROY IT AFTER YOU HAVE CONVEYED INFORMATION TO JOE.[24]

A few days later the Roosevelt landslide came as no surprise to Giannini.

CHAPTER TWENTY-FIVE

The Banking Crisis of 1933

BETWEEN the time of Mr. Hoover's defeat in November, 1932, and the inauguration of Franklin D. Roosevelt, on March 4, 1933, the country ran downhill faster than at any period since the market collapse of 1929. As the situation became critical it centered upon the ability of banks to perform their function, a part of which is the maintenance of confidence. This went on until other factors were almost lost sight of, and the episode has become known as the "banking crisis."

Roosevelt had campaigned on the issue that the government should play a larger role in the economic welfare of the people. He had called for "a New Deal." His proposals gave a shaken people hope, as did Giannini's "Good Times" campaign in California. After the election there was a psychological reaction. March 4 seemed a long way off. The drain on bank deposits continued, particularly in the Midwest and the East. People were hoarding money—gold when they could get it. More disturbing than that were the sudden, sporadic bank runs that broke out. In all, the feeling was one of mounting tension.

For the first time since the Reconstruction Finance Corporation had begun operation in February, 1932, bank failures showed an increase. Many of the failing banks had appealed unsuccessfully to the R.F.C., limited then to "fully and adequately secured loans." (Not until its second year was R.F.C. authorized to put new capital into banks by investing in their preferred stocks.) A notable failure occurred just before election when the Wingfield–Reno National Bank of Nevada was obliged to close. This institution was a chain of thirteen banks situated in nine Nevada towns. After appealing in vain for R.F.C. funds to reopen the bank, and to A. P. Giannini to start a

Transamerica bank in Nevada, the governor of the state proclaimed a banking holiday—the first of many that were to follow. George Wingfield's troubles stemmed from his efforts to carry Nevada's cattlemen. His bank had been obliged to foreclose on 150 ranches that owned nearly 800,000 head of cattle and sheep, or 70 per cent of the cattle and sheep in Nevada. So bad was the market that the bank realized as little as twenty-five cents for sheep on which it had loaned eight dollars a head.[1]

The Nevada situation and the bank closings in the Midwest disturbed California, particularly southern California where so many transplanted Midwesterners live. On the night of Saturday, December 31, 1932, national bank examiners got hold of Dwight L. Clarke, executive vice-president in charge of the Bank of America in the Los Angeles district. They said that unless Giannini took it over they would not permit the First National Bank of Redondo Beach to open on Tuesday, January 3 (January 2 was a bank holiday). This was an appeal Giannini had heard so often, over the years. Clarke advised against the take-over, on the basis of the bank's condition. Nevertheless, Giannini complied with the examiner's request.[2]

Other banks were the victims of panicky runs. Several small ones closed, in the north and the south of the state. Giannini was cheered, however, by the absence of serious repercussions on the neighboring Bank of America branches. The next general alarm came from a distance—from St. Louis, Missouri, where runs on a number of suburban banks finished sixteen of them. That was the country's first concentrated series of runs that seemed apt to be contagious. Contagious it was, and the next place the virus of fear struck was Sacramento, California, where, on a Saturday morning, the California National Bank and its savings affiliate failed to open. Full-fledged runs began at once on all other banks in town. The Bank of America's five Sacramento branches were liable for deposits of $40,000,000.

In San Francisco, Russell G. Smith, the bank's cashier, ordered a million in currency from the Federal Reserve. It takes about an hour to count and check off a million dollars in working denominations —bills of twenty dollars and less. The Federal Reserve also was filling orders from the other Sacramento banks. When Giannini learned that this money was to go by slow armored truck, he said that he wanted cash in Sacramento quicker than that. Though it was a foggy day, "Jake" Fischer, a veteran of the Santa Rosa run of

1921, hired an airplane and a pilot. He took off with another million. A third million followed by Leon Bocqueraz's limousine—in case Jake should have an accident. By nightfall ten more million, making thirteen in all, were on the way to the Sacramento and nearby branches of the B. of A.

On Monday afternoon the run died out. Withdrawals from Bank of America branches in the affected areas had exceeded deposits by only $104,000. The other banks, too, came through all right, though they were harder pressed.[3]

The story was different in Detroit, where mounting unemployment and home mortgage delinquencies had Michigan's two leading bank groups on the brink of insolvency. On February 13, the $51,-000,000 Union Guardian Trust Company, a link in the chain of twenty-one banks run by the Guardian Detroit Union Group, Inc., concluded it could not weather another day. Since the July previous the R.F.C., foreseeing the chaos that would ensue from the closing of these banks, had loaned $15,000,000 to the Trust Company. The Fords, heavy investors in the holding company, had begun as early as 1930 attempts to pull the Guardian group through. Their loans to it aggregated $9,500,000. Henry Ford, however, turned down a last-minute appeal by the R.F.C. for a further contribution to a joint salvage.

"Let the crash come," said the automobile manufacturer. It would serve as a "cleaning-up process," after which everybody could settle down to work, beginning all over once more. "Whatever happened," Mr. Ford "was sure he could again build up a business, as he still felt young."[4]

"Happenings" came fast and they brought down the banking structure of the nation. On February 14, the first day the Guardian banks did not open their doors, the governor of Michigan ordered all the banks of his state to remain shut. The banking holiday would continue for eight days, he said. It continued for four weeks, less one day. Meantime the fears of depositors reached hysterical pitch. Maryland's banks were closed on February 25; Ohio, Indiana and Illinois slapped restrictions on withdrawals; Arkansas fixed her limit at "5% or $15 whichever is larger." Two days later Arkansas proclaimed a banking holiday, as did Kentucky, Tennessee and Alabama. The panic was on.[5]

2

The President-Elect summoned A. P. Giannini to New York where, at his town house, Mr. Roosevelt was holding day-and-night conferences concerning ways and means of dealing with the crisis that grew more ominous by the hour. The banker arrived on February 21. Rumors flew every which way. Mario Giannini telegraphed one of the latest to reach San Francisco. It was that, on taking office, Mr. Roosevelt would declare a "national emergency" under a wartime statute and name B. M. Baruch the head of some governmental superbody, with extraordinary powers. This story did not anticipate the qualities of *personal* leadership that Franklin D. Roosevelt was to display as President of the United States. By no means was he to shrink from the invocation of extraordinary powers—for himself, however.[6]

Mr. Giannini's appointment was for the twenty-third. That morning Mr. Roosevelt announced that his Secretary of the Treasury would be William H. Woodin, president of the American Car & Foundry Company. (Carter Glass thought that he himself could be more useful in the Senate.) At the Roosevelt residence Giannini found Mr. Woodin, Norman H. Davis and Jesse H. Jones, a Texas banker destined to head the R.F.C. Giannini knew Jones and he had met Woodin once before when he had gone to his office to solicit American Car & Foundry's account for the Bank of America N. A. He got the account. The Californian and Mr. Roosevelt spent an hour together. They discussed plans for the country's rehabilitation that went beyond banking, per se.

In a telegram to his son, Giannini dismissed the national-emergency story by quoting Mr. Roosevelt as saying there was no statute under which it could be done. "Governor [Roosevelt] was very cordial," the banker continued.

Jones is very friendly and boosted us to Governor. Governor is going to propose legislation take care of farmers and home owners, issuing couple or three billion bonds in place of present mortgages on a basis around sixty or seventy per cent present face value. Henry Morgenthau, Jr., is to be chairman agricultural agency into which is to be merged all or about eight existing agencies on agricultural credit. Eugene [Meyer] is to go in due course . . . and there is likelihood of reorganization FRB, with new memberships . . . in about five or six months. I was so encouraged. Of course this should mean elimination of our friends Calkins and [Federal Reserve Bank chairman Isaac B.] Newton.[7]

All came true except the surmise concerning Calkins and Newton.

As banking activities ceased in state after state the drain on institutions in neighboring states, and particularly on New York, became excessive. More states closed their banks. Where governors failed to act mayors frequently took the law into their hands. Charles Partridge, in New York to woo back large accounts that had left the bank during the proxy fight, gave Will Morrish a picture of the situation on March 1:

> Everyone is terribly jumpy and scared of his shadow. Within the past two weeks over 750 millions have been taken out of New York banks by out-of-town correspondents. . . . Most of the big banks are selling their short-term paper to get cash. Potter of the Guaranty told us . . . he was ready to go into the Federal Reserve for 100 millions. . . . An officer of the City Bank told me that in one day they had dropped over 50 millions. The treasurers of all the companies are scared to death. Edwards of U. S. Steel showed us over twenty wires he had received today about banks. . . . Potter looks for government guarantee of deposits. Jackson Reynolds is one of the opposite opinion. Everyone has a different idea. . . . I know we are suffering less than these fellows are in the Middle West, East and South.[8]

Partridge was right. During the month of February, the worst month in the history of banking in the United States, the Bank of America N. T. & S. A. had lost only $22,376,000 in deposits. Of this $21,000,000 was withdrawn by Eastern banks and Eastern commercial depositors, nearly half of it during the last four days, an indication of their distress.[9]

On March 2 the governor closed the banks of California. Next morning, Friday, March 3, when Roosevelt left New York for Washington lines were in front of the windows of metropolitan banks. Twenty-nine states had invoked moratoria or some sort of restrictions. Yet, a quarter of a billion dollars was drawn from banks that were open on that day. That night Governor Lehman, himself a banker, shut the banks of New York. Nearly all the other states that had not already acted followed suit. The New York and Chicago stock exchanges did not open on Saturday.

Giannini, also, was in Washington on March 3. Roosevelt had not as yet said what he was going to do about the banks. To protect himself against an opening of them before confidence should be restored Giannini applied to the R.F.C. for two loans—one in the amount of $13,000,000 and one for $35,000,000. Of the second request the banker said "this commitment may not be used." As we shall see, neither commitment was used, nor needed.[10]

3

A. P. Giannini was an absorbed and approving observer of the inauguration of Franklin D. Roosevelt, the most momentous occasion of its kind since 1861. He liked Roosevelt's words. "The only thing we have to fear is fear itself." Giannini himself had used somewhat the same words time and again in California. Giannini warmed to Roosevelt's excoriation of "the unscrupulous money changers . . . [who stand] indicted in the court of public opinion. . . . They only know the rules of a generation of self-seekers. They have no vision, and where there is no vision the people perish." The speaker promised "action, and action now," to remedy that state of affairs. "Happiness lies not in the mere possession of money; it lies in the joy of achievement, in the thrill of creative effort. The joy and the moral stimulation of work no longer must be forgotten in the mad chase of evanescent profits." The Californian had damned Wall Street in much the same fashion, and his life was an exemplification of the new leader's philosophy concerning the possession of wealth.

As the inaugural fell on Saturday, the Executive had until Sunday night to decide whether the banks should open on Monday morning. It was a burdensome week end, of which Giannini had an inside view. He sat in some of the continuous conferences of bankers and officials that helped to shape the Administration's immediate course.

When a President of the United States has the will to do a thing it usually turns out that he can find the authority. That has been the history of every bold and natural leader in the White House. The President's constituted legal adviser, Attorney General Cummings, duly reported that a wartime statute gave the Executive authority to keep the banks closed. Thereupon, Roosevelt proclaimed a four-day bank holiday. He forbade the exportation of gold and the redemption of currency in gold or gold certificates. He called upon Congress to meet in special session the following Thursday, March 9. So much for one phase of "action now."

Though vastly relieved and encouraged by the vigor and optimism with which Roosevelt had taken hold, Giannini, nevertheless, had a few misgivings. For one thing, he thought the four-day holiday too short. When the banks opened there would be a pent-up demand for money and the demand might become panicky. It was proposed that Clearing House scrip be used to amplify the supply of currency, as had been done in 1907. Giannini, whose bank had declined to use scrip in 1907, did not think it was necessary to issue it now. But if it were issued, he intended that the Bank of America be entitled to its share. Consequently he was concerned when he heard from San Francisco that the Clearing House there had refused to issue the proposed scrip on the basis of mortgage loans, of which the Bank of America held $230,000,000. He attributed this to Calkins and started home to deal with the problem, telegraphing Mario en route:

Advise extreme tactful caution as to distribution [of Clearing House scrip], for you must remember enemies [Calkins, etc.] still at the helm. . . . You have one advantage over the competitors in that you have everything questionable charged off while they are yet to do this. Don't hesitate to shout from the house tops . . . that the stuff you still have on your books is absolutely good and is there with the approval of comptroller's department after a very thorough check . . . by him . . . of every item in the entire system.[11]

As Giannini traveled westward the holiday was extended, and Secretary Woodin abandoned the plan to use scrip. Privately Woodin said that he wanted to avoid anything that looked like "stage money." "We don't need it. We can issue currency against sound assets of banks."[12]

This was Giannini's thought exactly. So when the San Franciscan reached home on Friday, March 10, he thought one of his problems out of the way. To newspapermen he extolled "the initiative and leadership displayed by President Roosevelt." With the Bank of America in excellent shape—Giannini called it "the cleanest bank in the country"—the banker anticipated no difficulty about being allowed to reopen. At the same time he distrusted John U. Calkins in that connection—as it turned out, with very good reason.[13]

4

Giannini went straight from the train to No. 1 Powell. Announcement from Washington had been received that "eligible," meaning solvent, banks would be reopened by degrees under license of the Treasury. Institutions in the twelve Federal Reserve cities would be opened on Monday, March 13. On Tuesday, banks in 250 other cities having Clearing House Associations would open. On Wednesday, March 15, eligible banks elsewhere would open.

At once Giannini telegraphed Secretary Woodin for permission to open on Monday. He gave the salient facts of the bank's position. Word then came from Washington that licenses would be granted upon the recommendation of the district Federal Reserve banks and that applications should be made to them, and not to Washington. That brought Calkins into the picture. Giannini telegraphed the two California senators, Johnson and McAdoo, and C. W. Collins, the bank's Washington attorney, to watch over the bank's application.

All three sent reassuring replies, of which McAdoo's was strongest. After talking to Acting Comptroller F. W. Awalt (the comptrollership was vacant, Pole having resigned), the senator said he could not "imagine any ground for uneasiness on your part."[14]

That night—Friday, March 10—a disastrous earthquake in southern California added to Giannini's burdens. The shocks lasted throughout the night. At Long Beach 120 were killed and 4,000 injured. Three days went by before the Bank of America's directors resolved to "extend all possible aid" to the stricken community. In previous emergencies they had always acted with speed. The reason for the delay was that Giannini, during those three days, was pretty well occupied with aiding his institution to escape the untimely fate the governor of the Federal Reserve Bank of San Francisco would have liked to see overtake it.

All day Saturday Giannini waited in vain for the license to open the Bank of America on Monday morning. Despite the assurance of Senator McAdoo, by nightfall the banker was frankly disturbed.

Early Sunday Giannini returned to his desk in the bank. With bankers all over the country on the anxious seat, he could imagine the hordes of appeals descending upon Washington by telegraph, telephone and personal emissary. Nevertheless, he resolved to break through to the responsible officials, harassed as they were, and find out what had happened to the Bank of America's application. He wired Collins to go to the Treasury. He wired the California senators again. He wired Jesse Jones and he wired Marvin McIntyre, the President's secretary. Collins reported that Secretary Woodin had cleared the bank's license "early" Sunday morning. As Washington time is three hours earlier than California time, that would have been very early on Sunday in San Francisco. The same cheering word came from Johnson and McAdoo.

When no official confirmation of this news had been received in San Francisco by Sunday noon—3 P.M. Washington time—Giannini telephoned the senators. They were surprised to hear from him. That morning Secretary Woodin had assured them that he had cleared the bank. They volunteered to go again to the Treasury.

Not content with the efforts of the senators, Giannini telephoned John Francis Neylan, counsel for W. R. Hearst whose newspapers had supported Roosevelt during the campaign. Neylan knew many of the key people about the President. In a little while Neylan called back from his country place near San Francisco. He told Giannini that he had been in touch with Washington and that the bank was "all right."

Yet Sunday afternoon wore away, and still the license did not come. At six-thirty in the evening—nine-thirty Washington time—Senators Johnson and McAdoo telephoned the astounding news that Secretary Woodin had reversed himself, revoking his clearance for the Bank of America to open. The Secretary had taken this action on an "adverse report" about the bank from John U. Calkins. Concerning this report McAdoo added something that seems incredible, but was true, nevertheless. Woodin's conclusions were based on an examination of the Bank of America that was *more than a year old*. Calkins had forwarded to Washington that old report, notwithstanding there was in his office the results of a federal examination of the bank made in November, 1932, reflecting the institution's recovery after nine months of Giannini administration.

Giannini managed to get through by telephone to Secretary Woodin. It did no good. "Try as hard as we might," A. P. said later, "to convince him that the figures he had received were erroneous, we were not able to do so."[15]

At seven o'clock (ten o'clock Washington time), President Roosevelt went on the air for the first of his "fireside chats." Every step he had taken in the banking crisis during the past eight days had been calculated to allay the panic that had stricken the American people, and to restore their trust in the banks that were worthy of it. This talk was designed to complete that work.

The President began by reviewing the "bad banking situation" that had led up to his proclamation of the banking holiday.

Some of our bankers had shown themselves either incompetent or dishonest in their handling of the peoples' funds. . . . This was, of course, not true in the vast majority of our banks, but it was true in enough of them to shock the people for a time into a sense of insecurity and to put them in a frame of mind where they did not differentiate, but seemed to assume that the acts of a comparative few had tainted them all. It was the Government's job to straighten out this situation and do it as quickly as possible—and the job is being performed.

The President then gave an account of the emergency legislation Congress had enacted during the holiday and outlined the program under which the banks would reopen. The prohibition on gold payments by banks would continue; also the executive order requiring the redeposit of gold. The twelve Federal Reserve banks would issue an adequate supply of currency as fast as the Bureau of Engraving and Printing could turn it out, the additional currency being shipped to every part of the country. This was sound currency, backed by actual good assets of the banks.

"I do not promise you that every bank will be reopened or that individual losses will not be suffered," Mr. Roosevelt concluded,

but there will be no losses that possibly could be avoided; and there would have been more and greater losses had we continued to operate. I can even promise you salvation for some at least of the sorely pressed banks. We shall be engaged not merely in reopening sound banks but in the creation of sound banks through reorganization.[16]

5

One can imagine Giannini's emotions as he listened to the President's words. Yet he did not give up. He dare not. The bank was perfectly qualified to open, and it *must* open.

He telephoned Jack Neylan, who, in turn called William Randolph Hearst at his estate at San Simeon. The publisher agreed that the failure of the Bank of America to open would be a catastrophe for California. He told Neylan to insist on speaking to the President, personally.

At the White House, Marvin McIntyre informed Neylan that the President had gone to bed with a cold. Nevertheless, McIntyre summoned Secretary Woodin from his office in the Treasury a block away. Raymond Moley of the "brain trust," Acting Comptroller Awalt, and other officials were on hand. Later Senators Johnson and McAdoo came in. The stage was set to thresh out the matter and, if necessary, to awaken the President to make the ultimate decision. Mr. Roosevelt's sleep was not disturbed for it took all night.

Some time after 11 P.M. (2 A.M., Monday, Washington time) Neylan had his first conversation with Secretary Woodin at the White House.

"He told me," Neylan later related,

[that] Calkins contended that the bank was hopelessly insolvent and that it could not possibly stand up.

I told him . . . that Calkins was violently prejudiced, and that the bank had made a remarkable recovery and that failure to open the Bank of America would be a disaster from which the Pacific Coast would not recover in twenty-five years.

He read to me from the Calkins report, and I had to confess I was unfamiliar with the figures. It was then agreed I would get more information and ring him back.

Neylan called Giannini at No. 1 Powell, and got the figures to refute Calkins. A few hours before, Giannini had tried to give the Secretary the same figures and had made no impression. In the light of hindsight it is difficult to reproach Mr. Woodin. A man of frail physique, he had gone through a week that might have broken an athlete. He listened attentively to Neylan and promised to check the whole situation and call back.[17]

Woodin put in a call for "a high banking official in San Francisco," as Raymond Moley described him in a subsequent account. The official was Calkins. "Then ensued a long telephone conversation . . . punctuated by strong language," continued Moley.

It wound up with Woodin's "Are you willing to take the responsibility for keeping this institution closed?" and the answer, from California, that the official refused to take that responsibility. "Well, then," said Will [Woodin], "the bank will open."[18]

At 3:30 A.M. California time (6:30 Washington time) the Secretary of the Treasury called Jack Neylan again.

"He . . . told me," said Neylan,

he had become satisfied of the prejudice of Calkins and that the Calkins figures did not reflect the current situation in the bank.

He then said, "If we let the Bank of America open, will you and Mr. Hearst underwrite it?"

I told him that, of course, such a thing was absurd; that even though Mr. Hearst was a man of large wealth, he could not underwrite a bank of that magnitude and that, of course, my means were microscopic in comparison with the bank.

He hastened to say he did not mean "underwrite" in the conventional sense, but what he meant was, he wanted our assurance that if anything happened to the bank and the administration was subjected to criticism, we would tell the facts and approve the steps that were being taken.

Neylan gave the promise and the Secretary said: "You can go to sleep. The bank will open."[19]

Thus A. P. Giannini received the welcome word with a little more than six hours to spare. One of the most anxious nights of his life was at an end. In a letter thanking W. R. Hearst for his and Jack Neylan's services, the banker said:

The conduct of Federal Reserve officials . . . was calculated to lull us into a sense of security, they having in mind to send in a last minute adverse report so that we would not have time or opportunity to defend ourselves.[20]

The opinion of Raymond Moley was no less damning.

Giannini had made many powerful enemies during his tremendous rise in banking, and some of them were ready in this emergency to strike him down.[21]

A tired but triumphant little group watched the big doors of the Bank of America N. T. & S. A. swing open at No. 1 Powell Street at ten o'clock in the morning of March 13, 1933. In an automobile Giannini made a tour of the Bay Area branches. At the end of the day he telegraphed Jesse Jones:

The opening of banks in San Francisco was very gratifying. Normal banking conditions prevailed everywhere. On my visits to our branches I found depositors cheerful and most willing to cooperate in the President's policies. I found everywhere high commendation of the President's Sunday speech and of the constructive actions taken by him. . . . Please convey to him my sincere appreciation and congratulations.[22]

The following day Marvin McIntyre wired from the White House that he was "tickled to death that things are working out so well." Giannini replied with more details of the first two days' operations since the reopening:

I want to particularly repeat that the President's talk last Sunday night did the trick as far as California is concerned. Fine reports continue to come in from all over the state not only concerning our own bank but concerning other banks. We have been particularly gratified at the showing in Los Angeles, Oakland, San Diego, Fresno, and Sacramento. Preliminary reports from the smaller cities throughout the state which were just opened for banking business today are also excellent. You will especially be interested in knowing that the amount of actual cash taken in throughout the branches of our system on Monday and Tuesday exceeded the cash withdrawn by one million two hundred twenty-five thousand dollars. This certainly shows that money is coming out of hoarding.

On Saturday, March 18, Giannini telegraphed Jesse Jones a cancellation of the tentative request for R.F.C. funds that he had made on March 3.[23]

The sweeping gains of the Bank of America continued. On June 29, 1933, it wiped out the last of its indebtedness to the Reconstruction Finance Corporation. Eight months later the Pacific Coast Mortgage Company, formerly the Bankitaly Mortgage Company, paid off the last of its $30,000,000 loan.[24]

The day after settling up with R.F.C., the Bank of America declared a quarterly dividend of seventy-five cents a share, the first dividend since October, 1931. This, and subsequent dividends, enabled Transamerica to pay twelve and a half cents a share to its stockholders in January, 1934, the first dividend since November, 1931.

Such was the performance of the bank that, less than four months earlier, was almost kept from reopening.

CHAPTER TWENTY-SIX

Giannini and the New Deal, 1933-1936

A. P. GIANNINI'S enthusiasm for the way Franklin D. Roosevelt had mastered the most immediate of his problems, the banking crisis, did not abate. He watched with growing approval as the new Executive sailed into one detail after another of the question of relief for the victims of the depression. This included the unemployed and their potential employers in business and industry; it included farmers under a burden of debt and confronted by prices for their products that did not meet the cost of raising them; it included homeowners faced with eviction through foreclosure. It included also reforms looking to the future: the Banking Acts of 1933 and 1935; the Securities and Exchange Commission, making Wall Street a safer place for the ordinary investor; and the development of public resources, as embodied in the Tennessee Valley Authority.

No banker got behind these measures with the force and ardor that Giannini brought to bear. "We are on the right road," he told newspapermen in 1933. "The system has to be changed. . . . There is something wrong with a system that lets 14,000,000 men get out of work." This unique support was deeply appreciated at the White House, where Giannini was an occasional guest. The banker got on close terms with some of the New Deal big guns, especially Jesse Jones of the Reconstruction Finance Corporation. "A. P.'s name was magic in Washington," an admiring Native Son has said. "When California wanted something from the New Deal, he was asked to get it."[1]

2

The Banking Act of 1933 represented a triumph for the Giannini point of view. "No other banking group gains from this act as many advantages as does Transamerica," C. W. Collins reminded the Californian. It had been Mr. Collins' job to follow the act through Congress as he had followed the McFadden bill of 1927, which the Act of 1933 supplanted.[2]

The chief author of the 1933 measure was Senator Carter Glass who, more than any other member of Congress, had been responsible for the branch banking features of the Act of 1927. The new law wisely incorporated the principle for which national banks had long contended—parity with state banks in the matter of branches. It permitted national banks to open branches anywhere in a state where state banks had that right.

The act enabled Giannini to merge his Bank of America (state) with the parent institution, Bank of America N. T. & S. A. The first step was taken on Christmas Eve, 1934, when 61 of the state bank's 70 branches were taken over. This gave the Bank of America N. T. & S. A. 423 branches in 255 California communities. The consolidation cut the state bank down to a skeleton of 8 branches and the home office. These were retained because, as a guard against unforeseen circumstances, Giannini thought it best he keep a state bank in California.

Under the Banking Act of 1933 Transamerica's First National Bank of Portland, Oregon, increased the number of its branches to 16 in 9 cities in Oregon. In 1934 Transamerica entered Nevada, as it had been asked by the governor to do in 1932 after the failure of the Wingfield chain. Carl Wente was persuaded to take the presidency of the First National Bank of Reno. Giannini wanted one of his best men there to get Trans off to a good start. This was in no sense a minor undertaking. Trans opened branches in towns that had been bankless for two years.

The new legislation also separated investment banking from commercial banking by obliging commercial banks to divorce themselves from their security-trading affiliates. This was directed at a notorious evil of the twenties. Moreover, bank holding companies, such as Transamerica, were placed under federal supervision in the same manner as national banks. Giannini had suggested this to the House Committee on Banking and Currency in 1930 and later he had mentioned it to Senator Glass.[3]

The act provided for the insurance of deposits up to $2,500. Glass had opposed this, but accepted it by way of a compromise. Giannini, too, was lukewarm until he saw how the provision made for confidence among depositors. Three months after the act came into force the San Franciscan surprised a convention of the American Bankers Association by welcoming the insurance feature, being the first big banker to do so. He praised the new law generally, singling out for mention "the provision that minority stockholders of a national bank have a right to elect representatives on the board of the institution in proportion to the stock they hold."[4]

It is little wonder that Giannini liked that feature of the law, since he was responsible for it. The situation that prompted him to act concerned the National City Bank of New York, in which Transamerica by this time owned a tenth stock interest. A part of the deal by which Walker had sold the Bank of America N. A. to National City was that Trans should forego board representation. This was so unfair that Giannini had Grant, the president of Transamerica, ask for recognition. Grant got nowhere. In the spring of 1933, Giannini had lunch with James H. Perkins, who had just succeeded C. E. Mitchell as chairman of the board of National City. Giannini liked Perkins whom he described later as "a gentleman of the old school." The Westerner marveled that, after long exposure to the "questionable practices prevailing in Wall Street, Mr. Perkins has so steadfastly stuck to his ideals." The New Yorker also liked Giannini and that lunch was the beginning of their long, close friendship. It did not, however, serve to get Giannini his places on the board. This he attributed to the opposition of Morgan.

From New York Giannini went to Washington and, in a week's time, was able to wire Will Morrish: "HAVE SUCCEEDED IN GETTING AMENDMENT IN GLASS BILL THAT WILL PERMIT MINORITY BEING REPRESENTED ON NATIONAL BANK BOARDS."[5]

After the bill had become a law John Francis Neylan, visiting in New York, found Mr. Perkins laboring over a letter inviting Mr. Giannini to become a director. Somewhat embarrassed, the banker was having difficulty expressing himself.

"Why not just call him on the phone?" suggested Neylan.

Perkins wondered if that would be the proper approach to a man "in Mr. Giannini's position." On Neylan's assurance that A. P. was no stickler for formality, the New Yorker reached for the telephone.[6]

The new directors were Giannini and Neylan.

In the fall of 1933, Giannini expedited an R.F.C. loan to help the grape growers of California tide over the transition involved by the repeal of prohibition. Prohibition had boomed the grape business. Prices in New York soared as high as $200 a ton, but with the doubling of the acreage they fell off to $12. In 1933 the bank had $6,000,000 tied up in vineyards that repeal was expected to make profitable once more. The crop was ripening when a promised R.F.C. loan got tangled in red tape. The grape center of Fresno had the jitters. Protests brought no action in Washington, and Morrish wired Giannini that the situation was critical. Twenty-four hours later A. P. telegraphed from Washington that the R.F.C. money was forthcoming. On top of that, branches in the Fresno area were instructed to make loans to vintners to purchase grapes and accept new wines as collateral. "The aid was hailed with jubilation," noted the San Francisco *Examiner*.[7]

In May, 1933, the Emergency Farm Mortgage Act halted farm foreclosures by providing for their refinancing through the Federal Land Banks. Before the legislation became effective the Bank of America announced that it had stopped foreclosures not only on all farm property but on all real estate "where the borrower is evidencing his good faith in attempting to work out his problems." Thus was anticipated by a month establishment of the Home Owners Loan Corporation.

"The importance of this step," remarked the Santa Barbara *Daily News,*

becomes more readily apparent when it is realized that this great financial institution has interests in almost every county of the state. . . . The move comes as a cooperative effort on the part of the bank officials to comply with President Roosevelt's . . . plans to build the nation a better economic structure than that which collapsed because of faulty foundations.[8]

When Mr. Roosevelt broadcast an appeal for re-employment under National Recovery Act codes, the Bank of America curtailed working hours without reducing employees' pay, and took on more help. "BEING WHOLEHEARTEDLY IN ACCORD WITH YOUR REEMPLOYMENT PROGRAM," Giannini wired the President, "IT MAY INTEREST YOU TO KNOW THAT THE BANK OF AMERICA HAS RETAINED MORE THAN 300 EXCESS EMPLOYEES THROUGHOUT THE DEPRESSION AND THAT ON JULY 1 WE

INCREASED SALARIES OF MORE THAN 2,200 EMPLOYEES PLACING THE IN-
COME OF 57 PER CENT OF OUR PERSONNEL ON A NORMAL BASIS."[9]

A matter in which Giannini did not succeed was the attempt to
procure the removal of John U. Calkins as governor of the Twelfth
Federal Reserve Bank at San Francisco. In his first interview with
Roosevelt in San Francisco during the campaign Giannini had mentioned Calkins and had received a candidate's answer: if elected Mr.
Roosevelt would look into the matter and "if he found things as we
stated, he would see that they were adjusted." After a postelection
talk with F. D. R. and Jesse Jones early in 1933, Giannini had felt
that Calkins would go before long.[10]

Then had come Mr. Calkins' attempt to prevent the reopening of
the Bank of America after the banking holiday. With the record of
the bank since then disproving in almost every particular the criticisms of Mr. Calkins, Giannini was sure he had a case that would
bring the speedy end of the Federal Reserve governor's official career. But in August, 1933, he received a wire from Senator McAdoo
saying, "I AGREE WITH YOU BUT VERY DIFFICULT TO GET ACTION HERE.
DOING ALL I CAN." Dourly Giannini commented: "Apparently things
don't work out so fast in that [Washington] neck of the woods."[11]

They did not work out in the Calkins case for nearly three years
and then only because of the Banking Act of 1935 which reorganized the Federal Reserve System. The title of the head officer in each
district was changed from governor to president. Mr. Calkins, then
seventy-two years old, did not receive the appointment in the
Twelfth District, but it went to his chief deputy, William A. Day.

3

The revelations of Ferdinand Pecora, counsel for the Senate Committee on Banking and Currency, comprised one of the inspirations
of the New Deal legislation having to do with banking, finance and
the securities markets. Pecora stripped Wall Street bare. On the
banking side, he sent into unhappy retirement the chairmen of the
nation's two largest institutions—Albert H. Wiggin of the Chase
National and Charles E. Mitchell of National City.

Pecora was just getting under way when a political intimate of
McAdoo wrote Giannini that the Bancitaly Corporation was to come

under the investigator's eye. "There is nothing," the banker replied, "I would welcome more than an investigation by Congress (or anyone else for that matter) of the affairs of the Bancitaly Corporation, or its successor, Transamerica." Bancitaly did not get on Mr. Pecora's agenda, however. Nor was Mr. Giannini called before the committee —as he would like to have been, for instance, when Leo Belden was shown to have been on J. P. Morgan's "select list" for financial favors. That was at the time when Belden was acting as Giannini's confidential agent in New York during the tussle with Morgan over the Bank of America N. A.[12]

Mr. Giannini had never regarded C. E. Mitchell as much of a banker, and the deal by which the National City had taken over, at a low valuation, from Walker the highly liquid Bank of America N. A. in New York was something the San Franciscan never forgot or forgave. Out of the National City Bank, Mr. Mitchell went back to selling securities. In 1936 he made a business call on Giannini at the Los Angeles headquarters of the Bank of America. To a friend who was also in the securities business, A. P. gave an indication of the nature of the interview.

> Certainly this fellow Mitchell has a hell of a crust to come in to see me. . . . I had to take advantage of the chance to unload on Charlie Mitchell a few of the things that have been rankling in me since the Walker deal. . . . So we did not have any chance to talk [about securities]. . . . He apparently was glad to get away.[13]

This period also witnessed the last of the Nolan-Hellman-Bell affair. After Giannini's return, a scrutiny of the loan situation brought to light additional cases in which ostensible borrowers were dummies for one or another of the dismissed officers who had received the funds. In November, 1932, Giannini suggested to the chief examiner of the Twelfth District that prosecutions be commenced.[14]

Meanwhile Charles R. Bell instituted a number of lawsuits against the Bank of America, the Transamerica Corporation and several affiliates on behalf of himself and other stockholders of the former Merchants National Bank and Trust Company of Los Angeles. Damages were asked in the amount of $89,000,000 for losses sustained in the decline of Transamerica stock.

In a bristling letter to Attorney General Cummings, Giannini called the Bell actions "blackmail." He asked that the government get ahead with criminal charges against Bell, Nolan and the Hellmans. Cummings referred the matter to the United States district attorney in Los Angeles who declined to act.

The suits against the bank and Transamerica were eventually resolved in favor of the defendants. Of the dismissed officers only Bell was in a state of solvency. On a countercomplaint the bank was awarded a judgment of $460,000 against him, and one for $312,000 against his wife, who was a member of a wealthy family. She had signed one of the notes in question. The bank accepted a settlement of $250,000.[15]

4

In July, 1938, Jesse Jones, chairman of the Reconstruction Finance Corporation, wrote Giannini as follows:

> DEAR A. P.—I noted with interest some days ago your statement about cooperation with the R.F.C. in industrial lending. From your statement you are employing more of your deposits, I believe, than any big bank in the United States.[16]

Mr. Jones was referring to small-business loans which, four years earlier, the Federal Reserve had been authorized by Congress to make jointly with local banks. With no encouragement from the government agency, Giannini had pushed these loans on the Pacific Coast. It was a difficult task for a number of reasons. Applications were from $2,500 to $10,000 and practically all represented "problem loans" requiring detailed study. Many applicants had no basis for credit and it took time to separate the chaff from the wheat. Moreover, the studies had to be made jointly by the local bank and by the district Federal Reserve Bank. When a loan was approved the local bank advanced from 10 to 75 per cent, and the Reserve Bank the rest on behalf of the Reconstruction Finance Corporation.[17]

This type of loan was new to the Federal Reserve Banks. Especially the San Francisco bank, under Calkins, was slow to respond. In October, 1934, four months after Congress had acted, Giannini was impatient with Calkins and, during a visit to Washington, carried his complaint to Jesse Jones of the R.F.C. Mr. Jones was about to hold a press conference, and invited Giannini to sit in. The subject was discussed before the assembled newspapermen, one of whom wrote as follows:

"We have offered more than 500 industrial loans to the Reserve Board [the Twelfth District Bank] for approval and only one has been approved," said A. P.

"If the loans are good, why didn't you make them yourselves?" Mr. Jones asked.

"They are long-term capital loans," Mr. Giannini replied. "Bank examiners and federal authorities would have cracked down on us had we made loans as slow as these."

"Out of that 500 there must have been some you could make safely," Mr. Jones remarked.

"You would not have made a single one," Mr. Giannini answered. "Houston's National Bank of Commerce [the Jones bank in Texas] is one of the most prosperous banks in the country—and it is also one of the most liquid."[18]

The newspaper accounts created a stir and this was what Jones and Giannini wanted. Though correct in the substance of his protest, Mr. Giannini's figures were not altogether accurate, as John U. Calkins promptly pointed out. The 500 loan applications (actually 466) were from all the banks in the Twelfth District, not from the Bank of America alone. The Bank of America had submitted 105 applications, of which 14 (not 1) had been accepted at the time Mr. Giannini was speaking. The significant fact, however, was that after Giannini's criticism things moved a great deal faster in the Twelfth District. In November, 1934, small loans closed aggregated $191,000 and in December $394,000, against $15,000 for October. Loans approved amounted to $330,000 in November and $603,000 in December, against $128,000 in October.[19]

The Bank of America also went along with a number of small businesses that were unable to qualify for R.F.C.-participation loans. In some of these cases the bank's only alternative would have been to write off advances already made, as the involvements were inheritances from the Merchants National Bank of Los Angeles. The judgment and good management of Keath L. Carver, an assistant vice-president of the Bank of America, were responsible for pulling out several such loans. Representing the bank, Carver participated in the management of such diversified undertakings as Armacost & Royston (growers of flowers and plants) and the Filtrol Company of California (processors of clay used in the purification of petroleum).

Armacost & Royston owed $250,000. Carver decided that one of the firm's best assets were 750,000 young orchid plants that would not bloom for five years. The bank officer studied horticulture and nursed the company along. When the orchids bloomed, the orchid market, all but extinguished during the depression, also was blooming again. The 750,000 plants pulled the company out.

At the same time Keath Carver was acting as president of the Filtrol Company. Capitalized at $1,250,000, this Los Angeles industry had just begun to make money when the depression struck. In 1932 it owed the Bank of America $88,000. Besides that, the bank owned 27.5 per cent of the company's stock, which former Merchants National officers had pledged as security for loans. Carver bowed out in 1945 with Filtrol booming, largely because of the wartime demand for aviation gasoline.[20]

5

The resumption of dividends by the Bank of America on July 1, 1933, brought a frown from the comptroller's department which had suggested that all banks consider the reduction or deferment of dividends in order to build up reserve and surplus. There was much to be said for the request, but it did not seem to apply to the Bank of America. After paying miscellaneous debts amounting to $140,-000,000 that had accumulated during the Walker administration and starting the speedy liquidation of the R.F.C. loans, indications were that the bank's net earnings for the year would be around $8,000,000. Giannini believed that a dividend paid at the annual rate of $2,000,000-plus would be "conservative" and a "boost" to West Coast morale.[21]

Nevertheless, the dividend question found its way into the report of S. Clark Beise, national bank examiner in charge of the examination of the Bank of America that began in September, 1933, and was finished the following January. Beise is an able man and a reasonable one. Subsequently he became an important officer of the bank he was then examining. As an examiner, his principal criticism concerned foreclosed real estate that had been taken off the bank's hands by the Transamerica subsidiaries, Capital Company (for urban property) and California Lands (farm property). He said this transaction represented an "undesirable investment" for the bank, and recommended that $7,500,000 be charged off at once.

To accomplish this (and for other purposes), Beise suggested that "all of the earnings of the bank should be utilized to improve its asset position and any diversion of earnings [such as dividends] which do not serve this purpose would not appear warranted."[22]

When an examiner finishes his work it is customary to discuss the findings with officers of the bank before sending them to Washington. In the present instance the conferences were conducted in a friendly spirit, though a wide difference existed between the bank officers and Mr. Beise and his superior, L. L. Madland, chief examiner for the Twelfth District. Madland suggested that, if the bank did not wish to appropriate "a very substantial proportion of earnings for the removal of the criticised assets," it should borrow from the R.F.C.[23]

By this time both the bank and the Pacific Coast [formerly Bankitaly] Mortgage Company had finished paying off all they owed the R.F.C. Giannini must have been shocked at the proposal that he borrow afresh. "To emerge from this depression," he wrote another banker,

it may be desirable for banks to make loans which an extremely critical examiner might technically regard as "slow," but which loans are undoubtedly good. To know a good loan of this type, there is no question but what the examiner should be first qualified and then inspired by the rule of reason premised on common sense in determining the classification of loans.[24]

The question was appealed to Washington and Giannini sent Vice-President Hugh L. Clary to settle it with Chief Examiner W. P. Folger. "Concerning the pending foreclosures," Clary told Mr. Folger,

it should be mentioned the Bank of America is the result of a merger of a great many banks—most of them state banks. These banks had large amounts of real estate loans. The foreclosed real estate now on our books represents an aggregate that would otherwise have been spread over several hundred banks with total deposits of about a billion and a quarter dollars. The Bank of America cannot and should not be compared with large commercial banks in New York or Chicago. Approximately 75% of the Bank's deposits are time deposits. It operates in more than 250 communities in California—most of them farming communities. Time deposits and mortgage loans are a natural and inevitable characteristic of its business and are a result of the needs and requirements of the state of California. In proportion to the deposits and the mortgages they represent and in consideration of the nature and extent of the bank's business the total foreclosures are not excessive and do not constitute the problem which the examiner's comments would appear to indicate.[25]

This argument effected a compromise. Instead of the $7,500,000 charge-off, the bank was permitted to set up a reserve against the liquidation of the loans involved. Five million of the reserve came from surplus, in which $30,000,000 still remained.

6

On October 13, 1934, A. P. Giannini accepted for the third time the presidency of the Bank of America. Mr. Morrish had resigned to head a toll bridge company. Giannini stipulated that he would continue to serve without pay. Four days later, from New York, he talked by radio to 6,000 employees who were gathered around dinner tables in 257 California towns to celebrate the bank's thirtieth anniversary. He commended the New Deal in these terms:

Our President's recovery program has been assailed by reactionaries who would have us believe he seeks to destroy the social order, and by ultra-radicals who would have us forsake him because he does not. We are celebrating tonight because we believe that selfish interests can no longer conceal from the public the fundamental improvement that has taken place. . . . Our own state and our own bank demonstrate the scope of the recovery. Recently I visited more than three hundred of our branches. . . . In some sections of California farmers have done even better than in boom times.

As an anniversary gift, Giannini announced a new pension plan for the employees. The bank's contribution the first year would be $300,000.

"To you, my co-workers, whose assistance has meant so much, I offer my congratulations," he said in conclusion. "The worst is over. Just watch things hum!"[26]

Things did hum. During the years 1935, 1936 and 1937 the bank added as follows to the number of its depositors' accounts and to the aggregate of its deposits:

	New Depositors' Accounts	Gain in Deposits
1935	190,380	$176,932,000
1936	129,954	143,711,000
1937	233,477	58,402,000

At the end of 1937 the bank had 1,911,035 deposit accounts, or one for every three and a half persons in California. The deposit total was $1,357,379,000, or more than double what it had been in March, 1932, when Giannini halted the deposit losses which had reached threatening proportions.

Earnings increased and with them dividends. In 1937 dividends aggregated $8,800,000, as against $2,250,000 upon resumption in 1933.

The three years just mentioned witnessed a surge of new branches —seventy-five in all. Of these forty-five were the result of purchases; thirty were started *de novo*. Included here as purchases were the head office and eight remaining branches of the Bank of America (state), which in 1937 passed out of existence. Aside from these, the largest purchase of the period was that of the Seaboard National of Los Angeles, which had four branches.

The disappearance of the Bank of America (state) did not leave Giannini without a Transamerica-owned state bank in California. The place of B. of A. (state) was supplied by the purchase of the Central Bank of Oakland, a $45,000,000 institution. This transaction ended a minor feud between Giannini and A. J. Mount who had been president of the Bank of America under Walker. On the return of Giannini in 1932, Mount went to the Central Bank of Oakland, from which, incidentally, Giannini had hired him in 1921. Mount began making it uncomfortable for borrowers who had pledged Transamerica stock as security. In return, Giannini obliged Mount to repay the Bank of America considerable sums he owed at the time of his departure. Then Giannini went out to obtain stock control of the Central Bank, which he accomplished in 1936.[27]

To reorganize the Central Bank, Oakland, as it is called, Carl Wente was brought back from Reno. Under the ownership of Transamerica, the Central Bank, Oakland, continues independently of the Bank of America. In addition to the head office, in January, 1953, Central Bank had eleven branches in northern California and resources of $164,216,892.

During this wave of expansion Giannini almost bought his largest San Francisco Bay Area rival; in fact his only real rival, in northern California—the American Trust Company, with ninety-one branches. He could have had it, but refused to pay the price asked. The bank was in the hands of Floyd Odlum, whose Atlas Corporation had picked it up at a depression bargain from the deflated Goldman Sachs Trading Corporation. Odlum cleaned up the bank, but decided to sell it because of prejudice against absentee ownership.

Odlum wanted $15,000,000. John M. Grant of Transamerica told Giannini that $13,000,000 was enough to pay. At one time an agreement seemed so likely that Transamerica's publicity department prepared a "release" announcing its consummation. Giannini planned to retain the name, American Trust Company, and merge with it his Bank of America (state), then down to eight branches. But the $2,000,000 gap was never bridged, and in 1936 Odlum sold control to a syndicate of Californians.[28]

7

The Banking Act of 1933 was something of an emergency measure. It was superseded by the Banking Act of 1935, the most important piece of banking legislation since the creation of the Federal Reserve System in 1913. The system was reorganized and its central authority in Washington strengthened at the expense of Wall Street and influential banks elsewhere. In this legislative battle A. P. Giannini played a very active part on the Administration's side; and for good reason.

A tentative draft of the 1935 bill provided for branch banking on a regional or trade-area basis, doing away with state lines where they had no economic significance. If enacted, this would have enabled the Bank of America to absorb the Transamerica banks in Oregon and Nevada. Giannini made ready by creating an advisory council of fourteen. His son Mario was named head of the council, and the other members were:

For the Bank of America: Frank N. Belgrano, vice-president; W. E. Blauer, vice-president and chairman of the general finance committee; Hugh L. Clary, vice-president and vice-chairman of the operating committee; Louis Ferrari, vice-president and counsel; F. A. Ferroggiaro, vice-president; Dr. A. H. Giannini, chairman, general executive committee; G. J. Panario, vice-president; A. E. Sbarboro, vice-president and vice-chairman of the general finance committee; Will C. Wood, vice-president.

For the Bank of America (state): A. J. Gock, vice-president and chairman of the general executive committee.

For the First National Bank of Portland, Oregon: E. B. McNaughton, president.

For the First National Bank of Reno, Nevada: Carl F. Wente, president. (This was before Wente was sent to Oakland.)

For Transamerica: John M. Grant, president.

These were the lieutenants on whom Giannini placed heavy reliance in 1935. The council did not get a chance to function in the matter of throwing all the Giannini banks into one because the regional banking provision was stricken from the bill before it reached Congress. The Administration leader, Governor Marriner S. Eccles of the Federal Reserve Board, a branch banker from Utah, at the time favored regional banking, but he consented to the withdrawal of the provision when Secretary of the Treasury Morgenthau suggested that insistence on its inclusion might defeat other sections of the bill which he deemed more important. Giannini did not protest his decision.[29]

Three features of the bill that the government particularly desired went through after an average amount of debate. These increased deposit insurance from $2,500 to $5,000 per account; expanded the volume of real estate loans permitted by national banks; and made permanent emergency legislation permitting Federal Reserve banks to lend on certain types of commercial paper previously declared ineligible. The real estate provision was important, of course, to the Bank of America. Under it, national banks might lend on real estate up to 60 per cent of its value for ten years; and, further, they might invest in real estate loans up to 100 per cent of their unimpaired capital and surplus, or 60 per cent of their savings deposits, whichever was greater.

The major battle developed over the Administration's attempt to minimize the chance of boom-and-bust cycles by concentrating authority over credit and currency in the hands of the Federal Reserve Board in Washington. That meant diminishing the authority of the twelve Federal Reserve Banks and of the private banks that exerted influence over the Reserve Banks, as Morgan and others did in New York. New York bankers let out a great uproar. Winthrop

Aldrich called the provision "an instrument of despotic authority." James P. Warburg declared "the proposal for political control of the banking and credit machinery is in effect . . . [a] step toward communism." Eccles, chief advocate of the control measure, was pilloried as a "radical." *Time* magazine said the bill would make him "the first 'financial despot' of the United States."[30]

Giannini was on the side of Eccles. "It is true," he said in a newspaper interview,

that one of the purposes of the Banking Bill is to lessen the authority of bankers to determine the monetary policies of the country, but it should be emphasized that bankers at large have had very little voice in the determination of such policies in the past. The group that has exerted the predominant influence has been the New York bankers. . . . Personally, I would rather that this power be exercised by a public body in the public interest than by the New York banking fraternity.[31]

He said the bill was

not a radical document sprung from the brains of theorists, but deep rooted in 20 years of practical experience with the Federal Reserve Act as tested by the worst depression in history. . . . I take no stock in the "political domination" argument. . . . The Federal Reserve Board is a political body only in the sense that its members are nominated by the President and confirmed by the Senate. So are the members of the Supreme Court.[32]

"GREATLY APPRECIATE YOUR STATEMENT," Eccles wired the Californian.

"IT WAS BOTH A PLEASURE AND A PRIVILEGE," A. P. replied.

When the amended bill passed Eccles warmly thanked Giannini.

It turned out better than I had reason to expect and we gained not only all the essentials which we desired but, especially with respect to eligible paper, much more than I imagined would be conceded. That, together with the real-estate provisions, ought to be very helpful at this time. I doubt if we would have been successful against the great weight of banking opinion but for the fact that a few voices—all too few—and yours most notably, were raised in behalf of the bill.[33]

8

The fight over the Banking Act of 1935 ended the honeymoon of the New Deal, when nearly everyone was its friend. By then times were easier, memories of the late crisis had begun to grow dim, and, above all, an election was on the horizon. The wealthy began to kick about taxes and about the national debt, which stood at $28,-700,000,000—an increase of $5,000,000,000 since Roosevelt came in. Giannini regarded the money as well spent and said so repeatedly. In September, 1935, the President wrote Giannini a thankful letter:

It is refreshing to know that some who occupy high places in the business and financial realms can remember conditions as they existed several years ago and today can realize the changes for betterment that have come to us as a Nation.

I have read several newspaper reports of the statements you made in this connection. Naturally, your observation that business in the Far West has shown such remarkable improvement and, in some sections, "is back where it was before the depression," pleases me much.

I expect to be in your State within a week or so and hope very much that it will be possible for us to meet once again.[34]

Mr. Roosevelt visited only the southern part of California, and Giannini purposely stayed in the north. He was more anxious that Roosevelt meet and exercise his famous charm upon those who were in need of conversion. To this end he advised Jim Farley to arrange for a nonpartisan reception committee, which Farley did.[35]

Late in November Mr. Roosevelt made a speech at Atlanta. He recalled the days when bankers were scared stiff and crying for the government to save them. The President said that in 1933 bankers had assured him that the national debt could be safely expanded to $70,000,000,000. The opposition press leaped on the statement. The Chicago *Tribune* could think of only two bankers who might have said such a "silly" thing—Marriner Eccles and A. P. Giannini.[36]

Giannini made no comment. In 1948 one of the authors of this book asked him if he had been one of the bankers who had advised Roosevelt about the debt. Mr. Giannini declined to take personal credit in the matter. "It wasn't any new idea," he said. "A lot of bankers thought that way about the debt limit. The important thing then was to lick the depression. There was nothing wrong with the government spending to bring back prosperity. It could afford it. Look at the size of the national debt today." At the close of 1947 it stood at $256,981,000,000.[37]

Shortly after Roosevelt's Atlanta speech Giannini was in Washington. He dined at the White House, and "informed sources" began to speculate about a government post for the San Franciscan. On his return home Giannini called San Francisco financial writers to No. 1 Powell.

"I intend to remain where I am, if the board of directors want me to," he told them. "The banking business is going to be more interesting than ever in the next twenty years. It's changing, everything is changing, and the troubles of the world would be much alleviated if everyone stuck to the thing he knows in such an era."[38]

In April, 1936, the banker was again a guest at the White House. A few evenings later, in Washington, he reviewed in a radio address the banking situation from 1933 on.

"Bank depositors of the United States today are in the safest position they have ever occupied in the history of the nation," Giannini began. He went on to speak of the salutary effects of R.F.C. investments in the preferred stock of banks; of the stabilizing influence of federal deposit insurance; the effective regulation of bank credit; and the separation of investment and commercial banking. All this had been accomplished because the President grasped the critical nature of the situation and exercised his leadership to remedy it. The latest report of the comptroller of the currency showed that deposits in national banks were at their highest point in the entire history of the national banking system. National banks which had operated at an annual loss since 1931 of two to three hundred million dollars operated at a substantial profit in 1935. The major features of the New Deal policies had put the nation's financial structure upon a sound basis. There was more protection to the public, less hazard to the stockholders and a brighter prospect of success and prosperity than had been evident in many years. "That," concluded Giannini, "is why I am proud to be a banker."[39]

The speech brought a note from F. D. R. "In the midst of so much misunderstanding and misinterpretation it was decidedly reassuring to hear your radio address."[40]

When the campaign opened Giannini expressed himself on several occasions. A representative statement:

I say to business: stop and consider before going on with this anti-Roosevelt campaign! . . . Take inventory and compare conditions as they were at the time Mr. Hoover left office with times as they are today. . . . I know business is complaining against higher taxes. I realize that the cost of government has caused apprehension, but I say there is no just cause for complaint. . . . The day of concentrated wealth in a few hands is passed. The people will no longer stand for a rule that makes the poor poorer and the rich richer. We must realize that the rank and file is entitled to more than it has received or there'll be an uprising. . . . I remember when we had 14,000,000 out of work. . . .

Give Mr. Roosevelt four more years and he'll cure the errors—errors have been made—and leave the office with a record that will stamp him as the greatest man of our times.[41]

After reading the newspaper interview, Mr. Roosevelt wrote the banker that he was "willing to accept the verdict [on election day] on the issues as you have so admirably stated them."[42]

On August 1 Jim Farley asked Giannini for a "true picture," the bad along with the good, of the political situation as A. P. saw it in California.

The banker replied that he had just completed a tour of his branches and that Roosevelt would carry the state "by at least 500,000 votes."[43]

He carried it by 930,000.

Recovery of the California Farmer

THROUGH his bank and some of its affiliates A. P. Giannini played a role in the comeback of the farmer that perhaps was more notable than that of any other Californian. This success would not have been possible, however, without the aid of the United States government. Nor would the country as a whole have been lifted from the depression without the help to the farmer accorded by the New Deal. After a lapse of nearly twenty years, defects in that program can be pointed out. But the program as a whole, swiftly conceived and swiftly executed in the heat of emergency, was a lifesaver. That it could be was something Giannini caught sight of at the beginning. Thereafter the Bank of America pitched in and used the program for all it was worth to California farmers. Giannini brushed off critics of the program who termed it "regimentation": "If such regimentation will better conditions of the farming population of our nation I am in favor of it."[1]

During his first month in office Mr. Roosevelt created the Farm Credit Administration, under Henry Morgenthau, Jr. It took over existing agricultural loan agencies and the new ones that were set up. Among the institutions of New Deal creation were twelve regional Production Credit Associations. Their function was to provide more short-term credit—for planting, harvesting and marketing crops, feeding livestock, repairing buildings, etc. There were also twelve regional banks for co-operatives. Their function was to make capital and commodity loans to farmers' co-ops. The Farm Credit Administration assumed operation of the Emergency Farm Mortgage Act of 1933, which halted foreclosures; also the Federal Farm Mortgage Corporation, and other New Deal farm agencies.

To adapt the Bank of America's farm-loan affairs to the New Deal program, Giannini brought back Pop Hendrick who had gone into retirement when the Walker people closed down the central real estate department. Pop, however, returned only in an advisory capacity, for his health was broken. His former associate, Carl Wente, took active charge of grappling with the bank's large investment in farm mortgages.

One of Wente's lieutenants, W. W. Hopper, late of the cow bank, was sent to Washington to see that California got its share of attention. Like a diplomat Giannini wrote Morgenthau that Hopper's mission was to be helpful in smoothing difficulties. Formulas suggested for the Middle West by its powerful farm lobby would not meet the needs of California, with more than two hundred crops to consider. Another job of Hopper's was to prepare for the liquidation of Hendrick's pride, the California Joint Stock Land Bank, as required by New Deal legislation.

California got its share. In four years government loans to Golden State farmers aggregated $219,000,000, or 7 per cent of the national total. Only Texas and Iowa received slightly more.

The largest single item concerned mortgages, of which at the end of 1934, the first full year of the Farm Credit Administration's operation, federal agencies, mainly the Land Bank at Berkeley, held $127,625,000 in liens on California farms. This was 25.67 per cent of the state's farm-mortgage debt of $497,148,000. The banks of California held $115,563,000, or 23.24 per cent. Of the banks' holdings, nearly half, or $55,146,000, were held by the Bank of America. California banks were doing more than banks did in other states. At the end of 1934, Kansas banks showed only $7,384,000 in farm mortgages. In Nebraska the figure was $4,248,000; in Illinois, $22,777,000; in Iowa, $26,240,000. Yet these states were as heavily mortgaged, relatively, as California.

By the end of 1939 the government's take-over of farm mortgages that other lenders were glad to relinquish had reached its zenith and was on the way down. Of California's farm-mortgage debt of $541,929,000, the F.C.A. held $135,228,000, against $105,416,000 for all banks. Of the bank-held' mortgages, $49,194,000 were with the Bank of America. In all B. of A. refinanced through federal loans 704 farm mortgages aggregating $4,372,000.

This part of the government's farm relief program was financed by the sale of Federal Farm Mortgage Corporation bonds. In the early days of the program, when the bonds were going slowly, the

Bank of America offered to take $5,000,000 worth at par to stiffen the market. "DEEPLY APPRECIATE YOUR OFFER," the Treasury Department wired. "YOU WILL FIND THE BONDS A GOOD INVESTMENT." The market for the bonds improved. The Bank of America made additional heavy purchases until, at the peak, its holdings amounted to $52,000,000.[2]

2

The operations of California Lands, Inc., should be examined in connection with the Bank of America's farm mortgage problems during the recovery period. It will be recalled (Chapter Nineteen) that this Transamerica subsidiary went in business early in 1929. Its function was to buy at cost foreclosed farms from the Bank of America, and later from the Central Bank, Oakland; the First National Bank of Reno; the Occidental Life Insurance Company; and the California Joint Stock Land Bank. More than half of the 4,015 farms thus acquired at an aggregate book value of $43,016,000 came from the Bank of America. About one-fifth of these foreclosures grew out of loans originally made by the Bank of America. The balance derived from purchased banks and from the other institutions named above.

The responsibility of California Lands was a heavy one, as Howard Whipple, its president, wrote early in 1930:

"In number of farms, diversity of production, variety and intricacy of farm operations, there is probably no farm-owning organization in the United States faced with problems even remotely approaching those which confront this organization."[3]

That was the situation when California Lands was handling 1,377 farms aggregating 216,000 acres. Mr. Whipple's successors, Bert Meek, who took charge later in 1930, and E. D. Woodruff, who replaced Meek in 1932, had much larger loads to carry. For three years, beginning in 1932, the farm foreclosures of the Bank of America ran just under the three hundred mark annually. The book value of this property was around $3,000,000 a year. In 1936 California Lands had 2,642 farms comprising 531,000 acres and growing some 60 crops.

The ultimate aim to get these properties to producing profitably under individual ownership could not be realized over night.

Though sales were pushed as vigorously as appeared desirable, for long periods the company was obliged to run the farms. It did this in two ways—by direct operation, and by lease to individuals.

A foreclosed farm is almost always a run-down farm, and often it has been a mismanaged farm. To rehabilitate properties and set things to rights entailed heavy expenditures. When money was scarce California Lands put from $100,000 to $200,000 a year in improvements, including the restoration of the soil. Frequently crops had to be changed. On its farming operations the company lost $550,000 in 1930, $557,000 in 1931, and $621,000 in 1932. The next year the corner was turned with an operating profit of $111,000. In 1937 it was $643,000. Some of the factors were better prices and improved marketing conditions; more leased farms and fewer farms directly operated by the company; a revision of tax assessments, saving $100,000; the abandonment for unpaid taxes of the heaviest and most hopeless of the losers. In 1933 properties that had cost $100,044 were given up.

It remained for A. P. Giannini to ferret out the hustlers responsible for sending up California Lands's profits in too much of a hurry. What they were doing was not the way he wanted the company to make money. The minutes of a board meeting record the curtailment of their activities.

Mr. Giannini clearly indicated that it was not the purpose of the California Lands Inc. to remain in the farming business except for the purpose of developing and caring for properties awaiting sale, and he expressed disapproval of a recommendation that first class properties bringing in a good income should be withheld from sale.[4]

The lease arrangement that worked out so well for California Lands was not sharecropping as the South knows it. With his investment in tractors, livestock and equipment, the California tenant would be among the first to resent the suggestion. He is a "renter." Fifty-two per cent of California Lands's tenants owned farm property and supplemented their acreage by renting. The turnover was not marked: 43 per cent stayed four or more years. Through the leasing program, California Lands pioneered a new method in California. Heretofore, renting had been done on cash terms or a crop-percentage basis. The thirties found the farmer often hard pinched to meet his rent. To relieve him, a sliding rental scale for many crops was developed, minimum rentals when the returns were low and rising rentals when justified by better prices. Both renter and landlord benefited. The farmer carried on during lean years when otherwise he would have failed; in good years the landlord was assured of a larger income.[5]

No better indication of the relationship between California Lands and its renters could be cited than the fact that the renters, at their own expense, yearly made improvements aggregating $25,000 on the rented properties. Many of them did this because they expected to buy the places. This was in line with Giannini's policy. Though profitable, he regarded tenancy as a steppingstone to individual ownership, through financing by the Bank of America or federal agencies.

In 1940 the land company's debt to the bank for farm properties was down to $5,000,000. Four years before it had been $15,000,000. In 1936 the company relieved the bank of six hundred foreclosed farms; in 1941 the number was eighty-eight. The returning prosperity of the farmer left California Lands with so little to do that it was merged with the Capital Company, originally formed to handle foreclosed urban real estate.[6]

The same favoring factors, plus the lending by government agencies, brought the bank's farm-mortgage portfolio to a low of $26,-774,000 in 1946. Thereafter, it increased gradually, reaching $42,-029,000 in 1952.

3

Thus the Bank of America, along with banks generally, had yielded considerable in the farm-mortgage field to the Federal Land Bank at Berkeley. Private banks, that had to return a profit on their operations, simply could not always compete with the subsidized federal institution which, after 1935, cut rates as low as 3½ per cent and made loans for forty years, against a maximum of twenty permitted to state banks and ten to national banks. This was not true, however, in other branches of the agricultural lending, where the incursion of government agencies stimulated banks to greater efforts.

Let us take the situation created by the advent of the Federal Bank for Cooperatives, also located at Berkeley. The mission of this regional bank was to make advances to farmers' co-operatives and it was in the hands of wide-awake men. The lending volume swelled from $4,764,000 in 1934 to $11,674,000 in 1938. More than forty crops were accepted as security.

The Berkeley bank made its bow with a public statement of what it intended to do for citrus growers. The object, it said, was to help the farmer "through low interest charges . . . [to] get out of debt, as contrasted to the policy of keeping him in debt." Vice-President Dwight Clarke, in charge of the Bank of America's operations in the south where citrus loans are heaviest, did not take kindly to this insinuation. He wrote A. P. Giannini: "I do not know of a single instance where a cooperative possessing anything like fair credit has been declined accommodation by this bank for a long time past."[7]

Giannini's answer was a drive for commodity loans. Certainly the bank was no stranger to such loans, having been a pioneer in backing co-ops. After a study of the situation, a commodity loan department was created early in 1936. In charge was Ivan R. Bean, who had entered the bank's service as a messenger. But at the close of the year, the commodity loan department had made only eighty-five loans for just under $6,000,000.

Bean said he needed a "free hand," if his department was to make a better showing. Fortunately he had the receptive ear of Mario Giannini. Nine months later Bean's loans climbed to $8,870,000 and he was "pleased to report several accounts [obtained] from the Berkeley Bank for Cooperatives." The government bank's rate was 2 per cent for commodity and 3 per cent for real estate loans, against B. of A. and other banks with rates of 5 and 6 per cent. The government bank, however, required that 5 per cent of each loan be invested in its stock. Another important consideration was the convenience of banking at home through a local branch.[8]

By this time branch managers, at first lukewarm on commodity loans, had become actively interested. That made matters easier for Bean. In addition to crops, industrial and building materials, from asphalt to zinc, were added to the list of things loaned on. In 1939 loans went to $20,814,000, and in 1940 to $42,444,000, when they represented nearly 6 per cent of all the new loans made by the bank in that year. The Bank for Cooperatives, and other competitors, were left far behind.

The re-education of customers was a feature of this growth. In reviewing his first three years, Bean found 170 accounts, with loans of $16,000,000, that never before borrowed on a commodity loan basis. Considerable of the new interest came from the bank's expansion in financing on field-warehouse receipts. Over many years, this type of credit had not been greatly favored. To most bankers warehouse loans had meant those secured by receipts issued by a general public warehouse or cold storage warehouse. For these loans borrowers bring their commodities to the warehouses. For a field-warehouse loan, the warehouse is brought to the borrower. The latter's appeal lies in what a canner, a vintner or any other rural borrower in need of a commodity loan saves by not having to move his products. In this way canner and winery groups put to use their own storage facilities, giving them, through insurance and bonding, all the protection afforded by the big warehouse in a city or town.[9]

Another government lending agency in the short-term field that banks came to regard as an active competitor were the Production Credit Associations which made seasonal loans to farmers, with crops and livestock generally the security. One result was to draw banks into a field which they had rather shied from theretofore. "We recognize the hazards incident to financing of this type," Mario Giannini wrote the branch managers in 1934, "but feel that competent management and careful selection will enable us to handle this business on a safe basis and at the same time provide bank credit for many farmers who are entitled to it."[10]

The P.C.A. rate was 5 to 5.6 per cent, against the bank's 7. There were, however, countervailing factors. As in the case of the Bank for Cooperatives, the P.C.A. required borrowers to take a portion of their loans in stock. The bank afforded greater privacy, and there was always the probability that the applicant was already a customer of the Bank of America and familiar with its people and its way.

At the end of 1938 the Bank of America held crop-production loans in the amount of $33,000,000, against $24,000,000 by the P.C.A.'s, and $47,000,000 by other California banks. During World War II these loans zoomed. In one year B. of A. loaned as much as $20,000,000 to the growers of cotton in California. The trend did not stop with the end of the fighting. At the start of 1952, B. of A.'s seasonal loans (including those for livestock) were $159,292,000 against $25,248,000 for the badly outstripped P.C.A.'s.

Giannini's cow bank became another active competitor of the

P.C.A.'s. This once flourishing institution (proper name, Bank-america [originally Bankitaly] Agricultural Credit Corporation) was in low estate in 1932. So was the livestock business. On the heels of starvation prices had come the drought. Ranges were bare alike of stock and of grass. Milk cows went for as little as three dollars. Pop Hendrick told A. P. that Walker's liquidation policy had about finished the cow bank's reputation with borrowers. Moreover, among the directors no one was left except Wente who could go among the cattle and sheep men and talk things over with a view to finding a way out for lender and debtor alike.[11]

Just at the time when the industry began to show the first faint signs of recovery the Production Credit Associations entered the field, making loans right and left that normally would have fallen to the cow bank. To restore the cow bank to favor, eleven field men, most of whom had grown up on the range, were sent over California, Oregon, Nevada and Arizona. In San Francisco three lending officers who talked the cowmen's vernacular were on duty in a ground-floor office across the street from the Palace Hotel, where cattlemen stay when in town. They had hard going. In 1933 cow-bank loans were only $2,000,000 at their high point. By 1936 they were $4,100,000. After that the rise was faster: $11,000,000 by 1942 when the independent existence of the cow bank was ended. It was taken over by the newly created livestock loan department of the Bank of America. This department did not last long. As loans ran even heavier, a better arrangement was to let each branch operate its own livestock loan department.

4

Another problem confronting the California farmer was that of getting rid of his harvests. During an era of surpluses this was not simple, even in states where one crop—such as cotton, wheat or corn —enjoyed a virtual monopoly. In California no crop or group of crops stood in this position. Certain crops were too specialized to warrant federal support; others, because of the high investment involved, were beyond the reach of the "plow-under" solution.

The situation called for a host of individual and special programs. As a young partner in L. Scatena & Company, A. P. Giannini had studied the individual problems of farmers, and had financed them.

As a banker he had gone deeper into those questions than any other banker had done. In twenty years' time he had had more than any other banker to do with the architecture of the intricate financial structure of agriculture in California. Mario Giannini had taken up these studies early in his banking career. From country banks that were absorbed had come some crackerjack men, real experts on one phase or another of California agriculture. In general charge of the special-programs work was Burke H. Critchfield.

The services rendered by these men stood California in good stead in the middle thirties. The Bank of America was everywhere. It had the confidence of growers and processors. It had the experience to draw on to meet some very knotty situations. What it was able to do played a considerable part in the bank's rapid growth. As the importance of special programs increased, in 1939 Mario engaged Jesse W. Tapp as the bank's agricultural economist, with the title of vice-president. Mr. Tapp came from the Department of Agriculture where he had occupied important posts, including that of president of the Surplus Commodities Corporation.

We will sketch the bank's part in some of these programs.

The prune grower had seen his last good year in 1929. The root of the trouble lay in the expansion during the twenties, when prune acreage increased from 104,000 to 171,000. Prune orchards still occupy the largest acreage among California's deciduous tree fruits. In 1932 the industry was laid low by depression prices and a substantial carryover. Under the leadership of Burke Critchfield and of experts from the Giannini Agricultural Foundation of the University of California, packers and vineyardists set up the California Prune Pool, designed not only to divert oncoming surpluses into by-products such as prune juice, but to enhance the fruit's reputation through a nationwide sales campaign.

The voluntary pool was continued through 1933, with some benefit to growers. In 1934 the California Prune Control Board took over, operating under a federal marketing agreement the principal object of which was to eliminate carryovers. Packers and growers wrangled over the means, with Critchfield serving as moderator in many of the bouts. The upshot was a government-supported pool to take care of surpluses. But the war solved the marketing problem as none of the experts was able to. After the war the export market returned with the Marshall Plan.

Now to peaches. Here there was no government program for the disposition of the surplus, and, in 1938, growers were faced with a crop that meant a carryover of 5,500,000 cases, the largest on record. The California Canning Peach Association recommended an old emergency solution, namely that a substantial portion of the ripened fruit be left to spoil in the orchards. The Bank of America was asked to endorse this program, and it did so. Nevertheless, nonmember growers refused to go along, and the plan was defeated. Harvesting began and the price dropped to about the cost of picking. Thereupon, the California Canning Peach Association proposed that it can, on its own, fifty thousand tons of clings grown by its members, gambling on a return above the price offered by regular canners.

To finance this bold undertaking the Bank of America advanced $3,228,925 with warehouse receipts as security. The R.F.C. guaranteed half the loan. As a result, Association members realized $7.55 a ton against an average of $6.00 during the 1938 season. "If the Association had been unable to borrow this money, the governing price for 1938 cling peaches, not only for our own members, but for every grower in the state, would have been the actual cost of harvesting," said W. J. Edinger, manager of the California Canning Peach Association.[12]

The 1938 loan was paid off in 1940. Thereafter, as in the case of prunes, war and postwar demands took care of the peach crop.

The raisin industry, to which the Bank of America devoted so much attention during the twenties, proved beyond the capacities of private lenders when the depression struck. Six million dollars loaned during the twenties was written off, the Bank of America, the Security–First National and the Anglo California absorbing $1,000,000 each, and the Federal Intermediate Credit Bank the remainder. Government agencies carried the ailing industry through the thirties until the war gave it a lease on life.

5

That still left wine grapes. Repeal had not taken care of their surplus and the industry was largely to blame. The vineyardist had been ill-prepared for repeal. During prohibition his grape had to be a tough-skinned variety which could stand the long trip East. Unfortunately it produced wines of mediocre quality. Wineries were poorly equipped and poorly manned. In the rush to make a dollar, they dumped new wines by millions of gallons onto an eager market. Giannini worked to improve the quality and the reputation of his state's wines. He selected the best brands to grace the White House table and shipped them to Mrs. Roosevelt, calling attention to his favorite, the Livermore sauternes.[13]

When the bumper harvest came in 1938 the bank had become the undisputed financier of the California wine makers. Vintage loans of $100,000 and over, approved by the executive committee in 1937, totaled $7,193,640. They went higher when the bank assumed a leading part in solving the problem of the 1938 crop.

Some of the Bank of America's best—W. E. Blauer, A. E. Sbarboro, Carl Wente, Burke Critchfield and Ivan Bean—tackled the problem. They came up with a remarkable solution, without recourse to feeding grapes to livestock or leaving them to rot in the fields, and without federal subsidy. The crush that year was 1,000,000 tons. With 85,000,000 gallons of wine in storage from past seasons, a 1,000,000-ton crush threatened to drive the price to the grower to a ruinous $3 to $5 a ton. Growers, vintners, bankers and shippers got together and evolved this scheme: 55 per cent of the crush, for which growers were to receive $15 a ton, was earmarked for wine; 15 per cent earmarked for high-proof spirits, growers to be paid a share of the profits, if any, from the sale of such spirits; 30 per cent, for which the growers were to receive $12.50, earmarked for brandy. High-proof spirits and brandy were thus the dump for the surplus. They could be warehoused longer than wine, and would improve with age while awaiting a favorable price.

The R.F.C. agreed to underwrite half of this program, which ultimately cost $7,400,000. Originally twenty banks offered to take the other half. Fifteen of the banks dropped out. The burden was borne by the Bank of America which contributed 80.4 per cent of the bankers' share, with four other banks contributing the remainder. Because of war demands the scheme worked out quicker and better than anyone had dared to hope.

"It mellowed into exceedingly smooth collateral," commented Jesse Jones, who granted the R.F.C. loan after Secretary Wallace, a teetotaler, declined to recommend it to the Commodity Credit Corporation. Mr. Jones found the outcome highly satisfactory. "The brandy stocks pledged to the R.F.C. were sold at a stimulating profit."

By the end of 1942 enough brandy had been sold to pay up all loans and leave 1,395,000 gallons debt-free for the vintner and grower. As a result growers received above $15 a ton for their 1938 crop, against an estimated $12 when the plan was born and a certain $3 to $5 had there been no plan.[14]

The brandy pool was a one-year remedy that could not be repeated very soon. Consequently in 1939, before the pool had a chance to work out, growers once more were pinched for cash. Another large crop was on the way, with a threat of prices that would be below the cost of production.

Some of the smaller vintners, unable to compete with their better financed contemporaries, had their backs to the wall. To keep from being gobbled up at distress prices by their bigger rivals the little fellows were shoving improperly aged "hot wine" on the market, thereby damaging the reputation of all California wines. In desperation a group of ten small vintners in the Fresno territory proposed to Critchfield and to Ralph Heaton an idea designed to save their hides and, incidentally, to benefit the entire industry in California. The idea was to establish a co-op called Central California Wineries, Inc., that would enable the little fellows to compete with the big boys. C.C.W. would provide money for the small vintners to pay growers a decent price, to meet processing costs, carrying charges and taxes without recourse to "hot wine." C.C.W. would hold title to and market the wine. It looked like a good scheme and the bank donated the services of Critchfield to help get it under way.[15]

Critchfield canvassed vintners and co-ops that were financed by other banks or by the Federal Bank for Cooperatives at Berkeley. Edmund A. Rossi, of the Italian Swiss Colony Wine Company, was enthusiastic. He said that if the scheme worked "the wine business was on the road to recovery." The manager of a government-financed co-op at Lodi asked: "Could we participate? Our growers are in bad need of money. Our advances from the Bank for Cooperatives have not been satisfactory." He and several others came in.[16]

Four million dollars were needed to launch the venture. Other banks were invited to participate, but only one of them did—the Farmers and Merchants Bank of Lodi. It took care of several small members, and the Bank of America did the rest. With wine grapes going for $6, C.C.W. began paying from $8 to $11 a ton. "The psychology of the entire wine market changed from one of extreme pessimism," noted the *Wine Review*. The price of grapes climbed to $15.[17]

In the spring of 1940 Central California Wineries proceeded to the next step, that of marketing. To this end a subsidiary called Central Winery, Inc., was created. Ralph Heaton retired as vice-president and manager of B. of A.'s Fresno main office to become its president.

Central Winery filled a real need. Over the years the small producer had been largely limited to the highly vulnerable bulk-wine market and, more often than not, he was at the mercy of the Eastern wholesalers. Lacking, too, were storage facilities to hold stocks for aging and blending. Heaton corrected these deficiencies. All this took capital, which the Bank of America advanced to the tune of $4,454,000.[18]

Central Winery was a success. Both growers and vintners profited, but nonmember producers began to complain about "price fixing." The Department of Justice in Washington was interested, and in 1942 it was preparing papers for an antitrust suit when the entry of Schenley Distilleries into California's wine industry ended that threat. The Roma Wine Company, a Schenley subsidiary, bought Central Winery and its inventory for $3,800,000. After paying all loans, Central Winery distributed a profit of $657,000. The parent organizations, Central California Wines, liquidated, its members receiving $895,000.

The bank's help to the wine industry during that critical period has not been forgotten. Today it is estimated that the Bank of America finances over 50 per cent of the wine storage capacity of California, which amounts to 302,000,000 gallons. Twenty of the principal bonded wineries, each with a storage capacity of above 500,000 gallons, are Bank of America customers.

6

There was more to do than to keep people on the land, growing and marketing crops. There was the problem of keeping water on the land, for without it crops were impossible. In California this is a bigger problem than it is in any other state. Five million acres, or 15 per cent of the productive surface of California, is under irrigation. This 15 per cent brings in 80 per cent of the state's farm revenue. The distribution of water over these five million acres is a great and costly undertaking which, like nearly everything else, ran into financial difficulties in the thirties.

With a few exceptions, California's ninety-seven irrigation districts are self-governing bodies which regulate their own affairs, as a county does. They elect officers, levy and collect taxes, vote and issue bonds, build and operate irrigation works and power plants. In 1930 the water districts numbered eighty-four, representing an investment of $233,000,000. All but two had bonded debts, in the aggregate of $94,500,000. The Bank of America, with $6,796,000, was the heaviest single holder of these bonds. More than that, its farm mortgages in the irrigated areas topped $26,000,000.

Water districts began to default on bonds early in the depression. Their distress sprang from two main causes. First was the collapse of farm prices which made it impossible for the growers to keep up their water taxes. Delinquencies ran as high as 50 per cent. Another source of revenue was the proceeds from the sale of water to power companies. A series of dry years cut this income to almost nothing in some districts. At one time thirty-eight districts could not meet the interest on their bonds. Some could not even pay operating expenses.

This was one of the many pressing problems to which A. P. Giannini gave his attention on his return to the bank in 1932. To handle the job he hired State Railroad Commissioner Fred G. Stevenot, who had organized California's department of natural resources. Stevenot was given the title of vice-president and placed in charge of the bank's corporate and public refinance division. "What is good for California is good for the bank," Giannini reminded him. Stevenot's principal assistants were Russell A. Kent, head of the bank's bond investment department, and W. D. Courtright, of the corporate and refinance department.[19]

In the solution of the irrigation district's difficulties the Bank of America played the biggest part of any outside agency. It contributed the largest amount of emergency funds, with the exception of the Reconstruction Finance Corporation. Its chief contribution was not in money, however, but in counsel and in leadership in devising and putting through plans for refinancing. Generally speaking, the bondholders consented to write down their investments, in instances almost to fifty cents on the dollar. Interest was also cut and sometimes unpaid back interest was forgiven—not without protests and, on occasions, court actions by minorities of the bondholders. In some cases water-tax rates were reduced and in some cases they were raised. The bank also interceded with the R.F.C., sometimes getting what it asked for and sometimes getting nothing.

So it was a long and hard work that Stevenot, Kent and Courtright had to do, and to do over and over, the formula varying with the needs of different districts. In the end they won out. As the depression decade drew to a close better prices, rains and a reduced debt load enabled the irrigation districts to begin to pull out. Agricultural prosperity during the war and after finished the job.

Though no one has ever figured it out exactly, Russell Kent believes the bank broke even on its irrigation bond investments. Losses through write-downs were balanced by gains on bonds bought at low prices which came back with the general recovery.[20]

7

It is possible in this book to sketch only one individual case, that of the Imperial Irrigation District, on the Mexican border. The dollar amounts involved were the largest of any district, and the resistance of minorities was tenacious. The problems were in general the problems of districts elsewhere, and the ultimate solution followed in a broad way the line of most other solutions, with the exception that there was no help from the R.F.C.

Leroy Holt, the bank's resident vice-president in Imperial Valley, had gone there in 1900, when, as he used to say, water was too scarce to wet the cloth on the outside of a canteen. The land was a desert so barren that little of it was entered on the tax rolls. In 1928 a half-million acres of this former desert was worth $140,000,000. They yielded a cash crop return of $40,667,000.

The water that worked this transformation came from the Colorado River, by way of a canal connecting with that stream on the Mexican side of the border. Gravity spread it over the floor of the valley, most of which is below sea level, having once been part of the Gulf of California. Walled off by mountains from the cooling Pacific breezes, the valley has long and dry summers when the mercury soars to 120. The place is one great hothouse, with an ideal "forcing" climate for melons and vegetables. The results are little short of miraculous.

The canal bringing water from Mexico was owned by the California Development Company. The valley boomed until 1905 when floods raged down the uncontrolled Colorado and plunged into the canal which became a torrent a mile wide. Most of the valley was inundated, parts of it to a depth of sixty feet. The drowned-out Development Company dumped its affairs into the lap of the Southern Pacific Railroad whose main line was imperiled by the waters. The railroad eventually turned back the river, but the valley was a sorry sight. In 1911 the Imperial Irrigation District was formed to attempt to restore prosperity.

To protect the main canal, seventy miles of levees were erected, sixty of them in Mexico. Secondary canals were extended until their combined length was 2,441 miles. From them extended a network of ditches. Diversion gates, checks, drops, siphons, flumes, waste ways and other structures numbered 15,000. A small army of men patrolled the system and kept it going. The cost of this all was enormous. In 1923 the district owed $16,000,000 on outstanding bonds that bore between 5 and 6 per cent interest. The budget was $3,000,-000 a year, yet the returns from the soil were so great that the district more than paid its way. Farmers had no quarrel with water rates that amounted to about $5 per $100 of assessed valuation. By 1930 the bonded debt had been reduced to $14,800,000.

Over this pleasant and thriving prospect hung a menace—the possibility of another Colorado flood. This seemed on the way to removal, however, when in 1932 Herbert Hoover got under way the Boulder Dam project to harness the mighty Colorado. The Imperial Valley rejoiced, and took further steps to safeguard its future. The canal that lay mostly in Mexico had been a constant source of controversy with the Mexican government and with property owners south of the border. The valley decided to substitute for that waterway an All-American Canal wholly on United States territory. The cost would be many millions, which the district itself engaged to repay to the government: this on top of its other debts.

The commitment for the All-American Canal was indeed a brave one, for in 1932 the valley was enduring the hardships common to farmers everywhere. The irrigation district no longer paid its way. A default on interest had been avoided in 1931 by issuing warrants. In June, 1932, the first default came when the district was powerless to meet an interest payment of $215,000. The Bank of America held warrants in the amount of $407,000 and bonds with a face value of $710,000. Purchased at 70, the bonds had slumped to 27 after the default. Mortgages brought the bank's investment in the valley to $4,-000,000, an investment that steadily increased, as valley conditions got worse before they got better. Giannini's faith in the valley was not shared by the Federal Land Bank of Berkeley, which had pulled out of there in 1918. It did not return until 1941 when the crisis was over.

The hard times were reflected at the Bank of America's three branches in the valley—in El Centro, Calexico and Brawley. In his examination of March, 1932, the national bank examiner classified $646,106 of the El Centro branch's loans as slow, $54,041 as doubtful, and $23,656 as losses. Though, as we know, Giannini did not think much of the examiners' appraisals of loans in those days, he asked Leroy Holt for an explanation. The veteran's reply showed that he realized the Valley was in for a long pull:

I want you to know I assume the full responsibility for the condition that exists at El Centro. I approved the loans made here, both real and chattel, based upon a reasonable percentage of the appraisal value at the time the loans were made. . . .

The success of every business in the Valley depends on the farmer. We have absolutely no income except from the soil. We must have better prices and a reduction in overhead to pay out.

It has been more than thirty years since I started the first bank in the Valley. I was manager and principal owner of three or four [banks] for many years. They all made money, and . . . I brought them through every depression in splendid condition, when every bank in the Valley had to be reorganized or liquidated except one. I hope I still know how to manage a bank well and, unless the conditions in this Valley are such that farming in general cannot be conducted profitably, with the advice of you and your associates we shall succeed.[21]

Advisers were at Holt's elbow. Representatives of the farmers, the bondholders, the State of California and the Bank of America met with officers of the Imperial Irrigation District. They reached an agreement which amounted to a four-year moratorium.

A formula for permanent relief was delayed by a series of dogfights among the interested parties. The Reconstruction Finance Corporation offered a refinancing loan at seventy-five cents on the dollar, plus $2,000,000 in addition for drainage—this on condition that 90 per cent of the bondholders agree. They did not agree. Stevenot, of the bank, got R.F.C. to promise to offer eighty cents if the district should request it. Both sides—debtors and creditors—were split into factions. No request was forthcoming and R.F.C. withdrew.

The patient labor of Fred Stevenot eventually dissolved the impasse. He assembled engineers and accountants to make an unbiased survey. They reported that both sides would have to make sacrifices. Bondholders would have to take less than the face value of their securities. Funds for drainage were called an imperative need to prevent much land from becoming unusable. Sobered by the experts' report, the district again approached the R.F.C., but Jesse Jones refused to better his last offer of seventy-five cents.[22]

Stevenot began to shape a scheme independently of the government. He enjoyed the advantage of better times and cooler tempers in the valley. "It is time the bondholder realized," wrote an El Centro editor, "that the district is not a deadbeat . . . and it is also time the district realized that the bondholders are not Shylocks." Another paper styled Stevenot "the Doctor in the District's troubles." The doctor evolved a refunding plan that called for a 25 per cent reduction in interest on bonds and warrants; a waiver of $400,000 interest to be spent for drainage; and $800,000 ceiling on debt service for any one year; the district to pay overdue interest.[23]

The district board endorsed the plan and submitted it to the voters early in 1939. Mario Giannini cautioned the bank's local personnel against overzealousness in the ensuing canvass. The voters approved the plan by nearly four to one. Though a handful of last-ditch objectors held up the actual refunding for several years, Stevenot's plan, Boulder Dam and the All-American Canal combined to usher a new era into the Imperial Valley. All the same, in 1939 record-breaking rains did a quarter of a million dollars' damage to crops. Except for the dam there might have been a repetition of the 1905 flood. Six months later an earthquake broke the levees of the Mexican canal in nine places, but the All-American, though not completed, furnished enough water to keep the fields green. Conditions and prospects alike were so flourishing that credit rushed forth to make up these losses. A. P. Giannini ordered branch managers in the Valley to use the radio to assure customers that the Bank of America stood "ready and willing to assist financially with repairs and rehabilitation." The managers took advertising space inviting people to "please call at your nearest branch."[24]

The district balanced its budget in 1940. Among the other benefits the All-American Canal conferred upon the Valley was the provision of water sufficient to bring under cultivation thousands of additional acres which duly went on the water-tax rolls. Incidentally, this tax had been reduced from $5.00 to $3.50 per hundred of assessed valuation. In 1952 the Valley marketed crops worth $125,000,000 or nearly thirteen times the return in 1938.

8

A postscript to the bank's history during the troubled decade of the thirties concerns two books that appeared in the spring of 1939. They were John Steinbeck's novel *The Grapes of Wrath* and Carey McWilliams' *Factories in the Field,* a report on the contemporary scene. Both addressed themselves to recognized evils in the state's agricultural scheme. McWilliams dealt with the problems of farm labor, especially migratory labor, at a time when there was not enough work to go around, when wages were low, and when workers were waging an uphill fight to better their lot by unionization. He dealt also with the landowners' struggle against debt, overproduction and low prices. *The Grapes of Wrath* touched most of these same topics as it took the Joad family from the dust and depression of Oklahoma over the long and crowded road to the Promised Land, and told of the migrants' disenchantment there.

They were crusading books, and you don't crusade by finding excuses for the *status quo.* Though they had their critics, the books nevertheless awakened people to real evils, and helped to set in motion corrective measures.

Both writers, McWilliams especially, were careless of some of the facts, as this passage from *Factories in the Field* shows: "When one realizes that approximately 50 per cent of the farm lands in Central and Northern California are controlled by one institution—the Bank of America—the irony of these 'embittered' farmers defending their 'homes' against shysters becomes apparent."[25]

The story of the bank's dealings with mortgages and other ills that beset the farmer has been told in these pages. When the McWilliams book appeared the bank had mortgages on 3.6 per cent of the arable land in central and northern California. Government lending agencies held mortgages on several times that amount. None of the lenders "controlled" the land. At the peak of its farm involvements, the bank's mortgages did not cover 10 per cent of the area McWilliams speaks of. At their peak foreclosed farms of the bank's then affiliate, California Lands, amounted to 1.7 per cent of the state's tillable soil.[26]

When the bank called the facts to McWilliams' attention he promised to make a change. The change was to substitute "a large percentage" for "approximately 50 per cent." To the date of this writing the bank still is occasionally in receipt of accusations and inquiries, published and otherwise, based on McWilliams' statements.

In Washington, Mario Giannini heard that Secretary of the Treasury Morgenthau had said "that the Bank of America had furnished thousands of dollars to finance the Associated Farmers, and referred to . . . *Factories in the Field* as evidence of the bank's attitude toward farm labor." The opposition of Associated Farmers, an organization of landowners, to the unionization of field workers, had led to much bitterness, and to occasional bloody encounters. Mario Giannini wrote to James Roosevelt, son of the President, that the bank had never contributed "so much as one dollar to Associated Farmers," despite urgent solicitation. Investigation by Russell Smith disclosed that, unknown to Mario, the bank had contributed $400 over a period of four years. Two hundred and fifty dollars was the subscription assigned to the Bank of America by the San Francisco Clearing House. One branch manager had made an unauthorized contribution of $50. Another had contributed $100 to a local organization that had turned the money over to Associated Farmers. The bank promptly admitted the contributions.[27]

For his part, John Steinbeck did not mention the Bank of America by name, but he gave an unpleasant picture of unnamed banks and land companies putting small farmers out of business. "The little farmers watched debt creep up on them like the tide. . . . This little orchard will be a part of a great holding next year, for the debt will have choked the owner. This vineyard will belong to the bank. Only the great owners can survive."[28]

Banks are usually under criticism from some quarter, and sentiment always is with a foreclosed farmer. Howard Whipple got the job of trying to discover whether the bank had suffered injury from the strictures in *The Grapes of Wrath*. He reported that, although the book probably had strengthened the notion "of land-grabbing on our part . . . it has not hurt us [as] shown by the extraordinary maintenance of our deposit levels."[29]

Mario Giannini and New Trends
in Banking

O N JANUARY 14, 1936, Lawrence Mario Giannini succeeded his father as president of the Bank of America National Trust and Savings Association. The elder Giannini retained the chairmanship of the board. Since 1932 Mario had been senior vice-president, first under Will F. Morrish, and, after Mr. Morrish's resignation in 1934, under his father. When A. P. Giannini was absent from San Francisco, and this was about five months out of the year, Mario had been in operating charge of the bank. So the new president was hardly new to his duties.

Mario was forty-one, and, as we have seen, he had worked for the bank since he was a schoolboy on summer vacations. In the personnel file the record of his progress from one job to another fills three pages. No one else in the bank, not even the founder, knew so much of the detail of the operation of that vast institution. One of the secrets of A. P. Giannini's success had been his ability to develop subordinates and give them heavy responsibilities. Details never concerned him too much. For that reason he seemed to have time to talk to whoever came to his desk. Of recent years, however, the elder Giannini had come to depend on his son as he had never depended on anyone else.

On the day of his election Mario received representatives of the press. "I don't like to make public speeches and all that kind of thing," he said. "This position really wasn't of my own choosing. I'd rather be in the background than out in front." Later in the interview he observed: "Bankers are supposed to be very conservative men. I might be just a little liberal—for a banker, I mean." He proved this by crediting "the money policy of the Administration" with having "something to do" with the fact that "business has definitely improved."[1]

2

Like his father before him Mario Giannini pioneered new trends in banking. These were destined to play a great part in raising the Bank of America from fourth place among the country's banks, the rank it held in 1936, to first place.

The number one problem confronting bankers in 1936 was to find more borrowers. Money was coming in the tellers' windows faster than it could be loaned out. In 1931 bank deposits in the United States aggregated $49,509,000,000 and loans $31,395,000,000. By the end of 1935 deposits had risen to $55,239,000,000 while loans had dropped to $20,302,000,000. As a result banks were loaded with government bonds, which assured a high state of liquidity but produced a low rate of income. For the Bank of America the problem was further complicated by the change in the character of its deposits. Since its founding the bank had been essentially a savings bank. Savings deposits are long-term deposits, eligible for long-term lending such as real estate mortgages. During the thirties the proportion of demand deposits gained rapidly, passing time deposits in 1941. After thirty-seven years this called for a departure in the development of the bank's lending program, a broadening into new fields.

Under Mario Giannini the Bank of America met these challenges in brilliant style, and in the established tradition of the bank as the friend of the little man. New borrowers were found by the hundreds of thousands. They fell into two classes, corporate borrowers and individual borrowers. In many cases the borrowing corporation was so small as to be simply another name for the individual who owned and operated it. This was little business, as contrasted with big business. Little business represented the backbone in the industrialization of California during this period. The population of the state had increased so fast, and its demands for manufactured articles was so great, that the time had come for California to make many of the articles that hitherto it had brought in from the outside.

This state of affairs, of course, had always been the aim of the Gianninis: more people to provide a home market for their state's abundances. The Bank of America became the principal backer of the small industrial concerns that began to sprout so notably as the depression receded. On the whole they have thrived, and some of them have grown into large concerns.

The individual borrowers were of the class who had not patronized banks before because banks regarded them as poor risks, or because the amounts involved seemed so trivial that overhead would eat up the lenders' profit. For the most part they comprised the great army of Americans who go into debt to buy household furnishings, automobiles, jewelry, clothing and so on, and pay their way out in installments. The interest charged ran as high as 30 per cent per annum. The Bank of America found that these people were good risks, and that the overhead on such loans could be kept to a point where the bank could handle the business profitably at rates running from 10 to a shade over 14 per cent, the average being about 13.

Accordingly, as the bank's deposits increased—from $1,299,000,000 in 1936 to $2,586,000,000 in 1942—loans increased in proportion. Though still the nation's fourth bank in amount of deposits, in 1939 the Bank of America became the first bank in the country in the amount of money loaned. That year the ratio of loans to deposits was 32.5 per cent for all banks in the United States, as against 48 per cent for B. of A.[2]

The nationwide business slump of 1937 was hardly noticeable in the figures of the Bank of America. Of the country's ten largest banks it was the only one to register a gain in deposits that year. It was one of the four banks to register a gain in the amount of money loaned. The Bank of America's loan gain of $98,376,000 was by far the country's greatest. The Manufacturers Trust of New York was second with $33,673,000; First National of Chicago, third; National City of New York, fourth.

Gains in loans were what the banks and the nation needed. "Banks must develop new lines which, while different, are just as sound as the old," A. P. Giannini was still saying in 1938. "It does not take much of a credit man to say 'No' to a borrower, but it takes time, labor and understanding to find a basis on which a loan can be made."[3]

The bank's history made Mario's task less difficult than otherwise it would have been. In 1929 a personal loan department had been established for borrowers needing from $100 to $1,000. Where no collateral was posted two cosigners of the note were required. Repayment was in installments. The rate was 13 per cent. The new department attracted borrowers who had formerly been obliged to patronize finance companies, whose rates were higher. The main uses to which the borrowers put the money were to furnish or improve homes, pay taxes and medical bills, and to finance educations and pleasure trips. Though the record of the department was excellent, with losses approximating eleven cents out of every $100 loaned, the service was not pushed until Mario became president. In 1936, his first year, the department loaned $12,260,000, which was more than the combined amount of small personal loans during the previous six years.[4]

Another forerunner of the small-loan development was ushered in by the Federal Housing Act of 1934. These loans were in part guaranteed by the government. Title I of the act enabled a successful applicant to borrow up to $2,500 to enlarge or modernize a home. The money was repaid so much a month. An electric refrigerator, for instance, could be purchased under the act. Title II offered loans up to $16,000 to build homes or to refinance existing mortgages.

No bank took quicker advantage of what F.H.A. offered than the Bank of America. At the end of the year it led all the banks in the country in the number of loans made—37,600—and in the amount of money advanced—$13,300,000—under Title I. In the intervening years, Title I has been broadened to include modernization of commercial properties, such as apartment houses and hotels. B. of A. wrote its millionth Title I loan in March, 1952, lifting the aggregate of this type of financing to $408,020,790. The borrower was James D. Boyer, a postal employee of Salinas, who got $400 to paint his house and build a fence.[5]

The record is similar with respect to the larger loans under Title II of the act. Growing California led all states in the number and amount of these home loans, and the Bank of America led all banks. By the end of 1940 it had participated in 53,000 such loans for $200,000,000. These represented 44 per cent of the Title II loans made in the state. Only 48 of the loans were in default. After the war, financing new homes under Title II has reached almost fantastic proportions. More will be said about the matter in Chapter Thirty-one.[6]

During most of the time, the bank's small-loan campaign was under the vigorous direction of E. A. ("Matty") Mattison. Mattison had learned that branch of the lending business with various finance companies of the type with which the bank was now in competition. Immediately before joining the bank he had been vice-president of the Pacific Finance Company of Los Angeles, well known in the automobile installment credit field. Lately Pacific Finance had organized a subsidiary, one of whose functions was to make household-appliance loans under Title I. The experiment was short-lived. The parent company decided to limit its operations to the profitable automobile field and the subsidiary retired from financing under F.H.A.

That left a number of household-appliance dealers, whose paper the subsidiary had been discounting, out on a limb to the tune of $500,000. Matty took the dealers' problem to Mario Giannini, who agreed to help these small businessmen. Mattison went to work for the bank, as the head of the newly-created installment credit department. In 1936 he coined the name "Timeplan," which the bank has copyrighted, to identify its installment-loan services. By advertising and by performance the Bank of America has made the word "Timeplan" almost as well known in California as Coca-Cola.[7]

We will glance at some of the Timeplan services.

3

Money lenders had a bonanza in the purchasers of automobiles. In 1934, 57 per cent of the nation's car buyers bought on time, and, when all the extras were figured in, they paid from 15 to 30 per cent per annum for the money they borrowed. Frequently there was a "cutback" to dealers, making it more profitable to them to sell a car on time than to sell one for cash.

In 1931, the Bank of America had had a brief and unprofitable fling at automobile-purchase financing. "We handled it like bankers," said Mario, "whereas it requires people trained in finance company methods." Mattison had that training and so in 1935 B. of A. made another try, starting with this arrangement. A prospective purchaser obtained a letter of credit from the bank covering what he needed toward the cost of the car. The dealer accepted the letter in lieu of cash and the car became the borrower's security while he repaid the bank in monthly installments. On a new car the rate was 9 per cent per annum for the first $400, and 7 per cent above that sum. On used cars the interest was 11 per cent on the first $400 and 9 for more.

The entry of the Bank of America into the automobile field alarmed the finance companies. Their representatives appeared along automobile row in San Francisco and in Los Angeles saying that the letter of credit plan would spell ruin for the dealers. The bank lost several million dollars in deposits when dealers closed their accounts. The press, however, received the innovation in different fashion. The Los Angeles *Daily News,* for example, hailed it as ending an era in which automobile buyers had been "gluttons for punishment."[8]

They had been, indeed, but car buyers displayed great eagerness to change their ways. In four months the Bank of America rose to third place among auto lenders in California. General Motors Acceptance Corporation was first. Soon installment rates began to drop to meet the Giannini bank's competition, not only in California but in other states. At the end of 1936, B. of A.'s auto loans were running a close second in California to those of G.M.A.C. For the year they amounted to $19,248,000 or 9 per cent of the state's automobile financing. It was only a matter of time before the Giannini bank took the lead on the Coast.

To the end of 1952 the Bank of America had made 3,329,313 automobile loans for a total of more than two and a quarter billion dollars. Over the years the average gross loss has been seventeen cents per $100 loaned. "Recoveries," in this case sale of the unpaid-for car, always lower average gross loss a few pennies by the time the loan is stamped "liquidated."

The letter of credit has long since been abandoned. Timeplan now affords the borrower three choices in financing purchase of his car: a personal loan; installment payments until the car's cost is liquidated; or financing by a dealer who has a line of credit with the bank.[9]

For the success of auto loans much credit is given the advertising campaign put on by L. E. Townsend, the bank's advertising director until 1952 when he retired. Townsend used newspapers, the radio and billboards to convey the bank's message: "Today 266 Cars Will Be Financed by Bank of America"; "Every Five Minutes Another Bank of America Financed Car."

In 1939, the bank's advent into the automobile field was still news.

After four years institutions outside California had not widely copied the idea. The conservative *American Banker* was moved to prod their attention to what it termed "this retailing of credit," thereby coining a phrase that has taken a permanent place in advertising lingo.

The Bank of America uses its advertising as a straight merchandising medium. It sells "loans" just as American Tobacco Co. sells Lucky Strikes. It never deviates and it never lets up. As a result, it is doubtful that there is a single literate person in California who has not heard of the willingness of the Bank of America to lend money.[10]

When Mattison introduced Timeplan, the minimum for small personal loans was reduced to $50. Loans under $300 to steadily employed individuals earning $1,500 or more a year could be made without cosigners. This constituted about 40 per cent of the business.

In 1941 Timeplan's personal loans amounted to $50,166,000. The money went to 280,000 individuals. Fifty thousand of them borrowed less than $100. That year the bank's annual report, with a note of pride, called attention to how much these borrowers had saved on the cost of their Timeplan loans, as compared with what they might have paid small loan companies charging the limit permitted by state law. For example,

On a $100 loan, repayable monthly over one year's time, the small loan company legal rate is $2\frac{1}{2}\%$ a month, 30% simple interest per annum. This compares with the Timeplan monthly interest rate of slightly less than 1%, or annual simple interest rate of 11.1%. Deducting the cost of life insurance in connection with Timeplan financing, the bank's effective simple annual interest rate is 9.23%.

By the end of 1952, the bank had made personal loans totaling $1,079,000,000. A considerable portion of this large sum has gone to borrowers with no better security to offer than reputation and prospects. The gross loss average on personal loans is sixty cents per $100, with recoveries naturally below those of other Timeplan categories.

When Mattison had been six months with the bank, at the end of 1935, the Timeplan type of loans amounted to $22,152,000. As the fiftieth anniversary of the bank approaches, the nineteen-year aggregate of I.C.L.'s, as installment credit loans are known inside the bank, hovers around the $12,000,000,000 mark. The gross loss average through the years is sixteen cents per $100 loaned, before recoveries.

Liquidation of Timeplan and other installment loans topped $2,000,000,000 during 1952. This continuous turnover of its funds in the course of a year provides the Bank of America with an unusual degree of liquidity. It is the explanation of why the Giannini institution can stand a higher ratio of loans to its capital funds than the majority of banks.[11]

A recent survey showed that Timeplan's lending fulfills upward of a hundred different purposes for borrowers. The purposes are sometimes out of the ordinary. One young man got $300 to buy a twenty-two-foot python when a motion picture company gave him a contract for the reptile's services. The bank demanded security for this particular loan. Until it was repaid—and it was—the python carried life insurance.

Somewhere in the vast collection of head office files, which contain the millions of individual loan histories, is a card for the borrower who volunteered an account of his experience with Timeplan long before the writers of this book knew of its existence. He's now maître d'hotel at one of San Francisco's big hotels. When his first child was born, he withdrew most of his savings to pay the hospital bill. As he was leaving the bank, he ran into A. P. Giannini, whom he knew. The banker told the young father to put his money back into his account and get a loan for the amount he needed. "You'll repay the loan quicker than you'll replace your savings," said A. P. This may not have been the bank's first loan to finance the birth of a Californian, but there's probably not a Giannini branch today whose books do not show loans to underwrite the new baby's arrival.

Timeplan had an effect on all kinds of new loan developments in the branches. For example, there was the start of small-boat loans to purse seine fishermen, who ranged the Pacific Coast for sardines. Purse seiners are not big business, but there are a lot of them. Often their families are the majority of the population in the half-dozen or so small coastal towns where they live, where their grandparents lived and from where their sons, in time, will take out the small boats that are their legacy. The purse seiner has never been much of a one for banking relations. Still, there have been times when a bank would have been helpful in tiding him over a bad season; or in getting him off to a good start in a good season.

In the Los Angeles–San Pedro area, purse seiners depended on advances from canners who customarily bought their catches. A few boat builders and engine companies also made loans. Until the late thirties, however, the banks kept their distance. The main reason was that mortgages on small craft had little value, the claims of all other liens and bills receiving priority. Another reason, as the manager of the San Pedro branch of the Bank of America advised the head office, purse seiners, taken as a whole, were unpredictable risks. "Some skippers can always bring in some sort of catch, while others have no luck at all."[12]

Luck or not, George W. Eckhardt, manager of the Monterey branch, felt he had watched too many years go by while the numbers of Monterey purse seiners diminished. This was a serious loss for a town whose second industry, the tourist trade, is somewhat dependent on the survival of the picturesque fisherman. Eckhardt's chances of aiding the small-boat owners brightened when Congress amended the Ship Mortgage Act to give small craft, such as fishing boats, the status of "preferred ship's mortgages." The change in law was the fruit of years of effort on the part of Peter J. Ferrante, a Monterey lawyer whose father was a fisherman. With this much security established, Eckhardt and Ferrante persuaded the head office to let the branch make a start on small-boat loans. That was in 1937. Because the Monterey branch made such a personal thing of them, even after Eckhardt had retired, the volume of its purse seine loans outdistanced that of the two larger fishing centers of Los Angeles and San Diego. The bank's rate was 6 per cent. They proved to be good loans. Down to 1949 the branch had not foreclosed on a fishing boat. That year saw the last of these loans. Sad to tell, after all that had been done to pioneer them, the sardine wrecked the whole scheme by disappearing from the Pacific Coast. Why, no one knows. Meantime, Monterey's harbor is filled with the little boats, bobbing at anchor and waiting. "Their future is very uncertain," said N. P. Hasselo, manager of the branch.

Though a number of Monterey canneries have shut down, the branch has not had much success with launching purse seiners in other lines of industry. A few have broken with tradition to fish for anchovies and mackerel, but barely meet expenses. At San Pedro, however, the fishermen have shifted to mackerel. The 1950 mackerel pack at Los Angeles' port was 850,611 cases; in 1952, small boats provided catches that filled 1,355,726 cases. Thus, purse seine loans at the San Pedro branch have begun to climb back to their heydey when canners thereabouts turned out nearly half a million cases of sardines annually.[13]

4

A credit innovation that had far-reaching effects on the industrial development of California was launched in 1937 by the Bank of America under the unexciting bookkeeping label of "financing accounts receivable." The purpose was to give small manufacturers, wholesalers and jobbers, who did not qualify for open lines of credit, the working capital to meet demands of seasonal peaks, expanding sales and other needs.

The mechanics of financing accounts receivable vary little from those of commodity loans in the agricultural field. The borrower posts his customers' accounts as collateral for a loan, and pays off his indebtedness as he makes collections. A variation of the accounts receivable technique is called "factoring." In this case the manufacturer, or the wholesaler, financially unable to guarantee his customers' accounts, sells them outright to the lender, who does his own collecting. Finance companies were already in the field, but banks were not except in rare instances. Even today, California banks generally avoid it. The painstaking investigation and supervision, involving both the borrower and his customers, make financing of accounts receivable and factoring more expensive operations than run-of-the-mill credit.

As used by the Bank of America, these forms of lending cover a variety of industries: jewelry, glassware, oil-well supplies, furniture, paper, janitors' supplies, lumber and many more. But textiles is the landmark in this phase of the bank's history. The growth of the textiles trade has been one of the marvels of Los Angeles. At the turn of the century the sole output was men's shirts for the local market. In the twenties, when Hollywood became a dateline and a trademark, a small amount of merchandise began to find its way into the national market. The boom started at the end of the depression when Los Angeles introduced the women's backless bathing suit, slacks, the dirndl skirt, "pedal pushers," "topper" and other styles suggestive of sunshine and outdoor life. In fifteen years, southern California's textile manufactures have mushroomed from a $50,000,000 business to more than $700,000,000 annually. Today Los Angeles is the second garment center of the United States.

The Bank of America is the garment district's principal banker. The development of this new line of business coincided with the sending of Alfred J. Gock to Los Angeles in 1939 to assume general charge of the bank's activities south of the Tehachapi. Al Gock had entered the banking business at the age of fourteen, with a small San Francisco institution. One of his duties was to sweep the floor. In 1912 he joined the Bank of Italy's Market Street branch as a clerk. A few weeks later A. P. Giannini, in Naples, Italy, noted, from the reports sent to him, a sudden gain in the number of accounts at the Market Street branch, and was informed that 138 of them were due to the industry of a new man named Gock. Giannini penned a note of congratulations to "Mr. Gock, % Market St. Brc, B of I," expressing the hope that "your future efforts will continue to be as successful as they have, so far, been." "Mr. Gock" did not disappoint his employer.[14]

In Los Angeles, Gock and Mattison piloted the textiles business through its hand-to-mouth stage. Both men give credit for the Bank of America's success as a backer of the textiles industry to Nat C. Green, who came to the Santee (now the Textile) branch as assistant manager in 1937. At this writing Mr. Green is still there. As a vice-president and the branch's manager, he is a key financial figure of Los Angeles' garment center.

It is little wonder that bankers shied away from backing beginners in the garment business. A small operator often started with a capital of $500, and an idea for a garment. He got his fabrics, rented a loft or an abandoned barn—anything that was cheap—hired his help and made his product. If it sold he cleaned up. If it didn't, he, or his creditors, lost about everything they had put into it. To this day little fellows start in business that same way. And big, successful outfits sometimes misguess the public's whims and take a smacking loss. The well-heeled amateur, splurging in a big way, can lose $100,000 in a season "and never know how he did it"—in the words of Mr. Green. Essential to success is a kind of a sixth sense about fabrics, styling and designing, and an instinct for catching the vagaries of the public (mostly the feminine half of it). The textile lender, too, must know something of these things.

In the early days two small Los Angeles banks were exceptions to the general rule among banks against factoring and accounts receivable. One of them, the Union Bank and Trust Company, was the first to back Los Angeles' manufacture of infant garments, and it still plays an important role in that field. The other bank was the Seaboard National, which Giannini bought in 1936. That transaction marked the entry of the Bank of America into the garment business. From Seaboard it acquired the Santee branch, on the edge of the garment district which was then beginning to boom. There were some inherited textile loans, and, during the first year under Giannini management, more were made. Results were not encouraging. That first year the branch wrote off $64,000 in bad garment loans.

Then came Nat Green, with an ambition to compete as a lender to this thriving industry with the finance companies whose rates were from 15 to 34 per cent. Mario Giannini approved the experiment. Green mixed with the people of the district and began his curious and special education. In many cases open credit, which an established manufacturer or merchant enjoys, was not to be thought of. Accounts receivable and factoring arrangements afforded the only practicable means. Interest rates ranged from 6 to 12 per cent per annum, the average being (in 1939) about 9. The experiment succeeded. Losses were very low. In 1938 the same services were extended to the San Francisco area where the apparel industry was fifty years old.

During the first six months of 1939 the Bank of America's accounts receivable operations in all lines, including textiles, amounted to $15,000,000 on 6,020 loans. Funds laid out to purchase invoices under factoring arrangements amounted to $8,548,000. San Francisco figures in the same categories were $8,500,000 and $4,871,000. Losses for the half-year were one-twentieth of 1 per cent. Up to 1953, the aggregate of accounts receivable loans had risen to $767,000,000.[15]

By no means does the above sum represent the Bank of America's over-all financing of textiles. As the industry became well established, loans, more and more, have reverted to the traditional in banking credit. Nowadays about only one-third of textile loans are of the factoring and accounts receivable type. The change has removed them from Timeplan into the realm of big commercial loans. Meanwhile, Nat Green has developed a staff of some fifty people who give advice to manufacturers and cutters on fabrics, colors, styles and marketing as well as financial counsel. They keep in touch with buying offices, the piece-goods market, the sources of raw material. They attend fashion shows, locate models and find factory locations for Eastern manufacturers who want to extend their operations to the West. Mr. Green goes East to visit mills, factories and outlets for California manufacturers.

Green is a mine of success stories. A favorite relates the rise of Jean Durain, a designer of little girls' dresses, whom Green loaned $1,000 in 1941 to go into business for herself. Jean Durain now has three factories and several hundred employees. Green started off other manufacturers and wholesalers with even smaller loans and has watched their businesses overreach the million-dollar-a-year mark. A few such: Sportclothes, Ltd., men's clothing; Anita Frocks; Morse & Morse, knit underwear; Klein-Norton Co., men's clothing.[16]

San Francisco's long-established apparel industry also grew healthily. In 1944 the leaders there conceived the idea of grouping the trade into an attractive center. After four local banks had turned down the proposal as unbankable, B. of A. worked the thing out. Land is scarce in San Francisco, but thirty acres, used as a trailer park was found in the Potrero district, south of the main business section. While the R.F.C. backed and filled, the Bank of America put up $1,175,000 to start construction. The first section of Apparel City opened in 1948 and rapidly acquired tenants. With the investment looking like a profitable one, the R.F.C. guaranteed 75 per cent of a $2,363,000 loan to carry the project to completion.

5

Though the Bank of America had proved that accounts receivable and factoring loans could be made safely, both the comptroller's office and the Federal Deposit Insurance Corporation were unconvinced. Throughout their pioneering stage, these loans constantly drew the criticism of national bank examiners. Many of them were classified as either "slow" or "doubtful," words of warning that, in effect, notified a bank to remove such loans from its assets. Moreover, examiners displayed no liking for the security of these small-business loans. The character and the prospects of the borrowers, on which the Giannini institution always placed a value, got no consideration from examiners.

According to their standards, the comptroller's men acted correctly. The trouble was that their standards were behind the times, a defect that banking authorities were shortly to correct. Even so, it was to take a long time for bank examiners to shake themselves free of old habits of thought.

Bankers generally had come to recognize the need for revision of examination practices, but few had the hardihood of A. P. Giannini to put up a fight for what they believed was right. Instead, they avoided argument by confining their commercial lending to gilt-edged propositions. Such a course was no help in getting business, particularly small business, back on its feet. It was no help to Jesse Jones, charged by the Administration with promoting industrial recovery through government loans. Mr. Jones frequently criticized the bankers publicly for their conservatism, though no one knew better than the R.F.C. chairman that they were not entirely to blame for failure to enter more fully into the purposes of his program.

The Bank of America was exempt from this criticism. Jones wrote A. P. Giannini that no other large bank in the country had co-operated so heartily with the R.F.C. in small-business loans. "It is refreshing to see a bank," he added, "willing to go to the trouble of originating loans in its own community rather than confining itself largely to buying 'tailor-made' credits in the way of low-yielding bonds and so-called commercial paper originated by others."[17]

Mr. Jones referred to the fact that banks, rather than argue with bank examiners, were lending to finance companies who, in turn, loaned to small business—at a price. This procedure, remarked Mr. Jones, would not achieve the large-scale business recovery that the New Deal had set out to get.

The so-called "Roosevelt recession" brought matters to a head. As an incentive to new undertakings that would provide more jobs, in June, 1938, Congress passed the Glass Act broadening the lending powers of the R.F.C. Important to banks, the new legislation permitted long-term industrial financing. This put the commercial borrower on the same footing with the installment buyer of goods. He could now liquidate his loan through time payments over a period of five years instead of nine months. This would seem to take care of the vexing problem of examiner criticism.

Jesse Jones hoped that the Glass Act would immediately place $3,000,000,000 of private capital in the hands of small business men.

He promptly sent copies of the new regulations to all directors and managing officers of state and national institutions. In an accompanying letter, he minced no words: "If banking is to remain in private hands it must meet the credit needs of the country." Then came a warning: "There still is persistent talk in Washington about the establishment of industrial banks throughout the country, to be at least partially owned by the government, to provide capital for local private businesses."[18]

This communication went to fourteen thousand banks. "Only 1 per cent acknowledged receipt of our letter," the chairman of the R.F.C. said later. "That seems hardly credible, because more than half of the banks had been directly assisted by the R.F.C. and all had been indirectly assisted."[19]

The memory of bitter quarrels with the comptroller's representatives lingered. Banks were not convinced that a new day had dawned. It hadn't. The Glass Act fell far short of realizing Mr. Jones's expectations, chiefly because bank examiners adhered to time-worn procedures. "Outmoded, unintelligent and officious examiner criticism," Jesse Jones called it a year later. It was almost as if Giannini were speaking.[20]

The Bank of America welcomed the Glass Act. Mario Giannini instructed the 493 branch managers as follows:

> It is definitely our policy to work along with these small business men and make capital loans if the moral risk is good and if they will work out in reasonable time. Therefore, the possibility of making a bankable loan out of an apparently unbankable application should be thoroughly explored. But when the application appears to be of the type you cannot handle . . . it is to be forwarded to our Loan Supervision Department at Headquarters. . . . Here the application will be reviewed and if no way can be found to develop it into a bank loan it will be forwarded to the R.F.C., where the responsibility of final acceptance or rejection will rest.[21]

From 1934 until the end of 1941 the Bank of America signified its willingness to participate with the R.F.C. in 324 loans to business. More than half of these applications were rejected, either by R.F.C. or the Federal Reserve. The bank wound up with 253 loans, only 144 of which were participation commitments.[22]

What the Bank of America pioneers in one decade other banks often take up in the next. We have seen plenty of this. Another example is the financing of motion pictures. During the latter 1930's the Bank of America found ample competition in this field. It came from New York, Chicago and Boston, and from banks at home— notably the Security–First National, the California Bank and the Union Bank and Trust Company, all of Los Angeles. But the Bank of America, which had been first in the field, remained Hollywood's principal lender.

In 1931, when Walker closed out the Bank of America N. A. in New York, Dr. A. H. Giannini established his home in Los Angeles. Nearly fifteen years before he had been the first man to see the possibilities of motion pictures from a banker's point of view. With the return of his brother to power, Dr. Giannini took charge of the Bank of America's affairs in Hollywood. Though times were hard in 1932, the Doc O.K.'d the bank's first million-dollar movie loan. It went to Samuel Goldwyn who was making *The Kid from Spain,* starring Eddie Cantor. Goldwyn was on the lot nearly every day, trying to keep down expenses. Commenting on his worries the producer said that his wife just that morning had remarked: "Sam, how drawn you look." "What she meant was overdrawn," observed Doc Giannini. Nevertheless, Goldwyn paid out, and a few years later he had an open credit of $4,000,000 with the bank.[23]

Dr. Giannini introduced the practice of accepting negatives as security. Finding a loan of $500,000 to Warner Brothers thus secured, a bank examiner questioned the value of the collateral. Giannini failed to convince the examiner, but before an adverse report could be drafted the loan was paid. Part of the security had been a negative of *Forty-Second Street,* which grossed $3,000,000 within a few months after its release.

By 1936 the bank's movie commitments amounted to $33,000,000 a year. From 1936 to 1952 it had financed upward of five hundred feature pictures and more than half as many shorts, representing an outlay (by the bank) of nearly half a billion dollars. Of the numerous clients, there is space here to mention only Walt Disney. The bank backed his first feature picture, the lovely and very successful *Snow White and the Seven Dwarfs,* and has since been Disney's banker through a succession of memorable productions.

When Dr. Giannini left the bank in 1936 his place was taken by Joseph H. Rosenberg. Wartime gas rationing kept people near home and made flush times for the pictures. Peace brought a near-collapse, with keener competition, vastly higher production costs and the loss, through tariffs, of much of the foreign market. Some lenders were badly singed. A few of them quit the movie field. The advent of television made further big dents in film income. As this is written (spring, 1953), Hollywood is in a state of confusion over the coming of three-dimensional pictures. Some companies look to them to put the movies back where they were before television got in its licks. Others believe 3-D is not here to stay. The only point on which all agree is that to convert and standardize theater equipment to exhibit the new pictures will be a costly operation.

In 1953, the Bank of America had outstanding $55,000,000 in movie loans. Bygone days have seen them in greater dollar volume. Bernard Giannini, a son of the Doctor, who died in 1943, has succeeded Mr. Rosenberg in charge of the bank's motion picture lending.[24]

6

While the events from 1934 to 1939 that are related in the earlier part of this chapter, and in preceding chapters, were going on, California was the scene of a sociopolitical struggle such as the state had never witnessed before. The issue was joined in the EPIC ("End Poverty in California") campaign of 1934 and in the "Ham and Eggs" campaigns of 1938 and 1939.

The struggle had its rise in human suffering. During the depression every state (even with the help of the federal government after the election of Roosevelt) was hard put to care for its own—the unemployed, the homeless and the hungry. No state, however, bore so heavy a burden as California. Not only had it to care for its own, but also the depression refugees who streamed in by the tens of thousands from other parts of the country. They had fled from the "dust bowls" of the Middle West; from the South, under the blight of six-cent cotton; from the paralyzed industrial cities. They came to California because for eighty years California had been another name for opportunity. California cotton pickers, for example, got (in 1937) ninety-five cents a hundredweight, against sixty-five in Texas. W.P.A. wages averaged $62.48 a month in California, $41.02 in Texas, $40.91 in Oklahoma. A year's residence in California entitled a dependent person of sixty-five to an old-age pension of $38.00 a month. Texas paid a comparable benefit of $8.91, and Oklahoma $17.58.

California could not absorb the whole of this army of job seekers, most of whom were destitute or nearly so when they arrived. In 1934 California had a million persons on relief. Wages had been cut, and workers in the cotton, lettuce and melon fields had to fight hard to keep their jobs. Newcomers offered to work for what they could get. Families camped by roadsides did not hesitate to steal rather than starve. Professional agitators moved among these miserable people.

In 1934 Upton Sinclair, a crusading former Socialist and a writer of distinction, won the Democratic gubernatorial nomination on his End-Poverty-in-California platform which was, in a word, state socialism. His Republican opponent was the incumbent, Governor Frank Merriam.

A. P. Giannini was as anxious as Sinclair to end poverty in California. He had done more toward that goal than any other banker, and probably any other citizen. He could not, however, accept the Sinclair platform. Yet, despite strong pressure, he refused to declare for Merriam until the day before the election.

Merriam polled 1,138,620 votes to Sinclair's 879,557. To the banker, the EPIC vote was "nothing short of amazing." "You can't tell me," he said, "that when a man like Sinclair . . . without any newspaper support, can get nearly a million votes there isn't something wrong somewhere. . . . Social security has got to come."[25]

Some of Sinclair's following drifted to the standard of a retired physician of Long Beach named Francis E. Townsend, who championed a $200 monthly pension for persons over sixty, not in California alone but everywhere in the United States. Dr. Townsend's movement petered out, but was revived as an exclusively California proposition under the name of "Ham and Eggs." Ham and Eggs called for the payment of $30 every Thursday to unemployed persons over fifty. To meet this outlay, it would have required a scrip issue of about $1,500,000,000 a year.

The proposal was put on the ballot in 1938 in the form of a constitutional amendment. The California Bankers Association called it a "crackpot idea." The members got the shock of their lives. Ham and Eggs lost by only 300,000 votes out of 2,500,000 cast. Culbert L. Olson, who had endorsed Ham and Eggs, was swept into the governorship on the Democratic ticket. He gave the proposal a second chance in a special election in 1939.

By then the state had outstanding $70,000,000 in warrants, representing a lien on the next year's taxes. Olson advertised an additional warrant offering of $3,800,000 to meet the July pay and relief rolls. The Bank of America was the sole bidder. In August there was another offering, and no one bid. The Bank of America then held $19,000,000 in state warrants, whose redemption was threatened by the specter of Ham and Eggs. Nevertheless, Russell Smith of the Bank of America worked out an arrangement whereby the state's credit was supported until election time by a syndicate of bankers that took $9,000,000 more in warrants.

The closing days of the campaign were hectic. "End Bankerism in California" was one slogan of the Ham and Eggers. The opposition came back strong. President Roosevelt called the Ham and Eggs proposal "fantastic"; Upton Sinclair called it "a cruel hoax"; Governor Olson deserted the cause; and A. P. Giannini took the stump.

"There is no escaping it," he told one audience, "something does not come for nothing."[26]

Ham and Eggs was beaten by a million votes. Giannini believed the crushing defeat was directly traceable to the doorsteps of the "large number of houses constructed under the F.H.A." He predicted the movement would not revive because California's preponderance of "home ownership and continued improved financial condition" would make the state "among the most conservative in the country."[27]

7

The lessons inherent in California's political foundering in the thirties were not disregarded. One fact stood out plainly. People wanted to feel secure. "At the very least, they are entitled to security," said A. P. Giannini who also saw the matter as a lesson in simple economics. "Proper housing, good food, good clothing and provision for old age are all requisites of prosperity."[28]

By 1938, the Bank of America had taken additional steps to increase its employees' stock ownership in the bank, and to provide for them other benefits, notably pensions. The reader will recall that in 1925 the bank began to set aside a portion of its earnings for the purchase of bank stock for employees. At that time shares were selling around 300. Under this earlier plan if an employee wished to purchase two shares, the bank would buy them and the employee could pay in installments. When the employee had fully paid, the bank would make him a gift of two additional shares. Thus he would get four shares for the price of two.

This went well until the bear raid in 1928 and the market crash of 1929. Employees found themselves paying for shares that were worth in the market much less than they had cost. During the regime of Elisha Walker, amid the grim conditions prevailing in 1930, the bank felt itself unable to take on any new engagements to match employees' purchases, share for share. Consequently the 1925 plan was abandoned. There was, of course, no repudiation by the bank of contracts already made. Employees who paid out on existing commitments, received gift shares as before. Many employees, however, became discouraged and ceased making payments.

The return of the Gianninis in 1932 revived wilting morale. The bank also relieved some of the material load by carrying the unpaid subscriptions and permitting dividends that had accumulated to apply against the employees' defaults.

As the bank continued its recovery, a liberalized retirement plan became effective in 1935. Payments into the pension fund were divided between the bank and employees, and were in addition to benefits under the Federal Social Security Act.

Progressively increasing stock ownership, however, was still a goal the Gianninis held for their employees. The bank was able to return to this objective in 1938. The new plan called for the payment of bonuses on salaries—7.5 per cent on incomes up to $500 a month and 5 per cent above that amount. The money was invested in bank stock and turned over to the employees at five-year intervals. At the end of 1949, the value of employee-owned shares had reached $22,766,000.

In 1950 the plan was again broadened. The bonus feature was done away with. Instead, a certain percentage of the bank's profits before payment of federal income taxes has since been set aside for employee benefits, including gifts of stock. Through 1952, the workers' "cut" each year has been 8 per cent. Most of the benefits—retirement, insurance, sickness, etc.—had previously been paid in part by the employees and in part by the bank. The bank has now assumed these obligations, paying entirely for all of them, except retirement pensions. It has, however, increased its contribution to the pension fund. The effect of the resulting decrease in payroll deductions has been to raise the amount of take-home pay. After benefit payments are covered, the remainder of the 8-per-cent-of-profits fund is invested in bank stock for employees. Under this latest plan the bank's contribution to employees' benefits and stock purchases amounted to $8,100,000 in 1952, as against something over $3,419,000 in 1949. Between 1938 and 1952 the bank invested in a total of 1,457,301 shares for employees. The market value of these shares at the close of 1952 was $45,176,321.[29]

Bank of America employees (more than 19,000 in 1952) have no union. One reason is that the management, like the managements of nearly all national banks, is opposed to unionization on the ground that national banks are arms of the federal government. This has not kept the C.I.O. and the A.F. of L. from trying to organize the employees. The last try by the A.F. of L. was in 1945, when the drive centered on the clerical force in twenty-six branches in the Oakland area. The result of the election ordered by the N.L.R.B. was 140 votes for a union and 320 against. An additional 41 votes against was challenged by the union.[30]

Grievances and criticisms find an outlet in the junior advisory council that the Bank of America formed in 1944. One function of this body is to hear what a junior has to say about how his superiors run the bank, and then to recommend improvements. The council is also a proving ground for young officers. The second generation looms stronger all the time, as the sons, and daughters too, of officers and employees start the upward climb. In 1953, the Quarter Century Club had over thirteen hundred members working in the bank. There is besides a considerable membership of employees who are retired.

A Showdown with Mr. Morgenthau

AN EFFORT has been made in preceding chapters to trace out the salient themes in the story of the growth of the Bank of America following the return of A. P. Giannini from retirement in 1932. In view of what has been written it may surprise the reader to learn that the soundness of much of that growth was seriously questioned in some official quarters.

Time is the infallible bank examiner. In the long run it reveals the wisdom or unwisdom of a banker's course. The trouble is that time reveals unwisdom too late to do victimized depositors and stockholders any good; therefore the need for other examiners, who labor amid the pulls and stresses of the hour. By now time has afforded a measure of perspective on the events of the 1930's, perspective that was not available to contemporary bank examiners.

Considerable of what the Gianninis, father and son, did in the thirties was new. Because of the responsibilities devolving upon it, banking is a conservative profession. New ways are suspect. Regulatory authorities are imbued with this conservatism. The reader has seen examples of this in the criticism such authorities have leveled at the Bank of America since it began in earnest its branchwise expansion before the first war.

In the late thirties, at the time the Bank of America was contributing so much to the lore and practice of banking in the United States, this criticism swelled in volume. What made it seem more important than it was, is the fact that a member of the President's Cabinet espoused the cause of the critics. He was Secretary of the Treasury Henry Morgenthau, Jr., who sought to bring national banks under the authority of the Treasury Department, somewhat as they had been three-quarters of a century before when the banking structure of the country was simple. If the contention of Mr.

435

Morgenthau and his allies was correct, much of the remarkable growth indicated by the Bank of America's statements was illusory. The critics said the bank was paying dividends it could not afford to pay, and was loaning many millions on poor security. The controversy lasted three years, during which Mr. Morgenthau brought to bear against the bank the enormous prestige of his office and of such of the regulatory machinery affecting banks as he had drawn under his control. In the end the Gianninis forced a showdown, and they won.

They won on merit, for time has proved Mr. Morgenthau was mistaken.

2

The story begins in 1937 when Senator McAdoo of California introduced two banking bills. One would permit national banks to operate branches anywhere within the federal reserve district in which their head offices were located. The other would prohibit holding companies from owning more than 10 per cent of the stock of any bank that was a member of the Federal Reserve. Giannini favored these bills. Many times he had said that bank holding companies could be done away with, if the law was amended to permit a bank to do business in more than one state. As a starter, within sixty days after the introduction of the McAdoo bills, 58 per cent of the bank's stock that was owned by Transamerica was distributed among the individual stockholders of the holding company. "The day of bank holding companies is gone," Giannini reiterated.[1]

By this time Transamerica owned banks not only in California but in Oregon, Washington, Nevada and Arizona—that is, in all but two of the states comprising the Twelfth Federal Reserve District. Should the McAdoo branch banking bill pass, the Bank of America could take over these institutions and become the nation's first regional bank.

The McAdoo bills did not pass and, in 1938, the agitation against holding companies, particularly bank holding companies, was taken up by President Roosevelt. Discussing the matter at a press conference, Mr. Roosevelt said that "investment trusts specializing in bank stock ownership should not be considered holding companies."

"[Mr. Roosevelt]," concluded the New York *Herald Tribune's* account of the conference, "seemed to exclude the Giannini-controlled Transamerica Corporation from this type of concern which the Administration was prepared to proceed against." In a letter to a colleague Giannini remarked that "the statement of the President is really along the lines we had in mind."[2]

Mr. Roosevelt fared no better than had Senator McAdoo in getting antiholding-company legislation.

Secretary Morgenthau persevered in his determination to have a large say in the conduct of the nation's banks. He was opposed, among others, by Marriner Eccles, head of the Federal Reserve Board, who contended for more liberal examinations for national banks. National bank examiners were under the office of comptroller of the currency, an arm of the Treasury which had long operated independently. Mr. Morgenthau was to succeed in depriving the office of its independence, and was the first Secretary of the Treasury to do so. When J. F. T. O'Connor resigned the comptrollership, a Morgenthau appointee, Deputy Comptroller Marshall R. Diggs, became acting comptroller.

The Secretary started to ride roughshod over Eccles' demand for an examination policy that would put more money, in the form of long-term loans, into business enterprises. This matter had taken on more urgency as the Roosevelt "recession" deepened and Jesse Jones blamed examiner criticism for the failure of R.F.C. to prevail on more banks to undertake the financing of small industry. Eccles brought the fight into the open by writing a letter to Senator Vandenberg of Michigan which Vandenberg gave to the newspapers. Morgenthau backed water and there was a compromise which saw the passing of word classifications for loans. "Slow," "Doubtful" and "Loss" were replaced with the Roman numerals I, II, III and IV which were intended to give examiners more latitude in defining loans and other banking investments.[3]

The examiners did not adapt quickly to this easing of restrictions which relied, in greater degree, on their good judgment rather than on application of hard and fast rules. Meantime the Bank of America was constantly in hot water over its ever-expanding lending policy. The situation might have been cleared up sooner with a Secretary of the Treasury more in sympathy with new banking trends.

"There was no love lost between Mr. Giannini and Secretary Morgenthau," said Jesse Jones who had a ringside seat at the contest of which this chapter tells.[4]

3

The development of differences between the bank and that part of Washington officialdom that the Secretary of the Treasury was bringing under his influence proceeded in various ways, some of them quite small in the beginning. There was the matter of applications for branches in the towns of Gonzales and Pinole. Gonzales is a little farming community in the Salinas Valley. Pinole, on the upper reaches of San Francisco Bay, is even smaller (population 934, in 1940). Before leaving office Comptroller O'Connor had approved the applications, subject to opening for business in January, 1938. When the bank found that it could not provide quarters for the branches that soon, Washington granted an extension.

In March the quarters—in one case a remodeled butcher shop— were ready, down to signs on the windows. But the permits were not forthcoming. From day to day the bank was put off, with vague excuses. Having tried to reach Mr. Morgenthau by other means, Giannini requested the President's secretary, Marvin McIntyre, to ask the head of the Treasury what was wrong. McIntyre's intervention brought word from Acting Comptroller Diggs that the branch applications were being held up because his office did not like the looks of the most recent examination report on the Bank of America. Diggs said the permits would not be forthcoming until some $6,000,-000 in "losses" were charged off.[5]

Here it is necessary to digress for a moment. The need for vigilance by the comptroller's office had just been demonstrated by a revelation of the condition of the so-called Fleishhacker bank of San Francisco, the Anglo California National. It appeared that for years the comptroller's office had failed to act on adverse reports on this institution submitted by local examiners. In 1938, however, the Fleishhacker brothers, Herbert and Mortimer, were forced out and the R.F.C. supplied $22,000,000 toward the reorganization of the bank. A. P. Giannini regarded Herbert Fleishhacker as an enemy as well as an incompetent banker. Nettled by what he termed the Treasury's "unprecedented treatment," Giannini could not resist the opportunity to telegraph congratulations to Secretary Morgenthau on the "belated housecleaning."[6]

Naturally, Giannini was anxious that Washington should not set up in its mind anything resembling a parallel between the Bank of America and the Anglo California. On May 6, 1938, Giannini wrote Diggs a long letter denying that items totaling $6,000,000 which Diggs called losses were losses in fact. He said that all such losses had been charged off. On the heels of this letter Russell Smith went to Washington to make in person any needful explanations. Smith reported a successful mission. The matter of losses was gone into with Chief Examiner Folger. The $6,000,000 was whittled down to $220,-000. Other important criticisms in the report likewise were adjusted. Smith also had sessions with Acting Comptroller Diggs and with a Treasury official close to Morgenthau. Everything seemed pleasant. He returned to San Francisco expecting favorable action on the branches "very soon."[7]

By July, however, the permits had not come through and Giannini wired McIntyre to ask what was the matter. No response from McIntyre is of record. Yet something serious was the matter, which vitiated the understanding Smith had reached in Washington. The Smith mission concerned the report of 1937. The examiner, L. H. Sedlacek, who had had charge of that examination, was in the final stages of his 1938 examination. A preliminary report made to the chief examiner of the Twelfth Federal Reserve District, William Prentiss, was quite critical. More severely than in his 1937 report, Sedlacek mentioned the bank's "frozen" real estate loans, its large lines of credit to Transamerica and subsidiaries, its dividend policy, and much more. As Mr. Prentiss was making a trip to Washington concerning the affairs of the Anglo California National, he availed himself of the opportunity to take the Bank of America report along.[8]

4

The bank's first warning of the approach of bad news was on September 13, 1938, a few hours before a regular meeting of the board of directors in Los Angeles. Mario Giannini, in the south for the occasion, received a telephone call from R. E. A. Palmer, resident national bank examiner, that he had been instructed to attend the meeting and read a telegram from Acting Comptroller Diggs. Mario asked what was in the telegram. Palmer said it had not been de-coded. Mario phoned Folger in Washington, but the chief examiner would not discuss the message. Then Mario wired Russ Smith to fly down from San Francisco.

The meeting opened at the scheduled hour, A. P. Giannini presiding. Sixteen directors were present and eight absent. Neither Palmer nor Smith had arrived. The chairman told of the forthcoming message from Diggs, and the meeting proceeded with its business. The only item of interest to this narrative was the continuance of the current dividend of sixty cents a quarter. At length Palmer arrived with Diggs's message, certainly the most astonishing communication to come before the board of the Bank of America since the Walker regime. It read:

> In view of the unsatisfactory asset condition of the bank, of real estate in excess of forty million dollars carried in loans and discounts and . . . of other items carried in assets of questionable value and of the aggregate of assets classified as doubtful and loss, it is imperative that the earnings of the bank be used to write off and reduce book value of such assets. Notwithstanding the condition as outlined above and the fact that the dividend policy has been repeatedly criticised, the dividend rate has been repeatedly increased . . . [since] nineteen thirty-three. . . . In the opinion of the comptroller of the currency the declaration of any dividends at this time would, unless proper provisions for such criticised assets were first made, be and continue an unsafe and unsound practice. . . . Accordingly the comptroller of the currency pursuant to section thirty of the Bank Act of Nineteen Thirty-Three hereby warns the bank, its officers, the board of directors and the members thereof to discontinue such unsafe and unsound practice.[9]

Section 30 empowered the comptroller to charge officers and directors with violations of banking practices and hail them before the Federal Reserve Board for trial and possible removal.

Giannini accepted the challenge forthwith. After Palmer had withdrawn the bank board voted to request a hearing before the Reserve Board. At this juncture Smith showed up. In view of his recent and apparently satisfactory adjustment in Washington of the very questions raised in the Diggs telegram, Smith was dumbfounded by the acting comptroller's about-face.[10]

In conveying to Diggs the bank's demand for a hearing, A. P.

Giannini rebuked the acting comptroller for the method he had adopted to deliver his message—a message "calculated to disturb public confidence," should its contents leak out. A few days later it developed that the acting comptroller had sent by ordinary mail copies of the wire to every member of the board at his business address. Disturbed by this treatment of sacredly confidential matter concerning the bank, Mario Giannini telegraphed Marriner Eccles of the Reserve Board for an early hearing. "I am prepared to leave here at a moment's notice."[11]

If the Gianninis found cause to be disturbed, so too did Secretary Morgenthau after hearing how the directors' meeting had reacted to the comptroller's telegram. The Secretary hastily summoned the following officials: Marriner Eccles, Leo T. Crowley, chairman of the Federal Deposit Insurance Corporation; Marshall Diggs, William P. Folger, Jesse Jones and Sam Husbands, president of the Federal National Mortgage Association. To the group Mr. Morgenthau announced that the Bank of America had "defied" the comptroller of the currency by paying dividends after he had instructed it not to do so. A portion of the subsequent discussion was reported by Mr. Jones:

> After seeming to question the soundness of Mr. Giannini's bank, Mr. Morgenthau said he thought he should withdraw from it the government's deposit of several million dollars. I reminded him that all government deposits were secured by government bonds. The Secretary said he didn't know that the Treasury's deposits in commercial banks were secured by government bonds. He turned to Mr. Folger who, of course, confirmed that fact for him.[12]

Such a punitive measure might have produced a lot of trouble for the Bank of America. Fortunately, the Gianninis kept the initiative in their hands, giving the Treasury Department little time to dwell on retaliatory action.

Press reports from Washington on that eventful September 13 of the bank directors' meeting clarified matters a little. By a departmental circular merging the legal staff of the comptroller's office with that of the Treasury, Mr. Morgenthau had practically assumed control of that office. Presently Marshall Diggs was transferred to the F.D.I.C. and Preston Delano, a distant relative of the President, was named comptroller of the currency.

Before Diggs surrendered the title of acting comptroller he signed two letters, dated September 23, bearing on the Bank of America situation. One was directed to L. M. Giannini. It remarked that, despite official warning, the bank board had declared a dividend. Mr. Diggs cited a law under which a bank could lose its charter and directors be liable for damages for actions that produced losses for shareholders and depositors. Mario replied that the dividend was voted before the telegram was received and before its contents were known to the board, though efforts had been made to ascertain what they were.[13]

Copies of the second letter were sent to each of the bank's directors. This communication constituted an argument in support of the points made in Diggs's telegram to the board, an argument that accepted as gospel Examiner Sedlacek's latest report, completed on September 15, 1938, two days after the episode of the Diggs telegram. The letter alleged that $137,818,000 of the bank's assets were "subject to adverse classification," and pointed out that this sum exceeded "the total capital structure of the bank by more than $25,000,000."

The principal item in the $137,818,000 figure, contended Mr. Diggs, was $76,000,000 in credits to Transamerica and subsidiaries. The largest component of this figure was $41,533,000 which California Lands, Inc., and the Capital Company were said to owe the bank on account of mortgage foreclosures those corporations had taken over.

Mr. Diggs contended further that the bank was undercapitalized to the extent of $42,000,000. He arrived at that conclusion in this way. Capital, surplus and undivided profits amounted to $96,447,000. Deposits were $1,385,000,000, representing a ratio of fourteen to one. This ratio he thought should be ten to one, which would mean capital funds of $138,000,000.

The acting comptroller spoke strongly on the subject of dividends. "The primary purpose of the management appears to be that of publishing large earnings statements and the payment of everincreasing dividends, rather than a frank recognition of . . . asset problems." The charge was reiterated that the directors had defied the comptroller's office by continuing current dividends *after* a warning not to.

There were other complaints, involving lesser matters.

The board of the bank was requested to consider this letter at a special meeting and to reply in detail over the signatures of the members attending.[14]

5

A. P. Giannini assembled the board at No. 1 Powell in short order —on September 30. Only three directors were absent, and they had good excuses. The Diggs letter was considered paragraph by paragraph, and a reply outlined. The drafting, approval and signing of this document of twenty-two pages took until October 11, when it was dispatched.

The directors agreed with almost nothing the acting comptroller had said. They contended that the $137,818,000 should have been $13,000,000, and cited the regulations of the comptroller's office to prove this. The larger figure included $124,766,000 in loans called "slow" by the examiner. The directors pointed out that, according to existing regulations, slow loans were "not subject to . . . 'adverse classification.'" The $13,000,000 remaining, consisting of loans the examiner called "doubtful" or "losses," was no longer $13,000,000 actually, but less than $10,000,000 because, since Mr. Sedlacek had inspected the loan portfolio, the bank had eliminated $3,219,000 of criticized items. "[This] does not seem to us to indicate a reluctance on the part of the Management to admit known losses and voluntarily charge them off, as stated in the second paragraph of your letter."

The $76,000,000 figure for bank credits to Trans and subsidiaries should have been $28,000,000, as of April 28, 1938, the date of the beginning of the examination. Since then it had been very materially reduced, the directors said.

On the matter of the bank's capital the divergence was greater yet. The bank's net capital funds amounted to $112,615,000 on September 30, 1938, an improvement of $16,000,000 since the date on which the examination began. Far from showing a capital deficiency, the directors contended that, according to the Banking Act of 1933 fixing capital requirements for national bank branch systems, the bank enjoyed a *capital position . . . more than twice as strong as the law requires.* The italics are in the original. In effect, the directors said a one to ten ratio of capital to deposits was something Mr. Diggs had pulled out of a hat, with nothing in the law to support him.

Spiritedly the directors defended the bank's earnings statements and dividend policy. They called the telegram Palmer had thrust upon them on September 13 a "startling performance," unjustified by the facts. Earnings statements were accurate, they declared, and dividends legal and reasonable.

A thread of criticism of the bank's management ran all through the Diggs letter. The implication was that many errors were of long standing. As we know, every one in the bank from A. P. Giannini down was proud of the bank's record since the return of the Gianninis in 1932. The directors did not miss the opportunity to lay before the comptroller an exhaustive comparative statement, as follows:

	3-31-32	4-28-38	Increase	Decrease
		(000 omitted)		
Conforming Real				
Estate Loans	$195,076	$ 220,409	$ 25,333	
Nonconforming Real				
Estate Loans	97,423	57,718		$ 39,705
Total Classified				
Loans	207,202	123,873		83,329
Slow	155,333	115,456		39,877
Doubtful	21,428	3,689		17,739
Loss	30,441	4,728		25,713
Loans Dependent				
Upon Trans-				
america Stock	20,535	4,817		15,718
Total of All Loans	499,655	571,663	72,008	
Uncollected Interest	8,070	6,502		1,568
Bonds & Securities	249,504	598,187	348,683	
Cash & Due from				
Banks, etc.	58,214	209,740	151,526	
Capital Surplus &				
Profits	94,209	110,621	16,412	
Demand Deposits	162,638	492,430	329,792	
Time Deposits	432,296	771,851	339,555	
Cashier's & Certi-				
fied Checks	8,164	26,029	17,865	
Total Deposits	622,530	1,385,491	762,961	
Bills Payable	138,182	Nil		138,182
Loans to Affiliates				
Classified	74,569	45,099		29,470
	(11-9-32)			(40%)

Loans to Affiliates Classified Adversely	14,315 (11-9-32)	335	13,980 (98%)
Statutory Bad Debts	28,984	9,235	19,749 (68%)
Net Sound Capital	56,300	96,447	40,147 (72%)
Bond Appreciation	—	7,636	7,636
Operating Income Before Recoveries	22,765 (1932)	39,026	16,261 (72%)
Operating Expenses Before Losses	20,323 (1932)	27,496 (1937)	7,173 (35%)
Loans Classified Adversely	51,868 (10% of Total Loans)	8,417 (1.4% of Total Loans)	43,451 (83% Imp.)
Net Earnings Before Depreciation, Amortization, Reserves & Dividends	7,601 (1932)	19,204 (1937) 11,603 (153%)	

"These figures," they added, "tell the story of the constant and successful effort of the Management in behalf of the bank."

Mr. Diggs had written that he hoped his letter would be helpful to the bank. He said he wanted to be fair to everyone. At the same time, implicit in nearly every line of the acting comptroller's letter was the assumption that the directors should accept his figures and do everything he suggested.

The directors did nothing of the kind. Instead, they frankly criticized the drastic nature of the Diggs letters:

The national banking laws confer upon the Comptroller of the Currency two rare and extraordinary powers. One in the Act of 1864 which permits the Comptroller of the Currency to bring suit in his own name for the forfeiture of the charter of a national bank when the Directors knowingly violate or knowingly permit a violation of the law, and the other in the Banking Act of 1933 which permits the Comptroller of the Currency to make a citation to the Federal Reserve Board for the removal of an officer or director for violation of law, or engaging in unsafe or unsound banking practices despite warning to desist. . . . They are desperate remedies and surely they were intended to be employed only after all other other efforts at conciliation had failed.

Yet in our case, a national bank with great earning capacity, a net capital position in excess of $100,000,000, twice the legal requirement, and not involved in any emergency situation, the Comptroller of the Currency, with no inkling theretofore to our Board, or to the Management, that he thought that any such procedure was even remotely contemplated, suddenly within a space of ten days threatened, in effect, to invoke both of these remedies against us.

The directors added that they felt sure that the differences between the comptroller's department and the bank could be removed "in the ordinary manner by conferences from time to time." They went to the heart of the dispute:

We believe that the chief difficulty between the examiners and the Bank is in the matter of the attitude toward real estate as security for loans. We have no reason to believe that this difficulty rests on anything else than an honest difference of opinion. The examiners seem always to have held a low opinion of real estate as security. We, on the other hand, taking into consideration our type of bank, have a high regard for the value of real estate as security for obligations.

Two closing paragraphs stated a prime article of the creed of the Bank of America:

Real Estate is the backbone of the country. It represents a greater proportion of the wealth of the country than does any other form of property. From it as a source of taxation the State, County and Municipal governments obtain their chief revenues. Ownership of real estate gives stability to the citizen. Our homes, farms, business houses, and industrial plants offer a fruitful field for long term financing. It is necessary for us to satisfy the diverse credit requirements of all the communities which we serve.

Bank of America National Trust and Savings Association, as its name implies, is in a large measure a savings bank. Its savings deposits in fact exceed those of any savings bank in the country. We therefore feel that the examiner should consider our real estate security in the light of the principles which should govern a sound savings bank practice.[15]

6

Three developments followed this exchange of letters.

First, there seeped out from Washington a trickle of rumor, insinuation and report to the effect that the Bank of America N. T. & S. A. of San Francisco was in trouble with the government. Sometimes the bank was named, and always it was pretty well identified. These reports traveled by grapevine, by means of guarded items in the lay as well as the business press, and by mention in other circulating mediums such as the Kiplinger *News Letter* and *Banktrends*. *Washington Banktrends* (current title) is a subscription service to bankers and businessmen supplied by the Washington correspondent of the *American Banker*.

The leak is a device well known in Washington, by which officials of high degree, including Presidents, under the cloak of anonymity and thus without accepting responsibility, grind axes, send up trial balloons, test public reactions and so on. At No. 1 Powell, Giannini assembled a collection of pertinent items. Believing them the result of an inspired leak from the Treasury, on November 1, 1938, he sent a stinging telegram to the Secretary.

The wire cited a recent example of the whispering campaign that had appeared in *Banktrends*. "Don't you think, Mr. Secretary," concluded the banker, "that your continued unwarranted and unjustifiable smearing has gone far enough?"

The Secretary indignantly denied everything. He had not "known" of the offending dispatch until receipt of Mr. Giannini's telegram. The "tone and text" of that telegram "would not merit either acknowledgment or reply" under ordinary circumstances. Mr. Morgenthau, however, was

impelled to write in the hope that the tactics of personal vituperation you adopted in this telegram do not represent your considered judgment but were prompted by momentary anger. . . . There are matters of grave import pending between the office of the Comptroller of the Currency, which is a bureau of the Treasury Department, and the financial institutions of which you are the responsible head. Let us not muddy the waters by personal animus.[16]

Giannini replied that the Secretary should be better informed. He appended a list of articles, with names and dates, and offered to send photostatic copies. Their wide circulation, Giannini continued,

[has] prompted some our most valued clients, such as Woolworth's, Penney's, Safeway, Montgomery Ward, and certain railroads, to make direct and indirect inquiry as to their meaning. As a result of the publicity given to these matters, a whispering campaign against the Bank got underway, and the rumor was circulated that the Bank would discontinue dividend payments. To meet a possible emergency arising in consequence of prevalent gossip, recently the management was obliged to accumulate ex-

cessive cash reserves by selling large blocks of government bonds and restricting lending activity, thereby suffering, unnecessarily, a loss in income
and prestige. . . . In the final analysis, Mr. Secretary, someone must accept
responsibility for the damage caused to Bank of America by reason of the
unwarranted and damaging method of attack.[17]

7

In contrast to the foregoing, the second development in the controversy between the bank and the Treasury was a thoroughly constructive one. The new comptroller, Preston Delano, accepted the
bank's proposal for a conference. Mario Giannini, Bill Blauer and
Russell Smith went to Washington. They met a host of officials—
apparently every one, excepting Mr. Morgenthau—who by any
stretch was concerned with the issues outstanding between the bank
and the Treasury. Among them were Delano; his chief deputy, C. B.
Upham; Chief Examiner Folger and assistants, including Sedlacek;
Eccles of the Federal Reserve Board; Jesse Jones of the R.F.C., and
his chief examiner; Crowley of the F.D.I.C.; and Undersecretary of
the Treasury John W. Hanes, whom Mario called "a gentleman . . .
honorable in his recognition of commitments." A word is necessary
about Upham. He was known as "Morgenthau's man," and, though
only recently made deputy comptroller, he was in many matters
more influential than Mr. Delano.[18]

Amid an atmosphere of friendliness, and impelled by an earnest
desire to adjust the differences outstanding, the conferees sat down
to work. With objectivity and singleness of purpose they continued
their labors, undistracted by the fact that almost simultaneously another government agency, the Securities and Exchange Commission,
launched, amid a blaze of publicity, a series of charges against the
Transamerica Corporation. Shortly your narrators will allude further to these allegations, but for the present we must stick to the
conferees. Considering the wide divergences of view so lately expressed, in an amazingly short time they reached a basis for settlement of the bank matter. On December 15, a seventeen-point program was agreed upon. It is necessary here to mention only four of
these points:

1. The bank agreed to increase its capital in an amount necessary
to establish a one to ten ratio of capital funds to deposits. Consider-

ing that the bank had not increased its capital stock since 1927, when it was half the size it was in 1938, this request seems reasonable and in no way an adverse reflection. Still, Mario had opposed it at first, because other national banks were not required to maintain a one to ten ratio, and many had a much lower capital ratio than the Bank of America. Jesse Jones expected that the R.F.C. would provide most of the new capital funds. He knew that a loan to the Bank of America, with its stock as collateral, would be an excellent investment for the government. Mario, however, disliked the idea of R.F.C. participation because so many people associated R.F.C. loans to banks with rescue operations.

2. No bank dividends unless the one to ten ratio was maintained.

3. By July 15, 1942, the aggregate of loans to Transamerica and subsidiaries to be reduced to 10 per cent of the bank's capital. This represented a fairly strict construction of the law, limiting the amount of bank loans to one individual or corporate interest.

4. Real estate contracts with California Lands and Capital Company to be terminated by December 15, 1943.[19]

On his way home for Christmas, Mario Giannini telephoned Jesse Jones from Chicago. Owing to the illness of Delano, Jones had presided at the last sessions of the conferees. Mario merely wished to check on some details. He was hopeful of peace. What Jones told him over the phone made him more so. "You've a great bank," the big Texan said. "Go home and tend to business and forget the situation here."[20]

Shortly after the first of the year (1939), Mario was back in Washington to close the deal about the stock issue. The bank had in mind a $25,000,000 flotation of convertible preferred shares. Mario proposed that what the public did not take Transamerica should buy with funds advanced by R.F.C., with the stock as security. Following a pattern established by his father, Mario wanted Trans, and not the bank, to be the borrower. Despite the fulminations of the Securities and Exchange Commission against Transamerica, this procedure was satisfactory to Jesse Jones. After R.F.C. examiners had been over Transamerica's books, Jones approved the corporation's application for a loan and forwarded it to Secretary Morgenthau.[21]

Here we had the spectacle of one government agency flailing away at Transamerica and trying to remove its shares from the trading lists of the stock exchanges, and another government agency willing to lend that corporation many millions of dollars. Mr. Morgenthau accepted the view of the hostile agency. He failed to endorse the loan to Trans, and the peace efforts of the conferees came to a standstill.

8

A word more about the S.E.C. charges. Without giving the corporation an opportunity to make any statement, they had been launched, and handed to the newspapers, a day or so before the conferees on the bank question began their sessions. This timing seems significant. Mr. Morgenthau admitted that he had been consulted in advance by S.E.C. This was obvious, because the commission's allegations showed careful study of the Sedlacek examination report on the Bank of America. Wall Street, anti-New Deal and anti-Giannini, watched the proceedings with glee, "because," as *Time* magazine put it, "the New Deal had bit the only big banking hand that ever fed it."[22]

The basis of the S.E.C. charges were alleged "false and misleading" statements in Transamerica's application to register the stock issued in 1937 when the Bank of America shares were distributed. Among other things, it was said that the $22,503,000 profit claimed by Trans in 1937 was virtually all fictitious. Hearings on the charges were scheduled to begin before the commission in January, 1939. In preparation for them, S.E.C. subpoenaed the top officers of the Bank of America, and ordered them to bring to Washington a great quantity of bank records.

Donald R. Richberg, who had held important Administration posts in the early New Deal, appeared as counsel for Transamerica. Richberg appealed to the courts. He contended that S.E.C. had acted unfairly in making public unsubstantiated charges; that the Secretary of the Treasury had had no right to reveal to the commission confidential data about the bank; that the commission had no right to subpoena bank officers or records to furnish evidence, involving confidential relations between the bank and its customers, in a proceeding to which the bank was not a party and concerning matters that were within "the exclusive visitorial jurisdiction" of the comptroller of the currency.

The bench ruled that Secretary Morgenthau's act "in furnishing the Commission with the reports of the bank examiners . . . was not inconsistent with law." It rebuked the S.E.C., however, for making public the contents of the reports and took it to task for pretrial publication of evidence, "labeled to be true." This "ought to be avoided, especially as emanating from the tribunal charged with the judicial responsibility of . . . assuring the accused a fair hearing." The National Bank Act, the court pointed out, "contemplates exclusive supervision of banks by the Comptroller of the Currency and the confidential treatment by him of . . . their internal affairs." Use of the Bank of America's records was "confined to the investigation of the charges" in preparation for the hearing. The subpoenas affecting the bank's officers and records were declared to be unenforceable.[23]

Though unanticipated by the Treasury Department, the decision, in reality, defined the powers and responsibilities of the comptroller's office and paved the way for the ultimate elimination of the Bank of America from the S.E.C. proceeding against Transamerica. That was what Mario Giannini had been working for.

9

Mario took up the broken thread of negotiations looking toward the settlement of the bank's differences with the Treasury. At first the situation looked hopeful. Delano seemed friendly. As a gesture of good-will he called Chief Examiner Folger into his office and, in Mario's presence, asked Folger to remove Sedlacek from the Bank of America assignment and select in his stead "one of your best qualified examiners, one upon whom he could definitely rely for a fair and impartial examination."[24]

The new examiner was H. C. McLean. His report was completed in July, 1939. It threw cold water on the hope for a settlement. This report repeated most of Sedlacek's criticisms, and raised to a matter of first importance a subject that had been overshadowed by other topics in Mr. Sedlacek's findings. This was the valuation of the bank's banking premises, scattered among 307 communities in California. The bank carried these properties, including furnishings, at $31,000,-000, McLean put their value at $21,834,000.

Knowing beforehand that this subject was coming up, Mario had discussed an independent appraisal with Irwin D. Wright, a seasoned examiner and successor to Prentiss as chief examiner of the Twelfth District. The bank engaged the American Appraisal Company, an independent organization, to value its premises.

As a preliminary, Mr. Wright suggested the division of the bank's numerous holdings into categories and the appraisal of some of each category for sampling purposes. This was done and showed promise of worth-while results. Before the end of the year, the appraisal was completed as to all the 317 individual holdings. The depreciated appraised value, as of December 1, 1939, of the bank's premises owned was $48,509,625. They had cost the bank, less depreciation, $51,423,-092 and the reproduction cost new was fixed at $62,244,085.

Although the bank was then carrying these premises at a figure far below their depreciated appraised value, the examiner would have required the bank to charge out an additional $9,000,000. Of course, bank premises, in a period of improving economic conditions, do not depreciate at any such rate between two examinations.

The McLean report ignored the seventeen-point program of the December, 1938, conferences. As Mario wrote Delano, "this sudden change of mind is evidence to us that Washington dictated the conclusions of the examination report." Certainly, the comptroller repudiated what he had agreed to in December.[25]

In the fall of 1939 Eccles of the Federal Reserve Board made an effort for peace. The two Gianninis went to Washington. There were meetings with various officials. The meetings were friendly but inconclusive, and, on the Gianninis' return to San Francisco in December, all hope for peace seemed knocked in the head by a letter from Delano which put things back where they had been fourteen months before.[26]

The comptroller called the bank's dividend policy "unsafe and unsound"; he demanded that the bank increase its capital; he brushed aside the independent appraisers' report and demanded that the bank adopt the McLean figure. If these things were not done, concluded Mr. Delano, "I shall be compelled to take such action as the law authorizes." He asked Giannini to pass the letter on to his directors.[27]

A. P. Giannini refused pointblank to do so. "Your letter contains matter which is grossly defamatory and libelous," he wrote.

If it is now the policy of the Comptroller of the Currency, under the directions of the Secretary of the Treasury, to enforce agreement to such opinions as he, or the Secretary, might have formed regarding the Bank of America National Trust and Savings Association, or the officers or Directors thereof, by openly charging violations of law and dishonesty, both corporate and personal, I shall have to ask that you use some instrumentality other than me for this purpose.[28]

10

Giannini's defiance opened the final phase of this controversy which brought the showdown and the swift retreat of the Treasury.

The bank asked for an examination of its condition by the Federal Reserve Board. The letter of application denounced the conduct of the Secretary of the Treasury. It called the S.E.C. hearings of charges against the Transamerica Corporation a "vicious" proceeding countenanced by the Secretary. "Publication of unproven charges against our bank . . . would have destroyed a bank whose good will was less strongly entrenched."[29]

The annual meeting of stockholders of the Bank of America was scheduled for January 9, 1940. Mario prepared to mobilize the shareholders in the fight against the Treasury. "We must strike from the shoulder," advised his father. "Nothing in the way of apologies, patronizing or humbling ourselves." Mario admitted the press to the meeting, an unprecedented step at that time, and he addressed personally the three hundred stockholders assembled. He struck from the shoulder, all right:

Were it not for the privilege that surrounds his office, Mr. Morgenthau would not dare to act as he has. We do not propose to relinquish our self respect and submit to his high-handed tactics. . . . We shall continue to contend for honest treatment and fair consideration of your Bank's affairs, and civil treatment of its directors and officers. If this cannot be accomplished rationally, and if it later appears that Mr. Morgenthau is to be permitted to continue to use his position arbitrarily to harass your bank, we may suggest that you consider its conversion into a State bank. It is not necessary to be a national bank in order to be a member of the Federal Deposit Insurance Corporation or the Federal Reserve System. Many of our long-established and highly regarded banking institutions function well in the State system, and your Bank formerly operated very successfully as a State Bank.[30]

The threat to withdraw the Bank of America from the jurisdiction of the Treasury and of the comptroller of the currency by reconversion to a state bank caused a sensation. "GIANNINIS OPEN 'WAR TO END' ON MORGENTHAU," read a typical headline. Mr. Morgenthau took refuge behind a somewhat bombastic statement. He would "protect the interests of depositors of all national banks . . . just so long as I have breath in my body." At the moment, however, the Secretary did not use any of his breath to discuss the most interesting question Mario had raised—that of reconversion.[31]

The bank went ahead with procedure looking to a change into a state institution. The skeleton of the Bank of America (state) was ready for that purpose. Before Mario addressed the stockholders, Charles W. Collins in Washington had, after quiet inquiry, reported that as a state institution the Giannini bank would be received as a member of the Federal Reserve System and of the Federal Deposit Insurance Corporation. Mario Giannini telegraphed Comptroller Delano that "WE PROPOSE PROMPTLY TO INITIATE [RECONVERSION] PROCEEDINGS. PLEASE ADVISE US WHETHER OR NOT THERE ARE ANY FORMALITIES PRESCRIBED BY RULES OR REGULATIONS OF YOUR OFFICE RELATING TO SUCH PROCEEDINGS WHICH ARE NOT PRESCRIBED BY STATUTE. SEND US THE NECESSARY FORMS." The Federal Reserve Bank of San Francisco also was notified. "BEFORE PROCEEDING FORMALLY . . . TO DISSOLVE THE ASSOCIATION AS A NATIONAL BANK, WE WOULD LIKE TO HAVE AN INDICATION FROM YOU AS TO THE FORMALITIES INVOLVED.[32]

Russell Smith conferred with California's superintendent of banks. That official said he would welcome the return of the Bank of America into his dwindling circle of state banks.[33]

Less than a month after the announncement to stockholders, leaks concerning the Bank of America once more were emanating from Washington. They were different from the leaks of 1938. As the ticker service *Banktrends* informed its subscribers: "Beginning to appear that the Treasury's conflict with Bank of America will be smoothly ironed out with no casualties. Treasury authorities were on the wrong track and advised they would be unable to prove their points. Morgenthau may discuss the matter with the President today."

The fact is that Mr. Morgenthau hadn't a leg to stand on.

In February Mario Giannini went to Washington. He met practically the same government people he had met in 1938. They soon reached an agreement which was less exacting than that of December 5, 1938. It was a sweeping victory for the bank. On March 15, 1940, Mario gave the terms to the press. The principal items were:

1. The comptroller's office conceded the right of the bank's board of directors to exercise their own judgment as to the amount of dividend declarations. The bank announced there would be no change.

2. The bank conceded the desirability of increasing its capital by $30,000,000 no later than June 30, 1940.

3. A reappraisal of bank premises by a committee of three chosen from the three bank supervisory agencies was agreed to. Meanwhile, the bank agreed to set up from the new capital a reserve of $6,900,000 to be used to reduce the carrying value of the properties, if the new appraisal turned out to be less than the bank claimed.

4. Concerning contracts of the Bank of America with Capital Company and California Lands, the bank agreed to obtain additional collateral, satisfactory to the comptroller, to secure the contracts, and to eliminate all such contracts from the bank's assets by December 15, 1943.

5. The obligations to the bank of Transamerica and subsidiaries were to be brought within the 10 per cent limitation of "one interest" by July 15, 1942, and to be eliminated by July 15, 1945.[34]

Mr. Morgenthau made his exit from the situation with the very brief comment that he was "satisfied" with the settlement.[35]

The terms of the agreement were all carried out on time or ahead of time. It is necessary to mention only two of them.

Although Jesse Jones again offered to supply R.F.C. funds to Transamerica to care for the $30,000,000 issue of convertible preferred stock of the bank, Mario Giannini set about to dispose of the shares through an underwriting by investment bankers. That spring Hitler fell upon Norway, Denmark, the Low Countries and France, and the British expeditionary force escaped through Dunkirk in May. Securities markets plunged. The public was not buying. Therefore Mario accepted Jones's offer and the R.F.C. loaned $27,533,000 to Transamerica. Four years ahead of time, in 1946, the bank retired the last of the preferred stock, and Transamerica finished paying off the Reconstruction Finance Corporation.

In the matter of the value of banking premises the appraisers again found in favor of the bank's figures. Nevertheless, Mario voluntarily reduced the carrying value of these properties by $4,004,000, in addition to depreciation.

The Securities and Exchange Commission hearings of its charges against Transamerica, launched with such fanfare in 1938, dragged on and on. Not until 1947 were they dismissed, "without," as A. P.

Giannini informed the stockholders, "the corporation altering any of the figures in its financial reports that had been challenged by the Commission." Moreover, there was no criticism of the directors or officers of Transamerica.[36]

II

On May 6, 1940, A. P. Giannini celebrated his seventieth birthday. The struggle with the Treasury was behind him. To employees, depositors and friends who filed past the veteran's desk at No. 1 Powell he said it was time "for folks to forget my birthdays." Some of the depositors in the greeters' line were carried into the bank in the arms of their parents, who had first made the acquaintance of Mr. Giannini in the arms of *their* parents. The employees' present was a pledge to increase the bank's deposits by $150,000,000 in one year. Vice-President Frank Risso, once Giannini's chauffeur, took charge of the campaign.

At the end of the year Giannini told the employees he was looking forward to his present. He said he wasn't running the bank any more. Mario was doing that, and had been for some time. "[During the coming year] I want to withdraw a little further and leave more of the active leadership in younger hands." But he would still be around, like "the family watchdog, ready to growl at any sign of danger from without, and ready to bark at you if I find any turning away from the ideals on which this institution was built. . . . We, as a bank, never could have survived the assaults of the past two years or more if we had not been clean and sound, with no guilty secrets. I have never locked my desk or a single drawer in it. I have nothing to hide, nor has the bank."[37]

On May 6, 1941, A. P. Giannini got his present, plus $31,000,000 extra. In twelve months the gain in deposits had been $181,000,000.

On the next day Mr. Giannini laid a cornerstone at Montgomery and Pine Streets. The stone bore the words:

ERECTED A.D. 1941

BANK OF AMERICA

NATIONAL TRUST AND SAVINGS ASSOCIATION

A. P. GIANNINI

FOUNDER

The time was near to say farewell to No. 1 Powell Street as the head office of the bank. In 1939 the Bank of America had begun to build a new home that was to fill the long block on Montgomery Street between Pine and California. It is in the heart of San Francisco's financial district, and a five-minute walk from the Bank of Italy's first home in North Beach.

It is twelve stories high, and there is no handsomer business edifice west of Chicago. The construction was done under the supervision of Giannini's brother-in-law, Clarence Cuneo, whom the reader may recall in connection with the early days of the Bank of Italy. In 1941 Mr. Cuneo was executive vice-president of the Capital Company. Three Hundred Montgomery, as the building has become known in financial circles throughout the world, was formally opened on December 9, 1941. There were only token ceremonies. Pearl Harbor was smoking from the attack of two days before.

The eleventh floor of the building is the officers' floor. They inhabit a huge, quiet, walnut-paneled room which, except for a few private consulting rooms, runs the dimensions of the building. The officers have their desks in the open, where A. P. Giannini always insisted a bank officer's desk should be.

When the building was finished Giannini consented to try one of the private rooms. This was to be a mark of his semiretirement. He couldn't stand it, however. "It's a gilded cage," he complained. In no time A. P. had his desk out in the big room, with those of the other officers.

The Bank and World War II

PARTLY because of its geography, in World War II California became a camp, an arsenal and a commissary for the troops. It was the jumping-off place for the Pacific theater of conflict. Peacetime modes of life changed more abruptly and profoundly there than in any other state. During the war years and the period of preparation preceding them, 2,000,000 Americans from other parts of the country poured into California to man its arms plants. The population of small towns mushroomed to 50,000 and upward. Communities of 10,000 to 25,000 sprang up where there had been next to no one before the war. Even the boom-studded annals of the West contained nothing like this up to then.

The major significance of this invasion was not the numbers but the character of the newcomers. Prior to 1940 agriculture had been the magnet that drew people to California to work. Despite the advances toward industrialization that had been made since the first war, the basis of California's prosperity was the field and not the factory. The war changed this. It brought a new face to the West Coast—the face of the industrial worker, headed for the plant and not for the farm. This change had a profound effect on the operations of the Bank of America.

First of all, these newcomers had to be housed. As they were engaged in a national undertaking, namely, the provision of the sinews of war, the nation bore the largest part of the burden of providing shelter. After Uncle Sam, far and away the heaviest contributor among private lending agencies was the Bank of America.

The building of the prodigious plants which the workers manned night and day was also a national concern, as was the financing of the contracts for airplanes and ships and so forth that these plants turned out. Here again, the United States government was the principal lender. But among private lenders the Bank of America was in the van. California's industrial war activity was not self-contained. It was linked with similar activity in the rest of the country. The Bank of America followed this spreading out. It became a national bank in a new sense, in that it helped to finance war industry in all parts of the United States.

Getting back to California, the great war plants that blossomed there did not receive all the Bank of America's attention by any means. Small industrialists employing maybe ten and maybe fifty hands were the bank's special concern. These little fellows were threatened with extinction, as their workers were drawn off to the big plants that were getting the contracts. This was true of the whole country as well as of California. In fact it was even a worse problem in parts of the country more fully industrialized than California. But it was a Californian whose ingenuity went a long way toward saving the day for the little fellows. A formula that Mario Giannini had tested in California did much to make possible the Smaller War Plants Corporation, a government agency to see that the little fellows all over the United States got a chance to do their part.

2

The nation's preparation for war began in earnest in the spring of 1940, with the fall of Western Europe to Hitler. We invoked military conscription, which had never been done before in time of peace, and let contracts to equip a large army and to increase the Navy to two-ocean scope. First call on our productive capacity, however, was Britain's. The contracts involved in these preparations were with big industrial concerns prepared to produce quickly and in volume. Plant expansion and retooling were financed almost altogether by the government. The banks had little to do with it.

One effect of this was to attract skilled labor to the favored centers. In California these centers were the aircraft plants around Los Angeles and San Diego, and the shipbuilding yards on San Francisco Bay. The boom towns were in the making. Small industries that the Bank of America had labored for years to build up would be snuffed out unless places could be found for them in the defense program. Thousands of parts go into the fabrication of an airplane or a ship. Many could be made in small plants, and shipped to a place of assembly. Washington realized this. "It is almost criminal negligence," said Sidney Hillman of the National Defense Advisory Commission, "if we do not make it possible for all plants to participate in the defense effort. Every shop in even the smallest community should be turning out defense materials."

This system was employed in England, where production for civilian uses had virtually ceased. Village blacksmiths worked on defense orders, by what was called the "bits and pieces" method. A. P. Giannini said that was the way to do the job here. "It is calculated to minimize 'boom town' problems, present and future," he observed.

It means the continued functioning of local industry, maintenance of payrolls, stabilization of employment for the skilled worker in established surroundings of which he and his family are an important part, greater production for defense, and a big step toward cushioning the readjustments which must follow the ultimate curtailment of the defense program.[1]

Upon suggestion from the Bank of America, Governor Olson called a conference on the subject at Sacramento. The principal sessions were linked to local meetings that the bank's branches organized throughout the state. As a result California adopted a "bits and pieces" program and the drive began to put the small factories into defense preparations. The bank dinned in the slogan: "Convert Your Plant to National Defense." More than simple conversion was necessary, as the bank knew. The government did not guarantee the loans of subcontractors as it did those of prime contractors. That was something to work for in Washington. While this was being done, a number of small industries in the Santa Clara Valley, near San Francisco, banded together as the San Jose Manufacturers, Inc. Their pool had sufficient basic equipment to bid as a prime contractor. A Bank of America officer, Vern C. Richards, was named business adviser of the association which the bank loaned $70,000 for retooling. Half a million more was promised to finance contracts.

The bank took energetic steps to land contracts, not for the Santa Clara people alone but for all the little fellows in California. In the Mayflower Hotel in Washington it set up an "Office of Defense Information." This official-sounding agency was in charge of Theodore Granik, a Washington lawyer who knew the ropes in the government bureaus. During the early stages Earl Lee Kelly, a former director of public works in California, who knew the state's small industries, also was on the ground. The staff of the Office of Defense Information went to the procurement agencies preaching subcontracting and more subcontracting. They kept the bank's California clients posted on priorities, cutbacks and the unending changes of the war economy. In three months' time this activity was very helpful in landing for the little fellows in California, nineteen hundred contracts totaling $42,500,000. The financing was facilitated by a new law which permitted banks to accept assignments of government contracts as collateral for loans.[2]

Then came Pearl Harbor. We were at war instead of getting ready for it. Contracting activity increased a hundredfold. American industry went on a total-war footing. For example, the last "civilian" automobile rolled off the production line, and the stocks of cars on hand went under a government rationing order. The automotive plants turned to work on tanks and three thousand other items for combat. Mario Giannini, who had been the inspiration of the small plants' participation during the pre-Pearl Harbor phase, meant to see that they did not lose out now. Moreover, he was far from satisfied with the voluntary pool. The San Jose pool had gone through three disappointing months of promises before landing its first contract. Something more was needed. Mr. Giannini suggested that the government form an agency to take over, for the benefit of small shops everywhere, the work that the Bank of America was trying to do in the way of obtaining contracts for those in California. That was only part of Mr. Giannini's suggestion. To enable small contractors to execute contracts, he urged that the government guarantee their loans, as they did those of the big fellows. Then banks could advance the small contractors the money they needed, as they did in the case of the big fellows.

Donald Nelson, chairman of the War Production Board, knew the California story. Mr. Nelson, of course, had a great deal else on his mind at this time, and a firm like General Motors which could turn out units by the thousand commanded more attention than a small-town shop whose production would be measured in dozens. A subcommittee of the Senate was considering the plight of small business. Mario Giannini sent E. A. Mattison to Washington to represent the views of the Bank of America. Presently Nelson was called before the committee. After the W.P.B. chairman had made his recommendations, Matty wired Mario:

YOUR ENTIRE PROGRAM ENDORSED BY MR. NELSON.[3]

Within three months Congress created the Smaller War Plants Corporation. This agency pried out work for subcontractors, and by the end of the war had made loans of $190,000,000, nine-tenths of which went to plants with less than a hundred employees.

By the time the Smaller War Plants Corporation came into being, the Federal Reserve Board had taken a great step toward financing war production, including that of small plants. It had promulgated what was known as Regulation V. Frankly designed to get more war production, Regulation V's terms were so easy as to make war work almost irresistible to contractors. For the first time subcontracts qualified for guarantee by the government, even up to 100 per cent if necessary. This was a boon to small plants, and what Mario Giannini had urged. It was also a boon to banks for it assured them of participation in the war effort. For a while, the bankers had feared their institutions would be used mainly as warehouses for government bonds. The maximum rate on V Loans was 5 per cent. Competition among lenders sometimes resulted in rates as low as $1\frac{1}{2}$ per cent.

Individually, V Loans ranged from a few hundred dollars to a billion. The billion-dollar loan, to General Motors, was subscribed by four hundred banks. Half the Bank of America's early V Loans were for less than $100,000.

In southern California, Clark Beise and Keath L. Carver were a good team at pushing out V Loans. Samples of some of the larger contracts thus financed: Technical Oil Tool Corporation, Ltd., with a loan of $136,000, turned out tachometers for Norden bombsights; Gillespie Furniture Company, $500,000, fuel drop tanks for aircraft; Grayson Heat Control, Ltd., thermostat manufacturer, $1,500,-000, converted to hydraulic control for aircraft wing flaps; Western Stove Company, $500,000, incendiary bombs; Cole of California, the maker of "Hollywood" bathing suits, $325,000, parachutes. Walt Disney Productions got a $1,000,000 loan and switched from Donald Duck to propaganda and educational films.[4]

3

California's greatest war effort had to do with the manufacture of airplanes. Of the 301,584 machines built in the United States during the forty-four months between Pearl Harbor and VJ Day, one-fifth were assembled in California. Employment in the Golden State's airplane plants reached a high-water mark of 243,000 in 1943, against 16,800 before Hitler started on his rampage. New plant construction cost $150,000,000, of which private capital furnished $79,000,000 and the government the rest. These figures are small beside the cost of the planes that were made or assembled in those California plants. That amounted to $10,203,359,000, or one-sixth of the $61,537,605,000 spent nationally. No other state enjoyed such a harvest. Michigan, the seat of the automobile industry, was second with $7,000,000,000 in contracts.

Subcontracting was the secret of the success of our achievement in aircraft. Very often a finished plane represented the assembly of parts from across the width of the continent. Some planes were made wholly within the State of California, and more were made wholly within the State of Michigan, but that was not the rule. For instance, Consolidated-Vultee of San Diego had branch plants as far away as Florida. Bendix Aviation of Detroit had a plant in North Hollywood. The chief thing that California made in quantity was airframes. Those not used at home went elsewhere in the country. Trainloads of motors and other parts for planes rumbled across the Rockies in continuous procession, to be fitted into airframes on the Coast.

Most of the large aviation loans were controlled by syndicates of Eastern bankers who commanded large resources. Having done business for years with the industrial giants involved, the Easterners had the inside track. The Bank of America had to work hard for most of its V Loans to the aviation industry.

The bank came out very well. Vice-Chairman Francis S. Baer devoted most of his time to stalking participations in the Eastern syndicates. Until its purchase by Transamerica, Mr. Baer had been president of the Pacific Finance Company, the bank's leading Western competitor in automobile financing. "I've always heard," he said when he went to 300 Montgomery, "so much about what this bank does for the little fellow that I'm going to try to do something for the neglected big fellows."[5]

He got his first chance with the Consolidated-Vultee Aircraft Corporation of San Diego. Though a California concern and one of the bank's heavy depositors, Consolidated's prime financial connections were with the East. The Chase National Bank of New York had organized a bankers' pool to float a $200,000,000 loan. Baer was delighted when he was able to tell the eleventh floor at 300 Montgomery that the Bank of America's participation would be equal to Chase's—$15,000,000.

The changes war wrought at the Consolidated-Vultee plant illustrate what took place in California in this period. In peacetime, Consolidated had less than 1,500 employees; at peak war employment they numbered 44,673. Two months after Pearl Harbor, the San Diego plant was operating the first continuously moving airplane assembly line the world had ever known.[6]

A little later Baer got for his bank $19,400,000 of the largest single V Loan flotation of the war, the billion-dollar loan to General Motors, which was managed by the Bankers Trust of New York. The Bank of America's largest single loan was $20,000,000 to another California corporation, Lockheed Aircraft. It was part of a $175,-000,000 flotation that also was in the hands of the Bankers Trust Company. Some of the other large participations, mostly for aircraft, follow:

Borrower	Total Commitment	B. of A. Commitment	Agent Banks
Allis Chalmers	$ 75,000,000	$ 1,725,000	First Nat'l. Bank of Chicago
Bendix Aviation	150,000,000	5,000,000	Nat'l. Bank of Detroit
Brewster Aero Corp.	55,000,000	13,750,000	Chase Nat'l. Bank
Edw. G. Budd Mfg.	20,000,000	1,250,000	Bank of New York
Chrysler Corp.	250,000,000	7,500,000	Nat'l. Bank of Detroit
Continental Motors	30,000,000	800,000	Nat'l. Bank of Detroit
Electric Auto Lite	17,000,000	250,000	Central Hanover Bk. & Trust Co.
Emerson Elec. Mfg. Co.	30,000,000	1,000,000	First Nat'l. Bk. of St. Louis
Hudson Motor Car	30,000,000	3,000,000	New York Trust Co.
Mack Mfg. Co.	50,000,000	500,000	Manufacturers Trust Co.
R.C.A.	75,000,000	1,000,000	Bankers Trust Co.
Sperry Corp.	125,000,000	11,500,000	Bankers Trust Co.
Westinghouse	200,000,000	7,000,000	Chase Nat'l. Bank[7]

These activities illustrate what was said earlier about the Bank of America becoming a national bank in the broadest sense. The tremendous resources it commanded were put to work all over the country. The very nature of the war effort, where industries like aircraft had to call upon the industrial might of the entire nation, led to its participation on a national scale. Thus, for the first time to any considerable degree, the Bank of America broke the isolation, the sectionalism, that had characterized its past. This was all a part of what was happening to California, where barriers to the eastward were falling before the Golden State's new-found industrial strength.

The Bank of America also had a long list of participations in V Loans to California aircraft companies. It advanced $3,000,000 to North American Aviation, Inc., whose B-25 medium bombers took Doolittle and his men to Tokyo. To Northrop Aircraft, Inc., went $3,060,000 for first developing and then producing the P-61, the Black Widow night fighter. Northrop is chiefly a research and development organization. The same is true of Ryan Aeronautical Company of San Diego to which the bank extended a direct line of credit for $841,000.[8]

Factories making plane parts boomed along with the prime contractors. The Bank of America financed a score or more of subcontractors, from tool makers to radio repairmen, who turned out bits and pieces required to make an airplane. Commitments ranged from a few thousand to several million dollars.

One contractor whose achievements the Giannini bank regarded with particular satisfaction was Solar Aircraft of San Diego, turning out stainless steel exhaust manifolds for such important craft as the B-29 Superfortresses. During the depression this company had managed to survive by making frying pans, bookends and so on. In 1939, with an initial loan of $100,000 from the Bank of America, it began to find its way back to prosperity. During the war, nearly $90,000,000 worth of contracts passed through Solar's plants. Bank of America's pool commitments to Solar reached $4,225,000 in 1944. That year Solar embarked on a program of research on the jet engine, and shortly before VE-Day went into mass production of heat-resistant parts for the jet. For the changeover a group of New York and Western banks underwrote a $12,500,000 V Loan. The Bank of America took the largest share, $8,000,000.[9]

4

Though less money was spent for ships than for planes during the war, California's share of the aggregate was greater—$5,096,-957,000, or 17.7 per cent of the total outlay of $28,840,595,000. The Bank of America's participation also was proportionately greater, thanks largely to its backing of A. P. Giannini's old friend, Henry J. Kaiser, who had never built a ship before.

In one respect California's performance in ship construction was more noteworthy than its performance with airplanes. Before the war California had an airplane industry on which to build. It had nothing comparable in the way of shipbuilding. Most of the four thousand men employed in the shipyards were in the United States Navy Yard at Mare Island, Vallejo. Not a merchant vessel had been constructed since World War I. At the end of the second war shipbuilding was California's second industry, with 313,000 on the payrolls. The government had poured $409,000,000 into plant construction, whereas private capital, remembering the lot of such plants after the first war, had ventured only $29,000,000. It was in the contracts executed in these yards that private lenders figured extensively. Under these contracts California turned out more oceangoing tonnage than any other state in the Union.

San Francisco Bay was the focal point of this endeavor. River towns such as Antioch (wooden minesweepers), Stockton (steel barges and wooden minesweepers), and Napa (lighters and oil barges) did their share. No part of the armament program utilized subcontracting more than shipbuilding. It was particularly adaptable to the production of Liberty ships, whose prefabricated sections of hulls and superstructures were assembled and welded together on the building ways. Throughout California small plants rushed out the orders for prefabrications, machinery, masts, booms, hoists and other miscellaneous castings and equipment. Prime contracts involving $50,000 or more for materials and equipment had been placed by government procurement agencies with some 380 concerns located in forty-five counties throughout the Twelfth Federal Reserve District. The shipyards themselves placed a substantial volume of subcontracts. Early in 1944 Mare Island, which farmed out little or no work prior to the war, had about nineteen hundred prime contractors and more than three hundred subcontractors in California, Utah, Colorado and Wyoming. These firms employed some 25,000 persons.

More than any other one man, Henry J. Kaiser was responsible for California's achievement. His seven yards in California, Oregon and Washington produced 1,490 ships, or 34.9 per cent of the total merchant ship deliveries in the United States during the war. Kaiser revolutionized emergency shipbuilding with his welding process. Prefabricated ship sections, stamped to a pattern, were welded together and delivered to the ways where they were joined by more welding to form cargo ships. It was assembly-line technique, requiring relatively little experienced labor. The Richmond, California, yard set a record assembling and launching a ship in eleven days.

Giannini and Kaiser had met in the twenties when Kaiser applied for a loan to execute a road-building contract. The two men were much alike: tireless innnovators who, in their separate fields, believed that in the distribution of rewards for labor there should be more for the many and less for the few. As a Bank of Italy client, Kaiser built roads in places as distant as British Columbia and Cuba; he laid pipelines; he constructed levees along the Mississippi. In 1931, the Six Companies, Inc., in which Kaiser was an important figure, got the contract for Boulder Dam. During the first weeks of Roosevelt in the White House, Kaiser carried the following handwritten letter to Washington:

MR. PRESIDENT:

I wish to introduce to you Mr. Henry J. Kaiser, President of Bridge Builders, Inc., one of the low bidders on the San Francisco–Oakland Bay Bridge. He is also Chairman of the Executive Committee of the Six Companies, who hold the contract on Boulder Dam.

Mr. Kaiser is in Washington on matters pertaining to the Bay Bridge, and while there would like to consult with you. He is a man of outstanding ability, very highly thought of in this community, and has been a friend and customer of the bank since the first day he came to California.

Any courtesies extended to him I shall greatly appreciate.

Respectfully,
A. P. GIANNINI[10]

During the first and second Roosevelt Administrations Kaiser had a part in the building of such works as the Grand Coulee, Bonneville and Parker Dams. Although he did not own a cement mill, he underbid competitors by thirty cents a barrel to supply all the cement for the Shasta dam. The Bank of America loaned $7,500,000 toward the building of the world's largest plant for Kaiser's Permanente Cement Company. During the war Permanente, with the capacity to turn out 14,000 barrels a day, supplied the bulk cement used in the construction of Pacific air and naval bases. Important as to timing, directly after Pearl Harbor Permanente was able to deliver from its own storage stockpile, most of the 65,000 barrels of cement that quickly put Honolulu's airfields back into action.

Kaiser got into the ship program by erecting yards for others. Much to the satisfaction of Admiral Land, chairman of the Maritime Commission, in 1941 the builder accepted a $40,000,000 order to construct twenty-four cargo vessels. From that point Kaiser branched out. When he could not get enough steel for his ships, he persuaded the government to lend him $112,000,000 to erect a steel mill at Fontana. Kaiser also erected a magnesium plant that turned out 82,000,000 tons of "goop," the secret incendiary material for bombs, and over 20,000,000 tons of magnesium ingots for airplane parts. Moreover, he made shells, airplane parts, and experimented with helicopters.

The government was Kaiser's principal financier. From the start, however, the cement company has been a private venture. Among private lenders the Bank of America ranked first in its contributions to the various Kaiser enterprises. At one time the industrialist's line of credit reached $43,000,000. This was the bank's largest advance to one business management.

Bank of America's loans to Kaiser have always been promptly repaid, some ahead of time. On ships he contracted to build for the Maritime Commission, Kaiser made deliveries promptly, if not ahead of time. In May, 1946, his government shipping contracts had reached a total dollar volume of $4,019,256,000. When Mr. Kaiser applied for a loan to start a synthetic rubber plant, R.F.C. turned him down. "I thought he had enough to do," said Jesse Jones.[11]

The Kaiser loans afford a striking example of the Bank of America's decentralization and of the responsibility Giannini reposed with trusted lieutenants. Kaiser's headquarters were in Oakland, where for years Fred A. Ferroggiaro, vice-president and manager of the Oakland main branch, had handled the builder's loans. In 1940 Ferroggiaro was moved to the head office as executive vice-president and vice-chairman of the general finance committee of the bank. He continued to handle the Kaiser account through the Oakland branch.

The bank's largest single advance pertaining to ships was not to Kaiser, but to the Rheem Manufacturing Company of Richmond, recipient of a direct V Loan of $15,000,000. Rheem had been a long-time customer of the bank. By 1940 the company had expanded from small beginnings to something like nationwide operation as a maker of oil drums and water heaters, with plants in Houston, Chicago, New Orleans and Newark as well as in California. During the war it acquired ten more plants, and filled a long list of naval contracts.

The old-established Moore Drydock & Shipbuilding Company, a customer of the Crocker bank, received a loan of $4,750,000. Three million went to the W. A. Bechtel Company, an associate of Kaiser at Boulder Dam, which also took up shipbuilding. There were loans of $4,000,000 and down to the makers of marine engines, and a multitude of advances in varying amounts to subcontractors.

Except for the government's contribution, the shipbuilding program in California was financed by West Coast bankers. When syndicate operations were resorted to, as in the case of Crocker with the Moore Company, other Western banks took what the managing bank did not care to take. This was a milestone in the West's long struggle for financial independence.

5

Though the plan that Mario Giannini engineered to bring small industry into the war program acted as a deterrent to the concentration of workers in boom towns, it did not forestall such concentrations by any means. On San Francisco Bay the city of Richmond, the principal seat of Kaiser's shipbuilding operations, went from 23,000 population to 115,000—and this despite the fact that thousands of Richmond workers commuted from Oakland over an emergency railway supplied with cars from an abandoned New York City elevated line. Across the bay in another direction from San Francisco, the town of Marin City grew from nothing to 6,000. A bay city, Vallejo, once the capital of California, went from 14,000 to 43,000. These are cited as examples merely.

In the south the story was the same. Los Angeles added one to each four of its population, but some of those who tried to find places to sleep there thought it was the other way around. Long Beach made room for 70,000 more, and finished the war with 212,-000 people. San Diego doubled in size, to 292,000. Again, these are merely examples.

The first problem was to provide shelter for the newcomers. The government provided 99,589 dwelling units at a cost of $306,064,000. From the end of 1940 to the end of 1945, the Bank of America made 99,624 residential loans for an aggregate of $444,992,000. All this outlay was not to provide housing for war workers, though most of it was. *All* the government's outlay was for that purpose. For example, when the war ended half of Richmond's population was living in 24,000 temporary housing units the government had thrown up at a cost of $50,000,000.

The government also participated in the bank loans as a guarantor. Under what was called Title VI, the Federal Housing Administration made provision for the needs of the war-boom communities. Most of the bank's housing loans were under that title, whose terms were very liberal. The maximum cost of a house was $4,500, with no down payment and thirty months to acquire a 10 per cent equity.

The bank has never segregated its Title VI F.H.A. loans from its Title II loans. We do learn, however, that in 1942 Title VI loans outstanding exceeded $30,000,000, and that during the first three-quarters of 1943 such loans were made in southern California towns as follows: Barstow, $204,000; Burbank, $741,000; Culver City, $400,-000; Fullerton, $163,000; Long Beach, $1,454,000; San Diego, $1,385,-000. By VE-Day Title VI loans in San Diego totaled $7,000,000.

As an indication of the speed and volume of wartime construction under Title VI, Paul W. Trousdale, who had a line of credit at the Los Angeles main office, estimated that his firm completed "two houses per day, seven days a week." During most of the period, Trousdale had three hundred houses underway at once. All told he provided more than three thousand homes for war workers' families. His advances from the Bank of America reached $8,000,000. The figure seemed large then, but it represents only one-fourth of the financing Trousdale got when he started building homes for returning G.I.'s.[12]

The boom towns inflated normal banking services into acute problems. The supplying of change—half-dollars, quarters, dimes, nickels and pennies—for payrolls and for the business needs of those swollen communities meant the counting, packaging and transportation of coin by the ton. Branches that formerly required $10,000 or $15,000 in till cash now provided currency—in $10 bills and smaller —to meet payrolls running into hundreds of thousands and even millions of dollars every payday. An incidental service the bank rendered was in connection with food coupons. The points surrendered by housewives were deposited in banks. Retailers, wholesalers and manufacturers drew against these deposits to replenish their stocks. The Bank of America handled sixty thousand such coupon accounts.

Branches in the boom areas lengthened their hours and multiplied personnel, which sometimes worked in shifts. In a single day the Richmond branch took care of more than ten thousand customers. Its deposits went from $2,500,000 to $19,000,000. The same was true to a lesser degree of southern California branches in communities where the airplane industry blossomed, such as Santa Monica (seat of a Douglas plant), Burbank (Lockheed), Inglewood (North American), San Diego (Consolidated) and North Long Beach (Douglas).

The bank's difficulties were increased by the refusal of the comptroller of the currency to authorize a sufficient number of new branches to handle properly the avalanche of business. The situation was met by consolidating certain branches in regions untouched by the boom, and transferring to areas of congestion the charter thus released. Actually, the Bank of America finished the war with three fewer branches than it had operated before Pearl Harbor. An application for a third branch at Vallejo was met with the assertion, by the deputy comptroller, that Vallejo was a trailer camp, not an industrial defense area. The bank spent $50,000 enlarging one of the Vallejo branches, doubled the staffs of both, and made arrangements for patrons to bank by mail. In 1946, when it was clear that Vallejo was there to stay as an industrial locality, the third branch was chartered.[13]

More will be said in a moment about the difficulties with Washington officialdom. Nevertheless, in 1942 Secretary of the Treasury Morgenthau awarded the Bank of America the department's citation for "distinguished service" for having sold $120,000,000 in War Savings Bonds in one year. The following year the bank sold $300,-000,000 in government bonds, and received a letter of commendation from the Treasury. From May, 1941, to May, 1945, the Bank of America disposed of United States securities worth $2,725,831,000, a record unequaled by any other private financial institution. Nearly a billion of this amount was in E, F and G bonds of relatively small denominations.

All banks acted without pay as agents for government bonds. The Gianninis devoted energy and money to the sales campaigns. The cost to the bank of the 1943 drive was $1,000 a day in newspaper advertising, billboards, radio programs, rallies and other promotion reminiscent of the "Back to Good Times" campaign of 1932. Every branch received a quota, based on the amount of deposits.

At the start of the war the bank discontinued its school savings deposits program, though the bank's collectors continued to visit the schools to accept the children's savings toward the purchase of war bonds. Speaking of the bond campaign as a whole, A. P. Giannini wrote in an office memorandum: "The pursuit of this program may temporarily decrease our savings deposits . . . but nevertheless we feel the possible selfish interest of the bank should be considered secondary . . . [to the welfare] of the country."[14]

6

The military camps, too, growing in number and in size, presented a banking problem. So, also, in some degree, did the near-by towns where the soldiers spent their off-duty time. On week ends the troops just about took over those towns by weight of numbers. Six months before Pearl Harbor, 20,000 G.I.'s were in camp outside San Luis Obispo, population 9,000. Paso Robles, with 3,000, was "downtown" to another 20,000. Monterey, 10,000, had 32,000 military visitors on its outskirts. The nearest bank to the Hunter Liggett Military Reservation, where as many as 100,000 troops went for maneuvers, was King City, with 1,800 permanent residents.

During the defense period the banking needs of the armed forces were taken care of by banks designated as "general United States depositories," and located in twenty-eight California cities. Twenty-five of the depositories were branches of the Bank of America. They handled pay checks of Army and Navy officers and of civilian employees; provided cash for the payment of enlisted men; carried the accounts of many military units; supplied change on settlement day for post exchanges, officers' messes and so on. In 1935 Giannini had obtained a charter for a branch at Hamilton Field, near San Rafael. With the onset of the emergency Hamilton Field grew like the green bay tree, as did military establishments everywhere. The branch kept pace, handling money matters smoothly. Branches on the ground seemed the ideal solution.

The Bank of America requested three additional "military" branch permits—for March Field, near Riverside; for Fort Ord, near Monterey; and for Camp Roberts, near San Miguel. Early in 1941 the comptroller of the currency denied the permits. A. P. Giannini packed his grip and started on a tour of his branches. What he saw led him, not for the first time in his life, to question the wisdom of a comptroller's decision. The boom towns were in the making. Before tellers' windows Giannini saw lines that extended into the streets.

As a remedy for the increasingly difficult situation in the military camps, Giannini hit upon a clause in the Banking Act of 1935 for the establishment of "seasonal agencies." Though intended for tourist resorts, the clause had been used to cover temporary branches at the San Diego and the San Francisco world's fairs, and, every year, at the state fair at Sacramento. The matter was broached to Deputy Comptroller Upham. Upham said he did not like the idea, and wasn't going "to see the Bank of America use the war as a means of expanding the number of its branches."[15]

Earl Lee Kelly laid before Mr. Upham communications from the commanding officers of the Naval Training Station at San Diego, a military hospital at Modesto and an army training center at Marysville petitioning the bank for services. "Will you have any objections to our selling money orders, cashing checks, and leaving with these centers full material or a complete kit to enable them to bank with us by mail?" asked Kelly. "You have no idea of the terrific pressure we are getting from all parts of California . . . to render some kind of service to the military."[16]

When no reply came from Upham within a month, Giannini took matters into his own hands. He told branch managers to install "limited" banking services at military posts upon the request of responsible officers. Several such requests were on file. The services amounted to about what Kelly had requested. Usually tellers would set up shop at a post for one or two days a week. Two bank examiners dropped in on Chet Warren, manager of the branch at Santa Ana, which provided services for the Army air base near by and had received $7,000 in deposits on the first day. "I assume that you have a permit to do banking at the camp," said the examiners. "As far as I know, we have," replied Warren. All the permit he had was from the camp commandant.[17]

About the same time an officer of the Federal Reserve Bank of San Francisco called Russell Smith's attention to the need for banking accommodations in the state's two relocation centers for Japanese residents. Directly after Pearl Harbor, the government had removed California's ninety thousand residents of Japanese ancestry to these centers, where they were held in protective custody until the end of hostilities. "This gives us an opening," Mario Giannini wrote on a margin of the Reserve official's letter. The Tulelake and Lone Pine branches did the rest.[18]

What happened next suggests that the Bank of America was still far from a favorite of Mr. Morgenthau. Yielding to pressure from Army posts and Naval stations, the Treasury announced that an Oklahoma bank had been permitted to open a "banking facility" in near-by Fort Sill, and that the department would entertain applications for similar "facilities" elsewhere. Facilities blossomed all over the map—except in California. Neither the Bank of America nor any other bank got a permit. It was a strange business. Giannini increased to fifty the number of his unofficial facilities, which he called "installations." He complained bitterly to Marriner Eccles of the Treasury's "discrimination." The installations performed indispensable services. In one month they provided $13,700,000 in currency for military payrolls, and cashed 220,000 checks for $20,000,000.[19]

After seven months of this sort of thing the Treasury consented, early in 1943, to authorize facilities for California's camps. As far as the Bank of America was concerned this meant official sanction, with a little broader powers, for Giannini's installations. At the close of 1944 the bank operated forty-four facilities in California camps, with the American Trust Company of San Francisco and the Manufacturers Trust of New York tied for second place with six each.

With the reduction of the military establishment after VJ-Day the number of Bank of America facilities dropped to twelve. Then came the Korea episode in June, 1950, and a threatening future that called for rearmament. In 1953, the bank had in operation thirty-one domestic and six overseas facilities.

7

Deposits rose abnormally during the war because nearly everyone out of uniform was gainfully employed and because there were fewer things to spend money on. At the time of Pearl Harbor the Bank of America's deposits were under $2,000,000,000. By VJ-Day they were nearly $4,600,000,000.

In the thirties the Bank of America had dealt with a deposit bulge by opening up the field of installment loans. Now the little fellow could pay cash down for what he could get, though he could get automobiles and electric refrigerators, for example, only in the secondhand market. Consequently small loans fell off, and the big ones to war contractors did not make up the loss. When we went into the shooting war, the bank had outstanding the remarkable total of 946,184 loans, for $914,569,553. By the end of 1945 the number of loans had shrunk to 426,400, and the dollar amount was just over $1,000,000,000.

Consequently all banks became heavy holders of United States government securities. At the end of 1945, the Bank of America headed the list with "governments" aggregating $3,135,746,000. Only two life insurance companies—Metropolitan and Prudential—were ahead of the Giannini bank in that particular, though not by much. The bank's investment in U.S. securities represented 56 per cent of its resources, against 8 per cent for real estate loans and 10 for other loans.

Like every other organization, the Bank of America was hit by material shortages. For instance, computing machines that went up to eight figures were out of the market. Deposits in twenty-one of the bank's branches crossed the $10,000,000 mark, with the result that tellers had to do some of their own arithmetic. There was also a shortage of tellers themselves, and of all other help. "We are having a H—— of a time with personnel," a vice-president complained before the war was a year old. There was, of course, no escaping the military draft. The bank sent 3,521, or almost a third of its force, to the services. What with the inroads made by the war contractors, the turnover in help rose to 64 per cent, against 28 in 1941. The growth of the bank, and the extra duties it took on, increased the staff from 9,765 to 11,677. Most of the newcomers were women, who made up 68 per cent of the staff in 1945, against 25 per cent in 1940. In 1953 they comprised 60 per cent.

There have never been any soft snaps for officers of the Bank of America. The spartan habits of A. P. Giannini did nothing to alleviate this condition during the war. Looking over a batch of officers' expense accounts, he encountered a vice-president's charge of $35 for automobile hire. "You might tell him [the vice-president]," the old gentleman wrote Al Gock, "that I have cut out my car and am traveling on trains, street cars and buses, and that if I can do this I don't see why he can't."[20]

As peace drew near, the bugbear of "reconversion" was attended by lugubrious talk in high official and business quarters about unemployment and depression. Giannini would have none of it. The country was all right, he said, and California was better than all right. "The West Coast hasn't even started yet," he went on. It would keep all the people who had come there during the war, and keep them busy. "All the new inventions of wartime—electrons, television, light metals, products of every description"—they would be converted to peace time uses. Kaiser, Bechtel and other Californians who had distinguished themselves during the war, would distinguish themselves transforming war plants to a peace basis. A rounded economy for the state was at last at hand, with industry balancing agriculture.

When Giannini said this a few days after the ceremonies on the deck of the U.S.S. *Missouri,* it wore the aspect of prophecy. He wound up his discourse with the point that gave him the most satisfaction. "The West," he said, "has all the money to finance whatever it wants to. We no longer have to go to New York for financing, and we're not at its mercy. Wall Street used to give a Western enterprise plenty of rope, and when it went broke it took over." That day was past.[21]

No one had a better right to make that announcement than A. P. Giannini.

The World's Largest Bank

O N MAY 5, 1945, the day before his seventy-fifth birthday and two days before the surrender of the German armies, A. P. Giannini resigned as chairman of the board of the Bank of America National Trust and Savings Association. Alfred J. Gock, thirty-four years with the bank and since 1939 in general charge of its operations south of the Tehachapi, succeeded to the chairmanship.

The "honorary" title of "founder-chairman," which none but he could ever bear, was created for the retiring chairman. A. P. Giannini was not ideally qualified to hold a purely honorary office. He was the world's greatest banker, and he continued to give proof of it until his death four years later. No decision of first importance to the Bank of America was made without the approval of the founder-chairman.

One of the early meetings of the board that Mr. Giannini attended in his new capacity was held in October, 1945. Senior Vice-Chairman Francis Baer was reading figures describing the bank's condition when the founder-chairman interrupted:

"For God's sake, Franny, give 'em the big news!"

The big news was that the Bank of America had passed the Chase National of New York in deposits and in assets, and therefore was the largest bank in the world. The figures:

> Chase: assets, $4,965,394,000.
> B. of A.: assets, $5,037,500,000.[1]

2

For months prior to the end of hostilities the Gianninis had been studying the bank's role in the postwar world. The principal departure from precedent was a projected drive for a larger place in the field of international banking.

As we know, the Bank of Italy had, from the first, a "foreign" flavor. For a small institution it did a large business in remittances, foreign exchange, drafts and so on. Its relations were close with the Banca d'America e d'Italia, the Milan branch system established under ownership of the Bancitaly Corporation. During the 1920's the Bank of Italy spread correspondent ties over much of the continent of Europe. This is not to suggest that the Giannini bank was much of a factor in the field of international banking as, for example, the Chase National or the National City of New York with branches strung around the world. The first foreign branch of the Bank of America was opened in 1931 in London. No great effort since had been put into the branch's development. For one reason, the depression, which witnessed the ruin of our foreign trade and played hob with tourist travel, hit the bank's foreign business heavily —with one exception. That was the sale of travelers' checks, which the bank had inaugurated in 1929. Just to give an idea—in the summer months of 1953, sales of checks averaged close to two million dollars a day.

As the preliminary to a larger concern with world banking, in October, 1945 A. P. Giannini and Russell Smith, head of the bank's international banking activities, flew to Europe to inspect the Banca d'America e d'Italia. This institution, sequestered by the Italian government after Pearl Harbor, had been turned back to its then owner, the Transamerica Corporation. They found the bank in good condition and took steps looking toward its participation in the huge task of rehabilitating Italy. The Californians decided that what that country needed most, and immediately, were imports of raw materials to start up the factories.

Accordingly, the Bank of America began extending lines of credit not only to the Trans-owned bank, but to other Italian banks as well. The first financing was largely for the purchase of cotton. At the end of 1947, nearly a year before the Marshall Plan got under way, advances to Italian banks and industrialists had reached an aggregate of $37,000,000 and covered both exports and imports of numerous commodities besides cotton.

The Italian venture was only a few weeks old when the White House took note of it. "The President [Mr. Truman] and I are pleased," John W. Snyder, head of the Office of War Mobilization and Reconversion, wrote A. P. Giannini. "I regard this type of action as a positive contribution to worldwide recovery."[2]

The restoration of trade in a world so largely exhausted and laid waste by the war stood, at the close of 1945, as the most comprehensive economic undertaking in the history of mankind. The situation was to become more urgent when the Soviet Union's design for world political conquest began to emerge. Mario Giannini was placed in a position to get something of an inside view of the whole problem when, in 1946, President Truman made him a member of the Committee for Financing Foreign Trade. The task of the twelve industrialists and bankers composing the committee was to survey "foreign trade potentials and make recommendations on financing for international reconstruction." They have contributed importantly to an over-all result that can be stated in a few words: the halting, for the time being at any rate, of the Soviet Union's march toward world conquest. The Marshall Plan and Mr. Truman's Point Four Program were parts, and parts only, in this vast undertaking.

By the time this came to pass, the Bank of America had launched its first postwar overseas branch on the opposite side of the world from Italy. In turning to the Pacific, the bank had no intention of quitting the Atlantic field. One feature of the postwar financing that annoyed the people at 300 Montgomery was the necessity of bowing to the accepted idea that European transactions were the prerogatives of New York banks.

"We don't like to see exports from San Francisco financed by New York lines of credit," Mario Giannini told a directors' meeting. "We expect to build the position of the Bank of America in the international field to a point where it will be comparable to the bank's position in the domestic field. We feel we owe it to the country, to our state, to our customers, and to the stockholders."[3]

3

Before the war the West Coast had enjoyed more than a third of the United States's trade with the Orient. Newly industrialized California looked to the resumption and augmentation of that trade as one means of keeping her plants busy in peacetime. In January, 1946, Mario Giannini's interest in banking conditions in one part of the

Far Pacific was stirred by receipt of a letter from Frank Belgrano, Jr., on leave from the Transamerica-controlled Central Bank, Oakland, and serving as financial adviser to Paul McNutt, United States High Commissioner to the Philippines.

"At the moment everything is needed here," Belgrano wrote. The Islands' banks had tightened up on credit, some of them demanding as much as 100 per cent security. Commissioner McNutt's financial adviser thought this a mistake. "The immediate future seems to me to hold great possibilities if the right sort of concerns are properly financed."[4]

Francis Baer was sent to look into the "possibilities." He recommended the establishment in Manila of a branch of the Bank of America. As a starter, Baer suggested that the "pessimistic" outlook of the local bankers be offset by generous crop loans for sugar, and loans for rebuilding homes, commercial buildings, bridges and power plants.[5]

The Bank of America promptly applied for the new branch. Though the comptroller of the currency approves domestic permits, the Federal Reserve Board has the say-so outside the United States. To Chairman Eccles' query as to whether conditions warranted the branch, Commissioner McNutt replied that he was "delighted" that the Giannini bank wanted to enter the Philippines. "Not only can the branch be of assistance to the larger industrial concerns in the Islands, but—more important—it can offer complete banking services to the people in general and to smaller firms in need of funds."[6]

When the license was granted, Russell Smith and Tom B. Coughran, vice-president and manager of the international banking department, took off to look after the opening of B. of A.'s first Far East branch. Francis J. Moore, designated as manager, and four other bank men began the training of sixty Filipino employees. By January, 1947, the branch was ready to begin operations. Among the first loans was $2,000,000 to help with the rebuilding of the Central Azucarera de Tarlac. Sugar, along with copra, is uppermost in the Islands' economy and the Japanese had done a thorough job of destroying the refineries. Thanks to additional advances, the sugar industry's comeback has been fairly rapid. As a result, the Manila branch has flourished. With resources of $40,000,000 at the start of 1953, it had risen from eleventh place to stand among the first five of the Islands' banks.

From the Philippines, Smith and Coughran went to Shanghai. "Without exception," Chinese bankers advised against a branch. Chiang Kai-shek's forces and the Chinese Communists were momentarily expected to resume fighting. Capital was already on the wing to less troubled centers, such as Hongkong; merchants were closing their shops; lucky people were getting out fast. Smith was inclined to take the advice given him.

Because Chinese trade has always held a major place in California's commercial life, the Bank of America, however, went ahead with plans to put a branch in China's busiest seaport. The Federal Reserve gave its approval early in 1948 and Lewis E. Davis, Far Eastern emissary of B. of A.'s international banking department, began negotiations with the Nationalist government for a license. It took months of oriental palaver before the branch finally opened in January, 1949. By that time Chiang's regime was done for. In May the Chinese Communists were in Shanghai. They froze the branch's assets and a "people's commissar" took a desk at the branch manager's elbow. Not much banking remained for his attention. All loans had been liquidated and deposits amounted to only $376. In May, 1951, the Shanghai branch closed down.[7]

Bangkok got a branch in December, 1949, marking the debut of Thailand's [Siam's] first and only American bank. There are high hopes for this Pacific outpost of the B. of A., should the specter of Communism cease to haunt the Malay Peninsula.

In 1950 a branch was made of the Bank of Guam, established in 1915 by the United States Navy. Military installations dominate the little island, which has a resident population of thirty thousand. The thrifty Guamanians have put a good share of their high wages into savings accounts, of which the branch, after three years, had upward of ten thousand, accounting for deposits of more than 3,000,000. Lending in the first year was negligible, but, since the extension of F.H.A. benefits to the island, Title I loans have been especially popular. At the most recent reckoning the branch had more than three thousand Timeplan loans.[8]

The busiest postwar banking center in the Orient has been Japan. The race there has been to outdistance the same dark cloud that threatened Italy. The economic problem of the two nations is basically the same: too many people with too few resources in too small an area. The objective has been to keep the Pacific's shipping lanes

filled with a continuously moving stream of goods and so speed the
return of Japan's foreign trade to prewar footing. The energetic recovery measures account for the four branches that the Bank of
America has established in the island empire.

The Tokyo branch got off to an auspicious start in 1947 when the
bank broke an impasse over a $60,000,000 loan to revive Japan's
textile industry. The loan had fallen through when New York banks
refused to participate because of a disagreement over rates and security. B. of A.'s international banking department submitted a plan
with the announcement that it would take $10,000,000 of the loan.
The Wall Street institutions quickly followed, the Chase and National City banks taking $10,000,000 each, and the J. Henry Schroder
Banking Corporation $1,000,000. The remaining $29,000,000 went to
the Export-Import Bank.

Subsequent years have seen other large commitments to further
Japan's revival. Meanwhile, the Korean War has piled on more
banking responsibilities. Since Tokyo, branches have been opened
in Yokohama, Kobe and Osaka. At the end of 1952 their combined
deposits totaled $138,549,000.[9]

Seven years, seven branches—that's the score in the Far East.
Shanghai would have made eight. There was progress, too, across
the Atlantic, though no B. of A. branch was added in Europe until
November, 1951.

4

Yet, throughout the seven years, Western Europe had been the
vital stake in the titanic struggle to save the world from economic
chaos, and thus from Communism.

The first item in the original scheme for restoration of Europe was
emergency, on-the-spot succor (mostly food and clothing) from the
United Nations Relief and Rehabilitation Administration. This was
followed by efforts of longer range, mainly financed by the Export-
Import Bank. These measures proved insufficient. One after another,
Russia grabbed five nations of Eastern Europe (one of which, Yugoslavia, has since broken away). Italy and France were tottering. Such
was the situation in 1947 when Secretary of State George C. Marshall
declared that the United States should help any nation that earnestly
tried to help itself to make its people self-sustaining. "Our policy," he

said, "is directed against hunger, poverty, desperation and chaos. Its purpose should be the revival of a working economy in the world so as to permit the emergence of social and political conditions in which free institutions can exist."

The Marshall Plan became effective in 1948, with $5,300,000,000 at its disposal for the first year's operations. (Ultimately $12,000,000,000 had been spent when the Mutual Security Administration took over at the end of 1951.) Mario Giannini promptly called together the officers and the five hundred heads of branches in preparation for lining up the B. of A. with the government program. "The Plan must be made to succeed," he told the gathering. "This world is going to be what Americans make it. We will make it a good world if we are intelligent, energetic and resolute."[10]

As dispersed by the Economic Cooperation Administration, Marshall Plan aid offered generous terms to the participating nations. Only one-fifth of the expenditures was to be repaid, the rest being a gift outright from Uncle Sam. E.C.A. guaranteed the repayable part of the grants, which was advanced by the banks. The policy was to let each country pick its bank. Naturally choices were influenced by previous dealings. As a result, during the four years the Marshall Plan continued, the Chase National of New York had commitments aggregating $977,034,650, the largest of any bank. The Bank of America was sixth on the list, with $388,775,847, topped by five New York banks that had operated in the international field for half a century or more. J. P. Morgan & Co., for a generation the best-known American banking house on the Continent, was a notch lower with $371,116,149. Because of the East Coast's control of the field, California banks, other than the B. of A., did not extend themselves in making commitments. West Coast runner-up to the B. of A. was the Bank of California with less than $2,500,000.

The Bank of America stood first among banks contributing to Italy's recovery under E.C.A. Commitments there exceeded $110,-000,000. Just about as valuable as dollars was the loan of Vice-President Harry McClelland, one of the bank's farm experts, who, in the fall of 1948, became chief of the food and agriculture division of E.C.A.'s Italian mission. In two years' time McClelland changed the agricultural pattern of Italy. Much of what he did there the Bank of America had already done for California farms. Over five million acres were drained, irrigated or improved in other ways. Steel plows and tractors replaced wooden plows and oxen. The dairying industry was built up. A community of twenty thousand in the toe of the boot, which had never raised enough to feed itself, became self-supporting when McClelland brought 150,000 useless acres into cultivation. Grateful Italians have fixed a plaque to a pumphouse on a reclamation project in the Po Valley. It recites that the project was started by the Duke Ferdinand in 1596 and finished by McClelland in 1950.[11]

A corollary of the E.C.A. program was the stepping up of the pool participations of private banks with the Export-Import Bank and the International Bank for Reconstruction (usually called the World Bank). Unlike disbursements under the Marshall Plan, these loans are repaid in full by the borrowing nations who earmark the funds for the development of their economy. Here, too, the Bank of America made its share of commitments that have put its dollars to work in far corners of the world. It has loaned to help build power plants in South Africa, to enrich the soil of Israel, and to drain or to irrigate round the globe.

The period of heavy recovery financing did not blind the Giannini institution to the fact that some day normal banking conditions would resume. Loans to foreign countries, independent of the U.S. government's guarantees, have been steadily encouraged, particularly in Latin America. To improve its farms, Nicaragua has received several sizable advances. Most of the Bank of America's gains south of the border have been made in Mexico, however, where New York banks had so long ruled the roost.[12]

Getting back to the salvation of Europe for which the B. of A. advanced more postwar financing than in the Far East, the prodigious lending operations there had to be carried out with the support of the lone London branch. This was not enough. When the Federal Reserve Board persistently refused branch licenses for the Continent, to spread the load the bank opened representative offices in key European cities and reached out for more correspondent banks.

The Reserve Board's lack of enthusiasm for B. of A.'s international aspirations was apparent as early as 1947 when applications for Bangkok and three German branches were submitted. The time seemed ripe for Germany. English banks had thirteen branches in Britain's zone; French banks were in France's zone; American Express Company offices were scattered through the American zone which was also served by three branches of the Chase Bank.

The board took longer than any time before to reach a decision on the four overseas applications. In the case of Bangkok, Russell Smith was more than a little embarrassed. His initial trip in 1946 had been made at the invitation of the Thai government and upon urging by the U.S. State Department. Thailand was eager to have an American bank that would aid her purpose to seek closer trade ties with the United States. Native policy is to let in no more than one bank from each nation. Accordingly, a place was held for the B. of A. branch while Mr. Smith returned to the United States to complete arrangements.

Not until two years after the permits were requested did the Federal Reserve Board act on them. Executive Vice-President Smith was asked to come to Washington in April, 1949, for a conference. Following two days of talks, the board approved the branch for Thailand, "because of the special circumstances." At the same time it refused the German licenses. This was a blow. At the moment the Bank of America had outstanding $2,500,000 in letters of credit covering German imports from California, a sizable nest egg for a branch's beginning. Bangkok would start with much less.[13]

The setback in Europe did not alter Mario Giannini's determination to build a place, and no insignificant one, for the bank in international banking. Taking a leaf from the elder Giannini's book, the familiar search for the legal way around the obstacle was instituted. The way was quickly found by following the course taken by the Chase National Bank of New York, the foremost American bank on the Continent. Thus it was that in February, 1950, the Bank of America organized a wholly owned subsidiary, called the Bank of America International, with its principal offices in New York. B. of A. International was created under an act of Congress which permits American banks to engage in international banking through subsidiary corporations. In the foreign field the subsidiary can exercise some of the privileges that were useful to A. P. Giannini in his California expansion. It can invest in the stock of a foreign bank and it can establish new branches, with the consent of the Federal Reserve Board and of the country concerned. So far (1953), B. of A. International has opened only one branch—in Düsseldorf in Germany's industrial Ruhr. Though permits for Osaka and a second London branch were issued after formation of the subsidiary, they were established as branches of the Bank of America. All the Pacific branches continue as parts of the parent bank.

It is too soon to speculate on the future of Bank of America International. From a modest start, its resources at the end of 1952 were nearly $100,000,000, more than three times what they were two years earlier. Of more than passing interest, perhaps, is the fact that the creation of the subsidiary marked the return of the Giannini institution to Wall Street. In the old Bank of America N. A., Giannini had a New York outpost that was a sort of cousin to the Bank of America N. T. & S. A. of San Francisco. B. of A. International, however, is a direct offspring which can compete with New York banks for foreign business, not only in the world's banking center but in any part of the globe. Competition will not be negligible, if the postwar growth of the international banking department is a weathervane. Early in 1953, the Department's resources stood at $373,789,000, as against $53,000,000 in 1945.[14]

5

The federal census of 1950 gave California a population of 10,586,-223, an increase of 3,678,836 in ten years, or 19 per cent of the population increase of the United States since 1940. It moved California from fifth place to second among the states. A. P. Giannini predicted that by 1960 his state would be ahead of New York. Maybe so. People are still coming. Through 1952, they came at the rate of more than forty thousand a month.

In the decade of World War II, the Bank of America grew even faster than California:

Year End	Deposits	Capital	Surplus & Undivided Profits	Loans and Discounts
1940	$1,632,228,397	$ 62,000,000	$ 82,278,753	$ 778,295,101
1950	6,191,705,871	150,000,000	244,822,146	3,256,953,558

Year End	Investments in Securities	Resources	Number of Deposit Accounts	Branches
1940	$ 668,676,296	$1,817,535,186	2,384,551	495
1950	2,243,415,107	6,863,358,214	4,338,930	526

With that kind of growth, the Gianninis believed that the Bank of America, for the first time in its history, was in a position to make the most of opportunity. It had enough branches—well, almost enough!—enough resources and enough talent among its large staff to reach into every corner of California and give the mass of new residents (and older ones, too) what they needed and what they wanted.

While most of Mario Giannini's time was taken up with banking problems of the war, his father had begun to think of the problems of peace, long before peace was anything but a wish. Some people were making very gloomy predictions. Ham and Eggs would be back, they said, or something worse. A. P. Giannini had no such dismal outlook. To glum prophets, he said: "Here is the heart of a great new empire—an area of unbounded possibilities."

His mind's eye roved the familiar length of the state, noting the piled-up demand for public construction. From Alturas to National City, there was not a town but had outgrown its public services and facilities. Just catching up would provide thousands of jobs. (Even the B. of A. had to catch up. Since the war, to 1953 the bank has built or rebuilt four hundred branches, spending $40,000,000.) New schools—and in numbers—were a necessity. Thousands of children were being taken care of on a part-time basis in classrooms running a two-shift schedule. Wide new highways were needed to accommodate the growing lines of motor freight that crisscrossed the state. The cities demanded swift freeways to relieve their traffic. More power plants, more sanitation, more irrigation—there was no limit to what California needed.

Russ Kent of B. of A.'s bond investment department, produced figures to prove that A. P. was not guessing. A survey of three hundred California localities revealed new and deferred projects requiring local, state or federal financing that totaled $3,500,000,000.

The bond department did its part to get public construction under way buying, in 1944, the entire $100,000 issue of the Seal Beach School District, the first sale of "municipals" of any consequence since Pearl Harbor. This was soon dwarfed by other purchases running high into the millions. In the postwar years, bidding competitively, the Bank of America has taken approximately half of California's bond issues. For instance, out of a total of $432,171,000 in 1952, it bought $211,906,000. As a result the Giannini institution has superseded the National City Bank as the nation's largest investor in municipals. Right down the line, Eastern institutions have been sup-

planted as the principal brokers in the Western field. The change
has been all to the good. Formerly, these issues went begging, if the
market was tight. Absentee security dealers had no incentive to obtain the best results. Since the Giannini bank assumed the leadership,
buyers have acquired a healthy respect for the credit of California
communities and their bonds are in demand.[15]

These communities, as nowhere else, depend on trucks in their
daily commerce. The more than nine-hundred-mile length of the
state has made trucking second only in importance to agriculture.
California has approximately 500,000 steadily employed truck driv-
ers. Any motorist who has driven the coast highway between San
Francisco and Los Angeles will not question the number. If he traveled by night, he will say he met them all, chugging along in the
largest and most powerful trucks on the road today. The "fleets," to
which most trucks belong, are big business in every sense of the
term. Out of the Golden State comes the longest hauler of them all
—the Pacific Intermountain Express—whose Diesel-powered refrigerator trucks deliver food and meat to Chicago in five days. P.I.E.'s
average haul is over fourteen hundred miles. The Bank of America
made an initial loan of $200,000 to the motor freight company in
1941. The peak was in 1947 when P.I.E. was advanced almost
$2,000,000 to replace its beat-up wartime gear. Meanwhile, other car-
riers were similarly accommodated by the bank. By 1952 fleet operators had lines of credit, in the $100,000 and over class, totaling more
than $30,000,000. Single lines of a million or more are not uncom-
mon.

Even larger sums have gone to those other freight haulers, the
Western railroads, whose equipment was worked to death in the
wartime job they were called on to do. Replacements run into thousands of refrigerator and all steel boxcars, hundreds of fifteen-hun-
dred-horsepower locomotives and seventy-ton hopper (dump) cars,
and mountainous quantities of maintenance items. The average trav-
eler has no conception of the costs. He is not usually aware of the
behind-the-scenes activity and rolling stock involved in the transportation of daily necessities. He does see the *California Zephyr,* the
shining, streamlined train with the "vista dome" that permits an ex-
pansive view of the West's scenic wonders. The *Zephyr* is a postwar
inauguration jointly owned by three railroads. Though their loans,
for the *Zephyr* and much besides, run into seven numbers, the rail-

roads make repayment in monthly installments just as do Time-plan's borrowers, with the B. of A. holding title to the equipment until it's paid for.

Less in the public eye, though requiring many postwar dollars, are California's public utilities. Even without the war these companies would have been hard put to keep up with population growth. They have built fast and boldly since VJ-Day. New hydro-electric powerhouses and steam-generating plants feed scores of additional substations from which thousands of miles of power lines stretch in all directions. The "Super Inch" pipeline has been laid twelve hundred miles into west Texas to tap an adequate supply of natural gas. The construction program of the Pacific Gas & Electric Company—largest ever undertaken by a utility company—will have passed beyond a billion dollars in cost by the end of 1953. The Bank of America in 1948 arranged the largest banking commitment so far made to a utility. Behind it was a syndicate of seventy-three banks lending $95,000,000 to the Southern California Edison Company for postwar expansion. The B. of A.'s participation was $17,500,000. The San Diego Gas and Electric Company was the beneficiary of an $8,800,000 loan, likewise provided by a syndicate managed by the B. of A. which took $5,500,000.[16]

6

The extraordinary spectacle in postwar California has been housing—miles and miles of new houses strung up and down the hill-sides and through marginal land that no one ever before wanted anything to do with. The notable feature of all the building has been the fact that many new homes acquire owners before the last nail is driven. An old acquaintance, the Capital Company, once the repository of the B. of A.'s foreclosures, recently completed development of a large subdivision near Oakland. All the houses were sold prior to the driving of the *first* nail.[17]

Important in the financing of California's postwar housing have been two pieces of legislation—the Servicemen's Readjustment Act (better known as the G.I. Bill of Rights) and the Federal Housing Act of New Deal days. The benefits under the G.I. Bill provided for loans (guaranteed up to $4,000) to acquire a home, start or improve a business, or to buy or equip a farm. The ceiling on interest was 4 per cent (raised to 4½ in 1953) and repayment could take up to twenty years.

At their peak, early in 1948 the Bank of America had more than $600,000,000 in loans outstanding to veterans, or about 10 per cent of the G.I. loans in the United States. Apart from the total, the record is remarkable. Out of 78,000 home loans, only 31 went bad. None of the 567 farm loans backfired. Up to 1952 only 313 of the 4,513 business loans had turned out badly, a surprising result considering the youth and inexperience of most of the borrowers. The explanation is not hard to find, however. After almost two decades of Timeplan, the Bank of America has developed great skill in the handling of small loans.[18]

In the case of both G.I. and F.H.A. borrowers, sometimes the individual builds his own house, according to his own ideas, and sometimes he buys an old house. But often he buys a new house in one of the new communities—the towns within towns—that mass-construction builders have created. In addition to all his other postwar activities, to be touched upon presently, Henry J. Kaiser has been such a builder. In partnership with Fritz B. Burns—"Mr. Housing U.S.A.," as California named this low-cost housing leader—Mr. Kaiser created Kaiser Community Homes to which was adapted some of the assembly-line methods of the shipyards. For instance, one basic floor plan has been utilized in hundreds of variations.

Kaiser's biggest project is Panorama City, two thousand homes on five hundred acres in the San Fernando Valley, north of Los Angeles, and complete with shopping center, schools, churches and playgrounds. Bank of America financing of Kaiser Community Homes began in 1946 with a line of $4,793,200 when ground was broken for Panorama City and a second housing development was under way in San Jose. Since then, the bank has advanced nearly $50,000,000 for the construction of about six thousand Kaiser homes.[19]

In San Francisco, the bank has steadily supplied the credit needs of Henry Doelger, a veteran builder who has done much to transform the sand dunes of the city's Sunset District into a residential section. Starting with a line of $110,000 in 1936, Doelger has subsequently received advances that total upward of $75,000,000. Westlake, a Doelger subdivision now rising on the city's western outskirts, will provide houses and apartments for twenty thousand persons.[20]

Large loans to large operators, like Kaiser and Doelger, are impressive, but inevitably in relating the history of the bank that was begun to help small borrowers, one comes back to them. This section will therefore end with the very human story behind one small-home loan.

In January, 1949, Mario Giannini handed Vice-President Walter E. Bruns a longhand letter of several pages.

"Walter," said Mario, "if this woman is as right as she seems to be from her letter, let's do something about it."

The woman was Mrs. Althea E. Burnett, living in a small farming community in the Sacramento Valley. Her husband, Eugene, had been for twenty years a rural mail carrier, who had always saved something out of his pay. A year before he had moved to the valley from southern California. He took a rural route and bought forty-seven acres of farm land for $1,700, paying $1,000 down. The family, which included two children and another on the way, lived in a home-made trailer and practically fed themselves off the land the first year. What they needed was a house. For $625 cash Mr. Burnett bought a military barrack at an abandoned camp near by, tore it down, and hauled the lumber to his place. His wife designed a house, which could be built, including plumbing and wiring, from the Army material for $3,000.

At the same time, Mrs. Burnett was interviewing builders and talking to the Bank of America manager at the local branch. The manager put the appraisal value of the house she had planned at $7,000 when completed. A direct bank loan seemed best under the circumstances. To get the loan the manager explained that certain regulations would have to be complied with, including the provision of a set of blueprints. Mrs. Burnett rather hesitated over the expense of blueprints. Though the builder had said her own drawings were sufficient for his purposes, to satisfy the bank Mrs. Burnett consented to have the professional drawings made.

The builder, certified by the bank as a good man, decided there was no need for him to wait on the prints. Accordingly, Mr. Burnett took his last cash—$600 he had saved toward a new car for his mail route—and let the builder begin work. When the prints came Mrs. Burnett brought them to the branch, where the manager told her that, according to the rules, not a nail could be driven until the plans were approved by the bank and the loan granted. This came as a shock to the Burnetts. The builder had driven a good many nails. The manager said the loan was off.

At this point Mrs. Burnett wrote her letter to Mario Giannini.

"I'm bothering you," she said in conclusion, "because I cannot feel that the branch manager represents the true policy of the Bank of America." Mrs. Burnett's was in no sense a begging letter. She stated her case with restraint. She said she thought it would be to the bank's advantage to make the loan.

Vice-President Bruns first visited the branch manager, who was simply following the rules laid down by the head office. After hearing out the manager, Bruns called on the Burnetts in their trailer. They made as good an impression as the wife's letter had made on Mario. They knew exactly where the money was coming from to repay the loan. The vice-president said he would recommend that it be made. It is pleasant to report that the Burnett mortgage has been paid off. That outcome runs true to form. In 1952, the bank's gross loss on home loans was one-tenth of 1 per cent, the lowest of all Timeplan divisions.

In telling her story, the authors of this history developed a great liking for Mrs. Burnett. Most readers are bound to feel the same way and so for that reason we cannot resist quoting the following from her final letter to Vice-President Bruns: "I gained much strength from the incident, no small part of which was the realization that if you have a reasonable honest request you can get the president of a huge concern to listen."[21]

7

In Chapter Twenty-eight Bank of America's financing of California industry, small and large, was set forth and figures brought down to the latest date publication of this history will allow. To present details of that type of lending in the postwar years would be to repeat much of what has already been said. However, two new developments in the field are worthy of brief attention.

The terms of Timeplan's business loans were liberalized in the spring of 1945. One purpose was to help an increasing number of veterans who came to the Bank of America seeking loans to start their own businesses. At the time, G.I. loans were not much help, due to delay in the enactment of necessary amendments. Another purpose was to aid small business men in converting to peacetime pursuits. Timeplan's revised terms have worked out so well that they continue to operate. Loans are from $500 up, with interest from 4 to

6 per cent. They are available with or without security, according to circumstances, and there is a choice of modes for repayment. The loss rate averages eighty-three cents per $100 loaned, not including recoveries. E. A. Mattison, Timeplan's inventor, resigned in 1952 to take charge of a Los Angeles finance company. He was succeeded as head of the I.C.L. department by Lloyd Mazzera who has represented the Bank of America in various branches and in many jobs. Mazzera began at Lodi as a messenger.

The second development concerns the postwar emergence of Henry J. Kaiser as one of the country's leading industrialists. The Gianninis have backed Kaiser since the end of World War I, when none of the three cut much of a figure in West Coast business life. They were drawn together by the mutual ambition to lift California to top rank among the states and, in so doing, to emancipate the Western economy from Wall Street's domination. They saw eye to eye on how this could be done: more and more industrial development to counterbalance the agricultural economy.

On the West Coast, Mr. Kaiser has created a well-integrated, industrial principality. In 1952 there were close to fifty plants turning out a couple of hundred products. Most of them are in the West. Kaiser's head office remains in Oakland, and Senior Vice-Chairman Fred Ferroggiaro continues to look after Kaiser's banking affairs. Kaiser sales in 1952 went beyond the half-billion-dollar mark; payrolls for upward of fifty thousand employees exceeded $130,000,000. Moreover, these employees have been provided with a low-cost health plan, including a string of hospitals, that has gone far toward making Kaiser companies one of the most popular employers in the country today. The health plan started in the wartime shipyards when the Bank of America loaned more than half a million dollars to buy and equip an idle Oakland hospital.

In the fifties, the bank's credit lines to various Kaiser industries have averaged around $25,000,000. Kaiser's aluminum company and the steel plant at Fontana in southern California have received the lion's share of the commitments. The Kaiser Aluminum & Chemical Corporation has become one of the three largest producers of aluminum in this country.

Two major loans have been made to the Kaiser Steel Corporation. In 1950 B. of A. put up $11,500,000, or nearly half of a credit pool that three banks established for Fontana's expansion. Again in 1952 the bank joined with six banks and seven insurance companies to lend Kaiser Steel $65,000,000 for more expansion. An addition that year at Fontana was a tinplate rolling mill, completed in August two months ahead of schedule, to help alleviate the shortage of cans that California packers of perishable foods faced as a result of the long steel strike. Kaiser kept in full operation during the shutdown, having signed independently with the union before the workers were called out.[22]

All Kaiser postwar industries have fared well, except the Kaiser-Frazer Corporation. Originally the plan was to manufacture the new automobile in California, thus adding another industry with a large payroll. When the government offered to lease Willow Run at a bargain, Kaiser-Frazer went to Detroit. Though disappointed, the Gianninis backed Kaiser's newest company with a credit line running up to $12,000,000. For two years, through 1947, K-F automobiles rolled off the assembly line, profitably enough to wipe the slate clean at the Bank of America. Then Kaiser decided he wanted to produce more cars for bigger gains. With what looked like a business slump in the offing, Mario Giannini advised against the sale of new shares.

The market broke early in 1948 as Kaiser-Frazer launched the new stock issue and it was withdrawn. To provide working capital, the Bank of America immediately granted a line of $10,000,000 for nine months. The automobile company rocked along unspectacularly for five years when it announced in March, 1953, the purchase of Willys-Overland, Inc., for sixty-odd millions. The B. of A. loaned $20,000,000 to help consummate the deal. Earlier Transamerica had agreed to acquire $15,000,000 of Kaiser-Frazer class A preferred stock. The merger gave Kaiser Motors Corporation (new name and Frazer cars discontinued) assets of $200,000,000 making it the fourth largest automobile manufacturer in the U.S.A. Thus Kaiser is still very much in the automobile business.[23]

8

The sketch given here of California's postwar development is a brief one, and so is that of the Bank of America's part therein because the relationship between the bank and its patrons is confidential. However, one thing stands out: the bank has grown and prospered as the state grew and prospered and together they have come of age. In the process, the B. of A. has played a larger part in the maturing of the California economy than any other institution, except the United States government.

Thus the last years of A. P. Giannini's life saw the fulfillment of the great dream he held for the bank he had founded in 1904, not to make money for himself but to help the people he had grown up among. The dream leaped the boundaries of North Beach to change the face of banking everywhere. This did not come easily. It was a fight every step of the way.

"I suppose," wrote Mario Giannini, "there always will be some scoffers and doubters."[24]

Some of the doubters were in the ranks of federal banking authorities. Death caught up with A. P. Giannini before the issue was resolved in the last of the battles in which he was a participant. This controversy may be regarded as a continuation of the Morgenthau fight which came to the fore in 1938. When Mario Giannini negotiated the 1940 agreement with Comptroller Delano (as detailed in Chapter Twenty-nine), he had not made peace with the Secretary of the Treasury. To the end of his service in the Cabinet, Mr. Morgenthau remained a doubter. For three years, through 1942, all B. of A. applications for new branches were summarily declined by the comptroller of the currency, whose department Mr. Morgenthau had brought under the thumb of the Treasury. To representatives of the bank Mr. Delano frankly admitted "that he was taking orders from the Secretary."[25]

Meanwhile the Secretary was endeavoring to plug up the loophole that had served Giannini in the past when state or federal officials had sought to halt his branch expansion. During two successive Congresses the Treasury sent to Capitol Hill bills outlawing bank holding companies. The bills did not pass, and with new branches denied the Bank of America, Giannini told Transamerica to resume buying banks.

This activity brought a new figure into the fold of doubters— Marriner S. Eccles, chairman of the Federal Reserve Board, who in the bank's earlier controversies with the Treasury had been an ally of Giannini. Eccles telephoned Mario Giannini that he was "very much disappointed" to hear that Transamerica had purchased a bank in Temple City, one of Los Angeles' "bedroom" communities, where war workers went home to sleep. The burden of catering to Temple City's mounting bank needs had fallen upon a near-by B. of A. branch in Pasadena, already swamped and making out as best it could in a former Greyhound bus station.

Eccles protested to Mario that the purchase was contrary to the "gentleman's agreement" that Mario had made in connection with the 1940 settlement of the bank's dispute with the comptroller. According to the Federal Reserve chairman, the understanding provided that no additional banks were to be bought without the approval of the government's three supervisory agencies—the F.R.B., the comptroller of the currency and the F.D.I.C.

Mario replied that "there was never any such agreement made at those conferences." He suggested that Mr. Eccles look at the "records of the Board in which doubtless there are copies of the agenda of the meetings that were held, and summarizations of the discussion." Mario also cited the points listed in Comptroller Delano's program which was the basis for the settlement. They contained, said Mario, "no reference to any provisions with regard to Bank of America branches or Transamerica Corporation's expansion." As Eccles was later to recall, Mario Giannini was "apologetic," saying that neither he nor his father wanted the "Board to feel that they were going contrary to an understanding."[26]

When Transamerica purchased a bank in Pasadena and applied to the Federal Reserve Board for permission to give that bank two branches, Washington returned an emphatic "No." Moreover, Transamerica was informed that the supervisory agencies had unanimously agreed to "decline permission for the acquisition directly or indirectly of any additional banking offices or any substantial interest therein by Transamerica Corporation, Bank of America N. T. & S. A. or any other unit of the Transamerica group."[27]

If the Bank of America had not already been bottled up by Secretary Morgenthau's "orders" to the comptroller, that would do it. But regardless of what Washington might say, Transamerica had a clear legal right to continue to buy banks, coming up against the "freeze policy" only when it attempted to obtain branches for them. These Mr. Eccles and his allies had joined hands to deny, and deny them they did, though this had slight effect on the holding company's acquisitions. The united front soon realized that, if the "freeze policy" was to be altogether successful, a little co-operation from Mr. Giannini was needed.

"I cannot understand why there should be this discrimination against us and our attempt to extend our services where the need has been definitely established," A. P. Giannini wrote Marriner Eccles. The door was open to negotiate. "Anytime you are in Washington," the Federal Reserve chairman replied, "I shall be glad to arrange conferences on this matter."[28]

Early in 1943 Giannini went to Washington. With the war on, an informal truce was arrived at. Giannini promised that neither the bank nor Transamerica would acquire an interest in additional banks without the Reserve Board's approval, provided the same pledge was obtained from other bank holding companies. The board readily agreed to let Giannini fulfill commitments Transamerica had already made to purchase stock in two banks.

In the light of subsequent events, a few lines from the F.R.B.'s record of the conference make interesting reading:

His [A. P.'s] discussion had the tone of one who felt that he was "boxed" at every turn of the road. . . . It appeared to the Board members who had known Mr. Giannini in the past that he retained his old vigor and aggressiveness, but on the other hand, that there was something of a tendency towards relaxation and a desire to be conciliatory, even at the sacrifice of his ideas of further expansion.[29]

The truce came to nothing. This seems to have been because no one in Washington had thought to ask A. P. to identify the two banks he was permitted to complete deals to buy stock in. At any rate, a month after the conference, when it developed that one of the banks was the Citizens National Trust & Savings of Los Angeles, with thirty branches, the Federal Reserve Board blew up and tried to change the conditions of the truce. Mr. Giannini was informed that pledges from other bank holding companies were unnecessary. In addition, Transamerica was to initiate no bank-buying negotiations except on the board's recommendations. Giannini flatly refused to accede to this.

A. P.'s message was delivered to the Federal Reserve by Charles W. Collins, who received in answer as formidable a threat as had ever emanated from the office of Secretary Morgenthau during the bank's battle with the Treasury. John McKee, one of the board members, declared that the board would

proceed against . . . Transamerica and the Bank of America by means of every weapon and agency within reach. . . . He said this was going to be an all-out fight, through federal legislation, through executive action, through acts of organized banking and through building up of public opinion against these institutions and the Gianninis.[30]

McKee's prediction was to turn out uncomfortably accurate, but for the moment Transamerica kept the initiative. The Bank of America had been refused a *de novo* permit for a branch at Lakewood Village, on the fringe of Los Angeles, where the bank had approximately $2,000,000 tied up in home loans to defense workers. A. P. Giannini believed that public convenience demanded a bank in the booming area, and, after the application for a B. of A. branch was rejected, he encouraged organization of a state-chartered institution called the Peoples Bank. Transamerica carefully refrained from subscribing for stock in it. The bank was admitted to the Federal Reserve System, with the proviso that Transamerica, the Bank of America, or any affiliate of either, could not acquire stock in the Peoples without F.R.B. approval, under pain of surrender of its Reserve membership. That meant the surrender also of membership in the F.D.I.C.

Giannini believed the proviso illegal, as well as unenforceable because a bank has no control over who buys its stock. Accordingly, Transamerica bought 540 shares, about a 10 per cent interest, and the Peoples Bank challenged the Federal Reserve's proviso in court. Trans picked Wendell Willkie to argue its case in the federal court, but Mr. Willkie died three days before the hearing began. The appearance was made by a partner in the Willkie firm. He contended that Reserve membership is the privilege of any sound bank and the board cannot impose a condition not granted it by statute. After nearly four years the case reached the Supreme Court which, by a five to two decision, held, in effect, that the Peoples Bank had nothing to fear since the Federal Reserve Board had made no move to enforce the proviso depriving it of its membership.[31]

By that time two things had occurred taking some of the pressure off the Bank of America and off Transamerica. The death of President Roosevelt brought about the resignation of Secretary Morgenthau. The bank celebrated Mr. Morgenthau's departure by sending thirty-five applications for branches to Washington. Nine of them were requests previously rejected. Most of the thirty-five were for locations in and around long-suffering Los Angeles, so underbanked that an institution without depositors' lines extending to the sidewalks was a rarity. Only two branches were granted, however, and C. W. Collins informed Mario Giannini that the wholesale rejections were the work of Eccles who was holding Comptroller Delano to the terms of the "freeze policy." Still, the bank was greatly encouraged by the fact that the comptroller had seen fit to lift the ban to the extent of giving it a couple of new branches.[32]

Mr. Delano did much better by the B. of A. the following year, after John W. Snyder became Secretary of the Treasury. Mr. Snyder was a banker and a respecter of the policy of letting the comptroller of the currency make his own decisions. Moreover, he did not consider his department bound by the policies of his predecessor, unless he deemed them good policies. In 1946, therefore, the B. of A. got seven branches. Though not granting all that were requested, the Snyder-Delano team was not ungenerous with the B. of A.

Year	Branches
1947	8
1948	9
1949	8
1950	1
1951	3
1952	9

The second thing that lightened the load for Transamerica was the fizzling out, in 1947, of the sensational but futile proceedings brought against it by the Securities and Exchange Commission. That such would be the fate of this action had been clear for some while. As early as 1945, Mr. Eccles had begun to look around for other means to stop Transamerica's expansion. After lengthy investigation, Attorney General Tom C. Clark reported to the Reserve chairman that no evidence had been found to warrant action against the holding company under the Sherman Anti-Trust Act.[33]

Thereupon Mr. Eccles turned to antibank-holding-company legislation of which little had been heard since Mr. Morgenthau's failures along that line. Senator Tobey of New Hampshire introduced the Federal Reserve's bill. It was soon known as the "anti-Giannini

bill." Actually A. P. Giannini had never been opposed to such legislation, provided it was impartial. "Legislating bank holding companies out of existence is more a worry to others than to us," he
wrote in 1943. Neither Giannini was invited to testify at Senate hearings on the Tobey measure. This made no difference in the outcome.
The bill never came to a vote. Mr. Eccles blamed this on the opposition of John W. Snyder.[34]

He had more than that to blame Mr. Snyder for when the Federal
Reserve got in a row with the Treasury over steps to be taken against
inflation. Eccles did not stop there, but scared the bankers when he
asked for authority to demand that they set up secondary reserves in
their institutions. As a result, President Truman demoted Eccles
from chairman to vice-chairman of the Federal Reserve Board.
When A. P. Giannini was asked if he was responsible for the demotion he said he wished he could take credit for it but he couldn't.
Nevertheless, Giannini's name continued to figure in the speculation
and pretty soon Mr. Eccles was blaming both Giannini and Snyder.
The rumor spread that Snyder presently would leave the government service and go to work for the Bank of America at a fat salary.
When the Senate took up the confirmation of Thomas B. McCabe,
a Philadelphia manufacturer, whom President Truman designated
to succeed Eccles, Senator Tobey asked Mr. Snyder about the reported Giannini job. The Secretary denied he contemplated leaving
the Treasury, and he did not leave until Mr. Truman did in 1953.
Then he went to work for the Willys-Overland automobile concern.[35]

Mr. Eccles has said that the real object of the demotion was to get
him off the Federal Reserve Board altogether, but that he swallowed
his pride and stayed on as vice-chairman so as to continue his pursuit of Transamerica. And he was already hot on the scent from a
new direction. The termination of the S.E.C.'s unsuccessful action
made available for other services the lawyer who had prosecuted that
case. His name is J. Leonard Townsend. Eccles brought Townsend
over to the Federal Reserve and put him to studying the possibilities
of taking action against Transamerica under an antimonopoly section of the Clayton Act. Never before had the board invoked this
law to bring such a case. Townsend said that it contained everything
the board needed to proceed against the bank holding company.
Whereas the Sherman Anti-Trust Law required "proof of abusive
tactics," the attorney pointed out that all that had to be shown under

the Clayton Act was "that a corporation was in a position to exert monopolistic power."[36]

Accordingly, in June, 1948, the Federal Reserve Board issued a complaint against Transamerica, charging that its banking acquisitions constituted a potential monopoly with the power to stifle competition, as defined by the Clayton Act. The threat, so the board declared, existed in Trans's holdings in forty-eight banks in California, Oregon, Washington, Nevada and Arizona. In forty-six of these banks Transamerica owed a majority of the stock. The two in which it had a minority interest were the Bank of America (22.48 per cent in 1948) and the Citizens National of Los Angeles (23 per cent).

A. P. Giannini won out over his legal staff and set the pattern for Transamerica's defense. The attorneys favored a few preliminary legal skirmishes to strengthen their cause through court rulings. The veteran Charlie Collins warned A. P. against rushing into hearings presided over by a member of the Reserve Board. "You will go into a kangaroo court," said Collins, "in a hearing not authorized by law and the case will be railroaded to a decision against you."[37]

All Giannini wanted was a chance to defend his achievements in a public hearing. When it was learned that the Federal Reserve had scheduled closed hearings, he consented to go to court and demand open ones. He got them without going to court. The public hearings were the key to A. P. Giannini's strategy. He had in mind something like the old proxy fight, with the people of California and the four other states coming before the hearing officer to tell what Transamerica and the B. of A. had done for them.

Hearings began in December, 1948, and lasted close to two years. Sixteen hundred Westerners—rival bankers among them—volunteered to testify and Giannini looked forward to their appearance with relish.

9

Amadeo Peter Giannini did not live to hear much of the testimony. He died on June 3, 1949, a few weeks after his seventy-ninth birthday.

Though the Transamerica Corporation and the Bank of America at that time were big business, very big business, to the last month of his life Giannini was as interested in the service they rendered to the little fellow as to the corporations. He, personally, would discuss a

$50 loan as earnestly and as patiently as he would discuss a $5,000,000 loan. That sort of thing alone, stretched over forty-five years, is enough to make a man remembered. Taken alone it is not enough, however, to create a great bank. Fortunately, in addition to a deep interest in the concerns of ordinary peole, A. P. Giannini had the gift to see horizons for banking that no one else had seen. He had the genius to realize them in the face of obstacles that at times seemed insuperable.

In 1945 when Mr. Giannini retired from the chairmanship of the board the prices of securities were rising. The banker described himself as "in danger" of becoming a millionaire. Shortly afterward he established the Bank of America–Giannini Foundation, and made over to it half of his personal fortune. The amount was $509,235. Objectives of the Foundation are to provide educational scholarships for employees of the Bank of America and to promote medical research.

At the time of his death Mr. Giannini's estate was appraised at $489,278. His will left $41,000 to various charities. It contained nine other bequests, of $1,000 each, to relatives and to an employee of long service. The residue went to the bank for the support of the Bank of America–Giannini Foundation. The lights that guided A. P. Giannini in his business life and his personal life shine forth in the final passage of his instructions concerning the aims of the Foundation:

The Trustor at his desk in his office, in the City and County of San Francisco, is executing this Declaration. The thoughts in his mind at this time are intimate and personal. He does not behold his Trustee as a cold, corporate entity, breathing only the life derived by it from the law. He sees through and beyond the corporate form, beholding the men and women who have worked by his side for the last forty years. To these devoted co-workers he cannot speak in the stern formalism of the law. His mind and his heart speak:

Administer this Trust generously and nobly, remembering always human suffering. Let no legal technicality, ancient precedent or out-moded legal philosophy defeat the purposes of this Trust. Like St. Francis of Assisi, do good—do not merely theorize about goodness. This is my wish and I confidently commit this Trust to your hands for its fulfillment.

In witness whereof, A. P. Giannini, the Trustor, has hereunto set his hand, at San Francisco, California, this 3rd day of October, 1945.

CHAPTER THIRTY-TWO

End of a Dynasty

IT HAS been a problem to keep this book from reading too much like a biography of A. P. Giannini. In truth, *he* was the Bank of America; *he* was the Transamerica Corporation, and all the other things that financial writers for twenty years had been lumping together as the "Giannini empire." The financial writers did not overstate. They could have pointed to the economic transformation of the Pacific Coast over a period of thirty years and called that Coast a partner of the Giannini empire, because A. P. Giannini had more to do with its transformation than anyone else. As we have said before, Giannini created his bank and achieved all that followed in the train of that institution without recourse to pretentious offices or titles, to money or stock interests. He ruled his empire because he had earned the people's trust.

The passing of such a figure creates more than a vacancy. A. P. Giannini's successor was his son Mario, who suffered from a minimum of the very real disadvantages that go with being the son of a great man. On the other hand he derived the maximum benefit from having been the president and actual administrative head of the bank for thirteen years during his father's lifetime. But he did suffer the handicap of an incurable malady, hemophilia.

Around 300 Montgomery Street there is a saying that A. P. Giannini ran the bank "by instinct," or "by ear." The details of a large or critical business deal did not concern him, unless there was trouble. Then he could reach into the heart of the matter faster than the lieutenants who habitually looked after the details. Mario Giannini did not make the mistake of trying to run the bank as his father had. The times were different. What was needed was a head of the bank to pull together the great, sprawling institution that had been so swiftly created and give its operations smoothness and efficiency.

Mario was the man of the hour. He had a mind for details and he worked himself to death attending to them. Before he got through, however, the Bank of America became the integrated organization that it is today, without losing the individuality and warmth that had been imparted by its creator.

From the time he became president in 1936, Mario worked hard, much to the alarm of his father who, with no success, cautioned him to take things easier. A. P. was delighted when, during the war, his son ceased making the fatiguing daily trip from his country home at Atherton and established his office in an apartment on Russian Hill, a ten-minute taxi ride from Montgomery Street. Mario would remain at the apartment until midafternoon answering correspondence, reading voluminous reports that came from the branches and the administrative departments of the bank (something his father never had the patience to do), meeting with committees and with individuals who came from everywhere in the world. Then he would go to his office on the Bank of America's eleventh floor, and usually stay until after the dinner hour. Mary McGoldrick accounts for her eleven years as Mario's private secretary by saying that she worked for "Mr. L. M." twenty-two years.

Before long A. P. had seen that the Russian Hill office enabled his son to work longer hours than he had before. The father began to concoct little schemes to lure Mario away from his desk. The schemes were as transparent as the plots of Italian opera. The elder Giannini connived with his daughter-in-law, Mercedes, and his granddaughters, Ann and Virginia, to insist that Mario accompany them on holidays. He asked Dr. Constantine Bricca to "scare" his son. "Tell him he is killing himself with overwork." He asked Jake Fischer to buy a new car for Mario, who remained an avid motorist. The game made Mario wary of his father's proposals.

One of A. P.'s "plots" resulted in the creation of the Bank of America's managing committee in 1944. The elder Giannini walked into a group of directors gathered for a board meeting and let fall casually that he thought the bank needed such a body.

"Dad, that's a fine idea," spoke up Mario.

Encouraged, A. P. went into particulars as to how the proposed committee should replace, and have more authority than, the existing operating committee. Then he said almost too much when he declared that the managing committee, as he saw it, would relieve

Mario of some of his load. Mario gave his father a long look and said: "Let me think it over for a few days."[1]

Directors liked the idea, however, and so did Mario. With Carl Wente as chairman and Clark Beise as vice-chairman, a managing committee was chosen. The original sixteen members were later pared down to ten. *The American Banker* called the move "another piece of Giannini wisdom." The managing committee provided "a shock absorber in case of loss of high executive ability through death, retirement or other cause."[2]

Though he had not been far away—merely in Oakland, as president of Transamerica's Central Bank—it was, indeed, a fine thing to have the veteran Carl Wente back at 300 Montgomery. This big un-ruffled man, who never seemed to have a worry in the world, knew California's farms, livestock interests, small business and big business and the ins and outs of Giannini banking as well as any man living, except the Gianninis themselves. Mario welcomed Wente to his new post with these words: "If I am here you can help me; if I am not here, you are in charge."[3]

After her father's death, Claire Giannini Hoffman was elected to A. P.'s place on the board. Mario was particularly touched, as the action had not been suggested by him. Mrs. Hoffman has taken over a duty that was peculiarly her father's. That is visiting the branches and maintaining a personal tie between patrons and personnel and the head office. Claire also has studied the problems of the bank's women employees, who now constitute 60 per cent of the force.

With all that he had to do, Mario took especial pains to get done some of the things that his father had been deeply concerned with when he died. For example, there was the matter of the Gonzales branch. Owing to the slender resources of the community that branch was never expected to amount to a great deal. Yet, for A. P. Giannini, it had become a symbol of governmental discrimination against the Bank of America, and he had fought persistently for eleven years for the right to serve the little town in the Salinas Val-ley.

As related in Chapter Twenty-nine, a license for a branch in Gon-zales had been granted in 1938, extended when alterations on a for-mer meat market were not ready on time, but not approved once the bank was prepared to do business. Regularly the request for a permit went to Washington, only to be denied on "orders" from Mr. Morgenthau. The building stood empty for more than a decade, its gold-lettered sign kept bright to proclaim it a branch of the Bank of America. The B. of A.'s budget planners recommended that the vacant branch be rented. A. P. Giannini would not allow it. "Our institution didn't get where it is today by giving up." More than once the Federal Reserve Bank of San Francisco wrote that "competing bankers" objected to the sign and asked that it be "obliterated." "Definitely nothing doing," replied A. P.[4]

It was no secret that the most active of the competitor bankers was Andrew C. Hughes of the Monterey County Trust and Savings Bank. "Andy" Hughes is proud of the institution he has developed since the early 1900's, and justly so. Before the Gianninis tried to get into Gonzales, Hughes's bank had eight branches in Monterey county, or three more than the B. of A. An active Republican, Mr. Hughes had no difficulty maintaining the status quo during the Hoover Administration. Under Roosevelt, the fight between the Gianninis and Morgenthau had served him just as well. "We stopped them [the B. of A.] from opening it [the Gonzales branch]," declared Hughes shortly before A. P. Giannini's death.[5]

Mr. Hughes's boast was all that Mario needed to put him full-steam behind a revival of the effort to get the Gonzales permit. The time was propitious. Mr. Morgenthau was out and Secretary of the Treasury John W. Snyder had given Comptroller Delano back his independence. Delano approved the transfer of the Camp Roberts license (this was before Korea and Roberts was almost empty) to Gonzales and the branch opened in October, 1949. Mario's triumph was tempered with one regret. "It would have been a great day for A. P. had he been there," he wrote to a friend.[6]

2

Aside from the day-to-day operation of the bank, the principal task to which Mario devoted himself in the three years of life that remained to him after the passing of A. P. Giannini was the defense of Transamerica against the charges brought under the Clayton Act by the Federal Reserve Board. Although only Transamerica was named in the action, the real target was the bank.

"If the Bank of America," said J. Leonard Townsend, the board's attorney, "were not to be considered as included . . . in these proceedings . . . I don't think there would be any complaint."[7]

The Federal Reserve Board had named one of its members, Rudolph M. Evans, as hearing officer. After a brief residence in Arlington, Virginia, across the Potomac from Washington, Mr. Evans had been appointed to the board upon recommendation of Chairman Eccles. Mr. Evans was not eligible for appointment from his native Iowa, that section of the country already being represented by another board member. Mr. Evans is not a lawyer. At his side, throughout the hearings, sat a "legal adviser," a lawyer in the employ of the Federal Reserve. The board's case was marshaled and presented by Mr. Townsend who, as the prosecutor of the government's complaint, was not expected to be impartial. Transamerica was represented by its New York counsel, Samuel B. Stewart, Jr., who had recently become the bank's chief counsel. Some of the hearings were held in Washington and some in San Francisco.

Off and on for six weeks in San Francisco, Townsend put unit bankers on the stand. Twenty-nine in all testified to the Gianninis' bank-buying reputation, some adding, under questioning, that they did not know the difference between the Bank of America and Transamerica. Typical was the testimony of Charles M. Mannon, president of the Savings Bank of Mendocino County. "They're out to acquire any bank they can get," he said. Not a single banker claimed an injury because of this, however.[8]

Bank examiners called to testify produced a staggering array of statistical exhibits, between thirty and forty feet in thickness, on loans, deposits and banking offices in the five states of California, Oregon, Washington, Nevada and Arizona. Statistical evidence was, in fact, the substance of the board's case.

Stewart argued that the evidence was misleading because whatever measure was used to show the size of the "Transamerica group," the B. of A. accounted for 85 per cent or more of the totals. The Bank of America, he pointed out, did not belong to the "Transamerica group"; it was not controlled by Transamerica which, shortly after the start of the Federal Reserve hearings, reduced its ownership of the bank's stock to an 11 per cent interest. Mr. Townsend contended that even if the holding company disposed of all its Bank of America shares, such an event "would in nowise affect the 'relationship' between the two." They were closely bound by "tradition" and "personal ties," he insisted, calling off the names of "important officials whose careers have placed them first in one and then another of the various TA organizations." As far as his case was concerned, the board's solicitor declared that

the most important "tradition" is the role TA has played in acquiring banks for inclusion within the Bank of America system. This has gone on without interruption since TA was first organized. The distribution of 58 per cent of Bank shares in 1937 did not abate the practice. . . . The disposition of its remaining shares is not likely to have this result.

Mr. Townsend professed to believe "it was obvious" that the Reserve Board's monopoly charges had "precipitated" Transamerica's "long-range program" to dispose of its B. of A. stock. To see the matter that way, the attorney had to ignore the fact that the program had been initiated eleven years before the F.R.B. filed its action and had continued ever since.

But this concentration on the interplay of "latent power" existing between the Giannini bank and the Giannini holding company was the evidence by which Townsend had to prove the Federal Reserve's charges. "If the Bank of America . . . were no longer controlled by Transamerica," he conceded, "there would be no case." The bank, the solicitor explained, "has been the hub around which has revolved this constant pattern of acquisition of bank stocks which today brings the entire organization, operated in a sense as a single unity, within the prohibitions of the Clayton Act."[9]

So the government's case proceeded with the Bank of America's totals on loans, deposits, etc., used as the yardstick to measure competitive effects, within their areas, of forty-seven banks in five Western states. California, the second most populous state in the Union, was joined bankwise with Nevada, the least populous state, to produce over-all averages that reflected the banking picture of neither state. Stewart argued that the board's statistics were "completely meaningless." Take away the business done by the California state-wide branch system and the "percentages [for the majority-owned Trans banks] for the entire five-state area are only 6.5 per cent for loans, and 7.0 per cent for deposits." The defense attorney hastened to add that he did not think much of his own statistics unless many factors were considered in relation to them.[10]

Not that the holding company or the Bank of America was unwilling to back up its case with statistics on banking services to Californians, and to others elsewhere. Stewart had more than sixteen hundred witnesses—customers, stockholders, competitors, public officials. Whole communities were ready to take the stand. Yorba Linda, a small citrus center where the Bank of America had opened one of the branches granted in 1945, had volunteered to send a delegation to tell its story. Following the bank holiday of 1933, the town had been bankless for twelve years and, as a result, failed to recover from the slump as readily as some of its neighbors. After the citizens failed to get support in organizing a bank, shopkeepers closed up and headed for more promising territory. Only the Bank of America was willing to take a chance, but it was refused a permit for a branch. When the license was eventually granted, the town rapidly took on new life.[11]

But Yorba Linda was not allowed to put its testimony on record. Nor were most of the sixteen hundred. About forty defense witnesses were heard. Mr. Evans repeatedly ruled out evidence relating to the services to communities and to individuals, on the ground that branch banking was not an issue in the case. Mr. Stewart took exception to the ruling. His purpose was not "to show the advantages of branch banking" in the hope of convincing "the Board of the soundness of Transamerica's business judgment." On the contrary, the defense attorney said, the evidence he offered was intended to bring out the "significant development and trends in the competitive pattern of the business." This seemed important, if the board was to sit in judgment on the "impact upon competition of Transamerica's acquisitions of bank stock."[12]

Oddly enough, one success story that was not admitted in evidence drew an admiring comment from the hearing officer who excluded it. The witness was Arthur G. Howard who has built at Rio Linda a poultry-breeding business with a national reputation. In 1933 Howard was broke and working as a bellboy while his wife worked as a waitress. From tips they saved $25 and made a down payment on an acre of land. Needing $90 more to start his hatchery, Howard went to a bank in Sacramento. When the banker refused the loan, Howard applied at a Bank of America branch. The manager made the loan. The branch has continued to support the Howard enterprise on its upward climb.

Along with everyone else in the hearing room, Mr. Evans had listened with interest to Howard's recital. "Off the record," he said as the witness left the stand, "that was a great story." It was, however, "irrelevant."[13]

In Washington Mario Giannini spent fourteen days on the witness stand, his testimony punctuated by frequent passages militantly defensive of his father's reputation. By then A. P. Giannini had been dead more than a year.

"There are darned few leaders in business who worry about their stockholders the way A. P. Giannini did," said Mario while being cross-examined concerning the market support given the Giannini stocks following the "Blue Monday" raid in 1928. Sam Stewart interrupted to tell Mario that he did not have to reply to Mr. Townsend's questions. "Well," the witness continued, "the way I feel about it is that I have no reason or desire not to give the information. I have a feeling of great pride in what we did in those years to stabilize the situation in the interest of all of the Transamerica stockholders."[14]

When the Federal Reserve's counsel intimated "that the affairs of Transamerica Corporation, and some of its subsidiaries were used on occasion for the specific purpose of the profits of the insiders in the organization," Mario broke in furiously: "That is a malicious misstatement."[15]

Mr. Evans several times called the witness to order for his sharp exchanges with Mr. Townsend. In one eruption Mario accused the attorney of having "made a career over the past 12 years of persecuting the institution with which my father was connected." He said Townsend had a "distorted approach to things . . . of trying to make black appear white, or white to be black."[16]

At times the questioning of Mario took on a fantastic quality, as when the lawyer said he proposed to show that in certain respects the methods of Transamerica were similar to those employed by the rulers of Soviet Russia. After this had gone on for half an hour, Mr. Stewart objected on the ground of irrelevancy.

From the record:

The Hearing Officer: Is it your intention Mr. Townsend, to demonstrate some connection?

Mr. Townsend: . . . I am probing Mr. Giannini's general attitude . . . to explore generally the philosophy of this man who is the closest link that presently exists between all of the institutions whose names have come up in the course of these proceedings, and, finally, sir, I propose to show that a great number of the methods pursued by Transamerica, and their satellite organizations, including their agents and including in the form of the witness on the stand [*sic*], bear a striking parallel to the methods employed by the Communists in attempting to undermine confidence in public officials, in public forums, in the free institutions that we have in this country. . . .

Mr. Stewart: It seems to me that I should add to the objection of irrelevance the suggestion that the slurring insinuation of counsel is so utterly uncalled for, and so contemptuous in character . . . that it should be excluded. . . .

The Hearing Officer: I am going to overrule the objection.

The Federal Reserve attorney's next question backfired.

Mr. Townsend: Mr. Giannini, there isn't any doubt in your mind, is there, but that the agents of Communism in this country have made some progress by their condemnation of our American way of life, particularly our free institutions, such as the courts?

The Witness: I think that more damage has been done to our American institutions by the abuse, or the attempted abuse, of power of misguided bureaucrats, such as Mr. Eccles . . . than anything that could be done by agents of a power outside this country. Mr. Eccles has just lost his perspective, and he forgets that in America . . . our public officials are servants of the people, and not their masters.[17]

A veteran financial writer who had heard A. P. Giannini testify at some Capitol Hill hearings remarked the difference in Mario Giannini's performance under examination. "He does not 'roar' like his father used to do, but his words have more of the rapier quality."[18]

3

The hearings droned on and on. While they were under way, Mario Giannini turned to another item of unfinished business that had been started by his father. This was the acquisition by the Bank of America of twenty-two California banks, with five branches, that Transamerica had accumulated since 1938. When the Clayton Act complaint was filed, Comptroller Delano had under consideration B. of A.'s request to purchase these banks. At Eccles' suggestion, Mr. Delano agreed to withhold his decision until the Federal Reserve Board's proceedings were resolved.

For two years Mario pushed the matter in Washington. The comptroller doubted that he had the legal right to approve the take-overs, inasmuch as they involved institutions listed in the board's action. Finally Delano consented to discuss the matter with counsel for the board and for the Bank of America. When the board failed to reply to the invitation to the meeting, the comptroller said he would approve the sale of the banks, providing the B. of A. increased its capital by $70,000,000. This was in April, 1950. The Federal Reserve Board was notified of the comptroller's decision. After a proper wait, the board's silence was assumed to mean that it would offer no opposition. The capital funds were quickly raised and on June 20, 1950, the comptroller issued the permits.[19]

Clark Beise, R. P. A. Everard, Frank Dana and P. C. Read of the Bank of America staff had spent close to three months working out details of the transfer. Tons of equipment, including newly printed checks, letterheads and deposit slips, had been moved into the Transamerica banks. The 130,000 depositors had been notified by letter of the impending change of ownership. The shift was formally set for Saturday, June 24, after the noon closing hour.

Mario Giannini and Comptroller Delano had reckoned without the Federal Reserve's solicitor. Arriving in San Francisco on June 20, Mr. Townsend waited until late afternoon of June 23 to obtain a temporary court order against the transfer on the plea that it would remove Trans's banks from the Clayton proceedings. On Saturday, the twenty-fourth, the Giannini lawyers argued that the order was void because the banks had ceased to exist at noon on that day. The court held otherwise and made the injunction permanent.

This left the Bank of America in a dilemma. On the one hand, it was committed to the comptroller to open the branches and continue banking services. On the other, the court order forbade the transfer of the banking assets to the B. of A. Given the fullest co-operation, it was not possible in one day, and that Sunday, to effect the changes necessary to re-establish the institutions as independent banks. Accordingly, Mario announced that the twenty-seven new branches of the Bank of America would open on Monday morning.

When the branches did open, Townsend asked the court to hold Mario Giannini, the Bank of America, Sam H. Husbands (Transamerica's president at the time) and the Transamerica Corporation in contempt. Some days later the court ordered Mario Giannini to reconvert the branches within thirty days, under penalty of possible fine or jail term. The B. of A. tried to hold up the order, pending a review by the United States Supreme Court, but failed. On August 7, the banks returned to the Transamerica fold.[20]

Shortly after this episode the Clayton Act hearings in the Transamerica case came to an end and Hearing Officer Evans began his study of the thirteen thousand pages of record. His conclusions were presented in June, 1951. In substance, Evans found that Transamerica's systematic acquisition of banks "tended to create a monopoly." He recommended that the board order the holding company "to divest itself of all such stocks," excepting that of Bank of America. On its face, the recommendation seemed to be a contradiction in terms. The holding company was to be permitted to retain its shares (at this point down to a 7.66 per cent interest) in the biggest private bank in the world, yet it must dispose of majority-owned banks in five states where it had been shown, "by the board's own calculations," they did less than 7 per cent of the banking business.

But the hearing officer had an explanation for his exception. It followed the line of Mr. Townsend's reasoning. The Bank of America, said Mr. Evans, is the "hard core" of Trans, its "center and principal support . . . intangible factors [that] provide sound reason to believe that even if Transamerica were required to divest itself of the stock it now holds in Bank of America, the existing relationship would continue."[21]

The Evans recommendations had barely subsided as financial page news when the instigator of the whole proceeding, Marriner S. Eccles, resigned from the Federal Reserve Board. "Now the time has arrived," he said, "when I can . . . return to my home."[22]

The departure of Mr. Eccles left only three of seven members who had been on the Federal Reserve Board at the start of the Transamerica hearings. A new chairman, William McC. Martin, Jr., a former governor of the New York Stock Exchange, and one new member were appointed in time to take part in the board's review of the Transamerica case. Two other members were named too late to participate. *Washington Banktrends* noted that the changes were all to the good. "It is not now a Board completely dominated by a single individual," meaning Mr. Eccles.[23]

In March, 1952, by a vote of three to two, the board adopted Mr. Evans' recommendations. Evans himself cast the deciding vote. The dissenters were James K. Vardaman, Jr., the only member with legal training, and Oliver S. Powell, the only member with practical banking experience. Their opinion advanced the basic issues on which the holding company presently asked the United States Court of Appeals either to dismiss the Federal Reserve Board's order of "divestiture" or require the board to hear evidence that Transamerica had not been allowed to submit. In part, the minority opinion read:

> The case was tried on too narrow a basis. . . . The Board did not have a clear objective in bringing the proceeding. . . . In the evidence and arguments to support the claim that competition has been restrained and a tendency to monopoly has been created . . . the record makes it clear . . . that keen competition is present in the five states in which Bank of America affiliates operate. . . . The Board finds that 38.85 per cent of all deposits and 49.97 per cent of the loans in the five states are owned by Transamerica banks. This might well indicate merely better service to the public by Transamerica banks. . . . The tables on deposit accounts . . . seem to show that the small depositor likes the Transamerica banks, especially in California. . . . The respondent should have been given full opportunity to present its evidence. . . . The Order does not in all respects square with the facts and the respondent has not had its day in court.[24]

4

Mario Giannini was too ill to be told that the Federal Reserve Board had accepted the findings of Hearing Officer Evans.

The president of the Bank of America had returned to California in the fall of 1950, worn by the two-week ordeal on the witness stand in Washington. "I am trying to carry on the great work to which my beloved father dedicated his life," he wrote to a friend. "I find it is a constant and hard battle."[25]

That was about as near a complaint as Mario ever uttered. With his strength sapped by his chronic affliction, hemophilia, early in March, 1952, he entered a San Francisco hospital for an operation for hemorrhoids. A week later he developed influenza. He had barely recovered from that when virus pneumonia struck. Then came pleurisy, and general decline affecting the heart.

Lawrence Mario Giannini died on August 19, 1952. He was fifty-seven years old. During his last months in the hospital, the bank was run by the managing committee, under the chairmanship of Senior

Vice-President Clark Beise. In September, Carl F. Wente, thirty-five years in the service of the Gianninis, was elected president of the Bank of America.

"My big job is to find my successor," said the new president. In March, 1954, Wente will be sixty-five years old, the B. of A.'s retirement age.[26]

The son had died no richer than his father. The inventory of Mario Giannini's estate placed its value at $461,331. His will left half to his wife and the remainder in trusts for his two daughters.

Honoring the memory of their late president, the directors voted to give $100,000 to the Bank of America–Giannini Foundation for medical research on hemophilia. In clearing up Mario's files, it was discovered that, in 1950, he had agreed to make a personal contribution of $8,000 annually to the Stanford University Medical School for laboratory and clinical investigations of the mysterious disease that he had inherited. The Foundation is continuing the contributions.

The death of Mario Giannini removed the last interlocking director of Transamerica and the Bank of America. Two months later Transamerica sold its remaining shares (by then down to 5.6 per cent of the total) in the bank. Thus the final corporate tie between the two institutions was cut, completing a program voluntarily undertaken fifteen years before. This was the reverse of what the Federal Reserve Board had ordered. The board's ruling, however, did not long survive. In July, 1953, the United States Court of Appeals set it aside, declaring that the Federal Reserve had failed to prove its monopoly charges against Transamerica. The opinion of the court was essentially the same as the dissenting opinion, quoted earlier, of two Reserve Board members. Subsequently the Supreme Court declined to review the case. The Gianninis had triumphed in their last, long, crucial battle to preserve the ascendancy of their banking institution.

Comments and Acknowledgments

THE AUTHORS undertook to write this book for pay, with the understanding that they would have a free hand to find the facts and to set them forth as they saw them. The Bank of America was to make accessible all its records and the business correspondence of its officers and employees.

To help examine this material, or such of it as seemed necessary, we employed researchers, unconnected with the bank, though the bank paid them. We also used some of the bank's personnel, though not many because the bank's people were so busy. The records turned out to be far more voluminous than we had counted on, and they were not always easy to find.

In the notes of this volume readers will find frequent reference to the "Bank of America N. T. & S. A. archives." When the work was begun there were, properly speaking, no such archives. The bank's records were everywhere and anywhere an unused branch basement could be found to put them in. Of necessity, Mrs. James began to assemble them. The yield was so rewarding historically that the bank itself took this up. Though our work is now done, the task of assembling the archives continues.

An important part of the collection is some six-hundred-odd volumes of minutes and ledgers acquired through the absorption of small banks by the Bank of America and its predecessor the Bank of Italy. Some of these institutions go back almost to the beginning of California's statehood and their minute books are new sources for historians.

Not the least of the archives' treasures is A. P. Giannini's correspondence, boxes and boxes of which we have read. Were this book a biography of the banker instead of a history of his bank more use would have been made of these letters than has been the case. Giannini saw things quickly and clearly. The language of his letters has the same directness and simplicity.

Naturally, sources outside the bank, including those sometimes hostile to it, were consulted to the extent that seemed needful. By and large, we two authors divided our work as follows. Mrs. James established residence in San Francisco for nearly three years. Not only did she administer the job of research; she actually did most of it herself. I stayed in the East and did most of the writing. Both jobs turned out to be more arduous than we anticipated because this book is contemporary history, and, throughout the span of the Bank of America, banking has undergone more changes than in any other period in the country's history.

Our greatest debt in the matter of research is to Albert E. Haase—the Al Haase in the notes. We met him through Gerald T. White, associate professor of history at San Francisco State College, whose suggestions and criticisms have contributed to the enrichment of this history. Al became one of the early research employees and the only one who stuck through to the end. A member of an old cattle-ranching family in the lower San Joaquin Valley, he came to us after three years in the Army where he wound up helping to write the history of the Army Air Forces. Al's principal contribution has been the research that lies back of the chapters that deal with the bank and California's agricultural problems. He has also been unremitting in his pursuit of the bank's records, or any records, from which this history could benefit. The archives have him to thank for rescuing some of their best items from imminent bonfires.

We also wish to acknowledge the help in research contributed by Vice-President George O. Bordwell, by Roscoe L. Evans and by W. N. Wholey, all retired. With a long record of service in the bank's accounting department, these three at one time or another were our accounting department. One of them has checked independently nearly every banking figure used in this history. Thanks to their instruction, at the end of three years Mrs. James had begun to find a national bank examiner's report light enough reading for a summer holiday.

Among the officers we saw most of was Vice-President Walter E. Bruns, whom Mario Giannini delegated to see that we got what we wanted. Mr. Bruns fulfilled that mission with distinction, as the material in this book, virtually all from original sources, is the best evidence. Another officer consulted frequently was Vice-President Luther E. Birdzell, whose knowledge of the legal history of banking has been heavily drawn on in telling about the controversies with state and federal banking authorities.

In the fall of 1947 Mrs. James and I made our first trip to San Francisco on this undertaking. On the first day, I was introduced to Mr. A. P. Giannini. "You know, Mr. James," he said, "I'm not for this book. We have a pretty good bank, and it's doing all right. I can't see that a book will help it do any better. But some of the boys have an idea they want a book. I'll go along with my boys, and since they want you to write the book, I'll help you all I can." The remark was characteristic. I did not see much of Mr. A. P., but Mrs. James did. He became truly interested in the history. His death in 1949 was a loss to it.

One of the original proponents of the history idea, Mr. Mario Giannini showed an active enthusiasm for the work until he died in 1952. Despite the additional responsibilities that came to him after the passing of his father, Mario was always accessible for discussion of moot points. The principal complaint the writers have to make about Mario is an unusual one. He consistently minimized or was silent on his own contributions to the bank's development.

That Mr. A. P.'s "boys" wanted a book was quickly evident from their eagerness in helping us round up our material. Mrs. James was scarcely settled at 300 Montgomery Street when the old-timers began trekking to her office to reminisce about the early years of the Bank of Italy. Their names are scattered through the earlier chapters or cited in the notes. Because they were old men the trip downtown was not an easy matter and we especially want to thank all of them for the effort they put forth in our behalf. Some of them, like the founder, did not live to see the book in print.

Active officers and employees have been generous with their time. Many of their names appear in the text or in the notes. We will not repeat their names here, but, instead, acknowledge our debt to others who have been equally as helpful though less written about:

R. J. Barbieri, H. M. Bardt, Alan Bartlett, J. F. Burns, Glenn E. Carter, W. G. Cuppa, F. M. Dana, Genevieve Daneri, C. W. Dechent, J. W. Durham, W. L. Eager, E. J. Feliz, W. J. Fraser, A. D. Harrington, Dorothy Hayes, P. L. Hudson, J. H. Hull, L. O. Knutson, D. S. Langsdorf, L. B. Lundborg, Margaret Mallory, J. V. Minehan, A. C. Meyer, T. McDonald, Mary McGoldrick, M. D. McGregor, Eugenie M. Nivoche, W. B. Nix, Jr., Mary E. Nugent,

R. M. Oddie, Mary Ottoboni, R. H. Pearce, J. H. B. Perlite, G. M. Peterson, Roland Pierotti, H. J. Pye, F. E. Reed, V. C. Richards, J. A. Smith, George Solari, A. E. Sbarboro, Leo P. Scaroni, G. D. Schilling, R. T. Shinkle, S. B. Stewart, Jr., Dorothy Sturla, H. L. Topping, L. J. Tobey, S. J. Tosi, Roy Troutman, H. A. Wagstaffe, H. G. White, R. C. Woodmansee, Fred Yeates, F. E. Young.

It was impossible to visit all the branches, though Mrs. James and Al Haase got around to a large number of them. We wish to acknowledge the helpful aid of the following branch officers:

R. J. Bender and W. Ginotti (San Francisco, Park-Presidio); E. A. Bonzani (San Francisco, Columbus Avenue); A. Beronio (San Francisco, North Beach); F. M. Buckley (San Francisco, Humboldt); A. C. Dimon (Bakersfield); R. C. Craddick (Fall River Mills); Julian R. Davis (Oakland, Main); T. C. Deane (Los Angeles, Main); F. Erickson and Joseph Firpo (Daly City); N. P. Hasselo (Monterey); Graydon Hoffman, O. T. Jensen, and K. A. Nairne (San Diego, Main); H. F. Hogan and J. Raggio (San Francisco, Day and Night); Henry C. Maier (San Francisco, Main); W. H. Nuss, Jr., deceased (San Luis Obispo); V. L. Puccinelli (San Francisco, Clay-Montgomery); R. L. Rehorn (Fresno, Main); A. Risi (San Francisco, Castro-Market); F. W. Shields (Santa Maria); J. C. Sloan (San Bernardino); B. F. Vandenberg, Jr. (Sacramento, Main).

We wish also to acknowledge the help of the following members of the personnel of Transamerica and the Capital Company:

W. L. Andrews, Sam Flint, J. Franceschi, Pearl Gaulette, G. M. McClerkin, Malcolm P. McLellan, George Panario, A. J. Elliott Ponsford, J. A. Smith, Tom Walker, E. D. Woodruff.

Outside the bank, too, we also wish to say "Thank you" to the following, several of whom have since passed on:

William R. Bacon, Clare Banta, Eda Beronio, Tom Bragg, W. B. Camp, W. W. Crocker, John U. Calkins, F. S. Cooley, Ira B. Cross, Elbert W. Davis, Marshall R. Diggs, Robert Easton, Federal Judge Herbert Erskine, Dr. E. A. Filipello, Mrs. Charles F. Grondona, Alvin Heyman, Mr. and Mrs. John P. Jennings, L. M. Klauber, L. G. Laughlin, Johnny Longo, Parker S. Maddux, Irving S. Metzler, Eugene Meyer, Jesse B. McCargar, Henrietta Setaro, W. H. Snyder, Charles F. Stern, A. Sweet, W. R. Williams, Mrs. L. G. Worden, George Zaro.

Our thanks are also due to the following institutions and individuals:

San Francisco *Examiner* and Dwight Newton and Larry Lieurance of the *Examiner* "morgue"; Federal Reserve Bank of San Francisco: C. E. Earhart, president, A. C. Agnew, vice-president, Marion H. Lynch, secretary, and Elizabeth H. Holden, librarian; San Francisco Public Library; Wells Fargo Bank and Edna Durkee, its librarian; Los Angeles *Times* and Romeo Carraro of the *Times* "morgue"; *Wall Street Journal* (Pacific Coast edition); Mechanics Institute Library (San Francisco) and Mary Carmody, librarian; Wine Institute Library (San Francisco) and Miriam F. Horn, librarian; National City Bank and Nathan C. Lenfestey, vice-president and cashier; Bancroft Library at the University of California, Berkeley; Los Angeles Public Library; New York Public Library; Library of Congress, Washington.

M. J.

Notes

1. The sketch of A. P. Giannini's career to 1902 was derived from extended conversations between Bessie R. James and Mr. Giannini and a few old-timers who knew Giannini in those days, notably Charles F. Grondona, G. B. Cordano, Dr. Guido E. Caglieri, Fred Ferroggiaro, Eda Beronio and Clarence Cuneo (a brother-in-law) of San Francisco, and Frank S. Cooley of Palo Alto, California. Among published works usefully consulted were Oscar Osburn Winther, *The Story of San Jose, 1777–1869* (1935), 43; Reed Hayes, *A Real Romance of San Francisco, The Story of the Bank of Italy and A. P. Giannini,* Chapters 1 to 7— a serial in the San Francisco *News,* beginning March 6, 1928; Julian Dana, *A. P. Giannini, Giant in the West* (1947), 6–45. A court opinion of Giannini's stewardship of his father-in-law's estate and the reasonable nature of his fee in that connection is in California Appellate Decisions, Volume 28, 709–13. In 1916 Frank J. Cuneo, a brother-in-law, had sued on the ground that the $36,994 fee paid Giannini was excessive. The court ruled otherwise.
2. A. P. Giannini and C. F. Grondona to B. R. James.
3. Ira B. Cross, *Financing an Empire* (1927), I, 268, 425–26.
4. A. P. Giannini to B. R. James.
5. Jesse B. McCargar, retired banker and lifetime friend of J. J. Fagan; C. F. Grondona, G. B. Cordano and others to B. R. James.
6. A. P. Giannini to B. R. James.
7. Italian-American Bank, Minute Book (1904), 62; Bank of Italy, Minutes, I, 1: Bank of America N.T. & S.A. archives; A. P. Giannini to B. R. James.
8. Bank of Italy, Minutes, I, 2–4; Bank of Italy, General Ledger No. 1, Bank of America N.T. & S.A. archives.
9. *Ibid.*
10. Bank of Italy, Minutes, I, 11; A. P. Giannini to B. R. James; *Bankitaly Life,* February 1921, 18. Copies of this magazine which the Bank of Italy issued for several years are in Bank of America N.T. & S.A. archives.
11. Data on early deposits and depositors taken from the bank's contemporary records by G. O. Bordwell, retired vice-president of the Bank of America N.T. & S.A.
12. A. P. Giannini and Dr. G. E. Caglieri to B. R. James.
13. Figures on loans are from Bank of Italy records and other contemporary sources, abstracted by G. O. Bordwell. Additional material came from A. P. Giannini, C. F. Grondona, Alvin Heyman and others to B. R. James. Mr. Heyman is a son of Jacob Heyman.
14. A. P. Giannini to B. R. James; General Ledger No. 1; Challis Gore, "Bank of America N.T. & S.A. Chronology," year 1905. This is an unpublished account derived from bank records, conversations with officers and other contemporary sources.
15. C. F. Grondona and A. P. Giannini to B. R. James.

CHAPTER II

1. Figures compiled by G. O. Bordwell from Bank of Italy records and other contemporary sources.
2. Bank of Italy, Minutes, I, 46, 64.
3. Details of the first day and night of the fire are from the recollections of A. P. Giannini, C. F. Grondona, Dr. G. E. Caglieri, J. B. McCargar, Clarence Cuneo and others as related to B. R. James; and also from various contemporary accounts, notably that of Frank E. Aitken and Edward Hilton, *A History of the Earthquake and Fire in San Francisco* (1906), and of Mary Austin in *The California Earthquake of 1906,* David Starr Jordan, editor (1907).
4. No copy of this letter has been found. The substance given in the text was obtained through interviews.
5. San Francisco *Chronicle,* April 27, 1906.
6. San Francisco *Examiner,* April 27, 28, 1906.
7. Leroy Armstrong and J. C. Denny, *Financial California* (1916), 134.
8. San Francisco *Chronicle,* April 26, 1906.
9. A. P. Giannini and C. F. Grondona to B. R. James; Joseph Laib, president Laib Sign Company to Jack Sassell, assistant vice-president, Capital Company; Dana, 59–60; *L'Italia* (San Francisco), June 6, 1906.
10. San Francisco *Examiner,* May 22, 1906.
11. *The Recorder* (San Francisco), June 23, 1906.
12. *L'Italia,* July 2, 1906.
13. C. F. Grondona to B. R. James. The two importers made out better with their fire insurance than did Bank of Italy. Secretary Grondona, as agent for the Rhine and Moselle Fire Insurance Company, had sold the bank a $3,000 policy. Though a total loss was sustained, the bank had to accept a compromise payment of $1,000 several years later. Bank of Italy, Minutes, I, 135.
14. *Ibid.,* 77.
15. San Francisco *Examiner,* October 21, 1906.
16. San Francisco *Call,* July 12, 1908.
17. Figures by G. O. Bordwell, from contemporary records.
18. A. P. Giannini to B. R. James.

CHAPTER III

1. A. P. Giannini to B. R. James.
2. Alexander D. Noyes, *Forty Years of American Finance* (1909), Chapters XIII and XV, *passim;* Bank of Italy loan figures by G. O. Bordwell from contemporary records.
3. San Francisco *Daily Journal of Commerce,* January 4, 8, 1907; Noyes, 329.
4. A. P. Giannini to B. R. James; clipping, dated 1907, from an unidentified New Orleans newspaper in files of advertising and publicity department, Bank of America N.T. & S.A., San Francisco.
5. Figures by G. O. Bordwell from contemporary records.
6. A. P. Giannini, C. F. Grondona and Clarence Cuneo to B. R. James.
7. Bank of Italy, Minutes, I, 109; *Mission Times* (San Francisco), August 3, 1907.
8. A. P. Giannini and J. B. McCargar to B. R. James.
9. San Francisco *Chronicle,* December 21, 1907; *Report of Bank Commissioners of California* (1908), 20–23.

10. San Francisco *Chronicle* October 30, November 1, 1907; *L'Italia,* undated clipping in files of advertising and publicity department, Bank of America N.T. & S.A., San Francisco.

11. L. M. Giannini and J. B. McCargar to B. R. James; Bank of Italy, General Ledgers Nos. 1 and 2.

12. *Proceedings of the Fourteenth Annual Convention of the California Bankers Association* (1908), *passim.*

13. *Proceedings 34th Annual Convention of the American Bankers Association* (1908), *230 et seq.;* Bernard Ostrolenk, *The Economics of Banking* (1930), 149–55; John M. Chapman and Ray B. Westerfield, *Branch Banking* (1942), 258.

14. A. P. Giannini to B. R. James.

15. *Coast Banker* (San Francisco), November 1908, 129.

16. C. F. Grondona and various old-timers to B. R. James.

17. *Proceedings of the Fifteenth Annual Convention of the California Bankers Association* (1909), 83.

18. Cross, II, 723 *et seq.*

Chapter IV

1. Bank of Italy, Minutes, I, 164.

2. Commercial and Savings Bank of San Jose, Minutes, 1908–1910, 12, Bank of America N.T. & S.A. archives; A. P. Giannini to B. R. James.

3. Commercial and Savings Bank of San Jose, Minutes, 1908–1910, 15–19.

4. San Jose *Mercury* and *Herald,* November 14, 1909.

5. Commercial and Savings Bank of San Jose, Minutes, 1908–1910, 24–28; Bank of Italy, Minutes, I, 167–68.

6. *Ibid.,* 177; A. P. Giannini to B. R. James.

7. Bank of San Francisco, Minutes, 1907–1910, 57, Bank of America N.T. & S.A. archives; *Coast Banker,* December 1910, 416; Bank of Italy, Minutes, I, 216.

8. C. F. Grondona to B. R. James.

9. Bank of Italy, Minutes, I, 289; Donaldson B. Thorburn, *The Story of Transamerica* (1931), 7; *Coast Banker,* November 1912, 378, and March 1913, 355; J. F. Cavagnaro to B. R. James.

Chapter V

1. J. A. Bacigalupi to G. W. McEnerney, April 30, 1925, Bank of America N.T. & S.A. archives; A. P. Giannini and W. R. Williams to B. R. James.

2. Gore, *op. cit.*

3. A. P. Giannini, I. S. Metzler and W. R. Williams to B. R. James; A. P. Giannini to A. Pedrini, October 12, 1913, Bank of America N.T. & S.A. archives.

4. Bank of Italy, Minutes, I, 363, 410.

5. Los Angeles *Tribune,* May 2, 1913.

6. W. R. Williams to B. R. James.

7. Los Angeles *Tribune,* June 14, 1913.

8. *Ibid.,* June 19, 1913.

9. *Ibid.,* July 3, 1913; Los Angeles *Herald,* July 8, 1913.

10. *Ibid.,* July 26, 1913.

11. *Ibid.*

12. Los Angeles *Tribune,* August 7, 24 and 25, 1913; Los Angeles *Herald,* July 29, 1913.

13. A. P. Giannini and Hal Stanton to B. R. James. Mr. Stanton, manager of the Vermont-Melbourne branch of the Bank of America in Hollywood until his retirement in 1948, was an employee of the Park Bank when the Bank of Italy took it over in 1913.

14. "A Comparison of the Growth of the Branches of the Bank of Italy with the Growth of Other Banks in the Same Communities," April 22, 1925, Bank of America N.T. & S.A. archives.

15. Bank of Italy, Minutes, I, 414, 422 *et seq.*

16. *Ibid.,* I, 431 *et seq.*

17. *Transamerica Corporation vs. Board of Governors of the Federal Reserve System,* in the United States Court of Appeals for the Third Circuit, Appendix, Volume 7, 4707a.

18. Bank of Italy, Minutes, I, 459 *et seq.*

19. *Ibid.,* I, 478.

20. *Ibid.,* II, 20, 22; A. P. Giannini to B. R. James.

CHAPTER VI

1. Figures on assets, etc. are from published statements of condition. Other pertinent facts about the branchwise growth of the bank, complete to 1930, appear in Committee on Banking and Currency, House of Representatives, 71st Cong., 2nd Session, *Hearings,* Volume 2, Part II.

2. Bank of Italy, Stock Book (1918).

3. Dr. G. E. Caglieri to B. R. James.

4. House Committee on Banking and Currency, *Hearings, op. cit.,* 1470; Hayes, Chapter 23.

5. A. P. Giannini and W. R. Williams to B. R. James; A. P. Giannini to J. A. Bacigalupi, May 20, 1917, Bank of America N.T. & S.A. archives.

6. *Coast Banker,* January 1918, 71.

7. *Ibid.,* October 1916, 295.

8. L. H. Roseberry to J. A. Bacigalupi, April 23, 1919, Bank of America N.T. & S.A. archives.

9. J. A. Bacigalupi to L. H. Roseberry, April 24, 1919; Roseberry to Bacigalupi, September 18, 1919; Bacigalupi's reply, October 1, 1919: *ibid.*

10. Superintendent of Banks of California, *Seventh Annual Report* (1916), 7.

11. J. A. Bacigalupi to G. W. McEnerney, April 30, 1925, Bank of America N.T. & S.A. archives.

12. Bank of Italy, Minutes, II, *passim,* 1916–18; W. R. Williams to B. R. James.

13. *Ibid.*

14. A. P. Giannini to B. R. James.

CHAPTER VII

1. E. J. Wickson and R. E. Hodges, *Farming in California* (1923), 17.

2. *California Fruit News,* June 7, and July 12, 1919; *Pacific Rural Press,* December 28, 1918.

3. *The Financier* (New York), January 1, 1918.

4. *Pacific Rural Press,* November 12, 1917.

5. Donald C. Horton, *Fluctuations in Outstanding Farm Mortgages, 1910–1939,* United States Department of Agriculture Publication (1942), 9; R. L. Adams, *Farm Management* (1925), 246–47.

6. *Pacific Rural Press*, March 4, 1916.

7. C. W. Thompson, *Costs and Sources of Farm Mortgages in the United States,* United States Department of Agriculture, Office of Market and Rural Organization (1916), Bulletin 384; E. J. Wickson, *Rural California* (1923), 339.

8. Merced *Evening Star,* June 9, 1916; House Committee on Banking and Currency, *Hearings, op. cit.,* 1547.

9. M. S. Blois and W. H. Lemmon to Al Haase. Mr. Blois, a state bank examiner in 1917–19, is a vice-president of the Bank of America N.T. & S.A. Mr. Lemmon, who started his banking career in the San Joaquin Valley in 1908, was manager of the Merced branch.

10. House Committee on Banking and Currency, *Hearings, op. cit.,* 1342; W. C. Tighe, member advisory board, Madera branch, to Al Haase.

11. House Committee on Banking and Currency, *Hearings, op. cit.,* 1547; Fresno *Morning Republican,* October 20 and 21, 1916.

12. R. E. Emberton to Al Haase.

13. W. A. Harter to J. L. Williams, March 1, March 19 and April 3, 1917; to Bank of Italy, April 13, 1917: Bank of America N.T. & S.A. archives.

14. Madera *Daily Tribune,* June 22, 1917.

15. *Ibid.*

16. *Bankitaly Life,* July 1918, 69.

17. Stockton *Record,* December 30, 1917.

18. *Bankitaly Life,* November 1918, 3.

19. C. R. Shaffer and W. C. Tighe to Al Haase. In 1916–18 Mr. Shaffer was branch manager at Merced.

20. House Committee on Banking and Currency, *Hearings, op. cit.,* 1566.

21. Memorandum, interview with William Pabst in 1928, Bank of America N.T. & S.A. archives.

22. Bank of Italy, Executive Committee Minutes, March 1, June 7, May 1, 1918, *passim, ibid.*

23. *Bankitaly Life,* March 1918, 24; R. S. Heaton to Al Haase. Mr. Heaton joined the Fresno branch in 1919, later becoming vice-president and manager.

24. House Committee on Banking and Currency, *Hearings, op. cit.,* 1347.

25. E. T. Cunningham to Al Haase.

26. Bank of Italy, "Order of Business for Advisory Boards . . ." (1918), Bank of America N.T. & S.A. archives.

27. *Pacific Rural Press,* October 4, 1918; Murray R. Benedict, *Farm Finance: Dangers and Opportunities in Wartime* (1942), 7.

28. California State Board of Agriculture, *Statistical Report* (1919), *passim;* R. L. Adams, *Farm Management Notes for California* (1921), *passim.*

29. Advisory Board, Hollister branch, Minutes, *passim,* Bank of America N.T. & S.A. archives.

30. Figures compiled by Roscoe Evans from Bank of Italy ledgers.

Chapter VIII

1. Chapman and Westerfield, 82–83; Ernest Ludlow Bogart, *Economic History of the American People* (1935), 813–16.

2. Parker H. Willis, *The Federal Reserve Bank of San Francisco* (1937), 113; Chapman and Westerfield, 93–94.

3. A. P. Giannini to John Perrin, September 18, 1917; A. C. Miller to A. P. Giannini, September 26, 1917: Federal Reserve Bank of San Francisco archives;

W. P. G. Harding to John Perrin, October 23, 1917, Bank of America N.T. & S.A. archives. The correspondence on this subject in the Bank of America files being incomplete, the Federal Reserve Bank of San Francisco kindly filled up gaps with letters from its files.

4. C. F. Stern to Bank of Italy, June 23, 1919, *ibid.*

5. W. R. Williams to C. F. Stern, August 1, 1919, *ibid.*,

6. *Ibid.*, September 24, 1919; C. F. Stern to Bank of Italy, November 10, 1919: *ibid.*

7. *Bankitaly Life,* October 1919, 3.

8. C. F. Stern to Bank of Italy, November 10, 1919, Bank of America N.T. & S.A. archives.

9. Stockholders Auxiliary Corporation, Minutes, I, 61, 67, 75, 91; J. A. Bacigalupi to G. W. McEnerney, April 30, 1925: Bank of America N.T. & S.A. archives.

10. C. F. Stern to B. R. James.

11. C. F. Stern to A. P. Giannini, February 21, 1920, Bank of America N.T. & S.A. archives.

12. *Coast Banker,* January 1920, 60.

13. C. F. Stern to Bank of Italy, May 31, 1920, Bank of America N.T. & S.A. archives.

14. Bank of Italy, Minutes, III, 11, 81–84.

15. *Bankitaly Life,* May 1921, 29.

16. A. P. Giannini to C. F. Stern, November 4, 1920, Bank of America N.T. & S.A. archives.

17. C. F. Stern to Bank of Italy, June 13, 1921, *ibid.*

18. C. F. Stern to B. R. James.

19. A. P. Giannini to J. A. Bacigalupi, undated but probably written in July, 1918, Bank of America N.T. & S.A. archives.

20. *Ibid.*, July 12, 1918.

Chapter IX

1. Willis, 151.

2. San Francisco *Bulletin,* reproduced from *Bankitaly Life,* July, 1919, 8.

3. M. S. Blois to Al Haase.

4. Bank of Italy, Executive Committee Minutes, October 24, 1919.

5. *Pacific Rural Press,* January 24, 1920.

6. A. P. Giannini to B. R. James.

7. Bank of Italy, Minutes, III, 103, 105, 112, 116, 133, 156, 161, 184, 195.

8. A. P. Giannini to Al Haase.

9. W. W. Flannigan to W. R. Williams, July 14, 1919; California Joint Stock Land Bank, Minutes, September 29, October 29, 1919: Bank of America N.T. & S.A. archives.

10. A. W. Hendrick to Farm Loan Board, November 25, 1919; E. C. Aldwell to same, December 31, 1919: *ibid.*

11. E. C. Aldwell to W. W. Powell, December 11, 1919; A. W. Hendrick to Guy Houston, February 24, 1920: *ibid.*

12. *Ibid.;* A. W. Hendrick to Farm Loan Board, April 17, 1920; Charles Lobdell to Hendrick, April 23, 1920; Hendrick to Lobdell, April 27, 1920; Houston to Hendrick, April 27, 1920; L. B. Williams to Hendrick, January 11, 1921; Hendrick's reply, January 12, 1921: *ibid.*

13. Various correspondence, see especially: A. W. Hendrick to Guy Houston, March 23, 1921; Powell to Hendrick, April 19 and May 3, 1921: *ibid.*
14. California Joint Stock Land Bank, Monthly Statement, December 31, 1921, *ibid.*
15. *Pacific Rural Press,* January 1, 22, 1921.
16. J. A. Bacigalupi to John Perrin, December 3, 1921, Bank of America N.T. & S.A. archives.

CHAPTER X

1. F. W. Laughlin, retired Santa Rosa attorney, to Al Haase; Santa Rosa *Press Democrat,* January 8, 1921.
2. C. B. Wingate to C. F. Stern, January 10, 1921; Special Report 616, Operative L-44, Burns Detective Agency, January 10, 1921: Bank of America N.T. & S.A. archives.
3. L. B. McGuire to Al Haase.
4. J. A. Lombardi and J. M. Fischer to Al Haase; Santa Rosa *Republican,* January 8, 1921; D. P. Wingate to C. F. Stern, January 10, 1921, Bank of America N.T. & S.A. archives. Mr. Fischer, at present an assistant vice-president of the Bank of America N.T. & S.A., was a teller in 1921. He made the trip to Santa Rosa with Scatena and the $1,500,000.
5. Statement, C. F. Stern, January 7, 1921, *ibid.*
6. J. A. Bacigalupi to branch managers, January 7, 1921, *ibid.*
7. J. A. Lombardi to Al Haase; Santa Rosa *Press Democrat,* January 8, 1921.
8. A. P. Giannini to C. F. Stern, February 9 and May 11, 1921, Bank of America N.T. & S.A. archives; C. F. Stern to B. R. James; Stern to Giannini, June 18, 1921, Bank of America N.T. & S.A. archives.
9. A. P. Giannini to B. R. James.
10. W. H. Snyder, M. S. Blois, A. Sweet and R. F. Cross to Al Haase. Mr. Sweet, a resident of Visalia, was a stockholder in the threatened bank. Mr. Cross was a Visalia real estate dealer.
11. M. S. Blois and R. S. Heaton to Al Haase; L. C. Hyde to E. C. Aldwell, June 5, 1921, Bank of America N.T. & S.A. archives.
12. R. F. Cross to Al Haase.
13. J. A. Bacigalupi to G. W. McEnerney, April 30, 1925; A. P. Giannini to C. F. Stern, April 15, 1921; C. F. Stern to Bank of Italy, April 18, 1921: Bank of America N.T. & S.A. archives.
14. C. F. Wente to B. R. James; *Coast Banker,* May 1921, 599. Exact figures on the condition of the two banks on the day of the take-over have not been found. Rand McNally's *Banker's Directory* gives these figures as of January, 1921: National Bank of Visalia: capital, $200,000; deposits, $1,775,000; loans, $2,420,-000. Visalia Savings Bank: capital, $200,000; deposits, $1,130,000; loans, $1,249,-000.
15. A. P. Giannini to C. F. Stern, May 11, 1921, Bank of America N.T. & S.A. archives.
16. A. P. Giannini and C. F. Stern to B. R. James.
17. C. F. Stern to A. P. Giannini, June 18, 1921, Bank of America N.T. & S.A. archives.
18. *Bankitaly Life,* June 1921, *passim;* A. P. Giannini to J. S. Dodge, June 23, 1921; J. A. Bacigalupi to C. F. Stern, June 25, 1921: Bank of America N.T. & S.A. archives.

Chapter XI

1. *Coast Banker,* January 1921, 27; J. A. Bacigalupi to G. W. McEnerney, April 30, 1925, Bank of America N.T. & S.A. archives.
2. *Bankitaly Life,* July 1921, 19; J. S. Dodge to Bank of Italy, July 5, 1921: *ibid.*
3. J. S. Chambers to L. V. Belden, July 11, September 3, 1921, *ibid.*
4. *Coast Banker,* February 1922, 152.
5. J. S. Dodge to Bank of Italy, July 12, 1922, Bank of America N.T. & S.A. archives. Superintendent Dodge is quoted from a letter written some nine months after the examination discussed. Unfortunately his earlier letter has not been found. In the later communication, however, Dodge mentions that he is repeating criticisms he made after the September, 1921, examination of the Bank of Italy.
6. J. Perrin to J. A. Bacigalupi, September 23, 1921, *ibid.*
7. J. S. Dodge to L. V. Belden, November 22, 1921, *ibid.*
8. J. F. Sartori to J. S. Dodge, December 3, 1921, *Bank of Italy vs. J. F. Johnson, Appendix to Brief for Petitioner,* Records of the Supreme Court of California, Volume 3726, 16.
9. San Francisco *Examiner,* June 14, 1921; John Perrin to W. G. McAdoo, May 12, 1922; J. A. Bacigalupi to G. W. McEnerney, April 30, 1925: Bank of America N.T. & S.A. archives.
10. John Perrin to A. P. Giannini, November 25, 1921, Federal Reserve Bank of San Francisco archives.
11. W. P. G. Harding to A. P. Giannini, December 1, 1921, *ibid.*
12. A. P. Giannini to W. P. G. Harding, December 15, 1921, *ibid.;* W. G. McAdoo to Giannini, December 23, 1921; Harding to Giannini, January 18, 1922: Bank of America N.T. & S.A. archives.
13. Chapman and Westerfield, 94–97.
14. Proceedings Conference Held at the Federal Reserve Bank of San Francisco, April 13, 1922, *passim,* see especially pp. 2–11, 21, 22, 44, 120, Bank of America N.T. & S.A. archives.
15. Superintendent of Banks of California, *Annual Reports,* 1920 to 1923 inclusive.

Chapter XII

1. J. S. Chambers to J. A. Bacigalupi, December 18, 1922, Bank of America N.T. & S.A. archives; *Coast Banker,* February 1923, 178.
2. J. S. Chambers to J. A. Bacigalupi, December 30, 1922; to A. P. Giannini, March 8, 1923: Bank of America N.T. & S.A. archives.
3. *Ibid.,* February 10, March 8, 1923.
4. Chapman and Westerfield, 97; *Annual Report of the Comptroller of the Currency* (1923), 5, 10.
5. W. G. McAdoo to J. A. Bacigalupi, July 3, 1923, Bank of America N.T. & S.A. archives.
6. A. P. Giannini to J. S. Chambers, July 30, 1923; Chambers to W. W. Douglas, November 15, 1923: *ibid.*
7. J. F. Johnson to Bank of Italy, July 13, 1923, quoted in House Committee on Banking and Currency, *Hearings, op. cit.,* 1520.
8. Memorandum of interview with Lee Brown (in 1928), Bank of America N.T. & S.A. archives.

9. W. T. Rice to B. R. James; House Committee on Banking and Currency, *Hearings, op. cit.,* 1519.
10. *Ibid.,* 1512, 1516–18.
11. W. H. Snyder, Louis Ferrari and C. L. Preisker to B. R. James. Mr. Ferrari was attorney for the Bank of Italy and Mr. Preisker for the Bank of Santa Maria. For Bacigalupi's account see House Committee on Banking and Currency, *Hearings, op. cit.,* 1513–14, 1519.
12. The lineup of the Federal Reserve Board given in the text omits Secretary of the Treasury Mellon, an *ex officio* member. Mr. Mellon rarely attended board meetings and so was not a factor in the branch bank fight.
13. J. A. Bacigalupi to A. P. Giannini, September 13, 1923, Bank of America N.T. & S.A. archives; Bacigalupi to M. C. Elliott, January 24, 1924, in House Committee on Banking and Currency, *Hearings, op. cit.,* 1511–20. Elliott was a member of the Bank of Italy's legal staff in Washington. The letter to him comprised the bank's detailed answer to Whipple's charges and included copies and documents relative to the Santa Maria case.
14. Memorandum to the Federal Reserve Board, October 8, 1923, signed by John S. Drum, Charles F. Stern and J. F. Sartori, Bank of America N.T. & S.A. archives.
15. *Commercial & Financial Chronicle* (New York), October 27, 1923.
16. Chapman and Westerfield, 101.
17. *Bankitaly Life,* December 1923, 18–19; *Coast Banker,* February 1924, 149.
18. K. Lyons to A. P. Giannini (quoting McAdoo telegram), November 7, 1923; A. Pedrini to H. C. Cartan (quoting Perrin telegram re James), November 14, 1923; M. C. Elliott to J. A. Bacigalupi, November 19, 1923; Giannini to W. H. Crocker, December 11, 1923: Bank of America N.T. & S.A. archives.
19. J. A. Bacigalupi to M. C. Elliott, January 24, 1924, *ibid.*

Chapter XIII

1. C. F. Stern to C. J. Carey, February 29, 1924, Bank of America N.T. & S.A. archives.
2. Deposition of W. D. Mitchell, *Loller vs. Bank of Italy et al., ibid.* This legal action, brought in 1925, by a stockholder of the late Valley Bank against the Bank of Italy, the Pacific-Southwest, and others forms a sequel to the take-over of the Valley Bank which is extraneous to this narrative. The record of the suit is useful, however, in reconstructing the story of the bank's rise and fall.
3. Superintendent of Banks of California, *Sixteenth Annual Report* (1925), 729.
4. Depositions of J. F. Johnson, J. J. Graves, J. A. Bacigalupi, W. H. Snyder, A. S. Hays and A. P. Giannini, *Loller vs. Bank of Italy, op. cit.*
5. Depositions of J. E. Fickett, A. S. Hays, C. F. Stern, A. P. Giannini and J. F. Johnson, *ibid.*
6. Depositions of J. F. Johnson, J. E. Fickett, C. F. Stern, A. P. Giannini and J. J. Graves, *ibid.*
7. Exact figures on the losses shouldered by the Bank of Italy and the Pacific-Southwest in the Valley Bank take-over are not available. The million-dollar estimate is by Carl F. Wente.
8. Bank of Italy, Minutes, IV, 228.
9. *Coast Banker,* August 1924, 7.
10. *Transamerica Corporation vs. Board of Governors of the Federal Reserve System, op. cit.,* Appendix, Volume 7, 4536a; Dr. C. R. Bricca, F. Risso and J. M. Fischer to B. R. James.

11. Bank of Italy, Minutes, IV, 352.
12. *Bankitaly Life,* January 1924, 20.
13. California Bankers Association, *Bulletin,* August 1924, 425; W. J. Braun-schweiger to B. R. James; Americommercial Corporation, Minutes, September 15, 1924, Bank of America N.T. & S.A. archives. Mr. Braunschweiger, subsequently to have a long career with the Bank of America N.T. & S.A., was vice-president of the Bank of America of Los Angeles when the merger of 1924 took place.
14. San Francisco *Chronicle,* July 11, 1925.
15. J. A. Bacigalupi to J. F. Johnson, March 12, 1925; Johnson to Bank of Italy, March 20, 1925; A. P. Giannini to Bacigalupi, April 22, 1925: Bank of America N.T. & S.A. archives.
16. *Bank of Italy vs. J. Franklin Johnson, Petition for Writ of Mandate,* records of the Supreme Court of California, Volume 3726, 27.
17. Shirley Donald Southworth, *Branch Banking in the United States* (1928), 84–85.

CHAPTER XIV

1. J. F. Johnson to the Bank of America of Los Angeles, March 5, 1925, Bank of America N.T. & S.A. archives.
2. Vallejo (California) *Chronicle,* July 24, 1925; San Francisco *Bulletin,* September 17, November 28, 1925.
3. San Francisco *Chronicle,* October 15, 1925; San Francisco *Examiner,* December 21, 1925.
4. San Francisco *Bulletin,* January 11, 1925.
5. J. A. Bacigalupi to Officer Addressed, February 24, March 2, 1925, Bank of America N.T. & S.A. archives.
6. A. P. Giannini to L. M. McDonald, August 29, 1925, *ibid.*
7. A. P. Giannini, to the Stockholder [of Bancitaly] Addressed, December 28, 1925, *ibid.*
8. San Francisco *Chronicle,* December 29, 1925.
9. *Ibid.,* January 16, 1926.
10. Los Angeles *Examiner,* December 14, 1925; San Francisco *Examiner,* same date; Stockton *Record,* December 17, 1925.
11. Bank of America of Los Angeles to J. F. Johnson, July 12, 1926, Bank of America N.T. & S.A. archives; Gore, "Family Tree."
12. J. F. Johnson to Bank of America of Los Angeles, March 5, 1926, Bank of America N.T. & S.A. archives.
13. E. Cullinan to G. W. McEnerney, March 9, 1926, *ibid.*
14. A. P. Giannini (unsigned cable) to J. A. Bacigalupi, June 27, 1926, *ibid.*
15. Bank of America of Los Angeles and Liberty Bank to J. F. Johnson, July 12, 1926, *ibid.*
16. J. A. Bacigalupi to A. P. Giannini, July 26, 1926, *ibid.*
17. A. P. Giannini to J. A. Bacigalupi, July 15, 1926, *ibid.*
18. J. F. Neylan to B. R. James; J. A. Bacigalupi to A. P. Giannini, July 26, 1925, Bank of America N.T. & S.A. archives.
19. L. M. Giannini to L. V. Belden, August 24, 1926; O. E. Monnette to A. P. Giannini, August 26, 1926: *ibid.*
20. Los Angeles *Times,* August 25, 1926.
21. J. A. Bacigalupi to A. P. Giannini, September 7, 1926, Bank of America N.T. & S.A. archives.

22. Various correspondence during the last week of August and the first week of September show the zeal with which the personnel of the Giannini banks went to work for Young. See also, Arthur MacLennan to A. P. Giannini, August 27, 1926; Giannini's reply, same date; L. V. Belden to Giannini, August 30, 1926: *ibid.*

23. Los Angeles *Times,* August 29, 1926; A. P. Giannini to B. R. James.

24. A. P. Giannini to L. V. Belden, August 30, 1926; to W. C. Wood, September 3, 1926; to C. C. Young, same date: Bank of America N.T. & S.A. archives.

25. J. A. Bacigalupi to A. P. Giannini, September 7, 1926, *ibid.*

CHAPTER XV

1. Committee on Banking and Currency, House of Representatives, 68th Congress, 1st Session, *Hearings* on H. R. 6855, 69.

2. *Ibid.,* 178.

3. *Ibid.,* 104.

4. *Ibid.,* 127.

5. *Ibid.,* 185–86.

6. L. T. McFadden to A. P. Giannini, September 17, 1924; Giannini's answer, October 8: Bank of America N.T. & S.A. archives.

7. C. Glass, "The Battle for the Banking Bill," *Nation's Business,* April 1927.

8. C. W. Collins, *The Branch Banking Question* (1926), 99–101; Chapman and Westerfield, 105–06.

9. *Congressional Record,* House, January 10, 1925, 1625.

10. C. Glass, "The Battle for the Banking Bill," *Nation's Business,* April 1927; A. P. Giannini to B. R. James; *Daily Times* of Santa Maria, March 17, 1926.

11. A. P. Giannini to L. M. MacDonald, April 20, 1926, Bank of America N.T. & S.A. archives.

12. C. W. Collins to A. P. Giannini, December 28, 1926, *ibid.*

13. A. J. Mount to A. P. Giannini, May 21, 1926; to J. A. Bacigalupi, July 26, 1926; L. Edwards to A. P. Giannini, March 25, 1926: *ibid.*

14. A. P. Giannini to J. W. McIntosh, May 13, 1926, *ibid.*

15. Representative McFadden quoted in telegram from A. P. Giannini to J. A. Bacigalupi, January 24, 1927, *ibid.*

16. San Francisco *Examiner,* January 5, 1927; A. P. Giannini to C. W. Collins, December 23, 1926, Bank of America N.T. & S.A. archives.

17. California Bankers Association, *Bulletin,* January 1927, 3.

18. Undated memorandum in the papers of W. C. Wood. This long memorandum, in the former superintendent's handwriting, was found by his son Willsie Wood after his father's death in 1939. Willsie Wood believes the memorandum was written about March, 1927, shortly after the mergers took place.

19. San Francisco *Chronicle,* January 27, 1927.

20. W. C. Wood to M. B. Harris, May 15, 1930, papers of W. C. Wood.

21. J. A. Bacigalupi to L. V. Belden, February 15, 1927, Bank of America N.T. & S.A. archives.

22. San Francisco *Examiner,* February 16, 1927.

23. J. A. Bacigalupi to L. V. Belden, February 15, 1927, Bank of America N.T. & S.A. archives.

24. L. V. Belden to A. J. Mount, February 17, 1927; A. P. Giannini to J. A. Bacigalupi, August 4, 1926: *ibid.*

25. L. V. Belden to A. J. Mount, February 17, 1927; J. A. Bacigalupi to Belden, February 16, 1927; A. P. Giannini to Belden, February 17, 1927: *ibid.*

26. J. A. Bacigalupi to L. V. Belden, February 19, 1927, *ibid.*

27. "The Spirit of the Bank of Italy," an address by J. A. Bacigalupi, May 14, 1927, *ibid.*

CHAPTER XVI

1. *Transamerica Corporation vs. Board of Governors of the Federal Reserve System, op. cit.,* Appendix, Volume 7, 4583a.

2. A. P. Giannini to B. R. James; *Bankitaly Life,* May 1918, 44–48; H. A. Wagstaffe, W. C. Marshall, J. W. Durham and T. McDonald to B. R. James.

3. M. G. Farber to W. H. McGinnis, Jr., November 29, 1926, Bank of America N.T. & S.A. archives.

4. H. C. Carr to W. W. Douglas, February 8, 1929, *ibid.*

5. F. Risso to B. R. James.

6. Bank of Italy, Minutes, IV, 481.

7. Survey for business extension department by W. H. McGinnis, Jr., 1926; McGinnis to J. A. Bacigalupi, January 31, 1927: Bank of America N.T. & S.A. archives.

8. Memorandum on business secured by R. Paganini, December 31, 1925; F. P. Tommasini to business extension department, September 20, 1922: *ibid.*

9. Report on Monterey by A. Ponzio, October 28, 1922; report on Monterey by R. Paganini, January 22, 1925: *ibid.*

10. Various correspondence, Italian department, 1922–27, *ibid.*

11. Memorandum, W. H. McGinnis, Jr., February 11, 1925; memorandum, Italian department, January 3, 1923: *ibid.*

12. Memoranda, Italian department, January 3 and February 17, 1927, *ibid.*

13. Memorandum, L. Valperga, April 8, 1925, *ibid.*

14. Memorandum, Italian department, 1921; C. E. Wagner to L. Valperga, October 17, 1921; memorandum, L. Valperga, January 3, 1924: *ibid.*

15. Memoranda, L. Valperga, undated, 1921, and January 3, 1923; W. H. McGinnis, Jr., to A. J. Mount, September 6, 1928: *ibid.*

16. R. Paganini to A. J. Mount, June 17 and August 6, 1928, *ibid.*

17. Memorandum, L. G. Perna, undated, 1923, *ibid.*

18. Memorandum, L. Valperga, undated, 1922; R. Paganini to A. Pedrini, March 2, 1925, and April 28, 1931: *ibid.*

19. R. Paganini to A. Pedrini, February 26, 1925; Paganini to J. A. Bacigalupi, July 10, 1927: *ibid.*

20. Figures from A. Pedrini file, *ibid.*

21. Survey for business extension department by W. H. McGinnis, Jr., February, 1926; M. A. Gunst to A. Pedrini, January 22, 1928; yearly summary of foreign divisions, 1930: *ibid.*

22. McGinnis survey, *op. cit.;* McGinnis to A. J. Mount, April 11, 1927; memoranda, B. Metropoulos to A. Pedrini, January 22, 1929, and February 2, 1929: *ibid.*

23. W. H. McGinnis, Jr., to W. W. Douglas, November 17, 1927, *ibid.*

24. Memorandum, W. H. McGinnis, Jr., March 29, 1926, *ibid.*

25. *Ibid.,* June 13, 1925.

26. *Ibid.,* June 17, 1926; A. Pilcovich to A. Pedrini, February 11, 1931: *ibid.*

27. W. H. McGinnis, Jr., to A. J. Mount, January 11, 1928; E. L. Dominquez to R. Paganini, May 6, 1930; Dominquez to A. Pedrini, November 10, 1930: *ibid.*

28. Memorandum, W. H. McGinnis, Jr., February 17, 1926; McGinnis to J. A. Bacigalupi, January 31, 1927; C. Shanowsky to A. Pedrini, October 3, 1928 (quoted in text) and December 4, 1929: *ibid.*

Chapter XVII

1. A. P. Giannini to C. W. Collins, September 29, 1927; Collins to Giannini, October 3, 1927: Bank of America N.T. & S.A. archives.
2. San Francisco *Examiner,* March 22, 1927; French-American Bank, Minutes, March 27, 1927; United Bank and Trust Company of California, Minutes, March 27, April 30, 1927: Bank of America N.T. & S.A. archives; California State Banking Department, *Bulletin,* April 1928, 5; San Francisco *Chronicle,* December 11, 1927; A. P. Giannini to L. V. Belden, March 23, 1928, Bank of America N.T. & S.A. archives.
3. W. C. Wood to C. C. Young, January 3, 1928, papers of W. C. Wood.
4. G. H. Taylor to Al Haase. Mr. Taylor was vice-president and cashier of the Lassen Industrial Bank.
5. W. C. Wood to C. C. Young, September 1, 1927, papers of W. C. Wood. Sequel to the robbery was a visit several years later from one of the hold-up men. Released on parole he came to tell Dean L. Sears, manager of the Lone Pine branch, that he was "sorry for all the trouble I caused." A personable young fellow, the ex-bank robber took a job in the town until his parole was up. Then he went home to Georgia where he had inherited a plantation. (The *Bank-American,* January 1933, 10.)
6. Security Bank and Trust Company, Minutes, February 2, 1928, March 15, 1928; Humboldt Bank, Minutes, December 8, 1927; Security Trust and Savings Bank of Los Angeles, press release, February 10, 1928: Bank of America N.T. & S.A. archives; *Wall Street Journal,* March 16, 1928.
7. Statistics compiled by Wm. Cavalier & Company, June 30, 1928, Bank of America N.T. & S.A. archives.
8. J. A. Bacigalupi to Louis Ferrari, September 6 and 7, 1928, *ibid.*
9. A. P. Giannini to B. R. James.
10. W. H. Snyder to Al Haase; Snyder to L. M. Giannini, April 25, 1928; deposition of Louis Ferrari, April 20, 1936, *Rogers vs. Transamerica Corporation:* Bank of America N.T. & S.A. archives.
11. Amended cross complaint, *ibid.*
12. Memorandum, September 28, 1935, *Inter-Continental Corporation vs. Rogers, Nolan and Bell;* A. P. Giannini to Lee F. Madlan, June 10, 1933; Giannini to Louis Ferrari, November 30, 1928: *ibid.*
13. Los Angeles *Examiner,* November 17, 1928.
14. Livingston *Chronicle,* December 6, 1928.
15. A. J. Mount to A. P. Giannini, December 24, 1929, Bank of America N.T. & S.A. archives.
16. Deputy Comptroller to Board of Directors, Pacific National Bank, November 9, 1927; Pacific National Bank, Minutes, July 9, July 22, September 3, 1929: *ibid.*

Chapter XVIII

1. Cleland, quoting C. McWilliams, I. Jones and F. Crowder, 208.
2. Los Angeles Regional Board, Minutes, March 9, 1927, Bank of America N.T. & S.A. archives.

3. A. P. Giannini to B. R. James; Los Angeles *Examiner,* September 14, 1921; *Los Angeles Investment and Real Estate Blue Book* (1924), 70.

4. W. W. Robinson, "The Southern California Real Estate Boom of the 'Twenties,'" *Historical Society of Southern California Quartely,* March 1942, 26.

5. *Atascadero, Program of the Second Anniversary Convention of the Real Estate Settlement Plan, May 27–30, 1927.* Copy in Bancroft Library, University of California, Berkeley.

6. W. J. Braunschweiger and R. Groner to B. R. James.

7. A. J. Mount to A. E. Connick, November 8, 1929, Bank of America N.T. & S.A. archives.

8. R. C. Groner to B. R. James; L. A. Winterton to C. F. Wente, March 11, 1953, Bank of America N.T. & S.A. archives.

9. Compiled from Bank of America N.T. & S.A. records by Roscoe Evans and J. W. O'Donnell.

10. Exchange of telegrams between Joe Toplitzky and A. P. Giannini, July 28–29, 1925, Bank of America N.T. & S.A. archives.

11. Analysis and research department, Bank of America N.T. & S.A., *Bulletin* No. 13, September 15, 1931, *ibid.*

12. R. E. Giffin (Hanford) to W. H. McGinnis, Jr., March 26, 1930; W. T. Rice to McGinnis, March 21, 1930: *ibid.*

13. O. T. Jensen to W. H. McGinnis, Jr., March 26, 1930, *ibid.*

14. Figures for 1928 compiled by W. H. Wholey from annual reports to comptroller of currency and to the superintendent of banks of California; figures for earlier years from the bank's files.

15. Los Angeles *Times,* August 29, 1926.

16. The involvements of Messrs. Lewis and Berman with various banks, notably the Pacific-Southwest and the First National, and with various bankers, is set forth at length in *The Great Los Angeles Bubble* (1929) by Guy Woodeward Finney.

17. A. J. Mount, memorandum entitled "Richfield Oil Company," July 3, 1930, Bank of America N.T. & S.A. archives.

18. *Wall Street Journal,* June 29, 1926.

19. J. E. Barber, "The Banker and the Moving Picture Industry," *Coast Banker,* June 1921, 664.

20. *Wall Street Journal,* June 29, 1926.

21. *Coast Banker,* April 1925, 127.

22. A. P. Giannini to J. F. Schenck, December 11, 1926, Bank of America N.T. & S.A. archives.

CHAPTER XIX

1. A. W. Hendrick to F. S. Barr, May 13, 1927; Hendrick to A. F. Cardon: March 24, 1928, Bank of America N.T. & S.A. archives.

2. *Know Your Bank Bulletin,* No. 13, 1931, *passim, ibid.* Though the figures are taken from statistics gathered at the end of the decade, they represent a fairly accurate measure of what had gone before.

3. Memorandum, C. E. Gruhler, Bank of Italy district supervisor, March 14, 1930, *ibid.*

4. House Committee on Banking and Currency, *Hearings, op. cit.,* 1389; A. J. Mount to C. W. Collins, August 21, 1929, Bank of America N.T. & S.A. archives.

5. Memorandum, W. H. McGinnis, Jr., June 8, 1926; statistical papers prepared for J. A. Bacigalupi, 1930: *ibid.*

6. Memorandum, District Supervisor W. T. Rice, March 25, 1930, *ibid.*

7. Memorandum, A. W. Hendrick, 1924; Hendrick to A. P. Giannini, February 18, 1932: *ibid.*

8. C. F. Wente to Al Haase.

9. Memorandum, C. E. Gruhler, March 14, 1930, Bank of America N.T. & S.A. archives.

10. *Know Your Bank Bulletin,* No. 13, 1931; A. J. Mount to All Branch Managers, December 30, 1930: *ibid.*

11. Notes for a speech made by A. W. Hendrick some time in 1922, *ibid.*

12. Figures taken from published and unpublished statements, California Joint Stock Land Bank, *ibid.*

13. United States Treasury Department, Federal Farm Loan Bureau, *Statements of Condition of Federal Land Banks, Joint Stock Land Banks, Federal Intermediate Credit Banks,* December 30, 1930, 14.

14. A. W. Hendrick to E. Meyer, September 21, 1927; to J. R. Rutherford, June 17, 1929: Bank of America N.T. & S.A. archives.

15. Fresno *Bee,* January 2, 1924; A. W. Hendrick to J. H. Guill, April 30, 1923, Bank of America N.T. & S.A. archives.

16. E. J. Wickson, *Farming in California* (1927), 39; L. B. Williams to W. F. Morrish, May 8, 1932, Bank of America N.T. & S.A. archives.

17. Survey, by international banking department, Bank of Italy, March 25, 1927; analysis of accounts, by same, December 30, 1926: *ibid.;* Fresno *Republican,* September 18, 1926; Madera *Mercury,* February 6, 1925; *Grape Stake* (Fresno), February 18, 1928; R. E. Giffin and G. M. McClerkin to Al Haase.

18. "Factors Affecting California Raisin Sales and Prices, 1922–1929," by L. D. Mallory, S. R. Smith and S. W. Shear, in *Giannini Foundation of Agriculture, Economic Papers,* September 1931, 20.

19. *Bankitaly News,* October 30, 1930; California Bankers Association, *Bulletin,* April 1930, 114.

20. Sacramento *Bee,* April 28, 1930; San Francisco *Call,* May 29, 1930.

21. A. W. Hendrick to M. Doherty, December 21, 1920, Bank of America N.T. & S.A. archives.

22. S. J. Lubin to A. P. Giannini, October 17, 1927, *ibid.*

23. Mrs. M. A. Monsen to President, Bank of Italy, November 26, 1928, *ibid.*

24. H. C. Carr to Mrs. M. A. Monsen, January 23, 1929, *ibid.*

25. H. C. Carr to S. H. Green, California Dairy Council, March 30, 1928; to G. E. Anderson, February 23, 1928: *ibid.*

26. F. T. Robson to F. L. Washburn, December 5, 1929; J. A. McNaughton to Washburn, November 12, 1928; R. H. McMullen to Washburn, September 20, 1929: *ibid.*

27. E. S. Sparks, *Agricultural Credit in the United States* (1932), 385 ff.; W. G. Murray, *Agricultural Finance* (1947), 274 ff.

28. Memorandum, A. W. Hendrick, March 1928, Bank of America N.T. & S.A. archives.

29. H. C. Carr to J. A. Bacigalupi, April 24, 1928; Bankitaly Credit Corporation, Minutes, April 9, 1928: *ibid.*

30. L. E. Wyatt to F. H. Tooby, November 2, 1928, *ibid.*

31. Memorandum, C. E. Gruhler, March 28, 1930, *ibid.*

32. G. A. Davidson to B. R. James; R. G. Smith to A. O. Martin, January 12, 1924, Bank of America N.T. & S.A. archives.

33. San Francisco *Examiner,* December 17, 1929.
34. Butte County *Times,* December 14, 1928.
35. A. P. Giannini to B. R. James; G. M. McClerkin to Al Haase.
36. Figures from general ledgers of the Bank of Italy.
37. A. W. Hendrick to E. S. Lander, April 19, 1924, Bank of America N.T. & S.A. archives; C. F. Wente to Al Haase; Fresno *Republican,* September 18, 1926.
38. *Western Sentinel,* clipping, undated, probably 1929 or 1930, Bank of America N.T. & S.A. archives.
39. *Know Your Bank Bulletin,* No. 6, 1931, *ibid.;* C. F. Wente to Al Haase.
40. C. F. Wente to C. P. Cuneo, September 1, 1922, Bank of America N.T. & S.A. archives; Wente to Al Haase.
41. L. M. Giannini to Al Haase; A. Sala to L. M. Giannini, November 24, 1924; Sala to W. E. Blauer, December 3, 1924: Bank of America N.T. & S.A. archives.
42. C. F. Wente to A. W. Hendrick, January 10, 1925; Valley Farms Committee, Minutes, 1925, *passim: ibid.*
43. Unsigned memorandum, "Ranch Operations for the 1927 Season," *ibid.*
44. Regional Board, Los Angeles Division, Minutes, May 9, 1928, *ibid.*
45. California Lands, Inc., Minutes, January 21, 1930, annual report of the president.

CHAPTER XX

1. Concerning the 1912 talks, J. F. Cavagnaro to B. R. James.
2. A. Pedrini and R. Paganini to A. P. Giannini, May 24, 1926; Bancitaly Corporation publicity release, February 8, 1927: Bank of America N.T. & S.A. archives.
3. *Annual Report of the President to the Shareholders of the Bank of Italy N.T. & S.A.,* January 10, 1928.
4. L. V. Belden to L. M. Giannini, October 28, 1927, Bank of America N.T. & S.A. archives.
5. R. Jonas to A. P. Giannini, June 10, 1941; memorandum, J. E. Rovensky to L. M. Giannini, September 1949: *ibid.* The account of A. P. Giannini's ill-starred dealings with the Corner is based, in part, on a memorandum, in the California banker's handwriting, found among the papers of the late Dr. Celestine J. Sullivan of San Francisco, and now in the Bank of America N.T. & S.A. archives. As this paper will be cited at other points in this book something will be said about it here. It is without date, but from the context seems to have been written in the fall of 1931, during the proxy fight by which Giannini regained control of the Bank of America N.T. & S.A. (the former Bank of Italy). This episode will be related in Chapter XXIII. Dr. Sullivan was an ardent Giannini supporter, and the purpose of A. P.'s memorandum doubtless was to provide campaign ammunition. At such times few persons write objectively, which is understandable when all the factors entering into that desperate situation are considered. The authors have used their best judgment in basing statements in the text on this partisan document.
6. Note in L. M. Giannini's hand at the bottom of the letter, G. W. McGarrah to L. V. Belden, March 23, 1928, *ibid.*
7. J. E. Rovensky to B. R. James.
8. Telegrams between L. V. Belden and A. P. Giannini, March 1 to 6, 7, 9, 1928, Bank of America N.T. & S.A. archives.
9. A. H. Giannini to A. P. Giannini, March 10, 1928; A. P. Giannini to L. V. Belden, March 15, 1928: *ibid.*

10. Memorandum, Transamerica Corporation to Federal Reserve Agent, New York, February 13, 1929, *ibid*.
11. Memorandum dated September 14, 1934, *Bancitaly Corporation vs. Commissioner of Internal Revenue, ibid*.
12. L. V. Belden to A. P. Giannini, March 23, 1928, *ibid*.
13. A statement of net profit by years of the Bancitaly and the Transamerica Corporations and the amounts of Mr. Giannini's yearly withdrawals appears in Dana, 343. See also, *Transcript of the Record* in the case of *Commissioner of Internal Revenue vs. A. P. Giannini,* a suit to determine who should pay income tax on the $1,500,000 gift. A fairly complete file on this litigation is in Bank of America N.T. & S.A. archives. For the sake of brevity the account of the establishment of the Giannini Foundation is simplified, though without misrepresentation of essentials. For example, the $1,500,000 was taken from commissions due Mr. Giannini from Bancitaly in the year 1929 as well as 1928.
14. San Diego *Tribune,* January 26, 1928.
15. San Francisco *Examiner,* February 10, 1928; *Wall Street Journal,* March 31, 1928.
16. San Francisco *Call,* February 9, 1928; San Francisco *Bulletin,* February 17, 1928.
17. San Francisco *Examiner,* April 23, 1928.
18. *Forbes Magazine,* March 1, 1928.
19. G. O. Bordwell to B. R. James; San Francisco Board of Management, Minutes, April 9, 1928, Bank of America N.T. & S.A. archives.
20. *Barron's,* August 13, 1928.
21. San Francisco *Call,* April 13, 1928; J. M. Fischer to B. R. James; San Francisco *Examiner,* May 2, 1928; Bank of Italy publicity release, May 1928, Bank of America N.T. & S.A. archives.
22. P. C. Hale to A. P. Giannini, August 2, 1928, *ibid*.
23. Of the three men who knew the inside of Bancitaly's support of Giannini stocks during the bear raid of June, 1928, P. C. Hale was dead when this was written, Bacigalupi had been out of the Giannini organization since 1932 and refused to be seen, and Mario Giannini said that he would not trust his memory on details of so remote an event. The fallibility of memory may be illustrated by a letter from Hale to A. P. Giannini dated August 2, seven weeks after the break began. Mr. Hale attempted to sketch the supporting operation day by day, telling in some instances what stocks had been bought, in what amounts, and at what times and what prices. Frequently his prices cannot be reconciled with those in the daily trade sheets of the San Francisco Stock Exchange and of the Curb Exchange. Prices given in the text are from the trade sheets. Hale's letter has been used, however, in reconstructing other features of the episode. See also Bacigalupi to A. P. Giannini, July 25, 1928, and Bacigalupi "To Whom It May Concern," February 2, 1932, *ibid*. The quotation alluding to scenes in brokerage offices is from *Barron's,* August 13, 1928.
24. P. C. Hale to A. P. Giannini August 2, 1928, Bank of America N.T. & S.A. archives.
25. Minutes, Regional Board, Los Angeles Division, October 10, 1928, *ibid*.
26. Robson Brothers to A. P. Giannini, June 21, 1928, *ibid*.
27. H. C. Carr to R. B. Burmister, August 17, 1928, *ibid*.
28. L. Ferrari to C. W. Collins, undated; Collins' reply, June 26, 1928: C. W. Collins' correspondence file, Washington, D.C.
29. J. A. Bacigalupi to the Shareholder Addressed, June 26, 1928, Bank of America N.T. & S.A. archives.

30. San Francisco *Examiner,* July 23, 1928.

31. San Francisco *News,* September 5, 1928.

32. Memorandum, A. P. Giannini to Dr. C. J. Sullivan, *op. cit.;* Belden to A. P. Giannini (radiogram), August 29, 1928: Bank of America N.T. & S.A. archives; San Francisco *News,* September 12, 1928.

33. J. A. Bacigalupi to A. P. Giannini, July 25, 1928, Bank of America N.T. & S.A. archives.

34. A. P. Giannini to the Stockholder Addressed, October 24, 1928, *ibid.*

CHAPTER XXI

1. Various letters and telegrams between A. H. Giannini and A. P. Giannini, and A. H. Giannini and A. Pedrini, January, 1929, Bank of America N.T. & S.A. archives.

2. A. P. Giannini to L. V. Belden, January 4, 1929; Belden to Giannini, January 7, 8, 1929: *ibid.*

3. A. P. Giannini to C. Stamer, January 18, 1929; L. V. Belden to A. P. Giannini, January 28, 1929: *ibid.*

4. Bartow and Reynolds interviews from an affidavit, made at Giannini's request, by P. C. Hale, March 13, 1933, *ibid.*

5. C. W. Collins to B. R. James; A. P. Giannini to G. W. McGarrah, February 13, 1929, Bank of America N.T. & S.A. archives; Transamerica Corporation to J. P. Morgan & Co., same date, C. W. Collins' files, Washington, D.C. On June 12, 1947, George Whitney, president of J. P. Morgan & Co., wrote A. P. Giannini of his "distress" upon reading the account given in the recently published Dana biography of the 1928–29 affair "with which I unhappily was connected." At the time Mr. Whitney had already become a Morgan partner. In his letter to "Dear Mr. A. P.," he complained: "There is an intimation that we were influencing in some way the action of the Federal Reserve . . . in various steps which they were taking with relation to your companies. This could not be further from the fact. The action we took was precipitated by suggestion we received from the Federal Reserve Board and others, from which we had little or no appeal.

"The suggestion that there was any actual quarrel between us is beyond my recollection but Frank Bartow is now dead and I was present only at the final meeting with you and him at my house and, while it was far from a pleasant occasion for me, there was no argument of any kind."

The present chapter of this book was written from sources Mr. Dana had at his disposal; and from still others, lately become available. Presumably, therefore, it will give Mr. Whitney additional distress. The chapter's generous documentation, however, should indicate that the authors have gone deeply into the Morgan incident and sincerely tried to present it as accurately as possible. As for the influence exercised over the Federal Reserve, one authority is Representative Louis T. McFadden, who had no reputation for loose oratory. In a speech which the *New York Times* published on July 4, 1930, the congressman said: "The parent Morgan Company acts as fiscal agent for Great Britain, France, Belgium and Italy . . . and is the most potential influence in the Federal Reserve System. . . . The Morgan control of the Federal Reserve System is exercised through control of the management of the Federal Reserve Bank of

New York and the mediocre representation and acquiescence of the Federal Reserve Board of Washington."

6. *The Participant,* July 1929; various old-timers to B. R. James.
7. Various correspondence, A. P. Giannini with W. H. Snyder and A. Pedrini, summer and autumn of 1929, Bank of America N.T. & S.A. archives.
8. J. A. Bacigalupi to A. P. Giannini, May 10, 1929, *ibid.*
9. Deposition of L. Ferrari, *R. I. Rogers vs. Transamerica Corporation et al., ibid.*
10. These are New York figures, to the nearest whole number. San Francisco Stock and Curb Exchange quotations may have differed slightly.
11. A. P. Giannini to H. P. Preston, October 29, 1929, Bank of America N.T. & S.A. archives.
12. L. M. Giannini to A. P. Giannini, February 8, 1930, *ibid.*
13. A. P. Giannini (quoting Walker) to L. M. Giannini, January 21, 1930, *ibid.*
14. Appendix to a letter marked "Personal and confidential," from L. M. Giannini and P. C. Hale to Elisha Walker and Jean Monnet, January 16, 1930, *ibid.*
15. "Proceedings at Transamerica Meeting, February 27, 1930," *ibid.*
16. San Francisco *News,* February 19, 1930.
17. House Committee on Banking and Currency, *Hearings, op. cit.,* 1555–56, 1565–66.

CHAPTER XXII

1. For a more detailed view of the year 1930 see Broadus Mitchell, *Depression Decade* (1947), Chapters II and III; Dixon Wecter, *The Age of the Great Depression* (1948), Chapter I.
2. E. Walker to Stockholder Addressed, July 12, 1930, Bank of America N.T. & S.A. archives; *Financial News,* August 29, 1930; San Francisco *Examiner,* August 22, 1930.
3. L. M. Giannini to E. Walker, July 5, 1930; A. P. Giannini to L. M. Giannini, August 10, 1930; to Walker, August, undated, 1930; Walker to A. P. Giannini, August, undated, 1930: Bank of America N.T. & S.A. archives.
4. E. Walker to A. P. Giannini, August 5, 1930; A. P. Giannini to L. M. Giannini, July 20, 1930: *ibid.; Wall Street Journal,* August 21, 1930.
5. A. P. Giannini to L. M. Giannini, August 6, 1930, Bank of America N.T. & S.A. archives.
6. Penciled memorandum by J. A. Bacigalupi, about July, 1930, *ibid.*
7. *Bankitaly News,* September 1930.
8. Healdsburg *Enterprise,* September 5, 1930.
9. Hollister *Free Lance,* September 6, 1930; press release, Transamerica Corporation, September 12, 1930, Bank of America N.T. & S.A. archives.
10. R. Paganini to A. J. Mount, October 14, 1930, *ibid.;* A. C. Dimon to Al Haase.
11. San Francisco *Chronicle,* December 17, 1930; A. P. Giannini to Armando Pedrini, December 25, 1930, Bank of America N.T. & S.A. archives.
12. L. M. Giannini to A. P. Giannini, January, undated, 1931, *ibid.*
13. L. M. Giannini to E. Walker January 24, February 2, 1931; to P. C. Hale, February 7, 1931: *ibid.*
14. *Time,* April 6, 1931.
15. Examiners' Report of the Condition of Bank of America N.T. & S.A., February 28, 1931, Bank of America N.T. & S.A. archives.
16. Review of June, 1931, earnings, July 20, 1931, *ibid.*

17. O. E. Monnette to A. J. Mount, January 5, 1931; J. M. Perry to Mount, April 28, 1931; Perry to W. F. Morrish, May 8, 1931: *ibid.*

18. P. Denis to J. Monnet, January 8, 1931; A. P. Giannini to L. M. Giannini, June 13, 1931: *ibid.*

19. A. H. Giannini to A. Pedrini, April 12, 1931, *ibid.*

20. W. F. Morrish to E. Walker, March 20, 1931, *ibid.*

21. P. C. Read to A. P. Giannini, September 7, 1933, files of C. W. Collins, Washington, D.C.

22. A. J. Mount to E. A. Baird, July 22, 1931, Bank of America N.T. & S.A. archives.

23. J. P. Kennedy to A. J. Mount, August 7, 1931, *ibid.*

24. J. A. Bacigalupi to F. Kerman, June 3, 1931, *ibid.*

25. No account of the New York meeting of the executive committee can be found in the Transamerica records. The summary given is reconstructed from subsequent records of the corporation at which action was taken on the New York program and from correspondence, particularly of A. P. and Mario Giannini and Bacigalupi, touching the matter.

26. Transamerica Corporation, Minutes, September 22, 1931.

27. A telegram from Giannini to "James A. Bacigalupi and my other California B. of I. and B. of A. co-workers," September 12, 1931, (Bank of America N.T. & S.A. archives) refers to receipt of the news by telephone at Badgastein. Many cables passed between Giannini and Walker on the subject, though none remains in the Transamerica files. When Mr. Walker and associates left Transamerica they took with them many letters and other papers. During the proxy fight by which Giannini regained control, Walker characterized the cables he had received from Giannini as "violent." If they resembled some that A. P. sent to Mario and Bacigalupi, copies of which are in the bank's files, the characterization is accurate.

28. Various cables passing between A. P. Giannini and L. M. Giannini and A. P. Giannini and J. A. Bacigalupi, June–August, 1931, *ibid.* The quotations are from cables to Mario dated July 11, July 4, June 13.

29. A. P. Giannini to L. M. Giannini, June 13, 1931; to J. A. Bacigalupi, June 27, 1931: *ibid.*

30. Transamerica Corporation, Minutes, June 17, 1931.

31. L. M. Giannini to J. A. Bacigalupi, June 25, 1931, Bank of America N.T. & S.A. archives.

32. A. P. Giannini to J. A. Bacigalupi, June 19, 20, 27, 1931; to L. M. Giannini, June 27, 1931; Bacigalupi to A. P. Giannini, June 19, 20, 29, 1931: *ibid.*

33. A. P. Giannini to J. A. Bacigalupi, June 20, 1931; Bacigalupi to Giannini, June 29, 1931: *ibid.*

34. A. P. Giannini to J. A. Bacigalupi, June 30, 1931, *ibid.*

35. J. A. Bacigalupi to A. P. Giannini, July 3, 1931; Giannini's answer, July 6: *ibid.*

36. A. P. Giannini to L. M. Giannini, July 6, 1931, *ibid.*

37. R. W. Hoover to A. J. Mount, June 26, 1931; D. Cardinale to E. Walker, June 29, 1931: *ibid.*

38. L. M. Giannini (conveying Hale's opinion) to A. P. Giannini, July 24, 1931, *ibid.*

39. A. P. Giannini to L. M. Giannini, July 29, August 13, 1931, *ibid.*

40. *Ibid.*, August 17, 1931.

41. San Francisco *News*, August 27, 1931.

42. Dana, 201; San Francisco *Examiner*, September 11, 1931; San Francisco *Chronicle*, same date.

CHAPTER XXIII

1. A. P. Giannini to J. A. Bacigalupi and others, September 13, 1931, Bank of America N.T. & S.A. archives.

2. J. A. Bacigalupi to A. P. Giannini, September 13, 1931; Giannini's answer, September 14: *ibid.*

3. San Francisco *Chronicle,* September 15, 1931.

4. J. F. Neylan to B. R. James.

5. Transamerica Corporation, Minutes, September 22, 1931.

6. Elisha Walker to Stockholder Addressed, September 22, 1931, Bank of America N.T. & S.A. archives.

7. *Barron's,* May 9 and 16, 1932.

8. *Business Week,* September 30, 1931; San Francisco *Daily News,* September 24, 1931.

9. *American Banker,* October 2, 1931.

10. San Francisco *Chronicle,* September 23, 1931.

11. *Ibid.*

12. San Francisco *News,* September 24, 1931.

13. A. J. Mount to Branch Manager Addressed, September 23, 24, 25, 1931, Bank of America N.T. & S.A. archives.

14. San Francisco *Examiner,* September 25, 1931; Fresno *Republican,* same date; A. M. Otis to A. J. Mount, September 30, 1931; Anna G. Park to J. A. Bacigalupi, September 30, 1931: Bank of America N.T. & S.A. archives.

15. Transamerica Corporation, Minutes, October 1, 1931; Transamerica Corporation, *Annual Report,* 1931; C. E. Mitchell to A. J. Mount, November 30, 1931, Bank of America N.T. & S.A. archives.

16. San Francisco *Examiner,* October 2, 1931.

17. H. J. Soher to G. A. Webster, October 7, 1931, Bank of America N.T. & S.A. archives.

18. P. Michelson to W. F. Morrish, October 4, 1931; A. J. Mount to A. E. Connick, October 8, 1931: *ibid.*

19. A. J. Mount to O. E. Monnette, November 10, 1931; W. Barkley to Mount, same date: *ibid.*

20. C. W. Fay to the Stockholders of the Transamerica Corporation, November 7, 1931, *ibid.*

21. F. Kerman to R. Hayes, November 9, 10, 1931; Hayes to Kerman, November 9, 12, 1931: *ibid.*

22. Santa Rosa *Press Democrat,* November 7, 1931.

23. O. E. Monnette to A. J. Mount, November 16, 1931; G. A. Davidson to L. P. Talley, November 9, 1931; Mount to Davidson, November 12, 1931: Bank of America N.T. & S.A. archives.

24. J. A. Bacigalupi to My Fellow Officers in Transamerica Corporation, etc., November 19, 1931, *ibid.*

25. *Stockton Independent,* December 4, 1931.

26. San Francisco *News,* December 6, 1931.

27. E. Walker and J. A. Bacigalupi to Stockholders of the Transamerica Corporation, December 9, 1931, Bank of America N.T. & S.A. archives; San Francisco *News,* December 11, 12, 14, 1931.

28. M. Mattei to J. A. Bacigalupi, December 21, 1931, Bank of America N.T. & S.A. archives.

29. W. J. Kieferdorf to G. D. Schilling, December 12, 1931; W. H. McGinnis, Jr., to District Executive Vice-President Addressed, December 10, 11, 12, 1931; H. P. Preston to Branch Manager Addressed, December 11, 1931: *ibid.;* A. Chiappari to B. R. James.

30. L. P. Talley to J. D. Perry, January 2, 1931; W. L. Vincent to A. P. Giannini, February 26, 1932; Bank of America N.T. & S.A., Minutes, VI, 410: Bank of America N.T. & S.A. archives.

31. H. L. Clary to W. F. Morrish, January 6, May 6, 1932, *ibid.*

32. Statistics compiled by Bank of America N.T. & S.A. analysis and research department, April, 1941, *ibid.*

33. San Francisco *News,* December 17, 1931; J. F. Neylan to B. R. James.

34. A. Fanelli to A. P. Giannini, January 7, 8, 1931, Bank of America N.T. & S.A. archives.

35. "Transcript of Proceedings at [San Francisco] Federal Reserve Board, January 9–11, 1932," 4; A. P. Giannini to L. M. Giannini, January 9, 1932: *ibid.*

36. A. P. Giannini to E. R. Black, July 12, 1934, *ibid.*

37. "Transcript of Proceedings . . . ," *op. cit.,* see especially pp. 8, 12, 30, 35, 36, 52, 54.

38. On the seriousness with which Washington regarded the situation: C. W. Collins to B. R. James; on the rumor about Pole's intention of taking over the bank: Federal Judge Herbert W. Erskine of San Francisco to Al Haase. See also various correspondence of J. W. Pole, J. Monnet, C. W. Fay, L. P. Talley and J. U. Calkins, January–February, 1932: Bank of America N.T. & S.A. archives.

39. A. P. Giannini to H. W. Johnson, December 13, 1931, A. J. Scampini's scrapbook.

40. Dana, 218; H. J. Soher to L. Ferrari, February 3, 1932, Bank of America N.T. & S.A. archives; A. J. Scampini to Al Haase; A. Chiappari and others to B. R. James.

41. Estimate of number of unvoted shares, L. M. Giannini to B. R. James; Fresno *Bee,* February 15, 1932.

42. San Francisco *News,* February 15, 1932.

43. *New York Times,* February 16, 1932.

44. *American Banker,* February 19, 1932.

45. San Francisco *News,* February 23, 1932.

CHAPTER XXIV

1. *American Banker,* February 23, 1932.

2. Mitchell, Chapters II to V, inclusive; Wecter, Chapters I to III, inclusive; Marquis James, the *Metropolitan Life* (1947), 294–95; Marquis James, *Alfred I. duPont, the Family Rebel* (1941), 478.

3. M. E. Ivory, Sr., to A. P. Giannini, April 7, 1932, Bank of America N.T. & S.A. archives.

4. Memorandum, C. P. Partridge to W. F. Morrish, February 17, 1932, *ibid.; American Banker,* February 23, 1932.

5. A. P. Giannini to M. S. Rukeyser, March 26, 1932; to branch managers, March 3, 1932: Bank of America N.T. & S.A. archives.

6. W. N. Wholey to B. R. James.

7. J. M. Grant to A. P. Giannini, March 18, 1932; A. Bozzani to Giannini, March 25, 1932; reply to Bozzani, March 29, 1932: Bank of America N.T. & S.A. archives.

8. The one California bank not to lose deposits during the depression was the Farmers & Merchants National Bank of Los Angeles, controlled by Jackson A. Graves. Graves was an old-school banker who regarded branch banking as a creation of the devil. His institution, the fourth largest in the south, enjoyed a rich and conservative clientele. Thus it was about as different from the Bank of America in mode of operation, philosophy and outlook, as a bank could be and still be a bank. From the end of 1930 to June, 1933, the Farmers & Merchants gained deposits continuously, going from $66,000,000 to nearly $88,000,000.

9. J. U. Calkins to A. P. Giannini, March 24, 1932, Bank of America N.T. & S.A. archives.

10. A. P. Giannini to J. U. Calkins, March 25, 1932, *ibid.*

11. Memorandum by W. R. Morrish, undated but written in June, 1932, *ibid.*

12. A. P. Giannini to C. A. Miller, March 3, 1933, *ibid.*

13. Figures on R.F.C. borrowings are from Bank of America N.T. & S.A. General Ledger for 1932.

14. Various correspondence and memoranda; J. W. Pole to A. P. Giannini, July 2, 1932: Bank of America N.T. & S.A. archives; E. Meyer to B. R. James.

15. W. F. Morrish to Leon Bocqueraz, July 18, 1932, Bank of America N.T. & S.A. archives; R.F.C. account from the bank's General Ledger for 1932.

16. *Time*, January 23, 1933, 46.

17. Publicity release, Bank of America N.T. & S.A., March 27, 1932, Bank of America N.T. & S.A. archives; Giannini quoted in *Lake County Bee*, May 4, 1932; on Barbieri plan, *Reader's Digest*, September 1947, 129.

18. A. P. Giannini to Herbert Hoover, August 22, 1932, Bank of America N.T. & S.A. archives. The total of the R.F.C. loans is given as $64,488,644 in *Fifty Billion Dollars*, Jesse Jones's memoir of his R.F.C. stewardship, written in collaboration with Edward Angly and published in 1951. See page 72. Mr. Jones's figure includes the sixth loan which Giannini applied for and then canceled.

19. Telegrams between A. P. Giannini and J. P. Kennedy, September 6 and 10, 1932; A. J. Scampini to A. P. Giannini, September 12, 1932: *ibid.*

20. San Francisco *News*, September 23, 1932.

21. A. P. Giannini to R. V. Morrison, October 19, 1932, Bank of America N.T. & S.A. archives.

22. San Francisco *Examiner*, November 5, 1932.

23. Press release, Bank of America N.T. & S.A., November 5, 1932, Bank of America N.T. & S.A. archives.

24. A. P. Giannini to J. F. Cavagnaro, November 2, 1932, *ibid.*

CHAPTER XXV

1. *Pacific Banker*, November 1932.

2. J. A. Purdy to S. B. Stewart, Jr., February 1, 1949, Bank of America N.T. & S.A. archives.

3. R. G. Smith to B. R. James; G. W. Peltier to W. F. Morrish, January 30, 1933, Bank of America N.T. & S.A. archives.

4. Jones with Angly, 62.

5. *Commercial & Financial Chronicle*, March 4, 1933, 1481.

6. L. M. Giannini to A. P. Giannini, February 21, 1933, Bank of America N.T. & S.A. archives.

7. A. P. Giannini to L. M. Giannini, February 23, 1933, *ibid.*

8. C. Partridge to W. F. Morrish, March 1, 1933, *ibid*.
9. R. G. Smith to W. F. Morrish, March 1, 1933, *ibid*.
10. A. P. Giannini to C. A. Miller, March 3, 1933, *ibid*.
11. A. P. Giannini to L. M. Giannini, March 8, 1933, *ibid*.
12. Raymond Moley, "Five Years of Roosevelt and After," *Saturday Evening Post*, July 29, 1939, 55.
13. San Francisco *News,* March 10, 1933; A. P. Giannini to W. F. Morrish, March 8, 1933, Bank of America N.T. & S.A. archives.
14. A. P. Giannini to W. H. Woodin, March 10, 1933; C. W. Collins to A. P. Giannini, same date; Giannini to H. W. Johnson, same date; W. G. McAdoo to Giannini, March 11, 1933; C. W. Collins to Giannini, same date: *ibid*.
15. A. P. Giannini to P. C. Hale, August 15, 1936, an account from memory of the events of March 12, 1933, *ibid*.
16. F. D. Roosevelt, *On Our Way* (1934), 26 ff.
17. J. F. Neylan to A. P. Giannini, October 13, 1947, an account from memory, of the events of the night of March 12–13, 1933, Bank of America N.T. & S.A. archives.
18. Raymond Moley, "Five Years of Roosevelt and After," *Saturday Evening Post*, July 29, 1939, 55; Dana, 243.
19. J. F. Neylan to A. P. Giannini, October 13, 1947, Bank of America N.T. & S.A. archives.
20. A. P. Giannini to W. R. Hearst, March 14, 1933, *ibid*.
21. Los Angeles *Times,* June 10, 1949; from Moley's syndicated column.
22. A. P. Giannini to J. H. Jones, March 13, 1933, Bank of America N.T. & S.A. archives.
23. M. H. McIntyre to A. P. Giannini, March 15, 1933; Giannini to McIntyre, March 15, 1933; to Jesse H. Jones, March 18, 1933: *ibid*.
24. Jones with Angly, 19.

CHAPTER XXVI

1. New York *Herald Tribune,* November 22, 1933; E. A. Rossi to Al Haase.
2. C. W. Collins to A. P. Giannini, June 14, 1933, Bank of America N.T. & S.A. archives.
3. San Francisco *News,* February 17, 1932.
4. Chicago *Herald and Examiner,* September 17, 1933.
5. J. M. Grant to A. P. Giannini, March 28, 1933; Giannini to G. Purcell, October 21, 1937; to W. F. Morrish, May 9, 1933; to J. M. Grant, May 16, 1933: Bank of America N.T. & S.A. archives.
6. J. F. Neylan to B. R. James.
7. W. F. Morrish to A. P. Giannini, October 7, 1933; Giannini's reply, October 8: Bank of America N.T. & S.A. archives; San Francisco *Examiner,* October 26, 1933.
8. Santa Barbara *Daily News,* May 25, 1933.
9. A. P. Giannini to F. D. Roosevelt, July 21, 1933, Bank of America N.T. & S.A. archives.
10. A. P. Giannini to J. A. Farley, December 31, 1935; to L. M. Giannini, February 23, 1933: *ibid*.
11. A. P. Giannini to W. H. Neblett, August 16, 1933, quoting McAdoo's wire, *ibid*.
12. A. P. Giannini to R. V. Morrison, March 31, 1933, *ibid.;* Ferdinand Pecora, *Wall Street Under Oath* (1939), 27; Committee on Banking and Currency,

Senate, *Hearings* on Banking and Stock Exchange Practices, May 23, 24, 25, 1933, Part I, 138.

13. A. P. Giannini to Sid Bazett, September 3, 1936, Bank of America N.T. & S.A. archives.

14. A. P. Giannini to T. E. Harris, November 21, 1932; to L. L. Madland, June 10, 1933; Madland to Giannini, June 30, 1933; Giannini to H. S. Cummings, November 22, 1933: *ibid.*

15. A. P. Giannini to H. S. Cummings, July 7, November 22, 1933; J. B. Keenan to Giannini, December 5, 1933: *ibid.* The files of the legal department of the Bank of America N.T. & S.A. contain the papers constituting the record of the so-called Bell actions against the bank, Transamerica, etc.

16. J. H. Jones to A. P. Giannini, July 5, 1938, *ibid.*

17. Memorandum, D. R. Thorburn to A. P. Giannini, December, 1934, *ibid.*

18. *Christian Science Monitor,* October 30, 1934.

19. San Francisco *News,* November 1, 1934; San Francisco *Chronicle,* November 2, 1934; San Francisco *Examiner,* November 9, 1934; Board of Governors, Federal Reserve System, *Annual Report* (1934), 85.

20. K. L. Carver and W. J. Braunschweiger to B. R. James; Credit Department Records on Filtrol, Bank of America N.T. & S.A. archives.

21. A. P. Giannini to W. F. Morrish, June 7, 1933; Minutes, VII, 192; Giannini to J. H. Jones, June 23, 1933: *ibid.*

22. Report of Examination Commenced September 18, 1933, Closed January 12, 1934, page 11, insert 24, *ibid.*

23. Memorandum (by R. G. Smith, the bank's cashier) summarizing discussions with Mr. Madland and Mr. Beise, January 19, 1934, *ibid.*

24. A. P. Giannini to F. M. Law, October 1, 1934, *ibid.*

25. H. L. Clary to W. P. Folger, February 9, 1934, *ibid.*

26. *Bankamerican Deposit Builder,* October 26, 1934.

27. A. P. Giannini to B. B. Meek, November 14, 1932; Giannini to A. J. Mount, October 19, 1932; E. S. Zerga to Mount, November 14, 1932; Giannini to W. F. Morrish, April 21, 1933: Bank of America N.T. & S.A. archives; *Time,* December 21, 1936.

28. J. M. Grant to A. P. Giannini, April 13, 1935; press release, undated, publicity department, Transamerica Corporation; Giannini to J. H. Jones, May 24, 1935: Bank of America N.T. & S.A. archives.

29. Transamerica Corporation, *Annual Report,* 1934; Chicago *Daily News,* May 5, 1935.

30. *Time,* February 18, 1935.

31. *New York Times,* April 28, 1935.

32. A. P. Giannini in the magazine *Today,* quoted from press release of the bank, May 29, 1935, Bank of America N.T. & S.A. archives.

33. M. S. Eccles to A. P. Giannini, April 29, 1935; Giannini to Eccles, same date; Eccles to Giannini, August 22, 1935: *ibid.*

34. F. D. Roosevelt to A. P. Giannini, September 24, 1935, *ibid.*

35. A. P. Giannini to J. A. Farley, September 26, 1935; Farley's reply, same date: *ibid.*

36. Chicago *Tribune,* November 30, 1935.

37. A. P. Giannini to B. R. James.

38. *Wall Street Journal,* December 17, 1935; San Francisco *Chronicle,* December 3, 17, 1935.

39. Bank of America, publicity department release, May 1, 1936, Bank of America N.T. & S.A. archives.
40. F. D. Roosevelt to A. P. Giannini, May 7, 1936, *ibid.*
41. San Francisco *News,* June 25, 1936.
42. F. D. Roosevelt to A. P. Giannini, July 8, 1936, Bank of America N.T. & S.A. archives.
43. J. A. Farley to A. P. Giannini, August 1, 1936; Giannini's reply August 5: *ibid.*

CHAPTER XXVII

1. Los Angeles *Daily News,* December 17, 1936.
2. W. F. Morrish to H. Morgenthau, Jr., March 27, 1934; W. I. Meyer to Morrish, March 29, 1934: Bank of America N.T. & S.A. archives.
3. California Lands, Inc., Minutes, January 21, 1930, Capital Company archives.
4. California Lands, Inc., *Annual Reports,* 1930 to 1940; California Lands, Inc., Minutes, September 24, 1936: *ibid.*
5. *The Farm Salesman,* a publication of California Lands, Inc., April 1940; California Lands, Inc., *Annual Report,* 1934: *ibid.*
6. Figures on sales from *Annual Reports,* California Lands, Inc., 1930–1940, *ibid.*
7. D. L. Clarke to A. P. Giannini, August 16, 1934, Bank of America N.T. & S.A. archives.
8. Report of the Commodity Loan Department, March 15, 1937, *ibid.*
9. *Ibid.,* May 12, 1939; "Field Warehousing," an address by L. M. Albedi before the Credits Conference, Louisville convention, 1940: *ibid.*
10. L. M. Giannini to branch managers, February 19, 1934, *ibid.*
11. Memorandum, C. F. Wente, November 14, 1932; A. W. Hendrick to A. P. Giannini, February 18, 1932: *ibid.*
12. W. J. Edinger to R. G. Smith, October 9, 1939, *ibid.*
13. A. P. Giannini to A. C. Miller, January 9, 1939, *ibid.*
14. *Digest of the Grape Situation in 1938,* compiled by W. N. Wholey from reports and ledgers of the Bank of America N.T. & S.A., *ibid.;* Jones with Angly, 103–04.
15. Tulare Wineries and others to Bank of America N.T. & S.A., July 26, 1939, Bank of America N.T. & S.A. archives.
16. Memorandum, J. W. Tapp, August 15, 1939, *ibid.*
17. *The Wine Review,* March 1940.
18. R. S. Heaton to R. G. Smith, September 27, 1943, Bank of America N.T. & S.A. archives.
19. F. G. Stevenot to Al Haase; Sacramento *Bee,* March 23, 1933.
20. R. A. Kent to Al Haase.
21. L. Holt to A. P. Giannini, October 10, 1932, Bank of America N.T. & S.A archives.
22. R. A. Hill to Bondholders Imperial Irrigation District, December 31, 1937; E. T. Hewes to J. Jones, April 19, 1938; W. D. Courtright to R. A. Hill, August 15, 1938: *ibid.*
23. El Centro *Morning Post,* May 5, 1938.
24. L. M. Giannini to B. L. Goodrich, February 28, 1939; A. P. Giannini to J. R. Thompson, May 29, 1940: Bank of America N.T. & S.A. archives; *Imperial Valley Press,* May 20, 1940.
25. Carey McWilliams, *Factories in the Field* (1939), 233.

26. Memorandum, Farm Operations of California Lands and Bank of America, undated, 1939, Bank of America N.T. & S.A. archives.

27. L. M. Giannini to James Roosevelt, December 4, 1939; R. G. Smith to J. J. Bergen, April 4, 1940: *ibid.*

28. John Steinbeck, *The Grapes of Wrath* (1939), 476.

29. Howard Whipple to R. G. Smith, June 26, 1939, Bank of America N.T. & S.A. archives.

Chapter XXVIII

1. San Francisco *News,* January 15, 1936.

2. Bank of America N.T. & S.A., *Annual Report,* 1939; Gore, "Statistics."

3. San Francisco *Examiner,* March 24, 1938.

4. Consolidated report of personal loans, October 31, 1934, Bank of America N.T. & S.A. archives; *Wall Street Journal* (Pacific Coast edition), March 31, 1938.

5. San Francisco *News,* March 8, 1952.

6. K. S. McBride to W. Dunn, December 12, 1940, Bank of America N.T. & S.A. archives; New York *Herald Tribune,* January 5, 1953.

7. E. A. Mattison to Al Haase.

8. L. M. Giannini to B. R. James; Los Angeles *Daily News,* October 23, 1935.

9. H. L. Clary to Joshua Garrison, Jr., January 6, 1937, Bank of America N.T. & S.A. archives. Unless otherwise credited, all figures—totals, ratios, etc.—pertaining to Timeplan were furnished by the bank's report and analysis department.

10. *American Banker,* September 25, 1939.

11. Bank of America N.T. & S.A., *Annual Reports,* 1941, 1951, 1952.

12. J. H. Crosby to S. C. Beise, November 16, 1940, Bank of America N.T. & S.A. archives.

13. R. G. Smith to L. M. Giannini, April 2, 1941, *ibid.;* G. W. Eckhardt to Al Haase; N. P. Hasselo to B. R. James, March 18, 1953; C. P. Donetti, manager San Pedro branch, to C. F. Wente, March 11, 1953: Bank of America N.T. & S.A. archives.

14. A. P. Giannini to "Mr. Gock," March 24, 1912, in the possession of A. J. Gock.

15. Nat C. Green and E. A. Mattison to Al Haase; J. M. Reed to Howard Whipple, October 2, 1939, Bank of America N.T. & S.A. archives.

16. N. C. Green to Al Haase.

17. J. H. Jones to A. P. Giannini, July 2, 22, 1938, Bank of America N.T. & S.A. archives.

18. J. H. Jones to Directors and Managing Officers of All State and National Banks, July 15, 1938, *ibid.*

19. Jones with Angly, 183.

20. *New York Times,* June 30, 1939.

21. L. M. Giannini to "Dear Co-Workers," June 21, 1938, Bank of America N.T. & S.A. archives.

22. K. S. McBride to Howard Whipple, January 1, 1942, *ibid.*

23. Los Angeles *Times,* January 17, 1933.

24. Frank J. Taylor, "He's No Angel," *Saturday Evening Post,* January 14, 1939; K. L. Carver to Al Haase.

25. *Wall Street Journal* (Pacific Coast edition), November 9, 1934.

26. San Francisco *Examiner,* October 20, 1939.

27. A. P. Giannini to J. F. Douglas, September 29, 1947, Bank of America N.T. & S.A. archives.

28. San Francisco *Examiner,* July 10, 1934.
29. Bank of America N.T. & S.A., *Annual Reports,* 1934–1952; additional figures supplied by the bank's personnel relations department.
30. L. M. Giannini to Bank of America N.T. & S.A. Employees, Alameda Branch, November 6, 1946; F. M. Dana to Bank of America N.T. & S.A. Employees, Oakland Main Office, November 7, 1945: Bank of America N.T. & S.A. archives; G. A. Ghiselli to Al Haase.

CHAPTER XXIX

1. *New York Times,* May 16, 1937.
2. New York *Herald Tribune,* January 16, 1938; A. P. Giannini to J. F. Cavagnaro, January 15, 1938, Bank of America N.T. & S.A. archives. The President is never quoted directly in reports of press conferences. The words in quotation marks in the text are the *Herald Tribune*'s paraphrase of the Executive's remarks.
3. U. V. Wilcox, *The Bankers Be Damned* (1940), 40, 44, 76, 78; M. S. Eccles to A. H. Vandenburg, June 16, 1938, quoted by *New York Times,* June 17, 1938; *Federal Reserve Bulletin,* July 1938, 563.
4. Jones with Angly, 37.
5. A. P. Giannini to M. H. McIntyre, June 5, 11, 1938, Bank of America N.T. & S.A. archives.
6. A. P. Giannini to Henry Morgenthau, Jr., October 28, 1938, *ibid.*
7. A. P. Giannini to M. R. Diggs, May 6, 1938; Memorandum by R. G. Smith on his visit to Washington in May, 1938, dated October 9, 1941: *ibid.*
8. A. P. Giannini to M. H. McIntyre, July 11, 1938, *ibid.;* L. E. Birdzell to Al Haase. It is not known exactly what the "preliminary" report of Sedlacek, which Prentiss took to Washington, consisted of. The references in the text are from his final report, dated September 15, 1938, a copy of which is in the Bank of America N.T. & S.A. archives.
9. M. R. Diggs to R. E. A. Palmer, September 13, 1938, *ibid.*
10. Bank of America N.T. & S.A., Minutes, X, 164; Smith, memorandum, *op. cit.: ibid.*
11. A. P. Giannini to M. R. Diggs, September 15, 1938; L. M. Giannini to M. S. Eccles, September 20, 1938: *ibid.*
12. Jones with Angly, 38.
13. M. R. Diggs to L. M. Giannini, September 23, 1938; Mario's answer, October 1: Bank of America N.T. & S.A. archives.
14. M. R. Diggs to Board of Directors, Bank of America N.T. & S.A., September 23, 1938, *ibid.*
15. Members of the Board of Directors, Bank of America N.T. & S.A., to Comptroller of the Currency, October 11, 1938, *ibid.*
16. A. P. Giannini to H. Morgenthau, Jr., November 1, 1938; Morgenthau's reply, November 5: *ibid.*
17. A. P. Giannini to H. Morgenthau, Jr., November 10, 1938, *ibid.*
18. *Remarks of the President of the Bank of America N.T. & S.A. to the Shareholders,* January 9, 1940, 6, *ibid.*
19. Memorandum, re Bank of America N.T. & S.A. and Comptroller's office, December 15, 1938; L. M. Giannini to P. Delano, December 15, 1938; *Remarks of the President . . . op. cit.: ibid.*
20. A. P. Giannini to J. F. Cavagnaro, December 17, 1938, *ibid.*

21. L. M. Giannini to J. H. Jones, April 3, 1939; to F. D. Roosevelt, February 9: *ibid.*

22. *Time,* December 12, 1938.

23. *Wall Street Journal* (Pacific Coast edition), November 28, 1938; *Business Week,* January 21, 1939; "Chronological Digest of Events in the Treasury Department and the Securities and Exchange Commission, Relations with Bank of America National Trust and Savings Association, 1938–1941, compiled by C. W. Collins, October 15, 1941," Bank of America N.T. & S. A. archives.

24. L. M. Giannini to P. Delano, July 28, 1938, *ibid.*

25. L. M. Giannini to P. Delano, July 28, 1939; Delano to L. M. Giannini, July 31, 1939: *ibid.*

26. L. M. Giannini to J. McKee, November 30, 1939; A. P. Giannini to Drew Pearson and R. S. Allen, November 25, 1939; to F. Murphy, January 5, 1940: *ibid.*

27. P. Delano to A. P. Giannini, December 12, 1939, *ibid.*

28. A. P. Giannini to P. Delano, December 22, 1939, *ibid.*

29. Bank of America N.T. & S.A. to Board of Governors, Federal Reserve System, December 29, 1939, *ibid.*

30. *Remarks of the President . . . op. cit., ibid.*

31. San Francisco *News,* January 10, 1940; *Wall Street Journal* (Pacific Coast edition), January 12, 1940.

32. L. M. Giannini to P. Delano, undated; to Federal Reserve Bank of San Francisco, January 23, 1940: Bank of America N.T. & S.A. archives.

33. Memorandum by R. G. Smith, January 30, 1940, *ibid.*

34. San Francisco *News,* March 15, 1940; "Requirements of the Comptroller of the Currency, March 6, 1940," Bank of America N.T. & S.A. archives.

35. Associated Press dispatch, March 18, 1940.

36. Transamerica Corporation, *Annual Report,* 1947, 10.

37. *The Bankamerican,* January 1941.

CHAPTER XXX

1. *The Bankamerican,* October 1941.

2. *Bulletin* No. 16 to Members of Advisory Boards, Bank of America N.T. & S.A., November 26, 1941, Bank of America N.T. & S.A. archives.

3. E. A. Mattison to L. M. Giannini, March 4, 1942, *ibid.;* Senate Committee on Banking and Currency, 77th Congress, 2nd Session, *Hearings,* 246.

4. Memorandum, W. F. Huck to L. M. Giannini, April 19, 1943, Bank of America N.T. & S.A. archives; K. L. Carver to Al Haase.

5. F. S. Baer to B. R. James.

6. Consolidated-Vultee Aircraft credit agreement, April, 1943; Bank of America N.T. & S.A. *Business Review,* March, 1942, 3: Bank of America N.T. & S.A. archives.

7. Figures from "Reports of Regulation V Loans Guaranteed by and Made Directly Through the Federal Reserve Bank of San Francisco, 1942–45," *ibid.*

8. Memorandum, W. F. Huck to L. M. Giannini, June 29, 1943; various Regulation V Loan memoranda in credit files at San Francisco and Los Angeles headquarters: *ibid.*

9. *Wall Street Journal* (Pacific Coast edition), April 24, 1945; Memorandum, V and VT Loan Applications, Southern Division, March 31, 1945: Bank of America N.T. & S.A. archives.

10. A. P. Giannini to F. D. Roosevelt, April 23, 1933, *ibid.*

11. *Facts in Brief about Henry J. Kaiser,* a digest of his testimony given at hearings before the House Merchant Marine and Fisheries Committee in September 1946, *passim;* Jones with Angly, 331.

12. Memorandum, March 2, 1949, "Estimated Number of Real Estate Loans Made Since 1940," Bank of America N.T. & S.A. archives; California State Chamber of Commerce, *Survey of Housing Problem in California* (1946), 3; memorandum, October 4, 1943, "Lines of Credit over $100,000, Southern California Excluding Metropolitan Los Angeles"; P. W. Trousdale to E. A. Mattison, August 9, 1946: Bank of America N.T. & S.A. archives.

13. Re Vallejo: memorandum by R. G. Smith of telephone conversation with C. W. Collins, March 10, 1942, *ibid.*

14. Bank of America N.T. & S.A., *Annual Reports,* 1942 and 1945; A. P. Giannini to M. S. Eccles, August 17, 1942; to R. G. Smith, July 22, 1943: *ibid.*

15. Memorandum, R. G. Smith, March 10, 1942, *ibid.*

16. E. L. Kelly to C. B. Upham, May 2, 1942, *ibid.*

17. I. E. Ogden to R. J. Barbieri, June 30, 1942, *ibid.*

18. W. M. Hale to R. G. Smith, June 3, 1942, *ibid.*

19. A. P. Giannini to M. S. Eccles, August 17, 1942, *ibid.; Wall Street Journal* (Pacific Coast edition), February 1, 1945.

20. A. P. Giannini to A. J. Gock, November 19, 1942, Bank of America N.T. & S.A. archives.

21. San Francisco *News,* September 14, 1945.

Chapter XXXI

1. A. J. Gock to B. R. James; *Time,* October 15, 1945.

2. H. A. Keith to Al Haase; J. W. Snyder to A. P. Giannini, December 15, 1945, Bank of America N.T. & S.A. archives.

3. Memorandum, R. G. Smith, April 20, 1949, *ibid.*

4. F. Belgrano, Jr., to L. M. Giannini, January 7, 1946, *ibid.*

5. "Report on Manila," by F. S. Baer, March 4, 1946, *ibid.*

6. P. V. McNutt to M. S. Eccles, June 5, 1946, *ibid.*

7. Memorandum, R. G. Smith, December 13, 1946, *ibid.;* T. B. Coughran to Al Haase; R. G. Smith to B. R. James. Figures on deposits, loans, etc. of the foreign branches given in this chapter were furnished by the several departments at the head office that supervise these branches.

8. *The Bankamerican,* August 1950; publicity release, Bank of America N.T. & S.A., February 11, 1952, Bank of America N.T. & S.A. archives; C. D. Terry, Jr. to B. R. James.

9. *New York Times,* April 22, 1948; C. D. Terry, Jr., to B. R. James.

10. *American Banker,* April 20, 1948.

11. San Francisco *Chronicle,* June 15, 1950.

12. *New York Times,* January 25, 1947; T. B. Coughran to Al Haase.

13. Memorandum, R. G. Smith, April 20, 1949, Bank of America N.T. & S.A. archives.

14. Bank of America N.T. & S.A. *Annual Report,* 1952, pp. 8–10; figures from international banking department, Bank of America N.T. & S.A.

15. Figures supplied by the bond investment department, Bank of America N.T. & S.A.

16. *Ibid.;* A. K. Browne to Al Haase.

17. San Francisco *Call-Bulletin*, April 26, 1951; Transamerica Corporation, *Annual Report*, 1952, 11.

18. Figures supplied by the report and analysis department, Bank of America N.T. & S.A.; B. C. Taylor to Al Haase.

19. *Kaiser Industries* (1950), publication of Kaiser Services; memoranda on Henry J. Kaiser Company and affiliated companies in Bank of America N.T. & S.A. archives.

20. *Transamerica Corporation vs. Board of Governors of the Federal Reserve System, op. cit.,* Transamerica Exhibit No. 308; San Francisco *Call-Bulletin*, April 26, 1951.

21. A. E. Burnett to L. M. Giannini, December 31, 1948; to W. E. Bruns, October 20, 1953: Bank of America N.T. & S.A. archives.

22. Memoranda, P. L. Hudson to F. A. Ferroggiaro, February 6, 1947, January 11, 1951, *ibid.;* New York *Journal of Commerce,* November 2, 1950; *Commercial & Financial Chronicle,* August 18, 1952, 600.

23. Kaiser-Frazer memorandum, P. L. Hudson, April 12, 1946, Bank of America N.T. & S.A. archives; Hudson to Al Haase; *Daily Commercial News* (San Francisco), December 29, 1947; San Francisco *Call-Bulletin,* February 1, 1947; San Francisco *Examiner,* March 1, 1948 and January 1, 1949; *Wall Street Journal* (Pacific Coast Edition), December 12, 1949; San Francisco *Chronicle,* March 23, 1953.

24. L. M. Giannini to E. Vukicovich, December 8, 1950, Bank of America N.T. & S.A. archives.

25. Memorandum of R. G. Smith, reporting E. Kelley's interview with Comptroller Delano, September 1, 1941, *ibid.*

26. *Transamerica Corporation vs. Board of Governors of the Federal Reserve System, op. cit.,* Appendix, Volume 1, 578a (Eccles' testimony concerning telephone conversation); Volume 7, 4641a (Mario's testimony).

27. C. Morrill to Transamerica Corporation, February 4, 1942, Bank of America N.T. & S.A. archives.

28. A. P. Giannini to M. S. Eccles, August 17, 1942; Eccles to Giannini, December 19, 1942, *ibid.*

29. *Transamerica Corporation vs. Board of Governors of the Federal Reserve System, op. cit.,* Appendix, Volume 10, 7161a.

30. A. P. Giannini to C. W. Collins, April 13, 1943, C. W. Collins reference file, Washington, D.C.; Collins to Giannini, May 13, 1943, Bank of America N.T. & S.A. archives.

31. *American Banker,* November 6, 1946, April 15, 1947, March 16 and April 1, 1948.

32. C. W. Collins to L. M. Giannini, November 7, 1945, Bank of America N.T. & S.A. archives.

33. M. S. Eccles, *Beckoning Frontiers* (1951), 445.

34. A. P. Giannini to L. M. Giannini, January 5, 1943, Bank of America N.T. & S.A. archives; Eccles, 446.

35. A. P. Giannini to B. R. James; *American Banker,* January 28, February 2 and March 31, 1948; *New York Times,* March 31, 1948; *Washington Banktrends,* April 5, 1948.

36. Eccles, 453, 446.

37. C. W. Collins to A. P. Giannini, November 19, 1948, Bank of America N.T. & S.A. archives.

CHAPTER XXXII

1. F. Yeates to Al Haase.
2. *American Banker,* September 2, 1952.
3. *Transamerica Corporation vs. Board of Governors of the Federal Reserve System, op. cit.,* Appendix, Volume 4, 2646a.
4. I. D. Wright to R. G. Smith, May 26, 1939; A. P. Giannini to R. J. Barbieri, February 24, 1941, and March 20, 1945: Bank of America N.T. & S.A. archives.
5. *Transamerica Corporation vs. Board of Governors of the Federal Reserve System, op. cit.,* Appendix, Volume 3, 1637a.
6. F. M. Dana to Al Haase; L. M. Giannini to E. L. Kelly, October 7, 1949, Bank of America N.T. & S.A. archives.
7. *Transamerica Corporation vs. Board of Governors of the Federal Reserve System, op. cit.,* Appendix, Volume 2, 1329a.
8. *Ibid.,* Volume 3, 1728a.
9. *Ibid., Brief for Respondent,* 68 *et seq.;* Appendix, Volume 2, 1330a, and Volume 1, 424a.
10. *Ibid., Brief for Petitioner,* 10.
11. P. S. Lucas to the Yorba Linda Banking and Business Betterment Committee, December 24, 1948, Bank of America N.T. & S.A. archives.
12. *Transamerica Corporation vs. Board of Governors of the Federal Reserve System, op. cit., Brief for Petitioner,* 49–50.
13. Memorandum, F. Yeates, October 25, 1949, Bank of America N.T. & S.A. archives.
14. *Transamerica Corporation vs. Board of Governors of the Federal Reserve System, op. cit.,* Appendix, Volume 7, 4951a, 4950a.
15. *Ibid.,* 4772a.
16. *Ibid.,* 4653a, 4950a.
17. *Ibid.,* 4650a, 4651a.
18. *Washington Banktrends,* October 30, 1950.
19. J. L. Robertson to T. B. McCabe, June 20, 1950, Bank of America N.T. & S.A. archives.
20. San Francisco *Chronicle,* June 25, 1950, and August 15, 1950.
21. *Transamerica Corporation vs. Board of Governors of the Federal Reserve System, op. cit.,* Appendix, Volume 1, 362a *et seq.*
22. *American Banker,* June 22, 1951.
23. *Washington Banktrends,* February 11, 1952.
24. *Transamerica Corporation vs. Board of Governors of the Federal Reserve System, op. cit.,* Appendix, Volume 1, 408a *et seq.*
25. L. M. Giannini to A. H. Jeffries, October 27, 1950, Bank of America N.T. & S.A. archives.
26. San Francisco *Chronicle,* September 11, 1952.

Index

TULELAKE
ALTURAS
CEDARVILLE

YREKA

DUNSMUIR McCLOUD FALL RIVER MILLS

SUSANVILLE

CRESCENT CITY

WESTWOOD

PORTOLA
QUINCY LOYALTON

REDDING
WEAVERVILLE ANDERSON

ARCATA RED BLUFF PARADISE
EUREKA CORNING
FORTUNA ORLAND CHICO OROVILLE NEVADA CITY TRUCKEE
FERNDALE GRASS VALLEY
BIGGS GRIDLEY COLFAX TAHOE CITY
WILLOWS LIVE OAK PLACERVILLE
YUBA CITY TAHOE VALLEY
GARBERVILLE COLUSA LOOMIS
MARYSVILLE AUBURN
WILLIAMS WHEATLAND LINCOLN NEWCASTLE
ARBUCKLE ROSEVILLE FOLSOM
UKIAH LAKEPORT ROSEVILLE IONE
KNIGHTS LANDING SUTTER CREEK
JACKSON
FORT BRAGG KELSEYVILLE LOWER LAKE DAVIS NORTH SACRAMENTO SONORA
WOODLAND SACRAMENTO ANGELS CAMP
MENDOCINO CLOVERDALE WINTERS ELK GROVE
GEYSERVILLE CALISTOGA DIXON LODI
HEALDSBURG ST. HELENA VACAVILLE
POINT ARENA SEBASTOPOL SANTA ROSA RIO VISTA OAKDALE
ISLETON STOCKTON MARIPO
NAPA SUISUN CITY MANTECA
VALLEY FORD BRENTWOOD RIPON MODESTO
TOMALES SONOMA TRACY TURLOCK
PETALUMA LIVERMORE LIVINGSTON
POINT REYES STATION HILMAR ATWATER
MERCED CHOWCHILLA
GUSTINE
LOS BANOS DOS PALOS KERM
FIREBAUGH
MILPITAS
SARATOGA SAN JOSE MORGAN HILL
LOS GATOS GILROY HOLLISTER
SANTA CRUZ SAN JUAN BAUTISTA
WATSONVILLE
SALINAS
SEASIDE SOLEDAD
GONZALES
MONTEREY KING CITY
PACIFIC GROVE
CAMB

SAN FRANCISCO BAY AREA

VALLEJO
HAMILTON A.F.B. BENICIA
FAIRFAX
SAN ANSELMO SAN RAFAEL
LARKSPUR PITTSBURG
MILL VALLEY MARTINEZ ANTIOCH
RICHMOND CONCORD
SAUSALITO ALBANY EL CERRITO
EMERYVILLE BERKELEY WALNUT CREEK
OAKLAND
ALAMEDA
SAN FRANCISCO DANVILLE
48 Branches
SAN LEANDRO
CASTRO VALLEY
SOUTH SAN FRANCISCO BAY-FAIR
DALY CITY HAYWARD
WESTLAKE PLEASANTON
COLMA SAN BRUNO
BURLINGAME MILLBRAE
CENTERVILLE
SAN MATEO
SAN CARLOS
REDWOOD CITY
HALF MOON BAY MENLO PARK
PALO ALTO
MOUNTAIN VIEW
PESCADERO SUNNYVALE
SANTA CLARA

N